Marketing Survey
SAVE ONE DOLLAR!

MW00650510

Help us make our books more useful to you by telling us something certificate worth $1.00 toward the purchase of other fishing, sports and outdoor books. Thank you for your cooperation.

1. How many days per year do you fish?
- ☐ 1-5
- ☐ 5-10
- ☐ 10-20
- ☐ 20-40
- ☐ more than 40

2. Do you fish fresh water, salt water or both?
- ☐ FW
- ☐ SW
- ☐ Both

3. Do you own a boat? ☐ Yes ☐ No
If yes, length _____
Type or make _____

4. Do you own an outboard motor? ☐ Yes ☐ No
If yes, how many HP _____

5. Where do you fish?
- ☐ East Coast
- ☐ New England
- ☐ Southeast
- ☐ Central States
- ☐ Great Lakes
- ☐ Hawaii
- ☐ Southwest
- ☐ Mountain States
- ☐ Pacific Coast

6. How many rods do you own?_____reels?_____

7. Check types of fishing you do.
- ☐ Trolling
- ☐ Bait fishing
- ☐ Bottom fishing
- ☐ Artificial lures
- ☐ Cane pole
- ☐ Fly fishing
- ☐ Spinning
- ☐ Bait casting
- ☐ Spin casting

8. Which of the following species have you caught?
- ☐ Bass
- ☐ Bluegill
- ☐ Trout
- ☐ Salmon
- ☐ Pike
- ☐ Walleye
- ☐ Snook
- ☐ Blackfish
- ☐ Bluefish
- ☐ Dolphin
- ☐ Muskie
- ☐ Catfish
- ☐ Perch
- ☐ Pickerel
- ☐ Striped bass (rockfish)
- ☐ Whiting
- ☐ Bonefish
- ☐ Grouper
- ☐ Albacore
- ☐ Yellowtail
- ☐ Weakfish or seatrout
- ☐ Sailfish
- ☐ Marlin
- ☐ Tarpon
- ☐ Permit
- ☐ Snapper

9. How many years have you been fishing?
- ☐ 1-5
- ☐ 5-10
- ☐ 10-15
- ☐ 15-20
- ☐ over 20

10. What magazines do you read on a regular basis?
- ☐ Field & Stream
- ☐ Outdoor Life
- ☐ Sports Afield
- ☐ Fly Fisherman
- ☐ Angler
- ☐ Salt Water Sportsman
- ☐ Other _____
- ☐ Fishing World
- ☐ Fishing Facts
- ☐ Florida Sportsman
- ☐ Southern Outdoors
- ☐ Bass Master

11. Where did you buy Angler's Bible?
- ☐ Bookstore
- ☐ Sporting goods store
- ☐ Military PX
- ☐ Other _____
- ☐ Newsstand
- ☐ Department store
- ☐ Discount store

12. Have you used the information in Angler's Bible in purchasing a fishing product?
- ☐ Yes
- ☐ No

13. Are you also a
- ☐ hunter?
- ☐ trap & skeet shooter?
- ☐ bow hunter?
- ☐ skin diver?
- ☐ target shooter?
- ☐ gun collector?
- ☐ camper/backpacker?

participant in other outdoor sports? _____
(Please specify which) _____

14. Why did you buy Angler's Bible?
- ☐ Wanted product information
- ☐ Recommended by a friend
- ☐ Recommended by a salesman
- ☐ Advertising
- ☐ Attracted by cover
- ☐ Price
- ☐ Other _____
_____

15. Age _____

16. Occupation _____

Please give your comments on the Angler's Bible: _____
_____
_____

Name (Mr.) (Ms) _____

Address _____
_____ **Zip** _____

Remove this entire card along the left edge perforation, fold along the dotted line, tape the bottoms together and drop the **prepaid** card in the mail. NO POSTAGE NECESSARY.

Thank you again for your assistance.

(fold along this line)

POSSESSED IN QUIETNESS

No life, my honest scholar, no life so happy and so pleasant as the life of a well-governed angler; for when the lawyer is swallowed up with business, and the statesman is preventing or contriving plots, then we sit on cowslip-banks, hear the birds sing, and possess ourselves in as much quietness as these silent silver streams, which we now see glide so quietly by us.

—Izaak Walton, *The Compleat Angler,* 1653.

Angler's Bible

No. 2
1977 Edition

Edited by
Mark Sosin

ART DIRECTOR:
Maria Barranco
ARTISTS:
Ronald Cutro
Mary Ann Entriken

SUPERVISORY EDITOR:
Irene Hinds
COPY EDITOR:
Alice Roberts

CHIEF EDITORIAL RESEARCHER:
Marleen Anderson
EDITORIAL RESEARCHERS:
Carol Altman
Judith E. Cohen
Mary Kannar
Andrea Kelley
Gritli Wolbach

MANAGING EDITOR:
George M. Horn
ASSISTANT MANAGING EDITOR:
John C. Rhodes
PRODUCTION EDITOR:
Bob Dana
ASSISTANT PRODUCTION EDITOR:
Jeff Arnold
PUBLISHER:
Robert F. Scott

Stoeger Publishing Company

Although every effort has been made to describe specifications and descriptions of fishing tackle and equipment accurately, the publishers can take no responsibility for errors or omissions.

Copyright © 1977 by Stoeger Publishing Company

All rights reserved

Published by Stoeger Publishing Company

Library of Congress Catalog Card No.: 76-54413

International Standard Book No.: 0-88317-031-0

Manufactured in the United States of America

Distributed to the book trade by Follett Publishing Company, 1010 West Washington Boulevard, Chicago, Illinois 60607 and to the sporting goods trade by Stoeger Industries, 55 Ruta Court, South Hackensack, New Jersey 07606

In Canada, distributed to the book trade by Nelson, Foster and Scott, Ltd., 299 Yorkland Boulevard, Willowdale, Ontario M2J 1S9 and to the sporting goods trade by Stoeger Trading Company, 900 Ontario Street East, Montreal, Quebec H2L 1P4

Contents

Foreword

Man has always been a fisherman. In the beginning, fishing was a means of securing food rather than a sport. Prehistoric fishermen fashioned the first simple but effective devices for taking fish. The first hooks—narrow pieces of flint called "gorges"—were straight or slightly curved, with a groove at the center to hold a line made from a plaited vine or animal sinews. When a fish swallowed the gorge, a jerk of the line would turn it crosswise in the fish's throat or stomach.

There is archaeological evidence that in ancient Egypt fishing had come to be a pastime of the wealthy. About the time printing began in Europe, books extolling the virtues of fishing were among the first to make their appearance. Perhaps the most notable work was Izaak Walton's *The Compleat Angler,* which overshadowed a host of contemporary volumes on the same theme.

The twentieth century has brought a new attitude toward fishing, part of the national concern over the wholesale destruction of fish and game as a result of organized pillaging and pollution of the woods and waters, and this concern is reflected in hundreds of books.

The launching of a book—like that of a ship—is always attended with a certain degree of peril. Therefore, the decision to make an annual volume out of any tentatively birthed book must surely be cause for celebration.

Two years ago, the first ANGLER'S BIBLE saw the light of day. Reader reaction was immediate and almost universally enthusiastic. Unlike most fishing compendia, the accent was on equipment, with supporting how-to articles, classics and reference sections. The experience gleaned from the work of putting together that initial ANGLER'S BIBLE has now been combined with the results of extensive reader surveys. The result is, I think, a better book—one that is more responsive to the fisherman's needs and wants.

As before, the ANGLER'S BIBLE is proud of its distinguished heritage, for it is modeled on the best-selling SHOOTER'S BIBLE, still going strong after more than fifty years of publication despite its many imitators.

Readers who are curious about statistics may find the following program notes about the creation of the latest ANGLER'S BIBLE interesting. To begin the work of product research, hundreds of letters were written to manufacturers and suppliers of fishing tackle and related equipment requesting that they furnish catalogs, descriptions, specifications and photos. This they did with a seeming vengeance.

Our research staff next attacked this mountain of raw material, converting it into detailed specifications and descriptions (and taking out the inevitable advertising puffery in the process) of the dazzling array of new equipment that confronts the angler in the marketplace each year.

At the annual show of the highly respected American Fishing Tackle Manufacturers Association in Houston, manufacturers' representatives were contacted and interviewed about sticky nomenclature problems. The information-packed specifications section of this year's ANGLER'S BIBLE is fitting testimony to the thoroughness of this monumental research. Introducing each major section is a product preview reviewing the newest and hottest items in each category.

As before, top fishing experts were asked to write and illustrate articles in their areas of specialization. And to demonstrate that neither fishing nor fishermen change over the years, we have included a number of "angling classics" to entertain readers.

It is always easy to say something pleasant about fishing; it is by far the most ecologically acceptable of all sports and recreations. The remarkable yet unifying characteristic of fishing is its diversity. The bonefisherman battling his furiously fighting quarry at Bimini, the sportfisherman trolling the waters off Catalina for swordfish, the surf fisherman after channel bass or stripers near Cape Hatteras, or the fresh-water angler after trout, salmon, black bass, muskies or pike—they are all brothers and sisters under the skin, often in adversity.

So, here is your newest and latest ANGLER'S BIBLE—a book we hope you will look forward to and profit from year after year. It is not intended to be all things to all men; yet, curiously, there is something here for everyone. It is at one and the same time an informative "catalog" of catalogs, a common-sense how-to book, an evening's good reading and a veritable treasure-trove of hard-to-find reference material.

If you would explore the wonderful world of angling, let this latest ANGLER'S BIBLE transport you to that world. Fishing has a marvelous way of putting things into perspective, of making clear the deepest verities of life. Most of all, this ANGLER'S BIBLE offers ample support for the belief that man—every man and woman, in fact—deep down is still an angler.

—ROBERT F. SCOTT

Tools and Techniques

The Case for Ultralight
by Jerry Gibbs

The popular trend in one-hand fresh water spinning and casting rods seems to be toward producing sticks whose primary purpose is setting a new world pole-vault record rather than subduing fish. Although the big bad lunker lashers will certainly dispatch large-mouths with ease (the blanks have long been used on far tougher salt water species), to suggest that such heavy equipment is the end-all answer for bass or any other gamefish is sheer folly.

I would be the last to say that heavy rods are out of place, especially in thick cover, for deep jigging, throwing big lures or natural baits, and other uses. But there are situations in both salt water and fresh water which demand light lines, tiny lures or extremely light plugs that can only be cast with more delicate tackle. Besides, using ultralight gear is just plain fun; unless you're in very good condition, your casting arm and wrist will feel a lot worse after a really full day of slinging a big rod than they will if you use some of the mini outfits.

In the final analysis light tackle is a relative matter, geared to the fish and the conditions under which you're operating. There's no pleasure or reason in fighting to exhaustion a fish that you plan to release if your tackle is not up to the job. Unless you hold such fish in slow, quiet water until they get their second wind, it is doubtful that they'll recover. Some species never will if they've been played to utter exhaustion.

There is no need for this to happen. While competitive bassing tackle has been getting the most attention, a quiet revolution has been occurring in the field of ultralight tackle. The result has been the development of lightweight, tough rods with a variety of actions that permit the casting of lures from 1/32 or 1/16 ounce up to 1/2 or 3/4 ounce. The heavy end of this range is really out of the ultralight class, but the range does indicate the capabilities of this new equipment. Action, plus new supersmooth guides, makes possible the use of extremely light lines down to 1-pound test. Superior tight-tolerance reels with smooth drags in small sizes matched to these rods have taken ultralight outfits out of the Mickey Mouse class. Most of this new tackle is spinning gear, but several firms now have at least one refined plug casting outfit to please revolving spool fans. Veteran anglers who recall the days of delicate rods used with an ancient revolving spool multiplier to cast fragile live baits may point out that tackle has now come full

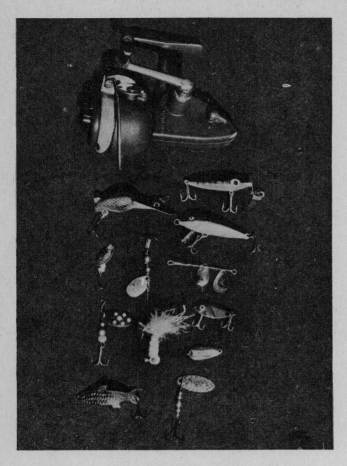

A selection of tiny lures for ultralight equipment that will be successful with most North American gamefish at one time or another.

A good ultralight spinning reel held with rubber bands to the corks of a fly rod is a great piece of equipment for exploring rivers and streams. Some rod builders are now putting together long, soft action spinning rods that handle 2- to 4-pound test line especially for river fishing and big salmon and trout.

circle, but they won't dispute the wisdom of the trend.

The increased interest in light tackle will be acknowledged by the keepers of world records. More entrants in salt water 6-pound class, and fresh water 1-, 2- and 4-pound class categories are received yearly. Whether you are casting a featherweight jig for line-shy bonefish in no-color water, tickling up cranky smallmouth from 40 feet deep, or coaxing a cannibal brown trout from his river lair, there is a mini tackle outfit that is perfect for the job.

I have broken down ultralight rod types into two categories, based on action, for all my angling. First, I've tossed out all so-called fast action rods: the blanks with very flexible tips and stiff butts. For fishing the tiniest lures, from 1/32 ounce to 1/8 ounce, I prefer a slow rod that bends from the tip down into the corks as you put more pressure on it. These I call soft action rods. To replace the fast-tip models, today there are ultralights with a great deal of stiffness, which will still scribe a bend that takes in the entire blank but

are capable of handling slightly heavier lures and working them in deeper water. I call these hard action rods. I use them primarily for lures in the 1/8- to 1/4-ounce class, but they will also handle 1/2-ounce lures well. The soft action rods dictate line in the 1- through 4-pound class, and the hard rods will handle 6 and 8 pound well. There are fewer of these hard action rods commercially made.

Many firms make good soft action ultralight spinning rods with a full-flex or parabolic bend. Not so many have soft plug casting rods. One possibility is to find a so-called spin-cast rod and see if your revolving spool reel will fit it.

Some of the new graphite spinning rods classified as "ultralight" by their manufacturers fall somewhere between the soft action fiberglass ultralights and the hard action ultralights. They have a good deal of bend yet possess the firm springiness typical of graphite. They are greatly tolerant in regard to lure size, being able to handle baits in a wide weight range.

Top quality ultralight spinning reels should have a fast retrieve ratio, smooth, easy operating bail, ball bearings and a very smooth line roller area. I like skirted spools which prevent stray line loops from slipping behind the spool, but I also use unskirted models. Revolving spool reels designed for light line work are scarce. Look for a light spool that will start turning quickly and easily and is designed to prevent small diameter line from slipping behind it.

When you are using light lines, it is imperative that your reel's drag be exceptionally smooth running. The drag on most reels can be fine tuned, and if you find that the starting drag (the force needed to start the spool slipping) on your reel is much more than the running drag (the force needed to keep it slipping) something must be done. Often, substituting cork or oiled leather drag washers for stock nonmetal washers in your reel will solve the problem.

In angling for panfish or small stream trout, the matter of drag is not so critical, but for big small-mouth, pike, and especially salt water fish or anadromous species such as salmon or steelhead, it is crucial. When you are using light lines for fish likely to make long runs, it makes sense to set the drag comparatively lighter than you would for heavier lines which usually have a bit more forgiving stretch. A rule of thumb is to set the drag for one-fourth of the line test; on 2-pound test line set it to slip at 1/2 pound, and so on. You'll probably think that this is extremely light, but it gives you a safety margin with a strong, freshly hooked fish. Later in the fight you increase the drag by applying additional pressure to the spool with your hands or fingers to keep the spool from slipping

Various handle styles on types of ultralight: *left to right,* Billy Westmorland custom hard action rod to which reel is taped; Billy Westmorland medium hard action rod with rings and light Foulproof guides; Garcia-Conlon soft action 5 foot 2121 A spinning rod with recessed corks on handle and sliding rings; Fenwick 5½ foot soft action FS 55 with sliding rings; Orvis 5 foot, 1⅝ ounce graphite spinning rod for 1/16- to 3/16-ounce lures but capable of handling heavier—action is somewhere between that of hard action glass or high modulus graphite and soft action glass; Fenwick G953 hard action graphite for 1/8 to 5/8 ounce lures, with fixed reel seat; Daiwa VIP 31 soft action spincast rod for use with revolving spool reel as a plug-casting outfit; Garcia-Conlon 8300 C 5½ foot medium hard action plug casting reel.

while pumping. If the fish makes a sudden lunge or run, you can quickly relax this pressure, returning to the pre-set light drag of the reel.

Another area of importance to the ultralight angler is that of line guides. Too few or incorrectly spaced guides on a rod will allow the line to pull down and rub against the rod blank. Poor quality guides will cut or burr quickly from the line or from being knocked on a solid object. Today the very popular aluminum oxide

You need ultralight tackle to throw effectively such feather-weight lures as this balsa wood Rapala.

guides are being used even on many ultralight rods, alone or in combination with Foulproof guides. They are smooth and hard. Light lines with a lower resistance to abrasion sometimes are roughened by seemingly smooth guides. If you notice a coarse texture on your line and have made sure that the fault is not in the guides, it may be smart to change brands.

I generally select one of the softer action rods for panfish, trout in streams, smallmouth (when they are not in deep water), spotted bass and small pike. The gentle resistance of these rods provides just the right cushion for line from 4 pounds down. The light line is absolutely necessary if you need any kind of distance when casting tiny spoons, spinners and jigs. I could use stiffer rods and slightly heavier lines for many of the situations in which I employ the more flexible tackle, but I don't. In addition to coaxing a fish to strike, the sport in sportfishing, to me, comes from handling a fish on tackle which allows little margin for error on my part. If I make a misjudgment, the fish breaks free, and I like that. It maintains the excitement. A more practical reason for the soft action tackle is that sometimes only the smallest lures will

For extra-secure connection and hand comfort, an ultralight Mitchell 408 is taped to the plain cork handle of a hard action ultralight rod.

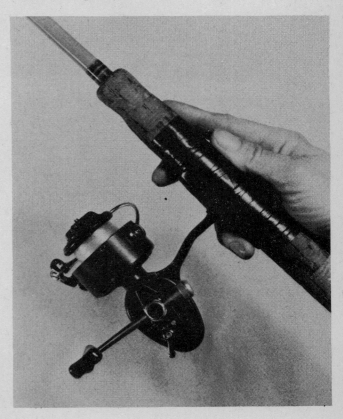

Ultralight spinning specialist Mike Baz proves that his featherweight gear is just right on big Vermont brown trout in both low water and deep fast-moving currents. Mike uses gold wobbling spoons for most of his fishing.

attract moody trout or bass and, as previously mentioned, this is the tackle with which to cast such lures.

Both soft and hard action ultralight spinning rods are wonderful tools with which to teach youngsters. Initially you may have misgivings about putting an expensive outfit into the hands of a child, but when you investigate the cheaper, so-called kid's combi outfits, you discover that the reels are often so stiff to operate that a child would be incapable of handling them. Watch the grin on the face of a youngster who has hooked a hefty bluegill or crappie with the ultralight gear, and you'll have no more reservations about letting him handle the good equipment. Besides, you can put it under your personal supervision the moment he's finished.

I think I find as much pleasure as any kid when I use soft action tackle on panfish. Dropping natural baits around long timbers jutting into the water, swimming little spinners along weed beds, plopping them into pockets or jigging them near brush brings sharp little strikes and a very satisfying bend in your rod. In streams, big old brown trout that cannot be coaxed any other way can often be fooled with mini wobblers of ribbon candy shape, as long as they are attached to 2-pound line. Soft action rods are ideal for pitching these lures side-arm far up under low hanging vegetation where these old lunkers like to lie.

Using this tackle on any slightly more toothsome fish calls for either a heavier leader or doubling the line at the terminal end where you attach the lure or hook. To double the line, I use either a Bimini Twist or Spider Hitch knot. I do not use this soft action tackle when fishing for larger pike.

With the hard action ultralight equipment you can handle almost any fresh water fish and many inshore salt water fish, provided there is room to fight them. You use a heavier leader in most instances, and you don't expect to land every fish you hook. The compensation for the latter inconvenience is that you will probably get more strikes with the light equipment than you would with heavier tackle.

With notable exceptions, it is hard to convince largemouth bass anglers—especially those working some of the big Southern impoundments—of the merits of ultralight for their kind of fishing. In dealing with underwater forests composed of both standing and knocked-down timber, ultralight may not be practical. But you can use it for dropoffs, light cover, banks, grass beds and rushes, flats, points and underwater channels. In spring and late fall, and in winter where there is open water, big bass have an appetite for plastic grubs, little jigs, mini spinnerbaits, little vertical jigging spoons and small pork baits. In summer, the little lures are often the only thing that will

The author uses ultralight for largemouth in water suitable for that equipment—light cover, no great snags of heavy timber.

coax hot-weather bass, and if you can work the edges of cover without having to rip a lure through thick vegetation, the hard action mini tackle is best suited to do the job. I also like this equipment for small-mouths in deep clear water lakes. It has all the guts needed to work a lure dropped to 35 or 40 feet and still maintain the sensitivity to feel the lightest hits from cold-weather fish. For this angling assignment I would not use soft action ultralights but they are ideal for dropping micro jigs for crappie that have suspended deeply in summer.

On float trips, I take both a soft and a hard action ultralight. I prefer the hard action for most work on stream smallmouths, but there are days when the moody bronzebacks will snap only at the tiniest lures or small model balsa plugs such as the Rapala, which are best tossed with the softer action rods. The more

The author holds a 12-pound river-run lake trout taken in swift water with 4-pound tackle and a hard action ultra-light rod. Lakers and northern pike are notorious loafers if tackle is not up to the job of subduing them, but the ultra-light combination proved satisfactory.

flexible rods are also a better choice for scrappy red breast stream sunfish. For shad fishing, I like the hard action rods, with slant-head shad dart jigs. This tackle will stand up to those tough-fighting gamefish very well.

Northern pike and lake trout can be notorious loafers if the tackle you're using is not strong enough to put pressure on them. With hard action rods and line testing 4, 6 and 8 pound maximum, I've had no problems in convincing these fish to fight and tire themselves quickly. Otherwise they would allow themselves to be winched in, then simply slide away when they moved too close to shore or boat. The result would be a drawn-out exercise with all the excitement of a magnetic crane moving scrap metal in a junkyard.

Ultralight rods are available in a variety of lengths. The shorter ones, slightly under 5 to about 5½ feet, are ideal when you are wading in brushy trout streams or float fishing for trout or smallmouth. In lakes, there are times when you must get under low-hanging branches as you cast to more open water or around and over a variety of obstacles. The short rods are perfect for this fishing, as they are for working in canals and ditches with close, high banks.

For long-running fish, especially in big rivers or rivers with a substantial current, longer rods are better. These allow you to keep a little extra line off the water. Excess line in the water gives fish addition-al leverage. Big-river striped bass, steelhead or salmon do not need such an advantage. In rivers, fish have the velocity of the main current to help them, plus stretches of fast or even white water. Besides the leverage factor, the more line underwater the greater the total drag. With ultralight lines this may cause breakoffs unless you relax the drag at the reel. A longer rod gives you a little edge.

Long rods are also an advantage when you have hooked a fish and are forced to move along a crowded riverbank, jetty or sea wall. With a large and vigorous fish—a big striper, for example, or a Pacific salmon or steelhead—the problem is magnified. A long rod will help you keep the line high and away from your fellow anglers' necks as you follow the fish.

Custom-rod-builder Dick Swan and his Michigan pals have refined the long ultralight spinning rod technique into a super-effective method along crowd-ed chinook, coho and steelhead rivers in the Midwest. Using 10- or 12-foot rods designed to handle 2- to 4-pound test line, these anglers regularly take hard-fighting fish weighing in the high teens. Sure, they lose a lot of fish but while they are standing shoulder to shoulder with other anglers, their hookup rate makes the others nearly weep, and, at day's end, it is the light tackle boys who have landed the most fish.

During freak cold snaps and low water conditions on steelhead rivers in Washington, I've put lightweight revolving spool reels and flexible action rods to work hooking and taking fish when others using heavier tackle and lines drew a blank in the air-clear water. The shorter plug rods were the ticket when floating in West Coast drift boats. If you really want to put your skill to the test, try these same outfits spooled with 6- or 8-pound line on the many inshore gamefish that roam our coasts. In most instances, you'll have to add a heavier leader. But don't use this method if you are fishing from a crowded party boat.

Inland or in bays or oceans, the new ultralight equipment is making an increasingly large place for itself in fishing sport, both for practical reasons and for pleasure. Next time you go fishing, take along one of the these mini outfits. After you give it the first real workout, the chances are you'll rarely leave it at home again.

Erik Lyngse nets scrappy Lake Champlain smallmouth for Vermont biologist Jon Anderson. The tiny lures best worked with ultralight tackle were needed for moody hot-weather bronzebacks.

Smallmouth Bass Mr. Thoroughbred

by Homer Circle

When the "Gashouse Gang" was making baseball history in St. Louis, a sign in the dressing room read: "When you call on a thoroughbred he will give you every ounce of heart and sinew in him. When you call on a jackass all he'll do is balk."

Score the smallmouth bass a thoroughbred. Few fish will give you so much in such a short period of time. From the instant you stick a hook in its jaw, you're tied to a raging roughhouser that can lose you more ways than a kid at a circus.

There was a time when I was a smallmouth nut. I pursued this hassler in every state where it surfaced in bragging sizes. And it has wiped my eye more times than I could possibly recall. But those memorable moments that remain with me are worth all the barren hours and frustrations.

There was the time I journeyed to the Snake River to fish with Frank Nachand, a man who probably has caught as many whoppers on a fly rod as any long-rodder in the nation.

We fished hard for three days, all the time I had left, and in spite of combined expertise, couldn't catch a smallmouth over three pounds. And yet, the ones we did catch gave us so much excitement that the trip was more than paid for.

One smallmouth in particular gave me an experience I'll never forget. I was fishing a fast-wriggling lure in heavy current when I felt tension on my line—not a jolting strike such as a smallmouth is capable of, but I knew I had a fish.

Although it was a strong fish, the connection was loose feeling. Puzzled, I finally brought in about a 2-pound smallmouth, and when I lifted it by the lower jaw to remove the lure, I saw the reason. It had been hooked previously and had broken loose from some angler's line. That angler had been using a 6-inch leader tied to a swivel which dangled from the bass's mouth. One of the points of my lure's rear treble was stuck through the small eye of the swivel.

Evidently that smallmouth made a pass at my lure, or was spooked by it, and somehow made close enough contact to get the swivel snagged on my hook. It would be hard to figure the odds of this happening, but it's typical of the screwy things that can occur when you're smallmouth fishing.

Another experience that stays with me took place in Lake St. Clair, that mini Great Lakes orphan between Lakes Huron and Erie. Here, Larry Helin lives to do battle with lake smallmouth whose average size is the biggest I've come across. And I can feel that fun-loving

Canadian smallmouth are among the tastiest and hardest fighting to be found.

Fast, deep, north-country rivers are the author's favored lunker hangouts.

Finn frowning at me for calling attention to his "honey hole." Still, he's had it virtually to himself for enough years, and it's large enough to stand a lot more angling pressure, so let's move in on Larry and help him keep those broad-shouldered smallmouths under control.

Twice each year the bigger ones, those averaging over 3 pounds, become predictable. In the spring they'll be around the pencil reeds. You cruise quietly and whenever you see one or more reeds sticking out of the water, you cast a lure past the stickup and hustle it through the spot.

Suddenly, before you realize it, three things can happen: (1) a lunker smallmouth has blasted your lure and erupted 3 feet into the air, throwing water in all directions; (2) you'll see your lure sailing through the air amid the spray as the smallmouth rejects it; and (3) you'll hear Larry chuckling fiendishly, "You gotta hit 'em now, friend; one second after now is like a day late."

Thus you learn to retrieve with no slack in your line, keep your rod tip continuously low, remain on a hair-trigger ready, and try to set the hooks just before that rascal strikes. Despite such readiness you will land less than half of the takers.

This led us into a discussion about the comparative speeds of smallmouth versus largemouth bass in the jumps. Fortunately for veracity's sake, our friend Glen Lau was along filming a segment on smallmouth bass for our TV show, "The Fisherman." We got some terrific jumping sequences, and overhearing our discussion, Glen said, "Well, when I get back to the studio, I'll put together footage comparing jumps of both fish and see what comes out."

Surprisingly, here's what we discovered. Film goes through the movie camera at the rate of 24 frames per second. By comparing leaps of both fish we not only could time the duration but also see exactly how high each leaped.

Out of hundreds of largemouth jumps, the highest was about 2 feet and lasted 27 frames, or 1⅛ seconds. It took the largemouth 10 to 12 frames to get airborne as it tailwalked to gain speed.

The smallmouth's best leap was over 3 feet and lasted 17 frames, or about 2/3 of a second. And the leaps were so explosively sudden that many were missed until we began using bright gold line so Glen could predict where the leap was going to occur.

So, despite my fondness for the largemouth bass, I'm forced to give the edge on hell-raising to its hard-muscled cousin, the smallmouth.

And speaking of hell-raisers, if you want to tangle with smallmouth under unusual fishing conditions try

below Wheeler Dam in Alabama. Smallmouth are tough enough in Lake St. Clair's still waters but in those swift-flowing waters they'll leave you standing with egg on your face.

One of my 'Bama bassing buddies, Nolen Shivers, a Birmingham police officer, sent me a picture of himself and Albert Gibson grinning over a two-limit string of smallmouth bass. Twenty bass weighed 97 pounds!

I began packing so fast my wife thought the house was on fire. Man, that stuff is strong! Especially when I read that the largest one was 8 pounds 1 ounce.

But Wheeler Dam is no place for a beginner at boat handling, because you're fishing water that boils out of the huge power-producing turbines which turn on

Flyrodding and wading for smallmouth is hard to top for hand-to-fin combat.

and off at unpredictable times. So go with an experienced friend, as I did, on your first trip.

The best lure Nolen has discovered is gizzard shad, and this area is a bait dealer's nightmare because it is alive with gizzard shad. All you need do is find a spot where they congregate along the dam's walls and dip all you need for an hour's fishing. Keeping them fresh and lively is easy here.

The hot spot is the eddy water below a turbine outpouring, where you can let two No. 4 split shot take the minnow right to the bottom.

As you bounce the minnow along the bottom, and drift, you watch your line closely. If it does anything unusual, such as going slightly slack, or momentarily tight, you set the hook because a smallmouth has sucked in the minnow.

We had a ball. And what made it more enjoyable was the fact that, intermittently, those big smallmouth would turn on and off throughout the day. When they seemed to disappear we fished for white bass, another hard-striking fish, around the dam's abutments.

If you would like to know more about Wheeler's smallmouth fishing write to Dan Long, Fisherman's Resort, Box 62G, Town Creek, Alabama 35672. Experienced guides are available, as well as neat, reasonable quarters and fine food. Nearby is Joe Wheeler State Park, also with excellent facilities.

Well, enough personality talk about Mr. Smallmouth. Let's take a look at its background and at some of the ways you can outdo this wily antagonist—remembering that it is more often the outdo-er than the outdo-ee.

Range. Originally the smallmouth was indigenous to the Great Lakes region, the St. Lawrence River system, and the upper stretches of the Mississippi, Tennessee and Ohio rivers.

Today, after transplanting in nearly every state, the strongholds are southern Canada bordering the Great Lakes, throughout the same river systems, and west through Arkansas, Oklahoma and Kansas.

Habitat. For reasons best known to the smallmouth it is found most often around rocky shores, bottoms or outcroppings in lakes and streams. When fishing an unknown lake I begin by cruising the shores and looking for rocky reefs, shoals, protruding points and bays.

Food. One good guess as to why the smallmouth prefers rocky habitat is that the food it seeks does too. Much of the diet is made up of crayfish, minnows, small fish, May flies, crustaceans and insect larvae.

Life Style. Each spring, when temperatures reach the 60- to 70-degree range, the smallmouth male prepares one or more nests and selects one or more females to join him in the spawning act.

The nests will be from a few feet to more than 20 feet down, depending on water clarity. The clearer the water the deeper the nest. After the eggs are spawned the male bass remains to fan the water with his tail and fins to keep the eggs free of silt.

In about ten days the fry are able to digest a variety of minute foods and at this time they are deserted by the male parent, who hasn't eaten for several weeks. The often-repeated story that he eats his own fry is not substantiated by observations. Some other bass's young, yes, and maybe some of his own after they have grown considerably and have been separated from him. So long as he is guarding his own brood, he is a good papa.

Suitable Tackle. Throughout their range smallmouth bass are caught on all types of fishing gear, even cane poles. But the more sporting the gear, the greater the enjoyment.

Whether you use spin casting, spinning, bait casting or fly outfits, the line or leader need not exceed 12-pound test for most smallmouth fishing. This is adequate even for strong fish in the 4- to 6-pound range, provided they are in open water.

My choice is the bait casting outfit because it is more suited to pinpoint casting. There are those times when the smallmouth wants a lure smack-dab against its hangout, not a couple of feet distant.

Whatever fishing outfit you are proficient with or presently own will do. Far more important is how you fish, because you have to find and tempt the smallmouth before you can hope to catch them.

Smallmouth are caught in both lakes and streams, but let's consider these separately because approaches and tactics differ.

Lake Fishing. Find those obviously rocky spots where clean, wave-washed shores or points draw you like a magnet. Your approach should be upwind, motor off, so you can use the wind to drift close enough to cast.

This sneaky approach is necessary because most of today's good smallmouth water gets a daily going over, heavier on weekends. And the bigger smallmouth bass don't reach magnum sizes by being stupid. The stupid ones got caught when they were small.

They are aware of man sounds and become wary when they hear them. So make as little noise as possible. Quietly anchor your boat a long cast away and systematically work lures over every foot of the near-shore and offshore cover.

Which lures? Well, over a period of nearly five

Author's wife, Gayle, center, took this 4-pounder on a bottom-nudging spinner.

decades a guy is bound to develop a preference for certain types of lures which repeatedly do business with smallmouth bass. And, believe me, they are sharp shoppers most of the time!

So, to be methodical, here's how I would fish my pet lures as I search for the "pattern of the day." The pattern could be which type of lure, even which size, which color, whether they want it on top, diving or grubbing the bottom. Again, it could be the type of cover or depth of water they're using.

For openers, I would be there at the beginning of day, first light, when visibility lets you barely discern the shoreline. Big smallmouth have a habit of feeding early, then holding quietly on the bottom for the balance of the day.

Because of the visual and auditory thrill, I begin with a surface lure that chugs, or one that has spinners, or an imitation minnow which I can make dart and flirt around. There's nothing like a small-mouth surface smash to start one's adrenalin flowing!

If half an hour of surface probing gets no results, I switch to a floating-diving lure, such as a Big-O. This

This is smallmouth country, and a canoe is a great way to fish it.

When you add the pull of current to the fight of a hefty smallmouth—that's sport!

has been the hottest smallmouth lure to come along in years, and its appeal probably lies in its superfast swimming vibration.

Another half hour with this and other floating-diving lures and if action hasn't occurred it's a logical conclusion that the smallmouth aren't on the shore at this time.

Now my mind, and lures, begin gauging the bottom cover in 10- to 20-foot depths. And my most dependable lure for telling me what's down there is a grub-jig, so called because the body of the lure is a soft-body, grublike variation of the plastic worm. These come in all colors and you just add one to the hook of a lead-head jig, preferably a quarter ounce.

Cast this past the dropoff and let it sink until the line goes slack, which tells you the lure is now on bottom. Reel the slack out of your line, lower the rod tip, and with a fast upsweep of the rod tip jump the grub-jig off bottom.

That's usually when you get results. A smallmouth has probably been eying your lure from the moment it hit bottom. When it jumps upward, that's more than a pugnacious smallmouth can stand, so he blasts it.

Once you learn to "feel" this lure over bottom, you will be able to use it as a sensor to tell you if that bottom cover is boulders, rock, sand, weeds, mud or whatever.

Another good bottom-type lure is a sinking, fast-wriggling type that imitates a minnow. Fish these on a countdown system. That is, count "one-thousand-one, two-thousand-two" until you see the line go slack. Suppose it did so at the count of fifteen. On your next cast, begin your retrieve at the count of fourteen and the lure will be swimming just over the bottom where most of the bigger smallmouth hang out.

A weedless spoon, with a plastic worm or a pork-strip attractor, also does fine for bottom fishing. Should the water grow calm during the day, it is wise to switch to surface and floating-diving lures. This way, you let the smallmouth tell you what *they* want and don't offer them only what you think they want.

Stream Fishing. You use the same lures and search for the pattern, just as in lake fishing. The essential difference is in the way you read the water, because in this case it is moving.

As it moves, it carries with it much of the food that small fish feed on. Where there are small fish feeding there will be the smallmouth feeding on them.

So look for holes where the water flows from a riffle into a deep, dark area. Especially good is an undercut bank or gravel bar bordering such water.

Here, again, try the full complement of lures from topwater to bottom, but the grub-jig tumbled with the current just over the bottom is about the deadliest thing I've found. At times the addition of an overhead spinner works like magic because it provides an attractor to grab the smallmouth's attention in murky water.

When wading, always walk the shallow side and work your lures quartering upstream, using the flow of water to animate and move them. In very clear water it can be particularly effective to fish a spinner lure upstream, reeling with rod tip high to keep the lure from fouling on bottom.

When drifting-fishing from a boat, always beach the boat above a long, deep hole and get out and walk the shore. A boat moves through these payoff areas too fast to allow you to fish them properly.

That's about it on smallmouth fishing, except for this small bit of Uncle Homer's counseling:

There will be hours, sometimes days, when the smallmouth will pound you right into the mud as it totally ignores your offerings and negates your skills. Then, suddenly, you find the magic pattern and you're 9 feet tall!

The smallmouth truly is a thoroughbred. And it takes one to catch one—especially the heavyweights!

Reading the Water
by Charles F. Waterman

Fish are found at the edges of things and that's the first principle of reading water. Before bass fishermen invaded fish privacy with electronic gear, thermometers, topographic maps and book learning, nearly all of them cast at shorelines. Those were edges they could see, and with all the gadgetry currently at their disposal they are still fishing edges, many of which they can't see.

An edge can be the point where temperature changes, where vegetation begins or one kind of plant borders another, where deep water meets shallow water or where slow and fast currents join. And that's only the beginning.

A long time ago I stood barefoot with a cane pole, small bobber and worm and stared hopelessly at a little Kansas creek from which the green sunfish seemed to have disappeared. I hadn't caught anything all afternoon. Except for about five strands of some kind of weed along a shallow place well out from shore, the creek was plain mud bottom and banks.

Without much hope I plunked the worm and bobber near the weed stalks and the cork went down with a plop. I heaved the sunfish to the bank, repaired the worm damage, and got the bait back in there. An hour later all but one of the weed stems had been drowned by my busy bobber and I had a string of sunfish. Those weeds were about the only feature in that stretch of creek. They weren't enough to provide real cover, but the fish had concentrated there, a demonstration of the Waterman theory, announced 55 years later, that fish like a reference point, even if it furnishes no shelter or food.

But anybody can see five weeds; it may take a little practice to notice less obvious features. Last summer on Montana's Yellowstone River, Ray Hurley beached his johnboat on a gravel bar and pointed to a spot where quick water chattered over slanting rocky shallows and then slipped along a deeper channel, making a patchwork of currents.

"Throw it right where that slow current comes in from the side and meets the fast stuff," Ray instructed. (A writer once recorded that Hurley is more quoted than Izaak Walton.)

I obediently made a couple of false casts and dropped my high-riding Trude fly in the designated area. Nothing. I dried it in the air and tried twice more, then began to change position a little. I'd waded a little deep and some of the gravel was washing from

Ben Williams fishes a big dry fly at the edge of white water during a stone-fly hatch. This stream is too swift for wading.

under my feet.

"Dammit!" yelled Hurley over the river's racket, "Throw it right where the currents meet!"

So I stared hard into the bubbling, curling flow and, sure enough, there was a barely perceptible line exactly where the currents joined. I dropped the fly there and a rainbow trout went "Glug!" I did it three more times and there were three more glugs. A foot away from the right place wasn't good enough and Hurley knew it.

Up on Bulkley River in British Columbia, another guide, Helge Byam, told me where to wade into the head of a big pool and then stood and watched by his high-bowed river boat pulled up on the sand. The river was wide and deep and moved swiftly at midstream.

"When you get opposite that old dead tree on the other bank you should get some action," Helge said.

It took time to work down that far, but opposite the old dead tree I felt a tentative tug and then the heavy surge of a big steelhead. The old dead tree was 10 feet back from the bank and had no relationship to whatever cover or vagary of current caused steelhead to lie in that particular spot, but Helge had used it as a marker for a long time. There was something out there in the river opposite that tree that generations of steelhead had liked. Even Helge hadn't figured out what.

You can go on and on about "structure" and current. Water reading is a part of all angling, whether it's a 50-foot sportfisherman looking for the shifting, dark-blue route of the Gulf Stream, giant of ocean rivers, or an Atlantic salmon fisherman studying the exact spot in a pool where fresh-run fish have rested since before he was born. It makes a romantic package, but there are some unglamorous facts about it that help fishermen.

Unless they are on the move, fish face upstream, a fact universally accepted by those used to fishing in fast water but perhaps unknown to some others. I was spouting off to a brand-new trout fisherman who had fished for years offshore in salt water and pointing to the swirls of rising trout in a Western brook. I was

Atlantic salmon fisherman plays fish hooked at edge of swift water. Guide readies net.

Trout angler hooks good fish where current is pinched between banks of watercress.

telling him how the fish, facing upstream, would rise up in the water and meet a fly coming down.

"How do you know they're facing upstream?" he asked.

That stopped me for a minute, as I assumed he had taken that for granted. Of course they face upstream to keep from being washed away. A fish has a reverse gear but it isn't strong enough to hold him all day against the current. The fact that it faces the water movement and prefers not to fray its fins fighting a torrent has a great deal to do with reading water— warm, cold, sweet or salt.

A fish may need cover for ambush, for concealment from real or imaginary enemies and for protection from sun or strong current. In most cases it is likely to be near the edge of its cover, especially if it expects

food to be passing by. It wants to be where it doesn't have to work too hard to hold its position, but if there is current, it is likely to be near it, because current brings food. Given food and some kind of cover (for a cover-using species), its main worry is temperature and every fish has a preferred temperature range. Other things being equal, it will head for the ideal temperature, whether it is a pumpkinseed sunfish hunting a spring hole or a blue marlin heading south for the winter.

It is trout fishermen who make the most of visual water reading. Where fast water enters a pool they expect fish to be waiting for food a little out of the main current. Where a boulder breaks the flow, they expect fish at the very edges of the quiet water immediately below the boulder, where they can face

Trout angler hooks fish at edge of underwater vegetation in deep slough.

food swept around either side without fighting to hold position. Less obvious is the "cushion" of slowed water above a fast-current boulder and many a heavy trout stays in that. Undercut banks are obvious shelter and so are tree roots, but it is harder to guess what is on the bottom in heavier flows. Any little bulge in a slanting current and any deviation from the straightest downstream course means something on the bottom. When water is very clear and you can look down from a bluff you'll be surprised at the bottom pockets where current is almost completely absent, even when the surface rushes, and big trout may lie in slight depressions with only the gentlest of tail and fin motions.

While offshore fishermen may probe for upwellings or deep bottom structures, coastal anglers can often read their water with a glance, but the beginner

seldom knows what to look for. Surf fishermen read the wave patterns to find bait-filled sloughs and make the most of special water movements caused by nearby inlets or obstructions. Complicated things happen around an inlet. There are the easily forcasted in-and-out tidal movements and the turbulence caused when an onshore wind meets a swift runout. Some ocean fish go in and out with the tide and others, migrating along the coast, feel the inlet's movement and are attracted to its mouth where they may postpone their travels.

We know now that the most productive parts of the sea are near shore and we know that brackish water is the most productive of all. Inland bays, rivers and marshes are the nurseries of many salt water fish. Some ocean species reproduce there and others meet the fresh water runouts to feed on species from both sweet and brackish water. So some of the most important water reading of all occurs inland, about the inshore islands and on the shallow flats bordering the ocean. The shallower the water involved, the more dramatic the hour-to-hour change. Fishermen working the Florida Keys flats and those of the Caribbean islands can read water changes by the minute.

Take the bonefish, who lives much of the time in fairly deep water but moves to shallow flats to feed, especially when these are barely covered. Some of the bonefish's favorite feeding areas are completely exposed at low tide and it likes it that way because some of the little crustaceans it feeds on become especially active just before and after their territory "dries up."

A "channel" on a bonefish flat can be no more than a few inches deeper than the surrounding water, but it is well worth knowing about because a fish can swim there when it would be grounded only a few feet away.

When the tide is out, the wet marl glistens in the sun and the wading birds walk where they please. Then the tide starts to fill and it's time for an ambush at one of the little channels. The bonefish wait just outside and when the channel becomes deep enough to cover them they begin their trip farther inshore to where they will feed with their fins and tails exposed. Then, when the tide goes out, they'll come back the same way after it's too shallow for comfortable swimming elsewhere. It takes no great intellect to figure that they will be traveling the little channel, but if

Snook came from small run-in in mangrove river.

you're a water reader you'll have learned of that channel ahead of time and you'll be ready for them.

A lot of water, fresh and salt, is read with a thermometer and there's more difference in temperatures over a small area than most of us suppose. Here we become stuck with rules that are not always correct. It turns cold and we assume fish will head for deep water, which chills slowly. Sure, they find it warmer when they go deep. But when the sun gets bright for a while, it's the shallows that warm first. The fish know about that and you should, too.

Back to the bonefish flats where the changes are so quick and drastic. I once had a friend with me who was on his first bonefishing trip and I was looking pretty good. I had our boat at the edge of a little channel when the tide was just beginning to cover a giant flat and we found the fish going up it. Then, when the water was deep enough farther inland, I poled along and gave my guest a dozen good shots at feeding and cruising fish. I felt pretty cocky about the whole thing and he was impressed.

Then, I simply quit seeing fish. I poled hard and I stared until my eyes smarted. Nothing. I was looking so industriously that I didn't notice where I was going and I poled the skiff aground on a little bottom ridge. When I jumped out in my canvas shoes to push us off the obstruction, the water was so hot it actually burned my feet. No wonder the bonefish were gone. It was leave or get broiled. There was a hot sun that day, hardly any breeze, and I had gone so far from deep water that there was no "exchange." In other words, the water just lay there and waited for the outside tide to fall. If I hadn't had an acute attack of stupidity, I could have figured that out without burning my feet.

In the mangrove swamp of Florida's west coast I happened to see a parade of small tarpon coming down a small creek with mangrove branches knitted together over it. We'd been fishing for snook where the little creek emptied into a river, but when the tarpon began rolling in we began to strafe them with streamer flies and they struck eagerly. I guess we jumped more than twenty without moving our boat.

Tarpon have a habit of going in and out with the tide but this particular case was an extreme. I went up the little creek and found it drained from some very large and very shallow bays. Only at high tide were the tarpon comfortable up there. In the years since I first saw tarpon coming down that creek I've caught them both coming out and going in and at high tide I've followed them into the shallow bays and done some business there. I was slow to catch on, but that parade of fish through that little brackish creek goaded me into some worthwhile water study.

Proper mixture of lily pads, grasses and nearby solid cover helps bass fisherman.

With our eyes glued to flashing, buzzing and even recording fathometers, we shamelessly invade the black bass's privacy in deeper water, but some otherwise scientific fishermen are not quite with it on shallow-water analysis. There are things to be seen besides overhanging banks and rotting stumps. Here, again, the business of a fish's living along the edge of something can be a bit on the subtle side.

On weedy lakes with hardly any water completely open, the "edge law" still works. Find a row of bullrushes so thick they can't be penetrated by the bass and it still makes an edge that can produce better than nearby water, even though there may be lily pads, eelgrass, peppergrass, arrowhead, cattails, pickerel weed, milfoil or what have you, all over the lake. In casting into weedy water from a drifting boat I always perk up when the scenery changes slightly, since there have been so many times when a bigmouth boiled up where the bonnets gave way to eelgrass or a little scattered arrowhead showed among some floating water lettuce.

Of course some kinds of grass or weeds make better shelter and a solid barrier can be nice to drive bait against, but the love of bass for lines of demarcation is hard to explain. An eelgrass flat may hold a lot of fish and a bed of lily pads may be good, but the point where they join is generally best of all. I can list a few theories.

One is that bait fish prefer a place where they can do a little foraging in fairly open water and then duck back into thicker stuff when danger appears.

Another theory is that a moving fish simply pauses when he comes to a change in scenery, causing a sort of traffic concentration.

Perhaps a line between two kinds of water serves as a reference area and becomes a familiar landmark (or watermark) and the fish acquire a habit of traveling along that line, whether it's easier or not.

A change of vegetation often means a dropoff or ridge which is known to attract fish. This is the most reliable of all the bottom attractions, and emergent vegetation can be a telltale.

While we're dealing with a "point of reference," I have a much maligned theory that fish use "structures" the way we use street signs, and I strongly suspect that many species of fish in big water will use any permanent fixture as a homing device to tell where they are. Why not?

Even if it isn't large enough to hide any worthwhile food, a little lump on an otherwise smooth bottom is likely to attract one or more fish which seem to use it as a base of operations. Old wrecks in salt water may crumble to nothing more than a vague outline of the original ship but they still hold their bait fish, even when there seems to be nothing for a fishlet to get under or into—and where the bait fish stay, the predators appear.

It is hard to explain just why a 20-pound dolphin

Offshore structures of any kind hold gamefish.

will take up residence by a 2-foot piece of board that neither conceals it nor hides any food but there are other cases when ambushing instincts are involved. A big barracuda may choose a buoy as a permanent residence because this conceals it from bigger barracuda and from bait fish that may be attracted to it or swim past it. After all, a buoy usually marks something concerning the bottom or the current and probably the edge of something. In some spots these are "ghost" barracuda. Catch one and there'll be a near-duplicate at the same buoy in a few days. It's just right for that size 'cuda.

With most of the world covered by water, a fisherman needs to pick out the best parts.

Putting Graphite in Perspective

by Mark Sosin

Most of us are spoiled. Relatively inexpensive fiberglass rods of every description, taper and design have dominated the fishing scene for more than a quarter-century, making it possible for the average angler to acquire adequate tackle at little cost and enabling the serious practitioner of the sport to amass an arsenal of sticks to handle casting, trolling, fly rodding or basic bottom bouncing.

Rod builders were beginning to master the intricacies of the material, and fishermen seldom let their minds wander beyond the realm of fiberglass. Everyone knew that progress in the form of new materials would come some day, but the timetable was obscure and no composite loomed on the horizon with the boldness of a thunderstorm.

In back rooms and off-limits laboratories, a handful of companies had been experimenting with a number of materials that might have potential for fishing-rod construction. Suddenly, without tipping their hands to consumers or other tackle companies, a couple of rod manufacturers announced the introduction of graphite as a rod-building material.

Proponents of graphite touted it as a panacea for every problem that ever plagued a fisherman and predicted the demise of both fiberglass and cane. More thoughtful observers concluded that graphite would probably take its place in the scheme of things but would neither push glass nor bamboo into the oblivion of the passenger pigeon.

While the majority of rod makers probed cautiously to test the acceptability of graphite before instituting crash programs, fishermen blinked in disbelief at the attention that was being focused on them. If they were confused initially, they were now totally lost. To compound the confusion, advertising people searched for words to make their product look better than any other. Engineering terms such as modulus (which refers to the stiffness of a material or its resistance to deflection) were casually tossed about. Some makers claimed that their rods were built from high-modulus graphite, while others boasted that theirs were low-modulus graphite.

If you deal in words, both are right, providing you know what the comparisons are. Compared to the modulus of fiberglass (3 million to 6 million psi) or bamboo (6 million to 7 million psi), graphite, with a modulus of 12 million to 19 million psi, is certainly high. If you match it against some graphites used in

A delicate touch is vital in steelhead fishing, and that is where the sensitivity of graphite makes a difference. The fact that George Maki knows this river better than the street where he lives also helps.

fisherman could tell the graphite content of a rod by looking at it or waving it around a store.

The test of any rod is its performance on the water, not the material from which it is made. However, different materials bend or deflect at different rates and this can affect performance. When you put pressure on a glass rod, the fibers stretch or elongate about 4 percent. Amazingly, bamboo will stretch from 8 to 10 percent. Graphite, however, elongates slightly less than 1 percent. In a composite rod of graphite and glass, the graphite will be at maximum stretch when the glass is only at about 25 percent of capacity.

There are a few rod builders who make blanks out of 100 percent graphite and a number of manufacturers who use a composite of glass and graphite. If you buy a rod from a reputable manufacturer, however, the glass content will be minimal (usually less than 25 percent) and the glass is used primarily to achieve a desired action.

Graphite fishing rods are not simply expensively dressed versions of fiberglass; they are high-performance tools designed to help you catch more fish. The key is sensitivity. A well-designed graphite rod helps you to feel a bait or lure much better than you ever could before, because the ability to transmit vibrations is a function of modulus. The higher the modulus of the material, the better it will transmit vibrations.

Don't underestimate the importance of this tactile sensation until you have tried a graphite rod. Anglers suddenly know what's happening to their lures, can feel strikes they only imagined before and, some claim, can actually sense a fish breathing on a bait or lure.

aerospace and totally unsuited for fishing rods, it is low. Almost all rod manufacturers, regardless of what they claim, use graphite in the 12 million to 19 million psi range.

Although the modulus of the graphite used in fishing rods is within a given range, all graphite rods are not the same. Fishermen already knew that all fiberglass rods are not the same and neither are all cane rods. But uneducated consumers began to believe that if a rod were black or gray, it was graphite and would perform miracles. That was not true in the beginning and it is no more valid now. Some rod makers merely put a touch of graphite in a rod and built most of it of fiberglass. There was no way that a

Feeding a live menhaden to a waiting striped bass or bluefish offers a new sensation if you try it with a graphite rod. You can feel every movement of the bait, and you'll even think you detect the predator breathing on the bunker.

The last may be purely fishermen's talk, but the sensitivity in good graphite is marvelous.

A graphite rod that duplicated the length, diameter, taper and wall thickness of your favorite glass rod would be three times as stiff. To make the rods perform comparably, the diameter and the wall thickness of the graphite rod would have to be reduced, which, in turn, would make the rod lighter. There is simply less material in a graphite rod than in a glass rod of the same strength and power.

We already know that graphite has a higher modulus of elasticity than glass and that means that it is stiffer. Since it is also lighter than glass, there is not enough weight in the blank to throw against this stiffness when you test the rod in a tackle shop, and therefore the graphite rod has a stiffer feel. This might make you think that the rod is too stiff. The problem is further compounded by graphite's ability to load over a shorter arc than glass. The combination of quickness and stiffness in a rod is a totally new experience,

especially if you try to measure the results with old-fashioned yardsticks.

The only practical way to test a graphite rod is to rig it up with a lure of the proper weight, or, in the case of a fly rod, with the correct fly line. Then take the rod outside and cast it. The results will be totally different and the graphite rod will suddenly come to life.

Because it absorbs and releases energy over a shorter arc and because the timing is faster, graphite will cast more accurately than glass. There is also less wind-resistance as you move the rod back and forth, and this fact, coupled with the lightness and quickness, means that you don't need as much energy to

Light rods made from graphite add a new dimension to fishing for popular species; this weakfish is an example.

Slender graphite fly rods make it easy to cast a longer line and to fish with much less effort.

cast. Since graphite also responds faster, you don't have to turn the boat over trying to set the hook. A shorter upward stroke of the rod will have the same effect on the end of the line as a long sweep with a glass rod.

Over the years, fiberglass rods were overdesigned. Anglers began to abuse them, and, since there was plenty of margin in the material, they were made so strong that a fisherman could use one as a boat hook or duel a tree stump with the tip to retrieve a snagged lure. On an equal-weight basis, graphite is four times as strong as steel and twice as strong as fiberglass, but this is true only when you compare them ounce for ounce or pound for pound. It does not mean that if you put the tip of a graphite rod in an open car door and slam the door shut, the car will be dented. You'll chop off the rod tip every time.

Top-quality glass today is designed to work in a fishing rod at about 40 percent of its breaking strength. Graphite, on the other hand, works at 60 to 70 percent. That means there is less margin for error, but you also get more out of the material as you work it at higher stress levels. A rod designed to be delicate yet durable should perform at somewhere between 50 percent and 75 percent of maximum. This range produces the greatest advantage as a fishing tool and the most sensitivity. Glass rods cannot be made to perform in that range because the right raw materials are not available and also because traditionally glass rods have been built as strong as wading staffs.

A quality graphite rod, like a fine watch, is a precision instrument that is tuned to a need. It can be carried every day, used anywhere and is rugged, durable and reliable. It is not a wading staff, however; nor is it a boat hook, lure retriever or a lever for a tug of war with a tree. Designers are working in the direction of sensitivity rather than overdesigning the stress levels.

The biggest question plaguing some anglers today in connection with graphite is whether they should buy a rod now or wait until the material has been around a lot longer. There's no question that the cost of a graphite rod is much higher than that of a glass one, but one is also buying a high-performance tool that is the result of a more costly and demanding manufacturing process. All of us have seen miracle products come on the market and, after a reasonable period, drop considerably in price. This has happened with all sorts of things, from ball-point pens and television sets to the newest pocket calculators.

Experts on graphite do not expect substantial price reductions in the next few years. Some of them talk of a new pitch process, which has not been fully developed but which, if successful, could cause prices to

Graphite surf rods are still expensive and there are not many of them around, but it won't be long before they become standard equipment for more serious surf fishermen.

drop. Ironically, a shotgunner often spends much more money on a scattergun that sees service only a few days a year. The gunner, however, knows that the balance of a better gun can make a difference, the barrel is truer and the firing mechanism is more reliable and perhaps more sensitive. Fishermen are going to have to realize that if they want the ultimate in performance, it will cost more money. There are those who contend that the question is no longer whether or not to buy a graphite rod, but how many an angler should own.

When graphite rods first came on the market, there was a certain amount of breakage, partly because of designers' misconceptions as to how thin the walls should be and partly because anglers were used to the excessive strength of glass. Graphite is a totally different material, which does not load in the same way that glass does. If you try to scribe a glass arc with a graphite rod, you may break it. It takes a little practice to develop the necessary feel, just as it does with bamboo or glass.

Interestingly, the major rod manufacturers who introduced graphite stood behind their products and replaced evey broken rod. The design problems were quickly solved; a graphite rod today is not the same as one made a couple of years ago. If you place your confidence in rods from a reputable and well-known manufacturer, you will be covered by his guarantee. Look for it on the rods.

Selecting the actual model is not easy, or at least not as simple as it is with fiberglass. You already know that you should rig up the rod and try it. If possible, compare it with a similar glass rod. One way of finding the right rod is to try those of friends who have already moved into graphite. You may not find the best rod the first time around, but almost any quality graphite rod is a better fishing tool than a glass one, so you can't lose in the transition.

Although graphite blanks are being made into more and more rod designs, certain applications are far

Bjorn Bjornson, one of Iceland's most famous anglers, still casts a two-hand bamboo salmon rod that is about 15 feet long. Rod builders are testing two-hand graphite models that weigh a fraction of this rod and will cast easier and farther.

Although they are light in weight and thin in diameter, graphite rods of any design have the power to slug it out with big tough fish such as this skyrocketing tarpon.

Countless casts are commonplace before an Atlantic salmon will strike a fly. Graphite fly rods provide an important edge in this type of fishing.

more significant than others and these are the areas in which you should look for your first graphite rod. Remembering that graphite is lighter than glass or bamboo, look for graphite to replace heavier rods and to obtain longer rods that didn't exist before. There is also something to be said for delicate rods made of graphite.

Fly fishermen tend to embrace graphite with a newly discovered enthusiasm once they try their first fly rod made from this Space Age material. The average caster finds that he adds at least 10 feet, and possibly 15 or more, to his present casting distance by using a correctly designed graphite rod. There are a number of reasons for this. Timing is easier to master with a faster-acting rod than with a slower one, and since graphite stores energy and unloads it faster than

Forrest Wood snaked this average-size bass out of some submerged branches. The sensitivity of his graphite rod helped him monitor the progress of his lure.

Longer fly rods tailored for lighter lines are one of the big advantages of graphite. A fly rod over 8 feet long makes it easier to roll-cast, mend a line and fish a stream.

other rod materials do, this is an advantage. More important, the tighter the loop you can cast in fly fishing, the farther the line will go. Loop size is determined by the power stroke. The shorter the stroke, the tighter the loop. It takes a lot of practice to develop the necessary power stroke with a glass or bamboo rod, but since graphite unleashes its energy over a very short arc, a graphite rod actually helps to shorten the stroke.

No matter how perfectly a fly rod of any material is designed, there are a certain number of up-and-down vibrations of the rod tip when you apply power in a cast. Known as natural frequency, these pendulum swings of the tip cause waves to occur in the fly line. Graphite deflects less to accept the same load and recovers faster. This greater dampening effect not only reduces the number of vibrations but shortens the distance between the peaks and valleys. Every time you cast a fly and move the rod, you must

straighten the line before it goes anywhere. It's exactly as if you were trying to move a lawn sprinkler by pulling the hose: you have to remove all the curves in the hose before the sprinkler begins to move.

The second major area of importance to the fly fisherman is the construction of longer fly rods for lighter lines and of long fly rods for one-hand and two-hand casting. The angler who tosses a bass tug from a canoe or wades waist deep in salt water to blind-cast for the elusive striped bass is bound to benefit from a 10½-foot fly rod that handles a 9-weight line. The same type of longer rod gives the fisherman an edge in a high wind or in working the shallow flats or even when there isn't much room for a back cast.

Stream fishermen sometimes select very short fly rods of unusually light weight, add a relatively heavy reel and line and then delude themselves into believing that they have chosen sporting and practical tackle. A far better approach is to use a longer rod which will permit better roll casts, superior line mending and easier fishing. Before graphite, exceptionally long rods were impractical, but that situation has changed. A 9-foot rod capable of handling a 5-weight line is superb for many kinds of fishing.

The bass aficionado who crawls a plastic worm over the umbrella limbs of a sunken tree or cranks a spinner bait can feel the vibrations through a graphite rod. The quicker release of energy aids casting accuracy and the lightness in weight can make a difference when you're chucking a lure ten times a minute.

Graphite surf rods are both longer and lighter than those made of glass and a far cry from the old Calcuttas that once stood majestically in sand spikes with revolving spool reels trussed to the cane with hose clamps. The greater length may make it possible to reach sloughs and bars that were out of reach of the standard surf stick.

Once you recognize that a graphite fishing rod is a tool and not a lever, you will begin to gain a tremendous edge. It provides the means of imparting a delicate and unique action to lures and of sensing the results through vibrations or even visually. With graphite, you'll get more out of a topwater lure than you ever did before, because of the quickness inherent in the material. When you raise your wrist to set the hook on a fish, you will be amazed at how rapidly the power is transferred.

Researchers state frankly that graphite has an ability to give performance that glass does not and probably never will have. Rated on a scale of 10, graphite would be either 8 or 9, while the best glass available now would barely make 5.5.

A lot depends on how you look at graphite and its effect on your fishing. In the final accounting, it may be a bargain at $100 to $200 per rod.

Tying and Fishing the Fur Nymph

by Poul Jorgensen

Trout fishing with a nymph can be a very exciting and rewarding experience, which, more often than any other method of angling in fresh water, will bring the lunkers up from feeding stations in deep pools and fast runs. It has often been said that fishing with artificial nymphs (imitations of the immature stage of May flies and other flying stream insects) is very difficult and was devised for professionals and anglers with special talent. This is simply not true. Nymph fishing is just another method of trout fishing and can be learned by anyone who can use a fly rod. What may cause confusion for the novice is the selection of flies. If you ask ten trout anglers to recommend nymphs, you will get ten different answers, none of which clears up the confusion. I know anglers who carry in their vest pockets boxes containing several hundred different patterns of nymphs, but they will tell you that they rarely use more than a few so-called standards in three different colors and many sizes. Such standards cover almost everything you need for a good day of nymph fishing. It takes only a few minutes to search the debris or turn over a few rocks and capture some specimens with a small aquarium net or seine to determine the size and color of the naturals found in the stream you are about to fish. With such evidence, you are able to pick an artificial that's sure to be a winner.

By far the best nymphs I have ever used are those made from the underfur of such animals as red and gray fox, woodchuck, black and brown bear, and others with fairly coarse pelts. The fur from a baby seal was long considered the very best for the tying of nymphs, but the import restrictions imposed on skins from these animals have made the stuff very scarce, and an excellent substitute called "Seal-Ex" is now being used instead. It dubs easily and has an even better sheen and translucency than actual seal fur. Regardless of which one you use, there is something about a juicy fur nymph that a trout just can't resist. If you know the fundamentals of fly tying, it is fairly simple to make effective fur nymphs by following the instructions given here. If you need to learn the basics of the fine art of fly tying, the section of this book called "The Angler's Bookshelf" lists books about various fishing subjects, including basic fly tying and how to identify materials.

Materials

To tie a selection of nymphs that will take fish anywhere in North America, you will need the following hooks and materials:

Hooks
Mustad #3906, Regular length
Mustad #3906B, Extra Long shank
Mustad #38941, 3X Long shank

These hooks have a sproat bend, which makes the nymph ride better in the current. Sizes range from 4 through 16.

Tying Thread
Herb Howard's 6/0 prewaxed, chosen to match the overall color of the nymph. The most common are tan, brown and black. (The prewaxed type is a must for dubbing in a spinning loop.)

For Tails
Fibers from the center of the tail of a ringneck pheasant. Both light

Tying Instructions

Step 1. Start the nymph by tying in three pheasant tail fibers. They should be about the same length as the hook shank. (It's always best to practice the tying of an unfamiliar pattern on a large hook such as a size 8 or 10.) When the tails are secured, form a spinning loop at the tie-in position. (To make a spinning loop release about 8 inches of tying thread between the spot where it leaves the hook and the tip of your bobbin. Place your index finger in the middle and double the thread over your finger and back to where it leaves the hook. Secure it with a couple of turns around the shank. If you wish, you can make a few turns directly around the loop tightly against the hook.) Now wind the thread forward to a position slightly past the middle of the hook shank.

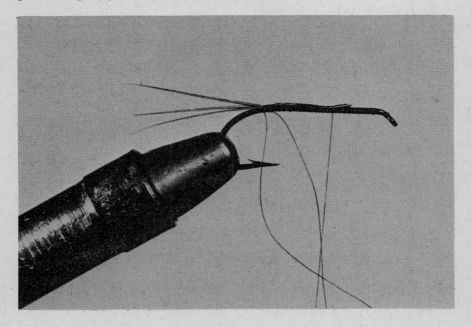

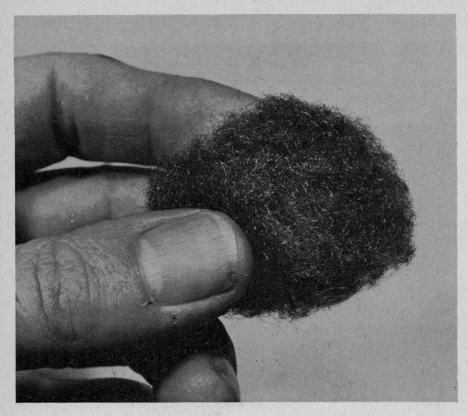

Step 2. Prepare the fur dubbing by mixing and fluffing it thoroughly with an electric blender or a small coffee grinder, or hand-mix well. Roll the dubbing into a fur puff between your hands.

Step 3. Draw enough fur from the "puff" to form a thin, tapered layer of dubbing about 3 inches long (measurement calculated for a Size 8 Extra Long hook 3906B).

and dark fibers are usually found on the same feather, but since the tails are relatively inexpensive, it is best to get a complete one to provide a better selection.

For Abdomens (Rear half of the body)

A selection of the fur dubbings and Seal-Ex mentioned earlier. The colors should be chosen so you can make a creamish-tan, medium-brown and blackish-brown body. The fur should be cut from the skin and mixed into the dubbing.

Thorax and Legs (Front half of the nymph)

Pieces of skin with underfur and guardhairs from the back of a brown rabbit and from the neck and sides of an Australian opossum. The neck portion of the latter gives you the dark-gray to blackish-gray shades, and the sides are cream to tan in color. All the types mentioned can be dyed but are usually acceptable in their natural shades. The fur should not be cut from the skin until you are ready to use it. If possible, get whole skins for better selection.

Wing Case (On nymphs this lays flat on top of the thorax portion of the body.)

Latex trimmed to shape. This thin rubber material is relatively new in fly tying; it can be purchased from a supplier in small sheets. For tinting of wing cases, use a good waterproof felt-tip marking pen, such as the Pantone Marker, that comes in a wide variety of colors and shades.

The same tying procedure is used for all the nymphs in the series, regardless of color or size. With practice, it is possible to dress quite a few of these little "winners"

Step 4. Insert the dubbing in the loop and fasten a pair of heavy hackle pliers on the end.

Step 5. Spin the dubbing into a ropelike tapered piece of material. (Use the pliers as a weight; just flip them with your fingers and they will spin the dubbing.) As the dubbing is being spun, help the fur around and spread it with your fingers to an even taper.

in the course of an evening. There are times when a nymph should be weighted with some thin lead wire wrapped around the hook shank. The lead is applied on the shank just before the abdomen fur is wound. This will aid the nymph to sink deeper and faster if necessary. The unweighted nymph is designed to be fished right under the surface, or in other situations where a slow-sinking nymph is desirable. In recent years it has become fashionable to fish the nymph as an emerger (a hatching insect struggling in the surface film to free itself from the nymphal chuck). For this purpose you can use the nymph unweighted but dressed underneath with some silicone floatant, and it will ride on the surface like a dry fly.

Fishing the Fur Nymph

Unlike dry fly fishing in which the angler is able to follow the fly and observe the take, nymphs are fished under water and will in most cases be out of the angler's vision. A take must be felt or observed from any erratic movement of leader or line. Many trout anglers fish a nymph by casting it across the stream and letting it work down with the current until the line straightens out directly below the casting position. When the line and leader straighten, short rhythmic flicks with the rod tip will give some motion to the nymph, encouraging a strike by a fish that may have followed it. This rather old-fashioned method enables you to cover a lot of water by systematically casting the same length of line and taking a few steps up or down before each new cast, but it will not get the most fish.

Today's successful nymph fish-

Step 6. Apply some clear cement on the hook shank and wind the dubbing to form the abdomen. Tie it off in the middle of the hook shank and trim away the surplus. Now form another spinning loop directly in front of the abdomen and wind the tying thread forward to 1/16 inch from the hook eye.

Step 7. Cut a thin layer of fur and guardhair from the skin without disturbing the natural direction of the fibers. (A little practice will enable you to cut just enough for a particular size of nymph). The fur color should match the rear body portion closely or be a little darker. Hold the fur layer with your fingers and trim the butt ends to make the fur and guardhair as long as one hook length.

Step 8. Insert the fur layer in the loop and spread it carefully so it occupies about 1½ inches. Note the position of the fur. The long tip ends extending to the left in the loop (one hook length) will form the legs and at the same time the short side will form the thorax when the fur is wound on the hook later.

Step 9. Spin a fur chenille as shown, using the same procedure as for spinning the dubbing (steps 4 and 5).

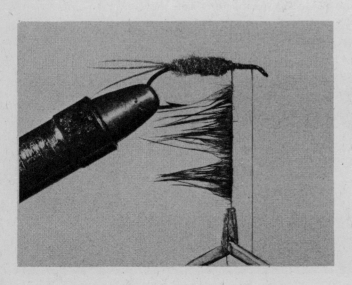

Step 10. Hold the fur chenille tightly away from the hook and moisten it a little before stroking all the fur and guardhair back so that it appears to be coming out from one side of the loop only. The tips should be pointing toward the rear.

Step 11. Apply some clear cement on the hook shank and wind the fur on the thorax portion in front of the abdomen. Tie off in front 1/16 inch from the hook eye and cut off the surplus, if any. The space in front is for tying in the wing case.

Step 12. Cut a piece of latex about 1 inch long and a little wider than the body width. Trim one end as shown to imitate the natural wing case.

Step 13. Trim away all the fur on top of the thorax portion, leaving it long on the sides and underneath to represent the legs. When the fur is trimmed away, lay the trimmed latex piece on top and tie it on in front. From the tie-in point the wing case should reach almost to the middle of the nymph. Secure it tightly, then apply a whip finishing knot or several half-hitches before cutting the tying thread.

Step 14. Trim the surplus latex in front, leaving enough to represent a small head. Tint the wing case with a waterproof marking pen to make it a little darker than the rest of the nymph. When it is tinted, take a pale-colored marking pen and wipe off the dark tint on the wing tips for an added effect. Add a little clear cement on the windings. This completes your nymph.

erman uses a short line (20 to 30 feet) upstream cast, which enables him to have good line control and to manipulate the nymph over underwater pockets and rocks where the fish have their feeding stations. This type of fishing is best done with an 8- to 10½-foot rod, slow action, taking a 5- to 7-weight line and a 9- to 12-foot tapered leader. Place your cast so the nymph will enter the water above a good riffle or run. When it hits the water, lift the rod tip slowly and leave as little line as possible on the water. If the cast is short enough, you will be able to see the nail knot between the line and the leader. As the current moves the nymph downstream, follow it with your rod tip at about eye level, assuming that the nymph moves at the same speed as the stream current. The advantage of this method of nymphing is that the fly comes down almost drag-free. The slight "arc" in the fly line suspended between the rod tip and the water surface gives you good control so you can see or feel when the fish takes. Pay close attention to the nail knot if you can see it. When it stops or moves in any direction other than down with the speed of the current, lift your rod tip gently and, *whammo,* the fish is on and running.

When you have nymph fished for some time and have discovered the many secrets and tricks you can use for various fishing conditions, you will also have learned that there is no single nymph or fishing method that will take fish all the time and that even nymphing has "dog days." But one thing is for sure: With a good selection of fur nymphs tied as described earlier, you are one step ahead of a potential catch.

Basic Rod Building
by Bub Church

The most difficult aspect of rod building is selecting what you want to build from the myriad of blanks and components on the market. The technique itself is within the scope of anyone's capabilities, and with a little practice you can become extremely good at it.

Fishermen not only save money by assembling their own rods (the cost is less than half the retail price of the finished rod) and have fun doing it but also get an extra sense of accomplishment from catching fish on tackle they have personally put together. Knowing how to build a rod also enables you to work up specialized designs that are not available in most tackle shops and it is a hobby that can provide ample enjoyment in the off-season.

Glass is the perfect blank mate-rial for the rod builder because it is strong and forgiving (usually over-designed as far as strength is con-cerned), the price is low, it is readi-ly available in a wide range of models and it is resistant to the elements as well as to most chemi-cals. Graphite is more expensive and a more delicate material to work with, but it certainly costs less to build your own graphite rod than to buy one. Bamboo is a ma-terial reserved for the very ad-vanced practitioner unless it comes in kit form or the sections are preglued.

If you know rods and their com-ponents, choosing the right mate-rials will be second nature. If you are a newcomer, it makes sense to visit a tackle shop that specializes in rod-building components and ask for help in selecting the right blank, cork, reel seat, guides and tip-top for your needs.

If you're ready, let's get started. Be sure to pick a clean place to work, and allow yourself ample room.

To make it easier, the following instructions are broken down into four sections. The first three deal with installing grips and reel seat, wrapping a guide and installing a metal ferrule if the blank isn't al-ready ferruled and you want a two-piece rod. One aspect of build-ing your own rods is the fun of decorating them distinctively, and the well-known diamond wrap is one way of doing this. Basic dia-mond wrapping is described in the fourth section; more intricate pat-terns are merely a matter of your own imagination.

I. Assembling the Grips

Step 1. After selecting the blank you are going to use, you next determine the spline. When the cloth is wrapped around the mandril during construction of the blank, the line where it stops creates a slightly stiffer side called the spline. To spline a rod, put the tip against a hard surface and, holding it gently in both hands as shown, push against the tip. You will actually feel the rod snap to one position. The guides can be placed along the spline or on the opposite side, depending on preference. Mark the spline so you can align the reel seat and guides with it later.

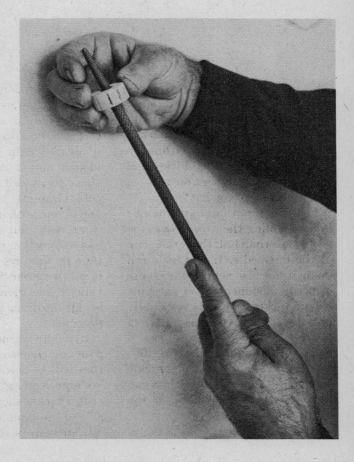

Step 2. If you are going to use cork rings for a grip instead of a preshaped grip of cork or other material, the inside diameters must be fitted to the diameter and taper of the blank. Use a round file to do this.

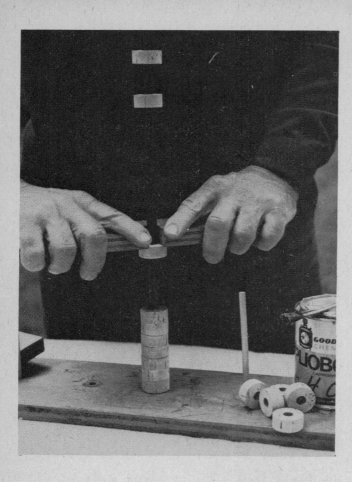

Step 3. By cutting a notch in a block of wood, you can use it to push the cork rings down on the blank. A good adhesive should be applied to each ring to glue it to the other rings. A dowel in a board enables you to hold the rod blank vertically while fitting the rings.

Step 4. When the cork rings are in place, put the blank in a lathe and while it is turning use sandpaper to shape the cork. Be sure to tape the reel seat and blank to avoid abrading these components if the sandpaper slips.

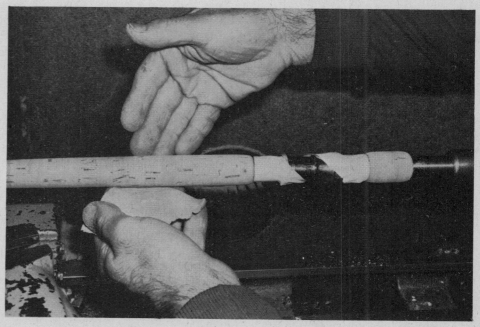

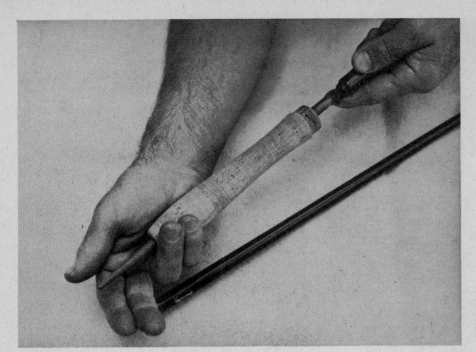

Step 5. Many rod builders are now using preshaped grips. These usually have to be reamed out until they fit the blank and this is done by trial and error.

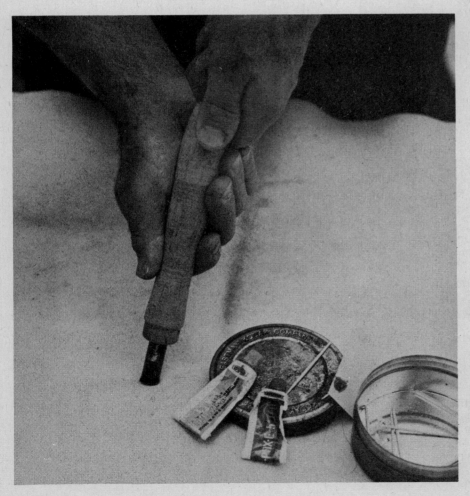

Step 6. Once the grip fits, apply epoxy, rubber-based cement or other adhesive and seat the grip.

Step 7. Install the sleeve under the reel seat and make sure it fits. Glue these in place.

Step 8. The reel seat is then glued and positioned. Install the foregrip and anything else that has to be slid over the blank; for example, a hozzle or winding check if you decide to use these items.

II. Wrapping the Guides

Guide spacing and determining the correct number of guides must be done before you begin to wrap. Too many guides seldom affect the rod, but too few can destroy performance. The first and most important step is to determine the distance between the face of the reel (assuming one were in the reel seat) and the first guide.

As a general rule and to help you get started, you can try the following distances: ultralight spinning, 22 inches; medium spinning, 25 inches; surf rod (over 8½ feet), 34 inches; bait casting, 17 to 19 inches; fly rod, 30 inches. Remember that the spacing between each guide gets progressively shorter as you work toward the tip-top. Spinning rods should have at least five guides and a tip-top; casting rods need five to seven guides and fly rods should have a minimum of eight guides.

The best approach is to tape the guides in place and then test the rod before wrapping them on permanently. You may, if you choose, use an underwrap or a more decorative wrap. The technique is the same as that shown for the basic wrap.

Step 9. For wrapping a rod, the thread must be maintained under tension. A simple way to do this is to drill a hole in a block of wood and install a bolt. With a spring and a couple of nuts to adjust tension, the gadget works and it can be clamped anywhere. Thread sizes are a matter of preference, but we recommend size A or D for fresh water rods and D or E for salt water. Once you gain experience, you can use finer threads if you prefer.

Step 10. Before placing the guides in position, use a file to taper the edges and to clean off any burrs that might remain. Filing insures that the thread will seat neatly.

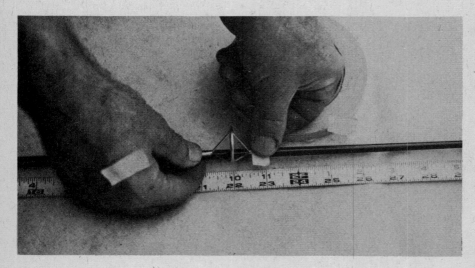

Step 11. Use a tape measure to place each guide correctly. As recommended, we have used 22 inches between the face of the reel and the center of the first guide. To help you align the guides, install the tip-top first and make sure it lines up with the fixed hood on the reel seat.

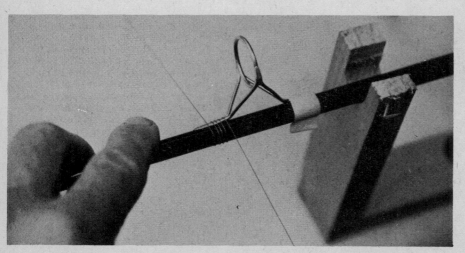

Step 12. When each guide has been taped in position, remove the tape from one foot of the first guide and begin to wrap. By putting four or five spaced turns over the guide and then pulling on the tag end of the thread, you can get a neat and even beginning.

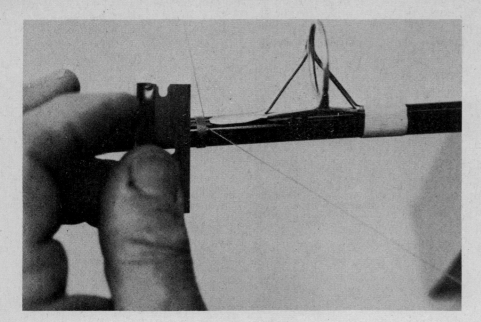

Step 13. After you have started the wrap, use a sharp razor blade to trim the tag end flush with the wrap. This should be done before the foot of the guide is reached.

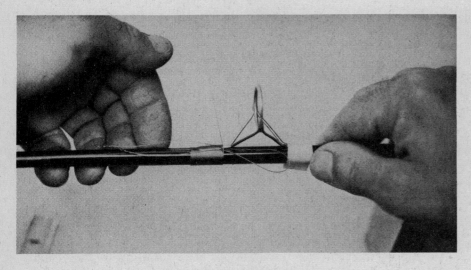

Step 14. When there are only five or six wraps left, insert a loop of thread or monofilament as shown.

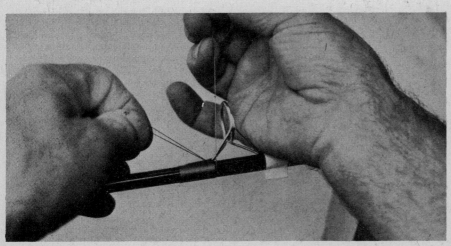

Step 15. Cut the thread after the final wrap and, while holding the threads in place, insert the tag end through the loop you have already tied in. Static electricity sometimes makes it tricky to insert the end of the thread. Moisten it with saliva and you won't have the problem. Pull the loop and the end of the thread is tucked neatly under the last six wraps.

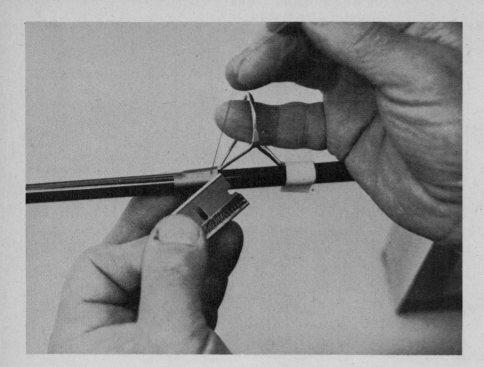

Step 16. Pull the thread tight with one hand and just touch a very sharp razor blade to it with the other hand.

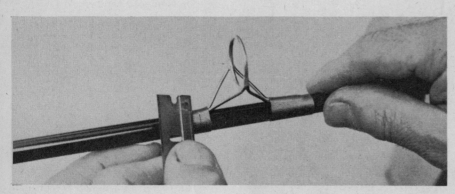

Step 17. Any openings in the thread can be closed by rubbing the back edge of the razor blade across them several times.

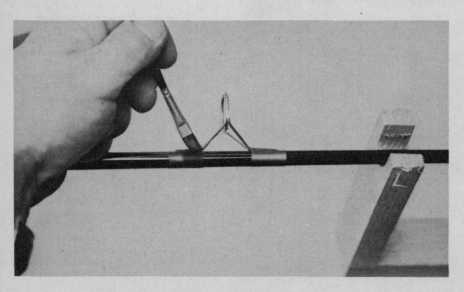

Step 18. The best way to apply a finish is to use a motor to rotate the rod slowly and continuously. There are a number of finishes available and each has its advantages. Polyurethane varnish or finish requires a number of coats, but once applied it creates a fine, durable coating that can be removed at any time. Epoxy and two-part polymer finishes are excellent but almost impossible to remove. Some of these, however, require only a single coat.

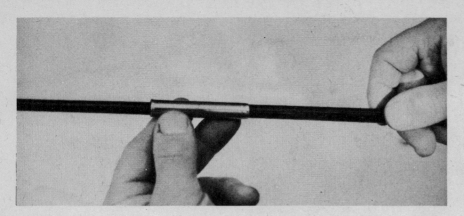

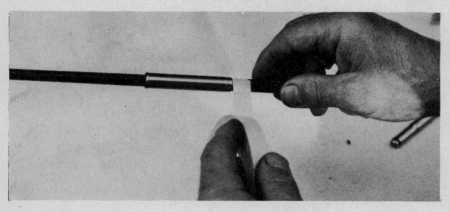

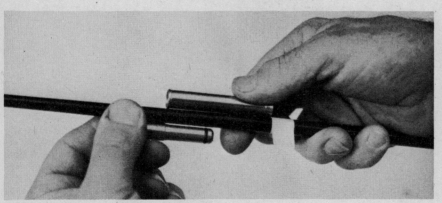

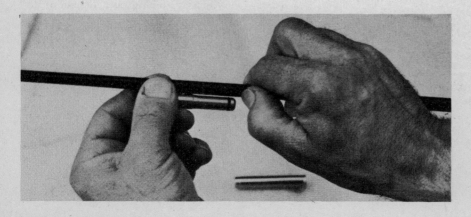

III. Installing A Metal Ferrule

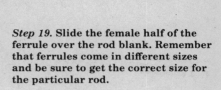

Step 19. Slide the female half of the ferrule over the rod blank. Remember that ferrules come in different sizes and be sure to get the correct size for the particular rod.

Step 20. When the female ferrule is seated, mark the blank by wrapping a piece of masking tape around it.

Step 21. Remove the female ferrule and hold it against the blank with the bottom of the ferrule touching the tape you just applied. With the other hand, hold the male ferrule in position exactly where it will seat when inserted in the female.

Step 22. Without moving the male ferrule, put down the female ferrule and mark the spot on the blank 1/8 inch below the base of the male ferrule. This is where you will cut the blank.

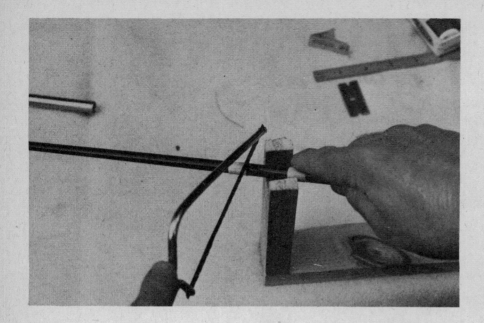

Step 23. You can use another piece of masking tape to mark the spot where the blank will be cut (see Step 22). Then carefully cut the blank.

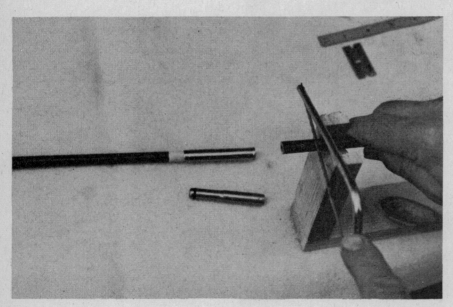

Step 24. Now the fitting process begins. In most aluminum glass-rod ferrules, the inside diameter of the male socket (where the tip of the rod will seat) is 1/64-inch less than the inside diameter of the female side. Continue to cut the blank until the male ferrule fits.

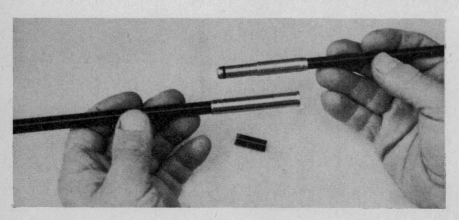

Step 25. Glue each section of the ferrule in place. You now have a two-piece rod.

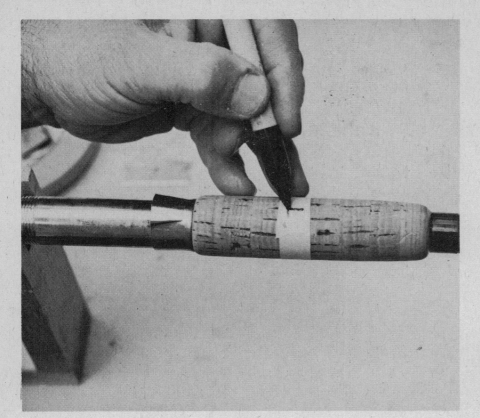

IV. The Basic Diamond Wrap

This basic decorative wrap is gaining in popularity and is very easy to do. As you gain experience, you may want to try more intricate patterns. The technique is the same; you merely add more threads.

Step A. Using the guides and fixed hood of the reel seat as a benchmark, mark the top of the rod. Then mark the exact bottom of the rod, which is the point directly beneath the top line. Do this carefully. If your marks are off, the diamonds will be off to the side.

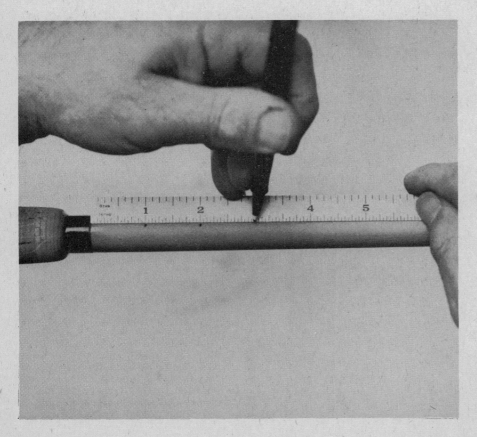

Step B. Determine the interval at which the threads will cross. You may, for example, select an interval of one inch on the top, crossing on the inch. Put a dot at each spot where the threads will cross.

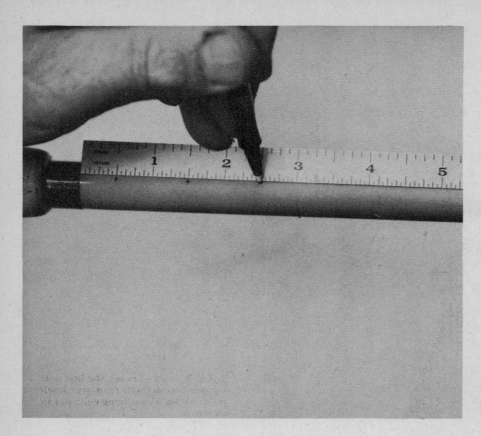

Step C. Although the bottom spacing is the same, the thread will cross half the distance between the top spacing. In this case, it is every inch on the half-inch. Put a dot at each junction.

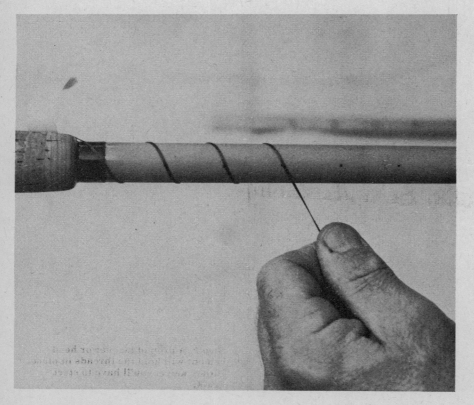

Step D. Take three strands of E thread of the first color and tape them to the foregrip of the rod. You'll have to adjust the position so that the angle will enable you to cross over the first dot. Very carefully rotate the rod and guide the thread so that it passes over each dot on the top and bottom. Position is important. If you are off, the spacing between diamonds will not be equal and they will not be aligned.

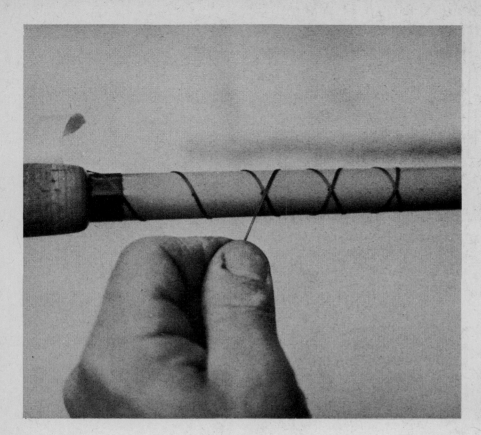

Step E. **When you reach the last dot, you must cross the thread over itself and work back, covering each dot in sequence.**

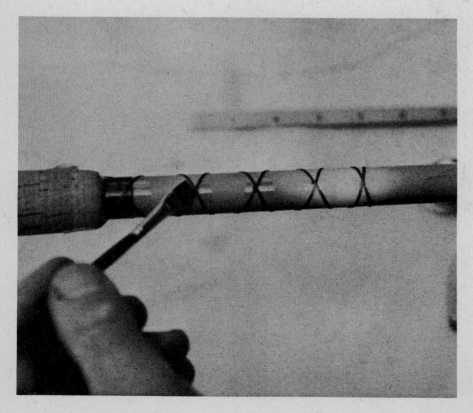

Step F. **A drop of lacquer or head cement will hold the threads in place. If they move, you'll have to start again.**

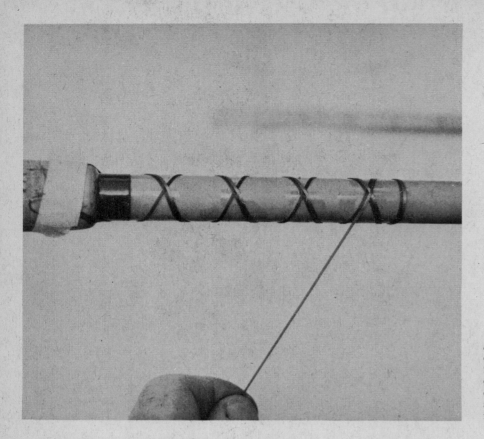

Step G. Take three strands of a second color, tape them to the foregrip, and repeat the wrapping process. The second color must lie alongside the first color. When you have worked forward and back, tape the ends against the foregrip.

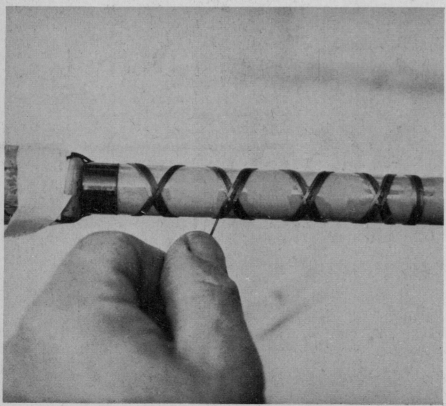

Step H. With another three strands of the second color, wrap forward and back along the other side of the first color. You will now begin to see the diamond pattern as the thread is worked back toward the grip.

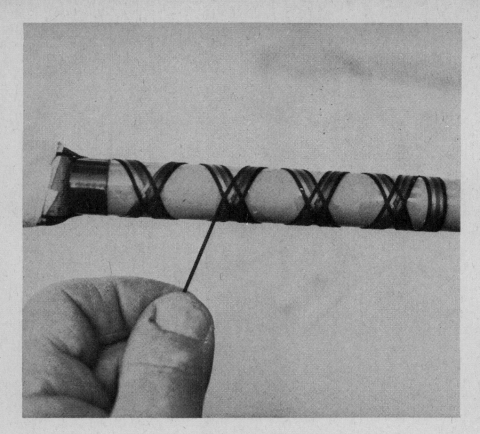

Step I. Introduce a third color, using three strands of E thread and wrapping them back and forth. You have now completed the basic diamond. If you prefer, you can underwrap before doing a diamond or space them closer together. We recommend, however, that you try the basic one first.

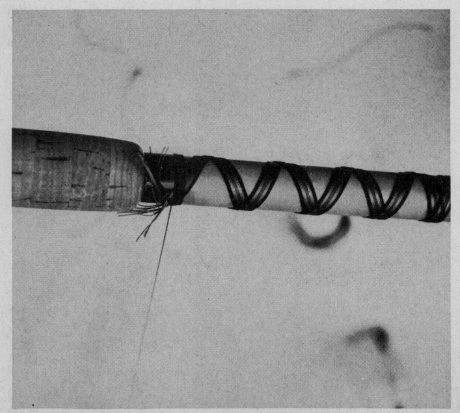

Step J. At this point, all the loose ends of the various threads are still taped to the butt. Using another piece of thread, start a single wrap from the end of the diamonds back toward the cork grip. Finish it off just as you would a guide. The purpose of this wrap is to hold all the loose thread ends. They should be trimmed after five or six turns of thread have covered them.

Float Tripping to Faster Fishing

by Erwin A. Bauer

Some of my happiest fishing adventures by far—and some of the most successful as well—have been float trips down the beautiful waterways of America. Not only has floating added a rich new dimension to my sport, but it has also taken me to places where few other anglers have preceded me and where the fishing pressure is relatively light. Drifting and casting with the current make a combination hard to match anywhere nowadays.

The first trips I can recall were made on such streams of southern and central Ohio as Rattlesnake, Big Walnut, Big Darby, Kokosing, Mohican and the Great Miami. Keep in mind that even thirty years ago Ohio was already a densely populated state which had suffered every kind of "development" and "improvement" man can inflict on his rivers, from unchecked pollution to channelization. It wasn't easy to find pure enough water to support gamefish, and everywhere there was great competition from the million other sportsmen in the Buckeye State.

Still a person with a boat could leave the highways, the crowded lakes and his fellow fishermen behind simply by launching on one of the streams mentioned and spending the day beyond the beaten tracks, which

rarely extend more than a short hiking distance beyond the bridges. We did exactly that at every opportunity and from the moment our canoe was caught in the lukewarm current, we enjoyed the very best sport a crowded, highly industrialized region has to offer.

One favorite trip was down a section of the Mohican which I will not identify because it is too small for intense pressure. This section covered about 5½ miles between two bridges which were our put-in and take-out points. That is approximately the right distance to fish leisurely but carefully on a typical spring day when the current is slow moving. At times, because of heavy May rains, the river was too high or roily to fish, but our batting average usually was high and we caught a good many fish.

In fact, this was smallmouth bass fishing as fast as any in the Midwest at that time. The fish averaged about 1½ pounds apiece, and every year or so somebody would boat one close to 4 pounds. Besides that, there were goggle-eyes and, in deeper holes along the way, channel catfish. If it became a warm and lazy day, Lew Baker and I would often pause at a midway point, take a refreshing swim and then at streamside

Float trips can be of any duration and long ones are possible if camping gear is carried along.

fry some channel cat fillets. That was living. But if it happened to be September or October rather than June, we would carry along a 22 and keep an eye peeled for the huge fox squirrels which lived in the wooded Mohican bottomlands. If there is anything more satisfying than a fishing float trip with a close friend, it is a fishing and hunting trip combined.

But take my word that float trips are not just for nostalgia. On the contrary, floating is today an angling technique as important as wading or plug casting. Some streams cannot be fished well any other way. No matter where the outdoorsman lives—in wilderness country or suburbia, East or West, near southern swamps or northern evergreen forests—the odds are good that float tripping can increase both his catch and his total fishing pleasure.

Exactly what is a float trip? What does an average fisherman need to try float tripping on his own?

Any downstream drift, or float, is the most quiet and economical means of fishing certain rivers. You use the current either entirely or mostly for propulsion while you concentrate on fishing along the way. No hard labor there. You might be casting for anything from sunfish to salmon, from perch to pike,

depending on the waterway and the time of year. Any number can play and for almost any length of time. One fisherman can drift alone, but perhaps it's even better with two; one can handle the boat while the other casts. A float can be for a day, a few hours or for a week or more if the participants care to take camping gear along. I have often done so, and camping also contributes much to the adventure.

Of course the main component is a suitable watercraft. This can be anything from a log raft, an inflatable rubber boat, a canoe, all the way up to a cabin cruiser, depending on the size and depth of the river. But here I am mainly talking about shallow-draft craft, fishing boats that will slide safely over riffles and still be comfortable for the occupants who may have to sit in place for hours at a time. The boat should also be easy to handle.

The type of water definitely dictates the type of boat. On some angry whitewater Western rivers, which I discuss later, a large rubber raft is the only answer. Rivers not quite so fast and wild can be managed in canoes if the anglers are familiar with these frail craft and feel confident in them. Canoes are hard to beat for many kinds of floating but, I must emphasize, *only* for

Fat northern pike taken by Bill Gressard while float tripping the Little Churchill River of northern Manitoba.

fishermen who have had some experience and attained some skill with them.

There is a bewildering variety of canoes on the market, some much less tippy and more reliable than others. As a rule of thumb, larger and wider is better. Sponsons (often called pontoons), built in along the tops of the gunwales to provide air spaces or flotation chambers, greatly reduce the chance of a canoe's capsizing. Some manufacturers, Grumman among them, offer pairs of polyurethane pontoons which can be clamped onto any canoe, as needed, in just a few minutes. My wife Peggy and I have used a number of different canoes for float trip fishing recently and have found two especially suit our needs and provide comfort, plus safety. One is the Delhi 15-footer by Delhi (Terry Bass Boats) of Louisiana; the other is the square-ended Grumman Sport Canoe, which we use when it is necessary or helpful to use a low-horsepower outboard motor. The power can be turned on when returning upstream or to hurry through occasional stretches of "dead" water.

Mostly because vast stretches of rivers in the Ozarks are now smothered forever, deep under giant

A shore dinner at midday breaks up a float trip during exploration of remote waters in northern Manitoba.

Would you believe that this scene of floating was taken on Rattlesnake Creek in highly developed, industrialized Ohio? It's good channel catfish water.

reservoirs, the once-famous float fishing on such streams as the White and Ouachita rivers has been forgotten. The craft formerly used were square ended, square sterned, super stable, with a very shallow draft and were known as Ozark or Arkansas "johnboats." But exactly this same design, built in either aluminum or wood, is still nearly ideal for many different kinds of float trips. A wandering angler will find these boats on many southern streams.

Although the current will do most of the hard work, paddles, a pole or a pair of oars will be necessary items. Add a life jacket per fisherman, a seat cushion, a cooler and/or lunch box (full, of course), a watertight container to keep cameras and other perishables dry in case of a sudden squall or upset, foul-weather gear—and of course the appropriate tackle. An anchor (to hold boat and fisherman in position to fish a likely hole) can be worth many times its purchase price.

Because a large percentage of all float tripping nationwide will be on small to medium streams, it is important (although not absolutely necessary) that the boat can be carried on top of a car. This requires at least one set of cartop carriers, of which dozens of different designs, for all cars from subcompacts upward, are readily available. It is normal procedure for two float fishermen to park one car near a designated take-out point and deliver the boat or canoe to the launch site with the other vehicle. Two persons can easily load and unload a craft which does not greatly exceed 150 pounds. With some cartop carriers roller bars and pulleys make the task even easier.

But keep clearly in mind that different kinds of float trips are possible. On many rivers, with an outboard, it is possible to motor upstream and then drift back down to the starting point. Or drift down to begin and motor back. One such adventure ranks with the most successful of all the float trips I can remember.

That time, Bill Gressard and I were fishing in the vast half-land-half-water wilderness west of Thompson, Manitoba, before it had been opened up by road construction. We were camped where the Little Churchill River poured out of Lake Waskiawaka, an area totally unfamiliar to us both. But we did have a small aluminum boat, an outboard and enough supplies to last a week or so.

"Let's just load up the works," Bill suggested, "take our sweet time floating down the Little C, and see what happens."

What happened is certainly worth telling. The faster-flowing sections of the rivers were not especially productive, although here and there we picked up more than enough walleyes for our meals. Our greatest discovery came where the current became sluggish

and the Little Churchill widened to form small lakes infested—no, almost choked—with emergent vegetation. Some of these lakes resembled huge salad bowls. In almost every one we found northern pike, and I mean bragging-size northern pike. From the way most of them charged up and out of the salad, they hadn't met many previous anglers who tossed surface lures. Neither of us can recall many other times when float exploring an unfamiliar waterway revealed such a remarkable fishing bonanza.

As I said at the beginning, the float trip may be most valuable in escaping other anglers in areas where the pressure is heavy, but as the preceding story shows, it is also a fine wilderness technique. Several summers ago we arrived at a camp in far northern Saskatchewan noted for its pike, lake trout and grayling. The time was August and that fact alone might have accounted for the slow action and the disappointment for the fishermen already on hand. They had pounded all of the lakes within reach and had only a few small northern pike to show for the effort.

"Let's look elsewhere," my companion Lew Baker suggested, "at least we can't fare any worse."

Of course that was the ticket. In a freighter canoe, we headed from the lake toward the nearest river, where we let the canoe drift freely just to see what would happen. The result was almost an instant replay of what happened on the Little Churchill. The pike here were concentrated in the deeper pools and backwaters at the bases of long swift runs, ready to strike our lures. And one evening, as a bonus, we found masses of whitefish wildly feeding on insects—in time on our own artificial ones as well as the clouds of natural ones. It was superb fly fishing for a species one rarely meets.

As time passes, more and more of the really good trout fishing on large Western rivers must be done, of necessity, by float tripping. Some are simply too large to be covered well by an angler strictly limited to how far he dares to wade in a powerful current. Parts of the Yellowstone River, for one example, remain a sanctuary against any fisherman confined close to shore in waders. The section north of the National Park boundary at Gardiner and Yankee Jim Canyon downstream to Livingston, Montana—which just could be the finest trout water on earth—is float tripped by everything from inflatable rafts to Mackenzie River boats. One very successful veteran guide, Ray Hurley, prefers a river skiff similar to the old Ozark johnboat for his clients.

The fact that many Western rivers (and a good many in the East as well) flow entirely through private properties has also made float trips a necessity.

Pause during a float on Gods River, Manitoba, near Red Sucker Rapids. Fish here are eastern brook trout.

A wilderness float on Wood River, Alaska, begins when a bush plane drops the fishermen at the starting point. The pilot will pick them up later downstream.

Pontoons can be clamped onto a Delhi canoe for greater stability during a river float. Dolphin box (center) is waterproof (for cameras, etc.) and also clamps to gunwales. Note bracket for mounting 3 horsepower outboard motor on the stern.

Inflatable rubber rafts are ideal for floating some turbulent rivers, but they are hard to handle in strong winds.

Trespassing is not permitted, but many river sections classed as "navigable" between public (Fish and Game Department) access sites can legally be fished by float boat, as long as the fishermen do not step out on the banks.

An extraordinary amount of fishing exists in deep canyons and roadless regions of the West where any access at all is strictly limited to rubber raft. Notable in this category are Hell's Canyon of the Snake River, Oregon's Rogue, Umpqua and John Day rivers, the Green and Yampa of Colorado and Utah, and in Idaho the Middle Fork of the Salmon and also the Main Salmon, better known as the River of No Return. In these remote places a fisherman will find everything

Angler John Moxley on a floating raft at Tikchik Narrows, a great fishing area in western Alaska.

from smallmouth bass and sturgeon (Hell's Canyon) and catfish (Yampa) to salmon, steelhead and Dolly Varden trout and squawfish (Salmon). But float trips on such intermittently turbulent whitewater rivers are not to be taken lightly or planned without care. A fisherman needs to engage a whitewater outfitter.

One of the best, who concentrates on the forks of the Salmon, is Terry Andreesen of Wild Rivers West, Salmon, Idaho. He custom organizes trips of any duration, for any number (if fairly small), and in the early fall, can include splendid chukar hunting. The total adventure of whitewater running with fishing in between could be the greatest thrill of an American outdoorsman's lifetime. Jim Campbell of Wild Rivers Idaho in Cambridge, Idaho, offers similar fishing expeditions through Hell's Canyon and other Western streams.

Except for such deep-canyon wilderness expeditions, fishermen can organize most of their own float trips. With a little investigation and reconaissance, they may be surprised at the numerous opportunities that exist at their back doors—or at least within short drives of their homes.

A good place to start checking, surprisingly enough, often is in the nearest county courthouse at the county seat. Go into the county engineer's (or surveyor's) office and ask for a county map, which will either be free or available at nominal cost. On that map trace the waterways, the bridges and the distances between them. Select a river where the interval between bridges is very short and try it out. It's a chance to get acquainted with your boat at the same time that you explore a new waterway. You may be amazed at what you find after leaving the bridge a mile or so behind you.

Another place to begin investigating is with the state Fish and Game (or Natural Resources) Department in your state capital. Many publish detailed stream charts, guides or booklets listing the best waterways in that state. It is also a good idea to consult local game wardens and rangers, as well as biologists at local fisheries, for suggestions and short-cuts. Many good float trips in the past were suggested to me by state wildlife personnel from Wisconsin to Texas.

Detailed maps of many American and Canadian rivers from Maine to Alaska, especially of the larger and more important fishing waters, are available from the Wilderness Sports Corporation, Eagle Valley, New York 10974. For instance a set of nineteen maps for the entire Yukon River (1 inch to the mile) costs $28.50. Seven maps of Ontario's Albany River run $11.20 and eight maps following Maine's famous Allagash River are sold for $9.60. Another example: Five maps of Georgia's canoe trails can be obtained for $6. They also have an unusual catalog listing all such maps available.

Downriver trips can be the secret of better fishing almost anywhere there is enough pure running water to float a fishing boat.

Knots for Fishermen

by Lefty Kreh

Two books and a number of articles on knots for fishermen have been published recently. In some cases knots were shown and explained that tested at little more than 60 percent of line strength. Statements about other knots were erroneous, and, most unfortunate, little consideration was given to rope, a material that almost every fisherman uses, either for his anchor, for tying the boat to his car carriers, or for attaching a winch line to the trailer.

There are many materials in which the fisherman makes his knots, but for fishing, more than 90 percent of what he uses will be nylon monofilament. As for ropes, there are several basic materials which are described later.

Monofilament
This single-strand plastic material revolutionized all areas of fishing from big game to taking brown trout with a tiny number 26 fly. For its diameter, mono is incredibly strong, and because it is inexpensive, it has become the most popular fishing line material for most uses.

There are many misconceptions about monofilament, and it also has some disadvantages.

Monofilament lines differ somewhat according to the company that produces them, depending upon the process each uses.

A fact that I've never seen mentioned in print but that many wise fishermen know is that different brands of nylon monofilament will produce higher strength with one knot than with another. This does not mean that one brand is better than another, because the line that has the greatest strength on the first knot tried may be weaker on the second.

I am not enough of a scientist to know why this is so, but my testing machine (which has no opinion) and my fishing experience have verified for me that if I tie a Palomar knot, for example, in three different lines, I will probably get three different strengths of knots, even though the material diameters all tested the same.

Another fact that I've never seen in print, yet one that I can easily prove, is that certain knots are best for certain line strengths or diameters. For example, the Surgeon's knot is one of my favorites for joining mono strands of different diameters, and I have used it for years instead of the more commonly used Blood knot, which is considerably weaker. But I have found that with line testing more than 60 pounds I cannot get a strong Surgeon's knot if I join to any line testing less than 20 pounds, and in any combination I find it difficult to get the desired strength.

In the case of the Surgeon's knot, I believe that the weakness of the knot when tied in line testing more than 60 pounds results from the fact that I cannot close the knot tight enough to keep it from slipping. But there are knots that I can tie with 4- to 12-pound monofilament that produce very poor knots with positive closure, and yet do comparatively better in larger diameters.

Many fishermen think that a spool of monofilament will last several seasons. That is not likely. First, there is deterioration from ultraviolet rays, which can ruin a good line that has never been fished. Any line stored either on the reel or on the supply spool should be kept from direct sunlight. Incidentally, fluorescent lights are rough on line, too.

A nicked line is another problem not generally recognized as serious, but any line that has a nick should have that portion discarded. Monofilament has great strength for its diameter, but a tiny nick in the line radically reduces the strength.

Most people have cut a section of garden or laboratory hose into pieces. If you have, you know that a tough hose can easily be cut if you bend it (putting stress on the material at that point) and then touch it at the same point with a sharp knife. The hose just parts.

That is exactly what happens to nicked monofilament. So, before you build a knot, test for nicks. It's easy to determine if a nick is present, even a tiny one. Take the suspected line and place it on your first finger so that it is trapped by the thumbnail. Be sure the thumbnail is pressed firmly against

the mono. Then draw the line through your fingers, keeping pressure on the thumbnail. Any slight nick is immediately felt.

In fact, a friend can conduct this test for you. You can place your fingers over his thumb and when he contacts a line nick, you can feel the bump that occurs as he draws the nicked portion through his hand.

The best knots in the world will do you no good with a nicked or an old line.

Some knots work well under slow steady pressure but fail under a snapping impact. The Spider Hitch is one of these. Under the very steady pressure of fighting a fish, this knot does fairly well, but should it receive a jolt, such as is caused by a big fish's lurching away from the angler, it is likely to fail.

In this case, the reason is that the knot is not drawn tight. In order to make it completely snug, the loops must feed a portion of the line through the knot, which tightens first and most securely on the reel end.

What happens with the Spider Hitch is that the knot looks tight, but as you fight a big fish and he bangs against the knot, the sudden tightening of the upper end of the knot throttles the mono and cuts it in two.

A number of people have stated that the Spider Hitch is a 100 percent knot and a good substitute for the Bimini Twist. That's only partly true. The Bimini Twist is still the *only* knot that gives better than 100 percent of line strength. The Spider Hitch is a good substitute only in that it is a fast, easy-to-tie knot that can be used in emergencies, but a serious angler, especially one battling salt water species on light lines, had better learn the Bimini Twist.

Rope

All fishermen use ropes: for stringers, for boats, for many uses that are so obvious that it is unnecessary to list them. But there is one knot that few outdoorsmen know, though it is not a new knot, but an old one. It was described in the early Boy Scout manuals and has been used for generations by the navy and by tree surgeons. It is a knot that every angler should know. It's called the Taut Line Hitch.

I find many uses for this adjustable knot, which is the major reason for learning it. It allows you to tie a line between two objects, then adjust, at will and with ease, the distance between them.

For example, if you car-top your canoe or boat to your favorite fishing hole, you probably tie it on in some manner, then attach a rope to the front of the car and the forward portion of the boat. Usually you have a difficult time getting the knot tight enough to prevent the boat from moving. Use the Taut Line Hitch. (The photographs in this article show how.) Simply tie the knot in loose line. Then pressing against the knot allows you to adjust it back and forth. The moment you release your finger pressure against the knot, it locks in position. When you want to untie the knot, press against it with your fingers, squeezing it hard; then slide the rope free. The knot will not come loose unless you squeeze on it. Tree surgeons hang from a loop in the rope formed below the knot and stake their lives on its reliability.

I'd like to suggest one more use for a Taut Line Hitch. Campers know that when it rains or snows, tents tend to contract and the guy ropes supporting the tent become so tight that the tents can be ripped or the stakes pulled from the ground. Place a Taut Line

Hitch between the tent and the stake and squeeze the rope between your fingers to adjust the tension.

There is another knot that I feel is vital if you want one that is secure and yet won't be too difficult to untie. That's the Bowline. The illustrations later in this article show just one of the many ways to make this hitch, which you can master in minutes.

If you fish, you should know something about ropes.

There used to be only natural fiber ropes made from one of four materials: jute, sisal, hemp and manila. In that order they demonstrated their qualities, with jute the poorest and weakest material for almost any use, and manila the best choice.

There are problems, however, with natural fibers. Mainly, they suffer from rot and mildew. I lost a very good home-made anchor years ago when a manila rope that appeared to be in excellent condition simply parted. It had rotted and I hadn't realized it.

Almost no natural fiber ropes are made in this country today; they have been replaced by synthetic ropes. There are four of these synthetics, and you should know a little about each to help you make the best and most economical choice for your purpose.

Polyethylene. This was perhaps the first synthetic rope on the market and is still the cheapest. It preceded polypropylene. It is very slippery, stretches badly, and, under a load pressure, is the weakest of all synthetic ropes. It is also easily affected by ultraviolet rays. It is rated at the bottom of the pile of synthetic ropes, yet I see it advertised for outdoor use by some companies. I'd suggest avoiding the use of polyethylene.

Polypropylene. This is the rope most frequently used by commercial fishermen to attach a plastic foam flat to a crab or lobster trap. It floats and is in general use as a ski tow rope. It's fairly inexpensive. Polypropylene has no stretch and because it is so slick, it is very difficult to tie knots in and to handle.

In its most common form, it is constructed with a hollow braid. Most people use a fid (a hollow pointed needle) to make loops used to attach this rope to objects.

Ultraviolet rays affect polypropylene badly and for this reason the rope is not recommended for uses in which it will get maximum exposure to the sun. While some fishermen use it for anchor ropes, it is not the best choice.

Nylon. This is the rope most commonly in use today. It has served us well, but rope authorities believe that a new rope material, polyester, may replace it.

Nylon and polyester have about the same comparative line strength, and both are superior to the two previously mentioned ropes. However, nylon is subject to deterioration from ultraviolet rays, tending to harden with exposure.

Another problem that shortens nylon rope's life is that it absorbs water. The alternate swelling and shrinking from water absorption is tough on the material.

Nylon stretches under extreme pull, but the amount of pull has to be considerable before stretch

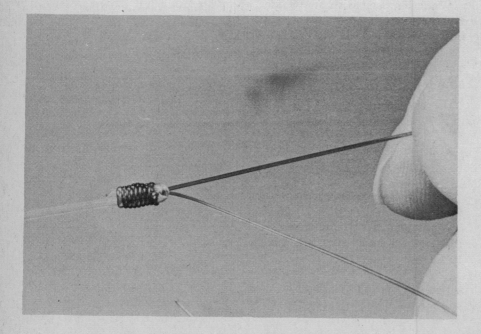

Step 1. **This is the completed Albright knot and would normally be trimmed. For the Albright insurance knot, leave at least 4 inches of the small strand extending beyond the knot.**

occurs, and generally a boat on the water does not generate enough force to cause the nylon line to stretch.

Polyester. This is the newest of the synthetic ropes and many authorities believe that it will soon replace nylon as the most popular rope material for outdoorsmen.

Polyester is not affected by ultraviolet, gamma or radio waves. It costs about the same as nylon and will probably be reduced even more in cost as it becomes more generally used. It does not absorb water (an important factor in rope life), but it abrades more quickly than nylon. Rope manufacturers tell me

that this can be overcome by the type of braid used. It has almost no stretch. It does not harden with exposure to the sun or with age.

The comparative strength of various ropes is interesting. If we use a 1-inch rope as a standard, we get the following line strengths in the various rope materials: manila, 9000 pounds; polypropylene, 14,000 pounds; nylon and polyester, 20,000 pounds.

The Albright Insurance Knot
I assume that the angler knows the Albright knot. If he doesn't, there are numerous pamphlets (Du Pont had a free one) and the book, *Prac-*

tical Fishing Knots, by Mark Sosin and Lefty Kreh shows it.

This knot is used to join strands of monofilament of great differences in diameter.

There has always been a problem with this knot. At times the smaller strands have loosened and the knot has parted. However, someone in South Florida, whose name I don't know, decided that it would be a good idea to put a small nail knot on the main line going to the reel, directly in front of the Albright. This eliminates any possibility of the knot's loosening. It works well and is easy to do.

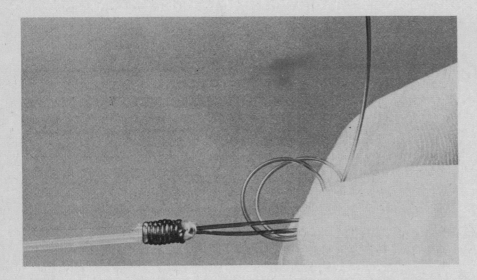

Step 2. With the loose end, make one wrap around the main line stem going to the reel. Then make another wrap between the formed coil and the Albright knot. When the two coils have been made it will look as shown in the pictures.

Step 3. Take the loose end from the left side and insert it through the two coils so that it travels through the coils in the same direction as the line going to the reel.

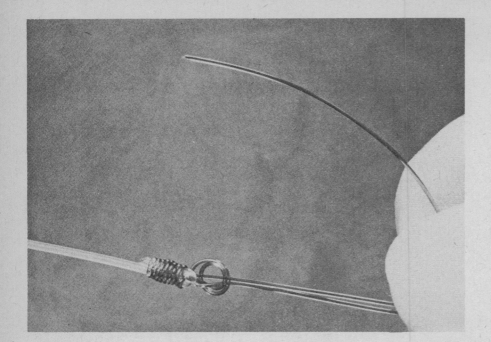

Step 4. Work the coils in the fingers to get them small and tease them down against the Albright knot.

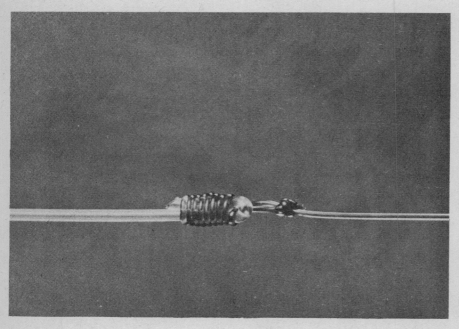

Step 5. Draw the loops tight and the Albright can never come loose.

The Thin Line Loop

I feel rather guilty about this knot. Someone sent me a drawing of it and I laid it aside, planning to run a series of tests on it when I had the chance.

Nearly a year later I found the drawing, but the letter was lost. But to whoever the fisherman was, I apologize, for this is the single best knot I have found to form a loop in a small line (from 15 pounds to 2 pounds in test) to obtain maximum action with the fly or lure.

In most cases the knot breaks either at full line strength or just under. Oddly enough, this knot does poorly in lines with a strength greater than 20 pounds, and I don't know why.

But for someone who wants to tie a loop from a thin plug, spinning or fly line to his lure or fly, the Thin Line Loop is a dandy. I owe a great debt of gratitude to the person who wrote me about it.

Here are the simple directions for tying the knot:

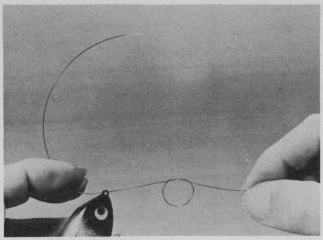

Step 1. Make an overhand knot in the line, leaving about 4 inches for the end. Then pass the end of the line through the hook eye.

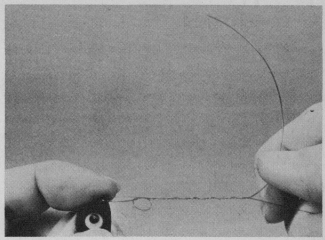

Step 2. Bring the line end back beyond the overhand knot (don't pass the end through the knot) and make five wraps around the main stem.

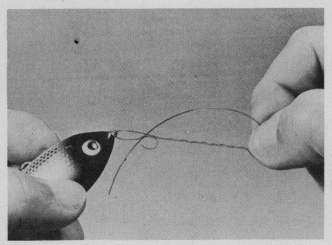

Step 3. Bring the line end back and insert it through the overhand knot loop.

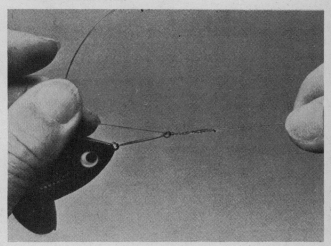

Step 4. Draw the knot tight. You can see the loop forming, and it should be obvious that the position of the overhand knot before you begin will determine the loop's final size.

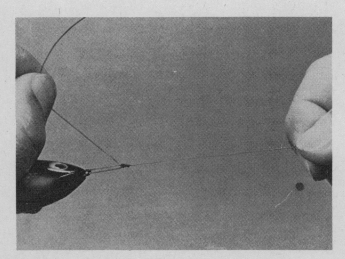

Step 5. Draw all strands tight.

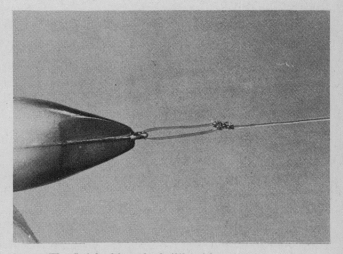

Step 6. The finished loop looks like this.

The Taut Line Hitch

This knot is used to connect two objects with a rope, allowing easy adjustment of length.

Step 1. Tag end of rope is passed around standing end as shown.

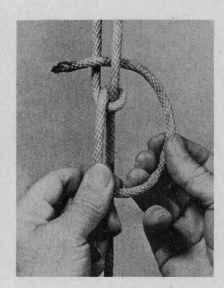

Step 2. The tag end is again brought through, as shown.

Step 3. Bring the tag end below the two turns already made and pass it through as shown.

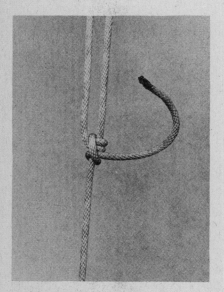

Step 4. At this point the knot is completed with the second pass through.

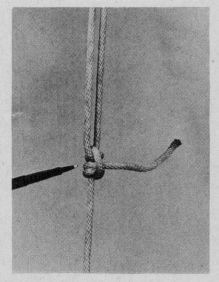

Step 5. Note that the second knot is formed below so that the tag end goes out at right angles to the main line. If the knot is tied correctly, the left side of the loop and the tag end, when held as shown, will be at right angles to the main line. If the knot is tied properly, the four wraps (two above and two below) cause the main line to form under the coils into an S shape, locking it in place.

Step 6. To adjust the knot along the main line, simply squeeze as shown. This takes the S out of the main line and allows the coils to slide easily along the main stem.

The Bowline

The Bowline is perhaps the best known of all nautical knots and is the only knot I know that is very easy to untie after severe pressure has been placed upon it. It is simple to learn.

Step 1. Grasp rope end as shown. The rope could have been passed around a piling or through a bow eye prior to starting the knot.

Step 2. Flip the end up and over as shown.

Step 3. Pass the line end around the main line, and return it through the opening as shown.

Step 4. Draw the knot tight and you're set.

Back to the Fly Rod for Bass

by Dave Whitlock

In spite of all the publicity given in recent years to scientific bass fishing with depth sounders, topographic maps, oxygen monitors and high performance bass boats, there is no challenge greater than that provided by using a fly rod on this popular gamefish. Fly fishing has characteristically and historically been the mainstay in the cold water world of the trout in both North America and Europe. Although a handful of anglers always cherished the fly rod for bass, there was little emphasis on this sport before the 1930's and 1940's.

Those were the days when it was delightful to ease past the lilypads along shore in either a rowboat or a canoe and toss a hairbug into every pocket. Panfish and pickerel as well as several species of bass responded to these grizzly offerings, and few of the early practitioners said much about it, because they didn't want to spoil a good thing.

In recent years, the ranks of fly rod bass fishermen began to swell, prompted by tackle improvements that made the sport easy instead of difficult. Perhaps the greatest boons were the refinements in fly lines and the wide range of densities and tapers that enabled anglers to cast without effort while covering every layer of water from the surface to pockets on the bottom.

Fly fishing in general has had a rebirth and anglers now pursue everything from trout and salmon to bass and marine species with the light wand. Think of the largemouth, smallmouth, Kentucky bass and other species as a common interest group and add pike, pickerel, panfish and anything else you can find to nail a fly in ponds, lakes and reservoirs.

Personal choice dictates how simple or how complex you want the fishing to be. You can fly fish on the surface or, by using special sinking fly lines and flies, seek out fish at depths to 30 feet with predictable success. You can start with the basic popping bug and run the range of imitations that bass will attack for food, fun or out of frustration and anger.

Every fly rod is a compromise and there is no single outfit that fits every situation, but a good choice to begin with is a rod that is 8 or 8½ feet in length, weighs 3½ to 4 ounces, and can handle a 7- or 8-weight fly line. Although you can spend more money if you desire, you can probably find something adequate in the $30 to $60 range. Choose a fly rod that appears to have a crisp, evenly graduated flex from the rod tip to the handle. Some people would classify this as a medium action.

Fit the rod with a moderately priced, good quality, single action fly reel that will hold a standard 30-yard fly line (7 or 8 weight) plus 50 to 100 yards of 18-pound test backing. Usually, a spool diameter of 3½ inches is about right for this capacity. Purchase an extra spool for the reel if you can. It will enable you to have two lines ready to fish and this will triple the scope of the waters you can challenge successfully.

The first line to buy is a floating special weight forward bass bug taper. With this line, you will be able to fish floating bass flies on the surface or sinking flies down to a depth of about 3 feet. You can use a floating level line of the same weight or a double taper, but neither is as effective as the weight forward. The bass bug tapered fly line is designed to cast the heavier, wind resistant flies and bugs more effectively. These lines also make it easier to cast under windy conditions and you can obtain greater distances with less effort than you can with a level or double taper line.

Your second fly line should be a high-density (fast

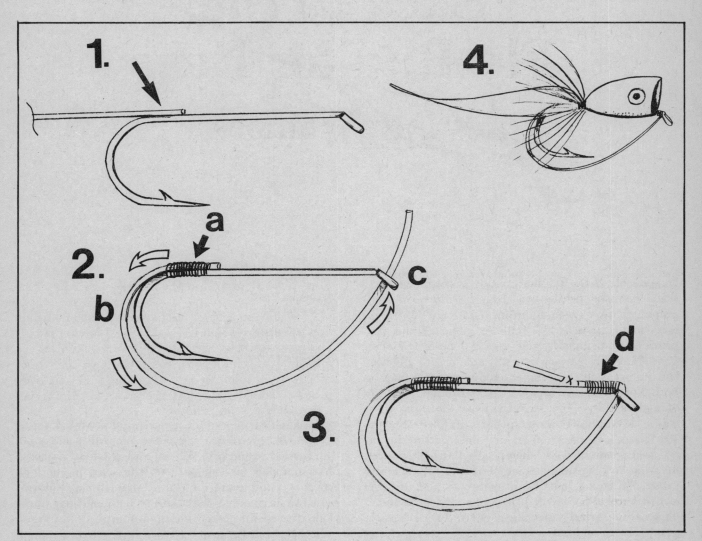

Step 1. Place hook in tying vise. Cut a 3- to 6-inch length of nylon monofilament approximately the same diameter as the hook's wire. Put one end down directly over the shank just in front of the hook's bend.

Step 2. *(a)* With fly-tying thread, wrap nylon filament securely on top of the hook's shank. Now tie whatever bass pattern you have chosen on the hook's shank. *(b)* After the fly is completed, bend nylon filament around hook's bend to form a loop below the hook approximately 1/2 to 1 times more than the width of the hook's gap. *(c)* Pass the filament through the hook's eye.

Step 3. *(d)* With tying thread, wrap nylon filament to the top of the hook's shank to complete the hook snag guard. Trim any excess filament not wrapped down.

Step 4. Typical bass bug with nylon loop snag guard. The guard makes any bass fly pattern practically snagproof from water obstacles.

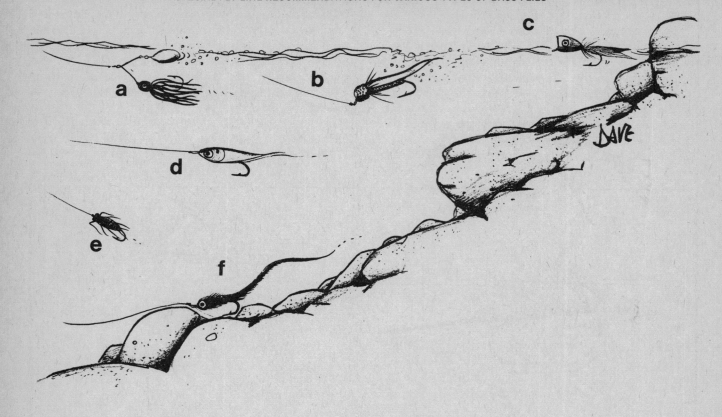

The line recommendations are numbered according to the author's general choice preference but he also considers various water conditions or special action needs.

a. Fly-Spinner Combo	1. Bass Bug Taper	2. Hi-D Sink Tip
b. Floating-diving Fly	1. Bass Bug Taper	2. Hi-D Sink Tip
c. Floating Bass Bug	1. Bass Bug Taper	
d. Streamer	1. Hi-D Sink Tip	2. Hi-D Wet Belly
	3. Bass Bug Taper	
e. Nymph	1. Hi-D Sink Tip	2. Bass Bug Taper
f. Eelworm Streamer	1. Hi-D Sink Tip	2. Hi-D Wet Belly
(or other special bottom flies)	3. Bass Bug Taper	

sinking), sink tip line. Make sure it is matched to your rod. This newly designed sinking-floating line has a fast sinking tip section that is about 10 feet long and will probe to a depth of almost 10 feet. The main body of the line floats, making it easier to pick up for another cast. The sink tip line has the same basic shape as the floating bass bug taper and it casts very well.

Use a nail knot to attach a knotless tapered leader to your full floating line. The leader should be 7 to 9 feet long and have a tippet strength of 8- to 10-pound test for most situations. The sink tip line should have a much shorter leader (3 to 4 feet) and the tippet section should test about 10 pounds.

These tackle recommendations are general, but if you are just turning to the fly rod for bass fishing, they offer an excellent starting point and will serve you well in most situations. When you are fishing for bass on the surface or even at moderate depth, casting accuracy is far more important than distance. Bass are cover-loving and they tend to ambush their prey from carefully selected vantage points. Before you even start to fish, learn to cast a controlled loop and spot your flies within inches of the intended target. Instead of reaching for the horizon, you can confine your casts to 15 to 40 feet and catch your share of fish, providing you can place the fly.

Now the fun begins. Fly casting is a completely manual method of fishing and, as soon as one gains modest casting control of the line and lure with the

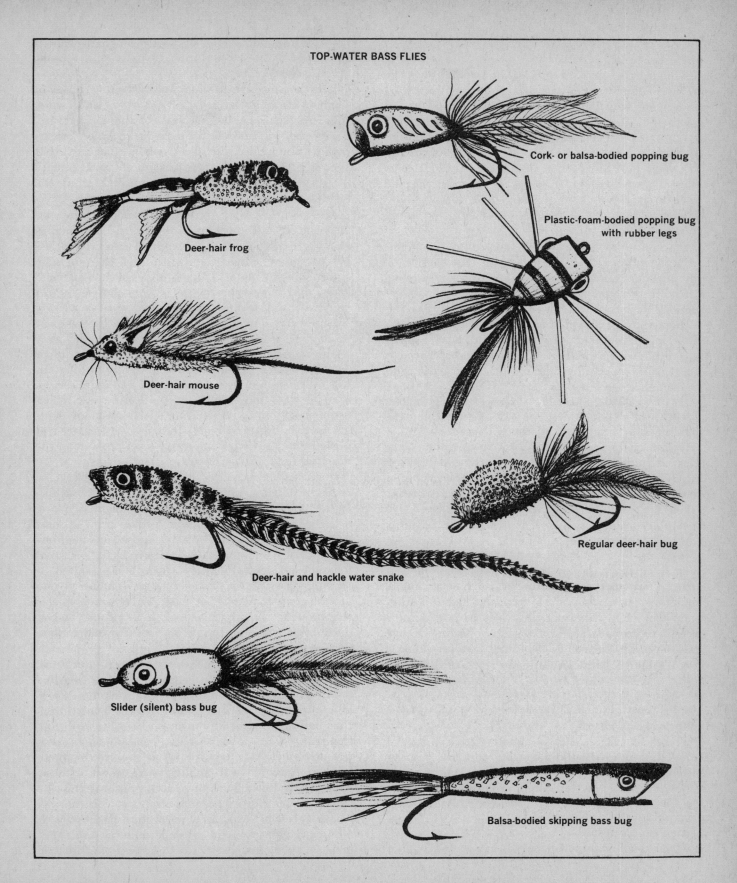

TOP-WATER BASS FLIES

Cork- or balsa-bodied popping bug

Plastic-foam-bodied popping bug with rubber legs

Deer-hair frog

Deer-hair mouse

Regular deer-hair bug

Deer-hair and hackle water snake

Slider (silent) bass bug

Balsa-bodied skipping bass bug

fly rod, a wonderful personal enjoyment becomes apparent. With a balanced rod and line and basic casting instruction, you can learn to handle the outfit in a few hours. Almost instantly, you will begin to understand why fly fishing is in a class by itself. As you cast the fly, a unique visual sensation occurs, almost hypnotizing you as you watch the loop unroll and the fly turn over on target. Each well-placed cast is a joy to experience and at this juncture a strike seems almost secondary. When you apply the power stroke to the rod, the long shaft responds in almost slow-motion sequence and the line transfers that same energy to the fly, turning it over gently.

The tackle and flies available today allow the fly rod to be effective almost as often as a bait casting or spinning outfit. A lot of bass anglers carry a fly rod but use it all too seldom, thinking that it is not capable of working most bass water. From a 30-foot depth to the surface, the fly rod will hold its own. Look for bass in the same prime areas that you would fish for them with other tackle and then try the fly rod. Determine the depth, pick the fly line to reach that depth, and you should be in business.

By using a wide range of fly styles coupled with both floating and sinking lines, you can increase the areas and times in which the fly rod will produce bass. I carry a large tackle box loaded with as great an array of special flies and color patterns as the average bass angler has of lures. These patterns are the results of continuous study and they form a total spectrum that allows me to fish most situations. Being a fly tier, I've been able to conceive, design and tie various patterns when I felt they would fill a need.

Bass are fierce, efficient predators and will, at one time or another, strike at any object that appears alive. They usually rely on foods that are most abundant, such as minnows, crayfish, shad and other baits, but they will vary their diet as opportunity offers. As the weather and water conditions change and seasons come and go, bass may swallow snakes, frogs, tadpoles, large aquatic and terrestrial insects, rodents, lizards, birds, turtles and salamanders. Your assortment of casting baits probably imitates or suggests a large number of these, so why not have flies that do the same?

The various bass patterns can be effective in natural colors that imitate their live counterparts but you can also have excellent success with exotic color schemes. Black, white, yellow and combinations of these three always seem to be productive. Occasionally, bass will go for very bright fluorescent reds, yellows, oranges and blue-greens. I have had great success also with purple and blue on patterns where these colors would

never be found in nature. Bass are fish of many moods and foods. That is unquestionably why they rank as our greatest gamefish.

Don't confuse the gullibility of the bass with lack of sophistication. Bass can be extremely selective when they are exposed to a great deal of angling pressure. By its very method, fly fishing appears to be able to cope with more of these selective bass than any other approach. A good fly rodder can present and animate his lures so realistically and temptingly that the technique can prove to be their nemesis.

Most waters that harbor bass populations are promising fly fishing areas. However, the large hydro-electric, irrigation or flood control lakes offer less potential for the light wand enthusiast than do more stable bodies of water. The shorelines of such artificial lakes, and hence the typical cover, change almost daily with the elevator-like action of water levels. By the time these lakes are a few years old, bass usually become permanent deep water residents and may return to the shallows only during spawning season or on slow rising water. That is why fly fishing for reservoir bass requires closer timing and more knowledge of bass movements and water levels. When fishing reservoirs, you will find that man-made floating boat houses and docks that are cable-placed to move in and out with the water level are among the most predictable bass homes.

In natural lakes, ponds, municipal water reservoirs, swamps, sloughs, oxbows, streams, rivers and brackish bays, some bass are almost always residents of shoreline cover or do most of their feeding from shallow water ambush hideouts. Cast to exposed and shallowly submerged aquatic vegetation such as lily pads and moss beds. Reeds, boulders, logs, ledges, fallen or standing trees, docks, flooded roadbeds and fence rows are all great hangouts for bass. In fact, any objects that provide a hiding place, such as old car bodies, duck blinds, sunken boats and beaver lodges, are perfect for fly rodding.

Bass use these various natural and unnatural structures for protection, bedrooms, ambush feeding points and, in some cases, spawning beds. By nature and for convenience, bass usually don't move far from their territory, especially in stable weather or during the daylight hours. A fisherman covering these spots will do best by keeping his lures as close to the prime cover as possible. Fly fishing is the most efficient means other than live bait of accomplishing this. No time is lost retrieving the lure after it is worked away from ideal cover. I can put three or four spot casts with a bug up against a cypress trunk, a pocket in the lily pads, or a cutbank edge in the same time that I would

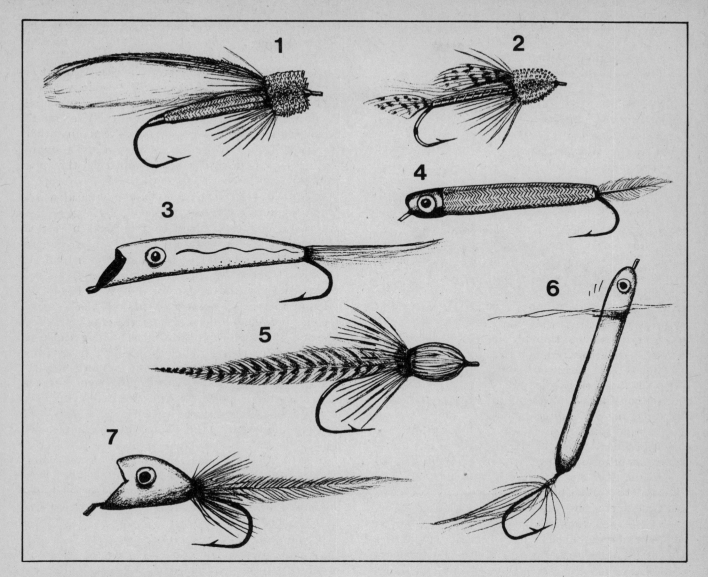

SPECIAL FLOATING-DIVING BASS FLIES

1. Marabou Muddler Minnow (enlarged head)
2. Muddler Minnow (enlarged head)
3. Diving Feather Quill Minnow
4. Mylar Quill Minnow (whygin argus)
5. Drake's Bullethead Deer-hair Minnow (Evert Drake)
6. Balsa Stick Cripple Minnow
7. Darter Bass Bug

need to crank in a lure from one cast with spinning or bait casting tackle. By using a loop roll false cast, I can work a fly back and forth in the same spot without any casting time lost.

Even an average fly caster can throw curves to put his fly in back of a log or behind a tree. The fly can also be skipped back under various overhangs and into small cover tunnels. This past fall, my wife Joan skipped her hairbug popper 3 feet back inside of a big

beaver's half-flooded tunnel in a clay bank and pulled out a 5-pound bass that was sharing the spot with the beaver.

Once you've tangled with a few decent-sized bass on a fly rod, you'll kick yourself for not starting sooner. I watch these winch-and-cable operators ski bass across the water and into the live well. If you question them, they'll tell you that the place to play with a bass is in the boat. I wish I could have a day with each of them to introduce them to the real joys of bassing.

A fly rod setup for bass is neither a willowy sissy stick nor a telephone pole with snake guides. It is an efficient and sensitive way to enjoy any fish that will share part of its day with you. A 2-pound bass—a nice average fish anywhere, I suppose—can really show what it is made of on an 8-foot fly rod. It may be hard

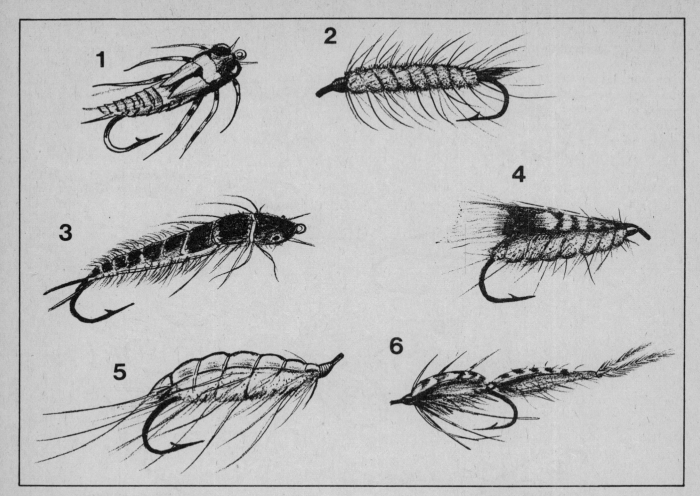

BASS NYMPHS

1. Dragonfly Nymph
2. Woollyworm
3. Helgrammite
4. Federmouse
5. Shrimp
6. Gray Wigglenymph

for some people to realize that a bass this size can make nice zippy runs and burst out five or six times before it's in the live box. This may sound harsh, but I can say it because I've been on the other side of the fence, too.

What a fly rod and reel lack in mechanical potential is more than compensated in your manual control over a diving, running, leaping fish. That is where another bonus lies. It is just more fun to "play" a punk bluegill, a 1-pound smallmouth or a hog-sized large-mouth with a long rod. I'd rather land one stream-bred Kentucky on a bug than ten of his brothers on even an ultralight casting outfit. Also, if I had to gamble $1000 on landing or losing a 10-pound bass in

most typical bass water, I'd opt for the fly rod and spot you 6 pounds on a line test. Even if I lost the old brute and my grand, I'd at least have enjoyed doing it.

Before I describe some modern tricks to take more bass with flies, let me tell you how to get close enough to them to put that fly where it might do the most good. I give any bass a lot more credit than some bass masters do, if the way they approach cover is any indication.

Today's bass boats are big, bright, high and noisy compared to those I sneak up on bass with. For a bass looking up at a modern bass boat from a hideout must be like a person looking out of a manhole at a two-trailer Diesel truck bearing down on him. There is no way these fishing machines can take most bass by surprise.

To fish cover close and efficiently, I like to use waders, a float tube or a canoe, and I use a paddle instead of a motor to get there and back. These quiet approaches are complemented by careful spot casting at "can't miss" range. With waders or tube floater I can also fish a fly that is absolutely line-controlled. A boat, even anchored, will constantly have some effect on your retrieves. With a crank or spinner bait this makes no difference. But, with a little frog, dragonfly nymph or slow crawling eelworm, fast dragbacks don't cut it for big bass that have been through that scene in their younger days.

To fish flies, you must become a master puppeteer, teaser and naturalist. If you know something about a bass's psychology that also helps. Shallow or deep, cold or hot, wind or calm, dark or bright, bass are worse than women for changing their moods. It also helps to have a nose for bass. That only means you can sort of smell that bass are there. No matter where you look for bass, watch for signs of its presence and tipoffs to its moods. Study the water's surface and try to see visually or mentally what is beneath.

Most bass bugs have buoyant enlarged heads made of materials such as balsa wood, cork, plastic and deer hair. Depending on shape and position in the water they swim, wriggle, pop, dive, or just sit there and look juicy. These bugs are fished with a floating line and usually mine are equipped with a snag guard to prevent snagging on surface obstructions.

With the floating line, the bug is dropped softly at or just beyond the target. Then it is animated to attract the eyes below. The most common action involves casting to the spot, letting the bug rest a few seconds, then beginning the series of slow to rapid erratic twitch retrieves. With this action a lot of surface

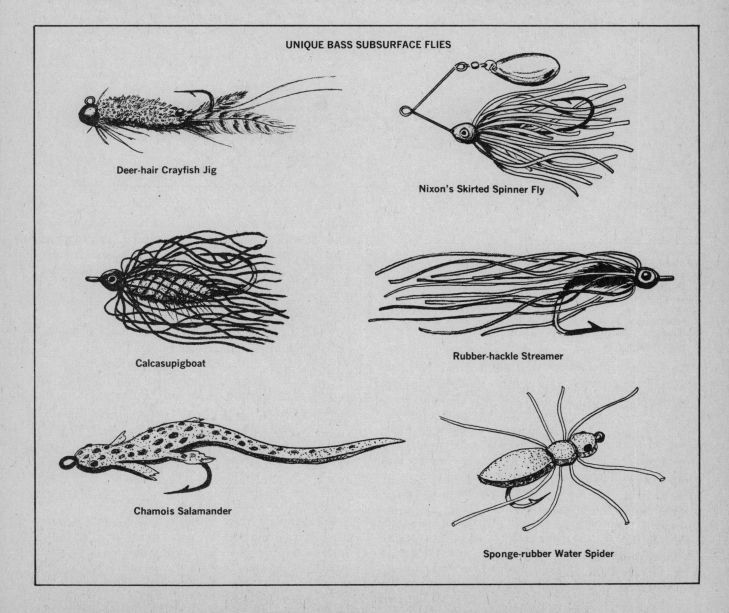

UNIQUE BASS SUBSURFACE FLIES

Deer-hair Crayfish Jig

Nixon's Skirted Spinner Fly

Calcasupigboat

Rubber-hackle Streamer

Chamois Salamander

Sponge-rubber Water Spider

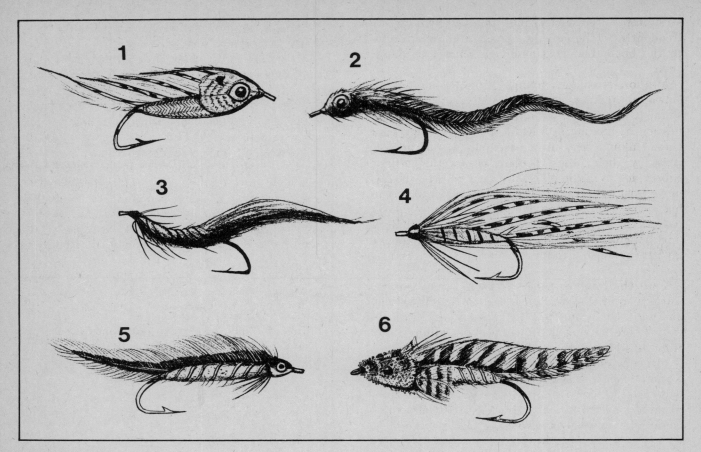

BASS STREAMERS

1. Marabou-mylar Shad
2. Eelworm Streamer
3. Green's Leech
4. Mylar Bucktail Streamer
5. Matuka Chub
6. Whitlock Sculpin

commotion is created that suggests fright, trouble or struggle.

For big bass, I prefer to work a well-placed bug very slowly. I cast into the cover or as close to it as I can. Once the bug gets in the water, I let it lie there motionless, or with only the slightest twitch or two as long as I can stand to. Then I slowly swim it out of the cover. Over the years this method has been more consistently successful for big bass than any other I have used. Large fish are usually extremely wary and don't commit themselves quickly. Flies must be worked very slowly and casts repeated to the same prime spot to score big.

Another topwater method I use involves rapid, skipping, splashy, erratic zigzag retrieves. This seems especially effective over open water where there is submerged cover or areas that have schooling bait fish such as shad. This is murder over good stickups. The

skipping, fast, erratic action can't be overdone. Sometimes it will take ten, twenty or thirty casts to pound them up, but watch out when it happens. Incidentally, this works best when two or more fly fishermen are pounding away at the same area. Besides bass, this works very well for offshore channel traveling sand-bass and school stripers.

The floating-diving flies are much like the popular crippled minnow, Rapala or Lucky 13 casting baits. That is, they incorporate float, surface noise and action with a dive and swimming retrieve. This action is generally accomplished with a floating line and special floating-diving pattern flies, such as a marabou muddler with a greased head, but can also be achieved with a regular popping or slider bug used with a sink tip fly line. If you like the fly to return to the surface on pauses, use the floater line. Sink tip is best if you want the bug to rise slowly but not surface or to continue swimming deeper.

I find this floating, diving, swimming, retrieve very productive when bass are not doing a lot of shoreline surface feeding but are chasing minnows or shad. Another good time to work the diver flies is when the water is cooler than ideal. Sometimes bass will only strike top waters just against the shoreline but will frequently hit the same lure below the surface almost to the boat. The floating-diving pattern is perfect then.

Minnow streamers, nymphs, spinner combos and eelworm streamers can be worked very effectively in shallow water with a floating line. When bass are nesting or holding in a shallow or slow slope bank, these sinking flies can be eased slowly off the bank right by their noses. I really enjoy this type of subsurface fly fishing. Usually, you will see the bass move, push a big wake toward the fly, and inhale it in a big swirl. Here, as on 90 percent of my floating patterns, I use a nylon loop snag guard so that the only hangups that I get are from the crushing jaws of an attacking fish. I think the guard is as important as the fly.

With the minnow-type streamer, I may vary my retrieve from slow regular strips to erratic twitches and pulls. Occasionally, I'll let the streamer sink and wait before moving it in any fashion—killing its retrieve until it hits the bottom then restarting.

The eelworm, my answer to the bait casters' plastic worm and jig and eel, should be fished exactly as its bait-casting cousins are. It is 4 to 8 inches long and is made of long floppy saddle hackles. Its head is overbalanced with weight to provide a jigging action. I use a Hi-D sink tip unless the water is less than 3 feet deep. I lay it back in the jungle and let it stick its head into every depression between the shoreline and the end of cover. It is also murder down the shady side of a standing timber trunk. Big bass suck it in and move off, usually at right angles. This crawling, undulating, swimming action rivals any worm I've ever used in both action and fish production per cast.

Other underwater flies, such as dragonflies, nymphs, leeches or crayfish, are usually fished with slow, erratic retrieves. I try to visualize the subsurface cover and work these flies over and in it as much as I can. This type of out-of-sight slow-retrieve fishing requires considerable patience and concentration. In bass rivers it is very deadly. I don't use these methods unless the fish are not active in the top or shallow areas. But it is still more fascinating to fly fish than to use other methods if the fish are above 10 or 20 feet.

If I wrote about all the things I would like you to know about fly fishing for bass I would fill two volumes the size of this *Angler's Bible*. I don't care how old you are. Starting today, you will find a full lifetime of charms and challenges with this bassing sport. A fly rod and reel and a box of bass bugs are all you need to sample it, but on that scale or with all the equipment you can carry, fly rod bass fishing is one hell of a great adventure.

Dave Whitlock's Favorite Bass Flies

Topwater
1. Cork-, plastic- or balsa-bodied popping bug, sizes 1/0 to 8
2. Balsa-bodied slider and darter bug, 1/0 to 6
3. Deer-hair popping bug, 1/0 to 8
4. Deer-hair frog, 1/0 and 6
5. Deer-hair mouse, 1/0 and 6
6. Deer-hair and hackle snake, 1/0

Floating-Diving Streamers
1. Marabou Muddler, 1/0 and 6
2. Muddler Minnow, 1/0 to 10
3. Balsa-bodied Minnow, 1/0
4. Quill-bodied Minnow, 1/0 and 4
5. Drake's Bullethead Minnow, 1/0, 4 and 6

Sinking Streamers
1. Marabou Shad, 1/0 to 8
2. Eelworm, 3/0 to 4
3. Green's Leech, 4
4. Mylar Bucktail, 1/0 to 6
5. Matuka Chub, 1/0 and 4
6. Sculpin

Nymphs
1. Dragonfly Nymph, 4 and 8
2. Woolyworm, 4 and 8
3. Helgrammite, 6
4. Federmouse, 1/0 and 6
5. Shrimp
6. Gray Wigglenymph

Dry Flies
1. White Wulff, 4, 6 and 8
2. Dave's Hopper, 4 and 8
3. Dave's Cricket, 4 and 8
4. Sofa Pillow, 4 and 6
5. Powder Puff, 4
6. Grizzly and Brown Bivisible, 6

Others
1. Deer-hair Crayfish Jig, 4
2. Nixon's Skirted Spinner Fly, 3/0
3. Calcasupigboat, 1/0
4. Rubber-hackle Streamer, 3/0 to 4
5. Water Dog, 1/0 and 4
6. Pork Rind and Spinner
7. Sponge-rubber Spider, 4 and 8
8. Tennis Shoe, size 9½D

Walleye Fishing Basics

by Jerome Knap

In many ways, the walleye is the most perplexing of fish. At times it is so simple to catch that only hungry panfish come easier, but on other days, trying to get a walleye to take a lure can be almost as difficult as coaxing a strike out of a muskie. A school of walleyes, like a flight of woodcock in October, may be in one spot one day and gone the next.

No one has ever awarded any laurels to the walleye as a gamefish. It is not a flat-footed slugger like the largemouth bass or a bouncing pugilist like the small-mouth. It possesses none of the aerial acrobatic skills of the steelhead or the native cautiousness of the brown trout. And it certainly doesn't smash a lure like the vengeful northern pike.

Yet in the northern Great Lakes states and in Canada, the walleye is one of the most sought-after fish. Why? I am a walleye fisherman, but I'm not sure what attracts me to this fish. It may be, in part, that on light tackle the walleye does give a satisfying account of itself. It is tenacious. Or perhaps I like the fish because juicy walleye fillets are hard to surpass on the dinner table, or even better at a shore lunch cookout. Perhaps it is partly the waters in which the walleye lives: clean running rivers, scenic rocky lakes and deep clean reservoirs. Then again perhaps it is the prospect of lots of action if the walleyes are biting well, or the challenge of finding them and making them strike if they're hard to catch.

To catch any species of fish, one must know something about the fish's habits, where it lives, how and on what it feeds, and even the water temperature range it prefers. Without knowing all these facts and using them, no angler can be truly successful.

The walleye gets its name from its large, glassy eyes, which are adapted to dim light. It is even possible that the walleye finds bright light uncomfortable, because the pupils of its eyes cannot contract to shut out excessive light. Therefore, the first tactic a walleye fisherman must employ is to take advantage of the fish's light-shunning ways.

This means fishing in the deep waters of lakes and reservoirs and in deep holes in rivers during the daylight hours. Only at nightfall do walleyes usually venture into the shallows, although they can be found in shallower water on cloudy days than they can on days that are bright and sun filled.

Walleyes also tend to be somewhat bottom oriented. They are not bottom dwellers like the catfish, but

There's no finer tasting fish than a freshly caught walleye.

they are more likely to seek bottom than are the lake trout. The reason for this is the walleye's diet, of which 30 to 40 percent is made up of crawfish and hellgrammites; the rest consists largely of minnows. In the walleye rivers of the northern seaboard states, young eels and lampreys are also favored foods.

A friend of mine, a fisheries biologist, once compared walleyes with wolves. The comparison is an apt one. Walleyes and wolves hang out in schools and packs, respectively. Like wolves, hungry walleyes pursue their prey in a direct and unrelenting manner. You won't see a walleye using stealth, as a pike does, to capture its prey. Rather, it pursues its prey continuously. When feeding on crawfish, for example, walleyes cruise about making short, accurate lunges.

Like a wolf pack, a school of walleyes has to keep on the move in search of prey. If it were to stay in one area too long, it would deplete its food supply. No doubt this is Nature's way of spreading the predation over a wide area. This is why walleyes in lakes can be in a certain place one day and gone the next. The only exceptions are walleyes in rivers; there they tend to stay in deep holes at the tails of rapids where currents continually bring fresh food.

All this means a number of things for the walleye

fisherman. Since walleyes tend to feed either at the bottom or close to it, that is where the angler must present his lure or bait.

The walleyes' slow pursuit of its prey means that an angler must work his lure to match that pace. An old walleye guide on Lake of the Woods once said to me, "There's no way a fella can troll too slow for walleyes." I'll buy that. More recently, I heard the same advice given in another way—use the right trolling speed and then cut it in half. That's how slow walleyes want it.

But don't make the mistake of working your lure only with a monotonous slow speed. Put 2 or 3 feet of fast motion into the lure once in a while by sharply sweeping your rod. This is particularly useful for jigs and deep-running plugs. The fast action draws attention to the lure. It may entice fish to strike, particularly when they are a bit reluctant. In such cases, you will probably find that most strikes come just as the lure has slowed down, or even come to rest on the bottom, at the end of the sweep.

The reason that walleyes never smash a lure with a wrist-wrenching strike is also directly connected with the fish's feeding behavior of slow pursuit and short lunges to catch prey. What does this mean to the fisherman? It dictates the choice of tackle. Tackle

Walleyes are strong fighters and will hit a variety of baits and lures. They are abundant in deep lakes.

should be light and fairly sensitive. I use a medium-light spinning outfit with an open-faced reel for nearly all of my walleye fishing—day and night. This seems to be the tackle preferred by most serious walleye fishermen, although some choose closed-faced reels, particularly for night fishing.

About the only time I use different tackle is when I am trolling. For that, I sometimes use a free-spool bait casting reel and bait casting stick with a sensitive tip. The outfit is lighter than a Southern bass fisherman would use.

I believe that 8-pound test monofilament line is about all that one needs for walleyes. It has more than enough strength to handle even a 12-pound trophy fish. I never use wire leaders for walleyes. I prefer to check my line periodically and to cut off a foot or two when the end becomes scarred and worn.

However, when fishing in lakes that also harbor northern pike, I use a 3-foot leader made of 20-pound mono. This is all one needs to hold the sharpest-toothed pike. And I don't use snap swivels on any jigs, bottom-bouncing lures or plugs, except when a spinner works better with swivels.

The only way one can catch fish is to be where the

Light spinning gear is ideal for school-sized walleyes, but it may take a bit heavier tackle if you happen to hang one over a half dozen pounds.

Some walleye anglers have never seen a 12-pounder. This one came from the Albany River in Ontario.

fish are and to present the lure or bait in a proper manner. For walleyes, this means that you must fish the likely holding waters, the proper structures. Since walleyes on lakes move about a great deal, you must move as well, trying all likely water until you find them. Knowing their preferred temperature range—generally about 54 to 62 degrees—helps. To find that temperature, an electronic thermometer is a must.

To find the right structures, a sonar is also a must, unless you have a contour map of the lake. Once you have found likely looking water, concentrate your efforts by fishing in the preferred temperature range, particularly in areas where that comes close to the bottom. Remember, the walleye is a bottom-oriented fish, but not exclusively so.

Learning to recognize likely looking walleye struc-

When water temperatures reach 45 to 50 degrees, walleyes begin to spawn, often ascending feeder streams to find a suitable gravel bottom. That's one time of year when you can find them in relatively shallow water.

tures is not difficult. In marshy Northern lakes or man-made compounds, I always look for dropoffs and holes. In rocky lakes, I look for shoals and bars that drop off or taper fairly suddenly into deep water. At night, don't fail to investigate rocky reefs and bars, or small sheltered coves where bait fish are likely to live.

On a strange lake or impoundment, I like to troll in all likely looking walleye spots. Or I may jig or live-bait, moving from one promising area to the next. Once I get a strike or catch a fish, I concentrate my fishing in that area. The trick of tying a balloon or bobber on a long line on a panfish so it will lead you to the school also works with walleyes. The reason, of course, is that walleyes are school fish. I know walleye fishermen who use this trick regularly, although I seldom do.

The balloon trick, however, is a good way to learn where walleyes move during a 24-hour period, where they spend the daylight hours, and on what shoals they feed. It is also good for discovering walleye holding waters in strange rivers.

In rivers, I fish eddy waters and deep holes during the daylight. As dusk approaches, or perhaps on a very cloudy day, I try both ends of the riffles, starting at the head of the riffle and working toward the tail.

Although I fish for walleyes any time I can, I rate night fishing as the most productive. This is when walleyes come out of deep holes to feed in shallow water. In rocky lakes and rivers, gravelly shoals and reefs are a good bet. This is where crawfish and hellgrammites live, and both of these invertebrates are really active only at night. Incidentally, dark

Walleyes are sometimes found in rivers, particularly in deeper pockets outside the fast water.

nights are not generally the best. Crawfish feed more actively on moonlit nights, and this attracts the walleyes.

A walleye fishing trick I learned very early is that on windy days the windward shore is the most productive. The reason is simple. Wind and waves cause plankton to drift toward the windward shore. Minnows and other small bait fish tend to follow the plankton, because it is one of their main sources of food. The gamefish, in turn, follow the bait fish.

I have found this to be true for many species of fish, including white bass, white perch, yellow perch and of course walleye. But don't expect the walleyes to be on the windward shore as soon as a strong zephyr comes along. Plankton drifts slowly, and the fish must alert themselves to what is happening. It takes two or three days of heavy blowing, from one direction, to bring any results.

To a large degree, the type of water determines the type of lure you should use and how you should fish. The time of year and the time of day are also factors.

For example, walleye lures for Northern lakes just

A bait casting outfit and a few walleye add up to fun and some tasty fillets for the table.

after the ice is out should be fairly dark in color—blacks or browns. This is because the ice has shut off much of the light and the days are short, and as a result, the natural baits have taken on dark colors. If you don't believe this, take a look at crawfish or even minnows at that time; you will find that they are darker than they are during the summer. Consequently, walleyes are accustomed to looking for dark-colored food then.

For walleye fishing in rocky lakes and streams, my favorite lures are jigs or any of the lead-headed bugs with rubber bodies and legs that resemble hellgrammites and crawfish. The reason has already been mentioned: crawfish and hellgrammites rate high on a walleye's menu. I particularly like to use them at dusk or at night in shallows where walleyes are known to feed.

Another very effective way to fish jigs and lead-headed bugs is from shallow to deep water. One mistake frequently made by walleye fishermen is fishing from deep water to shallow. Anglers tend to anchor on a reef or shoal, cast out into deep water, and bounce the lure back toward them in the shallows. This, in my walleye fishing book, is wrong. I anchor over deep water and cast over the shoal. Then I let bottom-bouncing lures roll off the bar into the deep water. In doing this, I try to imitate a crawfish falling over the ridge. Walleyes frequently lurk by dropoffs just to pick up such morsels.

I don't think there is a single best color for bottom-bouncing lures. I do use darker colors in spring, but if they don't produce, I try bright colors—yellows and white. My favorite colors are blacks with yellow or white bodies or bucktails. But solid browns and even solid yellows and reds should be included in a walleye fisherman's tackle box.

I am more adamant about the size of bottom-bouncing lures. I don't think the big ones are as effective as the smaller ones. I prefer them between 1/8 to 1/4 ounce in weight. Even big walleyes take small jigs, just as, I'm sure, big walleyes feed on tiny crawfish.

Another night-time walleye tactic I favor involves a big, floating Rapala, preferably with a gold and black finish. I cast or troll with this lure over shallow water, seldom more than 6 or 7 feet deep. To sink the lure, I use a large split-shot about 18 inches above the plug. My retrieve is very, very slow, and I work my rod tip from side to side to impart a zigzag motion to the lure. This tactic is particularly deadly for big walleyes.

In the spring or again in early fall, when the water is cool and the walleyes are in the shallows, my basic tactic is to cast for them using a spinner with a

Hank Andrews carefully removes a leadheaded bucktail from the mouth of a respectable walleye. These fish have teeth and it pays to be cautious.

willowleaf blade and a nightcrawler on a harness with two hooks in tandem. The Junebug spinner is also good at these times. This lure is particularly favored by experienced walleye fishermen for stream fishing on the Atlantic seaboard. They bait their Junebugs with small eels or lampreys.

However, I have caught shallow-water walleyes on almost all commercially made spinners in the spring or fall. On many spring walleye trips, nightcrawlers are not available to bait up the willowleaf.

For deep-water trolling, a baited willowleaf or Junebug spinner is again hard to beat. But this time I tie a three-way swivel about 6 feet ahead of the lure, with a big sinker on one arm of the swivel. I then slowly bounce the sinker along the bottom, letting the spinner work behind. This rig, incidentally, can also be used for casting, if your rod can handle the weight.

For deep-water trolling, I like to use a deep-running Riverunt or a deep-diving Rapala. I prefer these in dark colors. I suspect that some of the deep-running bass plugs might also work on deep-water walleyes in the summer, but I have yet to try them.

Walleyes can also be taken on a fly rod during the spring, or at night when they are in shallow water. River walleyes are more vulnerable than those in lakes. A number 8 or 9 bass rod, with sinking line and

weighted nymphs, streamers or bucktails, can be used. Any of the streamers that resemble minnows are a good bet; but perhaps the best patterns are those that resemble hellgrammites.

The best live baits for walleyes are minnows, crawfish and hellgrammites. Minnows are preferable for deeper water, particularly during the day. They should be rigged so that they will not have a chance to swim up more than 2 or 3 feet from the bottom. The best way to hook a minnow for walleye fishing is through the lips. This allows the minnow to swim in an active and lifelike manner, even in drift fishing.

Although minnows of any species can be used, my preference is the emerald shiner. Unfortunately emerald shiners are rather delicate. Keeping them alive on a hook is a problem. What frequently happens in summer is that the water in the minnow bucket is much warmer than the water in the lake at the depth at which you are fishing. When a bait fish is lowered into the colder water, it dies of shock because it cannot adjust to the new temperature fast enough. It is important to keep the water in the minnow bucket as close as possible to the water temperature at the depth you are fishing.

Crawfish are particularly effective on evenings or nights when walleyes come into rocky shoals to feed. The crawfish should be rigged so that the hooked crustacean cannot crawl on the bottom and hide under a rock. The best way to hook crawfish is through the first segment of the tail, the one closest to the body.

A good crawfish rig consists of a hook, a clear plastic bubble, a sliding sinker and a split-shot—in that order. The split-shot should be pinched on the line about 2½ feet above where the hook will be tied. The sliding sinker is slipped on next. Then the bubble is tied on about a foot above the hook. The hook comes last.

The sliding sinker must be heavy enough to sink the entire rig and must be free to slide between the bubble and the split-shot. This rig will let the bubble float about 18 inches above the bottom. The crawfish will trail about a foot behind. When the rig is retrieved, the crawfish will swim backward like any swimming crawfish. A swimming crawfish is much easier for a walleye to see, and hence much more deadly, than one fished on the bottom.

Hellgrammites are very potent walleye bait, particularly in streams and rivers. I fish them in the same way that I do for smallmouths. For this type of angling, an ultralight spinning outfit is my favorite tackle. I use only one split-shot for a sinker and a smallish hook. I hook the hellgrammite under the collar and cast out, letting the current take the bait

This 9-pound walleye taken in the Bay of Quintl is a trophy that an angler can boast about for a long time.

into the deep holes and eddy water. The pièce de résistance here is to clip off the claws on the hellgrammite's appendages so that the insect cannot cling to moss-covered rocks and hide. A hidden hellgrammite won't catch any walleyes.

Where should you go walleye fishing? Good walleye waters are found in many places. Minnesota, Manitoba and Ontario boast the best walleye fishing on the continent. But Northern walleyes are not the biggest. The deep reservoirs of the mid-South, where the growing season is longer, produce bigger fish. The 25-pound world record walleye came from Tennessee. Dale Hollow, Norris and Center Hill lakes in Tennessee; the Bull Shoals on the Arkansas-Missouri line; and Lake Cumberland in Kentucky are some of the best walleye waters in the mid-South. Other good waters are New York's Canandaigua Lake, Michigan's Manistee River and Wisconsin's Lake Geneva. Even Lake Erie, off Ohio, has again become a top walleye producer since commercial fishing there has been banned.

Navigation Aids
for Fishermen
by Frank T. Moss

With all the effective aids to navigation now available, few sport fishermen remember what it was like to navigate by compass, clock and "seat of the pants." Navigation is usually thought of as an exercise in going from one port to another without getting lost, but fishermen recognize the frequently pressing need to find a rock patch or wreck the size of a tennis court, out of sight of land and sometimes in thick fog.

Fishing navigators of the old school did surprisingly well at returning to superior offshore fishing grounds, provided they could see their ranges on shore. In this sense, a range is an imaginary line drawn through two objects on shore that are visible from out on the water.

Take, for example, a situation in which you have stumbled onto some really red-hot pan fishing, either at an inshore ocean area or on a large inland lake. You are 2 or 3 miles from shore and, judging from the way your depth sounder paints the bottom or your lures hang up, there is a substantial rock pile about 20 feet under the boat. The rock pile is loaded with bass, and you've caught your limit. You want to be able to return to the spot another day, and you don't want to leave a marker buoy that might give away its location to a rival.

The land lies roughly to your west. Looking northwest, you notice that a church steeple well back from the shore lies exactly in line with a small red boathouse on the beach. There's your northwest range. Looking to the southwest you see that a lone rock sticking up from the water a couple of hundred yards from shore is exactly in line with a tall pine tree on the edge of the beach. That's your southwest range, roughly at right angles to the first range.

Before you leave the spot, you write down a description of each range and draw a picture showing what each looks like from the fishing location. Thus, when you return a week later with a couple of buddies who are anxious to try your new secret spot, you are able to run down one range, going away from shore on that range until you close the other range. Then, you quickly stop the boat, anchor and start fishing. Of course, if your friends are as smart as you are, they'll locate the ranges too, and the spot won't be secret any more.

Locating potential fishing grounds, especially on many inland lakes, is much easier than it used to be. Topographical maps are now available for most man-made lakes and for a large number of natural bodies of

With radar, loran, flashing and recording depth sounders, VHF/FM and SSB radio, and automatic DF, this 42-foot Chris-Craft Tournament Fisherman is ready to go anywhere in the world.

water. Once you learn such bottom structures as old creek beds, submerged stone walls and house foundations, you can predict the parts of a lake that should yield fish to a smart fisherman.

Tools for this kind of exploratory fishing are the topographical maps just mentioned, a pair of binoculars, some kind of sounding device for measuring the depth of water, a compass, and a clock or wrist watch. It is also extremely useful to have a speed curve of your boat's performance at standard settings of the throttle or various engine speeds according to a tachometer.

Suppose, as an example, you have located on the map what looks like the submerged abutments of an

old bridge at a place where a road once crossed the river before the valley was dammed to make the lake. You suspect that the bridge abutments would be a prime fishing spot if you could find the exact location. With a straightedge and protractor, you determine that the abutments must lie southeast of the crest of the tallest nearby hill.

A line drawn on the map from the abutment area to the northeast intersects the ramp where you will launch your boat. By running southwest from the ramp until the crest of the hill is northwest of you, you can put the boat very close to the desired spot. Then you drop a small marker buoy overboard and fish around it in different directions until you locate the right spot. After that, you take two or three visual ranges and the bridge is nailed down in your record book forever.

For piloting and navigation of this kind, a hand-held compass of the eye-level sighting type is good. Just make sure that you don't have any magnetic material, such as a big knifeblade on your person, when you use the compass. Some specialists go to the trouble of providing themselves with an optical range finder for taking accurate distances from objects on shore when only one range can be obtained. In some cases, one accurate range, plus a range-finder reading for distance, checked by an accurate sounding, is all you need to locate a good fishing spot.

When you are spending hours out of sight of land or in thick fog, navigation of a different order is necessary. Before the days of radio direction finders, loran, radar and electronic sounding machines, offshore fishermen had to depend on keeping an accurate record of their courses, speeds and running times so they could determine their dead reckoning position whenever it was necessary. It was always a great relief to hear the familiar old foghorn blasting away, dead ahead, when you were returning from an all-day tuna trip in thick weather.

Nowadays, no serious offshore fisherman on salt water, or on the Great Lakes for that matter, ventures out of sight of land without at least a good sounding machine and a radio direction finder, in addition to his VHF/FM or CB radio telephone. The more elaborately equipped boats boast electronic navigating equipment that would have been right at home on World War II destroyers. So that we will know what we are talking about, let us take a look at the most important of these navigation devices.

Radio direction finder. The RDF, as it is usually called, is simply a sensitive receiver with a directional antenna that can be rotated to obtain the relative

Control station of a tournament-class fisherman: *1*. 200-fathom recording sounder. *2*. Loran-C receiver. *3*. Radio remote control station. *4*. Aimable fish-finding sonar. *5*. Master spherical compass. *6*. Radar scope and controls. *7*. Automatic direction finder.

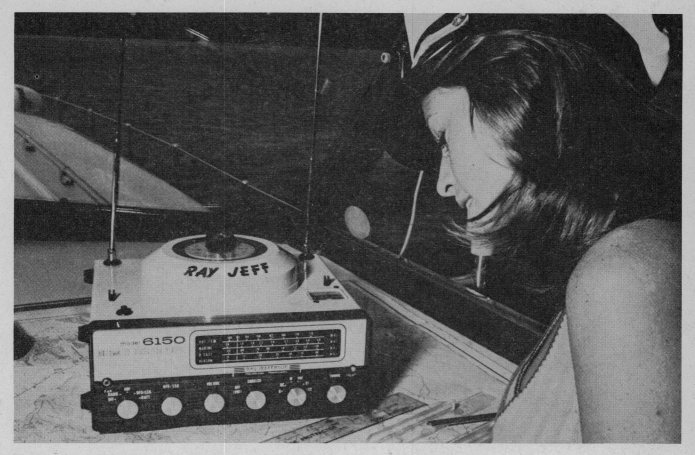

Portable automatic direction finder covers all bands and is a natural for a family fishing cruiser.

bearing of the "null," or position of least signal from a beacon, broadcast station or marine station. The position of least signal is selected rather than the position of greatest signal because lack of signal is easier to judge than maximum signal.

Modern RDF units come in three distinct types: (1) small, battery-powered, portable receivers that also double as multiband general-purpose news, weather and time-tick receivers; (2) highly sensitive, portable, single-band units with a built-in compass and sighting prism, designed almost exclusively for use on the beacon band; (3) larger, ship's-circuit-powered, permanently installed manually or automatically operated units for larger vessels, usually multiband in capability.

Because any RDF unit is a "passive" navigating instrument, depending on the strength and character of an incoming signal, the more sensitive and selective its receiver circuits, the better the navigation results. Accuracy is a direct function of distance from signal sources. Navigational fixes are obtained by taking two or more radio bearings and displaying them on the chart. RDF units vary in cost from under $200 for the least expensive portables to over $5000 for the largest and most accurate automatic models.

Radar. The term "radar" is a coined word meaning "radio detecting and ranging." Radar is not a navigating tool in the strict sense, even though it literally "paints a picture" of the area surrounding the ship on the display tube. Radar works by sweeping the surrounding area with a beam of radio pulses and receiving and interpreting the echos of radio waves coming back from objects swept by the radar-pulsed beam. The range of units suitable for medium- to large-sized sport fishing boats is from about 1/4 mile to as much as 32 miles, in graduated steps.

Radar for fishing boats and yachts costs from about $2500 up. The power consumption of new solid-state units is within the generating capability of a twin-screw power plant with two 30- to 50- ampere alternators working into a bank of 12-volt batteries. Larger units are usually powered by a separate auxiliary generator which also serves the boat's domestic,

Hand-held walkie-talkie (CB) works fine on the 17-foot Boston Whaler. A flashing sounder is console-mounted for easy viewing while fishing.

How much gear can you stack on a 26-footer? This Mako-26 inboard powered console fisherman has radar, loran, CB, VHF/FM, SSB and a combination flasher-recorder depth sounder. Some of the World War II submarine chasers were less lavishly equipped.

freezer, radio and special duty circuits. While radar is hardly a means of finding fish, its ability to bring a vessel safely through fog-shrouded coastal waters very greatly extends the operating capability of offshore boats. Maximum costs range from $5000 to $8000.

Loran. This term is another coined word, meaning, roughly, "long range radio navigation." Loran operates on what is called the pulsed hyperbolic navigation system. In laymen's terms, this is the way a loran position is obtained: Two loran transmitter stations, a "master" station and a "slave" station, are located several hundred miles apart. The master station continuously emits very accurately timed bursts of pulsed signals that are picked up and echoed by the slave station. The loran receiver on the boat picks up, interprets and displays in a numerical readout the information contained in the master and slave signals.

The readout in numbers corresponds to special hyperbolic curved lines on the loran chart. Each pair of stations will provide one line of position. Cross two or more lines of position from two or more pairs of stations and you have a fix. How accurate is loran? Loran-A, the type that has been around since World

War II, is generally considered to be accurate within 1/4 mile at most fishing distances offshore. Loran-C, a new and more elaborate system recently selected by the U.S. Coast Guard as the official American coastal-confluence radio navigation system, is said to be accurate to within 200 yards under average conditions, and to as little as 50 yards under optimum conditions.

Loran-A will be phased out by or shortly after 1980 when the Coast Guard will have fully implemented the new national Loran-C system, but until then it makes sense to invest in instruments with both Loran-A and Loran-C capability. Loran-A units are available for less than $1000, and combination units (Loran-A-C) run from about $1500 to upward of $4000. The more expensive units are completely automatic and extremely accurate, even hundreds of miles at sea.

Omega. This is another long range radio navigating system, one with world-wide capability. It is used more on the West Coast than on the East Coast, largely because the physical configuration of the

Pacific Coast does not lend itself to setting up a good Loran-A system. Omega has about the same accuracy as Loran-A. Units cost around $4000.

Sounders. Electronic sounding machines have revolutionized both fishing navigation and the fine art of fish detection under water. Basically, a sounder does in water with sound waves what radar does in the atmosphere with radio waves. Sounders vary from inexpensive, battery-powered "lunch box" portables to large, sophisticated directional sonar units capable of locating and tracking a school of fish 1/2 mile away. For small boats, the flasher mode of signal presentation is popular. Large boats usually utilize the permanent paper tape type of signal presentation. For medium-sized boats the combination flasher-recorder is often a very good buy.

Lest all this talk about spending thousands of dollars for sophisticated offshore navigation equipment scares you, let's climb down from the financial stratosphere and consider practical combinations of existing equipment that can be gathered together for a number of different types of salt water and fresh water sport fishing boats. In each case the costs reflect 1977 list values.

12- to 16-foot trailer and car-top boats

Compass, folding pocket prismatic	$ 10
Sounder, portable flasher, 60 to 100 feet	125
RDF, self-powered portable	125
Radio, CB walkie-talkie	40
Total	$300

16- to 22-foot fresh water bass boats

Compass, folding pocket prismatic	$ 10
Sounder, portable flasher, 60 to 100 feet	125
Radio, CB mobile	165
Total	$300

Console-mounted flashing sounder is handy to the control station of this MFG fresh water bass boat.

Hummingbird "Super Sixty" flashing depth sounder is waterproof for console-mounting on open boats like this typical fresh water bass boat.

17- to 23-foot center-console outboards

Compass, marine spherical, 3 inch	$ 90
Sounder, console-mount flasher, 120 feet	150
RDF, self-powered portable	125
Radio, CB mobile or 10-watt VHF/FM	235
Total	$600

23- to 30-foot center-console inboards, I/O's

Compass, marine spherical, 4 inch	$ 125
Sounder, flasher-recorder, 300 feet	500
RDF, self-powered portable	125
Radio, CB SSB, or 25-watt VHF/FM	450
Total	$1200

28- to 33-foot vest-pocket fishing cruisers

Compass, marine spherical, 4 inch (2)	$ 250
Sounder, flasher-recorder, 300 feet	500
RDF, all-band portable	350
Radio, CB mobile plus 25-watt VHF/FM	685
Total	$1785

33- to 42-foot family fishing cruisers

Compass, marine spherical, 4 inch (2)	$ 250
Sounder, flasher-recorder, 300 feet	500
RDF, manual permanent unit	450
Loran-A-C	1800
Radio, marine SSB plus 25-watt VHF/FM	2000
Total	$5000

42- to 50-foot tournament fishing cruisers

Compass, marine spherical, 5 inch (3)	$ 600
Sounder, console-mount flasher, 120 foot	150
Sounder, hi-fi recorder	1000
RDF, all-band automatic	2500
Loran-A-C	1800
Radar, 32-mile range	5000
Radio, all-band marine SSB	3000
Radio, 25-watt VHF/FM	450
Radio, CB mobile	235
Standby receiver, all band	265
Total	$15,000

Whether you are planning to equip a small fishing outboard for $300 or considerably less, or are planning to go for broke to outfit a big tournament cruiser, it is important to shop for good standard equipment which has stood the test of time and for which you can get good service when you need it.

If you have used electronic navigation equipment in fishing, you know that, as in any other form of endeavor, practice improves your skill and gives you confidence to use the right equipment at the right time—when the fog is thick, for example, or loquacious but invisible fellow fishermen are just over the horizon enjoying a Klondike of good fishing.

Never forget that it is the skipper's knowledge and skill that gets the fish, not the fancy electronic gadgets sitting on the console. A good fisherman can always catch fish with just a compass and a clock to tell him where he is. But give that same good fisherman a sounder and an accurate navigating system and he'll find fish where you never imagined fish could exist. That's the great thing about modern navigating equipment. It has opened up whole new worlds of fishing adventure to conquer.

California Kings

by Bob Edgley

Propelled by an instinct so strong that only death can destroy it, salmon gather together in the cold North Pacific and begin the annual migration to the gravel of their birth. Scientists tell us that these fish use their sense of smell as a navigational tool to find their way back to the very river in which they feasted on the yolk sac attached to the egg and spent their juvenile days. The mystery of these oceanic wanderers, however, is shrouded by the mists of time and has fascinated observers for centuries if not eons.

Although there are several species, the mightiest of Pacific salmon, sometimes called chinook, spring or tyee, to millions of Californians is "king," the official name given by the State of California. Known scientifically as *Oncorhynchus tshawytscha,* the king can grow to mammoth proportions. A 127-pound monster was captured in an Alaskan fish trap; the largest specimen to come from California was a whopping 85-pounder. Kings of such size are rare. They average about 20 pounds. Anything over 50 pounds is considered a trophy. This migrant ocean traveler ranges the Pacific from Southern California up through the Bering Sea and along the coast of Asia to Japan. Abundant from Monterey northward, the chinook is highly prized by both sport and commercial fishermen.

Kings are sometimes berated as sluggish because they often sulk deep when hooked. The light-tackle angler, unable to move the brute, must finally break the line in desperation. When this happens, it is because the fisherman is not working the salmon hard enough and the fish gets bored and goes to the bottom for a nap. My experience has been just the opposite. Here is a powerhouse with fins, which will pull like a posterior-hooked mule. To beat one, the pressure must be poured on and kept on or you may be out after dark trying to win the battle.

Though many salmon are caught by bank fishermen, a boat will greatly increase your chances of success if for no other reason than that more water can be covered. For the angler fishing alone on rivers with good access, a small skiff or pram of about 8 feet is ideal. A boat of this size can be carried easily and launched almost anywhere. Large streams like the Sacramento, where launch ramps are several miles apart and the current is swift, require a larger boat with a substantial kicker. I recommend as a minimum a 12-foot car topper with a 19-horsepower motor.

A 42-pound king from the Smith River in California.

Make sure you have a good anchor, often larger than recommended for your size craft. Navy, Danforth, grapnel and old-fashioned anchors are all good. There is nothing more annoying than to drop your hook in swift water and feel the anchor bouncing along the bottom. Down you go right into the spot you wanted to fish.

For the uninitiated, pursuing migratory fish like the king salmon can be a frustrating experience. The word "migratory" is the key, because whenever water conditions permit, these fish are on the move. The angler must be mobile and try to guess where the fish will be holed up next. Yesterday's hot spot can be as cold as day-old coffee. You must have mobility, whether you are river running in a skiff or following a streamside road. If the water is clear, use polarized glasses and check the river from a high bank, tree or bridge. If it is off color, watch a deep pool for a few minutes. Salmon are playful and break water frequently, which gives away their position. You can bet that for every fish that rolls there are a dozen more on the bottom of the hole.

Tackle for these giants runs the gamut from conventional ocean equipment to fly rods. Spinning gear is by far the most commonly used, with revolving spool and fly rodding next in popularity. No matter what you use, kings are powerful fighters and a good match for even heavy outfits.

It is hard to draw any hard-and-fast rules for selecting gear. Tastes differ. Some cast, others troll, and there is always a choice between spinning and conventional tackle.

Spinning tackle can be used effectively for trolling, but it is favored by the caster. Its simplicity of operation and care of casting have made it an all-around winner. Spinning gear that will handle kings must be stout. Rods should be in the light surfcasting class. Reels should be large, open-faced salt water jobs outfitted with 15- to 30-pound monofilament line. Salmon usually require a large bait or lure, so a heavy spinning rig will give you the muscle to make long casts over big water.

Conventional gear can be divided into two categories: casting and trolling. Trolling gear is generally the

Both of these fish were taken the same morning on the same fly, a #6 Horner Shrimp, from the same hole. They were twins.

same as that used for light offshore work. Rods around 6 feet, equipped with a reel in the 1/0 or 2/0 range and filled with 20- to 50-pound test line, are popular. More conventional tackle is used for trolling, but a handful of regulars prefer the revolving spool reel for casting. If you can remember the old days of scorched thumbs and birds' nests in the reel, I think you will agree that though this type of rig is harder to master, few anglers, once converted, ever turn back.

The lures or baits that will take king salmon come in all sizes and colors. Throw them in a pile and you would have a psychedelic nightmare. Good bets for salmon are chrome, brass or copper wobblers; spinners in the same finishes; silver or fluorescent red Flatfish lures or the old dependable Hot Shot. Baits are salmon roe and small fish, such as anchovies, herring or sardines. It has been my experience that a bright chrome lure works best in clear water. When the rivers are clouded with silt, the copper or brass imitation is superior. No matter what equipment you use, be sure

that you check the fishing regulations. Many Western waters are restricted to single hooks of size 1 or smaller and bait is often forbidden. Also, many streams have special closures on spawning areas. Be safe, not sorry.

Now, let's picture ourselves on a big California river such as the Feather. Deep holes are what we are searching for. Unless the fish are on the move, this is where they will be found. Kings stay deep, so it is important to get your bait or hardware close to the bottom. This takes a gut feel for the water, because you must guess the depth and adjust the sinker size accordingly. Many casters prefer an unweighted spoon or wobbler and adjust the depth fished by the distance the lure is cast upstream. When your barbed imitation has settled to the fish's level, it should be reeled in smoothly while the rod tip is being twitched and jerked to give your offering a seductive action.

Lures can be used without a sinker, but almost every bait rig must be weighted. Baits can be allowed to rest on the bottom or can be drifted downstream with the current. When you are drifting roe or other baits, the sinker should bounce gently along the bottom, which is the method used for steelhead fishing and takes a delicate touch to keep the drift snag free. The best outfit I have found for this purpose is a three-way swivel with surgical tubing tied to one side and a pencil sinker slipped up into the tubing. This rig seldom hangs up.

On large rivers like the Sacramento and its tributaries, a good portion of the salmon catch is landed by trollers. They use the same baits and lures mentioned earlier, but the water is covered in a different fashion. Using a three-way swivel or a wire spreader with a heavy sinker attached, the lure is held on or close to the bottom, while the boat works back and forth in the current barely making headway. A variation of this method is to anchor, let the spinner work deep, and frequently raise the rod tip a foot or so, then drop it back. Chinooks will often inhale the bait or lure as it flutters to the bottom. A favorite trick of Sacramento River trollers is to use a silver or fluorescent red Flatfish, often a big T-50 model, and sweeten it with a sardine fillet. Trollers usually have good success when the water is a little murky. As the river clears, the offering should be smaller and the tackle lighter. When a stream goes from slightly milky to gin-clear, the fly fisherman gets in his licks.

Hundreds if not thousands of anglers live with the misconception that salmon won't take a fly. I am told that this view is prevalent even in the Great Lakes region. It is *wrong,* for with good water conditions and the proper technique, salmon—kings in particular—can provide some wild action. How do you get one of

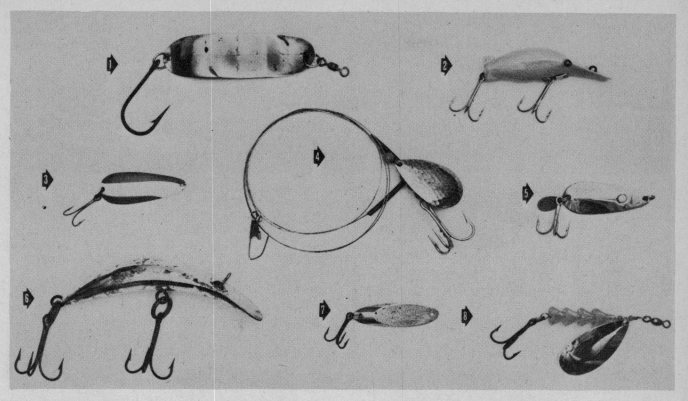

1, #5 Freak; 2, Hot Shot; 3, Dardevle; 4, Sacramento spinner and spreader; 5, Hotrod; 6, Flatfish T-50; 7, Kastmaster; 8, Tee spoon.

these silver submarines to inhale a fly?

The accepted technique is to cast a fast sinking line across the current and allow the fly to work deep, then strip in as the lure quarters downstream. The strike will most often come on the retrieve, and retrieves are as different as the fishermen who use them. I prefer a rapid, erratic nymph-type action with pulls of 3 to 8 inches, while others insist on a straight draw of about 12 inches spaced every couple of seconds. Another way to cover the water is to cast straight downstream and let that bright little imitation work deep among the big kings. This is an extremely effective technique because the lure is over fish most of the time. However, to cast down the chute, you must fish alone. Picture what would happen if a dozen fly rodders were quartering their casts on a good stretch of water and some hot shot fly flipper decided to fish down current.

Because the king is a strong fish that favors deep water, a fly rod with plenty of backbone is a must. I prefer a stick that takes either a 9-, 10- or 11-weight line. Whatever rod you choose, it should be accompanied by a complete shooting head system. [Editor's note: See "Shooting Head Systems" by Dan Blanton.] While lines are often critical, reels are not. Any

good-quality reel, either single action or anti-reverse, that is capable of holding a shooting head, 100 feet of 20- to 30-pound test mono running line, plus 200 yards of 20-pound braided Dacron will serve the purpose. Reels with nothing more than a click drag are fine. Flies for kings run the gamut of the tier's imagination, with bright patterns the most common. If I had to pick three favorite flies, they would be Cole's (or gold) Comet, Silver Comet and the Horner Shrimp. I am convinced that depth, retrieve and placing the fly in front of a salmon in a striking mood are more important than pattern. Fly hooks should be stout, and those who are well equipped will have a selection of sizes 2, 4 and 6.

The leader you select must be matched to water conditions, for kings are leader-shy. In clear water you may have to go down to 8-pound test. When waters are off-color, 15 pound is good. Equally important, keep the leader short, 6 feet or less; you defeat the purpose of a fast sink line when the fly can drift above it.

Several years ago I learned a lesson that just about doubled my batting average on winter kings. One sunny October day when the fishing was slow, I

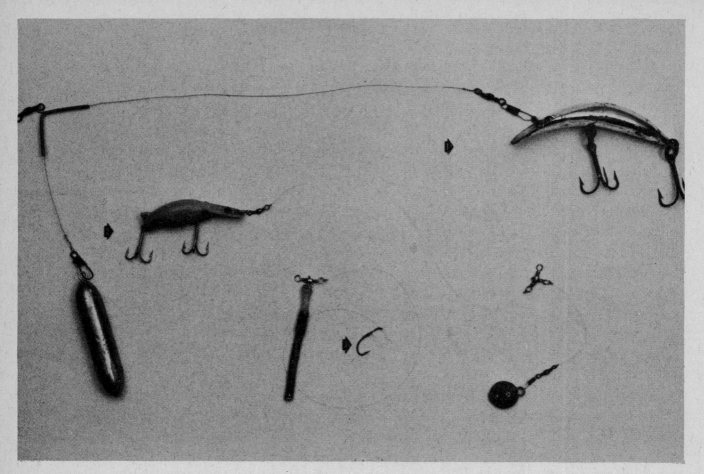

These rigs are popular on the Sacramento River: 1, wire spreader and Flatfish; 2, three-way swivel rig and Hot Shot; 3, bait gear with a pencil sinker and surgical tubing.

decided to watch from a high bank a school in 10 feet of clear water. A dozen or more fly rodders were dropping their flies over the fish with almost every cast, yet the lures weren't reaching their target. Since the river was low and clear, most flies were unweighted, so that when the fast-sinking lines hit bottom, the flies were no more than 4 feet below the surface. When retrieved, these feathered imitations were pulled down and away from the waiting salmon. Because the lines often snagged on moss as they came out of the hole, these anglers mistakenly assumed that their lures were passing in front of the fish. From that day on, my flies have all been heavily weighted, and when they picked up bottom debris, it was because the fly arrived first. I think it is best to have the fly sink slightly faster than the line. In the same vein, each cast should be counted down, so when a king is hooked or can be felt nudging the line, you can return the fly to the same spot time after time.

To land one of these heavyweights on light tackle is no easy chore, and I have more than once seen anglers make errors that cost them the fish of a lifetime. There are two common mistakes. The first is not working the fish hard enough, with the result that eventually either a tooth cut or knot failure parts the leader, or a hole is worn in the jaw and the hook falls free. The second is the tendency to pull the anchor too soon and try to follow the fish. As long as the fish hasn't left the hole, don't touch the anchor. It's hard to say how many times I have seen an angler frantically try to muscle a big chinook away from an underwater snag with the anchor up. As a result, salmon, boat and the guy that had a fish on his line all end up at the snag. If you are fishing near other boaters and have a hookup, work the fish till you land it or follow it safely out of the hole. Once it is in the clear, drop the hook and pour on the pressure. Fish over 30 pounds are best beach-landed. A fish that size is hard to lift into a net with light tackle. Furthermore, when playing a fish, keep the rod low and to the side. This tactic keeps the

The author's three favorite king salmon patterns: top, #6 Silver Comet; center, #2 Horner Shrimp; bottom, Coles Comet.

pressure on the side of the fish's head and throws it off balance, since it is strongest going straight away. When the salmon turns inward and swims the other way, swing the rod to the opposite side. This constant changing back and forth confuses your quarry and can cut landing time by 50 percent.

California is blessed with many rivers in which the mighty chinook migrates. Great streams like the Smith, Klamath, Eel and Sacramento produce good runs of this much-sought-after gamefish. I can know no other anadromous fish more available to Californians. For example, the Sacramento River has kings present year around. Fall-run fish start entering the Sacramento in August and continue through January, with the peak activity in October and November. This same stream produces winter chinooks which start around Christmas and are available until they spawn in May or June. Late spring brings yet another migration to this greatest of California rivers. April, May and June mark the peak of the spring run. Per numbers of fish and miles of fishable water, the Sacramento often has less angling pressure than smaller coastal streams. Other California waters that provide fishable stocks of king salmon almost all have fall runs which start in rivers like the Klamath in July, but by and large the peak months are October and November. It makes no difference whether you pursue this husky salmonoid in the spring or fall; to

When you try to muscle a big chinook away from a snag, keep the anchor down.

land one is its own reward.

Picture yourself on a Western river with the chill of approaching winter in the air, while bright fall leaves drift lazily with the current. A few yards away you witness silver-sided kings taking turns exploding the rippled surface. In my book, this is some of the most exciting fishing the West has to offer. When your favorite lure is going through salmon on every cast, your knees get a little weak and your breath comes quicker as you wait and work. Finally you feel a mighty tug and the line snaps taut—fish on.

Tidewater on California's Smith River. Lone angler is Ron Dong.

A New Look at
Bluegill and Crappie
by Bob Underwood

If you believe that the crappie is a lazy fish which prefers to strike tiny lures worked very slowly, this article is going to shock you.

Back in 1964, Dave Hill, a veteran Navy man now stationed in Maryland, and I were on the lake shortly after 8 a.m. for the specific purpose of catching as many blanket-size crappie as was legal. Our local community club had planned a fish fry for that afternoon and we had been elected to supply the fish. They had waited, however, until the previous night to notify us of our expected contribution. Now we were on the water in a "must" situation.

Fortunately, this happened during the "crappie time of year," which peaks in late January and February in our state of Florida. Dave not only had the fish located, he had the method of taking them down pat. We left the water around 3 p.m. with our limit of twenty-five each and enjoyed our role of heroes at the get-together. Twenty-six of those crappies weighed over 2 pounds each. Man, we did it up right!

What did we use to take them? Minnows? Jigs? A seine? Ha! We used a medium diving 3½-inch-long bass plug and we trolled this lure at better than 5 miles per hour. This was not merely a Florida fluke. I've tried it in at least nineteen other states with equal success. The method never fails to cause raised eyebrows among local fishermen who at first believe I'm trolling for bass. One fisherman in Texas (and I wish we had more like him) gave me a heated, 10-minute lecture on the evils of being a fish hog after he had watched me trolling for 4 hours and then asked how many fish I had in the live well. When I told him twenty-two, his face got all red and excited and he verbally lit into me. I had to show him that the fish were not bass before he would believe me.

The method of fast trolling with large (for crappie) lures is slowly spreading, and fishermen are beginning to note that it takes the huskier fish. With this method, the sonic, or vibrating, types of bass lures are the most popular, probably because, day in and day out, they are the most productive. Most crappie enthusiasts, however, still prefer their fishing slow and easy. I would hazard a guess that their choice of baits would probably be about 80 percent for live bait and 20 percent for artificials.

The jig is the most lifeless lure ever placed in the water unless one imparts some action to it. Retrieved on a steady line, it simply hangs there, moving with a deadness duplicated by no creature beneath the surface. Yet, it is the preferred method of trolling for crappie in certain Southern states and is rapidly spreading across the country. Simply drop the line behind the boat and let it hang there. Place a couple of rods so rigged into rod holders and motor along. Pick up the rod when a fish hooks itself and reel it in. In a small lake in Delaware I boated a limit for four consecutive days with this "dead" method.

The bluegill, like the crappie, often demands a departure from the time-honored and traditional methods. A lake near my home and another in Oklahoma yield the largest bluegills by trolling extremely slowly right down the middle with a 3-inch countdown Rapala lure practically kissing the bottom. There is no way the tiny mouth can inhale that large lure, but the fish eat up those rear treble hooks.

When I speak of modifying techniques, let me make a point that I feel needs to be made. Fish are changing, in a manner so subtle we aren't aware of it. You may scoff at this, but let me call your attention to the manner in which Nature takes care of her children and also give you something to think about. We'll see if you don't agree that the conditions are present, as never before, for such a happening to take place—that, indeed, it must eventually occur.

There are three stages that Nature puts creatures through for their own protection and survival. These are, in order: conditioning, conditioned instinct, instinctive knowledge.

Fish learn (this is not really the correct word) by a process known as conditioning. Basically, if a fish encounters an experience, good or bad, often enough, it begins to approach the "conditioned" stage. A few more occurrences of this incident and the fish is fully "conditioned." It has "learned."

Despite countless years of chasing these fish, crap-

The crappie and some of the lures that fool him. This particular fish was marked prior to release and came from a school the author was observing. Note the dorsal fin.

Some fly rod lures for bluegills. The flies are wet; the poppers for the top.

pie and bluegill fishermen have been relatively static in their methods for taking them. Lures, bait and types of presentation are no different today from what they were yesterday. The only significant modifications have been to add ultralight lines and to move into the deep water after the fish. We now catch crappie, for instance, during those times of year when they were once thought to be gone. So we've taken

an extremely short time of experience and added decades and decades of practice to it.

The crappie and bluegill, for an untold number of years, were fished only during certain seasons. The rest of the time they were, for the most part, safe. The crappie, relieved of the spawning duties which placed it in shallow water during its season, was then relatively safe in and over the depths. This set them up for a form of conditioning, a means of escape from pressure. For the past decade or so, there has been no escape from the constant pressure.

Conditioning, over the years, gradually takes on another form known as "conditioned instinct." This is present in every form of animal life in the wilds. Deer hunters get a better idea of how this works simply by thinking of the doe. If she had been hunted as long and as hard as the male, do you really think she would be as easy to spot as she is? Obviously, she would have all the instinctive alertness and caution of the buck. Humans are the only form of animal life that has not developed its instincts to anything approaching a meaningful level.

Conditioned instinct eventually becomes "instinctive knowledge" and is passed on from one generation to another through certain genes. Some call it "adaptability" but this is a misnomer. Adaptability is the ability to adjust, to modify. Instinct is an inborn ability, automatic, habitual. It is a survival must, a natural law.

So, while it has escaped notice, this phenomenon is beginning to take place beneath the surface of the water with the bluegill and crappie. Fishing pressure has never been greater and is rapidly increasing. No day goes by on which these fish are not subjected to it. Nature is making her adjustments. This is not going to be accomplished in one generation, but it will happen and I believe is happening. These fish are not going to become so smart that we will not be able to catch them, but we will have to develop new methods some time along the way.

Meanwhile, let's take a look at bluegill and crappie under water and learn better methods for taking them. With scuba equipment, I've spent considerable time in their living quarters, and, since you probably have not, I'll pass on a bit of what I've learned.

I've found both the bluegill and the crappie quite easy to observe. Bluegill are the easiest to approach under water and are curious, friendly fish. They do not frighten readily and rarely travel far from the scene. It's easy to get right in the midst of a school of bluegill and watch them feed within arm's reach of the diver. I've fed them from my hand. With crappie one must remain several yards outside the fringe of the school. Any continued attempt to do otherwise will cause the crappie to bunch tighter and move off. Bluegill will feed all around you; crappie tend to group together, and it is sometimes an hour or more before they will feed in your presence.

Light does not affect the eyes of either of these fish and, in itself, does not determine where the fish will be but the crappie seeks depth and shade more than the bluegill does. On a hot, bright and still day the crappie is likely to school right under your boat while the bluegill normally keeps its distance. This makes the crappie, in open water, perfect for the cane pole and minnow fishermen, while the bluegill, unless spawning, is likely to take the bait or lure a bit farther out. Years ago, my father used to row across the lake on a hot, still day spreading open sheets of newspaper behind him. Then he would row back, dapping a live minnow under the sheets, and fill his stringer with crappie. I wouldn't advise this now, however; I tried it not long ago and was castigated for littering. But, it works as well today as it did then.

Bluegill seek constant cover far more than do crappie, and, given a choice, they prefer underwater vegetation to rocks, stumps and logs. Bluegill spend most of their time either in or at the base of cover. However, they also spend time in the open, close to but not in cover. This popular panfish is much more of a bottom fish than the crappie is. I believe this is

The author's father, Allen Underwood, holds a stringer of bluegills from White River in Arkansas.

This bluegill took a wet fly fished at the edge of a weedbed.

because most of its food is found on or near the bottom. The crappie likes its food moving and off the bottom; small food fishes make up the better part of its diet. The bluegill prefers larvae or nymphs of insects, snails, worms and even fish eggs. It will also feed off vegetation when other food becomes scarce. The crappie will not.

There are times when both fish will feed on or near the surface, but the bluegill is more of a surface feeder than the crappie is. In times of insect hatches, for instance, both species will gorge themselves just below the surface and right on top. On such occasions a small popper, rubber spider or dry fly can be deadly for bluegill, and dry flies and small streamers will take crappie. From a small lake in Delaware (where the crappie is called the calico bass), I once boated and released 125 crappie in less than 2 hours, using only a hook tipped with a piece of my wife's white slip. With a fly rod, I simply cast the rig out about 40 feet and very slowly stripped line, keeping the lure just beneath the surface.

The sound, or lack of it, will often tell you which fish is feeding on the surface. The bluegill makes a sort of "kissing" noise on a surface take. The crappie simply leaves a little surface ring most of the time, but when it is feeling its oats, it makes a definite "slapping" sound. The time of day may also be used as a rough guide. The bluegill is likely to feed on the surface any time of the day. The crappie tends to restrict its surface feeding to the early morning and very late evening hours; unless actively spawning, it nearly always prefers to be in or over the depths.

In the Southern states, it is difficult to find an angler using a fly rod and wet flies or streamers for either of these species. Many use a fly rod but their mainstay for bluegill seems to be fishing poppers. I've yet to see a Southern angler using a fly rod and small streamer for crappie, though it may occur. Perhaps this is because Southern anglers haven't developed the instinct for the underwater strike that their Northern counterparts, many of whom are also excellent trout fishermen, have. Perhaps Southern anglers think that a fly rod and wet fly or streamer are difficult to use or have been conditioned to the cane pole and bobber, something they can see the fish take.

For the man who takes time to learn how, using a wet fly or streamer is much more exciting and is equally productive with either bluegill or crappie. Underwater, I've watched crappie ignore a live minnow anchored in their midst, yet take, one after the other, a streamer fly eased past their noses. I've also watched an entire school of bluegill, fifteen in number, taken one by one on a No. 12 wet fly allowed to settle

slowly to the bottom and then slightly twitched.

Both species are school fish. Where you locate one, you'll find others. Bluegill will normally bite from top to bottom at any time of day. But I've noticed repeatedly that crappie tend to hold at certain depths and often will not venture above or below those depths to take a lure or live bait. If I could offer only one bit of advice to a beginning crappie fisherman, it would be to vary his depth of fishing until the correct one is located.

Unless trolling or casting, the lure for crappie should be manually manipulated for a slight bit of action. Jigs should be kept moving and live bait should be kept alive. It isn't often that crappie will take a dead bait or a lure that is kept still. In color choice, nationwide, I would settle for yellow, white or a combination of both. If the action is slow, and you know you are over fish, try a green and white combination. Other colors sometimes work better, but these are the most consistent wherever you happen to be. Bluegill seem to prefer black in wet flies and, on the surface, a yellow and black combination seems to be the best choice on any given body of water.

Bluegill are territorial fish; crappie are wanderers.

The fly rod is the author's choice for bluegills.

The author holds a blanket-sized crappie that hit a small jig cast into a school. Finding the right depth is the key.

Take either a distance from their school and it will attempt to return to it. The bluegill will return to feeding within minutes after release, providing its stomach or throat has not been injured. The crappie, once hooked and released, will often not feed again for at least 30 minutes. A fish of either species, returned to the water obviously hurt to the point of bleeding, floundering or seeming crippled, is avoided by its mates. With bluegill, the rest of the school will continue to feed. With crappie, the rest of the school will normally stop feeding for a short time, unless they are on the spawning beds. When spawning, they hit regardless. This is more a protective than a feeding action.

In closing, let me pass on two outstanding methods of fishing for these species. One is for bluegill and one is for crappie. Try them and your days on the water will be blessed.

When fishing for bluegill over rocky, shell or sandy bottom, the most productive method by far is to fish the bait right on the bottom. I like to use live worms and I cast the bait out, using a splitshot to carry it down, then retrieve very slowly, but steadily. After several casts, as observed from underneath, the fish begin to watch for the bait and usually dart for it as soon as the retrieve is begun. The strike is quick and hard, the bait totally inhaled. I prefer a long-shank hook, about a No. 8 size, to facilitate easy removal, as the barb is usually buried in the throat.

The other method is for those times when crappie are in water of 10 feet or less. Using small jigs, place two cane poles, equipped with just enough line to hold the jigs barely off the bottom, into rod holders on

A float and live bait rank among the most popular methods for taking panfish.

opposite sides of the boat. Face the outboard motor and troll as slowly as it will allow. Tap the butt of each pole lightly and rhythmically with the palm of your hand. You'll find yourself taking crappie as close as 5 feet behind the motor.

Last, when fishing for crappie, remember that this fish likes its food moving. If you're using live bait, are not over the spawning beds, and the water is still and calm, you are handicapping yourself unless you ease the boat along with oars, paddle or electric motor.

Now, it is only a matter of cleaning your catch and cooking it. Call me when it's time to eat.

Put More Fish in Your Boat by Trolling

by Milt Rosko

Marty Hodes was bent over the fathometer, watching the stylus clearly draw the bottom conformation some 30 feet beneath his *Lisa Lee* as we slowly trolled along the perimeter of the Shrewsbury Rocks, a patch of rocky, broken, irregular bottom that plays host to a variety of gamefish off the Jersey coast each summer. The graph showed huge rocks extending up from the bottom as much as 10 feet, then dropping away abruptly to smooth sand.

"Get ready," said Marty. "The peak we just went over had a cluster of fish on it."

Marty's stern-drive churned along at 700 revolutions per minute (rpm), while 125 feet astern a pair of pork-rind-tipped spoons thumped rhythmically and an enticing surgical tube lure moved erratically through the water.

"There they go!" shouted my son, Bob as the two outboard rods arched over simultaneously, the reels emitting a banshee screech that was guaranteed to give even the most seasoned angler goosebumps!

Marty handled one outfit and Bob the other, and the fish ran off quite a bit of line, then came to the surface and thrashed it to foam. The pressure eventually took its toll, and first I swung Marty's tired adversary aboard and then Bob's. Both were bluefish of about 14 pounds. They had made the mistake of engulfing the pork-rind-tipped spoons, the first fish to have done so after almost three hours of trolling that morning.

We then fished to a pattern, trolling the rockpiles and looking for the patches of fish that were hanging on the peaks, and before day's end the fishbox included an 8-pound striper and a beautiful weakfish of the same size, plus several more bulldogging blues.

The CB disclosed that the chummers were faring poorly and anglers jigging or using natural baits were shut out for the most part. This was a case in which trolling was the right tool to cover a large area where gamefish were usually in residence and parlay good lures and sound techniques into a good catch. It was no blitz, just a slow, deliberate pick through the day that made it a fun day and, after all, that's what fishing is all about.

Many anglers will describe trolling as letting their lures astern and towing them around. Indeed, this is precisely what some anglers do, but it is not trolling as I think of it. The skilled troller employs a variety of techniques that result in his catching fish, while the angler who just tows his lures around often comes back with an empty fishbox.

Trolling, in general, falls into three distinct categories, according to the type of location. The situation described at the beginning of this article calls for inshore trolling, effective on open waters, primarily inshore, including broad bays and sounds as well as the inshore ocean. Sheltered-water trolling is employed in confined waters such as rivers and estuaries along the seacoast where the water is shallow and protected and the species are small. Blue-water or offshore trolling is practiced for the pelagic game species that roam the waters of the world and, for the most part, is done far from shore or where there is an abrupt dropoff and the water changes from the pale greens of the shallows to the deep cobalt of the open ocean.

For each of these three types of fishing there is specially adapted equipment that I have found perfect whether I fish the Atlantic, Pacific or Gulf coasts, or in Mexico, the Bahamas, Bermuda and the other exotic ports of call I visit.

For offshore trolling, I find regulation 30-pound-class tackle ideal for any species up to 100 pounds and have even landed heavier fish on the basic outfit. This includes fishing for the smaller tunas, such as the yellowfin, school bluefin and blackfin, and the smaller billfishes, such as the white marlin, sailfish and striped marlin. The outfit also works very well with the bonitos, amberjack, wahoo, dolphin, albacore and a

A 30-pound class outfit with a pair of balao baits and a swimming mullet bait. Note the pair of hooks rigged in each balao. The rear hook often catches short strikers such as king mackerel, which are notorious for cutting a bait in half and missing the hook.

variety of sharks.

Inshore trolling can be geared down substantially. While I use 20- or 30-pound test line for the most part, the rod is somewhat lighter than the class tackle version, and the reel holds 200 yards of line, which is more than adequate for most of the species encountered. You'll find plenty of variety inshore, including such Atlantic Coast favorites as striped bass, bluefish, weakfish and channel bass, plus the Atlantic and oceanic bonito which roam inshore at times, and also pollock. In Southern waters, the variety will be enhanced by jack crevalle, cobia, king mackerel, snook, tarpon and barracuda. West Coast anglers use this outfit for striped bass, silver and king salmon, Pacific bonito, Pacific barracuda and white sea bass.

For trolling in sheltered waters, I like what is called a plug outfit, a popping outfit or a bay outfit, depending on what section of the country you hail from. It's really a salt water version of a bait casting outfit, ideally suited to handling fish in the 2- to 10-pound class. The rod has a medium action and I use a level wind salt water reel that holds 200 yards of 15-pound test monofilament. This outfit works equally well for small bluefish, striped bass, weakfish and pollock in Northern waters and for Spanish mackerel, blue and rainbow runners, small snook, jack crevalle, and spotted weakfish in Florida and along the Gulf Coast; Pacific Coast anglers probing protected waters use it to catch bonito, school stripers, corvina and Pacific mackerel and enjoy fine sport.

With each of these three basic outfits, regardless of where I'm fishing, I always use a ball–bearing–type swivel at the terminal end of the line. With the 30-pound class outfit I'll use 8 or 10 feet of double line and then tie in a combination swivel and coastlock snap. With the other trolling outfits, I forego the double line and tie in directly to the combination swivel and coastlock snap. The swivel is important and it must have positive swiveling action, as the ball bearing type does, for in trolling many lures will twist your line into an unmanageable mess unless the swivel is doing its job.

The next item of terminal tackle is the leader. If you're fishing in Southern waters where toothy adversaries such as wahoo and king mackerel are plentiful it's best to use a leader of number 8 or 9 stainless steel single-strand wire or a light braided cable that tests out at around 75 pounds. If billfish and the tunas and bonitos are your target, then monofilament leaders are fine. For offshore fishing, I prefer my leaders

A 20-pound class inshore trolling outfit. The selection of lures includes a sparkling plastic coated spoon, a modern counterpart of a trolling feather with a plastic skirt, a stainless steel spoon, a cedar jig, a chromed spoon, a trolling feather, a bucktail jig, a painted cedar jig and a bone squid. All are standard on the trolling circuit and should be included in the kit of every troller.

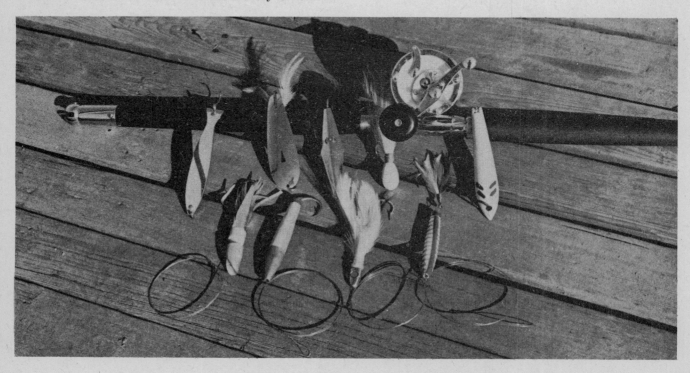

around 8 to 10 feet long, as this enables me to reel a fish close to the boat so that the person doing the gaffing doesn't have to handle a lot of leader before he can sink the gaff.

For inshore trolling, number 7 or 8 stainless wire is fine, but most often I use 30- or 40-pound test monofilament leader material and a coastlock snap at the end to facilitate changing lures. The leader's length is 6 to 8 feet, which I prefer. Some anglers use 25- to 30-foot-long leaders, but I see no purpose in it, because in practice you actually have to handline the fish the entire length of the leader to get it aboard.

In protected waters, a 6-foot leader is more than adequate, with 15- or 20-pound test monofilament leader material preferred. If the leader is too light, either a fish may bite through it or it may fray on sharp gill covers, fins or scales.

There are literally thousands of lures designed specifically to be trolled, but most fall into perhaps a dozen types that have universal appeal. Wherever I've fished, I've found that certain basic lures produce

A strip bait will catch fish no matter where you troll it. A fine barracuda is being swung aboard by Andy Heild, who guided the author while fishing off Walker's Cay in the Bahamas. The strip bait was cut from pork rind, and even the vicious teeth of the barracuda didn't ruin it. A strip bait may be fished effectively right on the surface or sent into the depths with the aid of trolling sinkers.

strikes from the same general species, even though local anglers may not have used them. The cedar jig of the East Coast angler worked very well on albacore off San Diego, yet I seldom observed other anglers using them. The strip bait so popular in Florida and the Bahamas has brought strikes for me from practically every species on the West Coast, the mid-Atlantic and especially the Gulf Coast. So include the basic lure or bait types in your trolling arsenal and try them even if local custom dictates otherwise.

The trolling feather is one of the most popular lures, regardless of the type of trolling you do or where you troll. It consists of a metal or plastic head with a collection of feathers tied to the head and partly covered with a plastic skirt. More recent types employ plastic streamers instead of feathers, but they work extremely well and are impervious to salt water, a big plus. Feathers are available in a variety of colors, with red and white, yellow, white, blue, green, and black all popular. The feathers when trolled resemble small forage fish and the size you use depends on the size of the bait in the area you're fishing. Inshore trollers often use 1/4-ounce trolling feathers, while offshore fishermen employ models with heads weighing a full 2 or 3 ounces.

The spoon ranks close behind on the popularity poll, with literally dozens upon dozens of shapes and sizes. Unlike the trolling feather which comes through the water with little action, the spoon is one of the most active lures used by the troller. Small 3- and 4-inch models are popular in protected waters where bait fish are small, while out in deep waters models that average 7 to 9 inches find the greatest use. The biggest spoons I've employed are known as bunker spoons; they measure a full 12 to 14 inches in length by 4 inches in width and are very effective when stripers, blues and channel bass are feeding on menhaden.

Cedar jigs collect a lot of fish wherever they're used and are most popular on the offshore grounds, especially for the tunas and bonitos on all coasts. The vintage cedar jigs are made of a hollowed dowel of natural cedar and are fitted with a lead head. When they are trolled, water rushes through the hollow jig and causes an erratic action that many gamefish find irresistible. Models ranging from 4 to 9 inches in length are most popular and, while the natural cedar coloration has always worked well for me, there are many jigs on the market today that are painted with an airbrush to simulate various bait fish. Some of the new plastic jigs with the styling of the cedar jigs also produce good scores.

The wide variety of lures made of surgical tubing or

The author inspects a modern-day counterpart of a feathered jig. It has a metal head and long plastic streamers, with a pair of hooks, and is a very effective lure for striped marlin. Here the author is working off Coronado Islands, on the Pacific Coast. The lure also accounts for a wide variety of gamefish, including the tunas, albacore, bonito and a host of others.

soft plastic also account for many species on the trolling grounds. Here, again, the size of the lure is usually matched with the bait fish in residence. Much must be said for the new plastics, for indeed some of the replicas of bait fish are so exact that they fool you at first glance.

Within the general category of plugs fall perhaps a dozen varieties and, at one time or another, most will catch fish when trolled. The best trolling plugs I've used are the swimming plugs, both surface and subsurface swimmers. The forward movement of the boat causes these plugs with metal or plastic lips to pulsate or swim enticingly when trolled at moderate speed. Deep-diving mirror plugs also take many fish, as do poppers, with the latter working best when jigged while trolling.

Bucktail jigs are still another fine trolling lure, which come in a mind-boggling variety of shapes, sizes and colors. Their fish-catching effectiveness may be enhanced by adding a few strands of Mylar to the bucktail skirt, a piece of pork rind or the new shimmering plastic bait-tails. Many anglers troll bucktail jigs at a steady pace, but they're most effective when you hold the rod as you troll and work the rod tip vigorously, causing the jig to dart ahead and then falter, much like a wounded bait fish. When you get tired of jigging, you know you're doing it right!

Bone squids and their plastic counterparts have a shape very similar to the spoon and a comparable action. They regularly account for many species that will hit a trolled lure. Block-tin, lead, stainless-steel and chromed squids are among the vintage lures used by trollers and must be included in the serious troller's kit.

The types I have described are by far the most popular and effective of the basic lures, but there are many others; and depending on time and conditions, most lures will coax a strike from a hungry gamefish in a feeding frenzy.

While the lures take a substantial toll of finned adversaries, natural baits also may be trolled with potent results. On the Atlantic Coast, the balao and mullet are favorites as rigged baits, although my own preference is for a rigged eel, as it can be used in situations ranging from close to the beach for striped bass to the offshore grounds for the tunas and white marlin. It's one of the toughest baits there is and can be struck repeatedly without being ripped from the hook.

On the West Coast, I've used sardines and flying fish with fine results on striped marlin and also trolled anchovies for king and silver salmon and striped bass.

Trolling is very effective in sheltered waters. The author used a combination of a bucktail jig and needlefish bait to coax a strike from this fine snook while trolling along the edge of a channel far back in the mangroves behind Marco Island on the west coast of Florida. A situation like this calls for a light popping outfit and 15-pound test line.

But if I had to choose only one natural bait for inshore or offshore trolling, I would succumb to the effectiveness of a strip bait. A strip may be cut from the belly of a tuna, bonito, dolphin or other fish. The finest strip I have ever used was cut from pork rind. It is extremely tough, will sustain repeated strikes, and will catch many fish before it needs to be replaced. I've used strips that measured only 5 inches in length by 1/2 inch in width while trolling for summer flounders and weakfish, and huge 14- by 2-inch strips while tangling with marlin, sailfish, and a variety of tunas and other scrappers on the offshore grounds. Properly rigged, the strip bait may be used as a surface skip bait, or sent deep with the aid of trolling sinkers where it shimmers and swims enticingly until a hungry gamefish wallops it.

Inshore, when fishing from a small boat in a protected river or creek, many anglers will simply use a pair of rods and stream their lines astern 60 to 75 feet, probing the depths, the rips and the eddies with their lures. Moving into bigger water and correspondingly bigger boats, it's often practical to troll three or four lines. Out on the blue water circuit, it's not at all unusual to troll a half-dozen lines: a pair straight astern called flat lines and from two to four lines fished from outriggers, which extend the lines well away from the boat and back anywhere from 100 to 150 feet.

There are a number of critical considerations in trolling and the veteran angler who catches a lot of fish is usually concerned with all of them. Line length is very important. You should know precisely the length of line you have behind the boat at all times, for once a fish is hooked, you can then return your lures to precisely the same distance behind the boat and often receive strikes in rapid succession. Tunas and bonitos are extremely fast and will often respond to lures trolled on the crest of the first or second wave churned up in your wake. They will strike a fast-moving lure more readily than a slow-moving one. Quite the opposite is true when you're seeking bluefish, striped bass, channel bass and weakfish. Motor noise will often spook these species and best results are usually achieved with lines measured at 125 to 150 feet behind the boat, with even more distance necessary if tide, current and depth of water dictate.

If you're trolling four lines, alternate their lengths, fishing a pair short and a pair long. Permit some of the lures to work near the surface, sending others a bit deeper through the use of any of the deep trolling devices, which include trolling sinkers, planers and downriggers. You can also employ solid Monel wire line or lead-core line, thus giving you an opportunity

Slowly trolling a rigged eel 125 feet behind an outboard skiff brought the author this 38-pound striper. Rigged eels are a very effective trolling bait as they are extremely durable and will survive repeated strikes. The author has caught a wide range of gamefish on eels.

to fish any desired depth. I mention wire and lead core as options available to the troller, but using these lines takes much of the sport out of catching gamefish.

Regardless of where you troll or what lures or baits you employ, it's extremely important that you troll at a speed that will allow your lures or baits to work properly. The speed cannot be determined by revolutions of your motor alone, because under one set of conditions your lures may work beautifully and fish strike them readily at, say, 600 rpm on your engine, while just a day later, or even hours later, under different conditions, it may require a speed of 900 or 1000 rpm to achieve the same action.

The variables that come into play are wind and tide, and both can have a pronounced effect on your results. Don't get locked into a specific pattern and ignore the wind and the tide, for then you'll score only when conditions are right, and not when they deviate too far from the norm. With lures such as plugs and spoons, you can watch your rod tips and will see that they are pulsating if the lures are working properly.

Watching skip baits such as balao and mullet will quickly tell the story. You want the bait or lure to be vibrant and full of life, not just dragging through the water listlessly.

It has been my observation that the chief mistake anglers make when trolling, is to troll too slowly and not to appreciate the speed with which a gamefish can seize a bait or lure. Trolling too slowly in some situations will keep even the finest lure from getting results. The fact that a lure isn't moving along and presenting a challenge can cause a fish to pay it little heed. That's why it often pays to work your rod tip vigorously while trolling, especially once a fish has been hooked from the school, for the erratic action will often bring additional strikes.

An old trick of veteran tuna fishermen is to leave a hooked fish in the water and to circle slowly, dragging the hooked fish, while the anglers in the cockpit deep-jig their lures, whether these are feathers, jigs, spoons or cedar jigs. Often, the tuna, bonito or other species will follow the hooked fish and immediately

Most types of boats can be used for trolling. This stern-drive rig is a fine platform for the angler intent on working the edge of a coral reef in search of gamefish. Keep alternating your speed and the length of your line until you hit the right combination.

pounce on any lure that is worked vigorously.

It's important to vary your pattern when trolling. Even many miles from shore there are swift currents, and if you simply troll in one general direction all day, you simply may never find the correct set at which the fish are striking. Work into the waves and then with them. Try cross current and lazy figure eights. Move your throttles ahead and ease back on them until you hit the combination that brings strikes.

If you are trolling with the rods in rod holders and one rod goes down under a strike, be alert to several things: speed, direction and the length of line on the lure that received the strike. Unless the fish is an extremely big one, don't stop the boat immediately. Keep moving ahead for at least 100 to 150 feet and let the hooked fish rip off drag. As you move ahead, you may be fortunate enough to hook two or three more fish from the same school. This is particularly true with bluefish, dolphin, king mackerel, albacore, bluefin tuna and bonito.

Most fish that feed on bait fish are accustomed to chasing and catching a fish that is excitedly dodging the predator in order to survive. Fish become furious as they chase something they're about to eat, and often both the pursuer and the fish being pursued leap out of the water in a frenzy. The troller can capitalize on this excitement quotient of gamefishing by putting a pair of teasers astern, simply to excite fish into striking the teasers and ultimately striking the lures being trolled close at hand. The most popular teasers

Many anglers who fish offshore waters do so from big boats such as the charter boat *Mitchell II,* which fishes out of Chub Cay in the Bahamas. Note the outriggers which are down and are used to keep the baits spread well apart. Boats such as this are ideal for sportfishing and have all the comforts one could possibly ask for while fishing far at sea.

King mackerel are extremely plentiful in Southern waters and during the height of the run an inshore troller can catch fish of the size shown until he is arm-weary. The 20-pound outfit used to subdue this small king is equally effective on the 20- to 30-pound marauding kings that may swat your bait.

in use today are constructed of plastic and resemble a huge popping plug with a concave head and a long plastic skirt. They are painted bright colors and, when trolled, they dive, jump and skip much like a bait fish attempting to elude a predator. Often, gamefish will zero in on a teaser and strike at it repeatedly. Then you can cautiously pull in the teaser and simultaneously ease a bait right into the slot where the teaser was. Invariably, the gamefish will be onto your bait in an instant.

I've used a variety of teasers, including a 3-foot-long common eel tied to a length of line, which white marlin will attack repeatedly before they finally move onto a bait fished close to the teaser. Some anglers use an 18- to 24-inch-long strip bait without a hook, and this, too, infuriates fish into ultimately striking an adjoining bait.

Watching for concentrations of sea gulls is of the utmost importance to the troller, since the birds often congregate to feed on the bait fish which are being herded to the surface by hungry gamefish below. Situations where the sky is alive with birds may

A balanced 30-pound class outfit produced this fine sailfish for June Rosko, who hooked it while trolling a mullet bait in the Bahamas.

develop in a quiet tidal estuary when you're trolling a bucktail jig for weakfish, on the inshore grounds where Spanish mackerel are cutting into pilchards, or many miles from shore where albacore and husky yellowfin tuna are gorging on squid, butterfish or herring.

When fish are chasing bait on the surface, they're usually in such a feeding frenzy that they're not difficult to catch. But one of the quickest ways to spook the fish is to run your boat right through them. This will often put the fish down, and sometimes they simply will not come back to the schools of bait fish on the surface. When you see surface activity or even see schools of nervous bait fish, the best approach is to work along the perimeter of the schools, trolling so that your lures skirt along the edge. This approach will often bring strikes, at which time it is wise to point your bow away from the fish and ease slowly away from them. Once a fish is aboard you can let your lines out and again work the perimeter of the school.

Sometimes you'll see fish cavorting on the surface and, troll as you may with every lure in your tackle locker, you simply can't coax a strike. This often happens with the tuna and bonito families, as well as with many other gamefish. At such times, you can often achieve strikes by determining in which direction the fish are moving, for often these cavorting fish are often just moving and not really feeding. Once you determine their direction, simply advance your throttles, overtake the fish, and deliberately spook them. Then, as your boat is immediately above where the fish were, quickly ease back on your throttles and have the anglers in the cockpit vigorously work their rod tips, causing the lures to dart about in the wake. Often, the fish will move excitedly back to the surface, spot the lures in the churning wake, and be onto them in a flash.

While admittedly this last technique is a direct contradiction of what I said earlier about working fish actively feeding on the surface, it has succeeded for me time and again on all three coasts and in Bermuda and the Bahamas as well.

One trick I make a habit of using wherever I fish has brought me many bonus fish, although at times it has also annoyed charter and private skippers intent on more formidable game than I was hooking. When I am trolling for marlin, sailfish or other exotics, I always put over a 30-pound class outfit with a small lure. If I'm trolling inshore with big bunker spoons or 9-inch-long plugs for big stripers, I'll ease over a small tube lure or bucktail jig. Just to be contrary, I always put out a smaller and different lure from the favorite being used. You know what happens? It catches fish. Lots of surprises come to the offbeat lure in the pattern. On the small offering, I've caught many big and exotic gamefish ranging from yellowfin tuna in canyon country off New Jersey to albacore a hundred miles off the coast of Baja California and dolphin around the oil rigs of Louisiana. The list goes on and on, and, to this day, while the deckhand or my host rigs up, I busy myself rigging up my offbeat combination to catch those fish that move up into the spread of primary lures or baits but happen to find my offering more to their liking.

Trolling is by no means the only way to catch fish consistently, but it is an extremely effective method that knowledgeable boatmen should put to use regularly to enhance their scores. For those who have been content with bottom fishing or chumming, it gives a new dimension, because the species that will take a trolled lure are many and they include some of the most formidable gamefish our oceans have to offer.

A Primer on Steelhead Fishing

by David Richey

Steelhead fishermen once believed that it was necessary to serve a two- to five-year apprenticeship on a steelhead stream before one could become proficient enough to take fish consistently. That concept is rapidly disappearing, in part because increased numbers of fish are being planted and more information on the sport is being provided. The result is a shortened span of time between the first steelhead strike and a gleaming silver fish quivering in the net.

It makes little difference whether the steelhead fishing techniques described here are practiced on Pacific Northwest streams or on rivers and lakes flowing into the Great Lakes. The methods work equally well in either location.

The first step toward understanding the steelhead and its migratory life style while in fresh water is to realize that the fish is almost constantly on the move. Steelhead leave the Pacific Ocean or the Great Lakes days, weeks or months prior to spawning time. Their primary purpose in ascending streams is to spawn and assure runs of steelhead in the future.

A steelhead will move upstream at its own pace, pausing now and then for a day or two and then pressing upstream again. This upstream migration

may take only a few days, as in the case of some steelhead streams in Michigan , Wisconsin or Minnesota, or a matter of one to three months in some of the larger rivers of Washington and Oregon.

Part of the secret of catching steelhead involves knowing *where* to locate the run of fish. Knowledgeable guides, game wardens and fisheries biologists are usually informed about the runs in their areas and can often pinpoint the location of fish quickly.

Steelhead, as they migrate upstream, will often pause for varying lengths of time in the same locations year after year. A trick many beginning steelheaders use is to watch veteran fishermen and see where they fish. A veteran often skips the unproductive water and heads straight for the best spots.

How does a beginner find a productive spot on a strange stream? Here it becomes a matter of knowing the type of water frequented by migrating steelhead. Certain areas will hold steelhead while other spots are often totally empty of any fish life. One of the best locations is the extreme tail end of a hole (steelheaders call them "drifts") where the water begins to increase its speed before spilling over into the next riffle. The tail of the drift should be from 3 to 6 feet in depth with

A grin of happiness totally engulfs this first-time steelhead fisherman's face as he leads an exhausted fish to the net.

a moderately heavy current flowing over a gravel or rocky bottom. If the drift contains some larger rocks or boulders, so much the better. Steelhead will often lie near these obstructions and pick off food as it drifts by.

Fairly deep runs (6 to 10 feet) along the edge of a riverbank are always good spots to try. Steelhead will normally be found lying toward the tail ends of runs. These fish often hold just to the outside of heavy flows of current. Many steelhead hotspots can be located by fishing the edges of the current or along the current sides of swirling eddies. Learn to read the current flows by watching drifting flotsam on the surface. Minor current flows often wash food into relatively quiet sanctuaries where steelhead can rest and feed without having to fight the full force of the current.

Any obstruction, such as a large boulder, sweeper (fallen tree top), submerged log or logjam, or tree roots, may serve as a buffer zone where steelhead can pause momentarily on their upstream travels. Steelies will normally lie directly in front, directly behind or alongside any obstruction that will divert the current flow and provide a small pocket of quiet water. It is possible to find 15-pound steelhead in a 3-foot pocket of water near a log or boulder. Never pass up this type of pocket water.

The head of a drift is often a good spot for feeding steelhead. They will rest just to one side of the in-rushing water and many times a quiet, observant fisherman can see them.

Deep, quiet drifts are not particularly productive. The majority of steelheaders may make a token cast

West Coast or Great Lakes—the ladies are getting in on the steelhead action. A 12-pound buck (male) steelhead is quite a load in this lady's net.

or two to a smooth, quiet drift, but most steelhead found in these areas are considered to be resting fish and not likely to strike. Most drifts can be fished better from one side of the river than from the other. Some drifts, however, are occasionally more productive when fished from the "wrong side." You should be willing to experiment with different casting positions and also try fishing from the more difficult side of the stream. This tactic has resulted in many steelhead for me from areas most fishermen overlook.

With the possible exception of trolling, the big secret in river fishing for steelhead is to present the offering *along the bottom*. This doesn't mean a foot off bottom. It means that the lure, bait or fly should be ticking along the gravel.

There are times when steelhead will rise off bottom to intercept a properly presented fly either on the surface or just under it, but these cases are fairly rare. Most steelhead are taken by allowing the offering to bounce downstream in a natural manner with the current.

Bait fishing is probably the number one method of steelhead fishing both on the West Coast and along the Great Lakes streams and open water areas. It is extremely productive, but it requires the delicate feel of an accomplished fisherman. As a rule, steelhead seldom strike bait hard. The bait just stops its downstream drift and the line may feel as if the hook has picked up a drifting leaf. Many times that's the case, but often a big steelhead will have the bait.

Successful steelhead fishermen use a variety of baits that include fresh steelhead or salmon roe (still in the membrane and cut in small chunks), spawn bags tied with ripe mature steelhead or salmon eggs, individual commercially processed salmon eggs, nightcrawlers, wrigglers (larvae of the May fly), small minnows, anchovies and corn.

Lures such as the Okie Drifter are commonly used instead of spawn bags because this lure bears a striking resemblance to a gob of fresh roe. A spawn bag or piece of roe still in the skein can increase the effectiveness of Okies on certain days.

Both natural bait and Okie Drifters are fished in much the same manner. The important point to remember here is to keep the offering bouncing naturally along bottom and at approximately the same speed as the current. This will require a bit of experimentation from drift to drift to determine just how much weight is needed to take the offering down to bottom and still keep it moving. Steelhead seldom strike a motionless bait in a stream.

The traditional method of fishing bait is to cast quartering across and upstream. Allow the lure or bait to sink to bottom and hold the rod at approximately a 10 o'clock position. As the sinker and bait drift downstream, reel occasionally to maintain a tight line and raise the rod tip slightly to ease the bait over bottom obstructions. Whenever the rhythmical nodding or bouncing of the rod tip ceases, set the hook. Once the bait works through the drift, reel in quickly and try again. Cover the drift thoroughly with casts, move downstream slightly, and probe the drift again with well-placed casts.

A variation on this basic bait fishing method is to cast directly upstream. Try to cast past the suspected steelhead lie so your bait or lure will be down to bottom when it drifts in front of the fish. Reel just enough to keep a tight line as the bait works downstream toward you. Strike at any hesitation of the line or bait.

Another modification of the bait fishing theme is practiced principally on the West Coast. It's called "plunking" and involves nothing more than fishing on bottom with a spawn bag. A heavy weight is used to anchor the bait in one spot in a deep, quiet pool. The

Nine pounds of fresh run steelhead is quite a handful.

bait and heavy sinker are allowed to rest motionless on bottom. The method takes its share of fish, primarily during winter months, and is normally associated with the more sedentary type of fisherman.

A Great Lakes innovation is the single egg method of fishing river mouths. River-mouth fishing is not as productive on the West Coast as along the exposed beaches of the Great Lakes. Single salmon eggs are used as bait, and light line (6 pound), long soft rods and number 10 to 14 single hooks are used. Naturally, with this type of light tackle, many of the really huge steelhead are lost. Enough fish in the 2- to 10-pound class are landed, however, to provide thrilling fishing for anyone.

Steelhead often congregate during fall months in front of a river mouth. Certain locations are more productive than others and, again, it is necessary to read the water. There is a point at almost every river mouth where incoming waves are buffeted by the out-flowing river current. This mixing action often creates small pockets of quiet undisturbed water where a depth of 3 to 10 feet offers safety for steelhead. The fish will seek out these pockets and pick up drifting food that is washed downstream into the lake. Fish the edges of the river current where it meets the lake waves. Many river mouths will change almost daily because of wind and wave conditions and the steelhead will shift position.

Single-egg fishing calls for using the lightest possible split shot. I've found that a single BB size shot is normally sufficient unless there are heavy waves. Bait up with one or two single salmon eggs and cast out

The author swings an 11-pound steelhead onto the beach.

into the small pockets of quiet water.

Two methods work at river mouths. I much prefer to work the egg-baited hook slowly along the bottom through the holding water. Some fishermen elect to keep the bait motionless on bottom or to allow the wave action to roll the eggs along bottom. Both methods work well. Newcomers to this light tackle sport must remember to keep the drag lightly set and the rod tip high. I've seen steelhead wrench out 200 yards of light line in a single nonstop rush. An improperly set drag will either seize up or break the line on the initial burst.

Many deep rivers require the use of a drift boat or some type of craft which enables fishermen to work various parts of the river. Two methods—the dropback and Hot Shotting—are especially suited to deep rivers.

The dropback method involves anchoring a boat directly upstream from a suspected steelhead lie. Level-wind bait-casting reels stocked with 20-pound braided Dacron are used, and the two favorite lures are U–20 Flatfish and a medium-sized Tadpolly. The Flatfish is used during low-water conditions, while the Tadpolly works best when the water is high and fast.

Once the boat is anchored above a holding spot, the anglers initially release about 20 or 30 feet of line. The lure is allowed to wriggle in one spot for 15 to 30 seconds (longer in very cold weather) and then another 3 feet of line is released. This drops the lure back downstream where it wriggles enticingly in front of a steelhead.

A long drift may be covered in this manner by two or three fishermen in one boat. After 50 or 75 yards, the anchor is raised and the boat is allowed to drift down to a new anchoring location. Unlike bait fishing, the dropback method of steelheading results in tremendous wrist-spraining strikes. Rods have been yanked overboard and lines snapped by the ferocity of a steelhead striking one of these lures.

The Hot Shotting method is practiced primarily on West Coast rivers from a Rogue River or MacKenzie River drift boat. The Hot Shot is the favorite lure and the drift boat is not anchored, as in the dropback method, but is worked across, downstream and upstream by the judicious use of oars. The guide rows the drift boat and he is responsible for placing the lures into the best holding water.

The fisherman normally releases only 10 or 15 yards of line and this allows the Hot Shot to drift downstream ahead of the boat. The guide, by rowing, can gradually change locations, slow the drift and wriggle of the lure, or drop rapidly downstream to a new location. Rowing will place the lure in strategic locations directly in front of and behind large boulders

where Western steelhead often hold. The strikes are arm wrenching and the battles long drawn out in the heavy flow of Pacific Coast streams.

Trolling is a deadly method of taking steelhead in certain inland lakes around the Great Lakes. Steelhead move upstream from the big lakes, travel a short distance through a connecting stream and enter an inland lake. These lakes, most of them in Michigan, are normally a mile or less from the Great Lakes and serve as a concentration point for migrating steelhead. The fish pause in the lakes for varying lengths of time before pressing farther upstream to the headwaters to spawn.

The key to taking steelhead by trolling is to remember that they seldom strike a fast-moving lure. The best lure for Michigan trolling is the X-5 or U-20 Flatfish. Hot colors are silver, red with black spots and orange with black stripe.

Steelhead trolling is a long-line affair with the lure wobbling about 50 to 75 yards behind a slow-moving boat. Concentration points have to be learned, but the major gathering of steelhead will be near the mouths of rivers flowing into the lake. Rolling or porpoising steelhead are a clue to the whereabouts of fish.

A 7- to 9-foot spinning rod with a reel loaded with 12-pound monofilament is an excellent choice for trolling. Make sure the drag is smooth and doesn't stick when a fish makes a long run. Troll a very slow zigzag pattern through 10 to 30 feet of water. The lures will be down about 6 to 10 feet, depending on the length of line released behind the boat. No weight is needed. Short, sudden bursts of speed and quick slowdowns will often bring about a strike from a trailing steelhead. I've found that raising my rod tip directly overhead and lowering it again will often trigger a strike. The best trolling in Michigan normally occurs from mid-October until the lakes freeze over. Early morning trolling is seldom productive. Top fishing usually occurs about noon and just before dark.

Fly fishing is a favorite method on the West Coast and also on Great Lakes streams. Western streams are much more open and easier to fish with conventional fly tackle, while many Midwest streams are narrow, brush-choked and difficult to fish. Consequently, various techniques have evolved to meet each situation.

Shooting heads, even lead-core varieties, are often needed on West Coast streams to enable the steelheader to make his 100-foot casts adequately and to sink the fly to the bottom where steelhead will be found.

Wet flies, streamers and, to a lesser extent, nymphs are the offerings fly fishermen cast to steelhead. Most

Stream fishing for steelhead in many areas of the Great Lakes calls for stealth. This fisherman is keeping his silhouette low to avoid spooking fish.

of the time the rivers are rain swollen and a fast sinking line is needed to pull the fly down.

The traditional method calls for making a cast quartering across and downstream. Advocates argue long and hard about the relative merits of making a dead drift with no action and of imparting action to the fly. Personally, I have taken more steelhead by presenting a motionless broadside fly to the fish than by giving the fly action.

Sinking lines or Wet Tip flylines are in common use on many steelhead streams. The majority of stream drifts being fished with flies will be from 4 to 8 feet deep. Where extremely deep water, such as California's Smith River, is involved, a lead-core shooting head is necessary to take the fly down. Lead-core shooting heads are tough to cast but they sink like a rock and enable a steelheader to fish areas that he would normally have to bypass.

Fly fishing on some of the brushy streams around the Great Lakes calls for entirely different tactics. Conventional fly fishing is practical in certain areas, but many streams are so narrow, swift and brush-choked that forward and back casts are out of the question. Even a roll cast can seem impossible.

Areas such as these demand a change in steelhead tactics. I've developed a method of fly fishing with fly rod and reel but using level monofilament for line. Split shot 12 inches above the fly enable the angler to deliver a soft lob cast that will place the streamer into place where a normal cast would never go. The wet fly, streamer or nymph is then fished exactly like bait. When a fly fisherman first tries this method, the results often surprise him.

Many Midwest steelhead streams provide enough room for fly casting but are so swift that it becomes extremely difficult to work the fly deep enough to take fish. A trick I've used over the years is to add a 12-inch length of Sevenstrand wire testing about 18 pounds to the butt of my leader. The extra length of wire sinks the fly rapidly and is practically invisible in the water. Steelhead come to the fly as eagerly as ever. It's an unconventional method, but one that pays off handsomely with steelhead.

Steelhead flies are often regional. On West Coast streams, I have found the following ties to be some of the best: Boss, Gold Comet, Black Demon, Golden Demon, Fall Favorite, Eel Optic, Mickey Finn, Polar Shrimp, Orange Shrimp, Thor, Silver Comet, Skykomish Sunrise, Umpqua, Royal Coachman, Van Leuven, Woolly Worm and various colors of Yarn flies.

Great Lakes favorites are often named after the tyer or for a famous river; among these are Betsie Special, Cowichan, The Crick, Dr. Rex, Hot Head, Little Manistee, Orange P.M. (Pere Marquette) Special, Platte River Special, Red P.M. Special, Richey's Platte River Pink, Spring's Wiggler, Baby Rattler and White or Chartreuse Yarn flies.

Picking the times when steelhead are in certain rivers can be foolhardy, but there are certain periods when steelhead can be expected to be in West Coast or Great Lakes streams.

Great Lakes streams are host to steelhead primarily during fall and spring. The fall runs normally begin in late September and continue through the winter. October through December are the peak fall months; March and April the peak spring months. There are steelhead in most streams during January and February although the weather is often severe enough to keep all but the most dedicated fishermen home. Only one river, Michigan's Sturgeon River in the Lower Peninsula, has a summer run of steelhead.

This fisherman unhooks a fresh run hen steelhead that struck a spinner.

West Coast streams normally receive their runs of steelhead later than their Great Lakes counterparts. Winter runs begin when heavy rains in November and December raise the river level and wash out sandbars at the ocean. Steelhead will then continue their migration throughout the winter and peak during the spawning time in February through April, depending on river and area.

The West Coast streams, especially some of the British Columbia and Washington rivers, are hosts to summer-run steelhead. These fish begin ascending the rivers late in the summer. They are active and come to the fly very well. They winter in the streams and spawn in late winter or early spring with later running fish.

A list of the better steelhead streams in the Pacific Northwest and the Great Lakes area could make an article by itself. The following paragraphs include topnotch streams in each state and Canadian province. The choice is based on predictability of steelhead runs, national and local reputation, size of fish, quality of the sport, guide services, access sites (where applicable) and other factors.

California has several first-rate rivers, such as the Eel, Klamath, Russian, Smith and Trinity. These rivers normally peak during the December to February period.

Oregon's Deschutes, Nestucca, Rogue, Siletz and Umpqua rivers are known throughout the country as fine steelhead streams. November through January are good times on these rivers. The Umpqua receives a good summer run from June through August.

Washington has the famous Cowlitz, Green, Hoh, Kalama, Queets, Skagit, Skykomish and Stillaguamish rivers to choose from. Look for peak winter action on these rivers from December through February. The Stillaguamish receives a good run of summer fish during July and August.

Idaho's steelhead situation looks bad for years to come. As this is written, the Idaho Fish and Game Commission is hinging its 1976 seasons on the condition of the fall 1975 Columbia River run; the prospects for steelhead fishermen in Idaho are poor.

British Columbia offers steelheaders one of the greatest opportunities in North America. Hundreds of streams along the mainland and the Vancouver Island shorelines contain runs of summer and winter steelhead. Summer steelhead can be caught during July and August in the Nitinat, China, Nahmint, Toquart,

The author hefts a 13-pound freshrun steelhead from the water. Steelhead should never be gilled unless the they are to be kept.

This fisherman plays a jumping steelhead on a Michigan river.

Heber, Stamp and Ash rivers. Winter running fish can be found in almost every stream flowing from Vancouver Island or from the mainland. Some of the best streams are the Cowichan, Little Qualicum, Oyster, Quinsam, Campbell, Nimpkish, Big Qualicum, Moyeha, Englishmans, Klahawa and Heber. Among the best-known steelhead streams in the world are the Babine, Skeena, Kispiox and Bulkley rivers. These rivers produce some of the largest steelhead taken in the world. Most winter steelhead streams are hot from October through December, although the rivers in the Skeena River drainage peak out from August through October.

Alaska has a veritable bonanza of steelhead streams, but many streams are too remote for fishing. Several of the best steelhead rivers, however, are found close to large centers of population. The Naha, Karta, Situk, Sitkoh, Anchor and Karluk rivers and Petersburg Creek are top choices. Best fishing is August through October.

Around the Great Lakes, steelhead streams are more plentiful and much closer to centers of population. This can lead to overcrowding on some streams.

Michigan's most favored streams are the Big and Little Manistee, Platte, Muskegon, Au Sable, Two Hearted, Ontonagon, Au Gres, Sturgeon and St. Joseph rivers. Peak periods are October through December and March and April. The Sturgeon River receives a summer run of steelhead during July and August.

Wisconsin has very few good steelhead streams. Most rivers are very short. Reibolts Creek and the Kewaunee, Manitowoc and Bois Brule rivers are some of the better streams. April and May provide the best fishing in most areas.

Minnesota also has few rivers worthy of note, because all are very short. River-mouth fishing is excellent in many areas from Duluth north. Try the French and Knife rivers for best results.

Ontario has an abundance of seldom-fished steelhead streams flowing into Lake Superior. Many of these streams don't see a fisherman for weeks on end. I'd suggest trying the Agawa, Coldwater, Baldhead, Montreal and University rivers along the north shore of Lake Superior. Ontario's Bighead, Nottawasaga and Saugeen rivers flow into Lake Huron and furnish good sport in that area.

The rest of the Great Lakes area does not provide outstanding steelhead fishing at this time.

Steelhead fishing is a fun sport, whether it is practiced during the winter rains on the Pacific slope or on a blustery spring day on a Great Lakes stream. Steelhead are becoming more plentiful in the Midwest with every passing year and more anglers are turning out yearly to sample this fine sport.

Follow the rules given in this article and I'm sure you will be just as hooked on steelhead fishing as I am.

The Shooting Head System

by Dan Blanton

Armed with a small plastic bag in his pocket and the willingness to shed the shackles of tradition and rigid thinking, the modern angler can pursue fly fishing almost anywhere, regardless of current speed or water depth. No longer is he limited to those situations where a floating fly line is the accepted approach or where short, well-placed casts are the order of business.

The shooting head or single taper is the core of the system and it is nothing more than the first 30 feet of a standard weight forward or double taper fly line. There is a small attaching loop at the back end to which is tied 75 to 150 feet of small-diameter shooting line. A half-dozen of these short heads, covering a broad range of densities from floaters to heavily leaded lines, fit neatly in a plastic bag the size of your hand and with them you can meet every angling challenge from dry fly fishing to hugging the bottom when the dam bursts or probing more than 100 feet below the surface of lake or ocean. Even for the average angler, casts approaching 100 feet or more can be routine.

Sunset Line and Twine Company of Petaluma, California, marketed the first commercially produced shooting head in August 1950 and "Shooting Head" is the company's registered trademark, but the concept goes back much further than that and originated in tournament casting. Marvin Hedge of Portland, Oregon, was the first caster to use a head in competition when he unveiled a homemade 50-footer fashioned from various diameters of braided silk and size I shooting line. Mr. Hedge set the casting world on fire with his unbelievably long throws and it was not long before every caster had an identical line.

The basic 50-foot silk shooting head was standard in tournament casting until 1946, when, by accident, a new dimension was added. Jim Green and Phil Miravalle of San Francisco's Golden Gate Casting Club were practicing for the national championships with the typical shooting heads of the time. Jim, who has always been an innovator, decided to tie some 8-pound monofilament from his newly acquired spinning reel to the holding line of the head. During the course of the session, the holding line broke and Jim decided to tie the monofilament directly to the shooting head. As Jim explains it, "The line took off like a bullet, adding at least 15 feet to our distance."

Until the championships at Indianapolis, shooting heads with monofilament running line were a closely

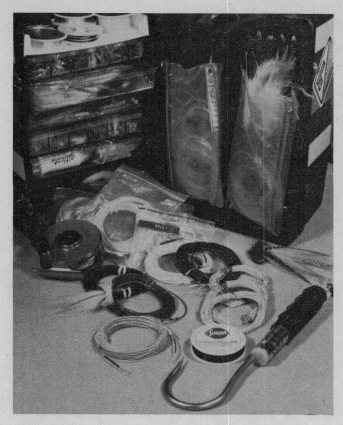
Shooting head systems are ideal for the traveling fly rodder. They take up little room, yet offer a broad range of lines that can be fished from top to bottom.

guarded secret. Jim Green swept the field with top honors and the rest of the team also cleaned up. From that moment, the shooting-head/mono combination became the accepted tackle for tournament casting, but others had different plans.

Charles Barfield is credited with being the first fly rodder to use mono shooting line behind a head in actual fishing. Jim Green had built Charlie a head around the time of the championships in 1946, and while Jim went to Indianapolis, Charlie went steelhead fishing. His enthusiasm about shooting heads prodded others to try, and mono running line has become standard equipment for salmon and steelhead in the Pacific Northwest, where long casts from armpit-deep water are the rule rather than the exception.

Although shooting head combinations as we know them today have been around for more than thirty years, it is only recently that fly fishermen across the land have begun to recognize their potential for everything from dry flies to nymphs to bass bugs and wind-resistant salt water streamers. The advantages

of heads are becoming more apparent. The distance capability heads the list. No other type of fly line will permit such long, effortless casts while still permitting accuracy at short range and the ability to roll cast effectively. Economy is another feature. Heads cost less than half the price of regular lines and will do an equally good or better job.

The heart of the shooting head system is the ability to change lines within seconds, selecting a density that will present your fly to the fish at the right depth. Veteran steelheaders, for example, may use two or three lines of different densities when fishing a single pool or run. They stop for a minute or two, switch lines, and continue fishing. The whole bundle of fly lines fits neatly in a ziplock plastic bag. You don't need extra reel spools.

Choosing the correct shooting line for the type of fishing you plan to do is the first step toward creating a system. Monofilament is more popular than small diameter level fly line, but each type offers distinct advantages.

Lightness and extremely small diameter coupled with low cost are the primary advantages of monofilament as a shooting or running line. Since it offers less resistance to both air and water, mono is the favored choice for maximum distance or maximum depth. It casts farther and it sinks faster, which can be important when you have to reach out for a fish or try to get a fly to the bottom in swift currents. Less water drag is also important when fighting a big fish, because the resistance of larger diameter lines in the water can break light leader tippets with no pressure on the reel.

Mono does have disadvantages. The tendency to tangle on a cast is by far the worst, and some of the rats' nests created can be repaired only by replacing the shooting line. Tangling is caused by several factors: not stretching the mono prior to using it for the day, repeatedly retrieving a fouled fly that spins in the water, and roll casting over and over again from the same side. An occasional backhand roll cast, by the way, will help to eliminate some of the twisting.

Ashore or afloat, wind can be the nemesis of mono, blowing it into an uncontrollable mess on the deck or at one's feet. Stripping the line on a wet towel or into a bucket with an inch of water in the bottom will help to counter the wind.

When mono is pulled across a finger or hand under pressure, its small diameter causes it to act like a buzz saw, often cutting into the flesh. This can be a problem with larger gamefish and sometimes occurs when casting. Wet mono is also slippery and difficult to grip or hold, which sometimes causes missed strikes.

A monofilament shooting line should be medium

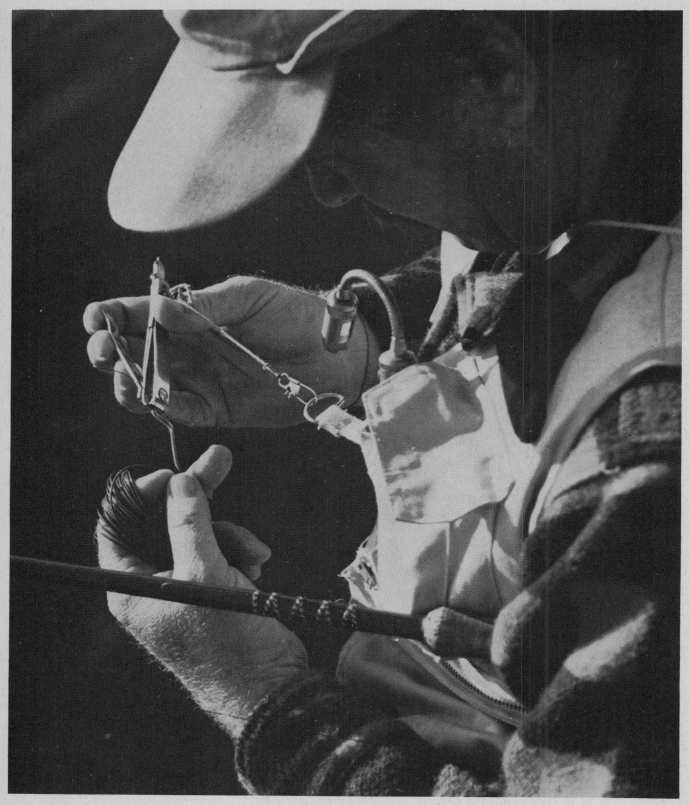

Changing shooting heads is as simple as cutting off a Clinch knot or unlooping attaching loops and re-tying or re-looping another head.

stiff or medium soft (depending on how you look at it) and should test between 20 and 40 pounds. Fresh water enthusiasts generally use 20- or 25-pound test, while their salt water counterparts favor heavier lines testing 30 to 40 pounds. With 9-weight shooting heads or lighter, 20-pound-test mono will allow longer casts and easier handling.

Several years ago, a handful of us who did most of our fishing on the West Coast began to experiment with level floating fly lines instead of monofilament for running lines. We found that they tangled less, made it easier to pressure a heavy fish out of structure, and enabled us to hook more fish because the line didn't slip through our fingers. There was also the advantage of being able to mend the line, and our hands and fingers lacked the cuts and slices that made them look like meat chopping blocks.

Floating shooting lines are ideal when neither extreme distance nor excessive depths are important. They must be used, however, from a boat or a solid casting platform. If you are wading, you will soon discover that the larger diameter (compared to monofilament) causes these level lines to cling to the water's surface, causing line drag and corresponding loss of distance. In extremely hot climates, the plastic finish on the level lines will tend to soften and tangles result. You can avoid this by using a wet towel or water in a bucket to keep the lines lubricated. Dressing the line frequently during the day with a line cleaner will also improve shootability.

When distance is more important than handling, your choice should be a number 2 level fly line with a diameter of approximately 0.029 inch. A level 3 floater or level 4 sinking line has the edge when you don't need casts over 100 feet and when you are fishing shallow reefs. These lines are also easier to handle when you are hooking or fighting a fish. Avoid lines with soft coatings because the finish will not hold up.

The shooting line can be joined to the shooting head in less than a minute, offering a quick change system that is important. With monofilament, you can simply tie a Clinch knot to the attaching loop on the back

Shooting lines should be dressed several times a day to obtain ease of casting and maximum distance. Any of the popular cleaners and dressings work equally well on monofilament or plastic-coated running line.

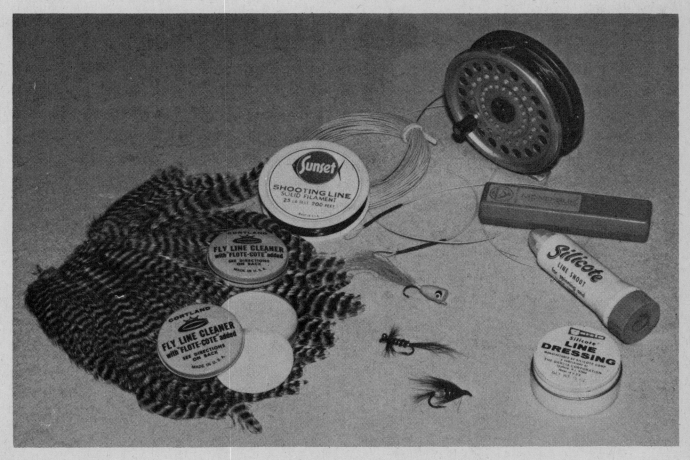

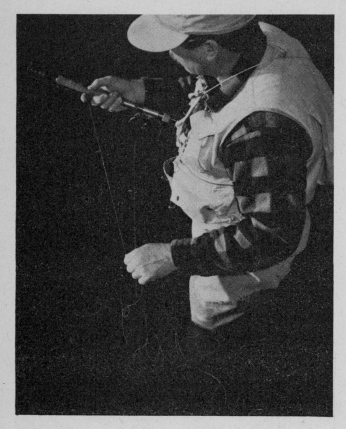

When properly dressed, monofilament running line will float on the water, making it easier to shoot during the cast.

length with a weight to match the rod and then splice a loop on the back. Some lead core has a plastic coating instead of the usual braid, and some casters believe that it shoots a bit better. This is questionable, and a coated line can shred into tatters in a matter of hours unless it is of top quality. There are fewer problems with the braided finish.

Bill Schaadt, a notable fly fisher and innovator from Monte Rio, California, had trouble getting his flies down to striking king salmon when the rivers were nearly at flood stage, so he developed a new idea. Taking a length of heavy Dacron fishing line, he inserted fuse wire to make a lead-core line. The result became known as "The Cable." It can be made from 2-, 3-, or 4-ampere fuse wire, weighing anywhere from 550 to 900 grains.

A system can always be improved, and Frank Bertaina of Santa Rosa, California, added a new twist to Bill's Cable. Frank removed 22 feet of the 1- ampere fuse wire from a 30-foot length and replaced it with 2-, 3-, or 4-ampere fuse wire, creating a tapered lead core line. With a little practice, you can strip the original fuse wire from a 30-foot length of lead core and replace it in about 45 minutes. Most of us prefer Buss Fuse Wire which is available from a number of West Coast fly fishing shops. Obviously, these cables must be used

of the head. With a level fly line, it is better to splice a loop in the end and then interlock that loop with the one on the shooting head.

Most commercially available shooting heads are in the larger line sizes and encompass the sinking densities. It is difficult to find a floating, intermediate, wet tip or lead core shooting head, because there has never been enough demand to prompt manufacturers to produce these. You will also have problems in locating heads lighter than perhaps an 8 weight.

The solution is to make your own and it's simple to do. Since a head is merely the first 30 feet of a double taper or weight forward fly line, you start with a pair of scissors. Buy the double taper whenever possible because you get two heads from the same line and it is cheaper than the weight forward version. Measure 30 feet from the forward taper and cut the line. Splice an attaching loop on the back and you have a shooting head.

Lead-core heads are made from 20- to 30-pound lead-core trolling line. It is available in 100-yard spools and will weigh between 11.5 and 12.5 grains per foot. Cut a

There are several methods of attaching shooting line to shooting heads and all provide a quick-change system. (Top to bottom) Interlocking loops connect lead core to level plastic-coated shooting line. Bimini Twist in Dacron backing looped to lead core head. Monofilament shooting line is connected to lead core with a Clinch knot. Monofilament shooting line and Dacron backing are joined by interlocking the loops formed by Bimini Twists. Note that interlocking loops must form a square knot.

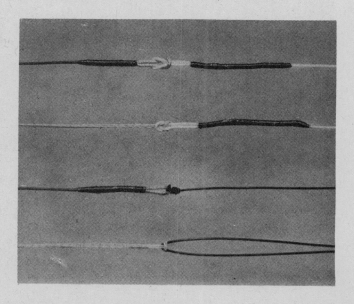

on fly rods that can handle at least a 12-weight line, but they permit fly presentations in depths and currents that were nearly impossible to fish prior to their development.

To help you design your own shooting head system, let's explore a few that have been proven on the water. Steelhead and salmon fishermen of the Pacific Northwest or in Michigan and other Great Lakes states would probably choose rods that handled 9- to 11-weight lines. Specific size depends on the type of water, but 8 heads could be assembled to meet any conditions. A floater, wet tip and slow sinker would handle activity near the surface, while a fast sinking line, extra fast sinker and three lead cores ranging from 250 to 650 grains would dredge the bottom no matter how fast the current.

The lake fisherman can add new horizons to his sport by starting with a floating head for surface or near surface work and switching to an intermediate line to work a streamer, nymph or wet fly in 3 or 4 feet of water. His outfit may handle anything from a 6-weight to a 9-weight line depending on where he fishes, and a wet tip for this outfit would cover water from 6 to 8 feet in depth. To get down to 15 feet, a slow,

A loop can be attached to lead-core line using 40- to 80-pound braided Dacron. (Left column from top to bottom). Fray the ends of 1½ to 2 inches of Dacron with a pointed tool. Fold the frayed sections over the lead core and wrap it securely with three layers of thread. Coat the splice with a rubber-based cement.

To splice a loop in level, plastic shooting line, fold about 1½ inches of line back on itself. Use a fly tying bobbin to spin three layers of thread over both the tag end and the running line. Coat with rubber-base cement.

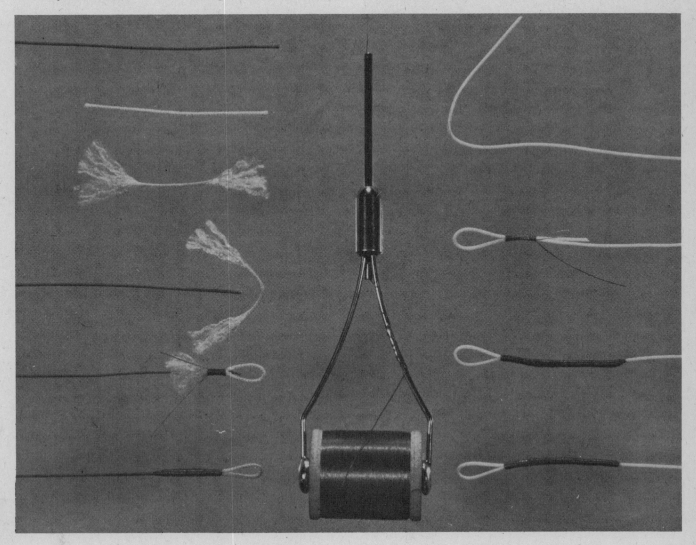

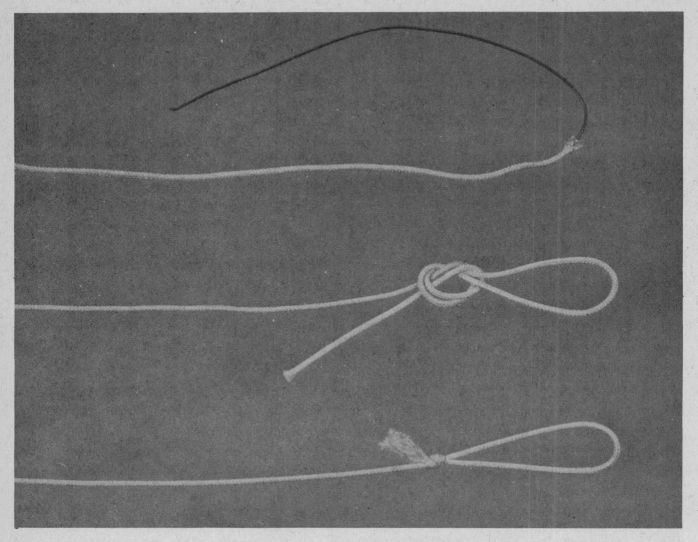

The quickest way to put a loop in uncoated lead core is to remove 6 inches of the lead and tie an overhand loop knot. Trim the tag end, but leave a quarter inch and fray it so the knot will slip through the guides easily.

fast and extra fast head would be perfect and for greater depths, a lead-core shooting head weighing from 180 to 250 grains. Think about the potential for lake trout, summer trout, and for black bass during the winter months.

Shooting heads enable the salt water fly fisherman to make longer casts, cover more water, and probe the depths. The lead-core lines and the Cables have made it possible to fly fish for species that were once considered inaccessible to the light wand enthusiast. Deep river tarpon fishing in Costa Rica is a prime example. The force of the current and the depth of the fish frustrated anglers until a few of us tried heavy lead-core shooting heads. Now, the fly rod is one of the most effective ways for taking these fish.

Myron Gregory, a West Coast fly fishing legend, was the first angler to use a lead-core shooting head in salt water. He developed it more than a quarter-century ago to take Pacific rockfish.

Salt water fly rodders use outfits that handle 9- to 13-weight lines, and a system of shooting heads can be developed for the various sizes and locations. Start with a floater for poppers or surface techniques and a wet tip for fishing 3 to 6 feet of water. You can skip over slower sinking densities and move right to extra fast sinkers for depths to 15 feet. After that, it's lead cores from 300 grains to 650 grains. You can always add intermediate, slow sinking or fast sinking heads if the situation demands it.

With the inclusion of lead-core shooting heads, you

will broaden your angling range regardless of where you fish. Blue water anglers, for example, are using lead cores on flies for sailfish because they get the fly a few feet underwater very quickly.

Tunnel-visioned anglers in many parts of the country have resisted shooting heads for years, preferring to write them off as a whim of a few West Coast steelheaders. Part of the problem is that these anglers have never had a chance to cast a properly tailored outfit, nor have they been schooled in the techniques. Once a fly fisherman learns the basics, he's usually hooked on the system. It could happen to you, if you are willing to keep an open mind and give the system a fair try.

A whole system of shooting heads can be stored in a clear plastic bag and attached quickly by interlocking the loops.

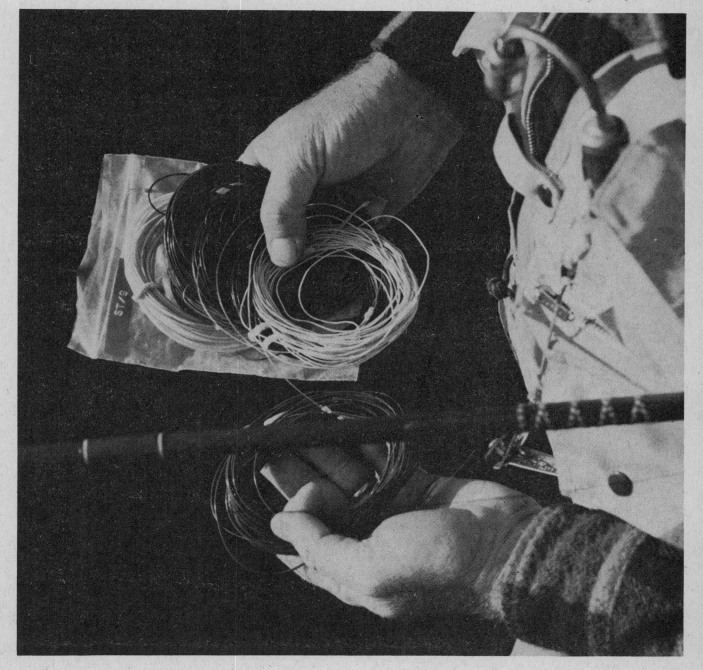

Shallow-Water Tackle

by Bob Stearns

Almost every angler has heard about fishing for the so-called exotic gamefish on the shimmering flats of South Florida and the Bahamas, and a great many enthusiasts have tried it themselves. The excitement of fishing the shallow water is so great that the newcomer may not realize the thought and careful development of techniques that lie behind this fine form of angling.

It was inevitable that the modern ultra-refined flats fishing associated with the clear water of the tropics should have started there: just seeing so many big gamefish—because the water was so clear—drove anglers into developing techniques that would enable them to take those fish.

The first essential was a small, shallow-draft boat and a long pole to push it around with. Perhaps the earliest pushpole was much like those you can still see today in remote out-islands of the Bahamas and the Caribbean—poles that are simply slender trees with bark and branches cut away. Then, because it was discovered that the bare end of a straight pole would sink deep into the mud and seriously hamper the efforts of the man using it, some sort of a "foot" or wide piece was added.

The early tackle used for flats fishing was mostly standard stuff. Spinning hadn't come into its own in those days, and anglers quickly learned that stiff boat rods with oversized revolving spool reels were not capable of accurate casting with any lure or bait that wasn't so heavy its splash would scare the quarry into a full-bore rush for deeper water. So anglers turned to the lighter, more easily casting fresh water tackle. This gear was capable of casting with ease and accuracy, but it had one serious drawback: once the fish was hooked, the equipment frequently didn't stand up to the rigors of battle.

Sometimes the reel did not have enough line capacity, and the fish simply ran away with all of the line. Or the metal-corroding properties of salt water quickly destroyed the vulnerable components of the tackle. Or perhaps, as was most often the case, the drag was too rough (if there was any drag at all) and the fish broke off. Gradually, though, tackle, boats, motors and pushpoles were improved.

Today, anywhere in the country you can buy tackle that will take practically any fish the flats have to offer, from the flighty bonefish or permit to the mighty tarpon, and everything in between. Even the better

Fishing the ultraclear flats of the Bahamas, boat and wading.

models of spinning and revolving spool reels are capable of this. In fact, those are what most anglers use there. Probably the fly rod is the only form of tackle that is radically different from that used in fresh water.

Before I go into detail about the tackle, boats and other equipment necessary for shallow water fishing in the tropics, I'd like to make an observation: shallow water fishing techniques are by no means limited to tropical areas. I know Northern anglers who, having once learned the techniques of poling a boat and casting in Southern shallow water, are doing extremely well with stripers, weakfish, blues, channel bass and other prime gamefish in the shallows off Middle Atlantic and New England states that had previously been ignored.

The same goes for fresh water. I've caught bass (big ones, too) by poling grass beds and shallow shorelines with the same type of small skiff that I use on the Southern flats. Because of the tremendous surge in popularity of electric trolling motors, particularly in fresh water, and their refinement to the point where they now make excellent positioning propulsion for the spot caster, we often forget that there are other ways to maneuver a boat in the shallows. In really shallow water, an electric motor will often alarm fish, or at least put them on their guard. I use electric motors in salt water and have often observed just this situation. A quiet, carefully handled pushpole is definitely an advantage here.

A brief look at the species of gamefish available in the shallows reveals an impressive list. Besides the obvious bonefish, permit and tarpon, there are snook, weakfish, barracuda, trout, snapper, jack crevalle, red drum (channel bass or redfish, if you prefer), pompano, black drum, bluefish, mackerel, sharks and even sheepshead. Some of these fish are found primarily in the clear shallows; others prefer darker, less transparent water, and a few like either.

Obviously, tackle selection is based on the type you prefer (spin, bait casting or fly) and its capability to handle the job at hand. For example, fishing clear

water requires pinpoint accuracy to present the lure or bait to the fish, while dark water means blind casting with not quite as much accuracy needed, except, for instance, when you are trying to place that plug alongside a fallen tree.

We can simplify the tackle situation by breaking down the types into three catagories: ultralight, light and medium. These catagories are based on line sizes (tippets in fly tackle) and are as follows: ultralight, 2- to 6-pound test; light, 8- to 10-pound test; and medium, 12- to 15-pound test. Lines over 15-pound test are seldom used in the shallows except for very large sharks (over 200 pounds), because they don't cast well.

A major factor in flats fishing is expressed in the old Boy Scout motto "Be prepared." You need to take advantage of every opportunity that presents itself,

Big jack crevalle can provide exciting action in the shallows.

Chico Fernandez of Miami, Florida, unhooks an 8-pound red drum (channel bass, redfish). This is a popular flats fish on fly, spin or bait casting tackle.

Several varieties of snapper are common on the flats; a mangrove is shown here.

water. The bail should be strong and have a positive closing mechanism, which means a strong bail return spring. Some "bargain" reels have springs so weak that the bail does not always return to the fully closed position. If you can use manual pickups, so much the better.

The line roller on the bail should roll easily. If you aren't thoroughly familiar with a particular brand of reel, check the roller with a piece of monofilament before leaving the tackle shop. Once the reel is in service, keep the roller properly lubricated so that it will keep on rolling. I use a mixture of Never-Seez (Never-Seez Compound, usually stocked by bigger hardware stores) and light machine oil, about one part Never-Seez to four parts oil. This is the most reliable lubrication for line rollers that I've found. Lubrication is extremely important with ultralight tackle. Any roller that "skips" or stops will chew up line faster than you would believe, and thin monofilament can't take this kind of punishment. It could break while you are fighting your first fish.

Bait casting reels, often called plug reels in Southern salt water parlance, are the typical revolving spool reels most popular with bass anglers. In general, with

Eternal vigilance and being always ready are the price of a good fish on the flats.

and if you are not prepared to do so, the odds are you'll miss some fine action. This applies to everything from proper tackle to rigging and lures.

Let's consider tackle, starting with spinning. The best reel, judging by long experience of many professional guides, is the open face type. Spin cast or "closed face" reels can be used in some situations, but they have certain drawbacks. First, many shallow water gamefish are sprinters in every sense of the word. Even species that are typically lungers in deeper water suddenly become racy when hooked in "skinny" water. Perhaps part of the reason is that almost any fish is nervous about being there, but it is there because food is abundant. Hooking one makes it even more uneasy, and its first reaction is to head for deeper water. So, it's extremely important to be able to check the reel spool visually when you're hooked up to a long-running fish, and that is not possible when the spool is covered. Often you must choose whether to stand your ground or pursue the fish, and in order to make that decision, you must be able to tell instantly just how much line is left on the spool.

Pick a reel that is made of high-quality materials and can withstand the devastating effects of salt the exception of the drag (more on drags later), the same qualities that make a reel a good bassing tool apply to fishing on the flats. It should cast well and easily and have a tough, reliable level wind system and close enough tolerances so that line cannot get between spool flange and the end plates if you get a backlash or overrun.

Clearance becomes critical if you use very light lines, and to date I have encountered only two reels capable of handling extremely light (4- to 6-pound test) lines without getting line behind the spool: the Ambassadeur 2500 C and the Childre Speed Spool. Both cast light lures exceptionally well. The line capacity of the 2500 C is about 230 yards of 6-pound test; that of the Speed Spool somewhat less.

Salt water fly reels are another matter. Those designed for the larger and faster species are quite different from the typical fresh water reel, which in most cases is used only for line storage. Probably the fresh water reels closest to those now popular for salt water are those designed for salmon and steelhead fishing, which have drag systems and capacity for backing.

Almost any salt water fish over a few pounds is

Sharks are popular shallow water gamefish.

going to get into the backing, and some do a pretty thorough job of it. I've had tarpon and sharks over 100 pounds run 600 to 800 yards across the shallow flats, necessitating a hasty chase. But that's the extreme end of the scale. Most of the gamefish encountered on the shallow flats will take anywhere from 25 to 100 yards of backing. Obviously, there are some "lightweights," such as bonefish, permit or jack crevalle, that are capable of longer runs, but most snook, red drum, weakfish, blues and so forth don't cover that kind of distance. Still, good backing capacity is part of the business of being prepared, so choose larger reels than you would normally use with fresh water rods of similiar weight.

There are a number of reels designed for salt water fly fishing, and not all of them are expensive. Reels like the Pflueger Medalist series have been used for many years on everything the shallows have to offer, except for the largest tarpon and sharks.

As I indicated earlier, line capacities are important. I prefer at least 200 yards of line (or backing, where fly reels are concerned), regardless of the tackle type and category. You will almost certainly encounter fish that will make it necessary to crank up and follow if you only have 200 yards on the spool, but at least that's enough line to give you time to get going in most situations. I've been completely stripped only a couple of times when using reels of that capacity and, in every case, it was because I refused to follow the fish. I have only my hard head to blame for that.

The most popular rods for both spinning and bait casting tend to be a bit longer than those commonly used for the same line weights in fresh water. I prefer a 6- to 6½-foot rod for ultralight spinning and one just a tiny bit shorter for bait casting with the same lines. For light (8 to 10) and medium (12 to 15), a 7- to 7½-foot stick is excellent.

An exception is the super long rod employed by some anglers for bonefishing with spin. In the old days, such rods were made from fiberglass fly rod blanks, and as spinning tackle they didn't cast as accurately as the 7-footers. But they did offer the advantage of helping keep the line elevated above obstructions when the fish ran. I've recently seen one or two 8½- to 9-footers made from some of the new, quality graphite fly rod blanks, and they offer a crispness in the action that the glass sticks don't have. The result is greater accuracy, so we'll probably see more of these long exotics in the future.

Even though the same length of rod is preferred for both light and medium line weights, the action varies. The light rod has a relatively slower taper and a smaller diameter near the butt section. As you would

Extra-long spinning rods, never really successful in fiberglass, show signs of returning in graphite, a material much better suited for such designs.

expect, it is a better casting tool than the medium rod. When you are dealing with heavy fish on 12- to 15-pound test lines, however, lifting power is the prime consideration. Therefore, medium flats rods (which are the shallow-water equivalent of heavy tackle) tend to be fast tapers, with larger diameters near the butt but still retaining enough lightness in the tip for some casting ability. This is true for both spinning and bait casting, and in fact both types of rod are often made from the same blank. I have a couple of rods built as "baitcasting/spinning" rods; they have straight reel seats (no hooked or offset handles) and can be used equally well with both types of tackle.

Fly rods for salt water, with the exception of those needed for the real heavyweights, are much the same as those used in fresh water. For flats fishing I frequently use light trout rods with light tippets (4 to 6 pound). Although these rods are designed for light dry fly fishing on small trout streams, they do a fine job on the flats if there is not too much wind. And they make supersport out of fishing for the typical smaller 2- to 4-pound bonefish common to the Bahamas and Caribbean flats. The trick there is to use a fly line two to three sizes heavier than the rod usually calls for. This slows down the dry fly "fast action" enough to cast long distances easily.

A good all-around fly rod for the flats is an 8- to 9-footer that will take a number 8 to 10 fly line. It's

Many shallow areas are prime for big snook.

Our *Angler's Bible* editor about to boat a permit.

light, easy to cast, and will take any fish except the biggest tarpon or shark. It will certainly do the job on anything under 50 pounds if you handle it properly.

When you get up to the big fish—tarpon and sharks that might top 100 pounds—you need a fly rod designed not so much for casting ease as for fighting such fish effectively. This means, as I've mentioned before, lifting power. There are a number of such rods on the market in both graphite and fiberglass; make sure you pick one that is specifically designed for such use by the manufacturer if that's what you want to try.

Regardless of the type of reel, the drag is all important. It must be smooth and capable of standing up under the punishment of long, fast runs. Fortunately, there are many reels of all types on the market today. That's a welcome change over ten years ago when an angler had to modify every reel before he could trust it.

There is also a major improvement in rod components: ceramic guides. The commonest types are aluminum oxides, and while they resemble the old-time agate guides in appearance, they are almost

friction free, providing two advantages that no previous guide ever offered—sharply reduced line drag and a dramatic reduction in line wear. I've found that all my lines, and particularly the ultralights, last much longer when I use rods with these new guides. Many companies are providing them as stripping guides on fly rods, and I think they give a little extra casting ease and distance.

Even though boats used for flats fishing in South Florida have evolved to a high stage of sophistication, any reasonably shallow draft hull under 19 feet can be used with fair success. Many Northern anglers trail their boats to Florida and do well, even though the

Boating a 20-pound permit on 8-pound test spin.

Sometimes wading with boat is effective in extremely shallow water if the bottom is firm enough. Here the guide points out fish for the angler.

Captain Lee Baker of Miami, Florida, stalks bonefish for an angler and puts him within casting range—the sort of thing a good guide can do for a novice.

craft were not designed for such fishing. The more open and uncluttered the boat is, the better it will perform under such conditions.

Although most serious flats fishermen and guides in South Florida have changed to fiberglass pushpoles, wood is still an acceptable material for such use. A wooden pole is not quite as tough as a fiberglass one and won't last as long, but it doesn't carry the $40 or so price tag that goes with the fiberglass item either. I've made many a good pushpole out of 1¼- to 1⅜-inch round stock, with a short piece of wood nailed to one end as a "foot." Another quick and easy way to make a foot is to saw off two 8-inch lengths of the pole itself and nail or screw one to each side of one end.

Most anglers prefer a 14- to 16-foot pole for water up to 4 feet in depth, and a 17- to 18-footer for up to 6 or 7 feet. At depths greater than those, poling is extremely difficult.

The best course of action I can recommend for a newcomer who is seriously interested in learning shallow water fishing techniques is to spend a day or two with a competent guide. You can learn more in one day, if you are willing to listen, than in two weeks on your own. And, although a good skiff guide can cost $100 to $120 per day (two can share the cost), it's easy to spend more than that in gas money alone and still not learn as much if you try it first on your own. Think of the day or two with a guide as a sound investment toward a future of one of the most exciting forms of fishing.

Score More in the Surf
by Jack Fallon

- The Nantucket bluefish saw the flash of hammered steel and within microseconds its reflexes had vectored it violently to port and onto the tin squid's trailing treble.
- Foraging through a trough that paralleled the Hatteras shore, the channel bass eagerly gulped the half-mullet, unaware that its fragrant flesh concealed a deadly sharp hook.
- The jig jumped enticingly along the Key West flat toward the murky patch of shimmering shapes. Suddenly a bonefish darted forward, grabbed the counterfeit shrimp, and streaked seaward as the hook was hammered home.
- The plug paused on its way back to the Sea of Cortez rockpile, perplexing the inquisitive totuava behind it. Following a brief drift, the plug twitched, then took off like a frightened sardine, and the totuava pounced.
- Her spawning completed, the cow striper had dropped back into San Francisco Bay. Eager to appease her ravenous appetite, she struck greedily at what appeared to be an injured anchovy. Too late, the feel and taste and stab and tug of her victim revealed her mistake.

Massachusetts bluefish, North Carolina channel bass, Florida bonefish, Mexico totuava, California stripers—what do all of these catches have in common? Success. And because fishing success, regardless of locale, regardless of species, can be broken down into a simple four-element formula, any surf angler on any stretch of ocean front can improve his score by analyzing these four elements in terms of how they apply to his kind of fishing. The four elements? The right place, the right time, the right lure and the right presentation.

The Right Place

Surf fishermen mature in three stages. As tyros they see only water; as veterans they see bottom; as pros they see fish. Alert novices notice many visible clues to fish's presence. By observing and exploiting bending rods, diving gulls, loud splashes, churning swirls and bright flashes, they cross the threshold between merely waiting for things to happen and actively seeking ways of making them happen. One day they're just guys who go surf fishing, the next they're on their way to becoming Surfmen, capital S.

These rocks provided an ideal ambush for Cape Cod Canal stripers when a sluicing tide was transporting bait.

When in doubt try a bucktail jig, the lure with perennial appeal.

Familiarity with a beach's bottom can enable you to predict the routes that feeding fish will follow. A deep indentation revealed by a receding tide might be occupied when the tide returns by a big channel bass lying in wait for passing prey. A trough might form a convenient *cul-de-sac* where bluefish can corral bait. A muddy patch might be patronized by flounder seeking worms, a cluster of rocks by blackfish seeking crabs. Study a beach at low tide and apply what you have learned when the tide is high, but return occasionally when water is low to update your intelligence. Beaches change. Last week's undulations can be erased by this week's storms.

Next time you're swimming, consider donning mask and flippers for a little nose-to-nose reconnoitering. While snorkeling, I have found stripers feeding closer to shore than I thought possible, and I have swum among bathers with bluefish that I thought were too spooky to tolerate people.

For the seasoned surfman, delicate wrinkles and tiny turbulences are enough to confirm the locations of underwater landmarks, but there is an ability beyond this that enables a few Super Surfmen to spot fish with the precision of sonar. Part of it is sensory—the discerning of subtle signs; part of it is cerebral—the interpreting of these signs, but mostly it's an intuition, a sensitivity that comes from a long and loving closeness to one's quarry.

My friend Arnold Clark exhibited it one long-ago dawn after we had plugged all night without a hit. A third man, who had fished with us, was not taking kindly to what he considered a wasted night.

"Bi-i-ig man," he jeered at Arn, "Bi-i-ig reputation. All night long, the whole ocean in front of us, and you can't produce a fish. Some fisherman."

Glancing at what looked to me like a mirror-smooth sea, Arn took two strides, cast his plug, and reeled in a striper.

"Here," he said, "is this what you're looking for?"

The Right Time

I am a charter subscriber to the credo that there is only one time to fish: *right now!* Life is too precious to be squandered on lesser pursuits. Day or night, fair weather or foul, there is a fish out there somewhere that will take me on if I offer the right enticement in the right way, and rarely is there anything I'd rather be doing than seeking that fish out.

Nevertheless, there is a distinction between fishing and catching fish, and since this article is about improving your score in the surf, let's consider factors that contribute to best times for catching fish.

"Early and late in the season, early and late in the day" is a dictum that has stood the test of time because of its fundamental infallibility. Migrating fish, for example, are notoriously cooperative just

A chunk of mullet off a Virginia beach took this 24-pound channel bass for outdoor writer Bob Hutchinson.

Yankees who exploit the cod's habit of foraging close to shore during cold weather enjoy fast action and fine eating.

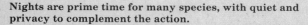

Nights are prime time for many species, with quiet and privacy to complement the action.

after moving in and just prior to moving out. This is why the annual striped bass and bluefish derby at Martha's Vineyard is scheduled from mid-September to mid-October, when fish are stoking their boilers for their trip south. Learn from your intelligence sources when early- and late-season action has erupted. Not just when it starts bubbling, but when it really bursts wide open. Then fish every available instant until peak action has passed.

Eyesight accounts for fishes' feeding activity at morning and evening twilights. Their pupils do not contract; like camera lenses set at a constant wide opening, they permit fish to see best in dim light. For the same reason, overcast days are likely to be more productive than those when skies are clear and sun is bright.

Nights can be the most productive (as well as the most exciting) times of all, but only when your quarry is a nocturnal feeder. In all my years in the suds I never have caught a flounder after dark, and only once, when a full moon made night more like day, have I caught a mackerel. Yet with species such as striped bass, tarpon, weakfish, channel bass and cod on the prowl during darkness, I not only enjoy red-hot fishing, but with bathers and boaters out of the way, I often have the best spots all to myself.

One nocturnal condition that shuts down fishing is when phosphorescence lights up lines like incandescent filaments and makes lures resemble Roman candles. Californians, I am told, actually encourage their plugs to glow by applying strips of fluorescent tape, but this is a far cry from the kind of fireworks I'm talking about. When there's fire in the water, stay home.

Weather reports can enable you to time your forays so they coincide with fishes' feeding binges. In New England, where I do most of my surf fishing, an onshore storm means up to three days of beach-battering blasts, during which fish generally abstain and all but the most ardent surfmen stow their gear. When winds abate, however, and seas subside, hungry fish move in to make up for missed meals. By heading for the shore as soon as the barometer starts rising, you can be there from appetizer through dessert.

Storms, by the way, are not all bad. I have enjoyed fast fishing when winds and waters have been high but manageable. Sometimes storms leave chumlines in their wakes. Sea clams, for example, can be uncovered by a prolonged battering. Exposed to air and sun during the next low tide, they open and die. On the following high, fish move in eager to feast on any convenient clam, including those placed there by enterprising anglers.

With a good tide running, chumlines can make right times out of wrong by tolling fish in when they normally would not be interested. Some surfmen simply toss a tethered chumpot into the foam, taking care while casting to avoid snagging its line. While standing in a tideway, I have attracted fish by clipping a perforated can of catfood to my stringer. One clever Yankee I know pounds mackerel chunks into the sand that has been exposed by a low tide, then reaps his harvest while the tide is high and frustrated fishermen on either side of him wonder what they're doing wrong.

Solunar Tables? I have seen them work too often not to pay attention to what they tell me, yet I have been disappointed often enough, especially in salt water, not to balance their predictions against other ambiences such as heavy seas, channel dredging and fish kills.

Tides are the ocean's chow lines: a mullet school is pulled through a pass between islands and tarpon are lurking; grass shrimp are carried down a tidal creek and weakfish are waiting; a tropical flat is flooded and bonefish move in to graze. Get familiar with tide tables; coordinate your fishing with flood, ebb, slack, spring and neap tides; and you will be well on your way to intercepting feeding fish.

Flood tide is the period during which water is moving in. Fish appreciate a flood because it inundates new feeding areas.

Ebb is when the tide is moving out, transporting food to waiting fish.

Slack water theoretically is that infinitesimal instant between ebb and flood when movement is neither in nor out, but generally the term refers to a brief period on either side when flow is slow. Traditionally, slack is regarded as poor fishing time because bait fish, having no current to contend with, can more easily escape from predators, but I have enjoyed too many successes during slacks to sit them out automatically. If a fish is hungry and has to work too hard to catch elusive bait fish, isn't it reasonable to assume that it will be more receptive to worms or clams or cut bait on the bottom?

Spring tides—nothing to do with the season, by the way—are those extra-high, twice-a-month tides that occur around new and full moons when the moon's and sun's attractions reinforce each other. Higher water and faster flow make these tides potentially more productive.

Neaps are the lower tidal ranges that occur between spring tides. While they lack the volume and velocity of spring tides, they have the advantage of concentrating fish more heavily in a given location and of enabling them to see your lures more easily in shallower-than-normal water.

The Right Lure

Ever hear of the Kitchen Sink Lure? A small plastic facsimile of a kitchen sink, complete with spinner and hook, it's designed for use after you've used everything but—that's right—the kitchen sink. Compared to some of the wild creations being touted in tackle shops these days, it doesn't even seem exotic.

Lures become less bewildering when you consider that almost every one of the seemingly infinite variety of artificial fish enticers is either a jig, a plug or a metal squid. Your arsenal should contain some of each.

A jig generally consists of a metal head and a bristle tail, with a single fixed hook among the bristles. Heads can have oval, ball, bullet, coin, cone and slanted shapes; tails can be of nylon, feather and plastic, as well as hair from the tail of a male deer. Designed to be retrieved with a jerking rod action, the jig is the most durable of lure designs.

The most popular plug types are the swimmer, whose wobbling action imitates an injured fish, and the popper, which attracts with noise and splashing. When you have become familiar with these styles, consider divers and darters for special applications.

With a compartmented plug box, you'll spend less time untangling, more time fishing.

The squid lure is a shaped piece of metal, usually stainless steel, that wobbles like a spoon yet is heavy enough for long-distance casting. Its shiny surface makes it especially effective on bright days.

A lot of unproductive casts are made by surfmen who either experiment randomly till they find a lure that works or stick resolutely with lures that worked well in the past but are inappropriate to the here and now. I encourage experimentation, especially with colors and color combinations, but tryouts should start with lures that suggest by their size, their color and, if possible, their shape the locally prevalent bait. Otherwise you might share the frustration that my wife and I endured a few years ago on Narragansett Bay when casters less than 100 yards away were filling their stringers with whopper weakfish while our offerings were being spurned. The reason: The bay was full of squid and our neighbors were fishing with squid strips; Peg and I didn't have a lure that even remotely resembled a squid.

We should have. A pre-departure phone call to a bayside bait shop had revealed the squid glut. Yet I was sure that the fish would gobble my yellow bucktail jigs just as they had the previous spring (and incidentally, as they did the spring following).

One of my early angling mentors told me, "There's only one sure thing about fishing: if you fall in, you'll get wet."

Early in the season and late in the day was the right time for this Plum Island bluefisherman.

A natural presentation is the key to success when fishing with live bait.

This was the same guy, by the way, who showed up one night with a 6-inch surgical tube rigged to swim a foot ahead of his plug.

"It's called a teaser," he explained. "Could just as well be a pork strip or a small jig, even a streamer fly. Supposed to look like a sand eel being chased by a mackerel. Seems to turn on a bass's appetite when it sees another fish feeding."

Whatever the reason, it worked. Sometimes the bass would hit the teaser in preference to the plug, suggesting that perhaps the combination triggers a competitive instinct. Occasionally, it even would deliver double-headers. Give teasers a try. For a little extra effort you might add appreciably to your catch.

Double-headers are more common in bait-and-wait fishing than in prowling and plugging. Up-and-down rigs, with a pair of snelled hooks about a foot apart above a terminal sinker, are favorites of frostbite cod fishermen. Flounder fans often take twin flatties on spreader rigs, a pair of hooks snelled to the ends of a horizontally fished foot of stiff wire with line and sinker attached to its center. With Florida pompano fishermen, even six and eight hooks in series are not uncommon.

Are natural baits better than their artificial counterparts? That's a loaded question, requiring a qualified response. What species? Locale? Time? Weather? What's the current bait supply? Which specific lure do you have in mind and how do you propose to present it? In fishing, simple answers seldom fill stringers. Squid strips were the ideal enticers for the Narragansett weakfishing I described earlier. Likewise those sea clams after a northeast blow. But bait heaved out haphazardly, without careful consideration of ambient conditions, is hit-or-miss fishing, usually with a lot more missing than hitting.

One of the most successful surfmen I know uses nothing but live bait.

"I feeds 'em what they's eatin'," he says, camouflaging his consummate skill in a cloak of simplicity.

No question, livelining can be devastatingly effective. A live eel, alewife, mullet, menhaden or anchovy can give you a decided edge in conning a fish because it is immediately recognized as the real thing. For this very reason, however, it must not behave in any unnatural way. The pull of your hook, the weight of your line, the tug of your rod all can signal DANGER! to a fish that owes its very existence to its built-in "look before you bite" discipline, and all are real risks when you must constantly control a live bait that's doing its darndest to avoid the very predator you're trying to catch.

By all means liveline the ocean's edges, but don't expect success to come automatically.

The Right Presentation

The need for proper presentation was impressed on me early when I jigged the base of a boiling Cape Cod tide rip for 20 minutes without a tap while the guy standing alongside me took thirteen stripers. Though I consciously tried to emulate his every move, I missed one nuance that made all the difference: he was casting about 15 degrees farther up current. Because his jig was swinging down as well as across, it reached the stripers' level; mine, they never even saw.

The first rule of presentation, then, is to make sure your offering is observed. Fish lying in ambush behind boulders or cruising roily tideways or foraging on sun-drenched flats will see your lure only if you adjust for their visual limitations.

Naturalness is the key to proper presentation. If you're trying to excite a fish's appetite, your lure must look and act exactly like a prospective meal. And how does a prospective meal act? Scared, that's how—fleeing, leaping, skittering, diving scared. Next time you find yourself retrieving slowly, casually, consistently, keep that in mind.

Fish strike out of anger, inquisitiveness and reflex as well as hunger. The sudden splash, the fleeting flash, the palpitating pause all should be part of your tactical repertoire.

How, then, to catch more fish in the surf? Same way as in any form of fishing: fish harder by keeping your lure working as much as possible; fish smarter by being in the right place, at the right time, with the right lure, presented the right way.

Rigging and Using the Striper Eel

by Russ Wilson

During the dog days of July and August trophy-sized striped bass can be as hard to locate as prayer books in a pool hall. But some of the more serious striper addicts have learned where and, more important, how to find and catch these giant-sized striped warriors.

Along much of the northeast Atlantic Coast jetties have been constructed to help control beach erosion. These moss-covered rock piles provide excellent hiding spots for big bass and also act as drawing cards for the many different species of bait fish normally preyed upon by the hungry stripers.

Bass are by nature lazy fish that prefer to do most of their feeding at night when things are quiet and bait fish are schooled up around the rocks. Regulars at fishing for super-sized stripers know this and do most of their fishing during the dark of the moon when time and tides coincide to make bass go into a feeding frenzy. Almost to a man they use only one lure—a rigged eel.

Rigging an eel is reasonably easy if you follow the illustrations in this article. Once rigged, the eel can be kept for quite some time in a brine solution. I make a brine by mixing 1 pound of kosher salt with 1 gallon of warm water. This solution is strong enough to keep the eels from spoiling but not so strong that it burns the skin and causes the eel to break apart at the first hit from a giant bass. Eels stored in this manner will last almost indefinitely if kept out of the hot summer sun. When not fishing, I usually keep the eel jar in the refrigerator but any cool spot out of the sun will do just fine.

Most of the regulars at rigged-eel fishing use spinning rather than conventional tackle. Not because it is better to fish with, but because when you are casting for long periods of time a heavy conventional outfit becomes tiring, whereas the spinning rigs are light and will not tire the caster so quickly. Many nights I spend 5 or 6 hours on the rocks and may make thousands of casts.

The rod I am presently using measures just over 7½ feet and will handle a 5-ounce weight without any trouble. Often it is necessary to stop a bass from making a run around the front of a jetty. Light equipment isn't capable of doing this and many big stripers are lost every season by anglers who are not using a rod with enough backbone to hold a good-sized fish.

The type of reel used isn't important but the reel should be capable of holding at least 200 yards

Russ Wilson drags a husky striper off a jetty. The fish struck a carefully rigged and skillfully fished eel.

of 20-pound test line. Chances are you will never need all 200 yards, but it is a lot easier to cast when using a reel with a full spool of line.

Leaders should be used whenever fishing from jetties because of the sharp barnacles and mussels the line drags across as it is retrieved. I use a 2-foot length of 40-pound test mono. To one end I attach a swivel to cut down on line twist. A big coastlock snap is attached to the other end.

The wide opening of the larger-sized coastlock allows the metal squid to wobble freely and this makes the eel swim in a natural manner. The same results can be obtained by using a short length of stiff piano wire between the squid and the leader.

Almost any jetty will hold some stripers, but, as with any type of fishing, some spots are better than others. The only way to find out which spots will always produce is to spend a lot of time pounding the rocks. Often you will locate a rock pile that can be counted on only during the low-water stages of the tide, while another jetty just a short distance away may produce best on the incoming water. Knowledge such as this comes only after spending many hours casting over the same waters.

I never fish the jetties during daylight hours, mainly because I have yet to catch a big bass in daylight. Very seldom will you find giant-sized stripers feeding when there is a lot of commotion. There are usually a lot of swimmers and boat traffic during the daytime, and I believe that this keeps the really large bass away from the jetties.

To a newcomer, figuring out where to fish a jetty can be frustrating. This can easily be overcome by using a method my father taught me many years ago. Start almost at the sandy beach end of the rocks and make a half-dozen casts in a fan pattern. Move out about 50 feet and repeat the pattern. With this system you will cover every piece of water that might harbor a big striper. After following this procedure a few times you will learn the spots that normally hold fish and can skip the unproductive spots, thus saving precious fishing time.

The beauty of fishing with eels is that they are a natural nighttime bait. Eels do not move around much during the daylight unless a heavy rain has muddied the water. So the bass expect to find eels swimming and feeding after dark, which makes them a natural bait for night fishing.

I usually rig my eels during the day so I can check to see whether they are swimming correctly. Any that are not can be adjusted by bending the metal squid up a little in the front. This causes the metal squid to wobble a little more, which in turn makes the eel swim. After fishing with rigged eels for a while you will be able to tell whether they are working by the feel of the line as you retrieve it, but until you get the knack it is strictly guesswork.

Stripers—big or small—do not fool around when they grab an eel. They hit it with all they have and there is no need to set the hook. Most times when a big striper grabs the eel you will think you have

Step-by-step Technique for Rigging an Eel.

Step 1. Eels for rigging should be starved first and then killed by immersion in a solution of 1 pound of kosher salt to 1 gallon of water. For the actual rigging, you'll need a block tin squid, tail hook, 50-pound Dacron, bait-rigging needle and pliers.

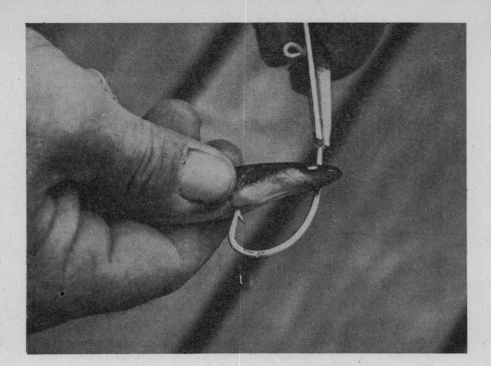

Step 2. Insert the point of the squid hook right behind the throat latch and push it through the head of the eel.

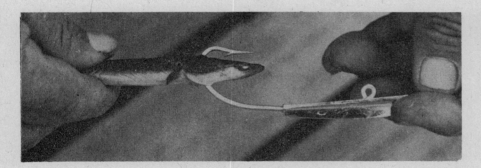

Step 3. With the hook positioned properly, the point is almost even with the mouth of the eel.

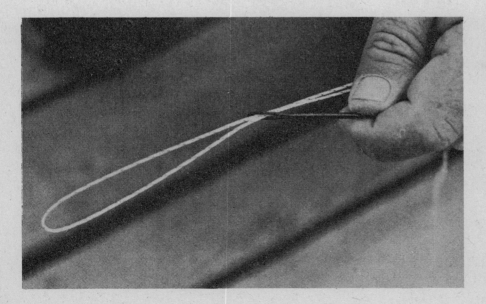

Step 4. Cut a 4-foot length of 50-pound test Dacron, double it in the middle, and thread the doubled end through the eye of the bait-rigging needle. Pull this doubled end all the way through the eye until the two tag ends remain.

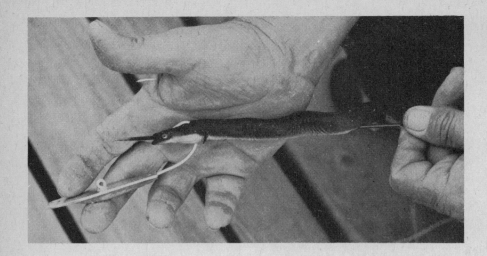

Step 5. Start the needle 1 inch behind the vent and push it all the way through the eel so that it exits at the mouth. Pull until only about 6 or 8 inches of doubled 50-pound Dacron remain under the belly of the eel.

Step 6. The tail hook is a short shank, 3 extra strong, tuna style, in a size 7/0 or 8/0. It has a big ringed eye so it can be tied securely. Slip the loop of Dacron through the eye of the tail hook and twist it around the hook three times, so the hook is secured.

Step 7. Carefully push the rigged hook into the body of the eel until the point and barb are parallel to the body.

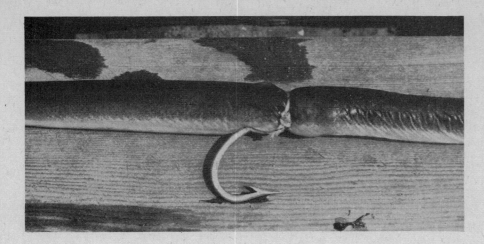

Step 8. Using another piece of Dacron, tie the hook in place. The Dacron should be seated right behind the big ringed eye and cinched down tightly so that the hook cannot turn sideways. If it does, the eel will not swim properly.

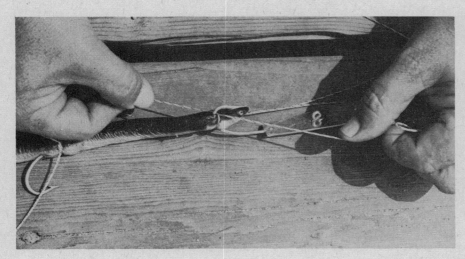

Step 9. With still another piece of Dacron, tie the squid hook to the eel. To keep this hook from sliding, make an X around the hook, passing the Dacron first in front of and then behind the hook. Tie it down snugly.

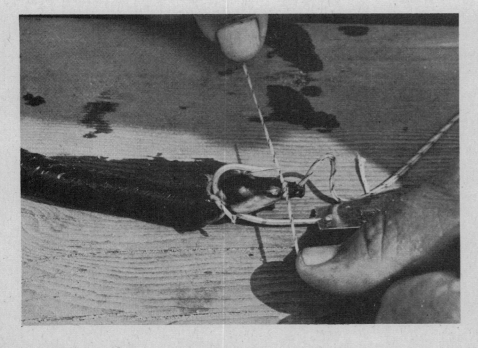

Step 10. If the mouth of the eel remains open, the bait won't swim right and the eel will break apart. To prevent this, tie the mouth shut just in front of the eyes.

Step 11. The two tag ends of Dacron running from the tail hook through the body of the eel and protruding from its mouth must now be secured to the ring eye on the squid. Remember that this is the only thing holding the tail hook; the knot should be fashioned carefully to prevent slipping.

Step 12. When you have trimmed the Dacron, the finished striper eel looks like this.

hooked on some obstruction on the bottom. The line just stops cold; then the fish turns and moves off with the eel. Very few bass are missed when fishing with rigged eels because of the power they use when grabbing the bait, but occasionally a fish will hit the eel with its tail, then turn and pick up the rig in its mouth. If you should feel a bump but not hook the fish, let the eel settle. Usually the bass will turn and hit the rig as it settles to the bottom.

The secret of success with rigged eels is the manner in which the lure is retrieved. A slow, steady retrieve will usually attract other fish besides the one that is speeding through the water. Many times I have found that it pays to do a bit of experimenting, and although on most occasions I have found the slow bottom-bouncing retrieve to be best, there are times when a fast eel brings more strikes.

When small bait fish such as mullet or rainfish are moving around the jetties, the stripers will be feeding higher off the bottom than usual. At times like this it may pay to try a fast retrieve. Another time when the fast retrieve will outproduce the bottom-bouncing method is when the stripers are chasing small bunkers. Usually the little bunkers will stay near the surface when they are being preyed upon by larger game fish. If you were to drag the rigged eel down near the bottom, it would not be seen by the feeding stripers.

Many states now are stocking the big linesiders in fresh water lakes. As techniques are refined and more anglers learn how to catch these large bass, I feel that the rigged eel will prove to be an exceptional fish catcher. Eels are native to most fresh water areas, and there should be no reason for these landlocked stripers not to feed on them.

Largemouth-bass anglers have already learned how effective a giant-sized plastic worm can be. Perhaps it would pay some of those specialists to try the rigged naturals. They might come up with a record-sized largemouth.

Beginner's Guide to Fresh Water Fishing

by Nick Sisley

How can a beginning fisherman get started on the right foot? I'll answer that by another question. What type of fishing is easiest and most convenient for you to reach? The answer will depend largely upon where you live.

Panfish such as bluegills, crappies and rock bass are ideal for beginning fishermen. They are within close reach in most areas and are fairly easy to catch if the right tackle and proper techniques are used. If you are an accomplished fisherman and would like to see your son or daughter or niece or nephew or the nextdoor neighbor's youngster enjoy the outdoors as much as you do, the best way to introduce them to the rewards of angling is through the panfish at a nearby lake or farm pond.

Trout fishing for brook, rainbow and brown trout abounds in mountain areas such as the Appalachian Chain, the Catskills, the Adirondacks, New England, even the Ozarks, and throughout the Rockies. Trout do well in other areas, too. Largemouth bass are especially abundant in Southern reservoirs. In that part of the United States, the U. S. Corps of Engineers has created numerous impoundments, and bass fishing has enjoyed a tremendous upsurge because of this.

Smallmouth bass have done well in some Southern reservoirs; in fact, a few of these produce the largest bronzebacks to be found anywhere. However, the smallmouth has a preference for flowing waters, and bass fishing in many of mid-America's larger streams is tough to beat.

As a fisherman becomes more skilled, there are several popular fresh water species that are widely distributed. These include northern pike, walleye and muskie. Northern pike are a good choice if you live near a lake where they are abundant. Walleyes are becoming more popular every year. State fisheries departments have learned a great deal about spawning this species and rearing it to stocking size. They strike readily, provide excellent food fare and are at home in lakes or streams where water temperatures are to their liking. Muskie fishing has enjoyed a great upsurge in recent years, and fisheries departments have also learned how to rear muskies to stocking size.

If you live near the East or West Coast or the Great Lakes, you will probably want to advance to salmon fishing when your skills are really developed.

The novice fisherman can't go wrong by purchasing a quality open-face spinning reel and medium action rod. Because such an outfit is basic and can be utilized for many types of fishing, this equipment should be the finest you can afford. Perhaps you've already acquired an inexpensive rod and reel of similar type—medium-weight, open-face, spin reel and medium action spin rod, say a 7-footer. In that case, don't make your next purchase a fly rod or a casting reel or an ultralight spin outfit. Instead, buy equipment similar to what you already have, but make it the very best you can afford. The problem with inexpensive fishing tackle is that it simply does not hold up to even moderate use or to big fish. The difficulties that I've encountered with inexpensive tackle would make another article as long as this one.

I recommend that the beginner start with panfish, trout or bass, progressing to larger fish later. The following recommendations for specific techniques and tackle will help him advance quickly down the road of angling success.

Panfish: Techniques and Tackle

In considering various panfish, let's talk about bluegills first. Bluegills (or bream) become active as waters warm in the spring. My experience has been that these little scrappers will take a lure or bait avidly soon after deciduous trees begin bearing leaves. Choose a warm, pleasant day. After all, panfishing is supposed to be fun.

Your basic tackle, medium spin gear, will be fine to start with. The reel spool probably came filled with 8- or 10-pound test. If you haven't done so already, buy a spare spool and fill it with 4- or 6-pound test for panfish. Also, acquire a cork arbor for the spare spool, so it won't be necessary to spool on so much line. If you don't have a spare spool, tie a short leader on your 8- to 10-pound test line. Use an Improved Blood knot or one of the new Uni-Knot connections to attach a 12- to 18-inch piece of 4- to 6-pound test.

Bluegills will be in the shallows during the spring, and spawning will be uppermost in their mind. You have your choice of live bait or artificials. Dry or wet flies produce excellent strings of bluegills, but flies require a little more expertise on the angler's part. I suggest you start with live bait. Bluegills go wild for worms or worm pieces in the spring. This is garden-digging time, so worms are readily available. Tie on a small bait-holder-type hook (my preference is for size 8 or 10) and cover the hook as best you can by threading the worm over the point two or three times. Use a tiny bobber that is almost submerged by the light weight of the worm. This will make it easier to recognize the bluegill nibbles. The bobber should be adjusted up and down the line, depending upon the depth of the

The author hefts a fine stringer of bluegills and rock bass taken with ultralight spin gear.

water you are fishing and your success. If you are not taking fish regularly, try positioning the bobber so that the worm is in deeper water, or move and fish in deeper water. Depending on how deep you have to go, it may be necessary to squeeze a split shot 14 or 16 inches above your hook.

At times bluegills take small lures almost as well as they take bait. One angler I know makes tiny jigs exclusively for panfish. I've seen him bring in eye-popping strings of bream and crappie from Tennessee's Reelfoot Lake. He fishes his minute jigs around weed edges with enticing movement of the rod tip. Sometimes he enhances the hook with a tiny piece of worm or a grub. No matter where you find bluegills, they can be finicky, preferring one special lure, color or bait over any other. At these times they can be as selective as brown trout rising to a hatch of Hendricksons. Usually, they're not that particular.

By the time farm ponds and small lakes have water temperatures approaching 72 degrees, bluegills begin to show a marked preference for flies. You can still take them with the basic spin gear I've recommended. Tackle shops sell an item called a casting bubble. Fill it with enough water to permit easy casting, attach it to your line like a bobber, then tie either a sinking or floating fly to the end of the line. With this equipment you can learn finesse—accurate casts into brushy places, and how to make the casting bubble and fly strike the water with minimal disturbance so that it won't spook your quarry.

Later in the summer, or in a year or two, you may have the desire to try panfish with a fly rod. It's great sport—lots of fun and lots of action. Stick with the concept I originally recommended—the very finest equipment you can afford. Ideal fly gear for bluegills would be a light 6½-foot to 8-foot fly rod that handles a 5-, 6- or 7-weight line. This same equipment is also ideal for trout fishing with flies. More about that later.

No doubt some anglers have no desire to move on to fly fishing but may want to acquire more specialized spinning equipment for bluegills—ultralight tackle. The very smallest fly reels are in order, and the very lightest wands will permit you to feel every surge.

Crappies, though similar in many ways to bluegills, require some different tactics. Basic medium spin gear is fine. Crappies are seldom interested in worms; minnows are always their meal-time entrée. They are easy to entice in the spring. Use a larger hook, size 2 or 4. Some prefer to clip the minnow through the mouth, others through the base of the dorsal fin. Many use a bobber, but I would rather spool a minnow (a few split shot above the hook) over the side of a boat and play the waiting game for a nibble while holding the line in my hand. Crappies often require a sensitive touch. Otherwise, you miss them.

These fish can also be taken with lures. Small spinners are good at times. Many use jigs and add a minnow to the jig hook. Crappies favor brushy areas. Experienced anglers take advantage of this trait by "salting" favored fishing areas with weighted limbs, small trees, and other brush during low-water conditions in the fall. In the spring these areas are flooded and the crappies move in to feed and spawn. Anglers who have marked these spots with buoys return. Many crappie fishermen use inexpensive cane poles or telescoping fiberglass crappie rigs.

The rock bass is one of my favorites. It is found in small streams, and your medium spin outfit will be ideal. It can be taken between bridges on short canoe trips or while wading. Minnows make up the major portion of its diet, so live ones are tough to beat. The rock bass is also a sucker for a jig or spinner. It is often encountered in waters that abound with smallmouth bass and is taken by the same techniques. Some look down their noses at goggle eyes, but, in my opinion, they are among America's finest and most underrated

A beautiful largemouth taken on a spinner bait and bait casting tackle.

This steelhead was taken on a fly from a small Lake Michigan tributary stream.

sport fishes. To graduate to even more fun with rock bass, move to ultralight spin gear.

Trout: Techniques and Tackle

I live in Pennsylvania, and in the Keystone State the trout is king. And this is so in many other areas of the country. Be they brook, brown or rainbow, trout are a great challenge, wonderful fun, and fishing for them can be enjoyed by virtually all anglers, rich or poor, experienced or novice.

Basic medium spin gear is ideal for the beginning trouter. I leave the option of bait or lures to him. Bait chunkers can choose from red garden worms, salmon eggs, small minnows, cheese balls—well, let's end the possibilities right there. Some of the trout baits these days border on the ridiculous. The trouting beginner who wants to cast artificials should choose small spinners, small spoons, tiny jigs and the like. Then, there is the world of fly fishing.

Let's take a brief look at lake fishing for trout, and a more extensive review of stream fishing, since that type of trouting is the most popular.

Trout have small mouths, so the angler using bait should select fairly small hooks, then try to cover them as best he can. This is easily done with a cheese ball or two salmon eggs, or by threading a wriggling red worm over the hook point and up the shank. Thread this on only once, however, so that the two ends of the worm twist and turn and are more attractive. I've found that the best way to fish lakes from shore is simply to cast out from the bank with one split shot pinched on the line about 15 inches above the hook. Prop the rod in a forked stick and hang a light bobber between the first and second spinning guides. Hang the bobber so that the line will pass through with no problem when you retrieve. The dangling bobber makes it easier to spot a nibble.

The lake angler casting for trout with spinners, spoons or jigs should "fan" his casts. Make the first cast directly ahead, the next to the extreme left or right, then a cast or two between each spot. If you don't encounter action, move 10 feet to 10 yards down the shoreline and fan your casts again. Trout in lakes school up occasionally, so if you take a fish, probe the same area with another cast or two a short time later.

The basic spin tackle is fine for stream fishing for trout. It is sometimes advisable to spool on 6-pound test, maybe even lighter, line, especially if the streams you fish are crystal clear. Lighter, thinner line is more difficult for the fish to see, and thus you encounter more strikes.

A red worm cast upstream and tumbled back over the rocks is the best trout killer I know of, bar none. I've fished with all manner of trout experts, including fly fishermen with finesse and unique abilities and those who caught fish consistently with a spinner/minnow combination, but none of them could match the fish-taking ability of one fellow who could make a red worm do everything but jump into a trout's mouth. Needless to say, he was not a beginner, but my experiences with him have proved to me that trout novices are well advised to start off their stream fishing with worms. Their chances of early success will be excellent, and the road toward achieving genuine expertise with this bait can be a long and interesting one.

Use only enough split shot to get the worm tumbling over the rocks. Depending on current and water depth, you may have to adjust the amount of weight continuously. Be willing to do so. Work upstream, directing short casts to the area just above trout holding places, then tumble your bait into each lair. The ability to recognize where trout are likely to take up feeding or resting positions is important. Once you have taught yourself where to cast, the ability to direct your casts accurately becomes paramount. The salmon egg fisherman who wades from spot to spot can work in a similar manner.

The man who concentrates on minnows is better off working downstream. His casts should be directed across the current; then the bait is permitted to "swing" through the likely looking spots. The most successful minnow chunkers thread their bait with a needle and attach either a double or a treble hook to the minnow's vent. This prevents missing trout if they

A fat Pennsylvania trout is in the net.

strike short. Many minnow purists rig a small spinner just ahead of the minnow for even more attraction. These minnow rigs can be made up or purchased commercially. The trouter who casts hardware should also work downstream, again casting across the current, permitting his small spinner or spoon to swing through the trouty looking water.

When a trout fisherman graduates from beginner to intermediate stage, there are two routes he can take. One is moving to ultralight tackle; the other, the highly regarded and intensely interesting sport of fly rodding for trout. The ultralight aficionado can use the basic trout techniques just described. His tackle might consist of whisper-thin lines: 1- or 2-pound test. To the trouter who opens the door to fly fishing, there is an area so vast and involved that I hesitate to approach it with only two or three paragraphs.

The fly rod suggested under "Panfish" is ideal equipment with which to start fly fishing for trout— the 6½- to 8-foot rod that handles a 5-, 6- or 7-weight line. The reel should be the single action type and matched in weight to balance with the fly rod. No worthwhile fly fisherman gives two cents for an automatic fly reel, though tackle companies sell them by the jillions.

Trout respond to the most delicate presentation. Level and weight-forward lines are preferred for many fly fishing circumstances, but when I am after wary trout, I'll take a double taper every time.

The trouter has his choice of dry flies, wet flies, terrestrials, nymphs or streamers. Entire books have been written about each and, by the time an angler has progressed to this stage, he has probably read at least some of the trout-angling literature. He should continue to read and learn. Some of the keys to success on trout are delicacy in presentation, putting the fly in front of the fish in the most natural manner and keeping out of sight.

Bass: Techniques and Tackle
In the last decade or so, thousands and thousands of outdoorsmen have been turned on to bass fishing, and they've turned on to a degree that tackle, boat and outboard motor manufacturers never dreamed possible. The sophistication that bass fishing has achieved with depth recorders or fish finders, foot-controlled electric trolling motors, bass boats, speedy outboards and structure fishing has opened up a whole new world of enjoyment and interest. The days of casting a Jitterbug on a farm pond at dusk seem to be gone

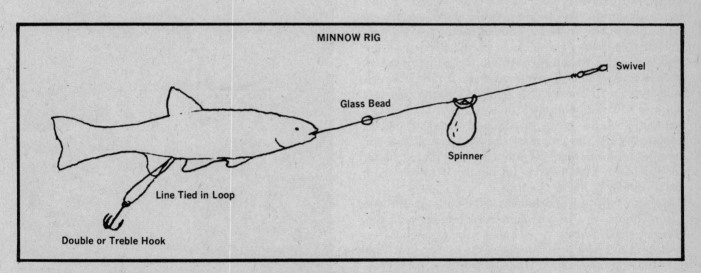

MINNOW RIG

Swivel

Glass Bead

Spinner

Line Tied in Loop

Double or Treble Hook

A minnow rig with a spinner is a great trout bait, and it will also take plenty of crappie, rock bass, largemouth, smallmouth and other fresh water battlers. The rig consists of a swivel, a short length of mono and a loop tied on the opposite end. A glass bead with spinner and clevis adds more attraction. Thread a loop of mono through the minnow with a slotted needle, attach the hook, then pull the hook back into the minnow's vent. You can tie these rigs yourself, but they are also available in tackle stores.

If you plan to fish small trout streams, select the shorter rod. If you are going to try your luck on larger trout waters, an 8-footer will be more in order. As you become more accomplished, you'll want to add more fly fishing equipment. Double tapered lines are best.

forever. Now, it's reservoirs full of standing timber, submerged stumps, fallen treetops—all manner of habitat that are ideal for the largemouth bass. Plastic worms and spinner baits that are threaded through these snag-infested morasses are the latest key to success. So, if you can't find the dropoff at a submerged creek channel and don't know how to probe 30 feet of water with a jig-n-eel, there is no way you can catch bass. Right? Wrong!

Farm-pond bass still attack top water lures at dusk just as avidly as they always have. You can get your feet wet bass fishing with that same medium spin gear that I recommended at the beginning of this article. If you get started with bass and find you enjoy it, there is no limit to the different bass fishing methods you can learn and the fish-taking equipment you can acquire.

If you try largemouth and become sold, your first pieces of specialized equipment should be a casting reel (one of the push button, free spool varieties) and a medium action bass rod about 6 feet long. An hour or two of practice on your driveway or lawn will be beneficial in showing you the how-to. Follow the casting directions that come with the equipment, and you'll soon realize that it takes only a small amount of dexterity to do the right thing with your thumb at the right time.

As you learn more and more about bass fishing, you'll probably expand to more equipment; say, several casting rods, maybe an ultralight spin outfit, even a fly rod so you can "bug" some bass. Where you take largemouth in reservoirs is as varied as the fish holding places available. The techniques are endless. Many of us get the most satisfaction out of fishing from a boat and casting toward the shore or visible stick-ups—targets we can see. Bass aren't always in the shallows, but that is where the beginner should start. First learn to take bass with three types of lures: plastic worms, spinner baits and alphabet plugs.

Plastic worms come in different lengths and in practically all the colors of the rainbow. Rig them weedless and cast into the worst-looking places: areas in which other anglers would be afraid to lob their baits for fear of losing them.

Spinner baits are another extremely important bass lure. Though not in the same weedless class as the Texas rigged worm, these lures are very snag-free because the upper arm rides over the hook point. The fact that spinner baits and plastic worms are cast into places where other lures aren't is one of the keys to their success.

Alphabet lures—Big O's, Little O's, Big N's, Little N's, Bagley B's—imitate the plentiful gizzard shad and threadfin shad that are so abundant in many impoundments. These lures can be obtained in numerous colors. They can't be thrown right into the worst spots, as the plastic worms can, but as your accuracy increases, you'll be throwing them closer and closer to tree tops, stumps, brush and bank edges.

With a cane pole and minnows the author's son had fine success with crappies.

While the greatest success in plastic worm fishing comes with edging the lure slowly through the bass's lair, the alphabet lures have the advantage of speed. Experts cover more water with them.

Heavier lines such as 14-, 17- and even 20-pound test are usually utilized by bass casting experts. These heavy lines are used because it is often important to pull a bass with sheer brute strength away from a stump, from under a submerged log, or over grass—situations where light lines are useless. Many bass experts keep several outfits rigged and ready in the bottom of the boat. One will have a topwater plug, another an alphabet, one with a plastic worm, and the fourth with a spinner bait, and so on.

These days, most bassing experts stick with bait casting and/or spin gear. They expand their horizons by learning more and more about structure fishing,

have a great deal to do with their satisfaction.

This discussion has had to do with largemouth bass; let's not forget smallmouth. In many mid-America streams, these fish are abundant, wary and challenging, a most worthwhile trophy. When it comes to putting up a fight, the smallmouth is the fresh-water champion.

Medium spin gear is perfect. Try topwater lures over slick stream pools morning and evening. Probe river depths with minnows or softshell crabs. Use bucktail or marabou jigs around river boulders, or cast plugs that closely resemble the commonest bait fish in your waters.

The smallmouth beginner who moves up to intermediate class will probably want to switch to ultralight spin gear, once he has learned his basic lessons. Some may want to graduate to fly rod fishing.

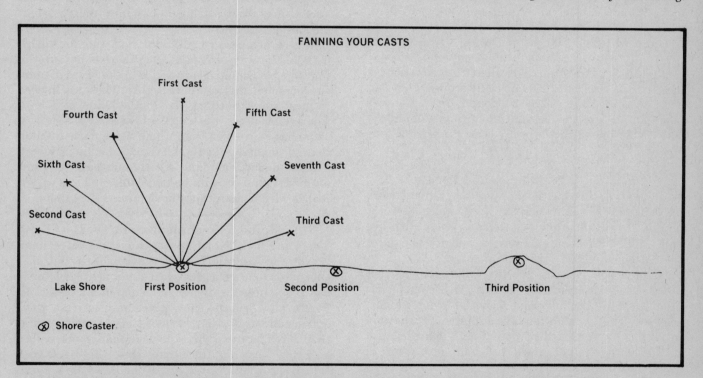

FANNING YOUR CASTS

First Cast

Fourth Cast   Fifth Cast

Sixth Cast   Seventh Cast

Second Cast   Third Cast

Lake Shore   First Position   Second Position   Third Position

⊗ Shore Caster

If casting from a lake shore try fanning your casts. After fanning seven or eight casts from the first position, move 10 feet to 10 yards along the shore and fan cast again. Little points that jut out into the lake are excellent casting positions.

add more types of lure to their tackle boxes and learn how to fish them, save for a down payment on a bass boat and motor, then finance the rig as they would a house or car. After that, there are depth recorders, electric trolling motors; the list goes on. Bass fishing on this scale can be expensive, but thousands of sportsmen consider it worth the money. The challenge, the variety and the constant learning no doubt

Smallmouth can be real suckers for bass bugs, poppers, streamers, even a well-hackled dry fly.

Northern Pike: Techniques and Tackle
As mentioned, a beginner is wise to start with panfish, trout or bass. Northern pike is a species the angler tries a little later. Medium spin gear can be perfectly suited to northerns. They strike lures willingly, so live

bait is seldom necessary. They like to lurk in weed beds, waiting for a tasty morsel to pass by. They prefer colder waters and are most abundant in the northern latitudes of North America. There is some excellent pike fishing in Michigan, Wisconsin and Minnesota, but the very best is found in lakes in the Canadian back country.

Red and white Dardevle spoons have long been the preferred bait for pike. Find weed beds and retrieve so that the lure wobbles right on top of the grass patch. A weedless spoon that you let sink directly into the weed field can sometimes be an even better producer. Trolling rocky shorelines can be another way to provide plenty of pike action. Pike's sharp teeth will sometimes cut through 8- and 10-pound monofilament. For this reason, many prefer to use short steel leaders, but I think more success is encountered with mono leaders, say 20-, 30- or 40-pound test, which are more difficult to see than cable.

Those who find pike fishing especially rewarding may want to move up from medium spin gear to a bait-casting outfit. Pike often take bright-colored streamer flies, so they are a good fish for the fly rodder. They can grow to respectable sizes—20 pounds or more—and pike spinning experts feel that the ultimate challenge is to try for one of these trophy-sized lunkers on 2- or 4-pound test.

Walleyes: Techniques and Tackle

Walleye is another species that beginners should work up to. These fish inhabit rivers, lakes and reservoirs, and I've always had my best luck on them with live bait. Trolled lures sometimes work well, if you can get them deep enough.

Medium spin gear is fine for walleyes. They are especially active early in the spring. Their main food is minnows, but they also have a special love for night-crawlers. They won't often take a spinner but they are attracted by the flash of one. That's why using a spinner with a gob of crawlers or a minnow is one of the secrets of walleye success.

When fishing in a lake, let the wind drift your boat. Use enough weight to get your bait to the bottom and throw a marker buoy when you have a strike. Keep drifting over the same area as long as it produces action. Walleyes are school fish. With walleyes, I like bigger hooks such as size 1, 2 or larger.

River fishing for walleyes can be done with the same spinner and bait combination. Also, marabou or bucktail jigs in white, red, yellow or combinations of these colors can be very effective. Some anglers, either lake or river fishermen, may be interested in progressing to ultralight tackle after they have learned the knack with the basic equipment.

Muskies: Techniques and Tackle

Muskies are another fish species for the intermediate angler. Learn basic techniques and tactics on panfish, trout or bass before trying these challenging devils. For your first experience with the muskie, standard spin gear will be borderline; try it to see if you like the sport, but move on to heavier stuff if you decide in the affirmative. Spin gear a notch stouter than basic medium tackle is in order. I suggest a reel that holds 180 to 200 yards of 14- to 20-pound test line, and a short, stout rod with plenty of backbone for setting hooks. Bait casting tackle is also great for muskies. Level wind push button free spool outfits that hold 200 yards of 17- to 20-pound test are usually preferred by the experts. Stouter rods permit casting heavier, larger lures, and setting hooks into the rock-hard mouths of these fish.

Muskie fishing is tough: a lot of casting for mighty little in the way of results. But there is no question that muskie fishing has gotten into the blood of many outdoorsmen, and it's there to stay. These are big fish. In most states nothing less than a 30-incher is legal. The average legal muskie taken these days runs 34 to 38 inches, and more than a fair share measure more than 40 inches. Add the fact that stocking by state fisheries departments has greatly increased the range of this fish and the number available, and it is easy to realize why so many sportsmen are seeking them.

Salmon: Techniques and Tackle

There are two North American types of salmon, Pacific and Atlantic. Neither is a fish for the beginner. One needs to learn a great deal about fishing before he can seek these two with any hope of success. Both Pacific and Atlantic salmon are born in fresh water and spend varying amounts of time in the stream of their birth before a physiological change takes place and they head for the ocean. Here they feed voraciously, growing to large sizes. When they are sexually mature they return to fresh water to spawn. This is when the fresh water fisherman tries to catch them. Because of their life in salt water, they seem to have greater vitality and a lot more fight than most fresh water fish.

While medium spin gear might be all right for the initial try at some species of Pacific salmon, the Atlantic salmon is by law a fly rod fish only. Let's look at Pacific salmon first. Today there is good coho and chinook salmon fishing in the Great Lakes and some of their tributary streams. There is also salmon fishing in Alaska, British Columbia, Washington and Oregon. In

Smallmouth bass abound in many mid-America streams, and provide super sport.

the latter two states problems have been created by a recent court ruling permitting Indians to take Pacific salmon and other anadromous sport fish by virtually any method they can. In Alaska the fishing is still truly fantastic.

In the mid-1960's, the Michigan fisheries department was successful in planting coho salmon smolts in tributary streams of Lake Michigan, and much publicity has been given to the success fisheries managers have had in planting coho, chinook, and rainbow or steelhead trout in Lake Superior, Lake Michigan, Lake Ontario and Lake Erie.

The techniques for catching these fish are not difficult. Try casting spawn bags of salmon eggs taken directly from recently caught females or cast commercially produced salmon eggs. Spoons or spinners that get to the bottom are also excellent. Pink, orange or red streamers are the primary choices of the fly fisherman. Anglers cast and troll the Great Lakes; then, later in the year, when the salmon move into the streams, they switch their attention to these.

These are tremendously strong fish, so if you find coho and king salmon are for you, it will be advisable to acquire some specialized tackle. For trolling the Great Lakes spin gear is fine, but the reel should be a little larger than your basic one. It should hold 180 to 225 yards of 12- to 15-pound test. The best rods for trolling the Great Lakes for salmon are 8½- to 9-feet long, with limber tips, but strong at the butt. Casting reels are also used for this trolling. Push button free spools are fine if they have a clicker to signal a strike. For stream fishing, the larger reels are in order, but try a shorter, stouter rod: one that will turn a powerful salmon, but short enough to cast a brushy, small stream. Fly fishing for salmon is becoming increasingly popular. It was originally believed that these fish could only be foul hooked, but they will take properly presented flies and an 8½- to 9-foot heavy action rod with 9-weight line is ideal. Some use a fly reel filled with nothing but 15-pound mono and make short "flip" casts.

Atlantic salmon are the world's premier fly rod fish. Currently, they are threatened by water pollution, poaching and a high seas commercial fishery. Salmon fishing in private and protected waters is also expensive. The best is in Iceland, Labrador and Scandinavia, but adequate Atlantic salmon sport is still available to those of more moderate means in New Brunswick, Quebec, Nova Scotia and Newfoundland.

Entire books have been written about salmon fishing techniques. Here are a few basics. The quartering downstream cast is in order and, as a rule, the fly should be from a few inches to a foot or so under the surface. Although in trout fishing drag is always to be avoided, the submerged fly that "swings" in the current is what usually attracts an Atlantic salmon from the depths and entices him to strike.

All types of fly rods will work. Experts might use 6- and 7-foot rods designed to handle 5- and 6-weight lines, but the beginner will be better off with an 8½- to 9-foot fly rod geared for an 8-, 9-, even a 10-weight line, especially if wind is a problem.

This coho salmon pulled the scale needle past the 12-pound mark. Both Pacific and Atlantic salmon provide supreme sport, but beginning anglers are advised to learn the basics before trying them.

Tips for Increasing Your Fishing Skills

How do you become a more accomplished fisherman? There is a little more to it than simply going fishing often, although that must be considered a key factor. If you notice a magazine article that covers a fishing subject you are particularly interested in, do more than read it. Study the piece, put it in a reference file, then read it again a year or two later. There are many specialized informative fishing books available.

Try to become acquainted with the fish wardens in the areas you fish most. It is their job to give advice willingly. You'll be surprised how cooperative they can be. Some of them are excellent fishermen. If the fame of a local angling expert reaches your ears, try to meet him. The learning experience with him, either on the stream, the lake or through conversation, could be most beneficial. Your area probably has one or two local outdoor writers. Seek their advice with regard to where you might find a fishing spot. Maybe they'll ask you to tag along. If they do, you'll probably learn something about techniques.

You should also join an organization that devotes itself to the species you are most interested in. If trout are your thing, you belong in Trout Unlimited, 4260 Evans, Denver, Colorado 80222. There are several organizations devoted to bass. One is the Bass Anglers Sportsman Society, P. O. Box 3044, Montgomery, Alabama 36109. Another is the American Bass Fisherman, P.O. Box 908, Cocoa Beach, Florida 32931. For the Atlantic salmon buff there is the Atlantic Salmon Association, 1405 Peel Street, Montreal, Quebec H3A 1S5, Canada. There are many others.

There are always new horizons to seek in fresh water fishing. Once you've arrived at the head of the class with medium spin gear, there is always a new type of tackle to take on, or a new fishing method, or a new lure type with which to become proficient. Become accomplished with all three angling methods: spinning, casting and fly. The techniques you learn along the way and the top tackle you are continually seeking will add much to your fishing enjoyment.

Remember that practice casting on a driveway or lawn is very beneficial. Accuracy and delicacy of presentation are extremely important ingredients to fishing success. Ten minutes a day with a practice plug or with a fly rod will make you an infinitely more accomplished angler. Knots, too, are of paramount importance, and you'll find they become more and more critical as your degree of fishing expertise increases. The place to practice new knots and old ones is in the comfort of your own home. Few of us go fishing often enough to become proficient knot tyers if we do it only when we are out on the water.

The beginner who follows the program outlined in this article will soon learn the basic techniques that put him on the right road to becoming a successful fisherman.

Keeping Tackle
out of Trouble
by C. Boyd Pfeiffer

Proper tackle maintenance at home is the first step toward preventing problems in the field, but there are many things that can be done on the water to keep tackle both out of trouble and ready for fishing at all times.

Suggestions for improvements often develop from examples of what went wrong. Several years ago, a friend and I were fishing for bass in a new lake. Not knowing what the fish would take or what tackle we would need, we brought along four rods each, about twice as many as we would normally carry in my 14-foot boat. With rods lying all over the place, my companion stepped on and crushed one of his outfits during the excitement of a strike. Moral: Keep rods out of the way in racks or along the gunwale.

Another friend and I were fishing the Ogeechee River in Georgia, dodging the branches of overhanging trees in one particularly tough stretch of river. A log just ahead forced me to swerve quickly. My friend shifted position, placing his hand on a pile of plugs he had been using for fishing. Moral: Run boats slowly enough to adjust for any sharp turns, but also put plugs in tackle boxes or in a small lure rack on the side of the boat.

While keeping tackle trouble free often involves just plain common sense, failure to do so may not only result in broken gear, but create dangerous fishing conditions as well.

The trick in working with any equipment is having a place for it and keeping it there, whether you are fishing from boat, bank, surf or shore. For example, allowing a rod and reel to lie on or in the sand can lead to disaster. Rod racks on beach buggies and sand spikes for walking anglers prevent the tackle from ever touching the stuff. No matter where you fish, you can leave gear in the car until you are ready to use it. Then, rest it on a forked stick or tackle box for bank fishing or place it properly in the boat.

Even a boat is no guarantee against trouble, as proved by my friend who stepped on his rod, broke it, and almost lost his balance in the process.

There are many types of rod racks for bass boats which can also be fitted on the gunwale or decks of other craft. Lacking such racks, the rods should be lined up neatly with one angler's rods on the starboard side, the other's on the port side. All rod tips and butts are now in the boat and out of the way of deck walking space.

Open boats like this one provide plenty of fishing space while keeping tackle out of the way and thus out of trouble. Cockpit arrangements differ, but all should be free of clutter for safety as well as fishing convenience.

Storage racks for rods will keep them out of the way, yet rigged and instantly available for casting a lure.

Many bass anglers store rods across the gunwales of a boat, but this can also bring grief. First, when moving out of a slip or away from a launch ramp, or tying up to a bulkhead or dock, any rods extending beyond the hull may be broken or crushed.

Similarly, a hooked fish near the boat can wrap a line around any protruding rod tips. The result too often is broken rods and lost fish. Fish are also lost on stringers, outboard engine skegs, bait buckets and anything else hanging over the side. Bring these inboard when a fish is hooked.

On large boats or when fishing with heavy tackle, overhead rod racks in cabins prevent breakage.

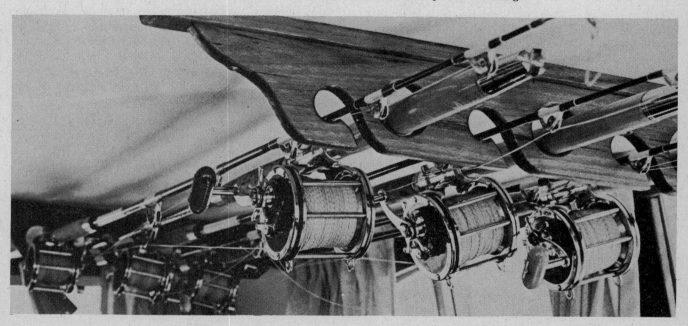

One way to keep tackle out of trouble is to rig rods ashore and store them where they will be out of the way.
Rigging equipment in a hurry when the fish are hitting often results in broken gear or in tackle left lying
around where it can be stepped on in the excitement of playing fish.

Larger boats with cabins should be fitted with overhead storage racks to hold the offshore and boat rods and reels safely out of the way, yet ready for instant use.

Rigging tackle ashore, down to the lure or fly on the end, is one easy way to be ready for the fish and to avoid damage to tackle in the field. Once you are on the water it is more difficult to put an outfit together. Rods can be broken while trying to string them in small boats, and reels often are dipped in the water while threading line through tip tops. Both sights are common on any popular fishing water.

Spinning reel handles and bails are particularly subject to damage even if tackle is carried in rod racks along the gunwales. One way to protect these two fragile parts is to fold down the bail (possible on many models of reels) and to reverse the handle so that it stores in close to the reel body. A rubber band will hold the reel handle and it can be removed quickly.

Handles and bails of spinning reels stick out so far

that they are most susceptible to damage from banging around. Since such knocks are entirely possible in upright rod holders and rod holders on the front of beach buggies, cut a slot in the tubing to hold the leg of the spinning reel and to keep it from swinging around. These slots in no way interfere with casting outfits dropped into the same rod holders.

Line can be damaged more easily than any other piece of equipment. Obviously, there is no way to "repair" line, but you can keep fish losses from line damage to a minimum if you follow a few basic procedures. When fishing rocky places, around stumps, or in heavy weeds, cut off about 6 feet of line every hour (more often if needed) and retie the lure each time. Another way to check for line wear is to run your finger along the line. Remove any line that is rough, brittle, frayed or twisted. If too much line gets frayed, replace the spool with one carrying new line.

Easily replaced spare spools are available for almost every fly, spinning and casting reel. Spare spools offer cheap insurance when line gets damaged in the field. They also make it easy to fish one reel with several different line sizes for changing conditions. I keep two to three spare spools for each of my spinning reels and at least one spare spool for every fly and casting reel.

To protect spare spools from nicks, corrosion and dirt, carry them in a small bag which can be stuffed in the bottom of your tackle box or wrap them in old socks, using rubber bands to separate the spools.

While tackle boxes are necessary, they are also

To keep bulky spinning reels from becoming damaged while traveling, fold back the bail *(circle).* **Reel handles on most reels can be backed off** *(arrow)* **and folded close to the reel body for protection.**

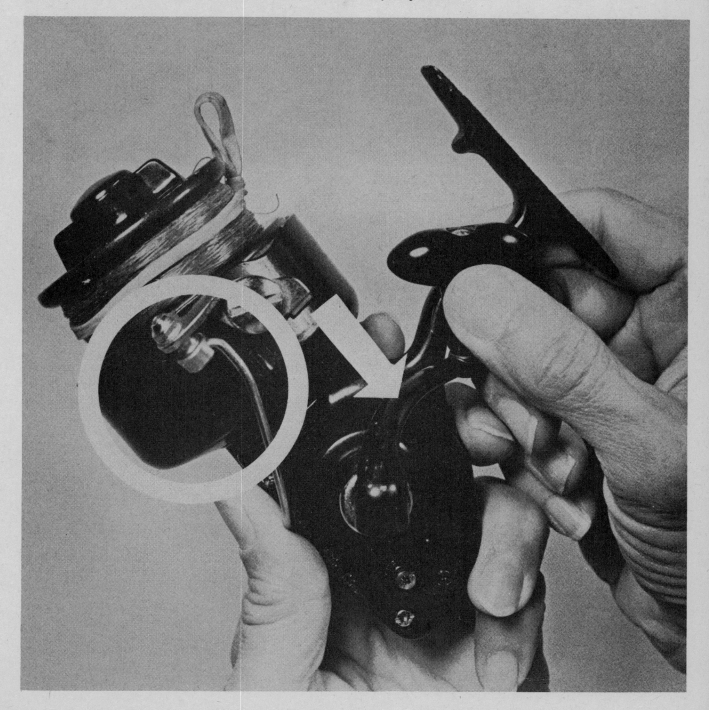

Reels will work better, rollers will turn better, and rods will cast better if reel spools are filled to capacity. The spare spool on the left has too little line, which can result in jerky casts that may snap a lure off. Avoid using old line which has turned white on the storage spool *(arrow)*.

stumbling blocks in many fishing situations. They must be placed where they can be reached to change lures and get at tackle but at the same time be kept out of the way as much as possible.

For small-boat anglers sitting down most of the time and chunking lures at bass "hidey holes," the hip roof boxes which open up like an alligator's jaws to disclose tray upon tray of lures create no problem. Since you tend to stay in the same seat for a day's fishing, the tackle box can be stretched out within arm's reach.

Carry spare spools in a bag such as the one shown to protect them from damage in the bottom of a tackle box.

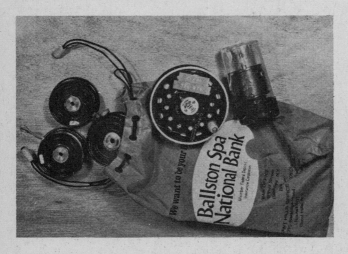

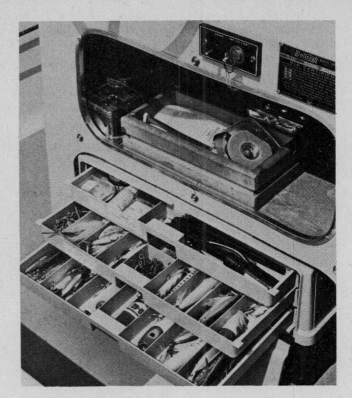

Tackle boxes that spread wide when opened can present a problem on a small fishing boat where space is limited. On such boats, the best tackle boxes are those with pull-out drawers that can be stowed out of the way and still provide access to several trays of lures.

Aboard larger fishing boats where it is necessary to move about to adjust trolling lines, down riggers and the like, boxes should be kept from underfoot. Space under seats, decks and center consoles will hold boxes within slide-out distance.

One of the best solutions is to get a tackle box with pull-out trays, so that the box will fit up against a gunwale or under a console or seat, yet still allow access to lures.

If your tackle box tends to slide, glue non-skid boat tape, indoor-outdoor carpeting, or rubber strips to the bottom to hold it in place. Epoxy glues work well for this purpose.

It is often more satisfactory to explore new fishing areas by switching back and forth among a few basic lures. This is difficult if you must dig in a tackle box each time to get out the necessary artificial. Keeping lures in a heap on the seat can be dangerous, as my friend and I found out on the Ogeechee. Lures piled in a heap must be untangled, which takes as much time as digging them out of a box. An easy solution is to fit your boat with a lure hanger along each gunwale at both the bow and stern. One of the easiest to make is a 12-inch length of 1- by 2-inch board, with 1/4-inch holes drilled 1 inch apart through the board. Fasten the board to the side of the boat so that lures can be hung by their hooks, out of the way and separately available. A similar hanger consisting of slots cut into one side of a sheet of clear plastic fitted to the windshield of a larger fishing boat will hold lures while keeping the running console clear of hooks and tackle.

Another lure storage method for those using rented craft or not wishing to add lure racks to their boats is to carry a small plastic container in which slots have been cut around the perimeter to hang lures. Plastic buckets or the bottom halves of plastic milk containers work well for this.

Fish are great to catch, but once in a boat they can make more mess and ruin more tackle in less time than a pack of Cub Scouts. The secret here is to handle the fish before bringing it aboard and giving it a chance to destroy tackle. Any netted species can be unhooked and placed on the stringer while it is held in

The steering console on this boat is free of clutter. Lures are hung on a slotted piece of plastic that slips over the windshield.

Rather than leaving lures in a jumbled mess, attach a strip of wood (drilled with holes 1 inch apart) to serve as a lure hanger. Artificials can't become tangled and are instantly available.

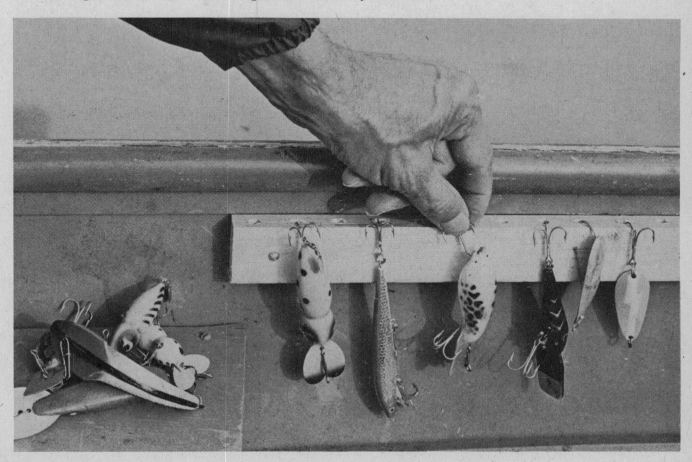

A frisky bass with a multihook lure in its mouth can tear up a landing net in short order. By unhooking a bass at the gunwale of the boat, you can prevent it from tangling the lure in the net or a pants leg while it is flopping around on the deck.

the net on the outside of the boat. Not only does this keep the fish away from the tackle but holding it in the net during the unhooking and stringing operation prevents the possibility of a loose fish flopping free and out of the boat.

Leaders tangled either while trolling or when landing a fish should be replaced as required. Since leaders behind planers or in-line sinkers are often long and even heavier than the line, they will not snap, but they can be more of a mess than a tournament caster's backlash. Usually these tangles are a problem only when you are changing lures or landing a fish. In either case, the leader should be discarded, since the work of straightening it is more than the short length of monofilament is worth.

Station wagon tailgates and car windows are particularly dangerous when removing rods from vehicles or when transporting long rods—especially fly rods— from one stretch of stream to another. I recently heard of an angler who slipped several of his favorite Orvis split bamboo rods into the back of a wagon. He got in the car, touched the switch to crank up the rear window, and cut about 12 inches off each rod. I did the same thing myself once with a hand-crank window, losing 2 inches off the tip of a glass blank.

Outside rod holders—with the rod placed butt forward—are the solution here, although on country roads brush or tree limbs can wreck the hardware or finish on a fine rod.

More rods are broken in home and car doors than on fish. Rods are also broken while walking through the woods. When a rod is pointed ahead it can catch on branches. The rod can get caught between two branches or in a limb fork and snap off without notice. Always walk through the woods with the rod pointed to the rear. Guides and the line (if the rod is already rigged) may catch occasionally, but without danger to the rod.

Nets can also be a nuisance when you are walking through the woods. Most are supplied with elastic cords. This is fine in open areas, but along wooded trout streams the net can catch in a branch. This stretches the cord so that when it is released, the net

Twisted and tangled leaders caused by trolling or by a fish should be cut off and replaced. Trying to straighten out such a leader is not worth the trouble.

handle comes back with rib-cracking force. The way to keep nets out of trouble is to sew a "D" ring onto the back center of your fishing vest or jacket and attach a French snap to the end of the net's handle. French snaps open in the center so that the net can be unsnapped behind you when you need it to land a fish.

Proper storage is the key to keeping reels in good condition, rods from being stepped on, lures and hooks out of danger, and boats, nets, fishing vests and tackle boxes in good shape.

"Have a place for everything and keep everything in its place" is an old maxim that is most appropriate for avoiding tackle problems in the field.

Sharks: Sportfishing's Newest Challenge

by Alex Chenoweth

More attention has been focused on the shark in the past decade than in all the 300 million years it has prowled the seas of the world. Basically a feeding machine and equipped to survive in almost any type of environment, the shark has remained virtually unchanged in shape and motivation for eons and eons.

As long as man has walked to the edge of the sea or sailed upon it, the sight of that triangular dorsal fin that rises above the water like the periscope of a submarine has elicited feelings ranging from awe and respect to outright terror. There are probably few people who can look at a shark without a reaction of some kind.

Until recently, few sportfishermen went out to catch sharks specifically. Those that were taken were incidental to the species of fish the anglers were primarily seeking, and these effective predators were often dispatched as cruelly as possible. Fishermen found it difficult to resist the temptation to slit the bellies of sharks or stab them several times. Others clubbed them with anything at hand. The first thought among seafaring people was to kill this monster that sometimes preyed on humans. They reasoned that every dead shark was one less threat.

All that is beginning to change, and much of the change is due to a continuing effort on the part of John G. Casey and his staff at the shark research project being conducted at the Northeast Fisheries Center of the National Marine Fisheries Service in Narragansett, Rhode Island. Casey has carried his research directly to anglers along both coasts and solicited their cooperation. His method has been one of education, attempting to persuade fishermen to tag and release sharks so that science can begin to gain the data necessary to understand them.

The process is a slow one, but progress is being made and Casey is pleased. He is equally delighted with the fact that thousands of years of apprehension and hate are giving way to curiosity and even concern for the shark both as a creature of the sea and as a useful resource.

As gamefish become more difficult to catch and more expensive to chase, small-boat fishermen and some shore-based anglers are now directing their big-game efforts toward sharks, because they present the only angling situation in which one can expect to catch a fish weighing from 100 to 200 pounds or more for a minimal amount of money. If you fish in the

ANGLER'S BIBLE

A shark close to the boat may thrash wildly and injure itself once you grab the leader.

Northeast, for example, you can almost be guaranteed a fish in that weight range if you specialize in sharks for a short period of time. The same promise is not possible for those whose goals are swordfish, tuna, marlin or sailfish. With these species, the cost is high and the success ratio relatively low. Your chance of catching swordfish is minimal unless you make it a vendetta and pursue them vigorously.

There are between 250 and 300 species of sharks around the world, ranging in size from one 6 inches long to the whale shark which can attain lengths of 60 feet and weights that are tremendous. Of these, perhaps a dozen species are taken regularly along American coasts and additional species occasionally. For many years it was believed that no matter how many sharks you killed there were always others to take their place. Now research has begun to show that the shark is actually a fragile resource and extremely susceptible to fishing pressure.

At present the main value of sharks in the United States is in providing recreational fishing. In 1970, sportfishermen caught 783,000 sharks (not including dogfish) with a total weight of 22 million pounds. Over 1 million dogfish with a total weight of 3 million pounds were taken that year. In 1965, 481,000 sharks were caught by recreational anglers; the catch has increased almost 63 percent in five years.

The population of sharks off our coasts is still considered virgin, but John Casey and others close to the scene feel that it is only a matter of time before these fish will be sought commercially. There is some evidence that this is already happening in the Gulf of Mexico and along the Southeast Coast of the United States.

When commercial fishing efforts start, documented evidence shows that populations drop drastically. Sharks are particularly slow-growing, taking many years to reach sexual maturity; they have a very limited reproduction potential compared to other species (most sharks give birth to their young alive) and they are easy to catch. This makes them targets for overfishing. Norwegian fishing for porbeagle sharks in the western North Atlantic started in the early 1960's. The landings of porbeagles in 1964 totaled over 8000 metric tons; only three years later, in 1967, commercial landings were zero.

Neither sport nor commercial fishing will totally eliminate a shark population, but it can easily be depressed to the point where it is no longer feasible to pursue. Then it takes a very long time for the population to restore itself, even if fishing pressure ceases. The typical porbeagle lives for over 20 years and it may be 12 or even 14 years old before it is sexually mature. It is always possible that the disappearance of a species reflects a shift in distribution, but it is more likely that the stocks were reduced and the catches reflected this fact.

With the renewed interest of sportfishermen in sharks and a probable entry into the arena by commercial fishermen, it is becoming increasingly important to learn as much as we can about sharks, and no one knows this better than John Casey. As the man in charge of shark tagging in the United States, Casey, his fellow biologists and almost 1500 cooperating sportfishermen along the coasts had tagged 14,368 sharks when the figures were totaled last year. Of this number, about 10 percent were tagged in the current year. Recapture rates average about 3 percent, with a total of 437 sharks recaught. Last year, 54 sharks representing eleven species were caught and recorded for the second time.

Tagging data is vital. It provides information on movement, growth rate, reproductive cycles and other critical facets of a shark's life cycle that will help scientists to learn how to manage the stocks. Without some data to determine growth rates and migration routes, proper management is not feasible. One of the key questions is identifying the stocks of sharks. Once migration is proved, it is obvious that management of the species must be on a worldwide basis.

The blue shark is one of the most common along the Northeast Coast and tagging of this species provided some dramatic results this year. A blue shark tagged off Moriches Inlet, New York, two years ago was recaptured off Guyana in South America, a distance of slightly over 2000 miles. Another blue shark that was released off Montauk, New York, two years ago turned up in the Cape Verde Islands off the African coast, some 3000 miles away. The latter capture was the first evidence of west-to-east trans-Atlantic migration for the species. A previously caught fish documented east-to-west migration from the Canary Islands to South America.

Because of these data and other information, scientists now believe that segments of the blue shark population may follow the clockwise flow of the major ocean currents of the North Atlantic. If this proves true, it is theorized that the fish may move eastward toward the Azores following the Gulf Stream, then southward with the Azores and Canary currents toward the African coast and back with the Equatorial Current that flows westward to the Caribbean. This may only be part of the migratory pattern. Other data point to a more complex pattern that involves separate coastal migrations on both sides of the Atlantic, as well as ocean crossings.

The result of all this study will be the determination of how and where to manage the stocks. John Casey is the first to admit that it would be an exercise in futility to attempt to manage locally a stock of fish that is involved in transoceanic movements and mixtures.

Sharks should be kept in the water. To release one, simply cut the leader. Don't try to reach down and remove the hook.

Sharks are taken regularly as part of the commercial longline operations, but most of the sharks taken in this high-seas fishery are discarded as trash. At present, there simply isn't enough of a worldwide market for shark flesh, hides, teeth or even the fins which the Chinese use for their famous shark-fin soup. The demand is developing, but for the commercial longliner, the decision is an economic one. There is only so much room aboard a ship for a cargo of fresh or frozen fish and other species bring more money, so the sharks are discarded. Without a market and an economical way to process sharks at sea, a longline or other high-seas fishery cannot develop.

Unlike the bony fishes, sharks have a cartilaginous skeleton, which means that the frame does have calcium but is made up primarily of cartilage. This gives the animal a great deal of suppleness, both in swimming and in ability to lash out with its tail or twist around with its head. Great care should be exercised in handling any shark, including small ones. In fact, veterans are convinced that the best way to handle any shark is to avoid getting it into the boat unless you intend to keep it. In tagging and/or releasing a shark, all the operations can be performed while the fish is in the water. If you are going to bring a shark aboard, it should be dispatched before it is slid over the gunwale. There are books filled with horror tales of the damage done by live sharks in boats. The tail alone can smash everything in sight and that doesn't begin to describe what they can do with the business end of their bodies.

Sharks do not have scales over their skin as other fishes do. Instead, they have tiny skin teeth called dermal denticles, which, like any other tooth, are somewhat pointed. If you rub your hand along the skin of a shark from head toward tail, it feels very smooth. This smoothness helps the shark to swim better because it increases the laminar flow of water along the body. But if you rub your hand from tail toward head (preferably on a dead shark), the skin feels as abrasive as coarse sandpaper. You are rubbing against the toothlike points of the denticles.

The toughness of sharkskin has forced researchers to design a stronger dart tag which will penetrate the skin and become imbedded about an inch or so beneath it. The dart head is curved so that the two rear points will face downward into the muscle when the tag is inserted. The tag is a spaghetti streamer with a capsule on the end. The capsule contains the following message, in English, Spanish, French, Norwegian and Japanese:

To assist biological research, kindly send this letter to address below, with species length and weight of

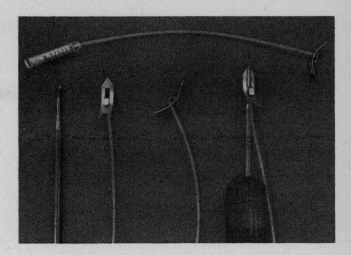

The dart tag has a plastic capsule with a number and instructions on the inside stating in five languages where to return it. The tag fits in a stainless needle that is imbedded in a wooden dowel.

fish and date, locality and method of capture. Please record number. Reward. Data on release of fish will be sent.

National Marine Fisheries Laboratory, Narragansett, Rhode Island 02882, U.S.A.

The dart tags fit in a special needle (supplied in a tagging kit), which is then mounted in a hardwood dowel 6 to 8 feet long. Rubber bands hold the tag in place. Each tag is attached to a card which must be filled in by the angler and mailed to the laboratory immediately after the capture.

Although the shark has survived so long in the same basic form, it is very fragile in some respects. Rough treatment can cause serious injury to a shark and this is more common with larger sharks. Sharks don't have air bladders and therefore most species must continue to swim at all times. Instead of the type of gills found on most fish, sharks have slits behind the head. On bony fish, gills open and close, forcing water with its oxygen through the mouth and past the gills. Sharks, on the other hand, have to keep swimming to force water through the gills and out the slits.

When you bring a shark alongside a boat for tagging, the operation should run smoothly. Long before the actual moment arrives, each person on board should be assigned a task. Those who are not involved in the actual tagging and release should be gathering the necessary biological data, but they should stay out of the way. Nothing is more dangerous than an inexperienced person trying to help without knowing what to do or how to do it. Tagging a large shark is a team effort and requires practice. The angler is in the poorest position to help, so the people who do

A long tagging stick makes it much easier to reach out and tag a fish before it becomes alarmed near the boat.

the tagging should be the most skilled (even if this means giving the rod to someone less experienced).

Placement of the tag is very important and overanxiousness is a major cause of missing the spot with the tagging stick. Another problem is caused if the tagging stick is too short to tag the fish while it is in a normal swimming position. When you grab the leader, the shark will twist and squirm, making tagging difficult if not impossible. Wait for the fish to settle down and assume its normal swimming position. Then drive the tag into the back of the fish near the first dorsal fin. You must hit the area to the side of the backbone and above the body cavity, and the dart must be inserted on an angle slanting toward the head of the fish so that the capsule will trail when the fish swims.

Tagging provides an opportunity to record accurate

Experienced shark taggers often try to tag the fish while it is swimming freely rather than to grab the leader first and have the shark twist and squirm.

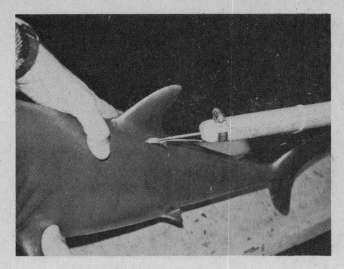

The tag should be placed on the side of the first dorsal fin of the shark on an angle toward the head so that the tag streams back.

This free-swimming blue shark with pilot fish has a tag trailing from the side of its dorsal fin.

information on the report card at the time the initial capture is made. During the heat of battle and the hectic time when the tag is being planted it is easy to overlook vital details or estimate the size of the fish incorrectly. Before the leader is cut and the fish let go, the team should agree on the size, the sex of the fish and the other details to be recorded.

Learning to identify the more common shark species is critical for a proper tagging job. Should you have doubts about the species, list the ones you think it might be. The first shark of a species to be caught should be studied carefully so that you will be able to identify the species when you see another example. Examine the shark in detail, following the identification procedure outlined in Casey's *Anglers' Guide to Sharks of the Northeastern United States*. Making a positive identification is not easy until you become familiar with the various species. You can then eliminate the species you know and recognize that this fish is different.

Shark fishing is gaining in popularity. Along the Northeast Coast, anglers chum with ground-up menhaden and an assortment of other goodies to lure sharks into the slick. Lines are baited with whole fish or large chunks of fish and held at a predetermined depth with a float, a piece of Styrofoam or even an inflated balloon.

Another form of shark fishing is equally exciting, although it may not yield fish as large as the offshore operations do. On shallow tropical flats, anglers are beginning to stalk sharks with fly rods, spinning tackle and plug-casting gear. The technique is to pole the

boat silently over the flats, drift with tide or current, or simply wait at a point where you know fish are going to pass. When you spot a shark, you must position the boat and make a cast so that the lure lands alongside the fish without alarming it. Sharks behave differently in shallow water from the way they do with plenty of depth under their bellies. In skinny water, a plug that lands too close will spook the fish and blow your chances. When the strike does occur, however, you won't experience sluggish performance. The shark will streak toward deeper water, throwing sand, mud and spray like a hydroplane that ran aground, and its speed will amaze you. Even if you are planning to chase bonefish, permit or tarpon, it pays to keep a rod rigged for sharks. When you see one, you're in business and you have a tough fight on your hands.

Whether or not the abundance of sharks continues along our coasts will depend on the pressures of both sport and commercial fishing, but without the efforts of men like John Casey who have devoted much of their lives to learning about sharks a successful management program would be inconceivable. A great deal of scientific fact must be collected before other countries of the world will be willing to cooperate, and that is exactly the direction in which John Casey has set out.

If you would like to participate in his tagging program, write him at National Marine Fisheries Service, Narragansett Laboratory, RR-7A, Box 522-A, Narragansett, Rhode Island 02882, U.S.A. Tell him Alex suggested that you write.

Bamboo:
The Rolls Royce of Rods
by Mario Riccardi

Keeping low and moving quietly, the angler crept slowly along the stream bank to a spot where he could study the glassy slick of water as it flowed smoothly along the weedy stream bed. There, motionless, he watched the water intently for telltale signs of feeding trout. A hatch of tiny, pale sulfur yellow duns had begun, and on the tippet of his finely tapered 12-foot leader he had tied a beautiful imitation of the insect, correct as to size and color.

Then his trained eyes saw them: four beautiful spotted browns that had taken up feeding stations from which they could intercept and devour the struggling little May flies as they drifted momentarily on the current.

The angler waited patiently until the fish began to tip up in a steady feeding rhythm. "Just about thirty feet and softly," he cautioned himself.

Carefully he rose, the delicate rod poised in his hand. Without apparent effort he worked out 20 feet of line, flicked one more backcast and made his presentation.

"That's it," he thought. "Slight hook to the right... ah, perfect!"

The fly landed softly, several feet in front of the nearest fish, drifted down on target, and suddenly was gone. A widening ring marked the spot.

The angler hesitated half a heartbeat, then gently cocked his wrist to the side and was instantly fast to the fish. The pulsing, tightly arched 2-ounce wand felt like a live thing in his hand.

Many minutes passed before the sensitive but unwavering pressure of the precisely tapered cane rod finally succeeded in sapping the great trout's strength. The angler lifted the rod above his head and drew the gasping brown over his waiting net.

For a moment or two he admired the fish, golden bellied with red spots on its flanks and white edges on its fins. Carefully removing the hook from where it was lodged in the corner of the trout's jaw he gently slid the fish from the net into the water. He held it upright facing the current until he felt its strength beginning to return, then let it slip away with a flick of its tail back into the depths of the pool.

Thousands of miles from this classic angling scene, there is a corner of the world where there are no trout streams or salmon rivers. In fact, the inhabitants have neither fished for nor even seen a trout or a salmon. Yet this small and distant piece of land, scarcely 25

The action in a bamboo rod enables an angler to pressure a heavy fish.

miles long, plays a vital role in the drama enacted daily on the greater and lesser trout and salmon waters of the world.

What special circumstance makes this relatively tiny spot of land so important in the world of angling, and where is this important place located?

The area is in the districts of Wai Tsap and Kwangning near the border between Kwangsi and Kwantung provinces, 75 to 100 miles northwest of the great city of Canton in the southern part of the People's Republic of China.

On the windswept hillsides of this region, a natural substance unique in all creation, the famous "Tonkin cane" *(Arundinaria Amabilis)* is cultivated.

This is the raw material from which the finest hand-crafted fly rods and many an angler's fondest dreams are made. This particular grass—bamboo is a grass, not a tree—contains straight, tough and highly elastic fibers that are perfect for the crafting of fly rods. It is also one of the curious mysteries of nature,

Landing a trout on a well-designed bamboo rod adds extra pleasure to angling.

for despite many attempts, Tonkin cane suitable for rod building has never been successfully cultivated on a commercial basis in any other place in the world.

To understand why this cane is so specially suited for rods requires a brief examination of its peculiar qualities.

Generally, trees which grow to significant heights increase in diameter at their base as they grow upward. This gives them sufficient strength to withstand the forces of wind and weather. Bamboos

Seasoned culms of first-quality Tonkin cane, the stuff an angler's dreams are made of.

however, grow to great heights without a commensurate increase in trunk diameter. Instead, they develop strong, highly resilient fibers. These fibers are therefore strongest and most highly developed at the base of the plant. In the skilled hands of the master rod maker, they become the "power fibers" which give the classic cane rod the great casting qualities that have made it a prized fishing instrument of anglers all over the world.

In this part of China, the constant prevailing winds combined with the favorable growing conditions have created an unique environment; this special ecosystem, for reasons still not understood, has been found nowhere else. Only from this one small corner of the globe does Tonkin cane attain the quality required for the finest bamboo fishing rods. Since the best part of the plant for rod making is the base or butt section, the finest cane rods are built from first quality butt-cut Tonkin cane.

Today, most fishing rods—including fly rods—are made from tubular fiberglass. In the past few years, rods fabricated from graphite (carbon) fibers, or from a combination of graphite and fiberglass, have gained increasing acceptance with anglers. Great progress has been achieved with these man-made fibers, and in fact most expert fly casters have shown a definite preference for glass or graphite rods for certain kinds of fishing.

In the United States, growing numbers of fly fishermen have turned to salt water species, such as tarpon, bonefish, striped bass, jacks, barracuda and even sailfish and marlin in their search for new angling challenges. Such fishing—often under windy conditions—requires the use of a rod that can effectively cast a number 9-, 10- or even 11- or 12-weight fly line. A bamboo rod capable of handling such heavy lines weighs about 7 ounces or more and usually must be a two-hand model. Glass rods weighing between 4⅞ and 6¾ ounces or graphite rods weighing even less are excellent for big game salt water fishing and do not require the angler to have the strength and stamina of an ancient Roman gladiator.

However, for the delicacy and finesse of fishing a 3-, 4- or 5-weight line with a long leader tapered to a spiderweb-like tip for casting a tiny midge fly to tempt wary trout in crystal clear water, many fly rod specialists still select a fine cane rod.

Undoubtedly tradition plays a part in this preference. The split cane rod was the chosen instrument of great names in fly fishing on all continents: England's Skues and Halford, America's Theodore Gordon, LaBranche and Hewitt. So too contemporary great anglers like Sawyer, the late Charles Ritz, Schwiebert,

Skilled hands machine a ferrule for mounting on a fine cane rod.

and the beloved American dean of the sport, Sparse Grey Hackle (alias Alfred Miller) all cherished their cane rods. In fact, Sparse Miller, who bridges the period between the age of the famous pioneers and our times, will not put his hand to anything but finely crafted cane when he goes trouting.

Throughout most of its history, the cane rod has essentially been "made by hand." Even today, with the introduction of precision beveling and milling machines and other powered tools, the building of a fine cane rod requires considerable skilled hand work. Rod-making skills must still be learned as an apprentice much as they were in the developmental years of the late 1860's and 1870's.

Deeply steeped in tradition and gaining the respect of anglers around the world, companies such as Pezon et Michel on the Continent and Hardy Brothers in England produced excellent rods. American rod builders originally emulated European builders, but eventually began to work in a slightly different direction.

Although Samuel Phillips of Pennsylvania is credited with making the first six-strip construction cane rod, in the history of the craft the name of Hiram L. Leonard is by far the best known. It was at the H. L. Leonard Rod Company, established in the 1870's in Bangor, Maine, that the school of famous American rod makers began. Great cane rod builders such as Edward Payne, Thomas, Hawes, Edwards and Chubb all served their apprenticeship under Hiram Leonard. The designs produced by Leonard and his successors have influenced the art of rod building right up to the present.

Methods and traditions established by these great rod builders continue to provide the basis for the work of the modern practitioners of the craft throughout the world. Although the advent of modern power machinery, improved adhesives and computer designed tapers has advanced the state of the art, the step-by-step process of building a six-strip rod from raw culms of Tonkin cane is still quite close to the original. The extraordinarily high prices brought by used classic rods in top condition that are sold in the

A master rod maker checks a section for straightness.

secondary market testify to the excellence of the craftsmanship of men like Ed Payne and his son Jim Payne, some of whose rods were built over 20 years or more ago.

Then as now, all individuals or companies making cane rods incorporate certain variations that they believe distinguishes their product from those of other makers. Some of these differences are controversial; each maker inevitably claims superior quality and construction as well as strength and casting dynamics.

Comparisons of the finished products are, however, largely subjective and a matter of the individual taste of the angler. This is to be expected: cane rods are made from a natural material that has individual variations from piece to piece. It is this natural variation that necessitates the handwork in the manufacture of a cane rod.

Because each culm of Tonkin cane has its own individual characteristics, the skilled hands of a master rod builder will always be required to compensate for these variations so that there will be a reasonable uniformity in the finished products. Each of the present day rod makers has standard models in his line of rods, and must be able to duplicate the model specifications as nearly as possible from rod to rod. Although no two rods of even the same model are exactly alike, few anglers, including the most experienced, can reliably detect the differences as far as casting and fishing are concerned.

The transition from a living fiber to a finished cane rod begins with the cultivation of the grass. When it is ready for cutting, the select first butt sections are used for the best rods. These sections, as culms, are seasoned and sorted before shipment. At the maker's factory, the culms are stored and subjected to further seasoning. Some makers remove a thin 1/4-inch strip running the length of the culm to allow for expansion, while others wait until a natural split develops and then open the culm along this line.

The outside nodes are smoothed down by filing and then either a half-culm or the whole culm (depending on the maker) is tempered by one of several heat processes. Some makers temper the cane at a much later point in the process, but the major makers prefer to do it at this stage. The dark color of some rods is due to the heat tempering, while lighter colored rods have much less heat treating. The tempering process is similar to that used in the making of tempered steel. Heating the fibers gives them greater elasticity and strength.

The old-timers simply used an open flame with an educated guess as to time and temperature. As man-

ufacturing know-how increased, more precise controls were introduced. Today heat tempering is precisely done with sophisticated equipment. Special automated ovens expose the culms to closely regulated temperatures for timed periods. There is some disagreement between makers as to how much tempering is desirable, but all agree that some is needed.

For the purpose of this article subsequent steps in the rod building process have been generalized, but where significant individual differences occur, these are pointed out. The treated culms are next split into smaller sections by one of several methods all of which require handwork, though some companies use power equipment. The sections are then prepared for further reduction into exact tapers by various rough sanding, filing or beveling operations. The tapering process was originally done by hand planing using Vee-shaped forms to develop the desired shape. Some individual rod builders with limited output still use the old planing-block method, but major producers use modern equipment.

By means of either a precision milling process or a closely controlled beveling device, the final taper is achieved. Tolerances in these operations are continually checked and are in the order of 1/1000 to 2/1000 of an inch.

Before the final tapering process, however, the rough sections must be matched in a particular way. The best quality canes have leaf nodes spaced 15 to 18 inches apart. In preparing the culm for rod building, these nodes are filed down to the level with the rest of the surface, thus making these spots weaker. In the

The rod maker checks the taper of a blank to tolerances of one to two 1/1000 inch.

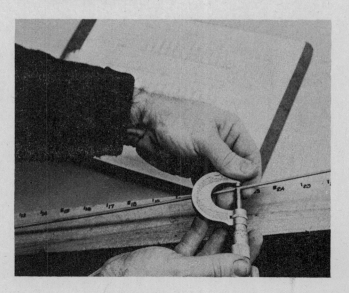

final assembly of the strips, these node points must be staggered so that not more than one occurs at any single spot along the length of the section. This process is called "mismatching."

Once the final taper has been completed—often with as many as a dozen separate inspections and measurements taken along the way—the strips (most of today's rods are six-strip construction) are joined in a bonding process. The type of adhesive varies among makers, but the modern rod has benefited greatly from the development of new adhesives such as thermo-bonding types that cure and create a stronger and stronger bond upon the application of heat. (Old-time makers generally used an animal glue that tended to soften with heat.)

After a day of fishing and casting in the hot sun, the fly fisher of yesterday had to straighten his cane rod over a small alcohol lamp to remove the set which developed during the day's use. Thanks to the use of much improved bonding agents, the modern cane rod does not have this same setting tendency.

After the adhesive agent is applied, usually by dipping, the bundle of sections is bound together by a pressure gluing machine which wraps the bundle spirally with thread or strong cord, under heavy tension. A number of different machines have been designed to do this, but the results are all quite similar.

A lot of handwork is involved in the gluing and binding process because it is not easily adaptable to automation. While the glue is still wet, the bound sections are rolled and straightened, and then the bundles are set aside at a controlled temperature for curing.

When the process is finished, the binding threads and excess glue are scraped off the "blanks," as the bonded bundles may now be called, (another hand process), and the blanks are checked and further straightened if necessary. A fine sanding is next performed to remove the thin outer husk and expose the power fibers and true grain of the cane. Such careful hand finishing requires great skill and constant micrometer checks to achieve the final taper specifications.

If the rod is to be impregnated with a special plastic or resin as many quality cane rods are, this is done now. Impregnation can take up to seven days, after which the sections undergo a final light sanding (to remove excess impregnation material), and then a buffing. The final assembly and finishing of the rod itself includes the installation of the grip (usually made from individual cork rings), reel seat, ferrules and guides. Non-impregnated rods are varnished as part of the final assembly. As many as five coats of varnish are used on the windings which hold the guides to the blank.

All of this is essentially handwork. The better makers construct their own reel seats from raw materials and manufacture their own hardware such as ferrules and butt caps, and other hardware.

Some of these components are of unique design, and certain makers are distinguished by their work. The final step is the application of details and finishing touches such as hand lettering, or application of the intended owner's name, if desired.

Each of the leading rod makers has developed a

Guide windings receive up to five coats of varnish.

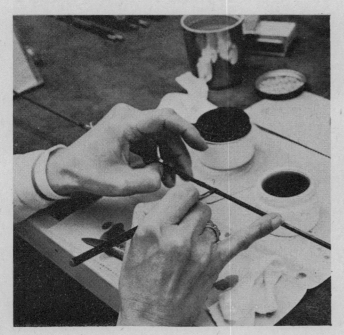

The components and the finished custom reel seat.

Shaping a cork grip.

series of tapers and designs to build a line of rods offering different actions and lengths for use in various angling situations. Some also offer custom rod building and will design and construct a special rod to the buyer's specifications. Prices for today's cane rods can run from $125 for a two-piece single tip model to as much as $500 or more for a custom-built rod. An average range for standard top-of-the-line models is $200 to $350 for a two-piece rod with extra tip.

Previously owned classic rods by certain famous makers, such as the American rod maker Payne, today command prices in the $450 to $800 dollar range for a rod in like-new condition.

So long as there are anglers who enjoy the aesthetic qualities as well as the fine fishability of rods made mostly by hand from natural cane fiber, there will be a market for the Tonkin cane rod. Like the appreciation of fine natural leather, hand loomed woolens, hand-made wooden furniture and hand-woven silks, the appreciation of a fine hand-built cane rod represents a standard in which value is placed on design and craftsmanship.

Finished cane fly and spinning rods receive final inspection.

There may be, now or in the future, rods mass-produced from synthetic materials that will cast and fish as well as a cane rod, but these will never give the aesthetically inclined angler the same feeling that he gets from the product of months of hand work and years of skill-learning apprenticeship. The fine cane rod will always have a place wherever skilled anglers practice their art in pursuit of trout and salmon.

Fishermen, Knots and Stresses
by Paul C. Johnson

When a fisherman ties a knot he is literally putting his skill on the line.

Most fishermen are aware that putting a knot in nylon monofilament weakens the line. How much it is weakened depends upon the type of knot and the way it is tied.

Some knots—the simple overhand loop is an example—are "cutting knots" which can reduce a line's break strength by more than 50 percent. For reasons not understood, other knots may lower line break strengths only a few percent. But to determine whether a knot has been tied properly is a problem.

If you analyze your own fishing habits, you will realize that you tie your favorite knot at least a dozen times in a single day. You tie it carefully and apply limited tension to test it before you continue fishing. You have undoubtedly noticed that some of your knots are strong and others mysteriously fail. Maybe you blame the line, the type of knot, or your technique. Did you ever consider that the cause might be a combination of all three factors?

Knot Science

As a fishing scientist, I have asked myself hundreds of questions about knots in nylon monofilament. Most fishermen ask themselves how they can learn to tie stronger knots; or what happens "inside" the knot; or whether some knots are really better than others and, if so, why. In this advanced scientific age, surely we should be able to tell a strong knot from a weak one before putting it to the fishing test.

So far, no textbooks have been written on the science of knots. The best book available is *Practical Fishing Knots* by Lefty Kreh and Mark Sosin, New York: Crown/Stoeger, 1975.

Fiber physicists are only beginning to gather data on textile fibers. It may be years before fishermen will get scientific answers to their questions. Meanwhile, their only guides are folklore, personal preferences and advertising gimmicks.

Today, however, fishermen are beginning to ask for facts. My job as one of a team of scientists is now to focus scientific tools and methods on answering questions related to sportfishing. Of all the areas studied, the "unscience" of fishing knots has proved the toughest. Part of the difficulty is in formulating the questions. For example, can any two fishermen tie the same knot, using the same mono, and achieve the same results? The first step toward answering this is to define the word "same."

Most fishermen have been led to believe that if they tie a knot carefully, after long practice they can expect to achieve reasonably uniform results.

Recently, I had an unusual opportunity to test the validity of this belief. Ten of the nation's top sportfishing experts visited the laboratories in which I work. All these experienced fishermen were skilled in tying a variety of knots.

I gave each a length of nylon mono from the same bulk spool and five medium-sized chromed swivels. Each was asked to join a swivel to a short section of mono by tying his best knot on five different samples. I watched as each carefully and methodically tied his own favorite knot. Each obviously was taking pains to tie better knots than his peers did.

The break-strength results were surprising—and controversial. Knot strengths varied as much as 50 percent between one tester and another. No two testers had comparable results. The testers were even more amazed when they saw the variation in test—as much as two times—among their five samples.

From the wide scattering of data it was impossible to state conclusively which tester had tied the best knot. Nor was it possible to decide which knot was the best. The heated discussions among the testers are probably still going on.

A fisherman might be disappointed with such a test. A scientist tries to identify the causes. Possible explanations include lack of uniformity within the nylon, variations in knot quality, insufficient numbers of samples, but also the human factor. No two people tie a knot exactly the same way.

Testing under Stress

How can you tell whether you have tied a really strong knot? You put load on the line and apply stress to the knot. If the line breaks easily, the knot is no good. If the line is difficult to break and the rupture occurs outside the knot, the knot is a good one.

Unfortunately, this is a go-no go type of destructive testing. You never really know whether it was a good knot until after you have destroyed it. Is there a way of telling that you have tied a good, strong knot without having to break it? And if there is, can it be related to the knot-tying method?

One place to begin is to study what happens when tensile stress is applied to a loosely tied knot. A logical starting point is a "bad" knot, such as the overhand cutting loop.

For these studies I used a binocular microscope set on low power (15x), an Instron tensile tester for applying load at a uniform rate of 10 inches pull per minute, and .030-inch diameter mono which had been only partially drawn during the manufacturing process. I chose partially drawn nylon because it retains a high amount of stretch that would "neck down" in diameter at the spots where maximum stress first appeared within the knot.

Load was slowly applied while observing knot behavior under the binocular microscope. At the first sign of mono neckdown, tensile load was cut off. After observing many samples of the overhand loop knot, I noticed that neckdown normally appeared first within the crossover points of the loop and then instantly spread beyond as the smaller-diameter mono slipped out beyond the knot zone. The bend radius of the mono became progressively smaller as further stress was applied and rupture within the loop eventually followed.

It certainly appeared that stress concentration points were created within the loop at each point where the mono crossed over itself. With the overhand knot there are two crossover sites. Slippage also occurred, but exactly what role it played within the knot could not be determined. Could it be that failure to localize stress caused premature breakage? Maybe "good" fishing knots could provide more information.

Trying to select a "good" fishing knot is like trying to pick a winner at a horse race. What value should be attached to looks, name and reputation? There must be more than a thousand different recorded fishing knots, each of which has been claimed to have fantastic qualities. Rather than engage in a stone-throwing contest, I decided to test three of the more commonly used and described knots: the improved clinch, the Palomar and the Crawford figure 8.

As you study these knots you will note that each has a distinctively different construction. On the improved clinch the line crossover points number seven or more, depending upon whether you tie a single strand or a double strand. To minimize complexity, I used the single-strand improved clinch. In contrast to the latter, the Palomar contains four crossover points and is remarkably similar to our villain, the overhand loop. The Crawford figure 8 contains six crossover points. In appearance it is more of a "jam knot" or so-called strangulation knot.

Each of the three "good knots" was tied very loosely, using premium quality 10-pound test nylon mono. Again, stress was slowly applied while observing effects under the binocular microscope. It was evident that something different was happening on these knots as compared to the overhand loop knots tested.

DOUBLE IMPROVED CLINCH KNOT

FIG. 1: Double 6 or 8 inches of your line and pass looped end half way through eye.

FIG. 2: Twist looped end 4 to 6 turns around main line (the easiest method is to hold both ends of line between thumb and index finger of one hand and roll hook shaft between thumb and finger of the other hand).

FIG. 3: Pass looped end of line through loop which hook is strung… then back up through big loop spanning knot.

FIG. 4: Pull up knot slowly until tight. Then trim both looped end near hook and single end at top of knot near main line.

THE PALOMAR KNOT

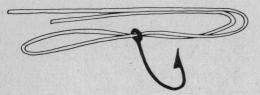

FIG. 1: Loop 3 or 4 inches of line end and pass loop through hook eye—short end must not pass through eye.

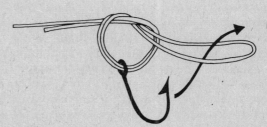

FIG. 2: Holding line and hook eye between thumb and finger, grasp loop with free hand and thread an overhand knot.

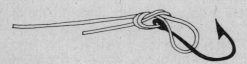

FIG. 3: Pass hook through loop and draw line while guiding loop over top of hook eye.

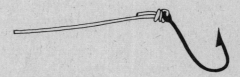

FIG. 4: Pull short end of line to tighten knot snuggly and trim short end to about 1/8″ to 1/4″.

CRAWFORD FIGURE 8 KNOT

FIG. 1: Pass line through eye and form loop.

FIG. 2: Cross over and form first portion of figure 8.

FIG. 3: Cross line over front completing figure 8.

FIG. 4: Pass line back through loop to secure knot. Draw tight.

Slippage and mono deformation within these more complex knots were occurring much faster, and stress propagation was more difficult to follow. What I really needed was "stop action" or, better yet, "instant replay" capability on the microscope.

Taking a high-speed photograph through a laboratory microscope is possible but because of the shallowness of field you get blurry pictures. A far better approach was to use the scanning electron microscope (SEM). Photographs taken through this at low magnification have a fantastic depth of field. But to use this tool I had to apply stress to a series of knots, stopping at a progressively higher tensile stress with each. With care, I could cut off the stress load the instant before rupture occurred.

As with a knotted rubber band, some relaxation of stress within the knots did occur. External change, viewed through the binocular microscope, appeared to be minimal. The SEM photographs show the progressive effects of stress with extraordinary fidelity.

As each knot is drawn tight, a surprising amount of stretch and slippage occurs within the knot zone. As further stress is applied, the circular mono is distorted.

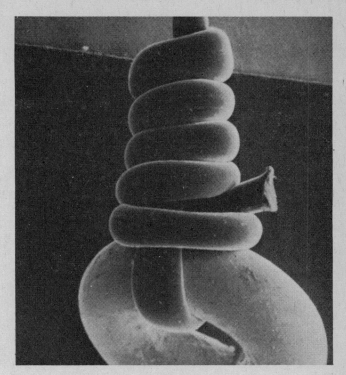

Improved clinch with 10-pound stress applied (SEM photo 20x).

Improved clinch barely tightened (scanning electron microscope (SEM) 20x enlargement).

Improved clinch with 14-pound stress applied (SEM photo 20x).

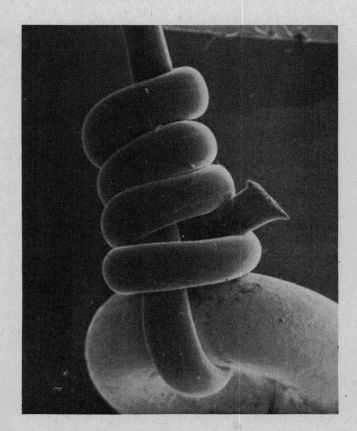

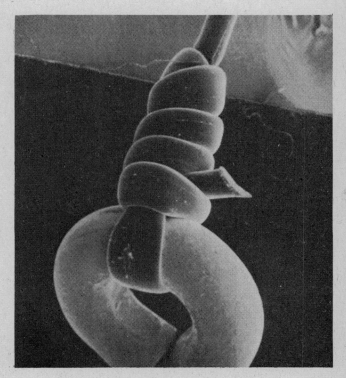

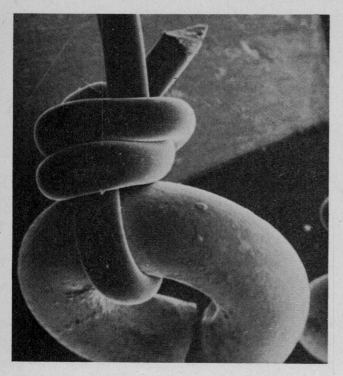

Crawford figure 8 barely tightened (SEM photo 20x).

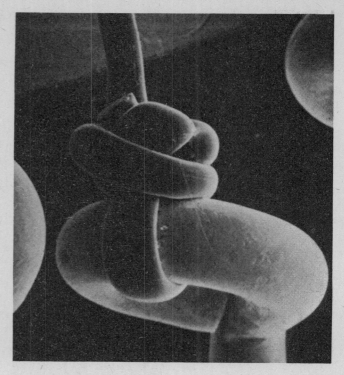

Crawford figure 8 with 10-pound stress applied (SEM photo 20x).

Palomar barely tightened (SEM photo 20x).

Palomar with 10-pound stress applied (SEM photo 20x).

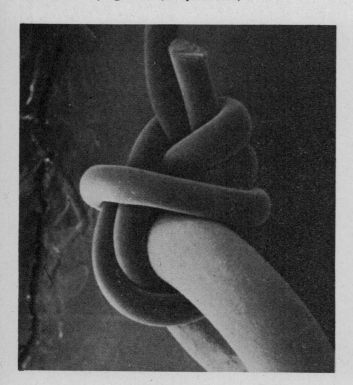

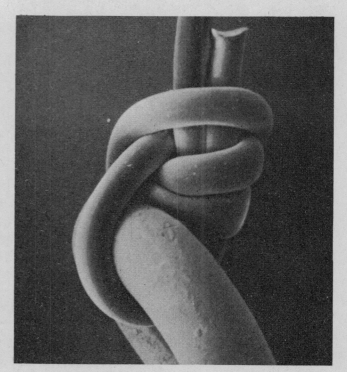

Palomar with 14-pound stress applied (SEM photo 20x).

Bend radii become smaller at each crossover site as the mono attempts to equalize stress concentration points. An instant before the stress reaches peak strength, additional slippage—estimated at a few thousandths of an inch—occurs. If you clip the tag end of a knot too close, you will discover the effect of this slippage.

At maximum stress the knot is grossly deformed and assumes a very tight, compact shape. The bend radius sites suggest that the mono is approaching its elastic limit. With the stronger knots, rupture occurred just beyond the knot in the short portion of mono that slipped outside.

Knot Slippage

It was not possible to measure accurately the precise amount of slippage and deformation that was occurring within these three different knots. The SEM photos showed what was happening on the surface of the knot, but I could only speculate on what might be happening inside.

Slippage might be related to the mono's surface and surface lubricity. It is common practice for manufacturers of synthetic fibers to apply organic chemical surface finishes to their products. In addition, fishermen commonly wet the mono in their mouths before

drawing up the knot. The object of both processes is to cut down friction, improve slip and minimize frictional heat build-up during the tightening operation. Does the finish or the saliva really help?

To try to answer that question I designed a series of tests using a bulk spool of premium 10-pound test mono. This particular mono is known to have high uniformity both of diameter and of physical properties.

Using the same three knots (that is, the single-strand improved clinch, the Palomar and the Crawford figure 8), I conducted five tests, breaking ten samples of each knot.

Test 1. Dry mono, knot tied loosely and slowly drawn tight to rupture on Instron tester

Test 2. Saliva-moistened knot, tied loosely and Instron-tightened to rupture

Test 3. Loose knot sprayed with silicone and drawn to rupture

Test 4. Mono coated with beeswax, loosely tied, and drawn to rupture

Test 5. Loose knot coated with a drop of Eastman 910 (an organic pressure curing adhesive), then drawn to rupture

The results of these five tests are summarized in Table 1.

Table 1 Average Break Strengths in Pounds of Ten Samples Tested (Unknotted control samples had an average break strength of 13.0 pounds.)					
Type of Knot	**Test 1 (dry)**	**Test 2 (wet)**	**Test 3 (silicone)**	**Test 4 (beeswax)**	**Test 5 (adhesive)**
Improved clinch (single strand)	9.0	6.2	10.6	9.2	9.0
Palomar	11.6	9.0	10.0	10.4	11.4
Crawford figure 8	9.2	10.5	11.1	9.8	9.5

From this limited data several hypotheses could be formulated:

- The improved clinch appeared to be the weakest knot and the Palomar the strongest.
- Wetting the knot appeared to weaken both the improved clinch and the Palomar but to strengthen the Crawford figure 8 slightly.
- Adding silicone helped the improved clinch and Crawford figure 8 marginally but appeared to weaken the Palomar.
- Neither beeswax nor Eastman 910 adhesive added any appreciable knot strength.

While these tests are far from conclusive, they do suggest that any attempt to increase or decrease internal knot slippage yielded unpredicable results. This area will require much more intensive study. In the meantime, the fisherman should be skeptical about applying any chemicals to his line in an attempt to improve knot strength. Wetting the knot with saliva produced mystifying results. Further examination of the reliability curves suggested only that saliva-moistened knots tended to break quite uniformly—that is, even the poor knots were consistently poor.

Knot Reliability

When you begin to compare hundreds of knot break strengths on nylon monos, you are confronted with a confusing mass of data. One fact, however, is obvious: knot strengths are far from being uniform or reproducible. The traditional approach has been to cite average knot strengths, but these tell nothing about reproducibility or reliability, which are what fishermen really need to know about.

Remember the old adage about "averages": a fellow with his feet in the oven and his head in the freezer *on the average* feels O.K. Average knot strengths are important, it's true, but reproducibility may be even more critical.

No statistical approach to the reliability of fishing knots has been reported. In fact, virtually nothing is known to help explain what may be inherent variations between one style of fishing knot and another. While some knots are far more complex and more difficult to tie than others, does this make them better? Could the most reliable knot actually be the one that is the least complex and the easiest to tie?

To answer these questions I devised a series of tests which became known later as "The Great Knot Tying Experiment." Rather than eliminate the human factor I decided to expand it. The test methodology consisted of finding 10 fishermen volunteers and asking each to tie 10 samples of each of the three knots already discussed. All testers would use mono from the same bulk spool of 10-pound labeled premium line. All would tie their knots against chrome-plated, medium-sized swivels. Thus, 100 samples of each knot reflecting the combined skills of 10 different fishermen, would be available.

Finding the volunteers was no problem. As with the earlier testers, competitiveness and cooperation were combined; each tester wanted to outperform the others. To serve as control samples, 10 pieces of mono were taken from each tester's spool and measured for unknotted break strength.

The results of the Great Knot Tying Experiment are presented in tabular form in Table 2 and pictorially in graphs I to III.

Table 2 The Great Knot-Tying Experiment (A total of 100 knotted samples, 10 samples tied by each of 10 fishermen, were tested. The unknotted control had an average break strength of 13.6 pounds based on 100 tested samples with a minimum of 12.2 pounds and a maximum of 14.9.)				
Type	Average break strength (pounds)	Range (pounds) Min	Max	Percentage of unknotted control
Improved clinch (single-strand)	9.6	5.8	13.5	71.6
Crawford figure 8	10.1	5.3	13.6	75.4
Palomar	11.5	7.9	13.8	86.4

The graphs best illustrate the variations in knot strength. Statisticians call these "distribution curves," but for our purposes we can consider them "knot reliability" curves.

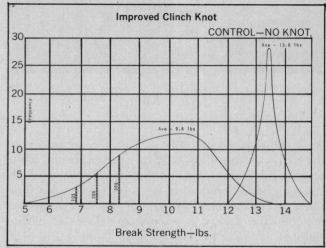

I. Reliability curve for the improved clinch knot

II. Reliability curve for the Crawford figure 8 knot

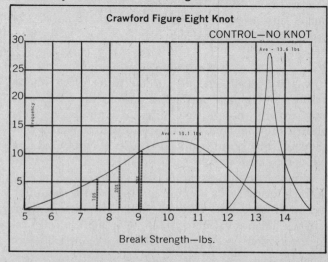

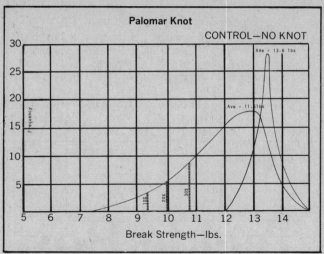

Palomar Knot

CONTROL—NO KNOT

Ave - 13.6 lbs

Ave - 11.5 lbs

Frequency

Break Strength—lbs.

III. Reliability curve for the Palomar knot

Each graph consists of two curves: a reliability curve for the unknotted control and a curve for the knotted test samples. Along the left-hand side of the test curve are dotted vertical lines labeled 10, 20 and 30 percent. These show the percentage of samples having break strengths equal to or less than the corresponding break strength shown on the bottom horizontal line.

Compare the shape of the reliability curves for the single-strand improved clinch and the Crawford figure 8. They are amazingly similar. There is only a slight difference in the average break strengths (9.6 pounds and 10.1 pounds, respectively), but comparison of the reliability percentages shows the Crawford figure 8 to be appreciably better.

Next, compare the reliability curve of the single-strand improved clinch to that for the Palomar. Not only the averages but also the shape of the curves are different. The Palomar curve is shifted far to the right (that's good); it has a narrower distribution with a sharper peak (that's better); and the knot is much more reproducible (that's terrific).

Clearly, in this series of tests with this particular mono, the Palomar knots were stronger, more uniform, more reliable. This may be because it is a completely different knot. Fishermen tying it for the first time often say that it is a simpler knot and easier to tie. Scientists may in time find other reasons but, for now, I am inclined to believe that the human factor will ultimately prove to be the most important element in the science of fishing knots.

Future Knots

Applying scientific tools and logic to fishing knots is confusing. For each answer found, a hundred new questions are raised.

My work continues. Each series of studies adds more understanding. Soon we may be able to analyze and predict knot strengths for existing designs. From there it is only a short step forward to devising new knots that have greater reliability, do not weaken the line and can be easily tied by fishermen.

The Offshore Tackle Box
by Dick Kondak

Concepts in tackle boxes are changing. There was a time not very long ago when the trend was toward massive satchels with a labyrinth of drawers and compartments and enough room to house half a tackle shop. For some types of fishing, this approach is valid. On the marine scene, carrying an impressive array of tackle may be ego-building and establish your status, but it also courts the destructive tendencies of salt water.

A modular system of relatively small specialty boxes not only protects your gear from the corrosive elements but allows you to get at the necessary equipment quickly without having to rummage through extraneous items. Rolling decks often tumble tackle boxes unceremoniously, spilling the contents everywhere just at a time when speed is vital.

Each specialty box should be labeled with a Dymo labeler or felt-tip marker as to its function, and, if you enjoy some basic tinkering, you can glue strips of Velcro on the top and bottom of each modular box. That way, the boxes can be stacked together and only separated when needed.

Each box should be a self-contained unit that harbors all of the necessary tackle for a particular type of fishing. My offshore bait-rigging box, for example, is equipped with an extra pair of Sargent fishing pliers and an extra knife. When the action is torrid, I don't have to look for these items in other boxes; it's all right there.

Depending on where you are fishing, you can keep a back-up stock of extra gear at home, in your car or in the lodge or hotel room if you are away on a trip. The modular box could then be replenished at the end of each day and brought up to capacity for the next day's sport. If you travel, you can pack your tackle in bulk and then break it down at your destination.

Although many offshore items are made of stainless steel, not everything is corrosionproof and a bit of precaution can prevent vital items from becoming rusty or failing to function because of the elements. Hooks and wire leader will often rust, while the bearings in some of the swivels will fail to turn efficiently because of corrosion. There are several solutions. One that has worked well for me is simply to pour a little talcum powder or cornstarch over everything in the box. This helps to absorb moisture and prevent damage. Silica gel is another agent that will remove moisture; it can be purchased in a camera

The small modular offshore tackle box contains all the necessary items for rigging bait and for trolling artificials short on flat lines.

Bait-rigging items should be kept together in one box. Among the gear, in addition to hooks, wire, sinkers, plastic skirts and floats (for squid), would be needles, a knife, pliers and soft wire. The file is for sharpening hooks.

shop or a pharmacy. That is the chemical that is packed with new cameras to eliminate moisture.

In establishing an offshore tackle box for rigging baits or dragging some trolling feathers, there is a general plan to be followed and a few specifics to tailor it to your part of the fishing world. Although baits vary from area to area, you should be prepared to handle balao, mullet, flying fish, squid, eels, mackerel and similar species. Since you may use any class of tackle from the newer 6 pound to 130 pound, you will need a variety of hook sizes and a few different styles.

For openers, you should have an assortment of sizes

The size and style of hooks are important and there should be enough variety to match any bait or class of tackle. Swivels should always be top quality.

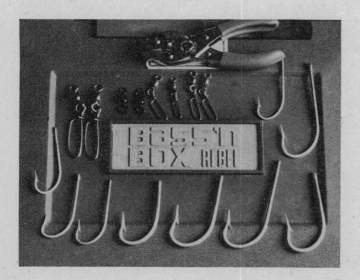

of Mustad's 3412, 3412A, and 3412C. The smallest I use is 4/0 and I would include 6/0, 7/0, 8/0, on up to 12/0 for big baits and heavy tackle. The 3412 is a forged needle-eye hook that is cadmium-plated and tinned. The 3412A is the same hook except that it is 2 extra strong. The 3412C is 2 extra strong, but it also has an extra short shank. These are O'Shaughnessy style hooks and the needle-eye is important for most bait rigging because it will slip inside the bait easily without tearing it. A ringed-eye hook will often rip the bait as it is pulled through.

When you rig a mullet or squid, however, the ringed-eye is important because it allows you to anchor the hook with wire through the ring and prevent it from sliding or turning. The Mustad 3407 is also an O'Shaughnessy style that is forged and has a ringed-eye. It's my first choice for this assignment. If the price factor is important, the 3407 is less expensive than the 3412.

Another hook that I carry for specialty applications such as tuna fishing is the Mustad-Sea Demon 7731A. This is a forged needle-eye hook that is cadmium plated. For live bait, such as blue runners, mackerel and even snapper blues, I prefer the Eagle Claw 318N because it has good hooking qualities, is lightweight and won't impede the action of the bait, and it can also be used with Jap feathers as a small trolling hook.

Whenever possible, I avoid using stainless-steel hooks, because the strength is not uniform and some will straighten out under pressure. There are different grades of stainless and, in spite of what hook manufacturers may claim, my experiences on the water

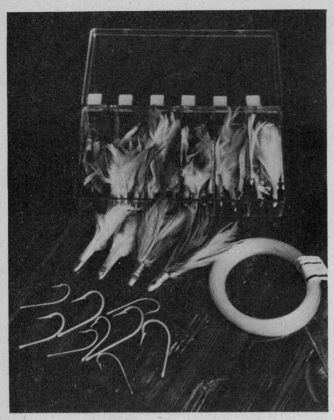

A small box of feathers with matching hooks makes it easy to rig these lures.

when I'm towing the Hawaiian type of lure that moves rapidly through the water with a lot of action. In a half-hour, the force of the water and the zigzagging of the lure will slice through mono, or kink and break single-strand wire. Cable can also be used on huge sharks or marlin of the size that many of us dream of catching.

For most of the daily work, however, the choice comes down to monofilament or wire. In my judgment, the weight of the wire has an effect on trolling a skip bait or swimming bait, giving you a better and more direct pull because the wire lies down properly. Mono can get gummed up with surface algae, and it is questionable which is more visible or invisible. There's security in single-strand wire.

With a Haywire Twist, wire can be quickly attached to hook or swivel. If it kinks or shows signs of wear, you can retie wire using only a few inches. The International Game Fish Association (IGFA) specifies leader lengths and for tackle up to and including 50-pound class you are limited to 15 feet of leader and 15 feet of double line. Both the double line and the leader can be 30 feet for tackle heavier than 50-pound class. On a standard-sized offshore boat, handling that much leader is no problem, but it can create a crisis on

There isn't much space on center-console boats, so it's important to keep the tackle organized and handy. Shorter wire leaders on the rigs are easier to handle on craft of this size.

have not necessarily matched the advertising copy. Some anglers who use light tackle exclusively argue that hook strength isn't very important with light lines, but then there is always the situation when someone grabs the leader and tries to snub a rampaging fish. The leader, of course, is much stronger than the line and that's where pressure can take its toll.

While we're on the subject of hooks, the most critical aspect is matching the right size and style of hook to the tackle you are using. It is difficult (if not impossible) to set a big hook with a light rod and matching line. You just can't drive the barb home. That's why it is important to pick hook sizes in relation to your tackle. The size of hook should also match the size of the bait. A big bait with a tiny hook can be a problem and the opposite combination is equally bad.

Leaders are more important than most fishermen suspect. The complete tackle box will be stocked with monofilament, wire and 49-strand cable in various sizes. Which type you use is a matter of personal preference, but my own experiences dictate wire for most situations. The only time I resort to cable is some of the smaller center-console models that have become so popular in recent years.

One way of getting around this is to use 3 or 4 feet of wire leader and then monofilament. Using a combination of knots that will pass through the guides, you can also reel the fish closer to the boat and not have to worry about leader coiled on deck if the fish should surge suddenly during the landing procedure.

Some veteran anglers prefer carbon-steel piano wire for leader material to the very popular stainless steel. The carbon steel is stronger for a given diameter, but it will rust and must be cared for. One difference of opinion is in whether to use coffee-colored wire or the bright variety. That's an argument that I choose to pass up.

Your box should contain wire in a variety of sizes. For most fishing, you will use Nos. 7, 8 or 9, and you should have some No. 12 wire on hand for big marlin or husky sharks. However, there are times when you have to go light (No. 4 or No. 5) and it pays to have some on hand. A typical example is with tuna. Even the big bluefins can be finicky feeders and seem leader shy. Sometimes, by using a very light wire such as No. 4, you'll begin to get strikes when the fish has passed up the same lure trolled with No. 6 wire.

Tuna, by the way, prefer a lure that does not swing erratically from side to side. They are not built to swerve quickly and will miss their target if it weaves. Wire instead of monofilament helps to dampen the action of a feather or cedar plug and should almost always be used for tuna.

A number of boat owners are ready to cut corners and costs when it comes to choosing a swivel. For some reason, they succumb to false economy, and, although they are spending a king's ransom to pursue the offshore sport, they are willing to take a chance on a vital piece of terminal tackle that is less than the best. There is no substitute for good-quality ball-bearing swivels. For bait rigging, you should have an assortment of black barrel swivels. There are no alternatives

The right combination of terminal tackle helped the author hook this tuna on a day when the fish were particularly finicky.

Trolling sinkers, egg sinkers for bait rigging and rubber-core sinkers to separate daisy-chained artificials are musts.

if you want to be rigged properly. A cheap swivel that breaks just as a mate reaches for the leader can be an extremely expensive item of tackle when it comes to measuring pleasure and performance.

No trolling box is complete without an assortment of egg sinkers for rigging baits, rubber-core sinkers to use as stops with feathers and artificial squids and standard tapered trolling sinkers to get a bait or lure down. The egg sinkers are used primarily as chin weights with a mullet or other fish and you should carry an assortment of sizes from 1/2 ounce to 3 ounces. You can always combine a pair of these sinkers to get the right weight.

Trolling weights should be carried in 2-, 4-, 6- and 8-ounce sizes. You can also use these in combination to get the desired weight. In my experience, I shun sinkers that are already rigged with bead chain, because the bead chain may break if subjected to a sharp angle. It's better to wire directly to an eye on the sinker and then use your own snap on the other end. Otherwise, if the sinker hits the boat when a fish is trying to dart beneath the hull, it could break the bead chain.

Keel sinkers are favored by some to prevent line twist with certain lures, such as spoons and some of the new surgical tubing lures. However, a good-quality ball-bearing swivel does more to prevent line twist than a keel sinker. Rubber-core sinkers are used when you daisy-chain squid, cuddlefish, feathers and other artificial lures. The rubber cores can be clamped to the leader and they will prevent the lures from moving below that spot while adding a bit of weight to keep the daisy chain skipping on the wave tops.

For the actual bait rigging, you will need a pair of needles (one 4 inch and one 8 inch), a deboner or two (depending on the size baits you use), soft balao wire, and either unwaxed dental floss, dental ribbon or cotton bait-rigging thread. If you intend to rig squids to swim on top, you will probably want some tiny floats (no larger than 1/2 inch in diameter).

A short paring knife with a 3-inch blade is ideal for bait rigging and both safer and more practical on a moving boat than longer knives. With the smaller blade, you can puncture the belly of a bait fish, cut thread or do other tasks with ease.

You'll also need a good whetstone to keep the knife sharp, a pair of Sargent fishing pliers and a file such as the Red Devil Wooodscrapers No. 15 for sharpening hooks. No hook should ever be put in the water without being triangulated and sharpened. This should be done before you rig baits and its importance should not be overlooked.

Mixing straws (used in any bar) can easily be cut to any length and used as a spacer on the leader. They can be put between the hook and egg sinker in a squid to keep the squid from sliding down the leader.

Before attaching a swivel or twisting a loop in the other end of the leader, you can slide a vinyl tail or skirt over the bait. The skirt keeps water from entering the mouth of the bait, which makes the bait last longer when being trolled. It also helps to reduce weeds and other debris on the bait. Also a skirt adds something different to interest a fish and makes it

When the action comes fast, it pays to have as much tackle as possible rigged in advance.

Every offshore tackle box should carry an assortment of artificials.

Trolling a properly rigged bait is the key to any successful fishing expedition.

easier for you to see and read your baits. Most skirts are brightly hued and easy to see. It's important to know where each bait is all the time, and fluorescent colors certainly improve visibility.

Small artificials trolled in the wake of a boat often account for a mixed bag, but there are some days when they are the ticket for the primary game species you seek. I make sure that I have a good selection of feathers, feather jigs, vinyl baits and bucktails in sizes ranging from 1/8 ounce through 1/4, 3/8, 1/2 up to 1 ounce. In some localities, you may want to carry lures as heavy as 3 ounces. Basic colors are red and white, black and white, and green and yellow, with red and white the hands-down favorite.

Rather than troll one large feather, I often slide three smaller feathers on to the leader so that they dovetail. This provides a different silhouette and I believe it is much more effective under most circumstances than a single feather. You also have the option of mixing colors when you rig three together. The first and third can be red and white and the center black and white, for example. It is surprising how often a fish, such as a tuna, will specialize on 2-inch prey and ignore larger offerings. Feathers, in these situations, are the answer.

Squid is the universal bait. It is found in all the waters of the world, and fish seem to recognize it as a steak dinner for them. In fact, a 10-pound fish will consume a 1-pound squid and a 100-pound fish will feast on the same bait. Yet the 10-pounder may reject an 8-inch mullet as being too large.

Because of the abundance of squid and the fact that fish prefer them, it makes sense to carry a supply of artificial squids in a variety of sizes. If you have 4-, 6-, 9- and 12-inch squids, you'll hedge all bets. They can be rigged singly or in tandem.

Finally, you should carry an assortment of trolling spoons in your box. The Drone spoon is good for slow-speed trolling and a size 3½ is about average. My favorite, however, is the Clark spoon, because it works at high speeds as well and it produces fish. These spoons are available from size 00 to size 6. Don't overlook the small ones. They are a perfect imitation of rainfish or glass minnows, and that is sometimes what the fish want. If you troll spoons, you may want to drag the smaller ones in a tight grouping to make it easier for a big fish to spot them.

In addition to the basic offshore tackle box, you can design modular tackle cases for inshore trolling lures. How many different boxes you have and what they should contain will depend on where you fish. It makes sense to put as much gear as possible for one type of fishing in a single box. Then when you stow the box aboard, you know that you are completely equipped for that species. (Remember that it is bad business to "borrow" from a box without replacing.) The alternative is to find yourself out on the water with an incomplete tackle box; that is pure frustration when you think of what you left at home.

Angling Classics

Going Home
by William Cowper Prime

THE SUN HAS GONE DOWN. The stars are beginning to be visible. The breeze has died away, and there is no ripple on the lake, nor any sound in the tree-tops. Let us go home.

The contentment which fills the mind of the angler at the close of his day's sport is one of the chiefest charms in his life. He is just sufficiently wearied in body to be thoughtful, and the weariness is without nervousness, so that thoughts succeed each other with deliberation and calm, not in haste and confusion. The evening talk after a day of fishing is apt to be memorable. The quiet thinking on the way home is apt to be pleasant, delicious, sometimes even sacred.

I am not sure but that many anglers remember with more distinctness and delight their going home after days of sport than the sport itself. Certainly the strongest impressions on my own mind are of the last casts in the twilight, the counting of the day's results on the bank of lake or river, the homeward walk or ride, and, best of all, the welcome home. For the sportsman's home is where his heart is; and most earnestly do I recommend all lovers of the rod to find their sport, if they can do so, where they can be accompanied by wives and daughters, even by children. On this account, if on no other, every one must be glad to see the formation of clubs whose arrangements include accommodation for the families of members.

There is no more graceful and healthful accomplishment for a lady than fly-fishing, and there is no reason why a lady should not in every respect rival a gentleman in the gentle art.

Shall I ever forget a day along one of the Connecticut streams, of which I have spoken in this volume, when four of us—a lady, two boys, and myself—took a superb basket of trout, and the lady beat us all? What a surprise it was when I saw her, far off across a meadow, standing alone, with her light rod bending as she gave the butt to a strong fish, to keep him from a last rush down the rapid! I hastened to her assistance, but it was useless; for before I reached her he lay on the grass, two pounds and three quarters exactly, the noblest trout I ever saw taken from a Connecticut brook.

Make your home, therefore, as near as may be to your sport, so, at the least, that you may always find it when the day is done.

I have described in this book a mountain lake, among the Franconia hills, which is not known to many anglers. As I approach the last pages of the volume, I recall, from among a thousand scenes, with especial vividness, memories of that lake. I could easily tell why these memories are so clear, but the reasons concern only myself, and all anglers have their peculiar reasons for best loving memories of certain waters.

My last day's sport one summer ended with a glorious evening there. We—Dupont and myself—had reconstructed two old rafts of logs and brush, which we had abandoned once before as water-logged, but now found, floating indeed, but so deep that it was necessary to cut pine boughs and heap on them to give us footing out of water. The situation of the lake renders it very lovely, as well as very lonely. I have already described it.

It lies in a basin among lofty mountain-tops, and is itself some three thousand feet above the sea. The pine-fringed crests around form the edge of the basin, the slopes being an unbroken mass of forest, except on the north, where a huge, bare, rocky bluff rises about eight hundred feet into the air.

When the sun had disappeared behind the western mountain crest, the scene was exceedingly beautiful. The lonely pond was a mirror, all wind had gone down, and a soft darkness seemed to fill the basin in which it lay, while up above and down below the water, and all around us, sun-lit peaks were standing out in a clear blue sky.

I sat down on my floating island of pine boughs to watch Dupont—for I believe I am sincere in saying that I enjoy seeing another man throw a fly, if he is a good and graceful sportsman, quite as much as doing it myself; and there is no man's casting I like to see so well as my friend Dupont's. The lake was crowded with small fish, so that at every cast from one to a dozen would rise. They were four-ounce fish, capital for the table, but not what we wanted. At length, as he sent his tail fly over toward the lily pads, there came that swift rush and swirl in the water that is such music to the sportsman's ears, and then the slender Norris rod bent as two pounds of lively trout-flesh, fins and tail, were dragging it downward.

If you desire to know what is fishing under difficulties, try a light rod on a mountain pond, and cast from a log raft covered with pine boughs. Dupont's fish fought hard at a distance for a few minutes, then yielded to the steady pressure of the rod in a skillful hand, and came slowly in. But when he saw what hurt him—that is, when he saw the humanity on the raft—he did just as a hundred fish in every hundred do, rushed for the only dark place in sight, and that was under the raft. Now remember, you who do not understand fly-fishing, that there were three flies on the casting-line, each four feet from the other, and the trout hooked on the middle one. What would be the natural effect of such a rush among the overhanging pine boughs? Of course two hooks would make themselves fast somewhere, for a hook always finds solid attachment where it is not intended to catch. So Dupont watched his fish, and when, with a sharp rush, he tore off the first bobber (which, my uneducated friend, means the upper fly, nearest the rod), succeeded in swinging him off so that his next rush loosened the tail fly, and then, convinced that the dark spot under the raft was full of enemies, the trout went away into deep water. Here it was easy work to bring him to the landing-net, and I lay on my pine-bough island and saw him come out, shining in gold and silver and jewels, and said, "A fine fish! Now do it again." And he did it again and again, and the day went down almost into darkness, and we had forgotten the difficulties and dangers of the untrodden mountain-sides which we must cross on our way homeward.

The twilight lingered long up there, but we pushed our rafts to the shore in haste, and plunged into the forest. I think I have before alluded to our misadventure on this evening. We had traveled this route often enough to know it; but this evening we missed the proper line at starting, and the effect of that little error well-nigh proved a very serious matter. For a divergence of a few rods at the commencement widened to a fourth of a mile by the time we reached the mountain-top, and instead of our mossy descent—steep enough, but easy because we knew it—we found ourselves suddenly on the edge of a precipice. Below us the descent for full five hundred feet was a vast pile of rocks but a few degrees out from the perpendicular. It was too late to turn back, for the night was already coming on. We had not fifteen minutes of twilight left. So we commenced the far from *facilis* descent. It was a break-neck or break-leg operation. Dropping from rock to rock, sliding down sharp inclines, catching here and there at branches of trees or shrubs that gave way with us and let us fall into holes among the stones, out of which we climbed, to fall again and again into similar openings—how we reached the bottom of that descent safely I can not imagine. At the moment we laughed at our scrape and scrapes, but when we reached more sure footing and a less precipitous slope of the mountain we paused for a long breath, and looked into each other's faces before we pushed on in the dense under-brush. An occasional look at the compass by the light of a match—for it was now dark—kept us on the right course— east half north—until we heard before us the welcome dash

of the Pemigewasset over his rocky bed at the foot of the mountain. The road could not be far beyond it, and crossing the river on fallen tree, we pressed on, and emerged at last, with no small satisfaction, on the track of civilization.

The silence which filled the valley at the foot of Mount Lafayette as we came into the clearing was oppressive. I never knew the forest so still. No bird, no insect, no living animal uttered a sound. There was no wind to move the trees. The voice of the river was inaudible, for it flows gently by this opening. I sat down by the road-side to gain breath, more exhausted by the descent than I had been by the ascent of the mountain. Up above us, between the tree-tops, was a narrow line of sky, sprinkled with bright stars, that shone as you have sometimes seen them on a winter night.

While we sat there a soft breeze from the south began to steal up the valley, and then, borne on the gentle air, I heard from far below the sound of the river vexed among rocks, and dashing down heavy falls, but the sound was not angry; it was musical and mournful; it was the sound of mingled praise and prayer in some distant place of worship, as I have heard the great organ at Freiburg, when late at night I have been standing on the bridge over the chasm.

The horses were not waiting for us, though we were a half-hour beyond the appointed time. As we learned afterward, the boy who had been sent with them waited in the lonesome road until, in the gloom, the trunks of trees began to look like men, bushes became ghosts, stumps seemed to him wild beasts, and the darkness frightened him. So the poor little fellow, after resisting the terror that crept over him as long as he could, yielded at last, and drove home as fast as the horses would drag him. We had nothing to do but to foot it. It was no wonder the boy was frightened in that deep valley. As we walked up the road we several times saw groups of men ahead of us, which wholly vanished as we approached them. Once I saw a horse standing by the road-side, and Dupont saw it too, and we hurried on, thinking to find old Jack and the wagon, but there was no horse there; only trunks of trees, and the starlight creeping through and around them.

Again we sat down for awhile on a great rock by the road-side, and listened, if we might perhaps hear the coming wheels. But all was silent; only that sound of the river came up the valley, like the murmur of many voices in prayer.

"It is as if all the dead that lie in the valley were praying together in some old church down yonder," said Dupont.

"Do you think there is very much dust of humanity here in the valley?"

"They say the earth's surface has been used for graves, so that the dead lie under every foot of ground."

"That's all nonsense. If all the men and women and children that have died on the earth from the creation till this day were gathered, living now, and the breath of the Lord should sweep them into Lake Superior, they might sink to the bottom and find ample space to lie side by side, and have plenty of room to turn if their slumber should be restless. If the judgment were set, and all mankind called to stand up and answer, they could be ranged within sound of a cannon. I don't think that many men lie in this valley. The dust of the earth that has been man is, after all, very little of it. It is not that which hallows ground so much as the memory of man's life and love and suffering, and approach to his God. Old places of worship are always full of sacred associations. Even an old heathen temple is a very solemn place. How strange and sweet among our treasures are memories of prayer! Did you never linger in an old cathedral after the vesper service, and find the atmosphere full of holy calm, as if the golden vials of the elders had not yet inclosed the prayers of that day? If there be any thing which hallows ground on this poor earth of ours, it is that here or there man or woman or child has prayed. If I did not believe that little six feet of rock in the old church in Jerusalem to be the rock on which the feet of the Lord first rested when he awoke from the slumber of atonement, I would nevertheless revere it as the holiest place on earth, because more knees have pressed it in penitential prayer than any other spot in all the world. It seems to me that much good paper and ink have been wasted of late in discussing this subject of prayer, and answering a queer proposition of some one who, wise in certain ways, is ignorant from lack of experience in this matter. I have great pity for the man whose life lacks this experience of prayer and its answers. For such a man, knowing nothing of the power of faith, is like a blind man who knows nothing of color. I would not attempt to explain it to him, for I could not. He can not understand the terms I use, nor can I explain them to him. He will never be wiser for any explanations of mine, nor until he meets the Master in the way, and is directed to some Siloam, where he may wash his eyes and see. Then he will know all about it. Meantime he laughs at me; and I let him laugh, for it does me no harm. Strange that wagon does not come."

"This prospect of going home on foot is not just the thing after our experience on the mountain."

"No, not the thing at all, especially with a strained ankle."

"What, yours?"

"A little so, I fancy. But let's be moving."

So we walked along, I limping a little.

"Certainly this is not what we bargained for. Where can that boy be? I'm in a hurry to be at home. When home is bright and pleasant, it's never the thing to be going there slowly. We are always in a hurry when our faces are once set homeward. You and I have been a-fishing in this world a good while, on all sorts of waters, and have taken more or less, in the main with quiet contentment. What is life, after all, but just going a-fishing all the time, casting flies on many rivers and lakes, and going quietly home as the day is ending?"

"Don't waste time with any more moralizing, Effendi. What we have before us is now to get ourselves home in as sound condition as possible."

"Well, can't we talk as we go along? That's another of the similarities between life and a day's fishing; as we go home we like to talk, and generally to talk over the day's events. Your basket is heavy, but you carry it lightly, because you killed those large trout in the twilight. If it had fewer trout in it, it would feel heavier. Life's work well done makes a light load to carry home."

"Is your basket heavy?"

"To-night? Yes. It's not half full, but I am half inclined to empty it among the bushes. If it were not wasting the trout, I would. Here comes a wagon or a coach, or something—perhaps we can get a ride."

It was a late extra from Plymouth on the way to the Profile, and it was loaded to excess. There was scarcely room for our baskets of fish, and none for us. But the driver relieved us of our loads, and we plodded on.

"There you have a simile again. Any one will carry your earnings for you. Plenty of people go by you on the road of life ready and willing to relieve you of the results of your labor, but they don't care to take you up and help you along."

"That's not fair. These people would have carried us along, but they had no room; and they took the trout in pure good-will, intending to restore them to us when we are at home."

"Possibly—possibly—but there is a great deal of selfishness in the world that we don't know of."

"Come, come Effendi—you are surly and cross. If you did break the second joint of your favorite rod on a three-ounce trout, you need not be in an ill humor with all the world because of it. Let's walk faster."

"Walk on alone, if you want to; but I'm going to sit down on this rock and stay here till Jack comes, if it isn't till morning. My ankle won't stand any more."

And down I sat. One can't be always cheery; and somehow there came over me that evening a gloom that I could not at once shake off. For, to say truth, I was thoroughly used up, and had strained my ankle badly in the plunge down the mountain. When one is weary, a slight ache is a serious impediment. Dupont yielded at last to my persuasions, or rather to his own conviction that I must be sent for if I were to get to the hotel that night, and so pushed on, leaving me alone in the forest.

The moon had by this time come up above the southern ridge of Mount Lafayette, and was pouring a flood of silver light into the valley of the Pemigewasset. The light stole down among the trees, scarcely reaching the ground any where, but producing that well-known effect of moonlight—the entire transformation of objects—so that there seemed to be life and even motion every where around me.

I lit a cigar and stretched myself out on the rock. Imprudent? Yes, but comfortable. The great trunks of trees around me began to look like the forest of columns in Karnak. I wondered whether it were really true that only a couple of miles from me at that instant were hundreds of people in a great hotel, representatives of the civilization of the century, gathered in a vast drawing-room, blazing with gas-light, brilliant dresses, jewelry, and all the adornments of modern life. It seemed odd to be lying on a rock in an old temple and yet so near to the modern world. I asked myself, are they after all very different people, that gay crowd at the Profile, from the men and women who thronged the old temple? We people of the nineteenth cenutry are guilty of folly in our self-admiration, and vastly err in placing ourselves far in advance of all ages. Steam-engines and telegraphs and printing-presses are mighty powers, but the day and the place are far distant from which man will look back on this little world and judge impartially of the various evidences of various civilizations. Even now we can see barbarism in our own governments, and in our own houses, if we will but look at ourselves. I doubt very much whether the Egyptian lady from whose head I once took a curl of hair was not as refined, as civilized, as polished three thousand years ago as any lady in the Profile House to-night?

Here lies the curl before me as I write—a dark brown lock, which lights in the sun to-day as it lit when she was living ages ago. Her head was covered with curls. Before they wrapped her face in the grave-clothes, loving fingers twined all the dark masses of her hair into just such curls as she loved to wear, speaking, we should say in our day, of youth, gayety, grace, and loveliness. For a curl speaks. Around it, as it lies there, is a halo, from which I can hear voices uttering many evidences of civilization. She lived in luxury; she wore purple and fine linen; she had jewels on her fingers, and, though she never imitated the civilization of modern Africa, which wears rings in the nose, she was guilty of the barbarism of piercing holes in her ears whereon to hang gold and jewels to be looked at and admired.

I never found the head of a dead woman in Egypt adorned with false hair, but I have seen abundant specimens of it from the tombs, where it had been laid with other ornaments, as if perchance it might be needed in the far-off morning. And this curl adorned a head which in life had every claim to civilization which any lady possesses who may read these words, and those locks of hair have been seen in halls whose splendor surpassed our Western dreams among statesmen and soldiers, from whom, if we could unseal their lips, we might learn lessons of civilization unknown to us of the nineteenth century.

But what was that yonder in the forest which startled me so that I sat up on the rock and looked intently into the strange cross lights of the moon among the bushes? Who was that, standing beyond the great column by the obelisk? and that? and that? Was it a breeze swaying the dogwood and mooseberry bushes, or were those verily ghosts? A weary fisherman, resting on his way home may well see visions in such a lonesome forest and such a moonlight. Face after face looked at me around that old column. It was the trunk of a mighty birch, but it looked more like the stone reared by Osirei. There was visible an old man's face. Alas, for the old man. The years that have been counted and stored away in God's memory and the memory of men since he departed, have made those once solemn and commanding features dust, while they have drawn these lines on mine. He was the guide of my boyhood, the beloved companion of my maturing years. His voice was exceedingly musical, as he read aloud to me his favorite passages in Homer, and bade me translate while he recited from memory the impassioned eloquence of the Medea. He seemed to be wondering what his boy was doing there on that rock, his eyes flashing back the light out of his own. And while I sat there, he vanished and another stood in his place. Old Simon Gray, who taught me how to catch trout forty years ago, the good old friend of my childhood, looked around the column, and I caught the old smile on his face. How my heart leaped to see the good old man. How I longed to ask him if the chestnut locks of his beloved wife lay clustering on his breast in the land of his present abiding! And though he spoke not a word, the old man knew my thoughts and answered me: "She is here, the beloved of olden times," and as he spoke she looked over his shoulder. It was strange, the contrast. I had never known her, for she died long before I was born, but I had often heard him speak of her young beauty, and now they stood before me. He was old, very old, and his white locks lay thin on his head, and the smiles of heaven rested among the deep harsh lines of sad age. But she was in her young, pure, matronly beauty; and her eye, blue as the skies of summer nights, and flashing as the stars, gleamed with a joy that can not be described. Her long curls of chestnut flowed over her neck and down her shoulders, like a river of rich, deep, magnificent beauty, through which glimpses of her temples seemed like diamonds. And she looked at the old man, and did not seem to think him old, but lovingly (how lovingly!) she laid her head on his shoulder, and wound her arms around his neck, and led him away out of sight. And when they were gone, for a little while there were only bushes swinging in the wind, and now and then the moan of a tree that had fallen against another, and complained as the rising wind moved it. And then, down the slope, among the trees, where a silver stream of water ran over rocks hastening toward the Pemigewasset, I saw a vision of exceeding loveliness, which you might have thought the rising mist above the water, but which revealed to me a face of rare and perfect beauty; and a smile of intense joy was on those matchless features, as if they had brought with them a memory of the light of heaven. I could not count the years since the dust was heaped over those closed eyes now bright with the light of blessedness. I could not number the moons that have waxed and waned since those lips, closed, close shut, were pressed with their last caresses. And now eyes and lips were smiling the language of heaven.

It was a vision of blessed days. I did not love Maud ————. But my friend, my almost brother, did, and his love was the adoration of boyhood. And she returned it. And if there be among the dark books which the recording angel has gathered in his fearful library, one page of white glory, on that page will be found written in living letters, letters that will live forever, the story of that golden love. It perished! Passed out of life, out of earth, out of the sun and moonshine of this lower world, but who dare say it passed not into some starry home, where God hath appointed his children to love on forever and forever! Aye, forever! That is the word, written on the human heart in letters of fire, of glory, or of agony.

They died on the same day, though a thousand miles apart. The whitest wings of the angels wafted her homeward, and who shall tell the joy of meeting him there! She was brilliant, starry in the splendor of her young pure beauty, and more brilliant, more starlike now, as she looked at me, and turned her face archly away with that smile on it as she looked back into the forest and seemed to say to me, "Yes, he is there;" and I gazed and gazed into the forest, to see, if I could, my old friend, the boy with whom I had fished the mountain brooks a hundred times in the sunniest days of life; but I could not see him yet, and—

"What! asleep, Effendi? Well, if you don't pay for this with all manner of aches and pains."

It was Dupont, returned with Jack and the buck-board, and he had found me sound asleep on the rock.

And as the good horse Jack went up the road at a tremendous rate, I failed to answer very clearly the questions he put as to my folly in thus going to sleep in damp clothes on a rock in the open air. For I was thinking of home, and who would be there to welcome me.

"Better than walking this, isn't it, especially as the moon is clouded now?"

"Yes, yes, on foot or in a wagon, it's pleasant anyhow to be going home. Always pleasant, when the work of the day is all done, when the sunlight of the day is no longer bright, nor the twilight soft and beautiful, when the darkness has settled down and we walk only by the light of stars.

"And there's no doubt about it, when one looks up yonder through the forest-road, through the tree-tops, through the gloom, and thinks of the far-off home and the waiting welcome—there's no mistake about it, my boy, one can't help wishing he might be sent for with swift horses."

—from *I Go A-Fishing* (1873)

Trout: Meeting Them on the "June Rise"
by George Washington Sears

There is a spot where plumy pines
O'erhang the sylvan banks of Otter;
Where wood-ducks build among the vines
That bend above the crystal water.

And there the blue-jay makes her nest
In the thickest shade of water beeches;
The fish-hawk, statuesque in rest,
Keeps guard o'er glassy pools and reaches.

'Tis there the deer come down to drink,
From laurel brakes and wooded ridges;
The trout, beneath the sedgy brink,
Are sharp on ship-wrecked flies and midges.

AND OF THE SCORES of mountain trout-streams that I have fished, the Otter is associated with the most pleasant memories.

It is, or was, a model trout-stream; a thing to dream of. Having its rise within three miles of the village, it meandered southward for ten miles through a mountain valley to its confluence with the second fork of Pine Creek, six miles of the distance being through a forest without settler or clearing.

The stream was swift, stony, and exceptionally free of brush, fallen timber and the usual *débris* that is so trying to the angler on most wooded streams. Then, it was just the right distance from town. It was so handy to start from the village in the middle of an afternoon in early summer, walk an hour and a half at a leisurely pace, and find one's self on a brawling brook where speckled trout were plenty as a reasonable man could wish.

Fishing only the most promising places for a couple of miles always gave trout enough for supper and breakfast, and brought the angler to the "Trout-House," as a modest cottage of squared logs was called, it being the last house in the clearings and owned by good-natured Charley Davis, who never refused to entertain fishermen with the best his little house afforded. His accommodations were of the narrowest, but also of the neatest, and few women could fry trout so nicely as Mrs. Davis. True, there was only one spare bed, and, if more than two anglers desired lodgings, they were relegated to the barn, with a supply of buffalo skins and blankets. On a soft bed of sweet hay this was all that could be desired by way of lodgings, with the advantage of being free from mosquitoes and punkies. The best of rich, yellow butter with good bread were always to be had at Charley's and his charges were 12½ cents for meals, and the same for lodging.

The two miles of fishing above the "Trout-House" led through clearings, and the banks were much overgrown with willows, making it expedient to use bait, or a single fly. I chose the latter; my favorite bug for such fishing being the red hackle, though I am obliged to confess that the fellow who used a white grub generally beat me.

But the evening episode was only preliminary; it meant a pleasant walk, thirty or forty brook-trout for supper and breakfast, and a quiet night's rest. The real angling commenced the next morning at the bridge, with a six-mile stretch of clear, cold, rushing water to fish. My old-fashioned creel held an honest twelve pounds of dressed trout, and I do not recollect that I ever missed filling it, with time to spare, on that stretch of water. Nor, though I could sometimes fill it in a forenoon, did I ever continue to fish after it *was* full. Twelve pounds of trout is enough for any but a trout-hog.

But the peculiar phase of trout lore that most interested me, was the "run" of trout that were sure to find their way up stream whenever we had a flood late in May or the first half of June. They were distinct and different from the trout that came up with the early spring freshets. Lighter in color, deeper in body, with smaller heads, and better conditioned altogether. They could be distinguished at a glance; the individuals of any school were as like as peas in color and size, and we never saw them except on a summer flood. The natives called them river trout. They came in schools of one hundred to five times as many, just as the flood was subsiding, and they had a way of halting to rest at the deep pools and spring-holes along their route. Lucky was the angler who could find them at rest in a deep pool, under a scooped out bank, or at the foot of a rushing cascade. At such times they seemed to lose their usual shyness, and would take the fly or worm indifferently, until their numbers were reduced more than one-half. To "meet them on the June rise" was the ardent desire of every angler who fished the streams which they were accustomed to ascend. These streams were not numerous. The First, Second, and Third Forks of Pine Creek, with the Otter, comprised the list so far as I know. And no man could be certain of striking a school at any time; it, depended somewhat on judgment, but more on luck. Two or three times I tried it on the Otter and missed; while a friend who had the pluck and muscle to make a ten-mile tramp over the mountain to Second Fork took forty pounds of fine trout from a single school. It was a hoggish thing to do; but he was a native and knew no reason for letting up.

At length my white day came around. There was a fierce rain for three days, and the raging waters took mills, fences and lumber down stream in a way to be remembered. Luckily it also took the lumbermen the same way, and left few native anglers at home. When the waters had subsided to a fair volume, and the streams had still a suspicion of milkiness, I started at 3 P.M. of a lovely June afternoon for the Trout-House. An easy two hours walk, an hour of delightful angling, and I reached the little hostelry with three dozen brook trout, averaging about seven inches in length only, but fresh and sweet, all caught on a single red hackle, which will probably remain my favorite bug until I go over the last carry (though I noticed it has gone well out of fashion with modern anglers).

A supper of trout; an evening such as must be seen and felt to be appreciated; trout again for breakfast, with a dozen packed for lunch, and I struck in at the bridge before sunrise for an all day bout, "to meet 'em on the June rise." I didn't do it. I took the entire day to whip that six miles of bright, dashing water. I filled a twelve-pound creel with trout, putting back everything under eight inches. I put back more than I kept. I had one of the most enjoyable days of my life; I came out at the lower bridge after sundown— and I had not seen or caught one fresh-run river trout. They were all the slender, large-mouthed, dark-mottled fish of the gloomy forest, with crimson spots like fresh drops of blood. But I was not discouraged. Had the trout been there I should have met them. I walked half a mile to the little inn at Babb's, selected a dozen of my best fish for supper and breakfast, gave away the rest, and, tired as a hound, slept the sleep of the just man.

At 4 o'clock the next morning I was on the stream again, feeling my way carefully down, catching a trout at every cast, and putting them mostly back with care, that they might live; but for an hour no sign of a fresh-run river trout.

Below the bridge there is a meadow, the oldest clearing on the creek; there are trees scattered about this meadow that are models of arboreal beauty, black walnut, elm, ash, birch, hickory, maple, etc. Most of them grand, spreading trees. One of them, a large, umbrageous yellow-birch, stood on the left bank of the stream, and was already in danger of a fall by

"The swifter current that mined its roots."

It was here I met them on the June rise.

I dropped my cast of two flies just above the roots of the birch, and, on the instant, two fresh-run, silver-sided, red-spotted trout immolated themselves, with a generous self-abnegation that I shall never forget.

Standing there on that glorious June morning, I made cast after cast, taking, usually, two at each cast. I made no boyish show of "playing" them. They were lifted out as soon as struck. To have fooled with them would have tangled me, and very likely have scattered the school.

It was old-time angling; I shall not see it again.

My cast was a red hackle for tail-fly, with something like the brown hen for hand-fly. I only used two, with four-foot leader; and I was about the only angler who used a fly at all in those days, on these waters.

I fished about one hour. I caught sixty-four trout, weighing thirteen and three quarter pounds. I caught too many. I was obliged to *string* some of them, as the creel would not hold them all. But my head was moderately level. When I had caught as many as I thought right I held up; and I said, if any of these natives get on to this school, they will take the last trout, if it be a hundred pounds. And they will *salt them down*. So when I was done, and the fishing was good as at the start. I cut a long "staddle," with a bush at the top, and I just went for that school of trout. I chevied, harried and scattered them, up stream and down, until I could not see a fish. Then I packed my duffle and went to the little inn for breakfast. Of course every male biped was anxious to know "where I met 'em." I told them truly; and they started, man and boy, for the "Big Birch," with beech rods, stiff linen lines, and a full stock of white grubs.

I was credibly informed afterward, that these backwoods cherubs did not succeed in "Meeting 'em on the June rise." I have a word to add, which is not important though it may be novel.

There is a roaring, impetuous brook emptying into Second Fork, called "Rock Run." It heads in a level swamp, near the summit of the mountain. The swamp contains about forty acres, and is simply a level bed of loose stones, completely overgrown with bright green moss.

"Rock Run" heads in a strong, ice-cold spring, but is soon sunken and lost among the loose stones of the swamp. Just where the immense hemlocks, that make the swamp a sunless gloom, get their foothold, is one of the things I shall never find out. But, all the same, they are *there*. And "Rock Run" finds its way underground for 80 rods with never a ray of sunlight to illuminate its course. Not once in its swamp course does it break out to daylight. You may follow it by its heavy gurgling, going by ear; but you cannot see the water. Now remove the heavy coating of moss here and there, and you may see glimpses of dark, cold water, three or four feet beneath the surface. Drop a hook, baited with angle-worm down these dark watery holes, and it will be instantly taken by a dark, crimson-spotted specimen of simon pure *Salmo fontinalis*. They are small, four to six inches in length, hard, sweet; the *beau ideal* of mountain trout. Follow this subterranean brook for eighty rods, and you find it gushing over the mountain's brink in a cascade that no fish could or would attempt to ascend. Follow the roaring brook down to its confluence with Second Fork, and you will not find one trout in the course of a mile. The stream is simply a succession of falls, cascades, and rapids, up which no fish can beat its way for one hundred yards.

And yet at the head of this stream is a subterranean brook stocked with the finest specimens of *Salmo fontinalis*. They did not breed on the mountain top. They *cannot* ascend the stream. Where did they originate? When, and how did they manage to get there? I leave the questions to *savants* and *naturalists*. As for myself, I state the fact—still demonstrable—for the trout are yet there. But I take it to be one of the conundrums "no fellah can ever find out."

P.S.—A word as to bugs, lures, flies, etc. Now I have no criticism to offer as regards flies or lures. I saw a Gotham banker in 1880, making a cast on Third lake, with a leader that carried *twelve flies*. Why not? He enjoyed it; and he caught some trout. Even the guides laughed at him. I did not: he rode his hobby, and he rode it well. Fishing beside him, with a five-dollar rod, I caught two trout to his one.

What did he care? He came out to enjoy himself after his own fashion, and he did it. Like myself, he only cared for the sport—the recreation and enough trout for supper. (I cannot cast twelve flies.)

Now my favorite lures—with forty years' experience—stand about thus. Tail fly, red hackle; second, brown hen; third, Romeyn. Or, tail fly, red ibis; second, brown hackle; third, queen of the waters. Or, red hackle, queen, royal coachman. Sometimes trout will *not* rise to the fly. I respect their tastes. I use then—tail fly, an angle worm, with a bit of clear pork for the head, and a white miller for second. If this fails I go to camp and sleep. I am not above worms and grubs, but prefer the fly. *And I take but what I need for present use.* Can all brother anglers say the same?

—from *Fishing with a Fly* (1883)

A Fatal Success
by Henry van Dyke

BEEKMAN DE PEYSTER WAS PROBABLY the most passionate and triumphant fisherman in the Petrine Club. He angled with the same dash and confidence that he threw into his operations in the stock-market. He was sure to be the first man to get his flies on the water at the opening of the season. And when we came together for our fall meeting, to compare notes of our wanderings on various streams and make up the fish-stories for the year, Beekman was almost always "high hook." We expected, as a matter of course, to hear that he had taken the most and the largest fish.

It was so with everything that he undertook. He was a masterful man. If there was an unusually large trout in a river, Beekman knew about it before any one else, and got there first, and came home with the fish. It did not make him unduly proud, because there was nothing uncommon about it. It was his habit to succeed, and all the rest of us were hardened to it.

When he married Cornelia Cochrane, we were consoled for our partial loss by the apparent fitness and brilliancy of the match. If Beekman was a masterful man, Cornelia was certainly what you might call a mistressful woman. She had been the head of her house since she was eighteen years old. She carried her good looks like the family plate; and when she came into the breakfast-room and said good-morning, it was with an air as if she presented every one with a check for a thousand dollars. Her tastes were accepted as judgments, and her preferences had the force of laws. Wherever she wanted to go in the summer-time, there the finger of household destiny pointed. At Newport, at Bar Harbour, at Lenox, at Southampton, she made a record. When she was joined in holy wedlock to Beekman De Peyster, her father and mother heaved a sigh of satisfaction, and settled down for a quiet vacation in Cherry Valley.

It was in the second summer after the wedding that Beekman admitted to a few of his ancient Petrine cronies, in moments of confidence (unjustifiable, but natural), that his wife had one fault.

"It is not exactly a fault," he said, "not a positive fault, you know. It is just a kind of defect, due to her education, of course. In everything else she's magnificent. But she doesn't care for fishing. She says it's stupid,—can't see why any one should like the woods,—calls camping out the lunatic's diversion. It's rather awkward for a man with my habits to have his wife take such a view. But it can be changed by training. I intend to educate her and convert her. I shall make an angler of her yet."

And so he did.

The new education was begun in the Adirondacks, and the first lesson was given at Paul Smith's. It was a complete failure.

Beekman persuaded her to come out with him for a day on Meacham River, and promised to convince her of the charm of angling. She wore a new gown, fawn-colour and violet, with a picture-hat, very taking. But the Meacham River trout was shy that day; not even Beekman could induce him to rise to the fly. What the trout lacked in confidence the mosquitoes more than made up. Mrs. De Peyster came home much sunburned, and expressed a highly unfavourable opinion of fishing as an amusement and of Meacham River as a resort.

"The nice people don't come to the Adirondacks to fish," said she; "they come to talk about the fishing twenty years ago. Besides, what do you want to catch that trout for? If you do, the other men will say you bought it, and the hotel will have to put in another for the rest of the season."

The following year Beekman tried Moosehead Lake. Here he found an atmosphere more favourable to his plan of education. There were a good many people who really fished, and short expeditions in the woods were quite fashionable. Cornelia had a camping-costume of the most approved style made by Dewlap on Fifth Avenue,—pearl-gray with linings of rose-silk,—and consented to go with her husband on a trip up Moose River. They pitched their tent the first evening at the mouth of Misery Stream, and a storm came on. The rain sifted through the canvas in a fine spray, and Mrs. De Peyster sat up all night in a waterproof cloak, holding an umbrella. The next day they were back at the hotel in time for lunch.

"It was horrid," she told her most intimate friend, "perfectly horrid. The idea of sleeping in a shower-bath, and eating your breakfast from a tin plate, just for sake of catching a few silly fish! Why not send your guides out to get them for you?"

But, in spite of this profession of obstinate heresy, Beekman observed with secret joy that there were signs, before the end of the season, that Cornelia was drifting a little, a very little but still perceptibly, in the direction of a change of heart. She began to take an interest, as the big trout came along in September, in the reports of the catches made by the different anglers. She would saunter out with the other people to the corner of the porch to see the fish weighed and spread out on the grass. Several times she went with Beekman in the canoe to Hardscrabble Point, and showed distinct evidences of pleasure when he caught large trout. The last day of the season, when he returned from a successful expedition to Roach River and Lily Bay, she inquired with some particularity about the results of his sport; and in the evening, as the company sat before the great open fire in the hall of the hotel, she was heard to use this information with considerable skill in putting down Mrs. Minot Peabody of Boston, who was recounting the details of her husband's catch at Spencer Pond. Cornelia was not a person to be contented with the back seat, even in fish-stories.

When Beekman observed these indications he was much encouraged, and resolved to push his educational experiment briskly forward to his customary goal of success.

"Some things can be done, as well as others," he said in his masterful way, as three of us were walking home together after the autumnal dinner of the Petrine Club, which he always attended as a graduate member. "A real fisherman never gives up. I told you I'd make an angler out of my wife; and so I will. It has been rather difficult. She is 'dour' in rising. But she's beginning to take notice of the fly now. Give me another season, and I'll have her landed."

Good old Beekman! Little did he think—But I must not interrupt the story with moral reflections.

The preparations that he made for his final effort at conversion were thorough and prudent. He had a private interview with Dewlap in regard to the construction of a practical fishing-costume for a lady, which resulted in something more reasonable and workmanlike than had ever been turned out by that famous artist. He ordered from Hook & Catchett a lady's angling-outfit of the most enticing description,—a split-bamboo rod, light as a girl's wish, and strong as a matron's will; an oxidized silver reel, with a monogram on one side, and a sapphire set in the handle for good luck; a book of flies, of all sizes and colours, with the correct names inscribed in gilt letters on each page. He surrounded his favourite sport with an aureole of elegance and beauty. And then he took Cornelia in September to the Upper Dam at Rangeley.

She went reluctant. She arrived disgusted. She stayed incredulous. She returned—Wait a bit, and you shall hear how she returned.

The Upper Dam at Rangeley is the place, of all others in world, where the lunacy of angling may be seen in its incurable stage. There is a cosy little inn, called a camp, at the foot of a big lake. In front of the inn is a huge dam of gray stone, over which the river plunges into a great oval pool, where the trout assemble in the early fall to perpetuate their race. From the tenth of September to the thirtieth,

there is not an hour of the day or night when there are no boats floating on that pool, and no anglers trailing the fly across its waters. Before the late fishermen are ready to come in at midnight, the early fishermen may be seen creeping down to the shore with lanterns in order to begin before cock-crow. The number of fish taken is not large,—perhaps five or six for the whole company on an average day,—but the size is sometimes enormous,—nothing under three pounds is counted,—and they pervade thought and conversation at the Upper Dam to the exclusion of every other subject. There is no driving, no dancing, no golf, no tennis. There is nothing to do but fish or die.

At first, Cornelia thought she would choose the latter alternative. But a remark of that skilful and morose old angler, McTurk, which she overheard on the verandah after supper, changed her mind.

"Women have no sporting instinct," said he. "They only fish because they see men doing it. They are imitative animals."

That same night she told Beekman, in the subdued tone which the architectural construction of the house imposes upon all confidential communications in the bedrooms, but with resolution in every accent, that she proposed to go fishing with him on the morrow.

"But not on that pool, right in front of the house, you understand. There must be some other place, out on the lake, where we can fish for three or four days, until I get the trick of this wobbly rod. Then I'll show that old bear, McTurk, what kind of animal woman is."

Beekman was simply delighted. Five days of diligent practice at the mouth of Mill Brook brought his pupil to the point where he pronounced her safe.

"Of course," he said patronizingly, "you haven't learned all about it yet. That will take years. But you can get your fly out thirty feet, and you can keep the top of your rod up. If you do that, the trout will hook himself, in rapid water, eight times out of ten. For playing him, if you follow my directions, you'll be all right. We will try the pool to-night, and hope for a medium-sized fish."

Cornelia said nothing, but smiled and nodded. She had her own thoughts.

At about nine o'clock Saturday night, they anchored their boat on the edge of the shoal where the big eddy swings around, put out the lantern and began to fish. Beekman sat in the bow of the boat, with his rod over the left side; Cornelia in the stern, with her rod over the right side. The night was cloudy and very black. Each of them had put on the largest possible fly, one a "Bee-Pond" and the other a "Dragon;" but even these were invisible. They measured out the right length of line, and let the flies drift back until they hung over the shoal, in the curly water where the two currents meet.

There were three other boats to the left of them. McTurk was their only neighbour in the darkness on the right. Once they heard him swearing softly to himself, and knew that he had hooked and lost a fish.

Away down at the tail of the pool, dimly visible through the gloom, the furtive fisherman, Parsons, had anchored his boat. No noise ever came from that craft. If he wished to change his position, he did not pull up the anchor and let it down again with a bump. He simply lengthened or shortened his anchor rope. There was no click of the reel when he played a fish. He drew in and paid out the line through the rings by hand, without a sound. What he thought when a fish got away, no one knew, for he never said it. He concealed his angling as if it had been a conspiracy. Twice that night they heard a faint splash in the water near his boat, and twice they saw him put his arm over the side in the darkness and bring it back again very quietly.

"That's the second fish for Parsons," whispered Beekman, "what a secretive old Fortunatus he is! He knows more about fishing than any man on the pool, and talks less."

Cornelia did not answer. Her thoughts were all on the tip of her own rod. About eleven o'clock a fine, drizzling rain set in. The fishing was very slack. All the other boats gave it up in despair; but Cornelia said she wanted to stay out a little longer, they might as well finish up the week.

At precisely fifty minutes past eleven, Beekman reeled up his line, and remarked with firmness that the holy Sabbath day was almost at hand and they ought to go in.

"Not till I've landed this trout," said Cornelia.

"What? A trout! Have you got one?"

"Certainly; I've had him on for at least fifteen minutes. I'm playing him Mr. Parsons' way. You might as well light the lantern and get the net ready; he's coming in towards the boat now."

Beekman broke three matches before he made the lantern burn; and when he held it up over the gunwale, there was the trout sure enough, gleaming ghostly pale in the dark water, close to the boat, and quite tired out. He slipped the net over the fish and drew it in,—a monster.

"I'll carry that trout, if you please," said Cornelia, as they stepped out of the boat; and she walked into the camp, on the last stroke of midnight, with the fish in her hand, and quietly asked for the steelyard.

Eight pounds and fourteen ounces,—that was the weight. Everybody was amazed. It was the "best fish" of the year. Cornelia showed no sign of exultation, until just as John was carrying the trout to the ice-house. Then she flashed out:—

"Quite a fair imitation, Mr. McTurk,—isn't it?"

Now McTurk's best record for the last fifteen years was seven pounds and twelve ounces.

So far as McTurk is concerned, this is the end of the story. But not for the De Peysters. I wish it were. Beekman went to sleep that night with a contented spirit. He felt that his experiment in education had been a success. He had made his wife an angler.

He had indeed, and to an extent which he little suspected. That Upper Dam trout was to her like the first taste of blood to the tiger. It seemed to change, at once, not so much her character as the direction of her vital energy. She yielded to the lunacy of angling, not by slow degrees, (as first a transient delusion, then a fixed idea, then a chronic infirmity, finally a mild insanity,) but by a sudden plunge into the most violent mania. So far from being ready to die at Upper Dam, her desire now was to live there—and to live solely for the sake of fishing—as long as the season was open.

There were two hundred and forty hours left to midnight on the thirtieth of September. At least two hundred of these she spent on the pool; and when Beekman was too exhausted to manage the boat and the net and the lantern for her, she engaged a trustworthy guide to take Beekman's place while he slept. At the end of the last day her score was twenty-three, with an average of five pounds and a quarter. His score was nine, with an average of four pounds. He had

succeeded far beyond his wildest hopes.

The next year his success became even more astonishing. They went to the Titan Club in Canada. The ugliest and most inaccessible sheet of water in that territory is Lake Pharaoh. But it is famous for the extraordinary fishing at a certain spot near the outlet, where there is just room enough for one canoe. They camped on Lake Pharaoh for six weeks, by Mrs. De Peyster's command; and her canoe was always the first to reach the fishing-ground in the morning, and the last to leave it in the evening.

Some one asked him, when he returned to the city, whether he had good luck.

"Quite fair," he tossed off in a careless way; "we took over three hundred pounds."

"To your own rod?" asked the inquirer, in admiration.

"No-o-o," said Beekman, "there were two of us."

There were two of them, also, the following year, when they joined the Natasheebo Salmon Club and fished that celebrated river in Labrador. The custom of drawing lots every night for the water that each member was to angle over the next day, seemed to be especially designed to fit the situation. Mrs. De Peyster could fish her own pool and her husband's too. The result of that year's fishing was something phenomenal. She had a score that made a paragraph in the newspapers and called out editorial comment. One editor was so inadequate to the situation as to entitle the article in which he described her triumph "The Equivalence of Woman." It was well-meant, but she was not at all pleased with it.

She was now not merely an angler, but a "record" angler of the most virulent type. Wherever they went, she wanted, and she got, the pick of the water. She seemed to be equally at home on all kinds of streams, large and small. She would pursue the little mountain-brook trout in the early spring, and the Labrador salmon in July, and the huge speckled trout of the northern lakes in September, with the same avidity and resolution. All that she cared for was to get the best and the most of the fishing at each place where she angled. This she always did.

And Beekman,—well, for him there were no more long separations from the partner of his life while he went off to fish some favourite stream. There were no more homecomings after a good day's sport to find her clad in cool and dainty raiment on the verandah, ready to welcome him with friendly badinage. There was not even any casting of the fly around Hardscrabble Point while she sat in the canoe reading a novel, looking up with mild and pleasant interest when he caught a larger fish than usual, as an older and wiser person looks at a child playing some innocent game. Those days of a divided interest between man and wife were gone. She was now fully converted, and more. Beekman and Cornelia were one; and she was the one.

The last time I saw the De Peysters he was following her along the Beaverkill, carrying a landing-net and a basket, but no rod. She paused for a moment to exchange greetings, and then strode on down the stream. He lingered for a few minutes longer to light a pipe.

"Well, old man," I said, "you certainly have succeeded in making an angler of Mrs. De Peyster."

"Yes, indeed," he answered,—"haven't I?" Then he continued, after a few thoughtful puffs of smoke, "Do you know, I'm not quite so sure as I used to be that fishing is the best of all sports. I sometimes think of giving it up and going in for croquet."

—from *Fisherman's Luck*, (1899)

The Trout and the Indian
by General John McNulta

FROM MY INFANCY I had heard tales of the Big Woods, but do not remember ever having then seen anyone who had been in them. A party was being made up to go there, and my father, when the time for starting came, on account of feeble health was prohibited from making the trip, as he had intended. I was in despair, as I was to be left behind, and all of the fond hopes that I had nourished were to be shattered—the big trout, the deer, the bears, the panthers, the wildcats and other varmints that I expected to kill, I would not see. And then, most of all the Indians, real wild Indians, but friendly, in whose wigwams I was going to rest, I would not see them. I was almost heartbroken. One of the party, however, with whom my father and I had been on a stream, volunteered out of pure sympathy to look after me.

Consent was then given that I might go, but the apprehensions under which I labored lest it be withdrawn, of which there was strong indication, are among the most painful reminiscences of my life.

We finally set off, three strong men and one small, freckled, scrawny boy. As one of the party facetiously remarked: "He is about the size of a pound of soap after a hard day's washing." And another said: "About two good mouthfuls for an ordinary bear," and my particular champion replied: "A small but very lively bait."

We got off on a steamer with a deck passage to Albany; fare one dollar for man, fifty cents for boy; canal boat from Albany to Utica. This was in 1847 or '48, and the New York Central Railroad was, I think, being operated between Albany and Syracuse. We took the canal boat because it was cheaper than the railroad, and we also took a freight boat because it was cheaper than the packet boat—being one cent a mile, instead of two. It was slower, but time was of no value to us.

At Utica we hired a man with a team and wagon for the trip, but I do not remember the cost; it was approximately about what a sleeping-car porter would now expect as a tip for like time.

We went through Trenton over to Alder Creek and the big Black River Dam, where digging for a canal to Rome had just been started. Here we struck the primeval forest—no habitations beyond in that direction. A Mr. Williams had a sawmill at the dam, and there were a few small houses. We had traveled more than half the time in the woods after we left Trenton, often many miles at a time without seeing any sign of human life beyond the rough road over which we passed. A few miles before we reached Alder Creek, there was considerable clearing and a settlement of Welsh people, who were starting dairy farms.

From Alder Creek we diverged to the left and to the west, then northwest through the Steuben Hills, and again southwest on to Booneville, and there our team left us and went back to Utica. Here we met our guide, a Canadian-Frenchman voyageur named Marienne, who expressed in emphatic mixed English and Canadian-French his disapprobation of taking that puny, sickly petit garçon in the woods, who might get wet and die there.

After several day's delay we got started. There had been provided for me as a special guide and caretaker an Ojibway Indian of Herculean proportions, fully 6 feet 2½ inches in his moccasins, and weighing, I judge, about two hundred pounds.

My long-desired wish to meet the Indians had been gratified, but the effect was not what I expected. I was afraid of the Indian, and it soon became evident that the Indian entertained grave apprehensions of some kind about me. I was constantly uppermost in his mind, whether for good or evil I could not determine, but feared the latter, and always felt great relief when he put away a big butcher knife that he carried in a leather sheath on a belt around his waist. I avoided being left alone with him, and as he did not know a dozen words of English and I did not know one word of Indian, our conversation was limited. My desire to know Indians had become fully satisfied, yet I thought if I could meet this particular Indian when he had no knife—in the city in the presence of a good-sized squad of policemen—it would be more satisfactory. I avoided being left alone with him and shied away from him on our journey. When we came to a stream I would slip out a few yards from camp and try my flies, and soon he left me to my ways.

At one of our camps I found an exceptionally good place for casting near the top of a rapid; the only place, however, to get room for a back cast was from a point of vantage on a tree fallen across the stream, upon which I crawled out. When in the act of making the first cast my feet slipped and down I went in the cold, swift water over head and ears, the current holding me up against the submerged limbs and body of the tree under which I was partly drawn with my head still under, but perfectly composed and with no apprehension, being a good swimmer and diver. With a good hold I was about to make a supreme effort to raise myself against the current, when I was pulled, almost jerked, straight up out of the water and found myself being held up in the air at arms' length by the Indian, about as he would hold up for inspection a muskrat that he had caught by the nape of the neck. He looked me in the face, made a grunt, and carried me to the bank. When he saw that I stood up and was all right, he gave two or three more grunts with a different inflection, while the expression of his countenance indicated satisfaction. Then it dawned upon me that the Indian thought I was in danger of being drowned, which I was disposed to resent as a reflection upon my resourcefulness as an angler, my skill as a diver and my all-around qualities as an amphibian.

An impulse came over me to make a run for camp and get away from him, but I could not run, as my boots were full of water. All men and boys wore boots then—calfskin boots, coming near to the knee. Boots indicated the line of demarcation between babyhood and boyhood. Then it occurred to me if I did start to run, the Indian could catch me before I reached camp. I pulled off my boots and rolled up my trousers ready for a run. Then I observed the Indian was without his butcher knife, and he beckoned me to come out on the fallen tree and hold the rod while he released the line from its entanglement. I did so because I was afraid to refuse, and reeled up while he released the hard-braided, heavily waxed linen line. When he came to the horsehair leader and single-hair snells and artificial flies on tiny hooks

he was amazed and charmed. He had not only never seen but never heard of such an appliance. It was to him incredible that a fish could be caught without bait, on that imitation of an insect, and impossible to hold the fish on a single hair after he was hooked, or that that little hook would hold anything larger than a minnow. He made manifest his feelings in pantomime, and also indicated a desire to see the thing tried. This gave me some confidence in him, and I immediately began to gratify his desire.

A few casts brought up a good trout, fairly hooked and nicely held in the stiff current until successfully landed, the light rod showing all the curves from the straightness of an arrow to and beyond the perfect arch, the standard of a rod's capacity, to almost a perfect loop—the point of desperation, where nothing further in the way of line can be yielded, and where the only alternative is to hold or break. The little twig and single horsehair held in that swift current a vigorous two-pound trout—a true *Salvelinus fontinalis*.

The stoicism of the Indian melted away and was all gone; he was bubbling over with enthusiasm and continued to bubble until, without moving from that fallen tree, I had landed a full dozen, one a double of about a pound and a half each.

Radically opposite in race, in aspiration and traditions and physical endowments, two kindred spirits now communed together and understood every thrill and emotion that moved each. The man regarded the boy as he would a little weak bird fluttering between life and death, prematurely separated from the nest and brood. And the boy, terrorized by being alone in the wilderness with this gigantic savage, whose queer actions and dress filled him with distrust.

And then the desire of the Indian to witness a practical test of the angler's skill touched the boy's vanity. The interest and enjoyment of the Indian made a soul communion and coalescence, and all fears and distrusts were dissipated by confidence.

The two were children of one father, the one true and ever-living God, with like thoughts and aspirations. They became friends and remained so for life.

THE TROUT AND THE INDIAN originally appeared in *Field & Stream* magazine in May, 1900.

Steelhead Trout of the Rogue River
by W. F. Backus

IT'S THE BIG FISH THAT COUNT in fly fishing, not the big catches. In the early stages of his career, the angler will perhaps strive to bring in a goodly number of trout but the mere taking of many average fish soon begins to lose its flavor. Then it's a question of not how many, but how big, and a keen fly fisherman will travel any distance and spend as much as necessary in order to enjoy the best of all sport: taking large fish on the artificial fly.

Those who can afford it take up Canadian-salmon fly fishing. This is the sport for the very rich, as a man will usually spend a thousand dollars for the privilege of landing a few dozen salmon on the fly. It is quite evident, therefore, that salmon fly fishing is out of reach for most of us, so it is a question of where to get some real big trout, and we will assume that a five-pound trout is big.

Broadly speaking, there are but a few districts in all North America where five-pound trout can be taken with regularity. Occasional specimens of that size will be found in almost any locality where trout are plentiful, but I refer to places where the big fellows are fairly numerous. The lakes and streams of northern Maine yield annually many large trout. The Nipigon River, which flows into Lake Superior from the north, has long been famous for its large brook trout. In Colorado we have the Gunnison River, where rainbows up to ten pounds have been taken on the fly.

Among the Eastern angling fraternity, these waters are regarded as the best for big trout. Five-pound fish are probable, but by no means certain, while eight- and ten-pound fish are mighty scarce. Furthermore, the season for taking the big fellows on the fly is usually very short.

Do you know that we have a river here in Oregon which will yield more big trout on the fly than all the above-mentioned waters combined? I refer to the Rogue River in southern Oregon, the finest fly-fishing stream in the world for big trout.

On this wonderful river you can begin fly fishing early in July and fish every day until the last of October, and average half a dozen fish every day which will weigh over five pounds each. For over a hundred and fifty miles the Rogue is one vast trout stream, with fish weighing over ten pounds to be found within each and every mile of its course.

The fish here are a species of searun rainbow trout, usually called steelhead trout. In most of our rivers the rainbows which go to sea come back in the winter, and are commercially known as steelhead salmon. But in the Rogue all rules are suspended, and it seems that all the fish there travel back and forth from salt to fresh water.

The upstream migration begins in the early spring, and all summer a constant run of steelhead trout works slowly up the Rogue River. The earliest fish usually travel farthest upstream, so that the upper waters furnish the first fly fishing.

To be sure, it's no easy fishing. To take steelhead trout with the fly on the Rogue requires long and skillful casting, deep wading and lots of it, and a knowledge of the habits of the big fish. It's hard fishing, but who wants to get six- and eight-pound fish without working for them? None of our party was afraid of getting wet, and we all cast enough line to get into the game, so it was a question of locating fish. In this respect there are a number of don'ts to be observed.

Steelheads don't like shallow, pebbly riffles; they don't like deep, sandy-bottom eddies, and on a hot day they don't like open water of any kind if they can avoid it. Furthermore, they don't like to have flies presented to them the way we usually fish for ordinary trout. They seem to have a fondness for water with a bed-rock bottom. Rock-bottom riffles of moderate width, with the water from three to ten feet deep, are their favorite lurking places. If the bottom is full of seams and cracks, so much the better, as these crevices are ideal haunts for the big fellows. Then, when you have located such a place, don't drag your fly along the edge of the current, as in trout fishing, but work out a good length of line, casting it clear across the body of the stream and let it swing down without further motion. If you are in luck, the fish will do the rest.

Let us follow an angler as he walks slowly along the stream, his critical eye examining the water until he finds a pool to his liking. Here he stops and sets up his tackle. His rod, ten feet of seasoned split bamboo, has proven victor in many a bout on the river. The reel, a strong, sensible one of the single-acting type, holds a full fifty yards of heavy enameled line. A six-foot single leader and a No. 4 Coachman with flashing jungle-cock shoulders complete the equipment.

Shading his eyes with one hand, the angler carefully scrutinized the pool he had selected. A rocky formation extended from shore to shore, while the bottom was plentifully studded with big brown boulders. The water, perhaps ten feet deep, flowed swiftly over its stony bed and formed an ideal environment for steelhead trout. Of this the angler was convinced, but his inspection must necessarily end at the waterline. Had his eyes been gifted with the power of piercing those green depths, he would have been even more elated. Well out toward the middle of the stream, some sixty feet away, he would have noticed a waving, shadowy form behind one of the ragged boulders. A closer look would have revealed a huge trout, resting quietly behind his rocky breastwork.

Majestically he lay there, his strong gills moving with machinelike precision, heeding not a whit the water swirling wildly around his barrier. His broad, gleaming side, with its wide stripe of scarlet, flashed gaily with the movement of the gently waving tail. Although apparently oblivious to all surroundings, nothing on the surface escaped his watchful eye. Every leaf, every bit of floating twig was given one fleeting glance, then ignored. For the trout was watching, always watching, for something edible.

The angler was now ready and, entering the water, waded out to a favorable position. Swinging his rod back and forth, he gradually worked out his line. At each forward cast he stripped another yard from the reel, which shot through the guides and joined the flying line on the back cast. Very soon forty feet was out and allowed to settle on the water. Then the angler's experience came into play. Quickly stripping a dozen feet of line from the reel, he draped it over his left hand in several large coils; a quick swish of the rod lifted the line from the water, and it resumed its aerial flight. Back and forth it flew, fairly jerking the rod tip at the end of each forward cast. This was what the angler wanted, and as the line went out straight and true, the left hand came into action; one by one the loops were snatched from the waiting fingers and drawn through the guides. Like a thing of life the white-winged Coachman flew on until the line became taut; then it settled gently on the water, a good sixty feet away. With his body braced against the rushing current, the angler watched the fly sweep over the pool until, undisturbed, it reached the shallow water. Immediately the left hand drew in several coils of line, the rod lifted the remainder and, after a few flying passes, the fly again dropped, just a yard or two below the spot reached on the first cast. Then followed another cast, and yet another, but still no rise.

Surely, thought the angler, there must be a good fish in such a place; a better bit of steelhead water would be hard to find. So he went at it again, determined to cover every foot of the pool. Once, twice, three times the fly swept around in a bold circle, without result. But the fourth cast was well placed, indeed. The leader struck the water just above the waiting fish, and, as the plump-bodied Coachman came drifting along, the orange-hued eyes of its jungle-cock wings seemed fairly to wink at the fish below.

This was too much. For just an instant the steelhead's body stiffened; then with a quick, convulsive movement of fins and tail, he launched himself at the intruding insect. The wide-open jaws closed with a vicious snap; with a burning sting of retaliation the hook sank into the bend— and the fight was on.

The first lunge of the fish told the angler that he had hooked something worth while, and he made for shore with all speed. As he floundered waist-deep in the current, the fish began his first wild rush: fifty feet, eighty feet, one hundred feet of line went whizzing through the guides, while the staccato of the clicking reel became a whistling shriek. Ashore at last, the angler sprinted along the bank; the fish, in midstream, was strenuously insisting on more line, a demand which the almost empty reel could not supply, so the angler ran. On went the trout to the very end of the pool, pausing just where it broke into a heavy-tumbling rapid. Here the angler made his decision, took his stand: not another foot would he give, even though something broke.

The rod bent till it formed a half circle; a warning hum came over the tightened line, telling plainly that things were going the limit. For perhaps twenty seconds the fish yielded, allowing himself to be drawn into deeper water. But the truce was short-lived; a moment's rest and he was all action. Up into the air he leaped, his glistening body, with its broad scarlet stripe, making a beautiful picture in the sunlight. Three times he sprang, twisting, turning, trying with frenzied endeavor to shake loose the burning barb. Then up the pool, straight past the surprised angler, who found himself utterly unable to take up the rapidly slackening line. Reaching the upper end of the pool, he performed some more aerial tumbling, shaking his trembling body from head to tail, until it seemed as though the tiny hook must surely give way. But he was doomed.

With a well-hooked fish and a cool, careful angler, there can be but one ending. Gradually his struggles became weaker, his runs shorter and shorter as tired nature gave up. And then, like a true steelhead, he was all in. The angler waded slowly out until knee-deep in water; the landing net was cautiously dipped in behind him, and without a quiver the seven-pound steelhead allowed its waiting meshes to encompass his splendid form.

It's no wonder we Portland anglers are willing to travel three hundred miles to get near this grand fishing, and we want our Eastern brethren to get in on this sport too.

To all those who desire to get some of that Rogue River fishing I will give the following tip: Bring your best rod with you, and a pair of waders as well. Have your railroad ticket provide for a week's stop-over in southern Oregon, preferably at Medford, and you'll insure yourself some of the greatest fishing you've ever had.

Cristivomer Namaycush
by Robert Page Lincoln

ONE OF THOSE TIME-HONORED RULES and regulations an angling writer is supposed to abide by and carry out at any cost is never to dispute the dictum of some famous man who went before—an authority who issued "the last word" on a certain subject piscatorial, or published to the world his opinion of the fighting or nonfighting qualities of a certain fish.

Once in a while a faint chirp is heard when some brave soul decides to make a break and give his own opinions, but he immediately veils his assertions in obscurity, thereafter vanishing behind the scenes to wait for announcements. He may have committed an unpardonable act. While not put on a bread-and-water diet, his feelings may well be understood.

Now the reason for the above introduction is that I want to say something about the lake trout and I want to make that fish out as second only to the rainbow trout as a fighter.

Now every man who has ever fished for *Cristivomer namaycush* will look away into space and try to concentrate. "When did I ever catch a lake trout that put up a good fight?" It may be hard for you to remember. But if you think over the list of all the lake trout you ever handled, you will also agree that most of them were small fellows, a foot to twenty inches in length, and they were caught in anywhere from eighty to two hundred feet of water, with tackle sufficient in quality and temper to hold a tuna and with a chunk of lead on the end of the lines weighing all the way from eight ounces to one pound.

When you have hauled in a fish thus encumbered, you may have considered the specimen an empty sack so far as sweep and flourish is concerned. But what can a fish be expected to do at such a distance down in the water, where the pressure is so great, hampered in all of its rushes by the lead sinker and you putting all your strength into the pull upward to the surface? Catch a rainbow trout under the same circumstances and he would not be one whit better off than this deep-water rover.

And so it is that the dictum of a justly famous man stands as the last word on the subject. Herbert, who wrote so pleasingly under the *nom de plume* of Frank Forester, said many things about the lake trout which every angling writer has continued to repeat into the present day. He considered the lake trout hardly worth while catching, and, being an epicure to boot, he stated that the fish was worthless as table fare.

To capture the fish, he suggested using "a coarse, heavy, stiff rod and a powerful oiled hempen or flaxen line, on a winch, with a heavy sinker; a cod hook baited with any kind of flesh, fish, or fowl," stating that this was "the most successful if not the most orthodox or scientific mode of capturing him."

It is safe to say that Forester fished comparatively little for the lake trout under conditions that gave the fish a chance or he would have entertained a vastly different opinion. For instance, if he had followed the lake trout into the more shallow water in the spring or early summer, he would have been able to catch the fish in question by means of fly rod and flies, in which case the fish would, or should, have won his unstinted praise.

Now it should be obvious to everyone that any fish caught deep down near the bottom of a lake is taken at a distinct disadvantage. But strangely enough no one ever seems to remember this when considering the matter of lake trout fishing.

Mr. E. D. Calvert, of Rainy River, Ont., who has captured many Field & Stream prizes for both lake trout and muskallonge, is probably the most enthusiastic lake trout fisherman I know of. He has made more of a study of the fish than any other man and has perhaps caught more lake trout on regular fishing tackle than any active angler in this country. Added to this, Mr. Calvert has fished in a region teeming with the noble fish. Calvert told me:

"There is a general idea, you know, that lake trout do not give a good fight. It is quite true that in the summer, when fishing for them with a copper line and a pound of lead as a sinker, they do not put up a great fight, as they have very little chance to do much fighting, handicapped as they are with a heavy copper line or sinker. The difference in pressure between the surface and down a hundred feet or more also militates against any battle. As most lake-trout fishing is done in the summer, it is no wonder that they get their name as a poor fighter.

"To those who have caught these fish in the spring, when they are in shallow water, an entirely different story is unfolded. At that time they act like a real member of the trout family, often tearing off a hundred yards of line in their first rush, burning your fingers if you try to brake the reel too hard. They pull off several stunts, the most characteristic of which is a vertical circle which has the effect of making you lift your rod up and down quickly, if you don't want to give them slack line. One second your rod tip is in the water, the next second straight up in the air; then this is repeated several times in quick succession. I have had many fights with lake trout that have lasted over an hour; one I remember well which lasted two hours and five minutes!"

Those who have fished for the lake trout in many waters and under many conditions know that it is the time of the year and the mode of the capture that will prove the mettle of the fish. I have heard strong, able-bodied men lament at the limp fight that a pickerel of two or three pounds puts up—and they have caught the fish with a heavy hand line and have pulled it in as one would play tug-of-war. If that same fish were caught on a four-ounce fly rod, a light leader, spinners and flies of the wee sma' type, they could read another version in the capture of the same pickerel.

The trouble is that the average fisherman will not catch a fish otherwise than with heavy tackle; they are afraid the "meat" will get away and will take no chance of such a loss.

The lake trout, after a sojourn in the inshore waters in the spring, betake themselves to the medium depths and from there to the deepest holes in the lakes about the time August hangs like fire over the land. When it is said they are in the inshore waters directly after the going off of ice (as Calvert has stated, from three to four weeks thereafter), it is not meant that they are in close to the shoreline, or even so that they may be detected. They will keep themselves in water from eight to twenty feet in depth, probably going in a little closer to the shore when they wish to feed near the mouths of streams flowing into the lake.

Lake trout feed more or less heavily at this time, which is proved by opening their stomachs. Stream mouths prove a good place to seek them, using a variety of tackle and lures and proceeding about the fishing in a certain manner which I shall later describe. After the trout have gone into the depths, they do not issue forth again into the more shallow water until some time during September. The month of October finds them visiting the shallow water in great numbers, although they keep their presence hid from view and one would not be the wiser.

Generally one gets his first inkling of the closeness of the lake trout to shore when, trolling in the ordinary manner for great northern pike, muskallonge and wall-eyed pike-perch, there is a sudden strike and a fight will follow that will prove interesting. Your fish will be a lake trout and you will catch him off a reef or sandbar, along the sloping sides of which they are then to be found. Where a stream has built sand out into the lake and a "step-off" or drop is formed, there you will find them hobnobbing with many

other forms of fish life.

The fact that lake trout are thus caught in comparatively shallow water, when they are usually found in deep water only, leads many anglers to believe they are not lake trout, but some other form of trout. Just so surely has *namaycush* been branded a bottom rover.

In the more shallow water, the trout will prove astonishing in his fighting ability. If the tackle is light, he will at once make a dash and the reel will shed most of its line. Here, with no heavy drag in the shape of a dipsy sinker of eight ounces to a pound, *Cristivomer namaycush* will promptly prove he is a close relative of *fontinalis*. He will tussle well and he will bore down; he will make many rushes, but will rarely break surface as a rainbow trout will under the same circumstances.

The man who has been wont to catch these same fish of fifteen to eighteen inches in length in the very deep water will be surprised. Have no doubt about that, for most of the lake-trout fishermen angle for *namaycush* deep down and with the unyielding lead sinker or copper line.

During the early part of September the lake trout are on the move. Lake trout spawn in the autumn, not in the spring. There is generally a closed season on lake-trout fishing after the first of October, such being the case in the state of Minnesota, where the closed season is from October 1 to November 15. This is not to say that spawning actually takes place in October; indeed, in some places of the northern half of the country (the natural range of the lake trout), they will not spawn until November.

In September, however, the trout are on the move. One will catch a larger proportion of lake trout from fifteen to twenty inches in length at this time, a large majority of them not being spawners at all but what may be termed "camp followers." That is, they go along to see what is going on and to aid in the destruction of the eggs that the larger trout lay.

Comparatively few real large lake trout (of the fifteen and twenty-pound class) are found in the shallow water. One is more apt to get these in the very deep water in the summer and spring by deep fishing. But during spawning time, or in the weeks before that event, these large fellows seem to pass up the lure.

It is said that few lake trout can be induced to take the artificial fly. That is because even if they come to the shallow water, they will not rise to the surface for flies, as will the brook trout and the rainbow. Or rather it may be said that most of them—nine out of ten—will not. Some lake trout of a pound and a pound and a half at times will slip up to the surface to take the fly, both live and artificial, but this happens mostly in the spring and early summer and often is the case in the Adirondacks.

In October you will have good success in the reef-wise water with the fly rod, spinners and flies. The addition of a spinner makes all the difference in the world with a lake trout; it will give the lure the illusion of a minnow-like form, which will prove too much for *namaycush*. The addition of some split shot on the leader will serve to carry it along down some ten or fifteen feet and, a decent cast having been made, it can be moved along by twitches of the rod tip, with now and then a start or jerk to hurry any fish that is interested.

It makes a most thrilling fight some late September day, off a Northern stream mouth in a lake, suddenly to catch one of these spirited ones. And where one is to be found there are others. The lake trout of the inshore class, of the autumn, are not only impelled in by the lure of the spawning season, but also, in the case of the smaller fish, to take in fuel for the winter, when they can live on the fat they accumulate.

A bass fly tied to the regulation 1-0 hook, with a spinner about a half-inch long on a shaft above it, will prove very "taking" off the reefs and sands anywhere along toward the end of glorious September. In some of the Northern lakes, lake trout can be caught by the hundreds at such times. A No. 3 spinner with a pork rind strip of the bottled sort attached to the single hook also proves alluring. But when casting the No. 3 spinner or spoon and the rind attachment, use a light bait rod and a bait-casting line of the twelve-pound-test type with a sinker up ahead on the line a matter of sixteen to eighteen inches, the sinker being of the long kind with a wire ring in either end—a sinker of the ordinary sort, in other words.

Or you will have better results by taking common strip lead and twisting this along the line to give it sufficient heft to bring it down. You can make your own strip lead by shaving a lead pipe. Wrap on a sufficient amount of this, covering a distance of four feet or so to bring the line down to the level desired. Strip lead, by the way, is far better than a sinker, since it is distributed over a certain space equally and does not hang in one spot, pulling the line sheer down as a result and making trolling more or less unnatural.

There are several types of the wobbling and darting spoons that are exceedingly "catchy" at this season of the year. One type of spoon, at least, is heavy enough so that it will sink of its own weight and still retain its gyrating motion or dart this way and that in the water, which is meant to give it the illusion of a disabled fish. An enthusiastic lake-trout fisherman has stated there is one peculiarity about the wobbling spoon: it seems more perfectly fitted for catching lake trout than any other artificial lure.

There seems to be something about a wobbling spoon which a member of this fish species will willingly commit suicide on, although he will hang aloof from the regulation spoon-hook affair. Because of its especially successful career in the lake-trout field, the autumn angler for this fish would be wise to stock up before he goes forth in his quest.

A live lure always proves interesting to the lake trout at any season of the year, but certainly when all fish are feeding heavily and the competition is great. A minnow of four or five inches seems to be the ideal size for lake trout. The ordinary way of fishing with a minnow is to fish it dead, attached to the many-hooked archer spinner, the standard contrivance for lake-trout fishing in the North.

Fishing the minnow alive off the bars and reefs is another matter. But let me warn you: using a live minnow thus you lay yourself open to the assault of any one of four or five varieties of preying fish. A muskallonge may happen along; he will never pass it by. A great northern pike of about twenty pounds may rush the lure open-jawed and take it into his very gullet. A wall-eyed perch or a large bass may encounter it.

None of them would pass by a live minnow fished in the right way in the golden month of September. So, therefore, it behooves you to prepare yourself. You must have a gimp

leader at least six to eight inches long attached to the hook to meet the emergency. The strength of the line you are to use and the weight of the rod depend largely upon your skill in using them so as not to come to ruin.

The minnow should be, in preference, one that has been taken from still water—more desirably from pond water. A minnow of this sort, four or five inches long, will have much strength, much kick in him and will not die. The hook is seated in the corner of his mouth in such a way that his progress through the water is not made too difficult.

In fishing in this manner, which I shall call drifting—a method of fishing I have not read of—the sinker is not used close to the lure but up, say, eighteen or more inches from the hook. This is let down to the desired depth and, as you row with the utmost ease, the minnow will swim in a natural manner, the sinker being a light one—just heavy enough to take the minnow down so that it will not swim along the surface. One "drifts" around or along a reef or sandbar in this manner, and one after another the lake trout will fall victims to its charms, for the minnow thus used is unfailing in its attraction.

When a lake trout seizes the minnow, do not set the hook but let the fish "run" with it, for, upon grabbing this minnow lure, the fish will probably just be holding it crosswise, with the hook still outside his mouth. It will then dash away with the prize, as any fish will, and after a twenty-foot race will stop to turn it and swallow. During this interval one can set the hook without fear of losing the frisky fellow.

Do not fear to let the fish have the lure and go with it. It is not the nature of any fish thus capturing a live lure to abandon it. Set your hook and upon capture row away as silently as possible, quite well away from the reef or bar, and there fight and net the fish. Then return; and in the meantime you will not have disturbed the others around that same spot.

Lake-trout fishing is too often followed up in the crude manner of years ago. This consists of ground baiting, by chopping up fish and dumping it to the bottom, the idea being to attract the fish to the spot. Then the common method is to anchor a boat over the place and drop a heavy line, baited with a piece of fish, to the bottom and wait results.

This is, at best, a clumsy manner of fishing; that it proves of worth does not necessarily mean that the lake trout is a fish to be placed in a class with the suckers and dogfish. Were the fish scientifically fished for, with light tackle and attractive lures, far more success would be had.

The knowledge of the average lake-trout fisherman is limited to the known truth that lake trout can be fished for over baited holes. But if he were also possessed of the knowledge that September sees the fish moving into the more shallow water over a wide area in a lake, he would at once shift his fishing tactics and gain more fish and really not take the finny one at a disadvantage.

Reference and Directory Section

Standard Check List of the Common Names and Scientific Names of the Principal American Sport Fishes

FRESH WATER FISHES

Bass, Largemouth: *Micropterus salmoides*

Bass, Rock: *Ambloplites rupestris*

Bass, Smallmouth: *Micropterus dolomieui*

Bass, Spotted: *Micropterus punctulatus*

> (This is the game fish somewhat generally known as the Kentucky Bass, but as its range is far beyond that one state, the acceptable name is used in this list.)

Bass, White: *Morone chrysops*

Bass, Yellow: *Morone mississippiensis*

Bowfin: *Amia calva*

> (Also known as the Mudfish and the Dogfish.)

Bluegill (See Sunfish)

Bullhead, Black: *Ictalurus melas*

Bullhead, Brown: *Ictalurus nebulosus*

Bullhead, Yellow: *Ictalurus natalis*

Carp: *Cyprinus carpio*

Catfish, Blue: *Ictalurus furcatus*

Catfish, Channel: *Ictalurus punctatus*

Catfish, Flathead: *Pylodictis olivaris*

> (Also known as Shovelhead Catfish.)

Catfish, Spoonbill (See Paddlefish)

Catfish, White: *Ictalurus catus*

Char, Arctic: *Salvelinus alpinus*

> (Also known as Arctic Trout and Sunapee Trout. Is found all over Europe where it is known as the Char.)

Chub, Columbia: *Mylocheilus caurinus*

Chub, Creek: *Semotilus atromaculatus*

Chub, Silver (See Fallfish)

Cisco: *Coregonus artedii*

Coaster (See Brook Trout)

Crappie, Black: *Pomoxis nigromaculatus*

Crappie, White: *Pomoxis annularis*

Dogfish (See Bowfin)

Drum, Freshwater: *Aplodinotus grunniens*

Fallfish: *Semotilus corporalis*

> (Also known as Silver Chub in Northeast.)

Note: There are four species of Gars now recognized by the American Fisheries Society, but the Alligator Gar is of chief interest to the sportsman-angler.

Gar, Alligator: *Lepisosteus spatula*

Gar, Longnose: *Lepisosteus osseus*

Gar, Shortnose: *Lepisosteus platostomus*

Gar, Spotted: *Lepisosteus oculatus*

Grayling, Arctic: *Thymallus arcticus*

Grayling, Montana: *Thymallus arcticus tricolor*

Mudfish (See Bowfin)

Muskellunge: *Esox masquinongy*

Ouananiche (See Salmon)

Paddlefish: *Polyodon spathula*

> (Last remnant in this country of a group of fossil fishes and confined to the Mississippi River system. Once abundant, but gradually disappearing. Taken chiefly in nets, but will take a hook. Also called Spoonbill Catfish, but is not a member of the Catfish family.)

Perch, White: *Morone americana*

> (This is a misnomer as this fish is a bass and not a perch, but this common name is so prevalent all over its range it would be unwise to change it.)

Perch, Yellow: *Perca flavescens*

Pickerel, Barred (See Redfin Pickerel)

Pickerel, Redfin: *Esox americanus*

> (Sometimes known as the Barred Pickerel.)

Pickerel, Chain: *Esox niger*

Pickerel, Grass: *Esox vermiculatus*

Pike, Northern: *Esox lucius*

> (An effort was made to call it simply Pike, but some of the pickerel are called pike in many localities, so it was decided too much simplification would lead only to more instead of less confusion.)

Pumpkinseed (See Sunfish)

Salmon, Atlantic: *Salmo salar*

Salmon, Chum: *Oncorhynchus keta*

> (Also referred to as Dog Salmon.)

Salmon, Coho: *Oncorhynchus kisutch*

> (This species is sometimes called the Silver Salmon.)

Salmon, King: *Oncorhynchus tshawytscha*

> (This species is sometimes called the Chinook Salmon.)

Salmon, Kokanee: *Oncorhynchus nerka*

> (This is the small Sockeye Salmon that is landlocked and is artificially propagated and planted in large numbers in the trout waters of the Northwest, especially the state of Washington.)

Salmon, Landlocked: *Salmo salar*

> (This is the game finny fighter so much sought after in Maine and parts of Canada and is being spread to other sections by artificial propagation. It is now landlocked by preference rather than by necessity. Sometimes referred to as the Sebago Salmon.)

Salmon, Ouananiche: *Salmo salar ouananiche*

> (The committee does not agree with those who hold that this

fish is just a landlocked phase of the Atlantic Salmon, because in most of the area where they are taken they have easy access to the sea if they choose to take it.)

Salmon, Pink: *Oncorhynchus gorbuscha*

(Most salmon are more or less humpbacked during the spawning season, but this odd deformation is more exaggerated in this species than all the rest. In fishing circles, this species is generally known as the Humpback Salmon.)

Salmon, Sebago (See under Landlocked Salmon)

Salmon, Sockeye: *Oncorhynchus nerka*

(Commercially referred to as the Red Salmon.)

Sauger: *Stizostedion canadense*

Shee-fish: *Stenodus leucichthys*

(This is the mystery fish of the frigid waters of the Arctic Circle of Alaska. Mainly native to Northern Siberian waters, it is taken frequently enough in Alaska from the Kuskokwim River to Demarcation Point to be given a place in this listing. Sometimes called the Inconnu, which means "unknown.")

Squawfish, Coastal: *Ptychocheilus umpquae*

Squawfish, Columbia: *Ptychocheilus oregonensis*

Squawfish, Sacramento: *Ptychocheilus grandis*

Steelhead (See under Trout)

Stonecat: *Noturus flavus*

Note: While Sturgeon are taken in salty waters only by commercial fishermen, two fresh-water species furnish splendid sport in the waters of Northern Minnesota and Wisconsin and Idaho.

Sturgeon, Shovelnose: *Scaphirhynchus platorynchus*

Sturgeon, Lake: *Acipenser fulvescens*

(Also known as the Rock Sturgeon.)

Note: While the various species of sunfish continue to be the special joy of the small boy, present-day artificial propagation and stocking of farm ponds has resulted in some crossing of species. There is also a tendency to drop some of the oldtime common names such as the Shellcracker, the Stumpknocker and the old-fashioned Pumpkinseed.

Sunfish, Bluegill: *Lepomis macrochirus*

(This species has come to be "the sunfish" of the country through its tremendous propagation and stocking. Unfortunately sometimes it has crossed with other species of the family.)

Sunfish, Green: *Lepomis cyanellus*

Sunfish, Longear: *Lepomis megalotis*

Sunfish, Pumpkinseed: *Lepomis gibbosus*

Sunfish, Redbreast: *Lepomis auritus*

Sunfish, Redear: *Lepomis microlophus*

(In the South commonly known as the Shellcracker.)

Sunfish, Spotted: *Lepomis punctatus*

Togue (See Lake Trout)

Trout, Arctic (See Arctic Char)

Trout, Blueback: *Salvelinus alpinus*

Trout, Brook: *Salvelinus fontinalis*

(This is the native Eastern Brook Trout, now found in many states thanks to artificial propagation. Known in localized areas as Squaretail and in some few areas they drop down to the mouths of tidal estuaries and are known as Coasters.)

Trout, Brown: *Salmo trutta*

(This introduced species has come to be the salvation of trout fishing in worn out Eastern streams. Like many other fresh water game fish of the West, it has in some places become sea-run. Formerly the non-migratory Brownies were known as *S. fario* and the sea-run fish as *S. trutta*, but modern listing makes no difference between the two, both being known as *S. trutta*.)

Trout, Cutthroat: *Salmo clarki*

(Some of this species have become sea-run, this tendency being manifested from Puget Sound northward through British Columbia to Southeastern Alaska.)

Trout, Dolly Varden: *Salvelinus malma*

(This species reaches its greatest concentration in Southeastern Alaska, where most of them are sea-run. Actually it is the Western form of the Eastern Brook Trout. Over much of its habitat it is known as the Salmon Trout.)

Trout, Golden: *Salmo aguabonita*

(Native only to the high Sierras at 10,000 feet or over. Several attempts have been made to reintroduce this species in California where it was once native.)

Trout, Kamloops: *Salmo gairdneri*

(This is one of the many subspecies of the Rainbow Trout, whose differences from the parent stock are either imaginary or due entirely to environment. The Kamloops reached its highest concentration in Pend d'Oreille in Northern Idaho, although it has been introduced elsewhere.)

Trout, Lake: *Salvelinus namaycush*

(This splendid game fish of northern waters is also known as the Togue in those parts of its habitat contiguous to Canada.)

Trout, Loch Leven (See under Brown Trout)

(Both the Loch Leven and the European Brown Trout were introduced into this country about the same time. In due course these two introduced species were crossbred until the present strain known as the Brown Trout resulted. It is doubtful if any true strain of Loch Leven Trout remain in this country.)

Trout, Rainbow: *Salmo gairdneri*

(Originally native to Western America, it has been introduced widely wherever suitable habitat can be found. Because of its wide geographic range, it has developed many localized subspecies, of which the more important are included in this list. Its sea-going members of the species are called Steelheads, but ichthyologists refuse to differentiate between the two scientifically. Hence, both are known as *S. gairdneri*).

Trout, Steelhead: *Salmo gairdneri*

(This is the accepted name of the sea-run branch of the Rainbow Trout, but is claimed by the experts to be the same fish in every other respect and so carries the same scientific name. In California the sea-run Cutthroat Trout is also called a Steelhead.)

Trout, Sunapee (See Arctic Char)

Walleye: *Stizostedion vitreum*

Warmouth: *Lepomis gulosus*

Whitefish: *Coregonus clupeaformis*

Whitefish, Rocky Mountain: *Prosopium williamsoni*

> (Sometimes erroneously referred to as a Grayling in some Western sections.)

SALTWATER FISHES

Albacore: *Thunnus alalunga*

Amberjack: *Seriola dumerili*

Amberjack, Pacific: *Seriola colburni*

Barracuda, Great: *Sphyraena barracuda*

> (This is the big fellow most abundant off the Florida coast and found ranging the seas alone or in groups of two or three.)

Barracuda, Pacific: *Sphyraena argentea*

> (This species is much smaller than the preceding and roams the seas in large schools. Sometimes called the California Barracuda.)

Bass, Channel: *Sciaenops ocellata*

> (This is the great battler of the Atlantic surf. A list of 22 common names have been collected, of which Red Drum in the Chesapeake Bay area and Redfish in Florida are the more generally used.)

Bass, Kelp: *Paralabrax clathratus*

Bass, Sand: *Paralabrax nebulifer*

Bass, White Sea: *Cynoscion nobilis*

Bass, Black Sea, (See Sea Bass)

Bass, Giant Sea: *Stereolepis gigas*

Bass, Spotted Sand: *Paralabrax maculatofasciatus*

Bass, Sea: *Centropristis striata*

> (The young of this popular sport and food fish come into tidal estuaries in great numbers and are called Black Wills. Also known as the Black Sea Bass along the upper Atlantic coast.)

Bass, Striped: *Roccus saxatilis*

> (This is the Rockfish of the Chesapeake Bay area, where it is claimed that about 90 percent of all the Atlantic population of this species are spawned. Transplanted to the West Coast, it now flourishes all along the California and lower Oregon coast.)

Blackfish (See Tautog)

Black Bonito (See Cobia)

Bluefish: *Pomatomus saltatrix*

> (This species is an erratic wanderer. However, its young under the names of Snapper Blue and Tailor run into tidal estuaries along the Atlantic coast in great numbers, providing great sport on light tackle.)

Bonefish: *Albula vulpes*

Bonito, Atlantic: *Sarda sarda*

> (Although distributed all along the West Coast, is generally called the California Bonito.)

Bonito, Oceanic (See Tuna, Skipjack)

Bonito, Pacific: *Sarda chiliensis*

Broadbill (See Swordfish)

Catfish, Gafftopsail: *Bagre marinus*

Catfish, Sea: *Arius felis*

Cero (See King Mackerel)

Cobia: *Rachycentron canadum*

> (This great battler is known by many names in many places, among them being Cabio, Sargeant Fish, Black Bonito, Ling and Lemon Fish.)

Cod: *Gadus morhua*

Cod, Pacific: *Gadus macrocephalus*

Corbina, California: *Menticirrhus undulatus*

Crevalle (See Jack Crevalle)

Croaker, Atlantic: *Micropogon undulatus*

Croaker, Black: *Cheilotrema saturnum*

Croaker, Spotfin: *Roncador stearnsi*

Croaker, White: *Genyonemus lineatus*

Croaker, Yellowfin: *Umbrina roncador*

Cultus (See Lingcod)

Cunner: *Tautogolabrus adspersus*

Cutlassfish: *Trichiurus lepturus*

Devilfish (See Manta)

Dolphin: *Coryphaena hippurus*

Drum, Black: *Pogonias cromis*

Eel: *Anguilla rostrata*

> (A true fish and has a right to be included in this list.)

Flounder, Starry: *Platichthys stellatus*

Flounder, Summer: *Paralichthys dentatus*

> (This is the well-known Fluke of lower New England and upper Middle Atlantic waters and its newer name will be hard to make stick, but is used in this list for simplification. There is also a species *P. lethostigmus* commonly called Southern Fluke. Its range overlaps with *P. dentatus*.)

Flounder, Winter: *Pseudopleuronectes americanus*

Fluke (See under Summer Flounder)

Fluke, Summer (See under Summer Flounder)

Gag (See under Groupers)

Graysby: *Petrometopon cruentatum*

Greenling: *Hexagrammos decagrammus*

Grouper, Black: *Mycteroperca bonaci*

Grouper, Coney: *Cephalopholis fulva*

Grouper, Gag: *Mycteroperca microlepis*

Grouper, Jewfish, Black: *Epinephelus nigritus*

Grouper, Jewfish, Spotted: *Epinephelus itajara*

> (This is the largest of the Groupers.)

Grouper, Nassau: *Epinephelus striatus*

Grouper, Red: *Epinephelus morio*

Grouper, Rockhind: *Epinephelus adscensionis*

Grouper, Yellowfin: *Mycteroperca venenosa*

Note: The Grunts are a large family of tropical fishes. The following seven species are most familiar to anglers.

Grunt, Black Margate: *Anisotremus surinamensis*

Grunt, Bluestripe: *Haemulon sciurus*

Grunt, French: *Haemulon flavolineatum*

(Also called Yellow Grunt.)

Grunt, Pigfish: *Orthopristis chrysopterus*

Grunt, Gray: *Haemulon macrostomum*

Grunt, Margate: *Haemulon album*

Grunt, White: *Haemulon plumieri*

Haddock: *Melanogrammus aeglefinus*

Hake, Silver: *Merluccius bilinearis*

Halibut, Atlantic: *Hippoglossus hippoglossus*

Halibut, California: *Paralichthys californicus*

Halibut, Pacific: *Hippoglossus stenolepis*

Herring, Common: *Clupea harengus*

(Primarily a commercial species but used extensively for bait by anglers.)

Hind, Red, *Epinephelus guttatus*

Jack, Bigeye: *Caranx marginatus*

Jack, Crevalle, *Caranx hippos*

(Sometimes called simply Crevalle.)

Jack, Green: *Caranx caballus*

Jack, Horse-eye: *Caranx latus*

Jewfish, Black (See Groupers)

Jewfish, Spotted (See Groupers)

Ladyfish: *Elops saurus*

(This species is often confused with the Bonefish and is also called the Chiro and Tenpounder.)

Lemon Fish (See Cobia)

Ling (See Cobia)

Lingcod: *Ophiodon elongatus*

(Also called Cultus.)

Lookdown: *Selene vomer*

Mackerel, Atlantic: *Scomber colias*

(Also referred to as the Common Mackerel.)

Mackerel, Cero: *Scomberomorus regalis*

(Sometimes called the Painted Mackerel; also the King Mackerel; is often miscalled the Cero in some Atlantic waters.)

Mackerel, Chub: *Scomber colias*

Mackerel, King: *Scomberomorus cavalla*

(Called Cero in some Atlantic waters and sometimes called the Kingfish by commercial fishermen.)

Mackerel, Pacific Chub: *Scomber japonicus*

Mackerel, Spanish: *Scomberomorus maculatus*

Manta: *Manta birostris*

(This is not exactly a sport fish, but it furnishes fine sport with the harpoon. Also known as the Devilfish.)

Marlin, Black: *Makaira indica*

(The real range of this species is south of the border of the United States, but enough stragglers are taken or seen above the line to call for insertion in this list.)

Marlin, Blue: *Makaira nigricans*

(Occurs in the Atlantic and Tropical Pacific oceans.)

Marlin, Striped: *Tetrapturus audax*

Marlin, White: *Tetrapturus albidus*

Menhaden: *Brevoortia tyrannus*

(An extensively used bait fish; also called the Fatback.)

Moonfish: *Vomer setapinnis*

Mullet, Striped: *Mugil cephalus*

(This is chiefly a food and bait fish, but in some sectors is taken also for sport as well as for bait.)

Muttonfish (See Snapper)

Palometa: *Trachinotus glaucus*

(This species of pompano is not too numerous anywhere, but is taken frequently in Florida waters.)

Permit: *Trachinotus falcatus*

(The young of Permit are called Round Pompano.)

Pigfish: *Orthopristis chrysopterus*

Pollock, Atlantic: *Pollachius virens*

Pollock, Pacific: *Theragra chalcogramma*

Pompano: *Trachinotus carolinus*

Pompano, African: *Alectis crinitus*

Porgy, Grass: *Calamus arctifrons*

Porgy, Jolthead: *Calamus bajonado*

Porgy, Northern: *Stenotomus chrysops*

(Called Scup in some parts of its range.)

Porkfish: *Anisotremus virginicus*

Queenfish: *Seriphus politus*

Note: While the Rays cannot be classed as sport fishes exactly, they do furnish quite a bit of fun to the angler in some sections and so the more familiar species are presented to complete this check list.

Ray, Eagle: *Myliobatus freminvillei*

Ray, Northern Sting: *Dasyatis centroura*

Ray, Southern Sting: *Dasyatis americana*

Ray, Stingaree: *Dasyatis sabina*

Ray, Spotted Eagle: *Aetobatus narinari*

(Also known in some waters as the Spotted Whip Ray.)

Redfish (See Channel Bass)

Robalo (See Snook)

Rockfish (See Striped Bass)

Rockhind (See Groupers)

Runner, Blue: *Caranx crysos*

Runner, Rainbow: *Elagatis bipinnulata*

Sablefish: *Anoplopoma fimbria*

Sandfish: *Diplectrum formosum*

(Also known as the Sand Perch.)

Note: Icthyologists are at odds over several subspecies of Sailfish, but there is no need to recognize any of them for the purpose of this check list except the two following species. Even these two are believed to be the same fish, whatever difference there may be in size or action when hooked being environmental in origin.

Sailfish, Atlantic: *Istiophorus platypterus*

Sailfish, Pacific: *Istiophorus platypterus*

Sailor's Choice: *Haemulon parrai*

Sawfish: *Pristis pectinata*

(Hardly a sport fish, but it has been taken often enough with rod and reel in the Gulf of Mexico off the Texas coast to gain a place in this check list.)

Schoolmaster (See Snapper)

Note: The controversy continues between the use of Weakfish or Seatrout as the basic name for the four species following. As far as can be determined, adherents of each are about evenly divided. For the purposes of this check list, the four species will appear under both of these names.

Seatrout: *Cynoscion regalis*

Seatrout, Sand: *Cynoscion arenarius*

Seatrout, Silver: *Cynoscion nothus*

Seatrout, Spotted: *Cynoscion nebulosus*

Shad: *Alosa sapidissima*

(Formerly a strictly commercial fish, of late it has become a fine sport fish being taken on a fly, streamer or spoon on its way to the spawning grounds in the upper reaches of tidal estuaries. Sometimes referred to as the White Shad.)

Shad, Hickory: *Alosa mediocris*

Note: Recreational angling for various species of sharks in the waters coming within the range of this check list is becoming more and more popular. Below you will find those species, and others, for which official records are kept by the International Game Fish Association.

Shark, Atlantic: *Isurus oxyrinchus*

(This shark is also sometimes called the Mackerel Shark.)

Shark, Blacktip: *Carcharhinus limbatus*

Shark, Hammerhead: *Sphyrna zygaena*

(Generally found in the open ocean and near the surface and gives a good account of itself whenever hooked on rod and line.)

Shark, Mako: *Isurus glaucus*

(This is the kingpin of all the sharks from the angler's viewpoint. Taken on rod and reel it gives the tops in sport. Also called Bonito Shark.)

Shark, Mackerel (See Atlantic Shark)

Shark, Porbeagle: *Lamna nasus*

Shark, Spinner: *Carcharhinus maculipinnis*

(This species is called the Spinner-Shark from its habit of shooting vertically out of the water and turning several times on its axis before falling back with a great splash.)

Shark, Thresher: *Alopias vulpinus*

Shark, Tiger: *Galeocerdo cuvieri*

Shark, White: *Carcharodon carcharias*

(This is the species sometimes called the Man Eater Shark.)

Sheepshead: *Archosargus probatocephalus*

Snapper Blue (See under Bluefish)

Note: The Snappers compose a large family, chiefly tropical. In the members of this family covered in this list there are two genera and seven species of interest to the recreational angler and four species that are important commercially.

Snapper, Dog: *Lutjanus jocu*

Snapper, Lane: *Lutjanus synagris*

Snapper, Mahogany: *Lutjanus mahogoni*

Snapper, Mangrove: *Lutjanus griseus*

Snapper, Mullet: *Lutjanus aratus*

Snapper, Muttonfish: *Lutjanus analis*

Snapper, Red: *Lutjanus blackfordi*

Snapper, Schoolmaster: *Lutjanus apodus*

Snapper, Silk: *Lutjanus vivanus*

Snapper, Yellowtail: *Ocyurus chrysurus*

Snook: *Centropomus undecimalis*

(Called by many the Robalo in parts of its habitat.)

Spot: *Leiostomus xanthurus*

Surf Perch: *Phanerodon furcatus*

(This is one of a number of similar small fish found in the Pacific surf, but of too little importance to be enumerated in full in this list.)

Swordfish: *Xiphias gladius*

(The only representative of its family hence it becomes unnecessary to use the prefix Broadbill.)

Tailor (See Bluefish)

Tarpon: *Megalops atlantica*

Tautog: *Tautoga onitis*

Tomcod: *Microgadus tomcod*

Toadfish: *Opsanus tau*

(Given a place in this list because of its great nuisance value to all fishermen.)

Tripletail: *Lobotes surinamensis*

Note: Following is the latest official listing of the Tuna family as published by the American Fisheries Society Committee. Authorities continue to differ over whether the Atlantic and the Pacific Yellowfin Tunas are the same fish. For the present at least, this list carries both.

Tuna, Allison (See Yellowfin Tuna)

Tuna, Blackfin: *Thunnus atlanticus*

Tuna, Bluefin: *Thunnus thynnus*

> (The young of this species migrate closer to the shoreline and are commonly called School Tuna. The fully developed Bluefins are often called Giant Tuna. This is the principal tuna of the sportsman-angler and the commercial fisherman.)

Tuna, Giant (See Bluefin Tuna)

Tuna, Little: *Euthynnus alletteratus*

> (This is a species sometimes called False Albacore, but it is a true tuna and is now recognized as such.)

Tuna, Skipjack: *Euthynnus pelamis*

> (Found off both coasts. Known as Oceanic Bonito on the Atlantic Coast.)

Tuna, School (See Bluefin Tuna)

Tuna, Yellowfin: *Thunnus albacares*

> (It is now agreed by most of the authorities that the so-called Allison Tuna is simply either an age or sex phase of the Yellowfin Tuna and so it has been dropped from the official check list.)

Wahoo: *Acanthocybium solandri*

Note: See statement regarding interchanging names of Weakfish and Seatrout under the Seatrout listing.

Weakfish: *Cynoscion regalis*

> (In one sector of its range, this species is known as the Squeteague.)

Weakfish, Sand: *Cynoscion arenarius*

Weakfish, Spotted: *Cynoscion nebulosus*

Whitefish, Ocean: *Caulolatilus princeps*

Whiting, Gulf (See Silver Whiting)

Whiting, King (See Northern Whiting)

Whiting, Northern: *Menticirrhus saxatilis*

> (This frequenter of the surf along upper Atlantic shores is also known as both the Kingfish and the King Whiting.)

Whiting, Southern: *Menticirrhus americanus*

Whiting, Silver: *Menticirrhus littoralis*

> (Also known as the Gulf Whiting.)

Yellowtail (See Snapper)

Yellowtail, Pacific: *Seriola dorsalis*

> —Compiled by the Outdoor Writers
> Association of America and reprinted
> with their permission.
> Revised, October 1976.

FISH IDENTIFICATION

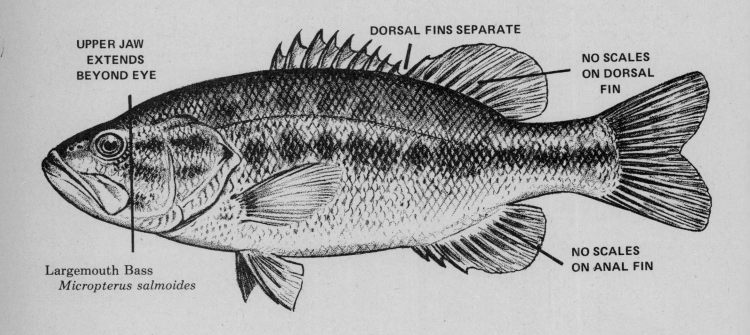

UPPER JAW
EXTENDS
BEYOND EYE

DORSAL FINS SEPARATE

NO SCALES
ON DORSAL
FIN

NO SCALES
ON ANAL FIN

Largemouth Bass
Micropterus salmoides

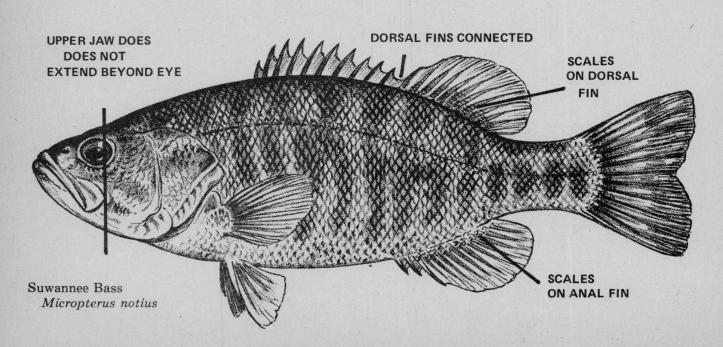

UPPER JAW DOES
DOES NOT
EXTEND BEYOND EYE

DORSAL FINS CONNECTED

SCALES
ON DORSAL
FIN

SCALES
ON ANAL FIN

Suwannee Bass
Micropterus notius

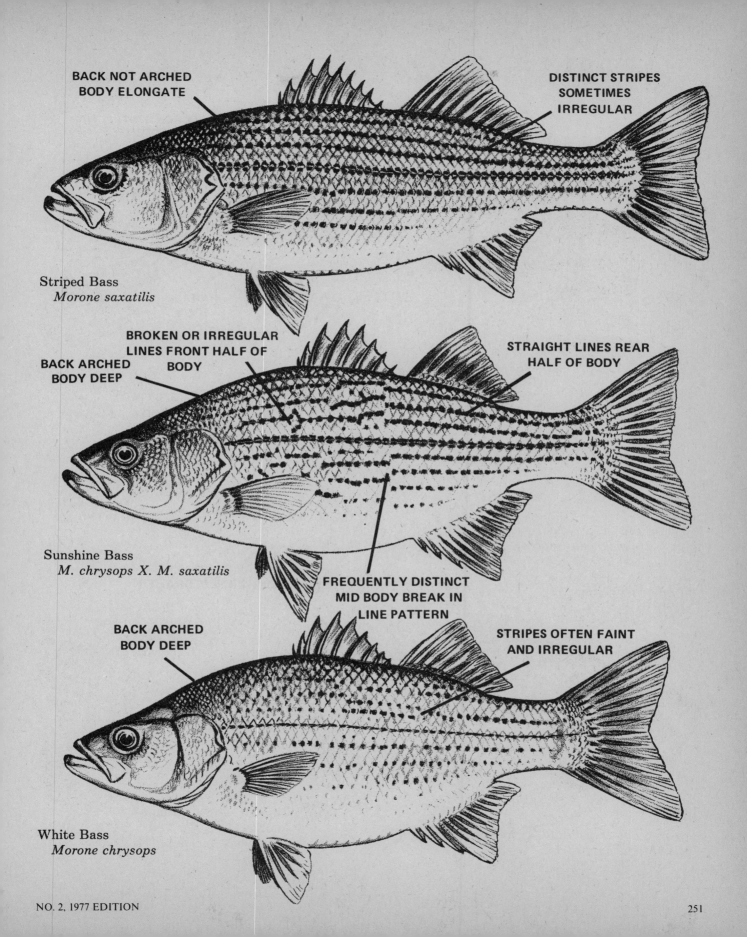

BACK NOT ARCHED
BODY ELONGATE

DISTINCT STRIPES
SOMETIMES
IRREGULAR

Striped Bass
Morone saxatilis

BACK ARCHED
BODY DEEP

BROKEN OR IRREGULAR
LINES FRONT HALF OF
BODY

STRAIGHT LINES REAR
HALF OF BODY

Sunshine Bass
M. chrysops X. M. saxatilis

FREQUENTLY DISTINCT
MID BODY BREAK IN
LINE PATTERN

BACK ARCHED
BODY DEEP

STRIPES OFTEN FAINT
AND IRREGULAR

White Bass
Morone chrysops

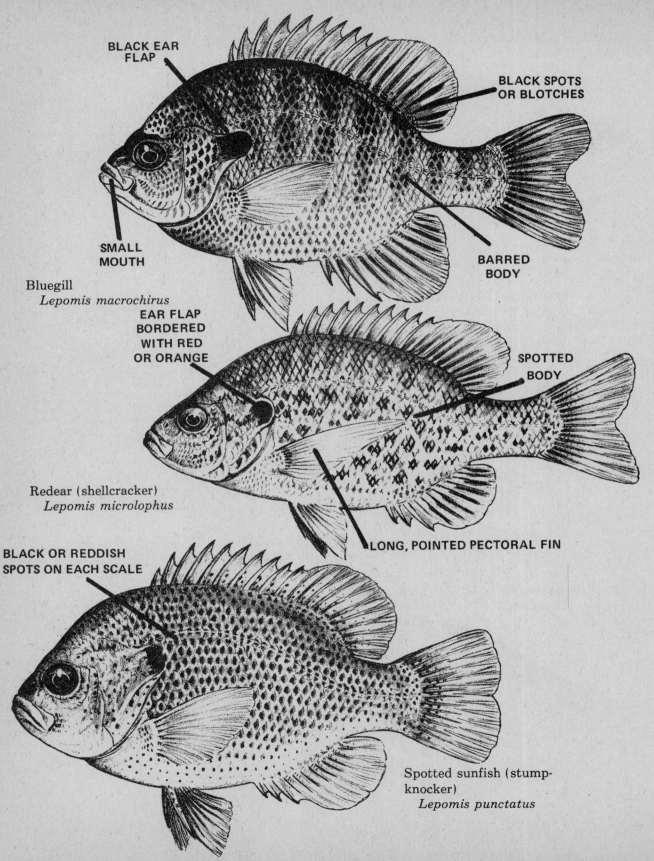

BLACK EAR FLAP

BLACK SPOTS OR BLOTCHES

SMALL MOUTH

BARRED BODY

Bluegill
Lepomis macrochirus

EAR FLAP BORDERED WITH RED OR ORANGE

SPOTTED BODY

Redear (shellcracker)
Lepomis microlophus

LONG, POINTED PECTORAL FIN

BLACK OR REDDISH SPOTS ON EACH SCALE

Spotted sunfish (stump-knocker)
Lepomis punctatus

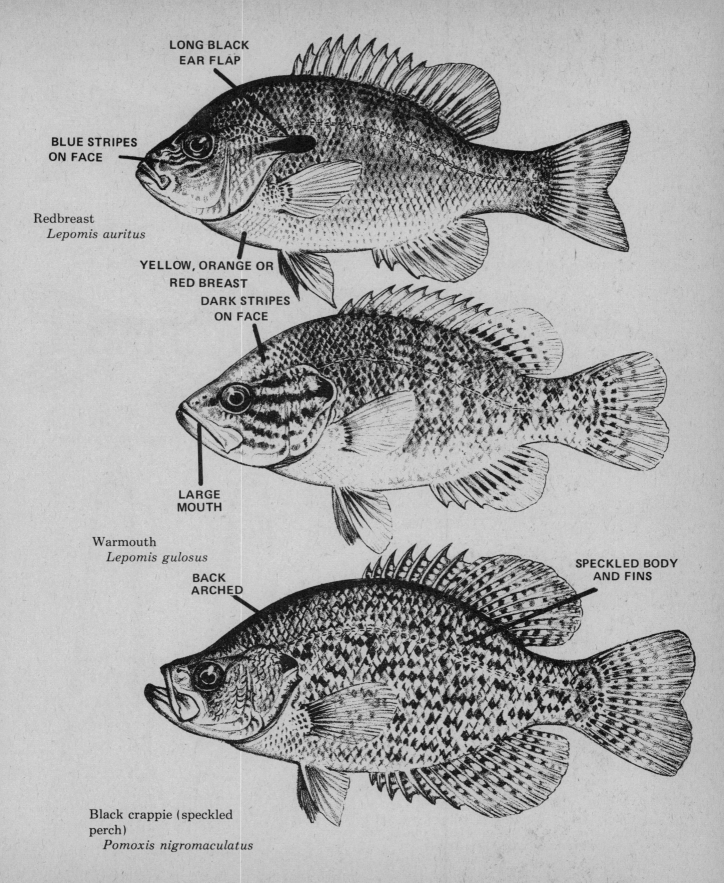

LONG BLACK
EAR FLAP

BLUE STRIPES
ON FACE

Redbreast
Lepomis auritus

YELLOW, ORANGE OR
RED BREAST

DARK STRIPES
ON FACE

LARGE
MOUTH

Warmouth
Lepomis gulosus

BACK
ARCHED

SPECKLED BODY
AND FINS

Black crappie (speckled
perch)
Pomoxis nigromaculatus

CHAIN-LIKE MARKINGS

DORSAL FIN RAYS
USUALLY 14

14-16
BRANCHIOSTEGAL RAYS

Chain Pickerel—*Esox niger*

SIZE TO 30 INCHES OR MORE

IRREGULAR VERTICAL MARKINGS

11-12 DORSAL
FIN RAYS

11-13
BRANCHIOSTEGAL RAYS

Redfin Pickerel—*Esox americanus*

SIZE—RARELY OVER 12 INCHES LONG

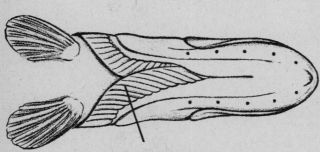

BRANCHIOSTEGAL RAYS

underside of pickerel head
showing branchiostegal rays

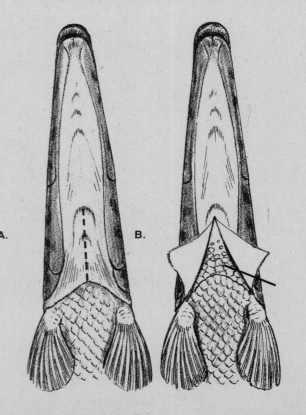

A.

B.

METHOD OF IDENTIFICATION OF SPOTTED
AND FLORIDA GARS

A. SPLIT SKIN OF ISTHMUS (OR THROAT)

B. FOLD BACK. SPOTTED GAR HAS SCALES PRESENT.
FLORIDA GAR DOES NOT. USE OF MAGNIFYING GLASS
IS HELPFUL WHEN MAKING EXAMINATION.

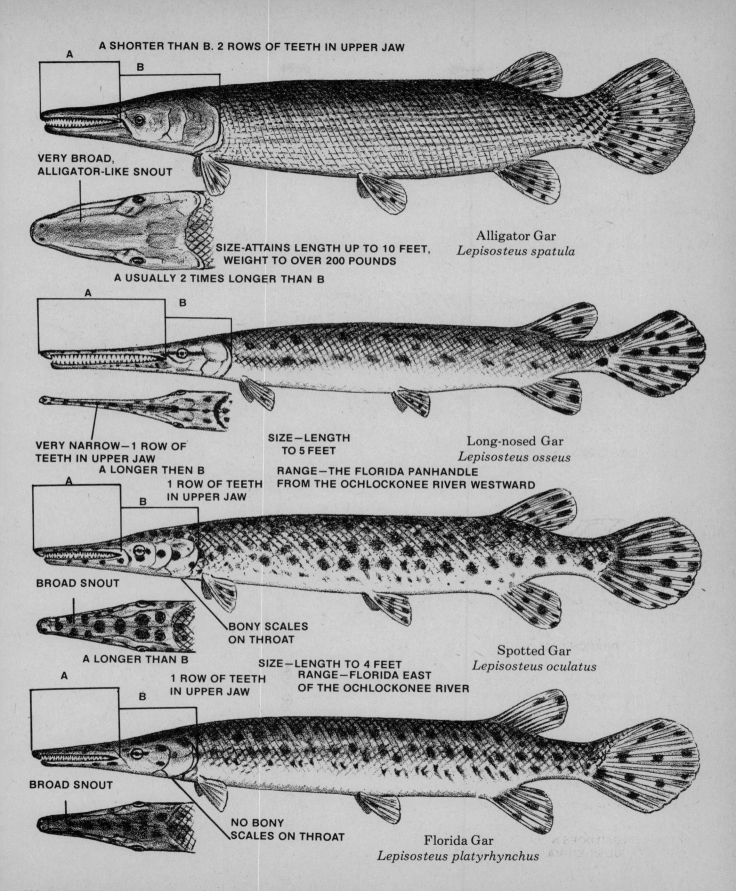

A SHORTER THAN B. 2 ROWS OF TEETH IN UPPER JAW

A

B

VERY BROAD,
ALLIGATOR-LIKE SNOUT

SIZE-ATTAINS LENGTH UP TO 10 FEET,
WEIGHT TO OVER 200 POUNDS

A USUALLY 2 TIMES LONGER THAN B

Alligator Gar
Lepisosteus spatula

A

B

VERY NARROW—1 ROW OF
TEETH IN UPPER JAW

A LONGER THEN B

1 ROW OF TEETH
IN UPPER JAW

SIZE—LENGTH
TO 5 FEET

RANGE—THE FLORIDA PANHANDLE
FROM THE OCHLOCKONEE RIVER WESTWARD

Long-nosed Gar
Lepisosteus osseus

A

B

BROAD SNOUT

A LONGER THAN B

BONY SCALES
ON THROAT

1 ROW OF TEETH
IN UPPER JAW

SIZE—LENGTH TO 4 FEET
RANGE—FLORIDA EAST
OF THE OCHLOCKONEE RIVER

Spotted Gar
Lepisosteus oculatus

A

B

BROAD SNOUT

NO BONY
SCALES ON THROAT

Florida Gar
Lepisosteus platyrhynchus

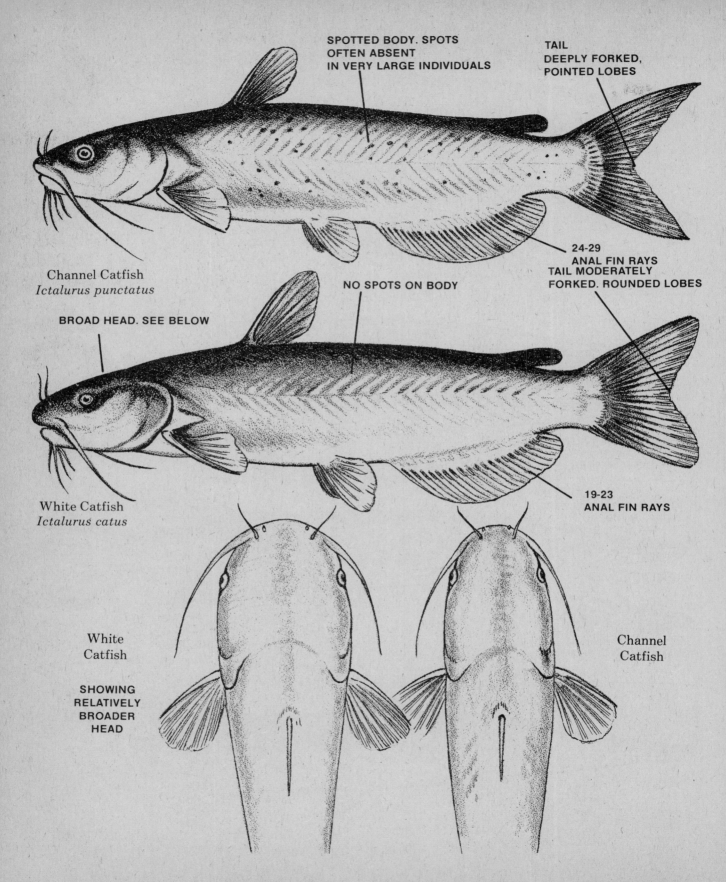

SPOTTED BODY. SPOTS OFTEN ABSENT IN VERY LARGE INDIVIDUALS

TAIL DEEPLY FORKED, POINTED LOBES

Channel Catfish
Ictalurus punctatus

24-29 ANAL FIN RAYS TAIL MODERATELY FORKED. ROUNDED LOBES

BROAD HEAD. SEE BELOW

NO SPOTS ON BODY

White Catfish
Ictalurus catus

19-23 ANAL FIN RAYS

White Catfish

SHOWING RELATIVELY BROADER HEAD

Channel Catfish

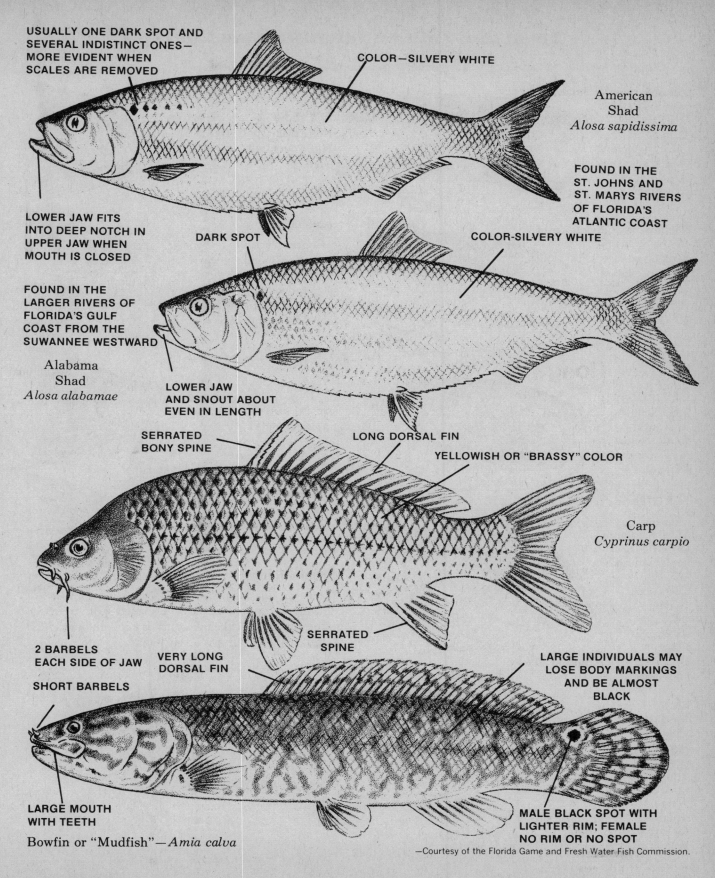

USUALLY ONE DARK SPOT AND SEVERAL INDISTINCT ONES— MORE EVIDENT WHEN SCALES ARE REMOVED

COLOR—SILVERY WHITE

American Shad
Alosa sapidissima

FOUND IN THE ST. JOHNS AND ST. MARYS RIVERS OF FLORIDA'S ATLANTIC COAST

LOWER JAW FITS INTO DEEP NOTCH IN UPPER JAW WHEN MOUTH IS CLOSED

DARK SPOT

COLOR-SILVERY WHITE

FOUND IN THE LARGER RIVERS OF FLORIDA'S GULF COAST FROM THE SUWANNEE WESTWARD

Alabama Shad
Alosa alabamae

LOWER JAW AND SNOUT ABOUT EVEN IN LENGTH

SERRATED BONY SPINE

LONG DORSAL FIN

YELLOWISH OR "BRASSY" COLOR

Carp
Cyprinus carpio

2 BARBELS EACH SIDE OF JAW

SERRATED SPINE

SHORT BARBELS

VERY LONG DORSAL FIN

LARGE INDIVIDUALS MAY LOSE BODY MARKINGS AND BE ALMOST BLACK

LARGE MOUTH WITH TEETH

Bowfin or "Mudfish"—*Amia calva*

MALE BLACK SPOT WITH LIGHTER RIM; FEMALE NO RIM OR NO SPOT

—Courtesy of the Florida Game and Fresh Water Fish Commission.

Trout and Salmon Identification Chart

Chinook (King) Salmon
Mouth — black.
Anal rays —
15 to 17.
Color — silvery
before spawning.
Dark during
spawning

Rainbow (Steelhead) Trout
Mouth — white.
Anal rays — 10
to 12. Color —
silvery may have
pinkish streak on sides.
Look-alike —
Salmon species

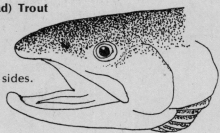

Coho (Silver) Salmon
Mouth — dark,
gums whitish.
Anal rays — 13
to 15. Color — silvery
before spawning.
Dark during
spawning.
Look-alike — Rainbow

Atlantic Salmon
Mouth — darkish
gums whitish.
Anal rays — 9.
Gill Rakers — over 18.
Tongue — pointed
with 5 or 6
small, weak
teeth.
Upper lip — extends to line with rear eye.
Look-alike — Brown Trout

Brown Trout
Mouth —
whitish or
pinkish.
Anal rays —
9 to 10. Gill Rakers —
under 18.
Tongue —
squarish with 5 or more strong
teeth per side. Upper lip — extends past
rear of eye. Look-alike — Atlantic Salmon

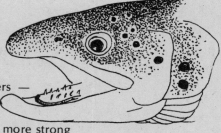

Chinook
Large black spots over tail
and upper portion of
body

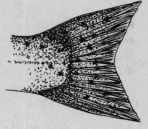

Rainbow
Pepper-size spots
radiating along the rays
on the entire tail.
Additional spots may or
may not adorn the upper
surface of the body

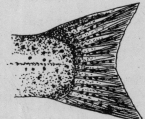

Coho
Small spots on upper
portion of tail

Atlantic Salmon
No spots on tail. X-like
spots on body. Tail
forked. Pectoral fins are
very dark.

Brown Trout
Pectoral fins light. Tail square. Lake-run browns
silvery with or without small x-shaped spots. Spots
become more distinctive as fish is kept out of water
and may take on a reddish hue.

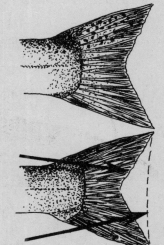

Atlantic Salmon
Hard bony plates in tail
will not compress and
makes it possible to hold
them by tail

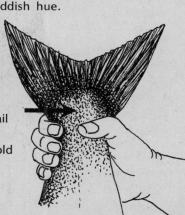

LAKE TROUT, SPLAKE AND BROOK TROUT

Generally these species may be distinguished from the other trout and salmon by their whitish spotted or wormy markings on their backs and by the white leading edge of their lower fins. Separation of the three is much more difficult.

Teeth on the Roof of Mouth

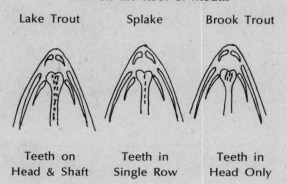

Lake Trout	Splake	Brook Trout
Teeth on Head & Shaft	Teeth in Single Row	Teeth in Head Only

On Brook Trout — Black Border on White

Tail Structure

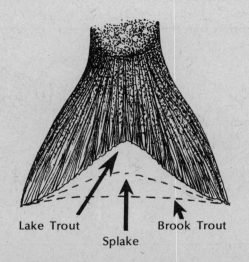

Lake Trout

Splake

Brook Trout

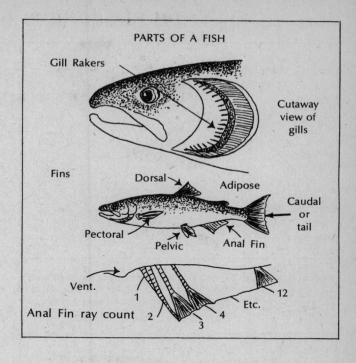

PARTS OF A FISH

Gill Rakers

Cutaway view of gills

Fins

Dorsal Adipose

Caudal or tail

Pectoral

Pelvic

Anal Fin

Vent.

Anal Fin ray count 1 2 3 4 Etc. 12

Less Common Salmon Species Found in the Great Lakes

Pink Salmon
Jaws of males very hooked during spawning season

Color — Silvery before spawning lateral line scales very small over 170

During spawning both sexes dark brown on top and white on belly

Male breeding hump (absent in females)

Normal body shape

Tail with large spots

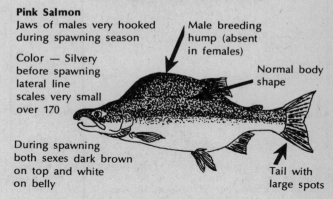

Kokanee Salmon
Jaws of males hooked during spawning season

Color — silvery before spawning both sexes bright red during spawning

Lateral line scales less than 145

Tail without spots

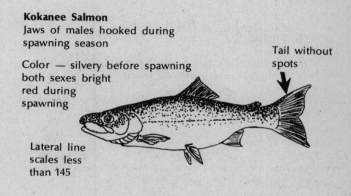

—Courtesy of Michigan Department of Natural Resources.

FILLET A CRAPPIE (Also Bass and Good-Sized Perch or Sunfish)

1a. Cut behind gill cover and fin down to backbone. (A sharp knife with thin, flexible blade is a must for filleting. Best is the Rapala, 6-inch blade. Gerber, Buck and other brands also available.)

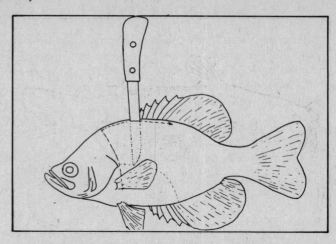

2a. Turn blade and cut along backbone following rib cage with knife point.

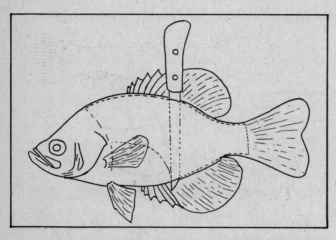

3a. When knife point passes last rib, push blade all the way through the fish. Blade should be flat against backbone. Follow backbone, cut fillet free at tail. Cut fillet free from ribs using knife tip and following rib contours.

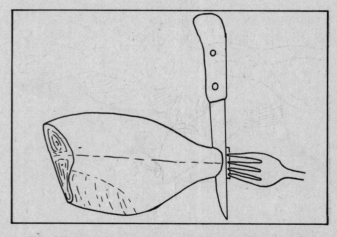

4a. Lay fillet skin-side down, hold tail end of skin down with a fork or fingernail and skin by sliding knife along table top. Knife is held nearly flat.

SCALE A SUNFISH

1b. Grasp sunfish with thumb on gill cover, scale with a large spoon—an old tablespoon with edge worn sharp is best.

2b. Make cut through backbone behind head—cut all the way through the fish.

3b. Pull head down and back removing paired fins and entrails.

Roll in corn meal and fry until tail is crisp. Dorsal and anal fins pull out easily when fish is done.

1b

DRESS A BULLHEAD

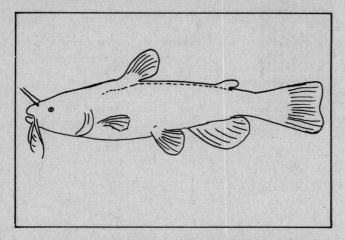

1c. Cut just under skin starting behind adipose fin. Slice off a half-inch wide strip up back. Cut down to backbone at base of skull under the dorsal fin.

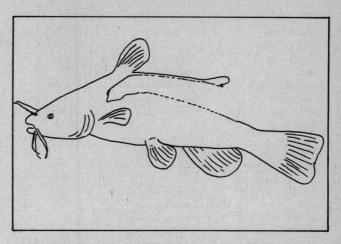

2c. Bend head down to break back (On catfish over 12-14 inches long split the skin down the back, around dorsal fin and head and pull skin off with pliers. Then fillet the skinned carcass.)

3c. Grasp broken end of backbone with pliers; pull head down and back.

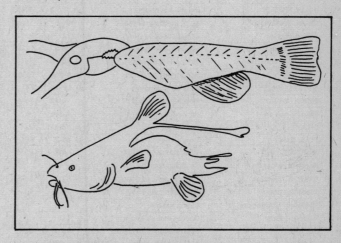

4c. Head, paired fins, entrails and skin are removed with one pull, leaving only caudal and anal fins on skinned carcass. These can be cut off, or left, as you wish.

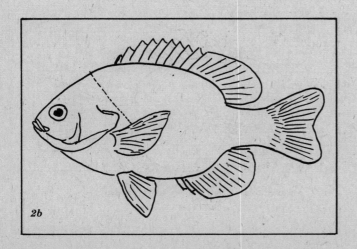

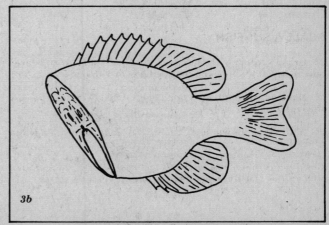

-Courtesy of the Idaho Department of Fish and Game.

World Record Fresh Water Fishes

SPECIES						CAUGHT BY ROD AND REEL		
Common Name	Scientific Name	Lb. Oz.		Length	Girth	Where	When	Angler
BASS, Largemouth	Micropterus salmoides	★	22-4	32½"	28½"	Montgomery Lake, Ga.	June 2, 1932	George W. Perry
BASS, Redeye	Micropterus coosae	★	7-8	23"	18"	Lazer Creek, Ga.	Apr. 9, 1975	Jimmy L. Rogers
BASS, Rock	Ambloplites rupestis		3	13½"	10¾"	York River, Ontario	Aug. 1, 1974	Peter Gulgin
BASS, Smallmouth	Micropterus dolomieui	★	11-15	27"	21⅔"	Dale Hollow Lake, Ky.	July 9, 1955	David L. Hayes
BASS, Spotted	Micropterus punctulatus spp		8-10½	23½"	19⅞"	Smith Lake, Alabama	Feb. 25, 1972	Billy Henderson
BASS, White	Morone chrysops	★	5-5	19½"	17"	Ferguson Lake, Calif.	Mar. 8, 1972	Norman W. Mize
BASS, Yellow	Morone mississippiensis		2-2	14"	13"	Lake Monona, Wis.	Jan. 18, 1972	James Thrun
BLUEGILL	Lepomis macrochirus	★	4-12	15"	18¼"	Ketona Lake, Alabama	Apr. 9, 1950	T. S. Hudson
BOWFIN	Amia calva		19-12	39"		Lake Marion, S.C.	Nov. 5, 1972	M. R. Webster
BUFFALO, Bigmouth	Ictiobus cyprinellus		47-2	43"	30"	Tippecanoe L., Ind.	May 10, 1975	David F. Hulley
BUFFALO; Smallmouth	Ictiobus bubalus		26-10	34½"	28¼"	L. Wylie, N.C.	Feb. 19, 1976	J. Gary Hill
BULLHEAD, Black	Ictalurus melas		8	24"	17¾"	Lake Waccabuc, N.Y.	Aug. 1, 1951	Kani Evans
CARP	Cyprinus carpio		55-5	42"	31"	Clearwater Lake, Minn.	July 10, 1952	Frank J. Ledwein
CATFISH, Blue	Ictalurus furcatus		97	57"	37"	Missouri River, S.D.	Sept. 16, 1959	Edward B. Elliott
CATFISH, Channel	Ictalurus punctatus	★	58	47¼"	29⅛"	Santee-Cooper Res., S.C.	July 7, 1964	W. B. Whaley
CATFISH, Flathead	Pylodictis olivaris		79-8	44"	27"	White River, Indiana	Aug. 13, 1966	Glenn T. Simpson
CHAR, Arctic	Salvelinus alpinus		29-11	39¾"	26"	Arctic R., N.W.T.	Aug. 21, 1968	Jeanne P. Branson
CRAPPIE, Black	Pomoxis nigromaculatus		5	19¼"	18⅝"	Santee-Cooper Res., S.C.	Mar. 15, 1957	Paul E. Foust
CRAPPIE, White	Pomoxis annularis	★	5-3	21"	19"	Enid Dam, Miss.	July 31, 1957	Fred L. Bright
DOLLY VARDEN	Salvelinus malma		32	40½"	29¾"	L. Pend Oreille, Idaho	Oct. 27, 1949	N. L. Higgins
DRUM, Freshwater	Aplodinotus grunniens		54-8	31½"	29"	Nickajack Lake, Tenn.	Apr. 20, 1972	Benny E. Hull
GAR, Alligator	Lepisosteus spatula		279	93"		Rio Grande River, Texas	Dec. 2, 1951	Bill Valverde
GAR, Longnose	Lepisosteus osseus		50-5	72¼"	22¼"	Trinity River, Texas	July 30, 1954	Townsend Miller
GRAYLING, American	Thymallus arcticus	★	5-15	29⅞"	15⅛"	Katseyedie R., N.W.T.	Aug. 16, 1967	Jeanne P. Branson
KOKANEE	Oncorhynchus nerka	★	6-9¾	24½"	14½"	Priest L., Idaho	June 9, 1975	Jerry Verge
MUSKELLUNGE	Esox masquinongy	★	69-15	64½"	31¾"	St. Lawrence River, N.Y.	Sept. 22, 1957	Arthur Lawton
PERCH, White	Morone americanus		4-12	19½"	13"	Messalonskee Lake, Me.	June 4, 1949	Mrs. Earl Small
PERCH, Yellow	Perca flavescens		4-3½			Bordentown, N.J.	May 1865	Dr. C. C. Abbot
PICKEREL, Chain	Esox niger	★	9-6	31"	14"	Homerville, Georgia	Feb. 17, 1961	Baxley McQuaig, Jr.
PIKE, Northern	Esox lucius	★	46-2	52½"	25"	Sacandaga Res., N.Y.	Sept. 15, 1940	Peter Dubuc
REDHORSE, Silver	Moxostoma anisurum		4-2	20½"	14"	Gasconade R., Mo.	Oct. 5, 1974	C. Larry McKinney
SALMON, Atlantic	Salmo salar		79-2			Tana River, Norway	1928	Henrik Henriksen
SALMON, Chinook	Oncorhynchus tshawytscha	★	92	58½"	36"	Skeena River, B.C.	July 19, 1959	Heinz Wichman
SALMON, Chum	Oncorhynchus keta		24-4	40½"	22⅞"	Margarita Bay, Alaska	Aug. 19, 1974	Richard Coleman
SALMON, Landlocked	Salmo salar		22-8	36"		Sebago Lake, Maine	Aug. 1, 1907	Edward Blakely
SALMON, Coho	Oncorhynchus kisutch		31			Cowichan Bay, B.C.	Oct. 11, 1947	Mrs. Lee Hallberg
SAUGER	Stizostedion canadense		8-12	28"	15"	Lake Sakakawea, N.D.	Oct. 6, 1971	Mike Fischer
SHAD, American	Alosa sapidissima	★	9-2	25"	17½"	Enfield, Connecticut	Apr. 28, 1973	Edward P. Nelson
STURGEON, White	Acipenser transmontanus		360	111"	86"	Snake River, Idaho	Apr. 24, 1956	Willard Cravens
SUNFISH, Green	Lepomis cyanellus		2-2	14¾"	14"	Stockton Lake, Missouri	June 18, 1971	Paul M. Dilley
SUNFISH, Redear	Lepomis microlophus		4-8	16¼"	17¾"	Chase City, Virginia	June 19, 1970	Maurice E. Ball
TROUT, Brook	Salvelinus fontinalis		14-8	31½"		Nipigon River, Ontario	July 1916	Dr. W. J. Cook
TROUT, Brown	Salmo trutta		39-8			Loch Awe, Scotland	1866	W. Muir
TROUT, Cutthroat	Salmo clarki		41	39"		Pyramid Lake, Nevada	Dec. 1925	John Skimmerhorn
TROUT, Golden	Salmo aguabonita		11	28"	16"	Cook's Lake, Wyoming	Aug. 5, 1948	Chas. S. Reed
TROUT, Lake	Salvelinus namaycush	★	65	52"	38"	Great Bear L., N.W.T.	Aug. 8, 1970	Larry Daunis
TROUT, Rainbow, Stlhd. or Kamloops	Salmo gairdneri	★	42-2	43"	23½"	Bell Island, Alaska	June 22, 1970	David Robert White
TROUT, Sunapee	Salvelinus aureolus		11-8	33"	17¼"	Lake Sunapee, N.H.	Aug. 1, 1954	Ernest Theoharis
TROUT, Tiger	Brown X Brook		10	27"	16¾"	Deerskin River, Wis.	May 23, 1974	Charles J. Mattek
WALLEYE	Stizostedion vitreum	★	25	41"	29"	Old Hickory Lake, Tenn.	Aug. 1, 1960	Mabry Harper
WARMOUTH	Lepomis gulosus		2	12"	12½"	Sylvania, Ga.	May 4, 1974	Carlton Robbins
WHITEFISH, Lake	Coregonus clupeaformis		13	32¼"	19"	Great Bear L., N.W.T.	July 14, 1974	Robert L. Stintsman
WHITEFISH, Mountain	Prosopium williamsoni		5	19"	14"	Athabasca R., Alberta	June 3, 1963	Orville Welch

Fresh water Records compiled by FIELD & STREAM   ★ Winner in Annual Field & Stream Fishing Contest

—Courtesy of *Field & Stream.*

International Game Fish Association
World Record Marine Fishes

ALBACORE

Other common name: longfin tuna
Scientific name: Thunnus alalunga

LINE CLASS	U. S. CUSTOMARY			METRIC			PLACE	DATE	ANGLER
	Weight lbs. oz.	Length inches	Girth inches	Weight kilo	Length cm	Girth cm			
M-6 lb.	27-8	37½	25	12.47	95.25	63.50	San Diego California, USA	Oct. 4 1972	Joe Bahan
W-6 lb.	14-8	31½	19	6.57	80.01	48.26	San Martin Island Mexico	Oct. 5 1975	Barbara McKinney
M-12 lb.	39-8	43½	32½	17.91	110.49	82.55	Balboa California, USA	July 23 1958	Dr. R. S. Rubaum
*W-12 lb.	29-8	37	24½	13.38	93.98	62.23	San Diego California, USA	Oct. 5 1963	Jane Holland
M-20 lb.	40-12	41½	29	18.48	105.41	73.66	San Diego California, USA	Oct. 4 1972	Glenn R. Bracken
W-20 lb.	50	45½	29	22.67	115.57	73.66	Ocean City Maryland, USA	Sept. 3 1970	Mrs. Carol R. Moss
M-30 lb.	70	47½	33½	31.75	120.65	85.09	Cape Point South Africa	Aug. 25 1974	Geoff. Sonnenberg
W-30 lb.	59-8	45½	29½	26.98	115.57	74.93	Montauk New York, USA	Aug. 14 1971	Eileen B. Merten
M-50 lb.	71-1	45¼	33¾	32.25	115.00	86.00	S. Miguel Azores	Nov. 17 1973	Eduardo do R. Melo
W-50 lb.	41	42	27	18.59	106.68	68.58	Morro Bay California, USA	Sept. 17 1967	Theresa Bullard
M-80 lb.	69-2	46	32	31.35	116.84	81.28	Montauk New York, USA	Aug. 21 1964	Larry R. Kranz
W-80 lb.	29	37	23	13.15	93.98	58.42	Morro Bay California, USA	Sept. 24 1967	Theresa Bullard
All-Tackle M-130 lb.	74-13	50	34¾	33.93	127.00	88.26	Arguineguin Canary Islands	Oct. 28 1973	Olof Idegren
W-130 lb.	Vacant — Minimum Acceptance Weight — 55 lbs. (24.91 kilos)								
*TIE W-12 lb.	29-8	37¼	24½	13.38	94.61	62.23	Morro Bay California, USA	Sept. 3 1973	Barbara Louise McKinney

AMBERJACK (greater)

Scientific name: Seriola dumerili

M-6 lb.	20	38	22½	9.07	96.52	57.15	Pinas Bay Panama	Jan. 23 1975	Edwin D. Kennedy
W-6 lb.	13	33½	17¾	5.89	85.09	45.08	Key West Florida, USA	Mar. 6 1973	Charlyne Terrell
M-12 lb.	80	66	35½	36.28	167.64	90.17	Miami Beach Florida, USA	May 19 1973	Jeffery F. Trotta
W-12 lb.	78-4	60¼	34½	35.49	153.03	87.63	Key Largo Florida, USA	Mar. 23 1969	Pamela J. Habicht
M-20 lb.	101-8	61	39	46.04	154.94	99.06	Palm Beach Florida, USA	Feb. 26 1964	Robert R. Boomhower
W-20 lb.	83-14	57¼	36	38.04	145.41	91.44	Challenger Bank Bermuda	July 28 1966	L. Edna Perinchief
All-Tackle M-30 lb.	149	71	41¾	67.58	180.34	106.04	Bermuda	June 21 1964	Peter Simons
W-30 lb.	101	67	45	45.81	170.18	114.30	Palm Beach Florida, USA	Mar. 31 1970	Mrs. Cynthia Boomhower
M-50 lb.	132	63	39¼	59.87	160.02	99.69	La Paz Mexico	July 21 1964	Howard H. Hahn
W-50 lb.	108	69	36	48.98	175.26	91.44	Palm Beach Florida, USA	Dec. 30 1967	Peggy Kester Mumford
M-80 lb.	142-14	71¾	42¼	64.80	182.24	107.31	Bermuda	Aug. 7 1969	Nelson Chesterfield Simons

AMBERJACK, greater (cont'd)

LINE CLASS	Weight lbs. oz.	Length inches	Girth inches	Weight kilo	Length cm	Girth cm	PLACE	DATE	ANGLER
	U.S. CUSTOMARY			METRIC					
W-80 lb.	106-8	65	39	48.30	165.10	99.06	Pinas Bay Panama	July 9 1960	Helen Robinson
M-130 lb.	133	66	37	60.32	167.64	93.98	Islamorada Florida, USA	Apr. 6 1968	Louis E. Woster
W-130 lb.	85	61	36	38.55	154.94	91.44	Palm Beach Florida, USA	Apr. 29 1971	Mrs. Cynthia Boomhower

BARRACUDA (great)
Scientific name: Sphyraena barracuda

LINE CLASS	Weight lbs. oz.	Length inches	Girth inches	Weight kilo	Length cm	Girth cm	PLACE	DATE	ANGLER
M-6 lb.	49-7	60	24	22.42	152.40	60.96	Cairns Australia	Sept. 25 1974	Robert Oliver
W-6 lb.	27-8	54½	18	12.47	138.43	45.72	Palm Beach Inlet Florida, USA	May 28 1974	Elizabeth Litchfield
M-12 lb.	49-4	56	21½	22.33	142.24	54.61	Margarita Venezuela, SA	Jan. 9 1960	Gerardo Sanson
W-12 lb.	44-4	59½	26	20.07	151.13	66.04	Key West Florida, USA	July 4 1975	Caroline Whittaker
M-20 lb.	60-10	64½	26½	27.49	163.83	67.31	Cairns Australia	Nov. 5 1968	Desmond R. Schumann
W-20 lb.	48	64½	26	21.77	163.83	66.04	Heron Island Australia	Aug. 21 1970	Mrs. Glen Mactaggart
M-30 lb.	70-12	64	29	32.09	162.56	73.66	Malindi Coast Kenya, Africa	Oct. 26 1973	Major D. C. Bagworth
W-30 lb.	43	60	26	19.50	152.40	66.04	Key Largo Florida, USA	Dec. 9 1956	Mrs. Robert M. Scully
All-Tackle M-50 lb.	83	72¼	29	37.64	183.51	73.66	Lagos Nigeria, Africa	Jan. 13 1952	K. J. W. Hackett
W-50 lb.	47-4	63	21	21.43	160.02	53.34	Pemba Channel Kenya, Africa	July 27 1973	Mrs. Ingrid Papworth
M-80 lb.	67	65	29¾	30.39	165.10	75.56	Islamorada Florida, USA	Jan. 29 1949	Harold K. Goodstone
W-80 lb.	66-4	70	25-1/5	30.05	177.80	64.00	Cape Lopez Gabon, Africa	July 17 1955	Mme. M. Halley
M-130 lb.	Vacant — Minimum Acceptance Weight — 62 lbs. (28.08 kilos)								
W-130 lb.	Vacant — Minimum Acceptance Weight — 62 lbs. (28.08 kilos)								

BASS (black sea)
Scientific name: Centropristis striata

LINE CLASS	Weight lbs. oz.	Length inches	Girth inches	Weight kilo	Length cm	Girth cm	PLACE	DATE	ANGLER
*M-6 lb.	4-14½	23	15¾	2.22	58.42	40.00	Virginia Beach Virginia, USA	Mar. 8 1974	Michael E. Hayes
*W-6 lb.	3-12	20½	14½	1.70	52.07	36.83	Virginia Beach Virginia, USA	May 1 1972	Mrs. Charlotte J. Wright
*M-12 lb.	5-6	21½	16	2.43	54.61	40.64	Virginia Beach Virginia, USA	May 16 1970	J. David Wright
W-12 lb.	4-4	20½	15¼	1.92	52.07	38.73	Virginia Beach Virginia, USA	May 21 1972	Mrs. Michael E. Hayes
M-20 lb.	6-1	24-1/8	17	2.74	61.27	43.18	Seabright New Jersey, USA	July 1 1958	William Young
W-20 lb.	5-2	23	15	2.32	58.42	38.10	Virginia Beach Virginia, USA	May 17 1971	Mrs. Charlotte J. Wright
*M-30 lb.	5-5	21	19	2.40	53.34	48.26	Virginia Beach Virginia, USA	May 29 1972	Michael E. Hayes
W-30 lb.	5-14	25	14	2.66	63.50	35.56	Cape Henry Virginia, USA	Oct. 2 1972	Mary Lou Penny Durney
All-Tackle M-50 lb.	8	22	19	3.62	55.88	48.26	Nantucket Sound Massachusetts, USA	May 13 1951	H. R. Rider
W-50 lb.	5-1	20½	16	2.29	52.07	40.64	Panama City Beach Florida, USA	July 21 1956	Mrs. R. H. Martin

LINE CLASS	U. S. CUSTOMARY			METRIC			PLACE	DATE	ANGLER
	Weight lbs. oz.	Length inches	Girth inches	Weight kilo	Length cm	Girth cm			
M-80 lb.	Vacant — Minimum Acceptance Weight — 8 lbs. (3.62 kilos)								
W-80 lb.	Vacant — Minimum Acceptance Weight — 8 lbs. (3.62 kilos)								
M-130 lb.	Vacant — Minimum Acceptance Weight — 8 lbs. (3.62 kilos)								
W-130 lb.	Vacant — Minimum Acceptance Weight — 8 lbs. (3.62 kilos)								
*TIES M-6 lb.	5-3	22½	16½	2.35	57.15	41.91	Virginia, USA	1974	Harry L. Hall, Jr.
M-6 lb.	5-2	23	15½	2.32	59.05	39.37	New York, USA	1974	John H. Windels, III
W-6 lb.	4-3	20	13¼	1.89	50.80	33.65	Virginia, USA	1974	Mrs. Charlotte J. Wright
M-12 lb.	5-10	22¾	16½	2.55	57.70	41.27	New York, USA	1974	Michael Harrington
M-30 lb.	5-8	24	15	2.49	60.96	38.10	N. Carolina, USA	1973	George F. Moore

BASS (giant sea)

Scientific name: Stereolepis gigas

LINE CLASS	Weight lbs. oz.	Length inches	Girth inches	Weight kilo	Length cm	Girth cm	PLACE	DATE	ANGLER
M-6 lb.	Vacant — Minimum Acceptance Weight — 56 lbs. (25.36 kilos)								
W-6 lb.	Vacant — Minimum Acceptance Weight — 56 lbs. (25.36 kilos)								
M-12 lb.	112-8	57	44	51.02	144.78	111.76	San Francisco Island Mexico	June 12 1957	D. B. Rosenthal
W-12 lb.	Vacant — Minimum Acceptance Weight — 90 lbs. (40.82 kilos)								
M-20 lb.	425	85	76	192.77	215.90	193.04	Point Mugu California, USA	Oct. 1 1960	C. C. Joiner
W-20 lb.	120	55	40	54.43	139.70	101.60	Malibu California, USA	Jan. 6 1957	Jane D. Hill
M-30 lb.	448	88	72	203.21	223.52	182.88	Coronado Islands Mexico	Apr. 13 1975	R. H. Gautier
W-30 lb.	108-8	55	42½	49.21	139.70	107.95	San Pablo Mexico	Dec. 29 1963	Frances Enfinger
M-50 lb.	557-3	88¼	78	252.73	224.15	198.12	Catalina Island California, USA	July 1 1962	Richard M. Lane
W-50 lb.	419	87¾	63½	190.05	222.88	161.29	Coronado Islands Mexico	Oct. 8 1960	Bettie Sears
All-Tackle M-80 lb.	563-8	89	72	255.60	226.06	182.88	Anacapa Island California, USA	Aug. 20 1968	James D. McAdam, Jr.
W-80 lb.	452	86¼	64¼	205.02	219.07	163.19	Coronado Islands Mexico	Oct. 8 1960	Lorene Wheeler
*M-130 lb.	514	86	82	233.14	218.44	208.28	San Clemente California, USA	Aug. 29 1955	J. Patterson
W-130 lb.	Vacant — Minimum Acceptance Weight — 425 lbs. (192.52 kilos								
*TIE M-130 lb.	514	90	80	233.14	228.60	203.20	Box Canyon California, USA	Nov. 15 1961	Joe M. Arve

BASS (striped)

Other common name: rockfish
Scientific name: Morone saxatilis

LINE CLASS	Weight lbs. oz.	Length inches	Girth inches	Weight kilo	Length cm	Girth cm	PLACE	DATE	ANGLER
M-6 lb.	38	48½	28	17.23	123.19	71.12	Atlantic City New Jersey, USA	Nov. 5 1973	Charles P. Bliss
W-6 lb.	32	45½	23¼	14.51	115.57	59.05	Cape Cod Bay Massachusetts, USA	July 3 1975	Mae B. Foster
M-12 lb.	61 - 10	53	30	27.95	134.62	76.20	Block Island Rhode Island, USA	July 5 1956	L. A. Garceau

BASS, striped (cont'd)

LINE CLASS	U.S. CUSTOMARY			METRIC			PLACE	DATE	ANGLER
	Weight lbs. oz.	Length inches	Girth inches	Weight kilo	Length cm	Girth cm			
W-12 lb.	47	49½	—	21.31	125.73	—	Umpqua R. Oregon, USA	Aug. 21 1958	Mrs. Margaret Hulen
*M-20 lb.	67	55	29½	30.39	139.70	74.93	Block Island Rhode Island, USA	May 31 1963	Jack Ryan
W-20 lb.	57 - 8	50	30	26.08	127.00	76.20	Block Island Sound New York, USA	Aug. 28 1959	Mary R. Aubry
M-30 lb.	63-8	52½	29	28.80	133.35	73.66	Jones Beach Inlet New York, USA	Aug. 17 1973	William E. King, Jr.
W-30 lb.	64 - 8	54	30	29.25	137.16	76.20	North Truro Massachusetts, USA	Aug. 14 1960	Rosa O. Webb
All-Tackle M-50 lb.	72	54½	31	32.65	138.43	78.74	Cuttyhunk Massachusetts, USA	Oct. 10 1969	Edward J. Kirker
W-50 lb.	64	50	31	29.03	127.00	78.74	Sea Bright New Jersey, USA	June 27 1971	Mrs. Asie Espenak
M-80 lb.	Vacant — Minimum Acceptance Weight — 54 lbs. (24.46 kilos)								
W-80 lb.	56	53½	33½	25.40	135.89	85.09	Sandy Hook New Jersey, USA	June 7 1955	Mrs. H. J. Sarnoski
M-130 lb.	Vacant — Minimum Acceptance Weight — 54 lbs. (24.46 kilos)								
W-130 lb.	Vacant — Minimum Acceptance Weight — 54 lbs. (24.46 kilos)								
*TIE M-20 lb.	67	54-1/8	32½	30.39	137.47	82.55	Greenhill Rhode Island, USA	Oct. 3 1965	Wilfred Fontaine

BLUEFISH
Scientific name: Pomatomus saltatrix

M-6 lb.	18-11	40	20	8.47	101.60	50.80	Atlantic Beach North Carolina, USA	Nov. 19 1972	Daniel W. Able
W-6 lb.	14-15	36	19	6.77	91.44	48.26	Nantucket Massachusetts, USA	Sept. 1 1972	Suzanne Cowan
M-12 lb.	24-3	41	22	10.97	104.14	5.58	San Miguel Azores	Aug. 27 1953	M. A. da Silva Veloso
W-12 lb.	16-10	36	19	7.54	91.44	48.26	Montauk New York, USA	June 24 1961	Gloria Better
M-20 lb.	23-12	40	28	10.77	101.60	71.12	Cape May New Jersey, USA	Oct. 9 1971	William Di Santo
W-20 lb.	24-8	40	23½	11.11	101.60	59.69	Nags Head North Carolina, USA	Nov. 12 1971	Mrs. Rita Mazelle
M-30 lb.	22	39	22	9.97	99.06	55.88	Avon North Carolina, USA	Nov. 27 1969	Michael E. Hayes
W-30 lb.	21-8	37	23	9.75	93.98	58.42	Truro Massachusetts, USA	Oct. 10 1970	Ruth M. Anderson
All-Tackle M-50 lb.	31-12	47	23	14.40	119.38	58.42	Hatteras Inlet North Carolina, USA	Jan. 30 1972	James M. Hussey
W-50 lb.	23-15	40½	23½	10.85	102.87	59.69	Nags Head North Carolina, USA	Nov. 19 1970	Mrs. Joyce Payne Bell
M-80 lb.	22-12	38	21-7/8	10.31	96.52	55.56	Arguineguin Gran Canaria	July 19 1971	Kenneth V. Oulton
W-80 lb.	21-8	39¾	21½	9.75	100.96	54.61	Virginia Beach Virginia, USA	Aug. 8 1971	Katherine K. Ayers
M-130 lb.	Vacant — Minimum Acceptance Weight — 19 lbs. (8.61 kilos)								
W-130 lb.	Vacant — Minimum Acceptance Weight — 19 lbs. (8.61 kilos)								

BONEFISH
Scientific name: Albula vulpes

M-6 lb.	13-2	31½	17 1/8	5.95	80.01	43.49	Islamorada Florida, USA	Oct. 25 1974	Russell Albury

BONEFISH (cont'd)

LINE CLASS	U. S. CUSTOMARY			METRIC			PLACE	DATE	ANGLER
	Weight lbs. oz.	Length inches	Girth inches	Weight kilo	Length cm	Girth cm			
W-6 lb.	13-2	29½	18	5.95	74.93	45.72	Islamorda Florida, USA	Apr. 5 1973	Charlotte Rowland
M-12 lb.	16	33½	18½	7.25	85.09	46.99	Bimini Bahamas	Feb. 25 1971	Jerry Lavenstein
W-12 lb.	15	32½	18½	6.80	82.55	46.99	Bimini Bahamas	Mar. 20 1961	Andrea Tose
*M-20 lb.	14	34¼	17½	6.35	86.99	44.45	Bermuda	Dec. 29 1950	Dr. H. R. Becker
W-20 lb.	13-12	30¾	17½	6.23	78.10	44.45	Exuma Bahamas	Jan. 3 1956	Mrs. B. A. Garson
All-Tackle M-30 lb.	19	39-5/8	17	8.61	100.64	43.18	Zululand South Africa	May 26 1962	Brian W. Batchelor
W-30 lb.	Vacant — Minimum Acceptance Weight — 14 lbs. (6.34 kilos)								
M-50 lb.	17-8	40	18	7.93	101.60	45.72	Oahu Hawaii, USA	Aug. 23 1952	Jack Yoshida
W-50 lb.	Vacant — Minimum Acceptance Weight — 14 lbs. (6.34 kilos)								
M-80	18-2	41½	17-15/16	8.22	105.41	45.56	Kauai Hawaii, USA	Oct. 11 1954	Wm. Badua
W-80 lb.	Vacant — Minimum Acceptance Weight — 14 lbs. (6.34 kilos)								
M-130 lb.	Vacant — Minimum Acceptance Weight — 14 lbs. (6.34 kilos)								
W-130 lb.	Vacant — Minimum Acceptance Weight — 14 lbs. (6.34 kilos)								
*TIE M-20 lb.	14-4	31½	19	6.46	80.01	48.26	Islamorada Florida, USA	Jan. 5 1972	Mike Hyman

BONITO (Atlantic)

Scientific name: Sarda sarda

M-6 lb.	Vacant — Minimum Acceptance Weight — 6 lbs. (2.71 kilos)
W-6 lb.	Vacant — Minimum Acceptance Weight — 6 lbs. (2.71 kilos)
M-12 lb.	Vacant — Minimum Acceptance Weight — 6 lbs. (2.71 kilos)
W-12 lb.	Vacant — Minimum Acceptance Weight — 6 lbs. (2.71 kilos)
M-20 lb.	Vacant — Minimum Acceptance Weight — 9 lbs. (4.07 kilos)
W-20 lb.	Vacant — Minimum Acceptance Weight — 9 lbs. (4.07 kilos)
M-30 lb.	Vacant — Minimum Acceptance Weight — 9 lbs. (4.07 kilos)
W-30 lb.	Vacant — Minimum Acceptance Weight — 9 lbs. (4.07 kilos)
M-50 lb.	Vacant — Minimum Acceptance Weight — 9 lbs. (4.07 kilos)
W-50 lb.	Vacant — Minimum Acceptance Weight — 9 lbs. (4.07 kilos)
M-80 lb.	Vacant — Minimum Acceptance Weight — 12 lbs. (5.43 kilos)
W-80 lb.	Vacant — Minimum Acceptance Weight — 12 lbs. (5.43 kilos)
M-130 lb.	Vacant — Minimum Acceptance Weight — 12 lbs. (5.43 kilos)
W-130 lb.	Vacant — Minimum Acceptance Weight — 12 lbs. (5.43 kilos)

BONITO (Pacific)

Other common names: Australian bonito / striped bonito
Scientific name: Sarda spp.

LINE CLASS	Weight lbs. oz.	Length Inches	Girth Inches	Weight kilo	Length cm	Girth cm	PLACE	DATE	ANGLER
	U. S. CUSTOMARY			**METRIC**					
M-6 lb.	Vacant — Minimum Acceptance Weight — 6 lbs. (2.71 kilos)								
W-6 lb.	Vacant — Minimum Acceptance Weight — 6 lbs. (2.71 kilos)								
M-12 lb.	Vacant — Minimum Acceptance Weight — 6 lbs. (2.71 kilos)								
W-12 lb.	Vacant — Minimum Acceptance Weight — 6 lbs. (2.71 kilos)								
M-20 lb.	Vacant — Minimum Acceptance Weight — 6 lbs. (2.71 kilos)								
W-20 lb.	Vacant — Minimum Acceptance Weight — 6 lbs. (2.71 kilos)								
M-30 lb.	7	27	14½	3.17	68.58	36.83	Palmar Sur Costa Rica, CA	Mar. 12 1975	Frank L. McGinn
W-30 lb.	Vacant — Minimum Acceptance Weight — 6 lbs. (2.71 kilos)								
M-50 lb.	Vacant — Minimum Acceptance Weight — 9 lbs. (4.07 kilos)								
W-50 lb.	23-8	35¼	23¼	10.65	89.53	59.05	Victoria, Mahe Seychelles	Feb. 19 1975	Mrs. Anne Cochain
M-80 lb.	Vacant — Minimum Acceptance Weight — 12 lbs. (5.43 kilos)								
W-80 lb.	Vacant — Minimum Acceptance Weight — 12 lbs. (5.43 kilos)								
M-130 lb.	Vacant — Minimum Acceptance Weight — 12 lbs. (5.43 kilos)								
W-130 lb.	Vacant — Minimum Acceptance Weight — 12 lbs. (5.43 kilos)								

COBIA

Other common name: ling
Scientific name: Rachycentron canadum

LINE CLASS	Weight lbs. oz.	Length Inches	Girth Inches	Weight kilo	Length cm	Girth cm	PLACE	DATE	ANGLER
M-6 lb.	45-8	54½	19½	20.63	138.43	49.53	Flamingo Florida, USA	Nov. 28 1973	Ray Cantarrana, Jr.
W-6 lb.	9-11	33	14¼	4.40	83.82	36.20	Daytona Beach Florida, USA	Aug. 7 1975	Shirley C. Gaines
*M-12 lb.	70	60	31½	31.75	152.40	80.01	Gulf of Mexico Texas, USA	May 13 1955	H. A. Norris, Jr.
W-12 lb.	55	60-5/16	29-3/8	24.94	153.19	74.61	Islamorada Florida, USA	Feb. 14 1971	Mrs. Marcia Maizler
M-20 lb.	91	56	30	41.27	142.24	76.20	Crystal Beach Florida, USA	Apr. 25 1962	Roy English
W-20 lb.	67	60	29	30.39	152.40	73.66	Cape Charles Virginia, USA	July 5 1968	Judith Anne Gingell
M-30	100	71½	36	45.35	181.61	91.44	Point Lookout Queensland, Australia	Oct. 4 1962	Peter R. Bristow
W-30 lb.	68-8	60	28½	31.07	152.40	72.39	Onancock Virginia, USA	June 6 1968	Mrs. Frances M. Roberts
All-Tackle M-50 lb.	110-5	63	34	50.03	160.02	86.36	Mombasa Kenya, Africa	Sept. 8 1964	Eric Tinworth
W-50 lb.	85	67	30½	38.55	170.18	77.47	Queensland Australia	Aug. 15 1964	Margaret Keid
M-80 lb.	90	65½	31	40.82	166.37	78.74	Ocean City Maryland, USA	Aug. 31 1949	Charles J. Stine
W-80 lb.	97	66½	33	43.99	168.91	83.82	Oregon Inlet N. Carolina, USA	June 4 1952	Mary W. Black
M-130 lb.	Vacant — Minimum Acceptance Weight — 83 lbs. (37.59 kilos)								
W-130 lb.	Vacant — Minimum Acceptance Weight — 83 lbs. (37.59 kilos)								
*TIE M-12 lb.	70-2	62	28	31.80	157.48	71.12	Key West Florida, USA	Jan. 27 1973	Alan H. Walton

COD

Scientific name: Gadus morhua*

LINE CLASS	U. S. CUSTOMARY			METRIC			PLACE	DATE	ANGLER
	Weight lbs. oz.	Length inches	Girth inches	Weight kilo	Length cm	Girth cm			
M-6 lb.	19-1½	38	22	8.66	96.52	55.88	Folkestone England	Jan. 10 1973	Christopher O'Hara
W-6 lb.	Vacant — Minimum Acceptance Weight — 15 lbs. (6.79 kilos)								
M-12 lb.	55	66	38	24.94	167.64	96.52	Plum Island Massachusetts, USA	July 6 1958	W. C. Dunn
W-12 lb.	17-7	36-3/8	21¼	7.90	92.39	53.97	Plymouth England	Sept. 19 1971	Mrs. Rita Barrett
All-Tackle M-20 lb.	98-12	63	41	44.79	160.02	104.14	Isle of Shoals New Hampshire, USA	June 8 1969	Alphonse J. Bielevich
W-20 lb.	71-8	58	31	32.43	147.32	78.74	Cape Cod Massachusetts, USA	Aug. 2 1964	Muriel Betts
M-30 lb.	81	54-7/8	35½	36.74	139.38	90.17	Brielle New Jersey, USA	Mar. 15 1967	Joseph Chesla
W-30 lb.	33-14	45	28	15.36	114.30	71.12	Fire Island Inlet New York, USA	Aug. 23 1975	Patty Ishkanian
M-50 lb.	80-9	58	38	36.54	147.32	96.52	Boston Massachusetts, USA	May 14 1972	William Bright
W-50 lb.	54-2	55¼	33	24.55	140.33	83.82	Nantucket Island Massachusetts, USA	Sept. 28 1970	Gail A. Mosher
M-80 lb.	Vacant — Minimum Acceptance Weight — 75 lbs. (33.97 kilos)								
W-80 lb.	81-12	59¾	39	37.08	151.76	99.06	Middlebank Massachusetts, USA	Sept. 24 1970	Mrs. Sophie Karwa
M-130 lb.	Vacant — Minimum Acceptance Weight — 75 lbs. (33.97 kilos)								
W-130 lb.	Vacant — Minimum Acceptance Weight — 75 lbs. (33.97 kilos)								

DOLPHIN

Other common name: dorado*
Scientific name: Coryphaena hippurus*

LINE CLASS	Weight lbs. oz.	Length inches	Girth inches	Weight kilo	Length cm	Girth cm	PLACE	DATE	ANGLER
M-6 lb.	46-5	61¾	30	21.00	156.84	76.20	Point Venus Tahiti, Fr. Polynesia	Feb. 10 1973	Alban Ellacott
W-6 lb.	30	52½	22½	13.60	133.35	57.15	West Palm Beach Florida, USA	March 27 1974	Mrs. Herbert L. Allison
M-12 lb.	59-8	64	33	26.98	162.56	83.82	Pinas Bay Panama	Jan. 28 1971	Russell M. Anderson
W-12 lb.	55-2	59¾	32½	25.00	151.76	82.55	Mazatlan Mexico	Oct. 18 1964	Marguerite H. Barry
M-20 lb.	64-12	69	32¾	29.37	175.26	83.18	Islamorada Florida, USA	June 7 1970	Donald H. Jackson
W-20 lb.	83-6	57½	37½	37.81	146.05	95.25	Mazatlan Mexico	Apr. 24 1972	Mrs. Eugene W. Wooten
M-30 lb.	66	68	36	29.93	172.72	91.44	Boca Chica Dominican Republic	Mar. 1 1975	Fernando Viyella
W-30 lb.	73-11	59½	43½	33.42	151.13	110.49	Baja California Mexico	July 12 1962	Barbara Kibbee Jayne
All-Tackle M-50 lb.	85	69	37½	38.55	175.26	95.25	Spanish Wells Bahamas	May 29 1968	Richard Seymour
W-50 lb.	67	68	31-3/4	30.39	172.72	80.64	Miami Beach Florida, USA	Jan. 2 1968	Janet Shepro
M-80 lb.	77	74½	35	34.92	189.23	88.90	Nags Head N. Carolina, USA	July 3 1973	Louis Van Miller
W-80 lb.	67	65	32	30.39	165.10	81.28	Chub Cay Bahamas	Mar. 13 1966	Ruth Stanley
M-130 lb.	72-8	58½	35¼	32.88	148.59	89.53	Honolulu Hawaii, USA	Mar. 13 1956	G. Perry
W-130 lb.	Vacant — Minimum Acceptance Weight — 64 lbs. (28.99 kilos)								

DRUM (black)

Scientific name: Pogonias cromis

LINE CLASS	U. S. CUSTOMARY			METRIC			PLACE	DATE	ANGLER
	Weight lbs. oz.	Length inches	Girth inches	Weight kilo	Length cm	Girth cm			
M-6 lb.	52	44	31½	23.58	111.76	80.01	Cape Charles Virginia, USA	May 10 1973	Harry L. Gerwin
W-6 lb.	Vacant — Minimum Acceptance Weight — 39 lbs. (17.66 kilos)								
M-12 lb.	89	51	40½	40.37	129.54	102.87	Delaware Bay New Jersey, USA	May 14 1971	John K. Osborne, Jr.
W-12 lb.	58-12	45-3/8	36	26.64	115.25	91.44	Atlantic Beach N. Carolina, USA	May 8 1959	Juel W. Duke
M-20 lb.	88-4	58½	40	40.02	148.59	101.60	Delaware Bay New Jersey, USA	June 8 1972	Josie A. Trolli, Jr.
W-20 lb.	80-8	52	39	36.51	132.08	99.06	Cape Charles Virginia, USA	April 27 1974	Louise M. Gaskill
M-30 lb.	107	53½	43	48.53	135.89	109.22	Cape Charles Virginia, USA	April 29 1974	Everette M. Masten, Jr.
W-30 lb.	80	52	39	36.28	132.08	99.06	Cape Charles Virginia, USA	May 24 1975	Diane Dattoli
All-Tackle M-50 lb.	113-1	53 1/8	43½	51.28	134.93	110.49	Lewes Delaware, USA	Sept. 15 1975	Gerald M. Townsend
W-50 lb.	93	50½	42	42.18	128.27	106.68	Fernandina Beach Florida, USA	Mar. 28 1957	Mrs. Stella Moore
M-80 lb.	111	56	45	50.34	142.24	114.30	Cape Charles Virginia, USA	May 3 1974	G. L. Hopkins
W-80 lb.	111	53½	45¾	50.34	135.89	116.20	Cape Charles Virginia, USA	May 20 1973	Betty D. Hall
M-130 lb.	Vacant — Minimum Acceptance Weight — 78 lbs. (35.33 kilos)								
W-130 lb.	Vacant — Minimum Acceptance Weight — 78 lbs. (35.33 kilos)								

DRUM (red)

Other common names: redfish/channel bass
Scientific name: Sciaenops ocellata

LINE CLASS	Weight lbs. oz.	Length inches	Girth inches	Weight kilo	Length cm	Girth cm	PLACE	DATE	ANGLER
M-6 lb.	32-4	43	25	14.62	109.22	63.50	Flagler Beach Florida, USA	Mar. 23 1975	Tony Ceribelli
W-6 lb.	30-4	43	25	13.72	109.22	63.50	Empire Louisiana, USA	Apr. 5 1973	Priscilla Jordan
M-12 lb.	69-3	52	32	31.38	132.08	81.28	Gwynns Island Virginia, USA	July 10 1975	John Oscar Everett
W-12 lb.	51-8	50¼	29	23.36	127.63	73.66	Cape Hatteras N. Carolina, USA	Nov. 19 1958	Joan S. Dull
M-20 lb.	72-7	55¼	31¾	32.85	140.33	80.64	Hatteras Island N. Carolina, USA	Nov. 27 1973	Wayne Plageman
W-20 lb.	53-8	50¾	29	24.26	128.90	73.66	Cape Hatteras N. Carolina, USA	April 16 1972	Mrs. Lucille Herbig
All-Tackle M-30 lb.	90	55½	38¼	40.82	140.97	97.15	Rodanthe N. Carolina, USA	Nov. 7 1973	Elvin Hooper
W-30 lb.	69-8	51 ½	33 ¼	31.52	130.81	84.45	Cape Hatteras N. Carolina, USA	Nov. 16 1958	Jean Browning
M-50 lb.	83	52	29	37.64	132.08	73.66	Cape Charles Virginia, USA	Aug. 5 1949	Zack Waters, Jr.
W-50 lb.	55	50	29	24.94	127.00	73.66	Smith Island Virginia, USA	Oct. 9 1966	Margaret M. Hutson
M-80 lb.	Vacant — Minimum Acceptance Weight — 68 lbs. (30.80 kilos)								
W-80 lb.	Vacant — Minimum Acceptance Weight — 68 lbs. (30.80 kilos)								
M-130 lb.	Vacant — Minimum Acceptance Weight — 68 lbs. (30.80 kilos)								
W-130 lb.	Vacant — Minimum Acceptance Weight — 68 lbs. (30.80 kilos)								

FLOUNDER

LINE CLASS	U.S. CUSTOMARY			METRIC			PLACE	DATE	ANGLER
	Weight lbs. oz.	Length inches	Girth inches	Weight kilo	Length cm	Girth cm			
M-6 lb.	18-3	33	31½	8.24	83.82	80.01	Fire Island, Bayshore New York, USA	Dec. 11 1974	Dr. Einar F. Grell
W-6 lb.	5	23 7/8	19¼	2.26	60.64	48.89	Gulf Breeze Florida, USA	June 30 1974	Rose Marie Bonifay
M-12 lb.	20	33	33	9.07	83.82	83.82	Topsail Island N. Carolina, USA	Oct. 26 1972	Chris A. Bowen
W-12 lb.	12-2	31¼	25¼	5.49	79.37	64.13	Avalon New Jersey, USA	Sept. 8 1957	Mrs. Alfred Bernstein
All-Tackle M-20 lb.	30-12	38½	30½	13.94	97.79	77.47	Vina del Mar Chile, SA	Nov. 1 1971	Agusto Nunez Moreno
W-20 lb.	16-15½	34½	28½	7.69	87.63	72.39	Captree New York, USA	July 4 1971	Florence Eidman
M-30 lb.	22-1	37	35	10.00	93.98	88.90	Caleta Horcon Chile, SA	Dec. 8 1965	F. I. Aguirrezabal
W-30 lb.	13-11	33	27½	6.20	83.82	69.85	Long Branch New Jersey, USA	Aug. 20 1953	Mrs. Leslie H. Taylor
M-50 lb.	22-7	35	34	10.17	88.90	86.36	Montauk, L.I. New York, USA	Sept. 15 1975	Charles Nappi
W-50 lb.	20-7	37	29½	9.27	93.98	74.93	Long Island New York, USA	July 8 1957	Mrs. M. Fredriksen
M-80 lb.	Vacant — Minimum Acceptance Weight — 23 lbs. (10.41 kilos)								
W-80 lb.	Vacant — Minimum Acceptance Weight — 23 lbs. (10.41 kilos)								
M-130 lb.	Vacant — Minimum Acceptance Weight — 23 lbs. (10.41 kilos)								
W-130 lb.	Vacant — Minimum Acceptance Weight — 23 lbs. (10.41 kilos)								

JEWFISH

LINE CLASS	Weight lbs. oz.	Length inches	Girth inches	Weight kilo	Length cm	Girth cm	PLACE	DATE	ANGLER
M-6 lb.	Vacant — Minimum Acceptance Weight — 40 lbs. (18.12 kilos)								
W-6 lb.	Vacant — Minimum Acceptance Weight — 40 lbs. (18.12 kilos)								
M-12 lb.	365-8	81¾	69	165.78	207.64	175.26	Flamingo Florida, USA	Mar. 31 1975	Kenny Bittner
W-12 lb.	110	58½	39½	49.89	148.59	100.33	Islamorada Florida, USA	Aug. 2 1961	Mrs. Gar Wood, Jr.
M-20 lb.	343	82	61	155.58	208.28	154.94	Flamingo Florida, USA	Jan. 6 1968	Ralph Delph
W-20 lb.	42-8	43	29	19.27	109.22	73.66	Florida Bay Florida, USA	Nov. 7 1969	Helen Robinson
M-30 lb.	430	96	67	195.04	243.84	170.18	Ft. Lauderdale Florida, USA	Apr. 25 1967	Curt Johnson
W-30 lb.	318	87	65	144.24	220.98	165.10	Dry Tortugas Florida, USA	Mar. 14 1966	Dottie Hall
M-50 lb.	369	77	65	167.37	195.58	165.10	Marathon Florida, USA	Apr. 25 1956	C. F. Mann
W-50 lb.	290	79½	60	131.54	201.93	152.40	Marathon Florida, USA	May 5 1967	Mrs. Leslie Lear
All-Tackle M-80 lb.	680	85½	66	308.44	217.17	167.64	Fernandina Beach Florida, USA	May 20 1961	Lynn Joyner
W-80 lb.	366	88½	68	166.01	224.79	172.72	Guayabo Panama	Feb. 8 1965	Betsy B. Walker
M-130 lb.	396	94	67	179.62	238.76	170.18	Islamorada Florida, USA	Mar. 22 1968	Frank J. Posluszny
W-130 lb.	327	80¾	54½	148.32	205.10	138.43	Flamingo Florida, USA	June 24 1969	Helen Robinson

KAWAKAWA

LINE CLASS	U. S. CUSTOMARY			METRIC			PLACE	DATE	ANGLER
	Weight lbs. oz.	Length Inches	Girth Inches	Weight kilo	Length cm	Girth cm			
M-6 lb.	19-8	34½	21	8.84	87.63	53.34	Port Stephens N.S.W., Australia	Aug. 3 1975	Jonathan M. Rowley
W-6 lb.	Vacant — Minimum Acceptance Weight — 6 lbs. (2.71 kilos)								
M-12 lb.	Vacant — Minimum Acceptance Weight — 6 lbs. (2.71 kilos)								
W-12 lb.	Vacant — Minimum Acceptance Weight — 6 lbs. (2.71 kilos)								
M-20 lb.	Vacant — Minimum Acceptance Weight — 9 lbs. (4.07 kilos)								
W-20 lb.	Vacant — Minimum Acceptance Weight — 9 lbs. (4.07 kilos)								
M-30 lb.	Vacant — Minimum Acceptance Weight — 9 lbs. (4.07 kilos)								
W-30 lb.	Vacant — Minimum Acceptance Weight — 9 lbs. (4.07 kilos)								
M-50 lb.	20-8	31½	22	9.29	80.01	55.88	Honolulu Hawaii, USA	Aug. 23 1975	Edward K. Jensen
W-50 lb.	Vacant — Minimum Acceptance Weight — 9 lbs. (4.07 kilos)								
M-80 lb.	21	34	22	9.52	86.36	55.88	Kilauea, Kauai Hawaii, USA	Aug. 21 1975	E. John O'Dell
W-80 lb.	Vacant — Minimum Acceptance Weight — 12 lbs. (5.43 kilos)								
M-130 lb.	Vacant — Minimum Acceptance Weight — 12 lbs. (5.43 kilos)								
W-130 lb.	Vacant — Minimum Acceptance Weight — 12 lbs. (5.43 kilos)								

MACKEREL (king)

LINE CLASS	Weight lbs. oz.	Length Inches	Girth Inches	Weight kilo	Length cm	Girth cm	PLACE	DATE	ANGLER
*M-6 lb.	44-1	58	23	19.98	147.32	58.42	Grand Isle Louisiana, USA	Apr. 13 1973	Robert Vaughn Beck
W-6 lb.	37-7	52¾	22	16.99	133.98	55.88	Empire Louisiana, USA	Jan. 26 1975	Pamela D. Levert
M-12 lb.	56	61	27½	25.40	154.94	69.85	Key West Florida, USA	Jan. 19 1974	Ralph Parlato
W-12 lb.	44-2	52	24½	20.01	132.08	62.23	St. Thomas U.S. Virgin Islands	May 7 1969	Gloria J. Applegate
M-20 lb.	77	65	29	34.92	165.10	73.66	Bimini Bahamas	May 12 1957	Clinton Olney Potts
W-20 lb.	65-8	64	25½	29.71	162.56	64.77	Palm Beach Florida, USA	Feb. 14 1965	Patricia E. Church
M-30 lb.	75	57	32	34.01	144.78	81.28	Walker Cay Bahamas	May 22 1966	Thomas J. Sims, Jr.
W-30 lb.	64	64	25	29.03	162.56	63.50	Palm Beach Florida, USA	Dec. 23 1973	Barbara Hinkle
All-Tackle M-50 lb.	78-12	65½	30	35.72	166.37	76.20	La Romana Dominican Rep.	Nov. 26 1971	Fernando Viyella
W-50 lb.	78	66½	28½	35.38	168.91	72.39	Guayanilla Puerto Rico	May 25 1963	Ruth M. Coon
M-80 lb.	Vacant — Minimum Acceptance Weight — 59 lbs. (26.72 kilos)								
W-80 lb.	67	60	29	30.39	152.40	73.66	Pompano Beach Florida, USA	Apr. 14 1972	Fran S. Colyer
M-130 lb.	76-8	63	31	34.70	160.02	78.74	Bimini Bahamas	May 22 1952	R. E. Maytag
W-130 lb.	71	60	31	32.20	152.40	78.74	Cat Cay Bahamas	June 19 1969	Ann C. Kunkel
*TIE M-6 lb.	44-5	53¼	23½	20.10	135.25	59.69	Empire Louisiana, USA	Feb. 10 1974	John R. Peters, Jr.

MARLIN (Atlantic blue)

LINE CLASS	U.S. CUSTOMARY			METRIC			PLACE	DATE	ANGLER
	Weight lbs. oz.	Length inches	Girth inches	Weight kilo	Length cm	Girth cm			
M-6 lb.	Vacant — Minimum Acceptance Weight — 40 lbs. (18.12 kilos)								
W-6 lb.	Vacant — Minimum Acceptance Weight — 40 lbs. (18.12 kilos)								
M-12 lb.	448	138½	55	203.21	351.79	139.70	St. Thomas U.S. Virgin Islands	Sept. 6 1971	Frank L. Miller
W-12 lb.	223-1	122½	42	101.18	311.15	106.68	Bimini Bahamas	Apr. 9 1960	Suzanne H. Higgs
M-20 lb.	430	138	54	195.04	350.52	137.16	St. Thomas U.S. Virgin Islands	Aug. 31 1970	Charles R. Senf
W-20 lb.	392	134¾	52	177.81	342.26	132.08	St. Thomas U.S. Virgin Islands	Aug. 14 1973	Elsie Senf
M-30 lb.	484-8	144	57	219.76	365.76	144.78	Near Hatteras N. Carolina, USA	June 3 1973	Charles Wade Bailey
W-30 lb.	542-8	162	56	246.07	411.48	142.24	Walker Cay Bahamas	May 2 1974	Mrs. Almeta Schafer
M-50 lb.	666	142	71	302.09	360.68	180.34	Hillsboro Florida, USA	May 24 1973	E. C. Brookshire
W-50 lb.	633-8	156	50	287.35	396.24	127.00	Bimini Bahamas	Mar. 27 1970	Mrs. Audrey Grady
M-80 lb.	1128	175	78	511.65	444.50	198.12	Hatteras N. Carolina, USA	June 5 1975	Fulton H. Katz, M.D.
W-80 lb.	705	167	64	319.78	424.18	162.56	St. Thomas U.S. Virgin Islands	July 8 1972	Gloria J. Applegate
All-Tackle M-130 lb.	1142	166	80	518.00	421.64	203.20	Nags Head N. Carolina, USA	July 26 1974	Jack Herrington
W-130 lb.	723	158	68	327.95	401.32	172.72	Bimini Bahamas	Aug. 10 1967	Mrs. J. M. Hollobaugh, Jr.

MARLIN (black)

Scientific name: Makaira indica

LINE CLASS	U.S. CUSTOMARY			METRIC			PLACE	DATE	ANGLER
	Weight lbs. oz.	Length inches	Girth inches	Weight kilo	Length cm	Girth cm			
M-6 lb.	41-8	66	25	18.82	167.64	63.50	Cairns Australia	Aug. 8 1975	Robert Oliver
W-6 lb.	Vacant — Minimum Acceptance Weight — 40 lbs. (18.12 kilos)								
M-12 lb.	368-2	116	53	167.00	294.64	134.62	Lizard Island Australia	Sept. 26 1975	Terry Russell
W-12 lb.	353	126½	55	160.11	321.31	139.70	Pinas Bay Panama	Mar. 6 1968	Evelyn M. Anderson
M-20 lb.	481	140	63	218.18	355.60	160.02	Pinas Bay Panama	Dec. 11 1974	Edwin D. Kennedy
W-20 lb.	418	130	59	189.60	330.20	149.86	Pinas Bay Panama	Jan. 11 1968	Mrs. Carl Dann III
M-30 lb.	816	152	69	370.13	386.08	175.26	Cairns Australia	Sept. 19 1971	Patrick Gay
W-30 lb.	552	147	62	250.38	373.38	157.48	La Plata Island Ecuador, SA	July 3 1953	Mrs. W. G. Krieger
M-50 lb.	1124	168	75	509.84	426.72	190.50	Cairns Australia	Oct. 31 1969	Edward Seay
W-50 lb.	584	150	68	264.90	381.00	172.72	Pinas Bay Panama	Jan. 14 1962	Helen Robinson
M-80 lb.	1218	176	81	552.48	447.04	205.74	Cooktown Australia	Sept. 24 1973	D. Mead Johnson
W-80 lb.	1028-8	157	75½	466.52	398.78	191.72	Cairns Australia	Oct. 29 1970	Mrs. Colleen Seay
All-Tackle M-130 lb.	1560	174	81	707.61	441.96	205.74	Cabo Blanco Peru, SA	Aug. 4 1953	Alfred C. Glassell, Jr.
W-130 lb.	1525	172	80	691.73	436.88	203.20	Cabo Blanco Peru, SA	Apr. 22 1954	Kimberley Wiss

MARLIN (Pacific blue)

Scientific name: Makaira nigricans

LINE CLASS	Weight lbs. oz.	Length inches	Girth inches	Weight kilo	Length cm	Girth cm	PLACE	DATE	ANGLER
	U.S. CUSTOMARY			METRIC					
M-6 lb.	Vacant — Minimum Acceptance Weight — 40 lbs. (18.12 kilos)								
W-6 lb.	Vacant — Minimum Acceptance Weight — 40 lbs. (18.12 kilos)								
M-12 lb.	248-4	120	48	112.60	304.80	121.92	Keahole Point Isle of Hawaii, USA	Aug. 12 1975	Stephen Zuckerman
W-12 lb.	Vacant — Minimum Acceptance Weight — 75 lbs. (34.01 kilos)								
M-20 lb.	224	115½	42	101.60	293.37	106.68	Keauhau Hawaii, USA	Mar. 22 1975	Warren Ackermann
W-20 lb.	406	135	52½	184.16	342.90	133.35	Mazatlan Mexico	May 18 1972	Marguerite H. Barry
M-30 lb.	438	159	53	198.67	403.86	134.62	Bay of Islands New Zealand	Dec. 2 1972	William W. Hall
W-30 lb.	264	120½	45	119.74	306.07	114.30	Kailua - Kona Hawaii, USA	Nov. 9 1965	Jeannette Alford
M-50 lb.	762	161	62	345.64	408.94	157.48	Kona Hawaii, USA	July 19 1974	Neil Nishikawa
W-50 lb.	565	149½	57	256.28	379.73	144.78	Keahole Point Hawaii, USA	Aug. 31 1975	Judith Ann Nakamaru
M-80 lb.	916	163½	72	415.49	415.29	182.88	Kailua-Kona Hawaii, USA	Aug. 28 1973	Eric Tixier
W-80 lb.	607-8	152	60	275.56	386.08	152.40	Keahole Hawaii, USA	Sept. 12 1973	Mrs. Lee Marvin
M-130 lb.	1100	165½	79½	498.95	420.37	201.93	Le Morne Mauritius	Feb. 20 1966	Andre D'Hotman de Villiers
W-130 lb.	669	156	66	303.45	396.24	167.64	Kailua-Kona Hawaii, USA	Aug. 27 1973	Mrs. Doris H. Jones
All-Tackle M-180 lb.	1153	176	73	522.99	447.04	185.42	Ritidian Point Guam	Aug. 21 1969	Greg D. Perez

MARLIN (striped)

Other common name: barred marlin
Scientific name: Tetrapturus audax

LINE CLASS	Weight lbs. oz.	Length inches	Girth inches	Weight kilo	Length cm	Girth cm	PLACE	DATE	ANGLER
M-6 lb.	205	114	40	92.98	289.56	101.60	Cabo San Lucas Mexico	Apr. 3 1972	W. Matt Parr
W-6 lb.	188	112	40	85.27	284.48	101.60	Cabo San Lucas Baja, Mexico	June 8 1974	Kathryn McGinnis
M-12 lb.	250	121	46	113.39	307.34	116.84	Palmilla Mexico	Apr. 16 1965	R. M. Anderson
W-12 lb.	210	114	40	95.25	289.56	101.60	Las Cruces Mexico	June 20 1959	Lynn F. Lee
M-20 lb.	338	125	47½	153.31	317.50	120.65	Sydney Australia	Oct. 20 1968	H. John McIntyre
W-20 lb.	321	127¼	47	145.60	323.21	119.38	Iquique Chile, SA	June 8 1954	Mrs. L. Marron
M-30 lb.	284	130½	46	128.82	331.47	116.84	Tutukaka New Zealand	Mar. 28 1975	Alan William Marshall
W-30 lb.	289	121	45	131.08	307.34	114.30	Iquique Chile, SA	May 18 1954	Mrs. L. Marron
M-50 lb.	365	134½	50	165.56	341.63	127.00	Whakatane New Zealand	Feb. 26 1972	A. T. Haultain
W-50 lb.	401	110	50½	181.89	279.40	128.27	Cavalli Islands New Zealand	Feb. 24 1970	Mrs. Margaret Williams
All-Tackle M-80 lb.	415	132	52	188.24	335.28	132.08	Cape Brett New Zealand	Mar. 31 1964	B. C. Bain
W-80 lb.	333	122	48	151.04	309.88	121.92	Ruahine Reef New Zealand	Apr. 20 1971	Jennifer Amos
M-130 lb.	398	128½	51	180.53	326.39	129.54	Mayor Island New Zealand	Dec. 30 1974	John Kenneth Boyle
W-130 lb.	Vacant — Minimum Acceptance Weight — 312 lbs. (141.33 kilos)								

MARLIN (white)

Scientific name: Tetrapturus albidus

LINE CLASS	U. S. CUSTOMARY			METRIC			PLACE	DATE	ANGLER
	Weight lbs. oz.	Length inches	Girth inches	Weight kilo	Length cm	Girth cm			
M-6 lb.	81	91½	29¾	36.74	232.41	75.56	Montauk, Long Island New York, USA	July 19 1975	Stephen Sloan
W-6 lb.	67	86½	26½	30.39	219.71	67.31	La Guaira Venezuela, SA	Sept. 20 1972	Kathryn McGinnis
M-12 lb.	103-8	96½	31½	46.94	245.11	80.01	Bimini Bahamas	Apr. 8 1952	G. A. Bass
W-12 lb.	122	99	44	55.33	251.46	111.76	Bimini Bahamas	Mar. 30 1953	Dorothy A. Curtice
M-20 lb.	128-8	102	36	58.28	259.08	91.44	Bimini Bahamas	Mar. 9 1960	James F. Baldwin
W-20 lb.	129-4	103	33½	58.62	261.62	85.09	Bimini Bahamas	Apr. 11 1963	Mrs. J. M. Watters
M-30 lb.	130-4	99	33	59.08	251.46	83.82	Bimini Bahamas	Apr. 18 1959	Leonard Hendrix
W-30 lb.	120-10	89¾	32¼	54.71	227.96	81.91	Bimini Bahamas	Mar. 29 1956	Mrs. M. Meyer, Jr.
All-Tackle M-50 lb.	159-8	108	36	72.34	274.32	91.44	Pompano Beach Florida, USA	Apr. 25 1953	W. E. Johnson
W-50 lb.	130	95	34	58.96	241.30	86.36	Montauk New York, USA	Aug. 13 1951	Mrs. P. Dater
M-80 lb.	Vacant — Minimum Acceptance Weight — 120 lbs. (54.36 kilos)								
W-80 lb.	142	98	34	64.41	248.92	86.36	Ft. Lauderdale Florida, USA	Mar. 14 1959	Marie Beneventi
M-130 lb.	Vacant — Minimum Acceptance Weight — 120 lbs. (54.36 kilos)								
W-130 lb.	Vacant — Minimum Acceptance Weight — 120 lbs. (54.36 kilos)								

PERMIT

Scientific name: Trachinotus falcatus

LINE CLASS	Weight lbs. oz.	Length inches	Girth inches	Weight kilo	Length cm	Girth cm	PLACE	DATE	ANGLER
M-6 lb.	38	41½	33	17.23	105.41	83.82	Key West Florida, USA	Mar. 19 1972	Stuart C. Apte
W-6 lb.	30-8	39	28¼	13.83	99.06	71.75	Loggerhead Key Florida, USA	June 27 1973	Kathy Marvin
M-12 lb.	50	43	34½	22.67	109.22	87.63	Miami Florida, USA	Mar. 27 1965	Robert F. Miller
W-12 lb.	38-8	45	31	17.46	114.30	78.74	Bimini Bahamas	Jan. 23 1975	Bess Greenberg
All-Tackle M-20 lb.	50-8	44¾	33¾	22.90	113.66	85.72	Key West Florida, USA	Mar. 15 1971	Marshall E. Earnest
*W-20 lb.	38	40	30½	17.23	101.60	77.47	Islamorada Florida, USA	Mar. 21 1954	Mrs. W. K. Edmunds
M-30 lb.	43	44½	31½	19.50	113.03	80.0l	Palm Beach Florida, USA	March 4 1974	Stephen I. Ray
W-30 lb.	38	43	31	17.23	109.22	78.74	Key West Florida, USA	Apr. 9 1963	Helen Robinson
M-50 lb.	47-12	45	32	21.65	114.30	81.28	Boca Grande Pass Florida, USA	May 5 1960	Frank G. Burke, Jr.
W-50 lb.	39	41	30	17.69	104.14	76.20	Islamorada Florida, USA	Apr. 2 1966	Shelagh B. Richards
M-80 lb.	34-8	36¼	28	15.64	92.07	71.12	Naples Florida, USA	Feb. 1 1951	R. R. Channel
W-80 lb.	Vacant — Minimum Acceptance Weight — 37 lbs. (16.76 kilos)								
M-130 lb.	38-8	40½	31¼	17.46	102.87	79.37	Boca Grande Florida, USA	Sept. 9 1953	R. H. Martin
W-130 lb.	Vacant — Minimum Acceptance Weight — 37 lbs. (16.76 kilos)								
*TIE W-20 lb.	38	43	33	17.23	109.22	83.82	Islamorada Florida, USA	June 11 1961	Louise Meulenberg

POLLOCK

Scientific name: Pollachius virens

LINE CLASS	U.S. CUSTOMARY			METRIC			PLACE	DATE	ANGLER
	Weight lbs. oz.	Length inches	Girth inches	Weight kilo	Length cm	Girth cm			
M-6 lb.	17-9½	35½	22½	7.98	90.17	57.15	Plymouth England	Jan. 1 1973	Roger William Palmer
W-6 lb.	15-2½	41½	22	6.87	105.41	55.88	Plymouth England	Mar. 10 1973	Mrs. Rita Barrett
M-12 lb.	36	47	32	16.32	119.38	81.28	Hunts Point Nova Scotia, Canada	Aug. 10 1965	Perry MacNeal
W-12 lb.	15-7	33¾	19	7.00	85.72	48.26	Nova Scotia Canada	July 9 1963	Janet D. Wallach
M-20 lb.	37-10	46¾	28	17.06	118.74	71.12	Fire Island Inlet New York, USA	Nov. 1 1974	Charles Fischett
W-20 lb.	38	47	14	17.23	119.38	35.56	Westport Nova Scotia, Canada	Aug. 20 1971	Ruth G. Verber
M-30 lb.	40	49½	27	18.14	125.73	68.58	Brielle New Jersey, USA	Oct. 22 1973	Tom Wier
W-30 lb.	35-1	47	26	15.90	114.30	66.04	Fire Island Inlet New York, USA	Aug. 23 1975	Patty Ishkanian
All-Tackle M-50 lb.	46-7	50½	30	21.06	128.27	76.20	Brielle New Jersey, USA	May 26 1975	John Tomes Holton
W-50 lb.	29	42	24¼	13.15	106.68	61.59	Manasquan New Jersey, USA	Nov. 3 1958	Ann Durik
M-80 lb.	Vacant — Minimum Acceptance Weight — 35 lbs. (15.85 kilos)								
W-80 lb.	36-1	43	25	16.35	109.22	63.50	Marblehead Massachusetts, USA	Aug. 26 1974	Mary E. Connolly
M-130 lb.	Vacant — Minimum Acceptance Weight — 35 lbs. (15.85 kilos)								
W-130 lb.	Vacant — Minimum Acceptance Weight — 35 lbs. (15.85 kilos)								

ROOSTERFISH

Scientific name: Nematistius pectoralis

LINE CLASS	Weight lbs. oz.	Length inches	Girth inches	Weight kilo	Length cm	Girth cm	PLACE	DATE	ANGLER
M-6 lb.	29-12	47½	25	13.49	120.65	63.50	Punta Colorado Mexico	June 24 1973	Bob Manos
W-6 lb.	34-3	48½	26½	15.50	123.19	67.31	Punta Colorado Mexico	July 5 1973	Pat Snyder
M-12 lb.	50-11	56	32	22.99	142.24	81.28	Guerro Mexico	Jan. 15 1961	Joseph Krieger, Jr.
W-12 lb.	45	52½	30	20.41	133.35	76.20	San Jose del Cabo Mexico	June 11 1951	Mrs. W. G. Krieger
M-20 lb.	85-13	58½	42¾	38.92	148.59	108.58	La Paz Mexico	June 15 1966	Willard E. Hanson
W-20 lb.	50-9	54½	30	22.93	138.43	76.20	Baja California Mexico	Nov. 20 1959	Lily Call
All-Tackle M-30 lb.	114	64	33	51.71	162.56	83.82	La Paz Mexico	June 1 1960	Abe Sackheim
W-30 lb.	99	59½	34½	44.90	151.13	87.63	La Paz Mexico	Nov. 30 1964	Lily Call
M-50 lb.	80	46	27¼	36.28	116.84	69.21	Cabo Blanco Peru, SA	June 13 1954	Clyoce J. Tippett
W-50 lb.	85-2	54	36	38.61	137.16	91.44	La Paz Mexico	Nov. 24 1956	Mrs. Esther Carle
M-80 lb.	90	59½	32	40.82	151.13	81.28	Loreto Mexico	Dec. 22 1960	Clement Caditz
W-80 lb.	66	56	29½	29.93	142.24	74.93	La Paz Mexico	Dec. 1 1964	Lily Call
M-130 lb.	100	54	32	45.35	137.16	81.28	Cabo Blanco Peru, SA	Jan. 12 1954	Miguel Barrenechea
W-130 lb.	Vacant — Minimum Acceptance Weight — 85 lbs. (38.50 kilos)								

RUNNER (rainbow)

Scientific name: Elagatis bipinnulata

LINE CLASS	U.S. CUSTOMARY			METRIC			PLACE	DATE	ANGLER
	Weight lbs. oz.	Length inches	Girth inches	Weight kilo	Length cm	Girth cm			
M-6 lb.	17-10	43¼	16¾	7.99	109.85	42.54	Isla Coiba Panama	Dec. 4 1974	Stuart C. Apte
*W-6 lb.	7	30	13	3.17	76.20	33.02	Madang, Papua New Guinea	Nov. 3 1974	Mrs. Joyleen M. Chan
M-12 lb.	18-12	38-7/8	20½	8.50	98.74	52.07	Las Cruces Mexico	May 31 1961	Bing Crosby
W-12 lb.	10-14	38¼	15	4.93	97.15	38.10	Key Largo Florida, USA	Aug. 10 1969	Pamela J. Habicht
M-20 lb.	25	48	23	11.33	121.92	58.42	Pinas Bay Panama	May 9 1965	Donald J. S. Merten
W-20 lb.	13-8	39	17	6.12	99.06	43.18	Cozumel Mexico	May 22 1974	Gloria J. Applegate
M-30 lb.	25-12	44¼	21	11.68	112.39	53.34	Oahu Hawaii, USA	Nov. 26 1967	Richard Y. Sakimoto, MD
W-30 lb.	12-2	40	16¼	5.49	101.60	41.27	Guerro Mexico	Jan. 21 1963	Mrs. Joseph Krieger, Jr.
M-50 lb.	28	49	21½	12.70	124.46	54.61	Pinas Bay Panama	Jan. 15 1967	Thomas C. Dickinson
W-50 lb.	23	42	19½	10.43	106.68	49.53	Oahu Hawaii, USA	May 9 1961	Lila M. Neuenfelt
M-80 lb.	28-6	49½	21½	12.87	125.73	54.61	Pulmo Reef Gulf of California	Nov. 11 1967	Joe C. Stuard
W-80 lb.	Vacant — Minimum Acceptance Weight — 23 lbs. (10.43 kilos)								
All-Tackle M-130 lb.	30-15	47	22	14.03	119.38	55.88	Kauai Hawaii, USA	Apr. 27 1963	Holbrook Goodale
W-130 lb.	Vacant — Minimum Acceptance Weight — 23 lbs. (10.43 kilos)								
*TIE W-6 lb.	7-4	33	13½	3.28	83.82	34.29	Pinas Bay Panama	Mar. 4 1975	Mary Wallace Josepho

SAILFISH (Atlantic)

Scientific name: Istiophorus platypterus

LINE CLASS	Weight lbs. oz.	Length inches	Girth inches	Weight kilo	Length cm	Girth cm	PLACE	DATE	ANGLER
M-6 lb.	85-15	91½	31½	39.00	232.48	79.98	Luanda Angola, Africa	Feb. 14 1974	Albino de Jesus Gaspar dos Santos
W-6 lb.	53	81½	24¼	24.04	207.01	61.59	Islamorada Florida, USA	Jan. 25 1973	Jacqueline E. Knight
M-12 lb.	99-13	107	32	45.30	272.00	81.00	Luanda Angola, Africa	March 27 1974	Albino de Jesus Gaspar dos Santos
W-12 lb.	83	83¾	32¼	37.64	212.72	81.91	Key Largo Florida, USA	Apr. 4 1965	Helen K. Grant
M-20 lb.	127-13	105½	33	58.00	268.00	84.00	Luanda Angola, Africa	Mar. 30 1975	Mario Rui Alves Da Silva
W-20 lb.	106-8	100 1/3	32¼	48.30	254.96	81.96	Luanda Angola, Africa	Mar. 15 1975	Mrs. Pamela Jean Durkin
M-30 lb.	116-5	103	32¼	52.75	261.62	81.91	Luanda Angola, Africa	Mar. 22 1972	Jose Eduardo Gaioso Vaz
W-30 lb.	84	98	29	38.10	248.92	73.66	Jupiter Florida, USA	May 3 1971	Jeanne C. Chatham
All-Tackle M-50 lb.	128-1	106¼	34¼	58.10	269.97	83.36	Luanda Angola, Africa	March 27 1974	Harm Steyn
W-50 lb.	108-4	105½	34	49.10	267.97	86.36	Luanda Angola, Africa	Mar. 30 1971	Mrs. Ellen Botha
M-80 lb.	Vacant — Minimum Acceptance Weight — 96 lbs. (43.48 kilos)								
W-80 lb.	Vacant — Minimum Acceptance Weight — 96 lbs. (43.48 kilos)								
M-130 lb.	Vacant — Minimum Acceptance Weight — 96 lbs. (43.48 kilos)								
W-130 lb.	Vacant — Minimum Acceptance Weight — 96 lbs. (43.48 kilos)								

SAILFISH (Pacific)

Scientific name: Istiophorus platypterus

LINE CLASS	U.S. CUSTOMARY			METRIC			PLACE	DATE	ANGLER
	Weight lbs. oz.	Length inches	Girth inches	Weight kilo	Length cm	Girth cm			
M-6 lb.	168	117¾	40½	76.20	299.08	102.87	Salinas Ecuador, SA	Sept. 7 1974	Santiago Maspons
W-6 lb.	116-4	115½	32	52.73	293.37	81.28	Pinas Bay Panama	July 19 1975	Lovern K. Scott (Bulauca)
M-12 lb.	159	119	36	72.12	302.26	91.44	Pinas Bay Panama	July 23 1957	J. Frank Baxter
W-12 lb.	146-8	108½	35½	66.45	275.59	90.17	Palmilla Mexico	Nov. 14 1962	Evelyn M. Anderson
M-20 lb.	174-14	110½	33	79.32	280.67	83.82	Mazatlan Mexico	May 4 1974	Morris A. Linsky
W-20 lb.	157	122	37	71.21	309.88	93.98	La Plata Island Ecuador, SA	Sept. 14 1961	Jeannette Alford
M-30 lb.	198	134	41	89.81	340.36	104.14	La Paz Mexico	Aug. 23 1957	Charles Kelly
W-30 lb.	178	119½	37	80.74	303.53	93.98	Santa Cruz Island Galapagos	Feb. 27 1955	Mrs. A. Hall
M-50 lb.	192-7	123	42	87.28	312.42	106.68	Acapulco Mexico	Oct. 4 1961	W. W. Rowland
W-50 lb.	192	125	40½	87.09	317.50	102.87	La Paz Mexico	Sept. 6 1950	Gay Thomas
M-80 lb.	198	126	33	89.81	320.04	83.82	Mazatlan Mexico	Nov. 10 1954	George N. Anglen
W-80 lb.	199	120	42	90.26	304.80	106.68	Pinas Bay Panama	Jan. 17 1968	Carolyn B. Brinkman
All-Tackle M-130 lb.	221	129	—	100.24	327.66	—	Santa Cruz Island Galapagos	Feb. 12 1947	C. W. Stewart
W-130 lb.	189	127	33	85.72	322.58	83.82	Yanuca Fiji	Dec. 7 1967	Mrs. C. L. Foster

SEABASS (white)

Other common name: white corvina
Scientific name: Cynoscion nobilis

LINE CLASS	Weight lbs. oz.	Length inches	Girth inches	Weight kilo	Length cm	Girth cm	PLACE	DATE	ANGLER
M-6 lb.	Vacant — Minimum Acceptance Weight — 30 lbs. (13.59 kilos)								
W-6 lb.	Vacant — Minimum Acceptance Weight — 30 lbs. (13.59 kilos)								
M-12 lb.	65	58	28	29.48	147.32	71.12	Ensenada Mexico	July 8 1955	C. J. Aronis
W-12 lb.	52-6	54	27¾	23.75	137.16	70.48	Newport Harbor California, USA	June 3 1959	Ruth Jayred
M-20 lb.	72	59¾	30½	32.65	151.76	77.47	Catalina California, USA	Aug. 13 1958	Dr. Charles Dorshkind
W-20 lb.	62	57	28	28.12	144.78	71.12	Malibu California, USA	Dec. 6 1951	Mrs. D. W. Jackson
All-Tackle M-30 lb.	83-12	65½	34	37.98	166.37	86.36	San Felipe Mexico	Mar. 31 1953	L. C. Baumgardner
W-30 lb.	59-8	55¼	30	26.98	140.33	76.20	Catalina Island California, USA	May 2 1968	Janice Jackson
M-50 lb.	77-4	61	33	35.04	154.94	83.82	San Diego California, USA	Apr. 8 1950	H. P. Bledsoe
W-50 lb.	44-3	53	25	20.04	134.62	63.50	Catalina Island California, USA	May 2 1968	Gail Cruz
M-80 lb.	74	63	33	33.56	160.02	83.82	Catalina Island California, USA	May 11 1968	Allan D. Tromblay
W-80 lb.	Vacant — Minimum Acceptance Weight — 63 lbs. (28.53 kilos)								
M-130 lb.	Vacant — Minimum Acceptance Weight — 63 lbs. (28.53 kilos)								
W-130 lb.	Vacant — Minimum Acceptance Weight — 63 lbs. (28.53 kilos)								

SEATROUT (spotted)

Other common name: speckled trout/spotted weakfish
Scientific name: Cynoscion nebulosus

LINE CLASS	U.S. CUSTOMARY			METRIC			PLACE	DATE	ANGLER
	Weight lbs. oz.	Length inches	Girth inches	Weight kilo	Length cm	Girth cm			
M-6 lb.	10-8	32¼	17 1/8	4.76	81.91	43.49	Cape Canaveral Florida, USA	June 16 1974	Beauford R. Franklin
W-6 lb.	8-1	29	15-7/8	3.65	73.66	40.32	Pensacola Sound Florida, USA	Apr. 24 1973	Rose Marie Bonifay
*M-12 lb.	14	38½	17	6.35	97.79	43.18	Ponce de Leon Inlet Florida, USA	Aug. 10 1972	Allen Kent Gibbens
W-12 lb.	10-4	30½	16	4.64	77.47	40.64	Jupiter Florida, USA	June 1 1958	Nancy Dukes
M-20 lb.	13-12	36	19	6.23	91.44	48.26	Vero Beach Florida, USA	Mar. 11 1957	W. Miller Shaw, Jr.
W-20 lb.	10	30	18	4.53	76.20	45.72	Pellicer Creek Florida, USA	Feb. 25 1950	Mrs. Bertram Lee
All-Tackle Tie M-30 lb.	15-6	33	23¾	6.97	83.82	60.32	Jensen Beach Florida, USA	May 4 1969	Michael J. Foremny
W-30 lb.	14	33	18	6.35	83.82	45.72	Stuart Florida, USA	Apr. 25 1970	Marilyn C. Albright
All-Tackle M-50 lb.	15-3	34½	20½	6.88	87.63	52.07	Fort Pierce Florida, USA	Jan. 13 1949	C. W. Hubbard
W-50 lb.	Vacant — Minimum Acceptance Weight — 10 lbs. (4.53 kilos)								
M-80 lb.	Vacant — Minimum Acceptance Weight — 10 lbs. (4.53 kilos)								
W-80 lb.	Vacant — Minimum Acceptance Weight — 10 lbs. (4.53 kilos)								
M-130 lb.	Vacant — Minimum Acceptance Weight — 10 lbs. (4.53 kilos)								
W-130 lb.	Vacant — Minimum Acceptance Weight — 10 lbs. (4.53 kilos)								
*TIE M-12 lb.	14-3	33	19	6.43	83.82	48.26	Jensen Beach Florida, USA	Feb. 21 1974	Les Mowery

SHARK (blue)

Scientific name: Prionace glauca

LINE CLASS	Weight lbs. oz.	Length inches	Girth inches	Weight kilo	Length cm	Girth cm	PLACE	DATE	ANGLER
M-6 lb.	205	95	36	92.98	241.30	91.44	Montauk, L.I. New York, USA	Aug. 19 1974	Stephen Sloan
W-6 lb.	193	108½	34½	87.54	275.59	87.63	Botany Australia	Dec. 15 1974	Mrs. Dulcie Chee
M-12 lb.	312	127	47	141.52	322.58	119.38	Montauk New York, USA	Oct. 28 1963	John S. Walton
W-12 lb.	150	96	32	68.03	243.84	81.28	Montauk New York, USA	July 22 1962	Dorothea L. Dean
M-20 lb.	218-2	117	42	98.94	297.18	106.68	Montauk New York, USA	July 22 1955	M. B. Mittleman
W-20 lb.	293	126½	44	132.90	321.31	111.76	Montauk New York, USA	July 21 1963	Lucette Rinfret
M-30 lb.	350	137	43	158.75	347.98	109.22	Sydney Heads Australia	Oct. 29 1961	John C. Kellion
W-30 lb.	284-8	128	42	129.04	325.12	106.68	Montauk New York, USA	Aug. 11 1959	Jacqueline Mittleman
M-50 lb.	371-8	135	47	168.51	342.90	119.38	Montauk New York, USA	Sept. 27 1969	Jack Bellock
W-50 lb.	298	138	40	135.17	350.52	101.60	Montauk New York, USA	Oct. 5 1959	Valerie Wuestefeld
All-Tackle M-80 lb.	410	138	52	185.97	350.52	132.08	Rockport Massachusetts, USA	Sept. 1 1960	Richard C. Webster
All-Tackle Tie W-80 lb.	410	134	52½	185.97	340.36	133.35	Rockport Massachusetts, USA	Aug. 17 1967	Martha C. Webster
M-130 lb.	341-8	121	45½	154.90	307.34	115.57	Las Palmas Canary Islands	Oct. 31 1966	John D. Nixon
W-130 lb.	334	128	47½	151.50	325.12	120.65	Rockport Massachusetts, USA	Sept. 4 1964	Cassandra Webster

SHARK (hammerhead)

Scientific name: Sphyrnidae

LINE CLASS	U.S. CUSTOMARY			METRIC			PLACE	DATE	ANGLER
	Weight lbs. oz.	Length inches	Girth inches	Weight kilo	Length cm	Girth cm			
M-6 lb.	101-13	71½	30¾	46.20	182.00	78.00	Luanda Angola, Africa	Dec. 29 1974	Manuel Quintela Maia de Loureiro
W-6 lb.	Vacant — Minimum Acceptance Weight — 76 lbs. (34.42 kilos)								
M-12 lb.	145-8	82½	33½	66.00	210.00	85.00	Luanda Angola, Africa	Dec. 15 1974	Albino de Jesus Gaspar dos Santos
W-12 lb.	121-4	81	32	54.99	205.75	81.28	Luanda Angola, Africa	Nov. 3 1974	Luisa Maria Picarra Baptista
M-20 lb.	352	103	50	159.66	261.62	127.00	Jibbon Point N.S.W., Australia	Dec. 12 1974	Paul Edward Caughlan
W-20 lb.	190	88	38½	86.18	223.52	97.79	Bay of Islands New Zealand	April 13 1974	Robyn Hall
M-30 lb.	357-8	125	51	162.16	317.50	129.54	Pinas Bay Panama	Jan. 24 1975	Roberto Estrada G.
W-30 lb.	Vacant — Minimum Acceptance Weight — 268 lbs. (121.40 kilos)								
M-50 lb.	380	129	54½	172.36	327.66	138.43	Folly Beach S. Carolina, USA	Sept. 1 1975	Thomas W. Rhodes, Jr.
W-50 lb.	460	124	56¾	208.65	314.96	144.14	Sydney Australia	Dec. 29 1974	Pamela Hudspeth
M-80 lb.	406	99	56	184.16	251.46	142.24	Shimoni Kenya, Africa	Mar. 9 1975	James Falkland
W-80 lb.	447	127½	68	202.75	323.85	172.72	Hobe Sound Florida, USA	May 26 1975	E.R. (Betsy) Browning
All-Tackle M-130 lb.	703	172	63	318.87	436.88	160.02	Jacksonville Beach Florida, USA	July 5 1975	H.B. "Blackie" Reasor
W-130 lb.	406	100	54	184.16	254.00	137.16	Lottin Point New Zealand	Feb. 26 1974	Mrs. H. M. Wood

SHARK (porbeagle)

Scientific name: Lamna nasus

LINE CLASS	Weight lbs. oz.	Length inches	Girth inches	Weight kilo	Length cm	Girth cm	PLACE	DATE	ANGLER
M-6 lb.	Vacant — Minimum Acceptance Weight — 30 lbs. (13.59 kilos)								
W-6 lb.	Vacant — Minimum Acceptance Weight — 30 lbs. (13.59 kilos)								
M-12 lb.	66	58	30	29.93	147.32	76.20	Montauk New York, USA	June 8 1958	M. H. Merrill
W-12 lb.	Vacant — Minimum Acceptance Weight — 51 lbs. (23.10 kilos)								
M-20 lb.	180	103½	37	81.64	262.89	93.98	Block Island Rhode Island, USA	Aug. 9 1960	Frank K. Smith
W-20 lb.	Vacant — Minimum Acceptance Weight — 135 lbs. (61.15 kilos)								
M-30 lb.	191-8	76	42	86.86	193.04	106.68	Montauk New York, USA	May 28 1964	Carl Monaco
W-30 lb.	222-8	75	44	100.92	190.50	111.76	Isle of Wight England	Aug. 14 1969	Mrs. Paula Everington
M-50 lb.	388	101½	62	175.99	257.81	157.48	Montauk Point New York, USA	Oct. 28 1961	John S. Walton
W-50 lb.	238-8	92	41	108.18	233.68	104.14	Montauk New York, USA	May 17 1966	Bea Harry
All-Tackle M-80 lb.	430	96	63	195.04	243.84	160.02	Channel Islands England	June 29 1969	Desmond Bougourd
W-80 lb.	230	87½	43	104.32	222.25	109.22	Montauk New York, USA	May 17 1965	Bea Harry
M-130 lb.	300	120	55	136.07	304.80	139.70	Falmouth England	Sept. 5 1973	Keith Stokes
W-130 lb.	369	102	48	167.37	259.08	121.92	Looe, Cornwall England	July 20 1970	Mrs. Patricia Winifred Smith

SHARK (shortfin mako)

Scientific name: *Isurus oxyrinchus*

LINE CLASS	U. S. CUSTOMARY			METRIC			PLACE	DATE	ANGLER
	Weight lbs. oz.	Length inches	Girth inches	Weight kilo	Length cm	Girth cm			
M-6 lb.	342	104	44½	155.13	264.16	113.03	Port Hacking N.S.W., Australia	Sept. 22 1974	Norman Richard Smith
W-6 lb.	115	71½	36	52.16	181.61	91.44	Botany Bay Heads Australia	Oct. 27 1974	Mrs. Dulcie Chee
M-12 lb.	261-11	88	44½	118.70	223.52	113.03	Montauk New York, USA	Oct. 1 1953	C. R. Meyer
W-12 lb.	183	86	39	83.00	218.44	99.06	Sydney Australia	Aug. 1 1971	Mrs. Pamela Hudspeth
M-20 lb.	347	102	49	157.39	259.08	124.46	Mercury Bay New Zealand	Jan. 3 1973	Donald Keith Butters
W-20 lb.	316	98½	48½	143.33	250.19	123.19	Bimini Bahamas	May 25 1961	Dorothea L. Dean
M-30 lb.	854	140½	73½	387.37	356.87	186.69	Port Stephens NSW, Australia	May 9 1971	John Howard Barclay
W-30 lb.	376	120	46	170.55	304.80	116.84	Sydney Australia	Sept. 7 1969	Helen Gillis
M-50 lb.	690	126	61	312.98	320.04	154.94	Cavalli Island New Zealand	Nov. 7 1970	Noel R. Brady
W-50 lb.	478	132	46	216.81	335.28	116.84	Broughton Island Australia	May 17 1957	Mrs. Ron Duncan
M-80 lb.	820	125	68	371.94	317.50	172.72	Cavalli Island New Zealand	Mar. 28 1964	T. Culshaw
W-80 lb.	880	131	75¾	399.16	332.74	192.40	Bimini Bahamas	Aug. 3 1964	Florence Lotierzo
All-Tackle M-130 lb.	1061	146	79½	481.26	370.84	201.93	Mayor Island New Zealand	Feb. 17 1970	James B. Penwarden
W-130 lb.	911-12	134	70	413.56	340.36	177.80	Palm Beach Florida, USA	Apr. 9 1962	Audrey Cohen

SHARK (thresher)

Scientific name: Alopias vulpinus

LINE CLASS	Weight lbs. oz.	Length inches	Girth inches	Weight kilo	Length cm	Girth cm	PLACE	DATE	ANGLER
M-6 lb.	18-8	62¾	18	8.39	159.38	45.72	Santa Monica Bay California, USA	Aug. 20 1974	Henry Galle
W-6 lb.	Vacant — Minimum Acceptance Weight — 18 lbs. (8.15 kilos)								
M-12 lb.	92-8	57	31	41.95	144.78	78.74	Long Beach California, USA	Dec. 12 1959	D. F. Marsh
W-12 lb.	Vacant — Minimum Acceptance Weight — 69 lbs. (31.25 kilos)								
M-20 lb.	207	139	39	93.89	353.06	99.06	Catalina Channel California, USA	Sept. 6 1975	Leo Dee
W-20 lb.	Vacant — Minimum Acceptance Weight — 120 lbs. (54.36 kilos)								
M-30 lb.	307	97	45	139.25	246.38	114.30	Tutukaka New Zealand	April 18 1974	Guy Pierce
W-30 lb.	300	152	45½	136.07	386.08	115.57	Bay of Islands New Zealand	June 23 1972	Mrs. Anne Clark
M-50 lb.	421	154½	51½	190.96	392.43	130.81	Bay of Islands New Zealand	May 27 1972	Barry McKenzie Hill
W-50 lb.	366	156	48½	166.01	396.24	123.19	Bay of Islands New Zealand	May 6 1972	Mrs. Avril Semmens
All-Tackle M-80 lb.	739	188	68	335.20	477.52	172.72	Tutukaka New Zealand	Feb. 17 1975	Brian Galvin
W-80 lb.	413	180	49½	187.33	457.20	125.73	Bay of Islands New Zealand	June 28 1960	Mrs. E. R. Simons
M-130 lb.	667	201	59	302.54	510.54	149.86	Mayor Island New Zealand	Jan. 5 1975	Vernon Coleman
W-130 lb.	729	196	61	330.67	497.84	154.94	Mayor Island New Zealand	June 3 1959	Mrs. V. Brown

SHARK (tiger)

LINE CLASS	U. S. CUSTOMARY				METRIC		PLACE	DATE	ANGLER
	Weight lbs. oz.	Length inches	Girth inches	Weight kilo	Length cm	Girth cm			
M-6 lb.	Vacant — Minimum Acceptance Weight — 50 lbs. (22.65 kilos)								
W-6 lb.	Vacant — Minimum Acceptance Weight — 50 lbs. (22.65 kilos)								
M-12 lb.	Vacant — Minimum Acceptance Weight — 100 lbs. (45.30 kilos)								
W-12 lb.	157-8	94	37½	71.44	238.76	95.25	Botany Australia	Jan. 12 1975	Mrs. Dulcie Chee
M-20 lb.	341	120	55½	154.67	304.80	140.97	Cape Moreton Australia	July 6 1957	Bob Dyer
W-20 lb.	294-8	110½	53	133.58	280.67	134.62	Sydney Australia	Feb. 24 1973	Pamela Hudspeth
M-30 lb.	494-8	119	62	224.30	302.26	157.48	Newport N.S.W., Australia	Jan. 29 1973	Peter Douglas Swavley
W-30 lb.	Vacant — Minimum Acceptance Weight — 370 lbs. (167.61 kilos)								
M-50 lb.	1018	159	68	461.76	403.86	172.72	Cape Moreton Australia	June 12 1957	Bob Dyer
W-50 lb.	458	127	57	207.74	322.58	144.78	Cape Moreton Australia	July 3 1957	Mrs. Bob Dyer
M-80 lb.	1305	163½	86	591.94	415.29	218.44	Coogee Wide, Sydne Australia	May 17 1959	Samuel Jamieson
W-80 lb.	1173	148	84	532.06	375.92	213.36	Cronulla NSW, Australia	Mar. 24 1963	June Irene Butcher
All-Tackle M-130 lb.	1780	166½	103	807.40	422.91	261.62	Cherry Grove S. Carolina, USA	June 14 1964	Walter Maxwell
W-130 lb.	1314	165	89	596.02	419.10	226.06	Cape Moreton Australia	July 27 1953	Mrs. Bob Dyer

SHARK (white)

LINE CLASS	Weight lbs. oz.	Length inches	Girth inches	Weight kilo	Length cm	Girth cm	PLACE	DATE	ANGLER
M-6 lb.	Vacant — Minimum Acceptance Weight — 40 lbs. (18.12 kilos)								
W-6 lb.	Vacant — Minimum Acceptance Weight — 40 lbs. (18.12 kilos)								
M-12 lb.	96-10	67	27½	43.82	170.18	69.85	Mazatlan Mexico	Apr. 30 1964	Ray O. Acord
W-12 lb.	Vacant — Minimum Acceptance Weight — 72 lbs. (32.61 kilos)								
M-20 lb.	1068	150	77	484.44	381.80	195.58	Cape Moreton Australia	June 18 1957	Bob Dyer
W-20 lb.	369	111	57	167.37	281.94	144.78	Cape Moreton Australia	July 6 1957	Mrs. Bob Dyer
M-30 lb.	1053	152	68	477.63	386.08	172.72	Cape Moreton Australia	June 13 1957	Bob Dyer
W-30 lb.	803	149	70	364.23	378.46	177.80	Cape Moreton Australia	July 5 1957	Mrs. Bob Dyer
M-50 lb.	1876	186	101½	850.94	472.44	257.81	Cape Moreton Australia	Aug. 6 1955	Bob Dyer
W-50 lb.	801	135	75	363.33	342.90	190.50	Cape Moreton Australia	June 11 1957	Mrs. Bob Dyer
M-80 lb.	2344	181	108	1063.23	459.74	274.32	Streaky Bay Australia	Nov. 6 1960	Alfred Dean
W-80 lb.	912	143	71½	413.68	363.22	181.61	Cape Moreton Australia	Aug. 29 1954	Mrs. Bob Dyer
All-Tackle M-130 lb.	2664	202	114	1208.38	513.08	289.56	Ceduna Australia	Apr. 21 1959	Alfred Dean
W-130 lb.	1052	166	72½	477.18	421.64	184.15	Cape Moreton Australia	June 27 1954	Mrs. Bob Dyer

SKIPJACK (black)

Scientific name: Euthynnus lineatus

LINE CLASS	U. S. CUSTOMARY			METRIC			PLACE	DATE	ANGLER
	Weight lbs. oz.	Length Inches	Girth Inches	Weight kilo	Length cm	Girth cm			
M-6 lb.	Vacant — Minimum Acceptance Weight — 6 lbs. (2.71 kilos)								
W-6 lb.	Vacant — Minimum Acceptance Weight — 6 lbs. (2.71 kilos)								
M-12 lb.	Vacant — Minimum Acceptance Weight — 6 lbs. (2.71 kilos)								
W-12 lb.	Vacant — Minimum Acceptance Weight — 6 lbs. (2.71 kilos)								
M-20 lb.	Vacant — Minimum Acceptance Weight — 9 lbs. (4.07 kilos)								
W-20 lb.	Vacant — Minimum Acceptance Weight — 9 lbs. (4.07 kilos)								
M-30 lb.	Vacant — Minimum Acceptance Weight — 9 lbs. (4.07 kilos)								
W-30 lb.	Vacant — Minimum Acceptance Weight — 9 lbs. (4.07 kilos)								
M-50 lb.	Vacant — Minimum Acceptance Weight — 9 lbs. (4.07 kilos)								
W-50 lb.	Vacant — Minimum Acceptance Weight — 9 lbs. (4.07 kilos)								
M-80 lb.	Vacant — Minimum Acceptance Weight — 12 lbs. (5.43 kilos)								
W-80 lb.	Vacant — Minimum Acceptance Weight — 12 lbs. (5.43 kilos)								
M-130 lb.	Vacant — Minimum Acceptance Weight — 12 lbs. (5.43 kilos)								
W-130 lb.	Vacant — Minimum Acceptance Weight — 12 lbs. (5.43 kilos)								

SNOOK

Scientific name: Centropomus undecimalis

LINE CLASS	Weight lbs. oz.	Length Inches	Girth Inches	Weight kilo	Length cm	Girth cm	PLACE	DATE	ANGLER
M-6 lb.	30	45½	25	13.60	115.57	63.50	Fort Lauderdale Florida, USA	June 26 1975	Steve Swisher
W-6 lb.	20-2	39	19½	9.12	99.06	49.53	Captiva Florida, USA	Aug. 2 1972	Wilma Bell Brantner
M-12 lb.	37	47	24½	16.78	119.38	62.23	Boynton Beach Florida, USA	June 18 1959	Durling Drake
*W-12 lb.	32-8	45	24	14.74	114.30	60.96	Jupiter Florida, USA	Aug. 2 1957	Mrs. Nancy Neville
M-20 lb.	41-8	42	29	18.82	106.68	73.66	Palm Beach Florida, USA	June 30 1968	H. Wilder Clapp
W-20 lb.	35	43	25½	15.87	109.22	64.77	Fort Myers Florida, USA	Feb. 16 1962	Mrs. Wade Miller
M-30 lb.	43	47	26½	19.50	119.38	67.31	Lake Worth Florida, USA	May 18 1952	Lee K. Spencer
All-Tackle W-30 lb.	52-6	49½	26	23.75	125.73	66.04	La Paz Mexico	Jan. 9 1963	Jane Haywood
M-50 lb.	40	44½	27¼	18.14	113.03	69.21	West Palm Beach Florida, USA	Apr. 8 1972	Ralph R. Boynton
W-50 lb.	31-8	41½	23	14.28	105.41	58.42	Stuart Florida, USA	July 17 1951	Mrs. B. N. Fox
M-80 lb.	39-8	46	28	17.91	116.84	71.12	Boca Raton Florida, USA	Mar. 22 1975	Ernie Hartness
W-80 lb.	Vacant — Minimum Acceptance Weight — 39 lbs. (17.66 kilos)								
M-130 lb.	Vacant — Minimum Acceptance Weight — 39 lbs. (17.66 kilos)								
W-130 lb.	Vacant — Minimum Acceptance Weight — 39 lbs. (17.66 kilos)								
*TIE W-12 lb.	32-8	46	23¼	14.74	116.84	59.05	Ft. Lauderdale Florida, USA	July 24 1966	Rosemary Schafer

SWORDFISH

Other common name: broadbill
Scientific name: Xiphias gladius

LINE CLASS	U. S. CUSTOMARY			METRIC			PLACE	DATE	ANGLER
	Weight lbs. oz.	Length inches	Girth inches	Weight kilo	Length cm	Girth cm			
M-6 lb.	106-8	105½	32½	48.30	267.97	82.55	Cabo San Lucas Mexico	June 11 1972	James Perry
W-6 lb.	Vacant — Minimum Acceptance Weight — 76 lbs. (34.42 kilos)								
M-12 lb.	120	103	33	54.43	261.62	83.82	Palmilla Mexico	June 1 1968	Russell M. Anderson
W-12 lb.	Vacant — Minimum Acceptance Weight — 90 lbs. (40.77 kilos)								
M-20 lb.	183-8	120	41	83.23	304.80	104.14	Cabo San Lucas Mexico	May 4 1971	Charles C. Yamamoto
W-20 lb.	157	108½	39	71.21	275.59	99.06	Baja California Mexico	Feb. 11 1972	Mrs. James Perry
M-30 lb.	314	131½	44	142.42	334.01	111.76	Catalina Channel California, USA	Oct. 4 1974	Larry Barrett
W-30 lb.	Vacant — Minimum Acceptance Weight — 235 lbs. (106.45 kilos)								
M-50 lb.	444	145	57	201.39	368.30	144.78	Pompano Beach Florida, USA	Apr. 27 1951	Fred J. Fleming
W-50 lb.	492-4	141	54	223.28	358.14	137.16	Montauk Point New York, USA	July 4 1959	Dorothea Cassullo
M-80 lb.	530	149	59	240.40	378.46	149.86	Shinnecock New York, USA	Aug. 26 1960	Walter P. Margulies
W-80 lb.	772	154	70	350.17	391.16	177.80	Iquique Chile, SA	June 7 1954	Mrs. L. Marron
All-Tackle M-130 lb.	1182	179¼	78	536.15	455.29	198.12	Iquique Chile, SA	May 7 1953	L. Marron
W-130 lb.	759	167	73	344.28	424.18	185.42	Iquique Chile, SA	June 30 1952	Mrs. D. A. Allison

TANGUIGUE

Other common name: narrow-barred mackerel
Scientific name: Scomberomorus commerson

LINE CLASS	Weight lbs. oz.	Length inches	Girth inches	Weight kilo	Length cm	Girth cm	PLACE	DATE	ANGLER
M-6 lb.	43	54½	22½	19.50	138.43	57.15	Grose Island Australia	Aug. 6 1972	Hilton Morrish Selvey
W-6 lb.	20-8	47	17¾	9.29	119.38	45.08	Cairns Australia	Aug. 25 1972	Dolly Dyer
M-12 lb.	53	64	24¾	24.04	162.56	62.86	Innisfail Australia	Nov. 24 1974	D.R.Henrickson
W-12 lb.	Vacant — Minimum Acceptance Weight — 40 lbs. (18.14 kilos)								
M-20 lb.	78	67½	33½	35.38	171.45	85.09	Queensland Australia	May 16 1970	Edward J. French
W-20 lb.	Vacant — Minimum Acceptance Weight — 59 lbs. (26.72 kilos)								
M-30 lb.	76	69½	30¼	34.47	176.53	76.83	Innisfail Australia	Mar. 28 1975	Alan Fitzmaurice
W-30 lb.	68	68	26	30.84	172.72	66.04	Hayman Island Australia	May 14 1969	Lady Joan Ansett
M-50 lb.	78	66	29	35.38	167.64	73.66	Cape Moreton Australia	Apr. 8 1967	Ronald G. Jenyns
W-50 lb.	63	67	25½	28.57	170.18	64.77	Hayman Island Australia	Apr. 26 1970	Marie Gloria Maestracci
All-Tackle M-80 lb.	81	71½	29¼	36.74	181.61	74.29	Karachi Pakistan	Aug. 27 1960	George E. Rusinak
W-80 lb.	64	67	26	29.03	170.18	66.04	Mozambique East Africa	Sept. 12 1959	Mrs. A. C. Lee
M-130 lb.	75-4	67	26½	34.13	170.18	67.31	Cairns Australia	Oct. 31 1974	Alexander Leslie Sinclair
W-130 lb.	Vacant — Minimum Acceptance Weight — 60 lbs. (27.18 kilos)								

284   ANGLER'S BIBLE

TARPON

Scientific name: Megalops atlantica

LINE CLASS	U. S. CUSTOMARY			METRIC			PLACE	DATE	ANGLER
	Weight lbs. oz.	Length inches	Girth inches	Weight kilo	Length cm	Girth cm			
M-6 lb.	71-8	64½	30	32.43	163.83	76.20	Big Pine Key Florida, USA	Mar. 13 1973	Stuart C. Apte
W-6 lb.	35-7	53½	23½	16.07	135.89	59.69	Islamorada Florida, USA	June 23 1973	Mrs. Albert H. Ehlert
M-12 lb.	170-8	84	40	77.33	213.36	101.60	Big Pine Key Florida, USA	Mar. 10 1963	Russell C. Ball
W-12 lb.	127	72	37½	57.60	182.88	95.25	Islamorada Florida, USA	Apr. 24 1975	Mrs. R. Michael Murphy
M-20 lb.	243	80	47	110.22	203.20	119.38	Key West Florida, USA	Feb. 17 1975	Gus Bell
W-20 lb.	150	80½	39½	68.03	204.47	100.33	Islamorada Florida, USA	May 24 1973	Shirley A. Hyman
All-Tackle M-30 lb.	283	86-3/5	—	128.36	219.96	—	Lake Maracaibo Venezuela, SA	Mar. 19 1956	M. Salazar
W-30 lb.	171	83	42¾	77.56	210.82	108.58	Marathon Florida, USA	May 21 1968	Mrs. Henry Sage
M-50 lb.	242-4	88-2/5	43-2/5	109.88	224.53	110.23	Cienaga Ayapel Colombia, SA	Jan. 7 1955	A. Salazar
W-50 lb.	190-8	84	45	86.41	213.36	114.30	Boca Grande Pass Florida, USA	May 27 1970	Patricia J. Mang
M-80 lb.	218	85	45	98.88	215.90	114.30	Tampa Bay Florida, USA	May 6 1973	Rick Wotring
W-80 lb.	203	95	44	92.08	241.30	111.76	Marathon Florida, USA	May 19 1961	June Jordan
M-130 lb.	210	86¼	45¼	95.25	219.07	114.93	Port Isabel Texas, USA	Nov. 13 1973	Thomas F. Gibson, Jr.

W-130 lb.   Vacant — Minimum Acceptance Weight — 180 lbs. (81.54 kilos)

TAUTOG

Other common name: blackfish
Scientific name: Tautoga onitis

LINE CLASS	Weight lbs. oz.	Length inches	Girth inches	Weight kilo	Length cm	Girth cm	PLACE	DATE	ANGLER
M-6 lb.	14-6	25½	22½	6.52	64.77	57.15	Virginia Beach Virginia, USA	May 17 1972	Linwood A. Martens
W-6 lb.	9	22	21	4.08	55.88	53.34	Bayville, L.I. New York, USA	July 20 1975	Deborah Kuno
M-12 lb.	13-3	26	19½	5.99	66.04	49.53	Virginia Beach Virginia, USA	Apr. 20 1975	Nicholas J. Durney, Sr.
W-12 lb.	10-8	23	18	4.76	58.42	45.72	Montauk New York, USA	June 2 1973	Mrs. Joseph M. Rinaldi
M-20 lb.	21	30	—	9.52	76.20	—	Jamestown Island Rhode Island, USA	Nov. 6 1954	C. W. Sundquist
W-20 lb.	10-12	24-5/8	18¾	4.87	62.54	47.62	Asharoken Beach New York, USA	May 7 1962	Trudy H. King
All-Tackle M-30 lb.	21-6	31½	23½	9.69	80.01	59.69	Cape May New Jersey, USA	June 12 1954	R. N. Sheafer
W-30 lb.	11-3	26	19½	5.07	66.04	49.53	Virginia Beach Virginia, USA	May 17 1971	Mrs. Charlotte J. Wright
M-50 lb.	20-14	32	30	9.46	81.28	76.20	Newport Rhode Island, USA	Oct. 20 1955	W. R. Peckham
W-50 lb.	17-6	27½	23¼	7.88	69.85	59.05	Virginia Beach Virginia, USA	May 5 1971	L. Trula Becker

M-80 lb.   Vacant — Minimum Acceptance Weight — 16 lbs. (7.24 kilos)

W-80 lb.   Vacant — Minimum Acceptance Weight — 16 lbs. (7.24 kilos)

M-130 lb.   Vacant — Minimum Acceptance Weight — 16 lbs. (7.24 kilos)

W-130 lb.   Vacant — Minimum Acceptance Weight — 16 lbs. (7.24 kilos)

TUNA (Atlantic bigeye)

Scientific name: Thunnus obesus

| LINE CLASS | U. S. CUSTOMARY | | | METRIC | | | PLACE | DATE | ANGLER |
	Weight lbs. oz.	Length inches	Girth inches	Weight kilo	Length cm	Girth cm			
M-6 lb.	Vacant — Minimum Acceptance Weight — 10 lbs. (4.53 kilos)								
W-6 lb.	Vacant — Minimum Acceptance Weight — 10 lbs. (4.53 kilos)								
M-12 lb.	Vacant — Minimum Acceptance Weight — 20 lbs. (9.06 kilos)								
W-12 lb.	Vacant — Minimum Acceptance Weight — 20 lbs. (9.06 kilos)								
M-20 lb.	Vacant — Minimum Acceptance Weight — 34 lbs. (15.40 kilos)								
W-20 lb.	46	43	31	20.86	109.22	78.74	N. Key Largo Florida, USA	Jan. 17 1959	Dorothea L. Dean
M-30 lb.	Vacant — Minimum Acceptance Weight — 50 lbs. (22.65 kilos)								
W-30 lb.	Vacant — Minimum Acceptance Weight — 50 lbs. (22.65 kilos)								
M-50 lb.	321-12	88¼	58¼	145.94	224.15	147.95	Hudson Canyon New York, USA	Aug. 19 1972	Vito Lo Caputo
W-50 lb.	Vacant — Minimum Acceptance Weight — 100 lbs. (45.30 kilos)								
M-80 lb.	271	78	53¼	122.92	198.12	135.25	Arguineguin Canary Islands	July 24 1975	Kenneth V. Oulton
W-80 lb.	62	43	31	28.12	109.22	78.74	St. Helena Atlantic Ocean	Oct. 30 1957	Mrs. Brenda Dunlop
All-Tackle M-130 lb.	335-1	100¾	60¼	152.00	255.90	153.03	Mogan, Gran Canaria Canary Islands	July 11 1975	Wilhelm Rapp
W-130 lb.	182	68	56	82.55	172.72	142.24	Cat Cay Bahamas	June 2 1958	Mrs. Matilde Catta

TUNA (blackfin)

Scientific name: Thunnus atlanticus

LINE CLASS	Weight lbs. oz.	Length inches	Girth inches	Weight kilo	Length cm	Girth cm	PLACE	DATE	ANGLER
M-6 lb.	29	35½	26¼	13.15	90.17	66.67	Challenger Bank Bermuda	Aug. 6 1972	Keith R. Winter
W-6 lb.	18-4	29½	21½	8.27	74.93	54.61	Southwest Bermuda	May 24 1973	Rosalind E. D. Dunmore
*M-12 lb.	29-12	36¼	27	13.49	92.07	68.58	Bermuda	Aug. 24 1968	Jay William Rewalt
W-12 lb.	26-12	35	23½	12.13	88.90	59.69	Bermuda	Oct. 18 1957	Mrs. L. Edna Perinchief
M-20 lb.	34-12	40	32	15.76	101.60	81.28	Bermuda	June 16 1974	Keith R. Dunmore
W-20 lb.	32-2	38	26¾	14.57	96.52	67.94	Bermuda	Oct. 23 1968	Mrs. Herbert N. Arnold
All-Tackle M-30 lb.	38	39¼	28¾	17.23	99.69	73.02	Bermuda	June 26 1970	Archie L. Dickens
All-Tackle TIE W-30 lb.	38	41	28	17.23	104.14	71.12	Islamorada Florida, USA	May 22 1973	Elizabeth Jean Wade
M-50 lb.	36	36¼	28-7/8	16.32	92.07	73.34	Bermuda	July 14 1973	Joseph E. Baptiste, Jr.
W-50 lb.	31	36	26-5/16	14.06	91.44	66.83	Bermuda	Aug. 30 1967	Mrs. Glenn Sipe
M-80 lb.	29-1	36	25½	13.18	91.44	64.77	Bermuda	Sept. 21 1974	Robert Byrom
W-80 lb	30	36	26	13.60	91.44	66.04	Islamorada Florida, USA	Oct. 17 1974	Margaret K. Dansyear
M-130 lb.	Vacant — Minimum Acceptance Weight — 29 lbs. (13.13 kilos)								
W-130 lb.	Vacant — Minimum Acceptance Weight — 29 lbs. (13.13 kilos)								
*TIE M-12 lb.	29-12	36	25¾	13.49	91.44	65.40	Bermuda	July 13 1972	Norman Cove

TUNA (bluefin)

LINE CLASS	U. S. CUSTOMARY			METRIC			PLACE	DATE	ANGLER
	Weight lbs. oz.	Length inches	Girth inches	Weight kilo	Length cm	Girth cm			
M-6 lb.	9-4	24	17	4.19	60.96	43.18	Atlantic Beach New York, USA	July 14 1974	Fred H. Hill
W-6 lb.	7-6	27	15½	3.34	58.42	39.37	Atlantic Beach New York, USA	July 7 1974	Meta Hill
M-12 lb.	23-9	35	23	10.68	88.90	58.42	East Rockaway, L.I. New York, USA	Sept. 8 1975	Harry Ross
W-12 lb.	33-15	40	28¼	15.39	101.60	71.75	Guadalupe Island Mexico	Dec. 20 1962	Mrs. Rae Pasquale
M-20 lb.	114-8	61	42	51.93	154.94	106.68	Montauk New York, USA	July 25 1959	Mundy I. Peale
W-20 lb.	93	53-1/8	37½	42.18	134.93	95.25	Provincetown Massachusetts, USA	Sept. 14 1958	Willia H. Mather
M-30 lb.	139	66	40½	63.04	167.64	102.87	Block Island Rhode Island, USA	July 29 1975	Donald J. S. Merten
W-30 lb.	117-8	61-3/16	42	53.29	155.41	106.68	San Diego California, USA	Sept. 10 1968	Gladys A. Chambers
M-50 lb.	640	110	72	290.30	279.40	182.88	Massachusetts Bay Massachusetts, USA	Sept. 5 1971	Joseph M. Di Carlo
W-50 lb.	518	109	69	234.96	276.86	175.26	Bimini Bahamas	May 13 1950	Mrs. William Myers
M-80 lb.	881	119½	80¾	399.61	303.53	205.10	Newburyport Massachusetts, USA	Sept. 20 1970	Wilbur E. Tobey
W-80 lb.	717	108	74	325.22	274.32	187.96	Prince Edward Island Canada	Sept. 1 1969	Mrs. Herbert L. Allison
All-Tackle M-130 lb.	1120	122	85½	508.02	309.88	217.17	Prince Edward Island Canada	Oct. 19 1973	Lee Coffin
W-130 lb.	1000	124	84	453.59	314.96	213.36	Gloucester Massachusetts, USA	Aug. 31 1973	Anna Cardinale

TUNA (dog-tooth)

LINE CLASS	Weight lbs. oz.	Length inches	Girth inches	Weight kilo	Length cm	Girth cm	PLACE	DATE	ANGLER
M-6 lb.	Vacant — Minimum Acceptance Weight — 6 lbs. (2.71 kilos)								
W-6 lb.	Vacant — Minimum Acceptance Weight — 6 lbs. (2.71 kilos)								
M-12 lb.	77-11	57	34	35.25	144.78	86.36	Lizard Island Australia	Oct. 1 1975	John Pelton
W-12 lb.	Vacant — Minimum Acceptance Weight — 12 lbs. (5.43 kilos)								
M-20 lb.	47-4	46½	29	21.43	118.11	73.66	Cairns Australia	Sept. 11 1974	William Allen
W-20 lb.	Vacant — Minimum Acceptance Weight — 20 lbs. (9.06 kilos)								
All-Tackle M-30 lb.	142-3	68½	45	64.49	173.99	114.30	Lizard Island Australia	Aug. 29 1975	John C. Johnston
W-30 lb.	Vacant — Minimum Acceptance Weight — 30 lbs. (13.59 kilos)								
M-50 lb.	49	48	28	22.22	121.92	71.12	Lizard Island Australia	Aug. 30 1975	Bob Oliver
W-50 lb.	95-4	58	35	43.20	147.32	88.90	Cairns Australia	Oct. 5 1974	Eleanor D. Inscho
M-80 lb.	122-4	65½	40	55.45	166.37	101.60	Cairns Australia	Oct. 10 1974	Colin L. (Bill) Hinchen
W-80 lb.	104-8	61	39	47.40	154.94	99.06	Cairns Australia	Sept. 11 1974	Gloria J. Applegate
M-130 lb.	111	63½	36	50.34	161.29	91.44	Cairns Australia	Aug. 29 1974	Robert Oliver
W-130 lb.	Vacant — Minimum Acceptance Weight — 92 lbs. (41.67 kilos)								

TUNA (longtail)

LINE CLASS	U. S. CUSTOMARY Weight lbs. oz.	Length Inches	Girth Inches	METRIC Weight kilo	Length cm	Girth cm	PLACE	DATE	ANGLER
M-6 lb.	27	43¾	22¼	12.25	111.12	56.51	Moreton Bay Q., Australia	Apr. 25 1975	Alan Tesch
W-6 lb.	Vacant — Minimum Acceptance Weight — 21 lbs. (9.51 kilos)								
M-12 lb.	45-12	48¾	28	20.75	124.00	71.00	Moreton Bay Q., Australia	Mar. 13 1975	Bob Bruce
W-12 lb.	37-8	47½	25	17.00	120.50	63.50	Moreton Bay Q., Australia	Apr. 5 1975	Christine Stoddard
M-20 lb.	42	48½	27	19.05	123.19	68.58	Tangalooma Q., Australia	Apr. 25 1975	Keith Waterman
W-20 lb.	Vacant — Minimum Acceptance Weight — 32 lbs. (14.49 kilos)								
M-30 lb.	Vacant — Minimum Acceptance Weight — 32 lbs. (14.49 kilos)								
W-30 lb.	Vacant — Minimum Acceptance Weight — 32 lbs. (14.49 kilos)								
All-Tackle M-50 lb.	60	56	30	27.21	142.24	76.20	Bermagui N.S.W., Australia	Mar. 17 1975	N. Noel Webster
W-50 lb.	Vacant — Minimum Acceptance Weight — 45 lbs. (20.38 kilos)								
M-80 lb.	Vacant — Minimum Acceptance Weight — 45 lbs. (20.38 kilos)								
W-80 lb.	Vacant — Minimum Acceptance Weight — 45 lbs. (20.38 kilos)								
M-130 lb.	Vacant — Minimum Acceptance Weight — 45 lbs. (20.38 kilos)								
W-130 lb.	Vacant — Minimum Acceptance Weight — 45 lbs. (20.38 kilos)								

TUNA (Pacific bigeye)

LINE CLASS	Weight lbs. oz.	Length Inches	Girth Inches	Weight kilo	Length cm	Girth cm	PLACE	DATE	ANGLER
M-6 lb.	29-8	41½	23½	13.38	105.41	59.69	Salinas Ecuador, SA	May 31 1975	Luis Alberto Flores A.
W-6 lb.	Vacant — Minimum Acceptance Weight — 22 lbs. (9.96 kilos)								
M-12 lb.	37	42½	28	16.78	107.95	71.12	Salinas Ecuador, SA	May 28 1975	Knud Holst
W-12 lb.	27-1	36¼	24	12.27	92.07	60.96	Salinas Ecuador, SA	Jan. 29 1970	Mrs. Marilyn Schamroth
M-20 lb.	108	51½	37½	48.98	130.81	95.25	San Diego California, USA	Aug. 10 1968	John E. Muckenthaler
W-20 lb.	27	34	24	12.24	86.36	60.96	Cabo Blanco Peru, SA	Aug. 13 1955	Mrs. O. Owinas
M-30 lb.	163	61	50½	73.93	154.94	128.27	San Diego California, USA	Aug. 15 1970	Forrest N. Shumway
W-30 lb.	133	62½	41¾	60.32	158.75	106.45	Coronados Islands Mexico	Oct. 7 1970	Mrs. Sally Johnson
M-50 lb.	280	83	52½	127.00	210.82	133.35	Salinas Ecuador, SA	Jan. 21 1967	Luis Alberto Flores A.
W-50 lb.	240	75¼	52¾	108.86	191.13	133.98	Salinas Ecuador, SA	Jan. 11 1969	Helen C. King
M-80 lb.	332	87½	58	150.59	222.25	147.32	Cabo Blanco Peru, SA	Jan. 26 1953	Emil Wm. Steffens
W-80 lb.	335	85	59½	151.95	215.90	151.10	Cabo Blanco Peru, SA	Mar. 25 1953	Mrs. Wendell Anderson, Jr.
All-Tackle M-130 lb.	435	93	63½	197.31	236.22	161.29	Cabo Blanco Peru, SA	Apr. 17 1957	Dr. Russel V. A. Lee
W-130 lb.	336	87	56½	152.40	220.98	143.51	Cabo Blanco Peru, SA	Jan. 16 1957	Mrs. Seymour Knox III

TUNA (skipjack)

LINE CLASS	U. S. CUSTOMARY			METRIC			PLACE	DATE	ANGLER
	Weight lbs. oz.	Length inches	Girth inches	Weight kilo	Length cm	Girth cm			
M-6 lb.	21	31	22	9.52	78.74	55.88	Keahole Hawaii, USA	July 19 1972	Rufus Spalding, Jr.
W-6 lb.	9-8	24	16	4.30	60.96	40.64	Port Stephens Australia	March 30 1974	Mrs. Marilyn Petersen
M-12 lb.	27-8	34½	23	12.47	87.63	58.42	San Juan Puerto Rico	Oct. 20 1974	Miguel E. Correa
W-12 lb.	24-6	30½	21	11.05	77.47	53.34	Walker Cay Bahamas	Mar. 26 1965	Patricia E. Church
M-20 lb.	35-4	36½	26	16.00	93.00	66.00	Tahiti French Polynesia	Aug. 17 1975	Alban Ellacott
W-20 lb.	25	33	22½	11.33	83.82	57.15	San Juan Puerto Rico	Oct. 1966	Carmen Perez Agudo
M-30 lb.	33-4	37	27	15.08	93.98	68.58	San Juan Puerto Rico	July 14 1966	Jose L. Campos
W-30 lb.	28-8	32¼	23	12.92	81.91	58.42	Waianae Hawaii, USA	June 8 1954	Mrs. C. T. Nottage
All Tackle *M-50 lb.	39-15	39	28	18.11	99.06	71.12	Walker Cay Bahamas	Jan. 21 1952	F. Drowley
W-50 lb.	31	34½	24½	14.06	87.63	62.23	San Juan Puerto Rico	Dec. 26 1954	Gloria G. de Marques
*M-80 lb.	38-8	34½	29	17.46	87.63	73.66	Waianae Hawaii, USA	June 13 1964	Sueo Okimoto
W-80 lb.	35	38	26	15.87	96.52	66.04	Kailua, Kona Hawaii, USA	Aug. 5 1975	Judith Ann Nakamaru
M-130 lb.	38	—	—	17.23	—	—	Black River Mauritius	Mar. 15 1961	Frank Masson
W-130 lb.	31	35	24	14.06	88.90	60.96	Kona Hawaii, USA	June 16 1963	Anne H. Bosworth
All-Tackle TIE *M-50 lb.	40	38¾	27½	18.14	98.42	69.85	Baie du Tambeau, Mauritius	Apr. 19 1971	Joseph R. P. Caboche, Jr.
*TIE M-80 lb.	38-10	36½	26	17.52	92.71	66.04	Kaiiwi Point Hawaii, USA	July 6 1975	Ralph J. Wilson

TUNA (southern bluefin)

LINE CLASS	Weight lbs. oz.	Length inches	Girth inches	Weight kilo	Length cm	Girth cm	PLACE	DATE	ANGLER
M-6 lb.	Vacant — Minimum Acceptance Weight — 12 lbs. (5.43 kilos)								
W-6 lb.	Vacant — Minimum Acceptance Weight — 12 lbs. (5.43 kilos)								
M-12 lb.	56	47½	32	25.40	120.65	81.28	S. Neptune Island Australia	April 12 1965	Eldred H. V. Riggs
W-12 lb.	39-8	44½	28	17.91	113.03	71.12	Tasmania Australia	May 27 1963	Mrs. Bob Dyer
M-20 lb.	Vacant — Minimum Acceptance Weight — 30 lbs. (13.59 kilos)								
W-20 lb.	Vacant — Minimum Acceptance Weight — 30 lbs. (13.59 kilos)								
M-30 lb.	172	65	45	78.01	165.10	114.30	Cape Pillar Tasmania, Australia	May 8 1959	C. I. Cutler
W-30 lb.	Vacant — Minimum Acceptance Weight — 50 lbs. (22.65 kilos)								
M-50 lb.	Vacant — Minimum Acceptance Weight — 75 lbs. (33.97 kilos)								
W-50 lb.	Vacant — Minimum Acceptance Weight — 75 lbs. (33.97 kilos)								
M-80 lb.	Vacant — Minimum Acceptance Weight — 100 lbs. (45.30 kilos)								
W-80 lb.	Vacant — Minimum Acceptance Weight — 100 lbs. (45.30 kilos)								
M-130 lb.	Vacant — Minimum Acceptance Weight — 100 lbs. (45.30 kilos)								
W-130 lb.	Vacant — Minimum Acceptance Weight — 100 lbs. (45.30 kilos)								

TUNA (yellowfin)

Other common name: allison tuna
Scientific name: Thunnus albacares

LINE CLASS	U. S. CUSTOMARY			METRIC			PLACE	DATE	ANGLER
	Weight lbs. oz.	Length inches	Girth inches	Weight kilo	Length cm	Girth cm			
M-6 lb.	33-8	41¼	25½	15.19	104.77	64.77	Bernier Island Australia	May 28 1973	Ivan Harold Quartermaine
W-6 lb.	10-8	27½	18	4.76	69.85	45.72	Sydney Australia	April 7 1974	Pamela Hudspeth
M-12 lb.	145	65½	40½	65.77	166.37	102.87	Port Stephens NSW, Australia	Aug. 23 1970	Don McElwaine
W-12 lb.	76	59	33	34.47	149.86	83.82	St. Thomas U.S. Virgin Islands	May 10 1969	Gloria J. Applegate
M-20 lb.	153	73	42½	69.40	185.42	107.95	Montague Island Australia	Feb. 15 1973	Thomas O. Mitchell
W-20 lb.	100	63	36	45.35	160.02	91.44	Sydney Australia	Nov. 20 1971	Mrs. Pamela Hudspeth
M-30 lb.	196	75¾	46½	88.90	192.40	118.11	Sir John Young Banks Australia	Mar. 23 1975	Michael P. Micallef
W-30 lb.	137	63½	41¾	62.14	161.29	106.04	Challenger Bank Bermuda	Sept. 12 1965	Jan T. Heisel
M-50 lb.	241	76	53	109.31	193.04	134.62	Kailua, Kona Hawaii, USA	Aug. 5 1975	Duane L. Pratt
W-50 lb.	229	78	50	103.87	198.12	127.00	Kailua, Kona Hawaii, USA	Aug. 7 1975	Mardi Jensen
M-80 lb.	302	87½	56	136.98	222.25	142.24	Soccoro Island Mexico	Jan. 14 1975	John Lighty
W-80 lb.	231	75½	52	104.78	191.77	132.08	Kailua Kona Hawaii, USA	Aug. 4 1975	Judith Ann Nakamaru
All-Tackle M-130 lb.	308	84	57	139.70	213.36	144.78	San Benedicto Island Mexico	Jan. 18 1973	Harold J. Tolson
W-130 lb.	254	75	52	115.21	190.50	132.08	Kona Hawaii, USA	Aug. 19 1954	Jean Carlisle

TUNNY (little)

Other common name: false albacore
Scientific name: Euthynnus alletteratus

LINE CLASS	Weight lbs. oz.	Length inches	Girth inches	Weight kilo	Length cm	Girth cm	PLACE	DATE	ANGLER
M-6 lb.	19	34	23½	8.61	86.36	59.69	Mayport Florida, USA	June 1 1975	Bradley Reed
W-6 lb.	12	29 7/8	18 7/8	5.44	75.88	47.94	Mayport Florida, USA	July 23 1975	Melissa Workman
All-Tackle M-12 lb.	21-12	33½	21½	9.86	85.09	54.61	Key Largo Florida, USA	June 29 1975	Paul F. Leader
W-12 lb.	13-8	32	18¾	6.12	81.28	47.62	Marathon Florida, USA	Nov. 3 1974	Patricia T. Williams
M-20 lb.	20-8	35	22	9.29	88.90	55.88	Northwest of Bermuda	Aug. 5 1975	Juan Prado, Jr.
W-20 lb.	15-9	31	19	7.05	78.74	48.26	Marathon Florida, USA	Apr. 20 1975	Jane E. Spruance
M-30 lb.	16-9	31½	20	7.51	80.23	50.80	Brunswick Georgia, USA	Apr. 9 1975	David Urquhart Ansley
W-30 lb.	3-15	21	11½	1.78	53.34	29.21	Empire Louisiana, USA	July 6 1975	Priscilla Jordan Claverie
M-50 lb.	17-11	34	20¾	8.03	86.36	52.70	Manasquan Ridge New Jersey, USA	Sept. 13 1975	Richard C. Mitchell
W-50 lb.	20-2	36¼	20 5/8	9.12	92.07	52.38	Charleston S. Carolina, USA	May 19 1974	Mrs. Alberta B. Herring
M-80 lb.	Vacant — Minimum Acceptance Weight — 17 lbs. (7.70 kilos)								
W-80 lb.	Vacant — Minimum Acceptance Weight — 17 lbs. (7.70 kilos)								
M-130 lb.	Vacant — Minimum Acceptance Weight — 17 lbs. (7.70 kilos)								
W-130 lb.	Vacant — Minimum Acceptance Weight — 17 lbs. (7.70 kilos)								

WAHOO

Scientific name:Acanthocybium solanderi

LINE CLASS	U. S. CUSTOMARY			METRIC			PLACE	DATE	ANGLER
	Weight lbs. oz.	Length inches	Girth inches	Weight kilo	Length cm	Girth cm			
M-6 lb.	28	53	19½	12.70	134.62	49.53	Coiba Island Panama	June 28 1973	George A. Bernstein
W-6 lb.	25-6	50	17½	11.51	127.00	44.45	Bird Island Seychelles	Dec. 26 1974	Georgette Douwma
M-12 lb.	74	69½	28	33.56	176.53	71.12	Coiba Island Panama	June 26 1973	George A. Bernstein
W-12 lb.	66	68	25	29.93	172.72	63.50	St. Thomas U.S. Virgin Islands	Feb. 27 1969	Gloria J. Applegate
M-20 lb.	115	75½	32	52.16	191.77	81.28	Bermuda	July 2 1961	Leo Barboza
W-20 lb.	83	71	30	37.64	180.34	76.20	St. Thomas U.S. Virgin Islands	Mar. 5 1968	Gloria J. Applegate
M-30 lb.	102-4	74 2/5	31¾	46.40	189.00	80.60	Rio de Janeiro Brazil, SA	Nov. 30 1974	Alberto Ivan de Freitas Briggs
W-30 lb.	107-4	72½	33	48.64	184.15	83.82	Eleuthera Bahamas	Apr. 4 1965	Mrs. S. F. Briggs Ii
M-50 lb.	124	76	36	56.24	193.04	91.44	St. Thomas U.S. Virgin Islands	Mar. 29 1967	Joseph H. C. Wenk
W-50 lb.	113	74	33¼	51.25	187.96	84.45	Yanuca Fiji	June 30 1967	Jan K. Bates
M-80 lb.	139	81	33¾	63.04	205.74	85.72	Marathon Florida, USA	May 18 1960	George Von Hoffman
W-80 lb.	104-8	78	30¼	47.40	198.12	76.83	Walker Cay Bahamas	May 2 1965	Mrs. Lloyd Dalzell
All-Tackle M-130 lb.	149	79¾	37½	67.58	202.56	95.25	Cat Cay Bahamas	June 15 1962	John Pirovano
W-130 lb.	110	73½	36½	49.89	186.69	92.71	Port Eades Louisiana, USA	June 22 1964	Mrs. Homer J. Moore, Jr.

WEAKFISH

Scientific name:Cynoscion regalis

LINE CLASS	Weight lbs. oz.	Length inches	Girth inches	Weight kilo	Length cm	Girth cm	PLACE	DATE	ANGLER
M-6 lb.	13-2	33¼	19	5.95	84.45	48.26	Bayshore, Long I. New York, USA	May 29 1974	Dr. Einar F. Grell
W-6 lb.	8-5	29-3/8	15¾	3.77	74.61	40.00	Fire Island New York, USA	May 13 1973	Mrs. Veronica Grebe
M-12 lb.	11-12	31	17½	5.32	78.74	44.45	Virginia Beach Virginia, USA	June 14 1975	Kenneth O. Few
W-12 lb.	9-9	31½	17½	4.33	80.01	44.45	Chesapeake Bay Virginia, USA	May 19 1975	Dorothy G. Arey
M-20 lb.	12-14	35¾	20	5.84	90.80	50.80	Babylon, Long I. New York, USA	May 19 1975	Walter J. Joseph
W-20 lb.	12-1	30¼	18	5.47	76.83	45.72	Virginia Beach Virginia, USA	May 17 1975	Dorothy G. Arey
M-30 lb.	10-10	36	—	4.81	91.44	—	Fire Island Light New York, USA	Sept. 20 1951	J. E. Bailey
W-30 lb.	Vacant — Minimum Acceptance Weight — 8 lbs. (3.62 kilos)								
M-50 lb.	Vacant — Minimum Acceptance Weight — 9 lbs. (4.07 kilos)								
W-50 lb.	11-12	31¾	18	5.32	80.64	45.72	Morehead City N. Carolina, USA	Oct. 29 1950	Mrs. L. A. Denning
All-Tackle M-80 lb.	19-8	37	23¾	8.84	93.98	60.32	Trinidad West Indies	Apr. 13 1962	Dennis B. Hall
W-80 lb.	Vacant — Minimum Acceptance Weight — 15 lbs. (6.79 kilos)								
M-130 lb.	Vacant — Minimum Acceptance Weight — 15 lbs. (6.79 kilos)								
W-130 lb.	Vacant — Minimum Acceptance Weight — 15 lbs. (6.79 kilos)								

NO. 2, 1977 EDITION

YELLOWTAIL

Scientific name: Seriola dorsalis

LINE CLASS	U. S. CUSTOMARY			METRIC			PLACE	DATE	ANGLER
	Weight lbs. oz.	Length inches	Girth inches	Weight kilo	Length cm	Girth cm			
M-6 lb.	38	50½	25½	17.23	128.27	64.77	Bangitoto Channel New Zealand	Dec. 17 1972	Dr. Gabriel D. Tetro
W-6 lb.	16	37	19	7.25	93.98	48.26	Sydney Australia	Sept. 24 1972	Pamela Hudspeth
M-12 lb.	65-8	54	30¼	29.71	137.16	76.83	Cavalli Islands New Zealand	July 13 1972	J. Farrell
W-12 lb.	52-8	51	27½	23.81	129.54	69.85	Cavalli Islands New Zealand	July 5 1969	Mrs. Avril Semmens
M-20 lb.	74	59	31¼	33.56	149.86	79.37	Cavalli Islands New Zealand	May 29 1969	William Pocklington
W-20 lb.	66-8	53	32½	30.16	134.62	82.55	Cape Brett New Zealand	July 12 1970	Margaret Niven
M-30 lb.	88	55½	33	39.91	140.97	83.82	Cape Brett New Zealand	June 25 1963	J. R. Chibnall
W-30 lb.	68	54½	32	30.84	138.43	81.28	Mayor Island New Zealand	Apr. 17 1969	Mrs. Marjorie West
All-Tackle M-50 lb.	111	62	38	50.34	157.48	96.52	Bay of Islands New Zealand	June 11 1961	A. F. Plim
W-50 lb.	82	62	35	37.19	157.48	88.90	Three Kings Islands New Zealand	Oct. 1 1975	Mrs. Francine Swales
M-80 lb.	108	—	—	48.98	—	—	Cape Brett New Zealand	Jan. 15 1962	Robin O'Connor
W-80 lb.	81	57½	32½	36.74	146.05	82.55	Cape Brett New Zealand	May 18 1960	Kura Beale
M-130 lb.	95	69	36	43.09	175.26	91.44	White Island New Zealand	Apr. II 1975	James Victor Bayliss
W-130 lb.	81	59½	32½	36.74	151.13	82.55	Mayor Island New Zealand	Apr. 8 1966	Patricia E. Jack

—Courtesy of the International Game Fish Association.

Salt Water Fly Rod World Records

15 lb. Tippet Class

SPECIES	SCIENTIFIC NAME	WEIGHT	WHERE CAUGHT	DATE	ANGLER	Recognized IGFA All Tackle Weights
ALBACORE	(Thunnus Alalunga)	27 lbs. 8 ozs.	San Diego, Cal.	8-15-70	Charles Davis	70 lbs.
AMBERJACK	(Seriola dumerili)	65 lbs. 4 ozs.	Key West, Florida	1-6-71	Jim Lopez	149 lbs.
BARRACUDA, Great	(Sphyraena barracuda)	37 lbs. 4 ozs.	Key West, Fla.	12-16-75	Roy Terrell	83 lbs ★
BARRACUDA, Calif.	(Sphyraena argentea)					
BASS, Calif. White Sea	(Cynoscion nobilis)					83 lbs. 12 ozs.
BASS, Channel	(Sciaenops ocellata)	25 lbs. 8 ozs.			J.T. Littleton	83 lbs.
BASS, Kelp	(Paralabrax clathratus)	3 lbs. 8 ozs.	San Miguel I., Cal.	10-5-72	Freddie Cox	
BASS, Sand	(Paralabrax nebulifer)					
BASS, Sea	(Centropristes striatus)					8 lbs.
BASS, Striped	(Roccus saxatilis)	51 lbs. 8 ozs.	Smith River, Oregon	5-18-74	Gary L. Dyer	73 lbs.
BLACKFISH	(Tautoga onitis)					21 lbs. 6 ozs.
BLUEFISH	(Pomatomus saltatrix)	16 lbs. 8 ozs.	Va. Beach, Va.	11-16-68	W. A. Thigpen	31 lbs. 12 ozs.
BONEFISH	(Albula vulpes)	12 lbs. 13 ozs.	Islamorada, Fla	2-21-74	Ron Wagner	19 lbs.
BONITO, Common	(Sarda sarda)	13 lbs. 6 ozs.	Key West, Fla.	11-30-75	Al Polofsky	★
BONITO, Oceanic	(Katsuwanus pelamis)	10 lbs. 15 ozs.	Santa Barbara, Calif.	12-7-75	Patt Wardlaw	40 lbs. ★
COBIA	(Rachycentron canadus)	52 lbs.	Key West, Fla.	3-16-71	Jim Lopez	110 lbs. 5 ozs ★
CORVINA, Calif.	(Menticirrhus undulatus)	7 lbs. 4 ozs.	Salton Sea, Calif.	8-23-75	Robert P. Ferguson	
DOLPHIN	(Coryphaena hippurus)	45 lbs.	Bahamas	12-17-71	Harold Siebens	85 lbs.
DRUM, Black	(Pogonias cromis)					109 lbs.
FLOUNDER	(Paralichthys)					30 lbs. 12 ozs.
GROUPER		21 lbs. 8 ozs.	Salinas, Ecuador	2-11-70	W. W. Pate, Jr.	
HALIBUT, Arrowtooth	(Atheresthes stomias)					
HALIBUT, Pacific	(Hippoglossus stenolepis)					
JACK CREVALLE	(Caranx hippos)	20 lbs. 1 oz.	Loreto, Baja, Cal.	3-27-73	Norman LeGore	
JEWFISH	(Epinephelus itaiara)					680 lbs.
LADYFISH	(Elops saurus)	4 lbs.	Indian River, Fla.	10-8-75	Dennis W. Hammond	★
MACKEREL, Atlantic	(Scomber scombrus)					
MACKEREL, Cero	(Scomberomorus regalis)	6 lbs.	Key West, Fla.	12-27-69	Stu Apte	
MACKEREL, King	(Scomberomorus cavalla)	42 lbs. 8 ozs	Key West, Fla.	1-12-71	Jim Lopez	78 lbs. 12 ozs.
MACKEREL, Pacific	(Scomber Japanicus)	2 lbs. 10 ozs.	Rancho Buena Vista, Mex	11-30-72	Nat Hillyer	
MACKEREL, Spanish	(Scomberomorus maculatus)	5 lbs. 14 ozs.	Cape Lookout, N. C.	10-14-74	George Harrelson	
MARLIN, Black	(Makaira Indica)	42 lbs. 6 ozs.	Cairns, Australia	9-8-72	W. W. Pate, Jr.	1560 lbs.
MARLIN, Blue	(Makaira nigricans)					1153 lbs.
MARLIN, Striped	(Makaira audex)	146 lbs.	Salinas, Ecuador	2-10-70	W. W. Pate, Jr.	415 lbs.
MARLIN, White	(Tetrapturns albidus)	80 lbs.	La Guaira, Venezuela	9-17-75	Wm. W. Pate, Jr.	159 lbs. 8 ozs. ★
PERCH, Ocean						
PERMIT	(Trachinotus falcatus)	29 lbs.	Key West, Fla.	6-2-75	Gene Anderegg II	50 lbs. 8 ozs. ★
POLLOCK	(Pollachius virens)	18 lbs. 8 ozs.	Pt. Maitland, N.S.	6-22-73	Lou Truppi	43 lbs.
POMPANO, African	(Hynnis cubensis)	14 lbs. 8 ozs.	Key Largo, Florida	5-28-73	Jim Thomas	
POMPANO, Common	(Trachinotus carolinus)					
QUEENFISH		18 lbs. 8 ozs.	Carnarvon, Aust.	1-21-71	Max Garth	
ROOSTERFISH	(Nematistius pectoralis)	25 lbs. 8 ozs.	Mulege, Baja, Calif.	5-17-74	Harold Winkle	114 lbs.
RUNNER, Blue	(Caranx crysos)					
RUNNER, Rainbow	(Elagatis bipinnulatus)	6 lbs. 2½ ozs.	Tongue of Ocean, B'hamas	11-18-74	Harold Siebens	★
SAILFISH, Atlantic	(Istiophorus albicans)	75 lbs.	La Guaira, Venezuela	9-18-75	Wm. W. Pate, Jr.	141 lbs. 1 oz. ★
SAILFISH, Pacific	(Istiophorus greyi)	115 lbs.	El Coco, Costa Rica	7-25-67	Gil Drake	221 lbs.
SHARK		95 lbs.	Dana Point, Calif.	9-24-75	Robert Edgley	2664 lbs. ★
SNAPPER		21 lbs.	Isla Coiba, Panama	3-12-73	Jim Lopez	
SNOOK	(Centropomus undecimalis)	25 lbs. 8 ozs.	Punta Gorda, Fla.	6-5-74	Leslie M. Ager	52 lbs. 6 ozs.
SWORDFISH	(Xiphias gladius)	25 lbs. 8 ozs.	Gasparilla, Fla.	6-6-74	William Wegener	1182 lbs.

SPECIES	SCIENTIFIC NAME	WEIGHT	WHERE CAUGHT	DATE	ANGLER	Recognized IGFA All Tackle Weights
TARPON	(Megalops atlantica)	162 lbs.	Islamorada, Fla.	4-15-74	Jim Lopez	283 lbs.
TUNA, Atlantic Big Eye	(Thunnus obesus)					321 lbs. 12 ozs.
TUNA, Pacific Big Eye	(Thunnus obesus)					435 lbs.
TUNA, Blackfin	(Thunnus atlanticus)	22 lbs.	Bermuda	7-7-72	Jim Lopez	38 lbs.
TUNA, Bluefin	(Thunnus thynnus)	9 lbs. 8 ozs.	Montauk, N. Y.	8-14-66	Stephen Sloan	1065 lbs.
TUNA, Little (False Alb)	(Euthynnus alletteratus)	17 lbs. 13 ozs.	Canaveral, Fla.	7-17-71	Skip MacKay	
TUNA, Yellowfin	(Thunnus albacores)	81 lbs.	Bermuda	7-10-71	Jim Lopez	296 lbs.
WAHOO	(Acanthocybium solandri)	20 lbs. 2 ozs.	Isla Coiba, Panama	10-12-75	Stuart C. Apte	149 lbs. ★
WEAKFISH, Common	(Cynoscion regalis)	4 lbs. 4 ozs.	Delaware Bay, N.J.	5-18-73	Richard C. Mitchell	
		4 lbs. 6 ozs.	Brandywine Shoal, N.J.	6-28-73	Ronald Conner	19 lbs. 8 ozs.
WEAKFISH, Spotted	(Cynoscion nebulosus)	11 lbs. 10 ozs.	Jenson Beach, Fla.	3-31-71	Clarence Snook	15 lbs. 6 ozs.
WHITING	(Menticirrhus)					
YELLOWTAIL	(Seriola dorsalis)	32 lbs.	Loreto, Baja, Cal.	3-27-73	Timothy Jewell	111 lbs.

12 lb. Tippet Class

SPECIES	SCIENTIFIC NAME	WEIGHT	WHERE CAUGHT	DATE	ANGLER	Recognized IGFA All Tackle Weights
ALBACORE	(Thunnus Alalunga)	25 lbs. 4 ozs.	Todos Santos, Mexico	8-7-66	Harry Bonner	70 lbs.
AMBERJACK	(Seriola Dumerili)	75 lbs. 12 ozs.	Cape Canaveral, Fla.	8-11-72	Wm. Leffingwell	149 lbs.
BARRACUDA, Great	(Sphyraena barracuda)	31 lbs.	Key West, Florida	12-29-70	Jim Lopez	83 lbs.
BARRACUDA, Pacific	(Sphyraena argentea)	7 lbs. 3 ozs.	LaJolla Kelp Beds, Cal.	7-23-63	Harry Bonner	
BASS, Calif. White Sea	(Cynoscion nobilis)					83 lbs. 12 ozs.
BASS, Channel	(Sciaenops ocellata)	38 lbs. 12 ozs.	Chesapeake Bay, Va.	8-8-67	Ree Ellis	83 lbs.
BASS, Kelp	(Paralabrax clathratus)	2 lbs. 1 oz.	Oceanside, Calif.	5-12-66	Harry Bonner	
BASS, Sand	(Paralabrax nebulifer)	2 lbs. 13 ozs.	Pt. Loma, Cal.	6-16-71	Dave Cox	
BASS, Sea	(Centropristes striatus)					8 lbs.
BASS, Striped	(Roccus saxatilis)	40 lbs. 4 ozs.	Umpqua River, Oregon	7-13-70	R. M. Wadsworth	73 lbs.
BLACKFISH	(Tautoga onitis)	1 lb. 12 ozs.	Warwick, R.I.	5-19-72	Dr. A. Chatowsky	21 lbs. 6 ozs.
BLUEFISH	(Pomatomus saltatrix)	17 lbs. 7 ozs.	Va. Beach, Va.	11-16-68	Jeff Dane	31 lbs. 12 ozs.
BONEFISH	(Albula vulpes)	13 lbs.	Islamorada, Fla.	10-30-69	Bart Foth	19 lbs.
BONITO, Atlantic	(Sarda sarda)	17 lbs.			Elmer Aldacosta	
BONITO, Oceanic	(Katsuwanus pelamis)	15 lbs.	Santa Barbara, Calif.	12-15-75	Patt Wardlaw	40 lbs. ★
COBIA	(Rachycentron canadum)	60 lbs.	Flamingo, Fla.	1-22-75	Richard W. Moore	110 lbs. 5 ozs. ★
CORVINA, Calif.	(Menticirrhus undulatus)	13 lbs. 6 ozs.	Salton Sea, Cal.	9-29-71	Dave Cox	
DOLPHIN	(Coryphaena hippurus)	58 lbs.	Pinas Bay, Panama	12-6-64	Stu Apte	85 lbs.
DRUM, Black	(Pogonias cromis)	10 lbs. 8 ozs.	Islamorada, Florida	8-22-55	Bart Foth	109 lbs.
FLOUNDER	(Paralichthys)					30 lbs. 12 ozs.
GROUPER		24 lbs. 8 ozs.	Key West, Florida	1-1-66	Al Pflueger, Jr.	
HALIBUT, Arrowtooth	(Atheresthes stomias)					
HALIBUT, Pacific	(Hippoglossus stenolepis)	23 lbs. 2 ozs.	San Francisco Bay, Cal.	4-29-73	Ronald Dong	
JACK CREVALLE	(Caranx hippos)	30 lbs. 8 ozs.	Sebastian Inlet, Fla.	11-19-72	Dave Chermanski	
JEWFISH	(Epinephelus itaiara)	356 lbs.	Islamorada, Florida	3-15-67	Bart Foth	680 lbs.
LADYFISH	(Elops saurus)	3 lbs. 12 ozs.			L. de Hoyos, Jr.	
MACKEREL, Atlantic	(Scomber scombrus)					
MACKEREL, Cero	(Scomberomorus regalis)	9 lbs.	Key West, Florida	12-27-65	Al Pflueger, Jr.	
MACKEREL, King	(Scomberomorus cavalla)	38 lbs.	Key West, Fla.	1-12-71	Jim Lopez	78 lbs. 12 ozs.
MACKEREL, Pacific	(Scomber Japanicus)	2 lbs.	Rock Pile, Mexico	10-2-66	Harry Bonner	
MACKEREL, Spanish	(Scomberomorus maculatus)	5 lbs. 12 ozs.	Port Canaveral, Fla.	10-3-72	Robert Trosset	
MARLIN, Black	(Makaira Indica)	38 lbs. 10 ozs.	Cairns, Australia	9-10-72	W. W. Pate, Jr.	1560 lbs.
MARLIN, Blue	(Makaira nigricans)					1153 lbs.
MARLIN, Striped	(Makaira audex)	148 lbs.	Salinas, Equador	5-67	Lee Wulff	415 lbs.
MARLIN, White	(Tetrapturns albidus)	55 lbs.	LaGuaira, Venezuela	9-10-74	W. W. Pate, Jr.	159 lbs. 8 ozs.
PERCH, Ocean						
PERMIT	(Trachinotus falcatus)	30 lbs. 2 ozs.	Key West, Fla.	5-3-70	C. W. Walton	50 lbs. 8 ozs.
POLLOCK	(Pollachius virens)	8 lbs. 8 ozs.	Trinity Ledge, N.S.	6-21-72	Lou Truppi	43 lbs.
POMPANO, African	(Hynnis cubensis)	33 lbs. 8 ozs.	Palm Beach, Fla.	12-21-69	Gil Drake, Jr.	
POMPANO, Common	(Trachinotus carolinus)	4 lbs. 5½ ozs.	Miami, Florida		J. T. Pearson	
QUEENFISH		19 lbs.	Carnarvon, Australia	2-17-73	Maxwell Garth	
ROOSTERFISH	(Nematistius pectoralis)					

SPECIES	SCIENTIFIC NAME	WEIGHT	WHERE CAUGHT	DATE	ANGLER	Recognized IGFA All Tackle Weights
RUNNER, Blue	(Caranx crysos)	3 lbs. 3 ozs.	Port Canaveral, Fla.	10-16-73	John F. Meyer	
RUNNER, Rainbow	(Elagatis bipinnulatus)					
SAILFISH, Atlantic	(Istiophorus albicans)	48 lbs.	Cozumel, Mexico	4-28-75	Frank H. Inscho	★
SAILFISH, Pacific	(Istiophorus greyi)	136 lbs.	Pinas Bay, Panama	6-25-65	Stu Apte	
SHARK		272 lbs.	Islamorada, Florida		Bart Foth	
SNAPPER		22 lbs. 8 ozs.	Isla Coiba, Panama	3-12-73	Jim Lopez	
SNOOK	(Centropomus undecimalis)	28 lbs.			Jean Crooks	52 lbs. 6 ozs.
SWORDFISH	(Xiphias gladius)					1182 lbs.
TARPON	(Megalops atlantica)	154 lbs.	Key West, Fla.	4-10-71	Stu Apte	283 lbs.
TUNA, Atlantic Big Eye	(Thunnus obesus)					321 lbs. 12 ozs.
TUNA, Pacific Big Eye	(Thunnus obsesus)					435 lbs.
TUNA, Blackfin	(Thunnus atlanticus)	28 lbs.	Bermuda	7-6-72	Jim Lopez	38 lbs.
TUNA, Bluefin	(Thunnus thynnus)	9 lbs. 15 ozs.	Long Branch, N. J.	8-20-74	Robert S. Bottino	1065 lbs.
TUNA, Little (False Alb)	(Euthynnus alletteratus)	13 lbs.	Long Branch, N.J.	10-12-67	Jas. Hawthorn	
TUNA, Large Scale		11 lbs.	Cape Covier, Australia	11-28-71	Max Garth	
TUNA, Northern Bluefin		17 lbs. 8 ozs.	Carnarvon, Australia	9-30-72	Max Garth	
TUNA, Yellowfin	(Thunnus albacores)	67 lbs. 8 ozs.	Bermuda	7-7-73	Jim Lopez	296 lbs.
WAHOO	(Acanthocybium solandri)	15 lbs. 4 ozs.	Isla Coiba, Panama	10-12-75	Stuart C. Apte	149 lbs. ★
WEAKFISH, Common	(Cynoscion regalis)	8 lbs. 10 ozs.	Deal, New Jersey	10-11-74	Robert S. Bottino	19 lbs. 8 ozs.
WEAKFISH, Spotted	(Cynoscion nebulosus)	8 lbs. 13 ozs.			J. A. Knight	15 lbs. 3 ozs.
WHITING	(Menticirrhus)	9 lbs.	Jensen Beach, Fla.	1-2-72	Elwood Colvin	111 lbs.
YELLOWTAIL	(Seriola dorsalis)	29 lbs. 4 ozs.	Loreto, Mexico	3-7-73	Norman LeGore	

10 lb. Tippet Class

SPECIES	SCIENTIFIC NAME	WEIGHT	WHERE CAUGHT	DATE	ANGLER	Recognized IGFA All Tackle Weights
ALBACORE	(Thunnus Alalunga)	26 lbs. 2 ozs.	San Diego, Cal.	7-15-72	Les Eichhorn	70 lbs.
AMBERJACK	(Seriola Dumerili)	74 lbs. 8 ozs.	Key West, Fla.	1-25-75	Frank Inscho	149 lbs.
BARRACUDA, Great	(Sphyraena barracuda)	29 lbs. 8 ozs.	Key West, Fla.	1-2-71	Mike Leverone	83 lbs.
BARRACUDA, Calif.	(Sphyraena argentea)					
BARRIMUNDI		16 lbs. 9 ozs.	Queensland, Aust.	6-13-70	Tom Davidson	
BASS, Calif. White Sea	(Cynoscion nobilis)					83 lbs. 12 ozs.
BASS, Channel	(Sciaenops ocellata)	10 lbs. 11 ozs.	Islamorada, Florida	8-2-73	Wm. W. Pate, Jr.	83 lbs.
BASS, Kelp	(Paralabrax clathratus)					
BASS, Sand	(Paralabrax nebulifer)					
BASS, Sea	(Centropristes striatus)					8 lbs.
BASS, Striped	(Roccus saxatilis)	64 lbs. 8 ozs.	Smith River, Oregon	7-28-73	Beryl E. Bliss	73 lbs.
BLACKFISH	(Tautoga onitis)					21 lbs. 6 ozs.
BLUEFISH	(Pomatomus saltatrix)	16 lbs. 12 ozs.	Manasquan, N. J.	11-18-73	Robert Bottino	31 lbs. 12 ozs.
BONEFISH	(Albula vulpes)	12 lbs. 9 ozs.	Islamorada, Florida	8-31-74	Flip Pallot	
BONITO, Atlantic	(Sarda sarda)	7 lbs. 6 ozs.	Montauk, New York	9-28-71	Robt. Popovics	
BONITO, Oceanic	(Katsuwanus pelamis)	15 lbs. 8 ozs.	Monterey Bay, Cal.	9-15-72	Bob Edgley	40 lbs.
COBIA	(Rachycentron canadum)	69 lbs.	Florida Bay, Fla.	12-9-67	Ralph Delph	110 lbs. 5 ozs.
COD		8 lbs. 14 ozs.	Port Maitland, N.S.	6-22-73	Lou Truppi	
CORVINA, Calif.	(Menticirrhus undulatus)					
DOLPHIN	(Coryphaena hippurus)	32 lbs. 12 ozs.	Key West, Fla.	3-15-67	Charles Frasch	85 lbs.
DRUM, Black	(Pogonias cromis)					109 lbs.
FLOUNDER	(Paralichthys)					30 lbs. 12 ozs.
GROUPER		18 lbs. 10 ozs.	Port Canaveral, Fla.	8-20-73	Dave Chermanski	
HALIBUT, Arrowtooth	(Atheresthes stomias)					
HALIBUT, Pacific	(Hippoglossus stenolepis)	36 lbs.	Whidbey Isl. Washington	7-31-69	John Smart	
JACK CREVALLE	(Caranx hippos)	33 lbs. 12 ozs.	Sebastian Inlet, Fla.	11-19-72	Dave Chermanski	
JEWFISH	(Epinephelus itaiara)					680 lbs.
LADYFISH	(Elops saurus)	3 lbs. 12 ozs.	Sebastian Inlet, Fla.	7-19-73	Dave Chermanski	
MACKEREL, Atlantic	(Scomber scombrus)	1 lb. 12 ozs.	Long Island, N.Y.	5-24-71	David Knight	
MACKEREL, Cero	(Scomberomorus regalis)					
MACKEREL, King	(Scomberomorus cavalla)	24 lbs.	Port Canaveral, Fla.	11-5-73	John F. Meyer	78 lbs. 12 ozs.
MACKEREL, Pacific	(Scomber Japanicus)					
MACKEREL, Spanish	(Scomberomorus maculatus)					

SPECIES	SCIENTIFIC NAME	WEIGHT	WHERE CAUGHT	DATE	ANGLER	Recognized IGFA All Tackle Weights
MARLIN, Black	(Makaira Indica)	38 lbs.	Cairns, Australia	9-14-72	Laura E. Pate	1560 lbs.
MARLIN, Blue	(Makaira nigricans)					1153 lbs.
MARLIN, Striped	(Makaira audex)					415 lbs.
MARLIN, White	(Tetrapturns albidus)	68 lbs.	Fort Pierce, Florida	12-23-72	Dave Chermanski	159 lbs. 8 ozs.
PERCH, Ocean						
PERMIT	(Trachinotus falcatus)	30 lbs.	Marathon, Fla.	5-12-72	Greg Costa, Jr.	50 lbs. 8 ozs.
POLLOCK	(Pollachius virens)	10 lbs. 12 ozs.	Newport, R. I.	11-24-68	R. H. Smith	43 lbs.
POMPANO, African	(Hynnis cubensis)					
POMPANO, Common	(Trachinotus carolinus)	3 lbs. 3 ozs.	Sebastian Inlet, Fla.	4-11-73	Dave Chermanski	
QUEENFISH		16 lbs. 4 ozs.	Carnarvon, Aust.	2-20-71	Max Garth	
ROOSTERFISH	(Nematistius pectoralis)	9 lbs 11 ozs.	Rancho Buena Vista, Mex.	11-27-75	Denton Hill	114 lbs. ★
RUNNER, Blue	(Caranx crysos)	4 lbs. 4 ozs.	Key West, Florida	1-21-70	Stu Apte	
RUNNER, Rainbow	(Elagatis bipinnulatus)	4 lbs. 4 ozs.	Tongue of Ocean, Bahamas	4-17-75	Harold Siebens	★
SAILFISH, Atlantic	(Istiophorus albicans)	49 lbs. 8 ozs.	Cozumel, Mexico	4-13-75	C. A. Peacock, Jr.	141 lbs. 1 oz. ★
SAILFISH, Pacific	(Istiophorus greyi)	101 lbs.	Costa Rica	8-11-73	Flip Pallot	221 lbs.
SHARK		117 lbs. 8 ozs.	Key West, Fla.	4-14-72	Flip Pallot	2664 lbs.
SNAPPER		23 lbs. 8 ozs.	Isla Coiba, Panama	3-12-73	Jim Lopez	
SNOOK	(Centropomus undecimalis)	28 lbs. 8 ozs.	Stuart, Fla.	7-10-72	Martin Gottschalk	52 lbs. 6 ozs.
SWORDFISH	(Xiphias gladius)					1182 lbs.
TANGUIGUE		35 lbs.	Carnarvon, Aust.	4-15-72	Max Garth	
TARPON	(Megalops atlantica)	105 lbs.	Islamorada, Fla.	5-19-75	Wm. W. Pate, Jr.	283 lbs. ★
TREVALLEY, Gold Spotted		16 lbs.	Cape Cuvier, Aust.	6-7-70	Max Garth	
TUNA, Allison		21 lbs. 4 ozs.	Bermuda	7-8-71	Jim Lopez	
TUNA, Atlantic Big Eye	(Thunnus obesus)					321 lbs. 12 ozs.
TUNA, Pacific Big Eye	(Thunnus obsesus)					435 lbs.
TUNA, Blackfin	(Thunnus atlanticus)	24 lbs.	Bermuda	6-30-73	Jim Lopez	38 lbs.
TUNA, Bluefin	(Thunnus thynnus)					1065 lbs.
TUNA, Large Scale		11 lbs. 8 ozs.	Cape Cuvier Aust.	11-28-71	Max Garth	
TUNA, Little (False Alb)	(Euthynnus alletteratus)	14 lbs.	Portuguese East Africa		Jos. W. Brooks	
TUNA, Northern Bluefin		20 lbs.	Carnarvon, Aust.	10-1-72	Max Garth	
TUNA, Yellowfin	(Thunnus albacores)	16 lbs.	Los Coronodos, Mex.	10-11-67	Harry Bonner	269 lbs. 8 ozs.
WAHOO	(Acanthocybium solandri)	16 lbs. 8 ozs.	Isla Coiba, Panama	10-12-75	Stuart C. Apte	149 lbs. ★
WEAKFISH, Common	(Cynoscion regalis)	7 lbs. 3 ozs.	Barnegat Inlet, N. J.	8-10-75	Robert E. Priel	19 lbs. 8 ozs. ★
WEAKFISH, Spotted	(Cynoscion nebulosus)	6 lbs. 3 ozs.	Sebastian Inlet, Fla.	9-9-72	John Meyer	15 lbs. 6 ozs.
WHITING	(Menticirrhus)					
YELLOWTAIL	(Seriola dorsalis)	32 lbs. 8 ozs.	Loreto, Mexico	3-14-72	Christy Blough	111 lbs.

6 lb. Tippet Class

SPECIES	SCIENTIFIC NAME	WEIGHT	WHERE CAUGHT	DATE	ANGLER	Recognized IGFA All Tackle Weights
ALBACORE	(Thunnus Alalunga)					70 lbs.
AMBERJACK	(Seriola Dumerili)	29 lbs. 11 ozs.	Sebastian Inlet, Fla.	9-15-72	Dave Chermanski	149 lbs.
BARRACUDA, Great	(Sphyraena barracuda)	15 lbs. 2 ozs.	W. Palm Beach, Fla.	7-16-72	Dave Chermanski	83 lbs.
BARRACUDA, Calif.						
BASS, Calif. White Sea	(Cynoscion nobilis)					83 lbs. 12 ozs.
BASS, Channel	(Sciaenops ocellata)	13 lbs. 13 ozs.	Banana River, Fla.	5-30-72	Dave Chermanski	83 lbs.
BASS, Kelp	(Paralabrax clathratus)	4 lbs. 15 ozs.	Point Fermom, California	7-8-71	Bob Hart	
BASS, Sand	(Paralabrax nebulifer)					
BASS, Sea	(Centropristes striatus)					8 lbs.
BASS, Striped	(Roccus saxatilis)	24 lbs. 12 ozs.	American River, Calif.	12-2-73	Alfred Perryman	73 lbs.
BLACKFISH	(Tautoga onitis)					21 lbs. 6 ozs.
BLUEFISH	(Pomatomus saltatrix)	11 lbs. 6 ozs.	Long Branch, N. J.	5-31-74	Robert S. Bottino	24 lbs. 3 ozs.
BONEFISH	(Albula vulpes)	13 lbs. 4 ozs.	Islamorada, Florida	11-6-73	Jim Lopez	19 lbs.
BONITO, Atlantic	(Sarda sarda)	6 lbs. 12 ozs.	Bermuda	6-28-72	Lefty Kreh	
BONITO, Oceanic	(Katsuwanus pelamis)	14 lbs. 12 ozs.	Santa Barbara, Calif.	12-7-75	Patt Wardlaw	40 lbs. ★
COBIA	(Rachycentron canadum)	39 lbs. 8 ozs.	Key West, Fla.	3-15-72	Roy Terrell	110 lbs. 5 ozs.
COD		5 lbs. 14 ozs.	Port Maitland, N.S.	6-22-73	Lou Truppi	
CORVINA, Calif.	(Menticirrhus undulatus)	14 lbs. 14 ozs.	Salton Sea, Cal.	8-27-71	Dave Cox	

SPECIES	SCIENTIFIC NAME	WEIGHT	WHERE CAUGHT	DATE	ANGLER	Recognized IGFA All Tackle Weights
DOLPHIN	(Coryphaena hipprus)	23 lbs.	Tongue of Ocean, Bahamas	3-6-75	Harold Siebens	85 lbs. ★
DRUM, Black	(Pogonias cromis)					109 lbs.
FLOUNDER	(Paralichthys)	8 lbs. 6 ozs.	Sebastian Inlet, Fla.	11-2-71	Dave Chermanski	30 lbs. 12 ozs
GROUPER						
HALIBUT, Arrowtooth	(Atheresthes stomias)					
HALIBUT, Pacific	(Hippoglossus stenolepis)					
JACK CREVALLE	(Caranx hippos)	19 lbs. 2 ozs.	Key West, Fla.	2-14-70	Lefty Kreh	
JEWFISH	(Epinephelus itaiara)					680 lbs.
LADYFISH	(Elops saurus)	3 lbs. 4 ozs.	Melbourne Bch., Fla.	10-31-71	Dave Chermanski	
MACKEREL, Atlantic	(Scomber scombrus)					
MACKEREL, Cero	(Scomberomorus regalis)					
MACKEREL, King	(Scomberomorus Cavalla)					78 lbs. 12 ozs.
MACKEREL, Pacific	(Scomber Japanicus)					
MACKEREL, Spanish	(Scomberomorus maculatus)	4 lbs.	Madeira Beach, Fla.	7-19-74	Richard Redd	
MARLIN, Black	(Makaira Indica)	46 lbs. 4 ozs.	Cairns, Aust.	9-14-72	W.W. Pate, Jr	1560 lbs.
MARLIN, Blue	(Makaira nigricans)					1153 lbs.
MARLIN, Striped	(Makaira audex)					415 lbs.
MARLIN, White	(Tetrapturns albidus)					
PERCH, Ocean						
PERMIT	(Trachinotus falcutus)	19 lbs. 8 ozs.	Isle of Pines, Cuba		Jos. W. Brooks	50 lbs.
POLLOCK	(Pollachius virens)	8 lbs. 14 ozs.	Pt. Maitland, N.S.	6-22-73	Lou Truppi	43 lbs.
POMPANO, African	(Hynnis cubensis)					
POMPANO, Common	(Trachinotus carolinus)					
QUEENFISH		16 lbs. 12 ozs.	Carnarvon, Austr.	3-10-71	Max Garth	
ROOSTERFISH	(Nematistius pectoralis)					
RUNNER, Blue	(Caranx crysos)	3 lbs. 9 ozs.	Port Canaveral, Fla.	8-20-73	Dave Chermanski	
RUNNER, Rainbow	(Elagatis bipinnulatus)	6 lbs.	Bermuda	6-29-72	Lefty Kreh	
SAILFISH, Atlantic	(Istiophorus albicans)					141 lbs. 1 oz.
SAILFISH, Pacific	(Istiophorus greyi)					221 lbs.
SHARK		74 lbs.	Florida Bay, Fla.	11-15-75	Sandy Moret	2664 lbs. ★
SNAPPER		6 lbs.	Panama City, Fla.	9-8-72	Al Pflueger, Jr.	
SNOOK	(Centropomus undecimalis)	22 lbs. 3 ozs.	Sebastian River, Fla.	7-24-71	Dave Chermanski	52 lbs. 6 ozs.
SWORDFISH	(Xiphias gladius)					1182 lbs.
TARPON	(Megalops atlanticus)	36 lbs. 8 ozs.	Flamingo, Fla.	9-30-74	Flip Pallot	283 lbs.
TUNA, Atlantic Big Eye	(Thunnus obesus)					321 lbs. 12 ozs.
TUNA, Pacific Big Eye	(Thunnus obsesus)					435 lbs.
TUNA, Blackfin	(Thunnus atlanticus)					38 lbs.
TUNA, Bluefin	(Thunnus thynnus)					1065 lbs.
TUNA, Little (False Alb)	(Euthynnus alletteratus)	18 lbs. 4 ozs.	Cape Canaveral, Fla.	7-24-72	Dave Chermanski	
TUNA, Yellowfin	(Thunnus albacores)					296 lbs.
WAHOO	(Acanthocybium solandri)	17 lbs. 10 ozs.	Isla Coiba, Panama	10-12-75	Stuart C. Apte	149 lbs. ★
WEAKFISH, Common	(Cynoscion regalis)	8 lbs. 15 ozs.	Delaware Bay, N. J.	5-19-75	Ronald D. Conner	19 lbs. 8 ozs. ★
WEAKFISH, Spotted	(Cynoscion nebulosus)	8 lbs. 3 ozs.	Banana River, Fla.	12-5-74	Dave Chermanski	15 lbs. 6 ozs.
WHITING	(Menticirrhus)					
YELLOWTAIL	(Seriola dorsalis)	15 lbs. 3 ozs.	Loreto, Mexico	1-30-73	Harry Kime	111 lbs.

—Courtesy of the Salt Water Fly Rodders of America, International.

The Angler's Bookshelf

Artificial Flies

Bates, Joseph C., Jr. **Atlantic Salmon Flies & Fishing.** (Illus.). 1970. 14.95. Stackpole.

Bates, Joseph D., Jr. **Streamer Fly Tying & Fishing.** (Illus.). 1966. 8.95. Stackpole.

Bay, Kenneth E. & Vinciguerra, Matthew M. **How to Tie Freshwater Flies.** 1974. 10.00. Winchester Pr.

Bergman, Ray. **Fishing with Ray Bergman.** Janes, Edward C., ed. (Illus.). 1970. 8.95. Knopf.

Bergman, Ray & Janes, Edward C. **Trout.** 1975. 15.00. Knopf.

Fulsher, Keith. **Fishing the Thunder Creek Series.** (Illus.). 1973. 7.95. Freshet Pr.

Gerlach, Rex. **Creative Fly Tying & Fishing.** 1974. 10.00. Winchester Pr.

Jennings, Preston. **Book of Trout Flies.** Lyons, Nick, ed. (Illus.). 1970. 7.50. Crown.

Jorgensen, Poul. **Dressing Flies for Fresh & Salt Water.** (Illus.). 1973. 12.95. Freshet Pr.

Kessler, Herman & Bay, Kenneth. **Salt Water Flies: Popular Patterns & How to Tie Them.** (Illus.). 1972. 8.95. Lippincott.

Lawrie, William H. **All Fur Flies & How to Dress Them.** (Illus.). 1968. 5.95. A S Barnes.

Leonard, J. Edson. **Flies.** (Illus.). 1950. 9.95. A S Barnes.

McDonald, John. **Quill Gordon.** 1972. 10.95. Knopf.

Nemes, Sylvester. **The Soft-Hackled Fly: A Trout Fisherman's Guide.** 1975. 7.95; pap. 3.95. Chatham Pr.

Orvis, Charles F. & Cheney, A. Nelson, eds. **Fishing with the Fly: Sketches by Lovers of the Art with Illustrations of Standard Flies.** (Illus.). 1967. Repr. 8.25. C E Tuttle.

Schwiebert, Ernest G., Jr. **Matching the Hatch.** (Illus.). 1962. 7.50. Macmillan.

Shaw, Helen. **Fly-Tying Materials-Tools-Technique.** (Illus.). 1963. 8.95. Ronald.

Sturgis, William B. **Fly-Tying.** (Illus.). 1940. 8.95. Scribner.

Swisher, Doug & Richards, Carl. **Selective Trout.** (Illus.). 1975. softbound. 5.95. Crown/Stoeger.

Veniard, John. **Reservoir & Lake Flies.** (Illus.). 1974. 17.50. St. Martin.

Veniard, John & Downs, Donald. **Fly-Tying Problems & Their Answers.** (Illus.). 1972. 4.95. Crown.

Bait

Earp, Samuel A. & Wildeman, William J. **The Blue Water Bait Book: Secrets of Successful Big Game Fishing.** (Illus.). 1974. 7.95. Little.

Evanoff, Vlad. **Fishing with Natural Baits.** (Illus.). 1975. 8.95; pap. 4.95. P-H.

Harris, John R. **An Angler's Entomology.** (Illus.). 1973. 8.95. A S Barnes.

— — **Introduction to Bait Fishing.** 1974. pap. 3.95. Stackpole.

Bass Fishing

Bauer, Erwin A. **Bass Fisherman's Bible.** (Illus.). 1961. pap. 2.50. Doubleday.

Bergman, Ray. **Fresh-Water Bass.** (Illus.). 1943. 8.95. Knopf.

Dalrymple, Byron W. **Modern Book of the Black Bass.** (Illus.). 1975. softbound. 5.95. Stoeger.

Fagerstrom, Stan. **Catch More Bass.** (Illus.). 1973. pap. 7.95. Caxton.

Gooch, Bob. **Bass Fishing.** (Illus.). 1795. pap. 5.00. Cornell Maritime.

Gresham, Grits. **Complete Book of Bass Fishing.** 1966. 8.95. Times Mirror Mag.

Gresham, Grits L. **Complete Book of Bass Fishing.** (Illus.). Repr. of 1967 ed. 8.95. Har-Row.

Grigsby, Red. **Bass, & How to Catch Them.**

1966. pap. 0.50. Claitors.

Hawk, Dave. **One Hundred Years on Bass.** (Illus.). 1970. 6.00. Naylor.

Hornsey, Bill. **Bass Fishing: Strategy & Tactics.** 1967. 2.00. Claitors.

Livington, A. D. **Advanced Bass Tackle & Boats.** (Illus.). 1975. 9.95. Lippincott.

— — **Fishing for Bass: Modern Tactics & Tackle.** 1974. 8.95. Lippincott.

McKinnis, Jerry. **Bass Fishing.** (Illus.). 1974. softbound. 2.95. Stoeger.

Rosko, Milt. **Secrets of Striped Bass Fishing.** 1966. 6.95. Macmillan.

Sosin, Mark & Dance, Bill. **Practical Black Bass Fishing.** (Illus.). 1975. Softbound. 5.95. Crown/Stoeger.

Underwood, Bob A. **Lunker!—A How-To for Fresh Water Bass Fishermen.** (Illus.). 1975. 12.95. McGraw.

Bibliographies

A Bibliography of African Freshwater Fish. Compiled by H. Matthes. 1974. pap. 10.00. (FAO). Unipub.

Fishing Industry Index International 1975. 22.50. Intl. Pubns Serv.

Huver, Charles W., compiled by. **A Bibliography of the Genus Fundulus.** 1973. 18.00. G K Hall.

Lauche, R. **World Bibliography of Agricultural Bibliographies.** 1957. 20.00. Intl Pubns Serv.

Cod

Jensen, Albert C. **The Cod.** 1972. 7.95. T Y Crowell.

Cod Fisheries

Lounsbury, Ralph G. **British Fishery at Newfoundland, 1634 to 1763.** 1969. Repr. of 1934 ed. 12.50. Shoe String.

Dictionaries and Encyclopedias

Bates, Joseph D. **Fishing: An Encyclopedic Guide to Tackle & Tactics for Fresh & Salt Water.** 1973. 14.95. Times Mirror Mag.

Bates, Joseph D., Jr. **Fishing: An Encyclopedic Guide to Tackle & Tactics for Fresh & Salt Water.** 1974. 14.95. Dutton.

Brander, Michael. **Dictionary of Sporting Terms.** (Illus.). 1968. 6.50. Humanities.

McClane, Albert J., ed. **McClane's New Standard Fishing Encyclopedia & International Angling Guide.** (Illus.). 1974. 40.00. HR&W.

Marston, A. N. **Encyclopedia of Angling.** 2nd ed. 1963. 15.00. Transatlantic.

Fish Anatomy

Chiasson, Robert B. **Laboratory Anatomy of the Perch.** 2nd ed. (Illus.). 1974. pap. 3.95. Wm C Brown.

Gans, Carl & Parsons, Thomas S. **Photographic Atlas of Shark Anatomy: The Gross Morphology of Squalus Acanthias.** 1964. 4.50 Acad Pr.

Gilbert, Stephen G. **Pictorial Anatomy of the Dogfish.** (Illus.). 1973. pap. 4.95. U of Wash Pr.

Kindred, James E. **Skull of Amiurus.** (Illus.). 1919. 8.50. Johnson Repr.

Kusaka, Takaya. **The Urohyal of Fishes.** (Illus.). 1974. 50.00. Intl Schol Bk Serv.

Ribelin, William E. & Migaki, George, eds. **Pathology of Fishes.** 1975. 3.50. U of Wis Pr.

Tehernavin, V. V. **The Feeding Mechanism of a Deep Sea Fish, Chauliodus Sloani Schneider.** (Illus.). 1975. 10.00. British Bk Ctr.

Wright, James E., et al. **Biochemical Genetics of Fish, 1.** 1974. Mss Info.

Fish as Food

Borgstrom, G., ed. **Fish as Food.** 4 vols. Incl. Vol. 1. **Production, Biochemistry & Microbiology.** 1961. 46.00; Vol. 2. **Nutrition Sanitation & Utilization.** 1926. 43.00; Vol. 3. **Processing** Part 1. 1965. 34.50; Vol. 4. **Processing.** Part 2. 1965. 34.50. Acad. Pr.

Heen, E. & Kreuzer, R., eds. **Fish in Nutrition.** 1962. 19.00. (FAO). Unipub.

Moore, Remedios W., et al. **Progress in Fishery & Food Science.** (Illus.). 1972. 15.00. U of Wash Pr.

Quick Frozen Fillets of Cod & Haddock. 1972. pap. 1.25. (FAO). Unipub.

Quick Frozen Fillets of Ocean Perch. 1972. pap. 1.25. (FAO). Unipub.

Quick Frozen Gutted Pacific Salmon. 1970. pap. 1.25. (FAO). Unipub.

Who Expert Committee. **Fish & Shellfish, Hygiene.** 1975. pap. 2.50. (FAO). Unipub.

Fish as Laboratory Animals

Institute of Laboratory Animal Resources. **Fishes: Guidelines for the Breeding Care & Management of Laboratory Animals.** (Illus.). 1974. pap. 5.00. Natl Acad Sci.

Neuhaus, O. W. & Halver, J. E., eds. **Fish in Research.** 1969. 15.00. Acad Pr.

Shul'Man, G. E. **Life Cycles of Fish.** Hardin, Hilliary, ed. Kaner, Nathan, tr. from Rus. (Illus.). 1974. 30.00. Halsted Pr.

Fish Behavior

Adler, Helmut E. **Fish Behavior: Why Fish Do What They Do.** (Illus.). 1975. 17.50. T F H Pubns.

Greenwood, P. H., et al, eds. **Interrelationships of Fishes: Supplement No. 1 to the Zoological Journal of the Linnean Society.** Vol. 53. 1973. 31.00. Acad Pr.

Ingle, David, ed. **Central Nervous System & Fish Behavior.** 1968. 15.00. U of Chicago Pr.

Kleerekoper, Herman. **Olfaction in Fishes.** (Illus.). 1969. 14.95. Ind U Pr.

Lateral Line Sense Organs & Their Importance in Fish Behavior. 1973. 21.10. Intl Schol Bk Serv.

Neil, E. H. **An Analysis of Color Changes & Social Behavior of Tilapia Mossambica.** 1964. pap. 1.25. U of Cal Pr.

Simon, Hilda. **Strange Breeding Habits of Aquarium Fish.** (Illus.). 1975. 5.95. Dodd.

Sosin, Mark & Clark, John. **Through the Fish's Eye.** (Illus.). 1973. 8.95. Har-Row.

— — **Through the Fish's Eye.** (Illus.). 1973. 8.95. Times Mirror Mag.

Wickler, Wolfgang. **Breeding Behavior of Aquarium Fishes.** (Illus.). 1973. pap. 6.95. TFH Pubns.

Williams, Russ & Cadieux, Charles L. **The Ways of Game Fish.** (Illus.). 1972. 24.95. Doubleday.

Fish Collection

Gulland, J. A. **Manual of Methods for Fish Stock Assessment Part 1: Fish Population Analysis.** (Illus.). 1969. pap. 5.00. (FAO). Unipub.

Fish Cookery

Aberson, Sarah D. **Blue Sea Cookbook.** Porter, Eleanor, ed. (Illus.). 1968. 8.95. Hastings.

Allyn, Rube. **How to Cook Your Catch.** pap. 1.50. Great Outdoors.

Angier, Bradford. **Wilderness Cookery.** (Illus.). 1970. pap. 3.95. Stackpole.

Barnett, Harriet & Barnett, James. **The Game & Fish Cookbook.** (Illus.). 1975. pap. 3.95. Grossman.

Beard, James A. **James Beard's Fish Cookery.** (Illus.). 1954. 6.95. Little.
— — **James Beard's Fish Cookery.** pap. 1.50. Warner Bks.
Beaton, I. M. **Fish Cookery.** (Illus.). 5.00. Soccer.
Better Homes & Gardens Books, ed. **Better Homes & Gardens Fish & Seafood Cookbook.** 1971. 3.95. BH&G.
Brown, Helen E. **Some Shrimp Recipes.** 1951. 2.50. Grant Dahlstrom.
Chekenian, Jane & Meyer, Monica. **Shellfish Cookery.** (Illus.). 1971. 12.50. Macmillan.
The Complete Fish Cookbook. pap. 1.50. Hippocrene Bks.
Dahlem, Ted. **How to Smoke Seafood.** pap. 1.00. Great Outdoors.
Davis, Charles J. **Fish Cookery.** 2nd Ed. 1967. 2.98. A S Barnes.
Day, Bunny. **Hook 'em & Cook 'em.** (Illus.). pap. 0.95. Funk & W.
Dufresne, Francine. **Cooking Fish & Wild Game: French-Canadian Style.** (Illus.). 1975. pap. 4.95. One Hund One Prods.
Dunaway, Vic. **From Hook to Table: An Angler's Guide to Good Eating.** (Illus.). 1974. 6.95. Macmillan.
Evans, Michele. **Michele Evans Easy Seafood Recipes.** 1975. 1.25. Dell.
Favorite Recipes Press, ed. **The Seafood Cookbook.** (Illus.). 1975. Repr. of 1971 ed. 4.95. Oxmoor Hse.
Festive Seafood Cookery. 1.95. Peter Pauper.
Fish & Shell Fish. (Illus.). 1973. 29.50. Radio City.
Frederick & Joyce. **Long Island Seafood Cookbook.** 1971. pap. 2.50. Dover.
Froud, Nina & Lo, Tamara. **International Fish Dishes.** 1974. 7.95. Hippocrene Bks.
Hamilton, Dorothy R. **How to Catch & Cook Shellfish.** (Illus.). 1973. pap. 1.50. Great Outdoors.
Hawkins, Arthur. **Complete Seafood Cookbook.** (Illus.). 1970. 6.95. P-H.
Heath, Ambrose. **Madame Prunier's Fishery Cook Book.** (Illus.). 4.50. Peter Smith.
Hull, Raymond & Sleight, Jack. **Home Book of Smoke-Cooking Meat, Fish & Game.** (Illus.). 1971. 7.95. Stackpole.
Kaufman, William I. **Fish & Shellfish Cookbook.** 1968. 2.95. Doubleday.
Kelley, Carolyn T. **Carolyn's Seafood Recipes.** (Illus.). 1972. 5.95. Intl Marine.
Knight, Jacqueline E. **The Cook's Fish Guide.** 1973. 11.95. Dutton.
Leamer, Robert B., et al. **Bottoms Up Cookery.** (Illus.). 1971. pap. 5.00. Fathom Ents.
Lewin, Esther & Lewin, Birdina. **Stewed to the Gills.** (Illus.). 1972. 7.95. Nash Pub.
Lose Weight Deliciously with Fish. 1969. pap. 0.95. Univ Pub & Dist.
McGrail, William & McGrail, Joie. **Catch & the Feast.** (Illus.). 1969. 20.00. Weybright.
MacIlquham, Frances. **Fish Cookery of North America.** 1974. 8.95. Winchester Pr.
Marshall, Mel. **Cooking Over Coals.** 1975. softbound. 5.95. Stoeger.
Mason, Phillip. **Shellfish Cookbook.** (Illus.). 1974. 8.95. Drake Pubs.
Miloradovich, Milo. **Art of Fish Cookery.** rev. ed. 1970. 5.95. Doubleday.
— —**Art of Fish Cookery.** pap. 1.00. Bantam.
Morris, Dan & Morris, Inez **Complete Fish Cookbook.** 1972. 10.00. Bobbs.
Patten, Marguerite. **Fish, Meat, Poultry, & Game.** rev. ed. (Illus.). 1970. 5.25. Intl Pubns Serv.
Priestland, Gerald. **Frying Tonight: The Saga of Fish & Chips.** (Illus.). 1974. 12.50. Intl Pubns Serv.
Prunier, S. B. **Madame Prunier's Fish Cookery Book.** 1971. pap. 2.50. Dover.
Reidpath, Stewart. **The Angler's Cookbook: Trout, Salmon & Eel.** 1973. 3.50. Reed.
Simon, Andre L. **Lobsters, Crabs, Etc.** 1957. 1.00. Wehman.
Steindler, Geraldine. **Game Cookbook.** (Illus.). 1965. softbound. 4.95. Stoeger.

Sturges, Lena. **Fish & Shellfish Cookbook.** (Illus.). pap. 1.95. Oxmoor Hse.
Sunset Editors. **Seafood Cook Book.** (Illus.). 1967. pap. 1.95. Lane.
Townsend, Sally & Ericson, Virginia. **Sea Cook.** pap. 2.95. Funk & W.
Vilkitis, James & Uhlinger, Susan. **Fish Cookery.** (Illus.). 1974. pap. 1.25. Greene.
Wall, Roy. **Game & Fish: From Field to Table.** 1972. 5.95. Naylor.
Zachary, Hugh. **Beachcomber's Handbook of Seafood Cookery.** (Illus.). 1972. 4.95. Blair.

Fish Culture

Atz, James W. **Aquarium Fishes: Their Beauty, History & Care.** (Illus.). 1971. 10.95. Viking Pr.
Davis, H. S. **Culture & Diseases of Game Fishes.** (Illus.). 1953. 10.50. U of Cal Pr.
Hickling, C. F. **The Farming of Fish.** (Illus.). 1968. 2.90; pap. 2.15. Pergamon.
Hoedeman, J. J. **Naturalists' Guide to Fresh-Water Aquarium Fish.** (Illus.). 1974. 30.00. Sterling.
Lee, Jasper S. **Commercial Catfish Farming.** (Illus.). 1973. 10.00. Interstate.
Lewis, William M. **Maintaining Fishes for Experimental & Instructional Purposes.** 1963. 5.00; pap. 1.45. S Ill U Pr.
Ostermoeller, Wolfgang. **Fish Breeding Recipes.** (Illus.). 1973. pap. 3.95. TFH Pubns.
Villiard, Paul. **Exotic Fish as Pets.** (Illus.). 1971. 4.95. Doubleday.

Fish Diseases and Pests

Anderson, Douglas P. **Diseases of Fishes, Book 4: Fish Immunology.** Snieszko, S. F. & Axelrod, Herbert R. eds. (Illus.). 1974. pap. 9.95. TFH Pubns.
Bauer, O. N., et al. **Disease of Pond Fishes.** Theodor, O., ed. Mercado, A., tr. from Rus. (Illus.). 1974. 21.00. Intl Schol Bk Serv.
Davis, H. S. **Culture & Diseases of Game Fishes.** (Illus.). 1953. 10.50. U of Cal Pr.
Elkan, E. & Reichenback-Klinke, H. **Color Atlas of the Diseases of Fishes, Amphibians, & Reptiles.** (Illus.). 1974. 30.00. TFH Pubns.
Fish Diseases (Immunology). pap. 9.95. TFH Pubns.
Fish Diseases Textbook. (Illus.). pap. 9.95. TFH Pubns.
Geisler, Rolf. **Aquarium Fish Diseases.** (Illus.). 1963. pap. 1.29. TFH Pubns.
Goldstein, R. J. **Diseases of Aquarium Fishes.** (Illus.). pap. 4.95. TFH Pubns.
Kabata, Z. **Fish Diseases: Crustaceans.** pap. 9.95. TFH Pubns.
Kingsford, Edward. **Diseases of Exotic Marine Fishes.** (Illus.). 1975. pap. 4.95. Palmetto Pub.
Mawdesley-Thomas, Lionel E., et al. **Diseases of Fish.** 1974. 17.50. Mss Info.
Reichenbach-Klinke, H. H. **Fish Pathology.** (Illus.). 1973. pap. 20.00. TFH Pubns.
Ribelin, William E. & Migaki, George, eds. **The Pathology of Fishes.** (Illus.). 1975. 35.00. U of Wis Pr.
— — **Pathology of Fishes.** 1975. 35.00. U of Wis Pr.
Schubert, Gottfried. **Cure & Recognize Aquarium Fish Diseases.** (Illus.). 1974. pap. 3.95. TFH Pubns.
Sinderman, C. J. **Principal Diseases of Marine Fish & Shellfish.** 1970. 26.00. Acad Pr.
Sindermann, C. J. **Diseases of Marine Fishes.** (Illus.). pap. 3.95. TFH Pubns.
Sniezko, S., et al. **Fish Diseases: Bacteria.** (Illus.). pap. 9.95. TFH Pubns.
Van Duijn, C. **Diseases of Fishes.** 3rd ed. 1973. 12.95. C C Thomas
Zoological Society of London - 30th Symposium. **Diseases of Fish.** Mawdesley-

Thomas, Lionel E., ed. 1972. 21.00. Acad Pr.

Fish Embryology

Armstrong, Philip B. & Child, Julia S. **Stages in the Development of Ictalurus Nebulosus.** (Illus.). 1962. 6.50. Syracuse U Pr.
Blaxter, J. H. **The Early Life History of Fish.** (Illus.). 1974. 40.20. Springer-Verlag.

Fish Finding

Dunlap, G. Dale. **Navigating & Finding Fish with Electronics.** (Illus.). 1972. 5.95. Intl Marine.
Fishing with Electricity: Its Applications to Biology & Management. 1967. pap. 9.50. (FAO). Unipub.
Meyer-Waarden, P. F. **Electric Fishing.** 1965. pap. 3.00. (FAO). Unipub.

Fish in Religion and Folklore

Howell, Robert L. **The Fish: A Ministry of Love.** 1973. pap. 2.50. Jarrow.
Titcomb, Margaret. **Native Use of Fish in Hawaii.** 2nd ed. 1972. 7.00. U Pr of Hawaii.
Trevelyan, Marie. **Folk-Lore & Folk-Stories of Wales.** 20.00. Norwood Edns.

Fish Migration

Harden, Jones, F. R. **Fish Migration.** (Illus.). 1968. 22.50. St Martin.

Fish Nomenclature

Norman, J. R. **A Draft Synopsis of the Orders, Families & Genera of Recent Fishes & Fish-Like Vertebrates.** (Illus.). 1975. 45.00. British Bk Ctr.
OECD, ed. **Multilingual Dictionary of Fish & Fish Products.** 1973. 1950. Intl Pubns Serv.

Fish Oils

Stansby, Maurice. **Fish Oils.** (Illus.). 1967. 20.00. Avi.

Fish Parasites

Dogiel, V. A., et al. **Parasitology of Fishes.** (Illus.). 14.95. TFH Pubns.
Hoffman, Glenn L. **Parasites of North American Freshwater Fishes.** 1967. 18.25. U of Cal Pr.
Hoffman, Glen L. & Meyer, Fred P. **Parasites of Freshwater Fishes.** (Illus.). 1974. pap. 12.95. TFH Pubns.
Scott, T. & Scott, A. **British Parasitic Copepoda.** 2 vols. in 1. 1913. 21.00. Johnson Repr.
Taylor, Angela & Muller, R., eds. **Aspects of Fish Parasitology.** (Illus.). 1970. 10.50. Lippincott.
Yamaguti, Satyu. **Monogenetic Trematodes of Hawaiian Fishes.** (Illus.). 1968. 15.00. U Pr of Hawaii.

Fish Physiology

The Aging of Fish. (Illus.). 1975. pap. 17.95. Unipub.
Agricultural Board. **Nutrient Requirements of Trout, Salmon & Catfish.** 1973. pap. 3.25. Natl Acad Sci.
Alexander, R. McNeill. **Functional Design in Fishes.** (Illus.). 1967. 3.75; pap. 3.50. Humanities.
Chavin, Walter. **Responses of Fish to Environmental Changes.** (Illus.). 1973. 19.75. C C Thomas.
Hoar, W.S. & Randall, D. J., eds. **Fish Physiology.** 6 vols. 1969-71. Vol. 1. 35.50; Vol. 2. 35.50; Vol. 3. 35.50; Vol. 4. 37.00; Vol. 5. 42.00; Vol. 6. 40.00. Acad Pr.

Kleerekoper, Herman. **Olfaction in Fishes.** (Illus.). 1969. 14.95. Ind U Pr.
Love, M. R. **Chemical Biology of Fishes.** 1970. 23.50. Acad Pr.
Neuhaus, O. W. & Halver, J. E., eds. **Fish in Research.** 1969. 15.00. Acad Pr.
Satchell, G. H. **Circulation in Fishes.** (Illus.). 1971. 8.00. Cambridge U Pr.

Fish Ponds

Balon, Eugene K. **African Fishes of Lake Kariba.** (Illus.). 1974. 14.95. TFH Pubns.
Betts, Leonard C. **Garden Pools.** (Illus.). 1952. pap. 1.50. TFH Pubns.
Farmer, Charles J. **Creative Fishing.** (Illus.). 1973. 6.95. Stackpole.
Nuffield Foundation. **How to Build a Pond.** 1968. pap. 3.00. Wiley.

Fish Populations

Cushing, D. H. **Fisheries Biology: A Study in Population Dynamics.** (Illus.). 1968. 11.50. U of Wis Pr.
Gulland, J. A. **Manual of Methods for Fish Stock Assessment Part 1: Fish Population Analysis.** (Illus.). 1969. pap. 5.00. (FAO). Unipub.
Weatherly, A. H. **Growth & Ecology of Fish Populations.** 1972. 13.50. Acad Pr.

Fish Preservation

Burgess, G. H., et al. **Fish Handling & Processing.** (Illus.). 1967. 11.25. Chem Pub.
Mead, John T. **Marine Refrigeration & Fish Preservation.** (Illus.). 1973. 14.95. Busn News. **Preservation of Fish by Irradiation.** (Illus.). 1970. pap. 5.00. (IA EA). Unipub.

Fish Trophies

Migdalski, Edward C. **How to Make Fish Mounts & Other Fish Trophies.** (Illus.). 1960. 6.95. Ronald.
Moore, W E. **Mount Your Own Fish Trophies.** (Illus.). 1975. 5.95. Doubleday.
Pray, Leon. **Nineteen Sixty-Five Fish Mounting Book.** rev. ed. 1965. 2.00. Reel Trophy.

Fisheries

Ben-Yomi, M., ed. **Russian-English Glossary of Fishing & Related Marine Terms.** (Illus.). 1975. 18.00. Intl Schol Bk Serv.
Bogdanov, A. S. **Soviet-Cuban Fishery Research.** 1973. 23.25. Intl Schol Bk Serv.
Browning, Robert. **Fisheries of the North Pacific: History, Species, Gear, Processes.** (Illus.). 1974. 24.95. Alaska Northwest.
Christy, Francis T., Jr. **Alternative Arrangements for Marine Fisheries: An Overview.** 1973. pap. 3.00. Johns Hopkins.
Christy, Francis T., Jr. & Scott, Anthony. **Common Wealth in Ocean Fisheries: Some Problems of Growth & Economic Allocation.** 1966. 10.00. Johns Hopkins.
Crutchfield, James A. & Pontecorvo, Giulio. **Pacific Salmon Fisheries A study of Irrational Conservation.** (Illus.). 1969. 8.50. Johns Hopkins.
Cushing, D. H. **Marine Ecology & Fisheries.** (Illus.). 1975. 27.50; pap. 9.95. Cambridge U Pr.
Cushing, David H. **Fisheries Resources of the Sea & Their Management.** (Illus.). 1975. 9.75. Oxford U Pr.
Everhart, W. Harry, et al. **Principles of Fishery Science.** (Illus.). 1975. 12.50. Comstock.
Finn, William. **Fishermen on Georges Bank.** (Illus.). 1972. 5.75. Little.
Firth, Frank F. **Encyclopedia of Marine Resources.** (Illus.). 1969. 27.50. Van Nos Reinhold.

Fisheries in the Food Economy. 1968. pap. 2.25. (FAO). Unipub.
Food and Agriculture Organization. **Fisheries in the Food Economy.** 1968. pap. 2.25. (FAO). Unipub.
Funk, John L., et al. **Black River Studies.** 1953. pap. 3.50. U of Mo Pr.
General Fisheries Council for the Mediterranean, Vol. 10. Proceedings. 1970. pap. 2.00. (FAO). Unipub.
— — **Proceeding & Technical Papers,** Vol. 11. 1973. pap. 3.00. (FAO). Unipub.
Gulland, J. A. **Manual of Methods for Fish Stock Assessment, Part I: Fish Population Analysis.** (Illus.). 1969. pap. 5.00. (FAO). Unipub.
Gulland, John A. **Population Dynamics of World Fisheries.** (Illus.). 1972. 7.50. U of Wash Pr.
Harden-Jones, F. R., ed. **Sea Fisheries Research.** 1974. 32.50. Halsted Pr.
Hazelton, J. E. & Bell, F. W. **Recent Developments & Research in Fisheries Economics.** 1967. 12.00. Oceana.
Ice in Fisheries. (Illus.). 1975. pap. 3.50. (FAO). Unipub.
Idyll, C. P. **Sea Against Hunger.** 1970. 8.95. T Y Crowell.
Johnson, Ralph W. & Van Cleve, Richard. **Management of the High Seas Fisheries of the Northeastern Pacific.** 1963. pap. 3.50. U of Wash Pr.
Kasahara, Hiroshi & Burke, William. **North Pacific Fisheries Management.** 1973. pap. 3.00. Johns Hopkins.
Konovalou, S. M. **Differentiation of Local Populations of Sockeye Salmon, Oncorhynchus Nerka.** Sagen, Leda V., tr. from Rus. (Illus.). 1975. pap. 10.00. U of Wash Pr.
Lang, Varley. **Follow the Water.** (Illus.). 1961. 4.50. Blair.
Mack, Jerry. **Catfish Farming Handbook.** 1971. 12.95. Educator Bks.
Manual of Methods for Fisheries Resource Survey & Appraisal, Pt. 2: The Use of Acoustic Instruments for Fish Detection & Abundance Estimation. (Illus.). 1973. pap. 4.00. (FAO). Unipub.
Manual on Fishermen's Cooperatives. 1971. pap. 3.00. (FAO). Unipub.
Miles, Edward. **Organizational Arrangements to Facilitate Global Management of Fisheries.** 1974. pap. 1.00. Johns Hopkins.
Moore, Remedios W., et al. **Progress in Fishery & Food Science.** (Illus.). 1972. 15.00. U of Wash Pr.
Nikonorov, I. V. **Interaction of Fishing Gear with Fish Aggregations.** Vilim, E., tr. from Rus. (Illus.). 1975. 19.00. Intl Schol Bk Serv.
Pontecorvo, Giulio, ed. **Fisheries Conflict in the North Atlantic: Problems of Management & Jurisdiction.** 1974. 13.50. Ballinger Pub.
Proper, Ida S. **Mohegan, the Cradle of New England.** (Illus.). 8.00. NH Pub Co.
Protasov, V. R. **Vision & Near Orientation of Fishes.** 1974. 15.85. Intl Schol Bk Serv.
Ricker, W. E., ed. **Methods for Assessment of Fish Production in Fresh Waters.** 2nd ed. (Illus.). 1971. pap. 10.50. Lippincott.
Ricker, William E. **Methods of Estimating Vital Statistics of Fish Populations.** 1948. pap. 5.00. Kraus Repr.
Rounsefell, George A. **Ecology Utilization & Management of Marine Fisheries: Alternatives for Management.** 1974. pap. 3.00. Johns Hopkins.
Royce, William F. **Introduction to the Fishery Sciences.** 1971. 14.50. Acad Pr.
Russell-Hunter, W. D. **Aquatic Productivity: An Introduction to Some Basic Aspects of Biological Oceanography & Limnology.** (Illus.). 1970. 5.95. Macmillan.
Sabine, Lorenzo. **Report on the Principal Fisheries of the American Seas.** (Illus.). Repr. of 1853 ed. 15.00. Kelley.
Saila, Saul B. & Norton, Virgil J. **Tuna: Status, Trends & Alternative Management**

Arrangements. 1974. 3.00. Johns Hopkins.
Saila, Saul B., ed. **Fisheries & Energy Production.** 1975. 14.00. Lexington Bks.
Stansby, Maurice E. **Industrial Fishery Technology.** 1975. Repr. of 1963 ed. 14.50. Kreiger.
Sunset Editors. **Sea of Cortez.** 1966. 14.95. Lane.
Symposium on the Oceanography & Fisheries Resources in the Tropical Atlantic, Abid; an, 1966. Proceedings. (Illus.). 1969. 17.00. (UNESCO). Unipub.
Training Course on Quality Aspects in the Handling & Storage of Fish. 1975. pap. 3.50. (FAO). Unipub.
Trilingual Dictionary of Fisheries Technological Terms: Curing. 1972. pap. 3.00. (FAO). Unipub.
Tussing, Arlon R., et al, eds. **Alaska Fisheries Policy: Economics, Resources & Management.** 1972. pap. 10.00. U of Wash Pr.
Wharton, James. **Bounty of the Chesapeake: Fishing in Colonial Virginia.** (Illus.). 1957. pap. 1.25. U Pr of Va.
White, Donald J. **New England Fishing Industry: A Study in Price & Wage Setting.** (Illus.). 1954. 7.50. Harvard U Pr.
Yearbook of Fishery Statistics: Fishery Commodities. Vol. 37. 1975. pap. 12.50. (FAO). Unipub.
Yearbook of Fishery Statistics 1973: Catches & Landings, Vol. 36. 1975. pap. 19.00. (FAO). Unipub.

Fisheries—Africa

Crutchfield, James A. & Lawson, Rowena. **West African Marine Fisheries: Alternatives for Management.** 1974. pap. 3.00. Johns Hopkins.
Symposium On Hydrobiology And Inland Fisheries, 4th, Fort-Larny, 1961. River Basins Subject to Heavy Seasonal Floods: Proceedings. 3.75. Intl Pubns Serv.

Fisheries—Great Britain

March, Edgar J. **Sailing Drifters.** (Illus.). 1972. 22.50. Intl Marine.

Fisheries—Indian Ocean

Bogdanov, A. S. **Soviet Fisheries Investigations in the Indian Ocean.** Golek, B., ed. Kaner, N., tr. from Rus. (Illus.). 1974. 13.00. Intl Schol Bk Serv.

Fisheries—Newfoundland

Lounsbury, Ralph G. **British Fishery at Newfoundland, 1634 to 1763.** 1969. Repr. of 1934 ed. Shoe String. 12.50.
Reeves, John. **History of the Government of the Island of Newfoundland.** 1793. 12.50. Johnson Repr.

Fisheries—Norway

Klausen, Arne Martin. **Kerala Fishermen & the Indo-Norwegian Pilot Project.** (Illus.). 1968. 12.00. Universitet.
Kobayashi, Teruo. **Anglo-Norwegian Fisheries Case of 1951 & the Changing Law of the Territorial Sea.** 1965. pap. 2.00. U Presses Fla.

Fisheries—Nova Scotia

Denys, Nicolas. **Description—Natural History of the Coasts of North America.** Ganong, William F., ed. 1968. Repr. of 1908 ed. 42.25. Greenwood.
Farstad, Nelvin. **Fisheries Development in Newfoundland: Aspects of Development, Location & Infrastructure.** 1972. pap. 8.00. Universitet.

Fisheries—Tropics

Tussing, Arlon R. & Hiebert, Robin A. **Fisheries of the Indian Ocean: Issues of International Management & Law of the Sea.** 1974. pap. 3.00. Johns Hopkins.

Fishermen

Anson, Peter. **Fishermen & Fishing Ways.** (Illus.). 1975. Repr. of 1932 ed. 12.00. Rowman.

Anson, Peter F. **Fishermen & Fishing Ways.** (Illus.). 1975. Repr. of 1932 ed. 15.95. British Bk Ctr.

Clifford, Harold B. **Charlie York: Maine Coast Fisherman.** (Illus.). 1974. 7.95. Intl Marine.

Critchfield, Richard. **The Golden Bowl Be Broken: Peasant Life in Four Cultures.** (Illus.). 1974. 12.50. Ind U Pr.

Curtis, Elwood A. **A Wet Butt & a Hungry Gut.** 1974. 6.95. Blair.

De Gast, Robert. **Oystermen of the Chesapeake.** (Illus.). 1970. 16.00. Intl Marine.

Finn, William. **Fishermen on Georges Bank.** (Illus.). 1972. 5.75. Little.

Firth, Raymond. **Malay Fishermen: Their Peasant Economy.** (Illus.). 1975. pap. 4.95. Norton.

Fisherman's Guide. (Illus.). 1975. pap. 5.95. Drake Pubs.

Forman, Shepard. **Raft Fishermen: Tradition & Change in the Brazilian Peasant Economy.** (Illus.). 1970. 10.00. Ind U Pr.

Grossinger, Richard. **Book of the Cranberry Islands.** 1974. 10.00; autographed edition. 15.00. Black Sparrow.

Jenkin, A. Hamilton. **Cornwall & Its People.** Repr. of 1945 ed. 13.50. Kelley.

Lang, Varley. **Follow the Water.** (Illus.). 1961. 4.50. Blair.

Miles, A. Graham. **Fisherman's Breeze: The Log of the Ruth M. Martin.** 1973. Repr. of 1929 ed. 2.50. South St Sea Mus.

Piper, Steven. **The North Ships: The Life of a Travelerman.** 1974. 12.50. David & Charles.

Schwind, Phil. **Cape Cod Fisherman.** 1975. 8.95. Intl Marine.

Smith, Frederick J. **The Fisherman's Business Guide.** (Illus.). 1975. 10.95. Intl Marine.

Van Winkle, Ted. **Fred Boynton: Lobsterman, New Harbor Maine,** (Illus.). 1975. 8.95. Intl Marine.

Fishery Law and Legislation

Johnston, Douglas M. **International Law of Fisheries: A Framework for Policy-Oriented Inquiries.** (Illus.). 1965. 30.00. Yale U Pr.

Kobayashi, Teruo. **Anglo-Norwegian Fisheries Case of 1951 & the Changing Law of the Territorial Sea.** 1965. pap. 2.00. U Presses Fla.

Leonard, Leonard L. **International Regulation of Fisheries.** (Illus.). 1944. 1750. Johnson Repr.

Lounsbury, Ralph G. **British Fishery at Newfoundland, Sixteen Thirty-Four to Seventeen Sixty-Three.** (Illus.). 1969. Repr. of 1934 ed. 12.50. Shoe String.

Pontecorvo Giulio, ed. **Conflict in the North Atlantic: Problems of Management & Jurisdiction.** (Illus.). 1974. 13.50. Ballinger Pub.

Riesenfeld, Stefan A. **Protection of Coastal Fisheries Under International Law.** Repr. of 1942 ed. 28.00. Johnson Repr.

Rothschild, Brian J., ed. **World Fisheries Policy: Multidisciplinary Views.** (Illus.). 1972. 9.50. U of Wash Pr.

Tussing, Arlon R., et al, eds. **Alaska Fisheries Policy: Economics, Resources, & Management.** (Illus.). 1972. pap. 5.00. U Alaska Inst Res.

Fishery Products

Brody, Julius. **Fishery By-Products Technology.** (Illus.). 1965. 19.00. Avi.

Chichester, C. O. & Graham, H. D., eds. **Microbial Safety of Fishery Products.** 1973. 13.50. Acad Pr.

Food And Agriculture Organization. **Fisheries in the Food Economy.** 1968. 1.25. (FAO). Unipub.

IPFC-IOFC Ad Hoc Working Party of Scientists 2nd Session. **Stock Assessments of Tuna. Proceedings.** 1975. pap. 3.50. (FAO). Unipub.

OECD, ed. **Multilingual Dictionary of Fish & Fish Products.** 1973. 19.50. Intl Pubns Serv.

Tannenbaum, Steven & Stillings, Bruce, eds. **Economics, Marketing & Technology of Fish Protein Concentrate: Proceedings.** 1974. 20.00. MIT Pr.

Fishes

Allen, Gerald. **Anemone Fishes.** 20.00. TFH Pubns.

Allyn, Rube. **Dictionary of Fishes.** pap. 1.95. Great Outdoors.

Ames, Felicia. **Fish You Care For.** 1971. pap. 1.25. NAL.

Artedi, Peter. **Genera Piscium: Emendata et Aucta.** (Illus., Lat.). 1967. Repr. of 1792 ed. 33.00. Stechert.

— — **Ichthyologia.** Linnaeus, C., ed. (Lat.) 1961. Repr. of 1738 ed. 21.55. Stechert.

Axelrod, Herbert R. **Freshwater Fishes.** Bk. 1. (Illus.). 1964. 20.00. TFH Pubns.

Axelrod, Herbert R. & Emmens, Cliff W. **Exotic Marine Fishes.** (Illus.). 1973. 15.00. TFH Pubns.

Bagenal, T. B., ed. **Ageing of Fish: Proceedings of an International Symposium.** 1974. Haessner Pub.

Benirschke, K. & Hsu, T. C., eds. **Chromosome Atlas: Fish, Amphibians, Reptiles & Birds.** Vol. 1. (Illus.). 1972. 14.80. Springer-Verlag.

Blaxter, J. H. **The Early Life History of Fish.** (Illus.). 1974. 40.20. Springer-Verlag.

Bloch, E. M. **Systema Ichthyologiae.** 2 vols. in 1. Schneider, J. G., ed. (Illus., Lat.). 1967. Repr. of 1801 ed. 55.00. Stechert.

Brittan, Martin. **Rasbora.** (Illus.). 1972. 12.95. TFH Pubns.

Cannon, Raymond. **How to Fish the Pacific Coast.** 3rd ed. (Illus.). 1967. pap. 2.95. Lane.

Chaplin, Charles C. & Scott, Peter. **Fishwatcher's Guide to West Atlantic Coral Reefs.** Livingston, Robert A., ed. (Illus.). 1972. 5.95. Livingston.

Check-List of the Fishes of the North-Eastern Atlantic & of the Mediterranean. Clofan. Vols. 1-2, 1974. Set. pap. 66.00. (UNESCO). Unipub.

Childress. **Conchy on the Halfshell.** 1973. pap. 0.75. G&D.

Clark, Eugenie. **Lady with a Spear.** (Illus.). 1953. 5.92. Har-Row.

Cooper, Allan. **Fishes of the World.** (Illus.). 1972. pap. 1.95. Bantam.

Curtis, Brian. **Life of the Fish: His Manners & Morals.** (Illus.). 5.00. Peter Smith.

— — **Life Story of the Fish.** 2nd ed. 1949. pap. 3.50. Dover.

Cushing, David H. **Recruitment & Parent Stock in Fishes.** 1974. pap. 7.50. U of Wash Pr.

Deemer, Philip, compiled by. **Fish Directory 1973.** 1973. pap. 1.00. Jarrow.

De Sylva, Donald P. **The Alfred C. Glassell Jr. University of Miami Argosy Expedition to Ecuador, Pt. 1: Introduction & Narrative.** (Illus.). 1972. 6.95. U of Miami Pr.

Dunaway, Vic. **From Hook to Table: An Angler's Guide to Good Eating.** (Illus.). 1974. 4.95. Macmillan.

Eddy, Samuel & Underhill, James C.

Northern Fishes. rev. 3rd ed. (Illus.). 1974. 10.00. U of Minn Pr.

Fish, Marie P. & Mowbray, William H. **Sounds of Western North Atlantic Fishes: A Reference File of Biological Underwater Sounds.** (Illus.). 1970. 16.50. Johns Hopkins.

Goldstein, Robert J. **Anabantoids Gouramis & Related Species.** (Illus.). pap. 5.95. TFH Pubns.

Goode, G. Brown. **Game Fishes of the United States.** (Illus.). 1972. Repr. of 1879 ed. 75.00. Winchester Pr.

Gosline, William A. **Functional Morphology & Classification of Teleostean Fishes.** (Illus.). 1971. pap. 6.00. U Pr of Hawaii.

Greenfield, David, ed. **Systemic Ichthyology: A Collection of Readings.** 1972. 14.00. Mss Info.

Greenwood, P. H. & Norman, J. R. **A History of Fishes.** 3rd ed. 1975. 17.95. Halsted Pr.

Gulland, J. A. **The Fish Resources of the Ocean.** (Illus.). 1972. 27.00. (FAO). Unipub.

Herald, Earl S. **Living Fishes of the World.** (Illus.). 1961. 19.95. Doubleday.

Herold, Earl. **Living Fishes of the World.** 1975. 19.95. Doubleday.

Hopkirk, John D. **Endemism in Fishes of the Clear Lake Region.** pap. 5.50. U of Cal Pr.

Innes, William T. **Exotic Aquarium Fishes.** 19th ed. (Illus.). 1975. 7.95. Dutton.

— — **Innes Exotic Aquarium Fish.** 4.95. TFH Pubns.

Jacobs, Kurt, **Livebearing Fishes.** (Illus.). 1974. pap. 9.95. TFH Pubns.

Janes, Edward C. **Fresh-Water Fishing Complete.** (Illus.). 1973. pap. 1.95. B&N.

Jocher, Willy. **Spawning Problem Fishes.** Incl. Book 1; Book 2. (Illus.). 1972. pap. 3.95 ea. TFH Pubns.

Jordan, David S. **Genera of Fishes & a Classification of Fishes.** 1963. 22.50. Stanford U Pr.

Juntunen, Erland T., et al. **Economic Icthyology.** 1973. pap. 3.75. Oreg St U Bkstrs.

Kyle, Harry M. **Biology of Fishes.** 1971. 12.95. TFH Pubns.

Lagler, Karl F., et al. **Ichthyology.** 1962. 18.50. Wiley.

Lampman, Ben H. **Coming of the Pond Fishes.** 6.50. Binford.

Lanham, Urless N. **The Fishes.** (Illus.). 1967. pap. 2.25. Columbia U Pr.

Lindberg, G. U. **Fishes of the World: A Key to Famlies & a Checklist.** Mills, H., ed. (Illus.). 1974. 42.50. Halsted Pr.

Madsen, J. M. **Aquarium Fishes in Color.** (Illus.). 1975. 6.95. Macmillan.

Marshall, N. B. **Explorations in the Life of Fishes.** 1971. 7.50. Harvard U Pr.

— — **Life of Fishes.** 1966. 12.50. Universe.

Mills, Derek H. **Salmon & Trout: A Resource, Its Ecology, Conservation & Management.** 1972. 18.95. St Martin.

Morris, Dan & Strung, Norman. **Fisherman's Almanac.** (Illus.). 1970. 5.95. Macmillan.

Muus, Bent J. **Collins Guide to Sea Fishes.** (Illus.). 1974. 10.00. Scribner.

Myers, George S. **How to Become an Ichthyologist.** 1970. pap. 1.50. TFH Pubns.

Neugebauer, Wilbert. **Marine Aquarium Fish Identifier.** (Illus.). 1975. 4.95. Sterling.

Nikolsky, G. V. **Ecology of Fishes.** Birkett, L., tr. 1963. 17.00. Acad Pr.

Ommanney, F. D. **Fishes.** (Illus.). 1970. 3.95. Time-Life.

Perlmutter, Alfred. **Guide to Marine Fishes.** (Illus.). 1961. 10.00; pap. 5.95. NYU Pr.

— — **Guide to Marine Fishes.** (Illus.). pap. NYU Pr.

Saila, Saul B. & Norton, Virgil J. **Tuna: Status, Trends & Alternative Management Arrangements.** 1974. pap. 3.00. Johns Hopkins

Schroeder, J. H., ed. **Symposium on Icthygenetics, 1st. Genetics & Mutagenesis of Fish: Proceedings.** 1973. 26.70. Springer-Verlag.

Stephens, J. S., Jr. **A Revised Classification of The Blennioid Fishes of the American Family Chaenopsidae.** 1963. pap. 3.50. U of Cal Pr.

Tirmizi, Khan. **Hand Book on a Pakistani Marine Prawn Panaeus.** 5.00. Panther Hse.

Trott, Lamarr B. **Contributions to the Biology of Carapid Fishes.** 1970. pap. 2.00. U of Cal Pr.

Vessey-Fitzgerald, Brian. **World of Fishes.** 1973. 5.25. British Bk Ctr.

Walker, Braz. **Oddball Fishes & Other Strange Creatures of the Deep.** (Illus.). 1975. 5.95. Sterling.

Weatherly, A. H. **Growth & Ecology of Fish Populations.** 1972. 13.50. Acad Pr.

What Fish Is That? (Illus.). 4.45. Purnell Lib Serv.

White, William, Jr. **The Angelfish: Its Life Cycle.** (Illus.). 1975. 5.95. Sterling.

Wourms, John P., et al, eds. **Genetic Studies of Fish.** 2 vols., Vol. 2. 1974. 19.50. Mss Info.

Fishes—Africa

Balon, Eugene K. **African Fishes of Lake Kariba.** (Illus.). 1974. 14.95. TFH Pubns.

Fryer, Geoffrey & Iles, T. D. **Cichlids of the Great Lakes of Africa.** (Illus.). 1972. 20.00. TFH Pubns.

Greenwood, P. H. **The Cichlid Fishes of Lake Victoria, Africa: Biology & Evolution of a Species Flock.** (Illus.). 1975. 25.00; pap. 15.00. British Bk Ctr.

Lowe-McConnell, R. H. **Illustrated Key to Freshwater Fishes of the Volta Lake.** 1972. 6.00. Panther Hse.

Playfair, R. Lambert & Guenther, Albert C. **The Fishes of Zanzibar.** (Illus.). 1971. Repr. of 1866 ed. 125.00. N K Gregg.

Fishes—Atlantic Ocean

Beebe, William & Tee-Van, John. **Field Book of the Shore Fishes of Bermuda & the West Indies.** (Illus.). 6.50. Peter Smith.

Breder, Charles M., Jr. **Fieldbook of Marine Fishes of the Atlantic Coast.** (Illus.). 1948. 5.95. Putnam.

Migdalski, Edward C. **Angler's Guide to the Salt Water Game Fishes: Atlantic & Pacific.** (Illus.). 1958. 10.95. Ronald.

Perlmutter, Alfred. **Guide to Marine Fishes.** (Illus.). 1961. 10.00; pap. 5.95. NYU Pr.

Fishes—Australia

Deas, Walter. **Australian Fishes in Color.** (Illus.). 1973. 6.75. Newbury Bks Inc.

— — **Australian Fishes in Colour.** (Illus.). 1974. 6.50. Intl Pubns Serv.

Fishes—Canada

Grundle, Jack, ed. **British Columbia Game Fish.** 1975. 8.95. David & Charles.

Fishes—Europe

Blanc, M., et al, eds. **European Inland Water Fish: A Multilingual Catalogue.** (Illus.). 1972. 22.00. (FAO). Unipub.

Lythgoe, John & Lythgoe, Lillian. **Fishes of the Sea: The Coastal Waters of the British Isles, Europe & the Mediterranean, a Photographic Guide in Color.** 1972. 15.00. Intl Pubns Serv.

— — **Fishes of the Sea: The Coastal Waters of the British Isles, Northern Europe & the Mediterranean.** (Illus.). 1975. 15.00. Doubleday.

Muus, Bent J. & Dahlstorm, Preben. **Collins Guide to the Sea Fishes.** 1975. 10.00. Scribner.

Vachon, Mrs. Claude. **European Inland Water Fish: A Multilingual Catalogue.** (Illus.). 1972. 22.00. (FAO). Unipub.

Wheeler, Alwyne. **Fishes of the British Isles & North-West Europe.** 1969. 25.00. Mich St U Pr

Fishes—Great Britain

Bagenal, T. B. **Observer's Book of Fresh Water Fishes.** (Illus.). 2.50. Warne.

— — **Observer's Book of Sea Fishes of the British Isles.** (Illus.). 2.50. Warne.

Lythgoe, John & Lythgoe Lillian. **Fishes of the Sea: The Coastal Waters of the British Isles, Northern Europe & the Mediterranean.** (Illus.). 1975. 15.00. Doubleday.

Muus, Bent J. & Dahlstrom, Preben. **Collins Guide to the Sea Fishes.** 1975. 10.00. Scribner.

Wheeler, Alwyne. **Fishes of the British Isles & North-West Europe.** 1969. 25.00. Mich St U Pr.

Woodward, A. Smith. **Fishes of the English Chalk.** Part 1-7. Vols. 56-56, 61-65. Nos. 263, 266, 291, 300, 308, 313, 320. Repr. of 1912 ed. Set. pap. 40.50. Johnson Repr.

Fishes—Japan

Marr, John, ed., **Kuroshio: A Symposium on the Japan Current.** 1970. 17.50. U Pr of Hawaii.

Fisheries—Mediterranean

General Fisheries Council for the Mediterranean. **Proceedings & Technical Papers.** Vol. 7. 1964. pap. 10.00. (FAO). Unipub.

— — **Proceedings & Technical Papers.** Vol. 8. 1967. pap. 15.00. (FAO). Unipub.

— — **Proceedings & Technical Papers.** Vol. 10. 1970. pap. 2.00. (FAO). Unipub.

— — **Proceedings & Technical Papers.** Vol. II. 1973. pap. 3.00. (FAO). Unipub.

Fishes—New Zealand

Bodeker, Philip. **The Sandgroper's Trail: An Angling Safari from Perth to the Kimberley.** (Illus.). 1971. 8.95. Reed.

Doak, Wade. **Fishes of the New Zealand Region.** (Illus.). 1974. 29.95. British Bk Ctr.

Moreland, John M. **Marine Fishes of New Zealand.** (Illus.). 1967. 5.50. Reed.

Fishes—North America

Beebe, William & Tee-Van, John. **Field Book of the Shore Fishes & the West Indies.** (Illus.). 6.50. Peter Smith.

Herald, Earl S. **Fishes of North America.** (Illus.). 1972. 9.95. Doubleday.

Herbert, Henry W. **Frank Forester's Fish & Fishing in the United States & British Provinces of North America.** (Illus.). 1970. Repr. of 1850 ed. 16.00. Arno.

Jordan, David S. & Evermann, Barton W. **American Food & Game Fishes.** (Illus.). 1969. pap. 5.00. Dover.

Morrow, James E. **Illustrated Keys to the Freshwater Fishes of Alaska.** (Illus.). 1974. pap. 2.95. Alaska Northwest.

Walls, Jerry G. **Fishes of the Northern Gulf of Mexico.** (Illus.). 1975. 9.95. TFH Pubns.

Westman, James. **Why Fish Bite & Why They Don't.** 1961. 4.95. P-H.

Zim, Herbert S. & Shoemaker, Hurst H. **Fishes.** 4.95; pap. 1.95. Western Pub.

Fishes—Pacific Ocean

Burgess, Warren E. & Axelrod, Herbert R. **Pacific Marine Fishes.** Bk. 5. (Illus.). 1974. 20.00. TFH Pubns.

Fitch, John E. & Lavenberg, Robert J. **Deep-Water Fishes of California.** (Illus.). 1968. pap. 2.25. U of Cal Pr.

Fowler, H. W. **Fishes of Guam, Hawaii, Samoa, & Tahiti.** Repr. of 1925 ed. pap.

4.00. Kraus Repr.

— — **The Fishes of Oceania, Supplement 3.** pap. 14.00. Kraus Repr.

— — **Fishes of the Tropical Central Pacific.** Repr. of 1927 ed. pap. 4.00. **Kraus Repr.**

Fowler, H. W. & Ball, S. C. **Fishes of Hawaii, Johnston Island, & Wake Island.** Repr. of 1925 ed. pap. 4.00. Kraus Repr.

Fowler, Henry W. **Fishes of Oceania.** 4 vols. in 1. (Illus.). 1928-1949. 105.00. Johnson Repr.

Gosline, William A. & Brock, Vernon E. **Handbook of Hawaiian Fishes.** (Illus.). 1960. pap. 7.50. U Pr of Hawaii.

Gotshall, Daniel W. & Zimbleman. **Fishes of the Pacific Coast: An Underwater Guide, Alaska to the Baja.** (Illus.). 1974. 5.95. Livingston.

Guenther, A. **Andrew Garrett's Fische der Suedsee.** 3 vols. in 1. 1966. Repr. of 1873 ed. 99.00. Stechert.

Howard, John K. & Ueyanagi, Shoji. **Distribution-Relative Abundance of Billfishes (Istiophoridae) of the Pacific Ocean.** (Illus.) 1965. Set. pap. 5.50. U of Miami Pr.

Jordan, David S. & Evermann, Barton W. **The Shore Fishes of Hawaii.** (Illus.). 1973. pap. 8.50. C E Tuttle.

Kizevetter, I. V. **Chemistry & Technology of Pacific Fish.** IPST Staff, tr. from Rus. (Illus.). 1974. 22.00. Intl Schol Bk Serv.

Migdalski, Edward C. **Angler's Guide to the Salt Water Game Fishes: Atlantic & Pacific.** (Illus.). 1958. 10.95. Ronald.

Pietschmann, V. **Remarks on Pacific Fishes.** Repr. of 1930 ed. pap. 4.00. Kraus Repr.

Schindler, O. **Sexually Mature Larval Hemiramphidae from the Hawaiian Islands.** Repr. of 1932 ed. pap. 4.00. Kraus Repr.

Fishes—United States

Allyn, Rube. **Florida Fishes.** Allyn, Charles, ed. (Illus.). 1969. pap. 1.25. Great Outdoors.

Burgess, Warren E. & Axelrod, Herbert R. **Pacific Marine Fishes.** Bk. 4. (Illus.). 1974. 20.00. TFH Pubns.

Dahlberg, Michael. **Guide to Coastal Fishes of Georgia & Nearby States.** (Illus.). 1974. pap. 5.75. U of Ga Pr.

Eddy, Samuel & Surber, Thaddeus. **Northern Fishes.** 5.75. Branford.

Fitch, John E. & Lavenberg, Robert J. **Deep-Water Fishes of California.** (Illus.). 1968. pap. 2.25. U of Cal Pr.

— — **Tidepool & Nearshore Fishes of California.** (Illus.). 1976. 8.95; 3.95. U of Cal Pr.

Funk, John L., et al. **Black River Studies.** 1953. pap. 3.50. U of Mo Pr.

Hubbs, Carl L. & Lagler, Karl F. **Fishes of the Great Lakes Region.** (Illus.). 1964. 9.95. U of Mich Pr.

Jordan, D. S. & Evermann, B. W. **American Food & Game Fishes.** (Illus.). 10.00. Peter Smith.

Jordan, David S. & Evermann, Barton W. **The Shore Fishes of Hawaii.** (Illus.). 1973. pap. 8.50. C E Tuttle.

Koster, William J. **Guide to the Fishes of New Mexico.** (Illus.). 1957. pap. 1.65. U of NM Pr.

Rafinesque, Constantine. **Ichthyologia Ohiensis, or, Natural History of the Fishes Inhabiting the River Ohio & Its Tributary Streams.** 1970. Repr. of 1820 ed. 8.00. Arno.

Ricciuti, Edward R. **Dancers on the Beach: The Story of the Grunion.** (Illus.). 1973. 3.95. T Y Crowell.

Schultz, Leonard P. **Keys to the Fishes of Washington, Oregon & Closely Adjoining Regions.** (Illus.). 1936. pap. 2.00. U of Wash Pr.

Smith, Jerome V. C. **Natural History of the Fishes of Massachusetts.** (Illus.). 1970. boxed. 10.75. Freshet Pr.

Titcomb, Margaret. **Native of Fish in Hawaii.** 2nd. ed.1972. 7.00. U Pr of Hawaii

Wall, Roy. **An Angler Reflects: How to Catch the Wily Ones.** 1974. 7.95. Naylor.

Fishing

All-Union Conference, Murmansk, Feb.-Mar., 1968. **Fish Behavior & Fishing Techniques: Proceedings.** 1973. 14.00. Intl Schol Bk Serv.

Allyn, Rube. **Fishermen's Handbook.** pap. 1.00. Great Outdoors.

Annesley, Patrick, ed. **Hardy's Book of Fishing.** (Illus.). 1971. 13.95. Dutton.

Anson, Peter. **Fishermen & Fishing Ways.** (Illus.). 1975. Repr. of 1932 ed. 12.00. Rowman.

Anson, Peter F. **Fishermen & Fishing Ways.** (Illus.). 1975. Repr. of 1932 ed. 15.95. British Bk Ctr.

Arnov, Boris. **Fishing for Everyone.** (Illus.). 1970. 4.95. Hawthorn.

Babcock, Havilah. **Jaybirds Go to Hell on Friday.** 1964. 4.95. HR&W.

Babson, Stanley M. **Bonefishing.** rev. ed. 1973. 6.95. Winchester Pr.

Barrett, Peter. **In Search of Trout.** (Illus.). 1973. 7.95. P-H.

Bashline, L. James, ed. **The Eastern Trail.** (Illus.). 1972. 8.95. Freshet Pr.

Bates, Joseph D., Jr. **Fishing: An Encyclopedic Guide to Tackle & Tactics for Fresh & Salt Water.** 1974. 14.95. Dutton.

— — **How to Find & Make Them Strike.** (Illus.). 1975. 8.95. Har-Row.

Bauer, Erwin A., ed. **Fishermen's Digest.** 9th ed. 1973. pap. 6.95. Digest Bks.

Bayless, Kenneth M. **Complete Book of Sportfishing.** (Illus.). 1973. pap. 4.95. Petersen Pub.

Bennett, Tiny. **Art of Angling.** 1970. 9.95. P-H.

Bergman, Ray. **Fishing with Ray Bergman.** Janes, Edward C., ed. (Illus.). 1970. 8.95. Knopf.

Berlin, Sven. **Jonah's Dream: A Meditation on Fishing.** (Illus.). 1975. 6.95. W Kaufmann.

Blackwood, Elsie M. **Many Rivers.** (Illus.). 1968. 1.98. A S Barnes.

Blaisdell, Harold F. **Philosophical Fisherman.** 1969. 6.95. HM.

Bradford, Charles. **The Brook Trout & the Determined Angler.** (Illus.). 1970. boxed 6.75. Freshet Pr.

Bradner, Enos. **Fish-on!** 3.95. Superior Pub.

— — **Inside on the Outdoors.** (Illus.). 1973. 9.95. Superior Pub.

Briscoe, Lawrance. **Fisher's Alley.** 7.95. Vantage.

Brooks, Joe. **Complete Book of Fly Fishing.** rev. ed. 1968. 7.95. A S Barnes.

— — **Complete Guide to Fishing Across North America.** (Illus.). 1966. 10.95. Har-Row.

Casson, Paul. **Decoys Simplified** (Illus.). 1973. 14.95. Freshet Pr.

Catham, Russell. **The Angler's Coast.** (Illus.). 1976. 7.95. Doubleday.

Clark, Eugenie. **Lady with a Spear.** 1974. pap. 2.00. Ballantine.

— — **Lady with a Spear.** (Illus.). 1953. 5.92. Har-Row.

Clotfelter, Cecil F. **Hunting & Fishing.** 1974. 7.50. Libs Unl.

Cole, Len. **Fishing All Waters.** (Illus.). 1973. pap. 1.50 Stadia Sports Pub.

Cone, Arthur L., Jr. **Fishing Made Easy.** (Illus.). 1968. 6.95. Macmillan.

Congress on Fishing Gear, 3rd, Reykjavik, 1970. **Modern Fishing Gear of the World, Three: Fish Finding, Purse Seining, & Aimed Trawling.** Kristjonsson, H., ed. (Illus.). 1972. 38.00. (FAO). Unipub.

Crahall, Joseph. **The Completest Angling Booke That Ever Was Writ.** (Illus.). 1970. boxed 27.50. Freshet Pr.

Crowe, John. **Modern ABC's of Fresh Water Fishing.** pap. 0.95. Funk & W.

— — **Modern ABC's of Fresh Water Fishing.** (Illus.). 1973. pap. 3.95. Stackpole.

Cullen, Anthony & Hemphill, Patrick. **Crash Strike.** (Illus.). 1971. pap. 8.75. Intl Pubns Serv.

Culley, M. B. **The Pilchard.** 1972. 27.00. Pergamon.

Cushing, D. H. **Detection of Fish.** (Illus.). 1973. 20.00 Pergamon.

Dahlem, Ted. **How to Make & Mend Cast Nets.** pap. 1.25. Great Outdoors.

Dalrymple, Byron. **Sportsman's Guide to Game Fish.** 3rd ed. 1971. 6.95. T Y Crowell.

Decker, Maurice H. **How to Take Fresh Water Fish in Lake, Pond & Stream.** rev. ed. (Illus.). 1958. pap. 2.25. Sentinel.

Denny, George. **The Dread Fishwish.** (Illus.). 1974. 8.95. Freshet Pr.

DeRohan-Csermak, Geza. **Sturgeon Hooks of Eurasia.** (Illus.). 1963. 8.50. Aldine.

Dodd, Ed. **Mark Trail's Fishing Tips.** (Illus.). 1969. pap. 1.00. Essandess.

Doogue, Raymond. **Seafishing for Beginners.** 1974. pap. 3.50. Reed.

Downey, Earl. **How to Fish for Snook.** pap. 1.00. Great Outdoors.

Dunaway, Vic. **Modern Saltwater Fishing.** (Illus.). 1975. softbound. 5.95. Stoeger.

Earp, Samuel A. & Wildeman, William J. **The Blue Water Bait Book: Secrets of Successful Big Game Fishing.** (Illus.). 1974. 7.95. Little.

Elliot, Bob. **Bass Fishing in New England.** (Illus.). 1973. 6.50; pap; 3.50. Stone Wall Pr.

— — **The Making of an Angler.** (Illus.). 1975. 8.95. Winchester Pr.

Elliott, Charles. **Outdoor Observer: How to See, Hear & Interpret in the Natural World.** 1970. 4.50. Dutton.

Evanoff, Vlad. **Another Thousand & One Fishing Tips & Tricks.** (Illus.). 1970. 7.95. Har-Row.

— — **Another One Thousand & One Fishing Tips & Tricks.** 1975. pap. 3.95. Hawthorn.

— — **Best Ways to Catch More Fish in Fresh & Salt Water.** (Illus.). 1975. 7.95. Doubleday.

— — **Complete Guide to Fishing.** (Illus.). 1961. 4.50. T Y Crowell.

— — **Complete Guide to Fishing.** pap. 2.00. Wilshire.

— — **How to Fish in Salt Water.** (Illus.). 1975. 7.95. A S Barnes.

— — **One Thousand & One Fishing Tips & Tricks.** (Illus.). 1966. 7.95. Har-Row.

Fabian, John. **Fishing for the Beginner.** 1974. 5.95. Atheneum.

Fallon, Jack. **Teaching Your Children to Fish.** 1974. 6.95. Winchester Pr.

Fallon, Jack. **Teaching Your Children to Fish.** (Illus.). 1975. pap. price not set. Macmillan.

Congress on Fishing Gear, 3rd, Reykjavik, 1970. **Modern Fishing Gear of the World, Three: Fish Finding, Purse Seining & Aimed Trawling.** Kristjonsson, H., ed. (Illus.). 1972. 38.00. (FAO). Unipub.

Farmer, Charles J. **Creative Fishing.** (Illus.). 1973. 6.95. Stackpole.

Farrington, S. Kip, Jr. **Fishing with Hemingway & Glassell.** 1971. 5.95. McKay.

Fichter, George S. & Francis, Phil. **Fishing.** Zim, Herbert S., ed. 1974. 2.95. Western Pub.

Field & Stream. **Field & Stream Reader.** facs. ed. 1946. 15.00. Bks for Libs.

Fishing Ports & Markets. (Illus.). 1971. 30.00 (FAO). Unipub.

Flick, Art. **Art Flicks New Streamside Guide to Naturals & Their Imitations.** (Illus.). 1970. 4.95. Crown.

Forbes, David C. **Big-Game Fishing in British Waters.** (Illus.). 1973. 8.95. David & Charles.

— — **Successful Roach Fishing.** (Illus.). 1973. 7.95. David & Charles .

— — **Successful Sea Angling.** (Illus.). 1971. 6.95. David & Charles.

Forsberg, Foy. **Beginner's Guide to Shorecasting.** (Illus.). 1975. 9.50. Transatlantic.

Fox, Charles K. **The Book of Lures.** (Illus.).

1975. 14.95. Freshet Pr.

Freeman, Jim. **California Steelhead Fishing.** (Illus.). 1971. pap. 1.95. Chronicle Bks.

— — **California Trout Fishing.** (Illus.). 1971. pap. 1.95. Chronicle Bks.

— — **Fishing with Small Fry: A Parent's Guide to Teaching Children How to Fish.** (Illus.). 1973. pap. 2.95. Chronicle Bks.

— — **Klamath River Fishing.** (Illus.). 1971. pap. 1.95. Chronicle Bks.

— — **Shasta Lake Fishing.** (Illus.). 1971. pap. 1.95. Chronicle Bks.

— — **Trinity River Fishing.** (Illus.) 1971. pap. 1.95. Chronicle Bks.

Fridman, A. L. **Theory & Design of Commercial Fishing Gear.** Kondor, R., tr. from Rus. (Illus.). 1974. 35.00. Intl Schol Bk Serv.

Gerlach, Rex. **Creative Fly Tying & Fishing.** 1974. 10.00. Winchester Pr.

— — **The Complete Book of Casting.** (Illus.). 1975. softbound. 5.95. Stoeger.

Gingrich, Arnold. **The Fishing in Print.** 1974. 12.95. Winchester Pr.

— — **Well Tempered Angler.** (Illus.). 1965. 7.95. Knopf.

Goadby, Peter. **Big Fish & Blue Water.** 1972. 14.95. HR&W.

Goodwin, J. **Angling.** (Illus.). 1975. 3.50. T Y Crowell.

Grey, Zane. **Zane Grey Outdoorsman: Zane Grey's Best Hunting & Fishing Tales.** Reiger, George, ed. (Illus.). 1972. 9.95. P-H.

Haig-Brown, Roderick. **Fisherman's Fall.** 1975. 7.50. Crown.

— — **Fisherman's Spring.** 1975. 7.50. Crown.

— — **Fisherman's Summer.** 1975. 7.50. Crown.

— — **Fisherman's Winter.** 1975. 7.50. Crown.

— — **Return to the River.** 1974. 7.50. Crown.

— — **River Never Sleeps.** 1974. 7.50. Crown.

Hall, Henry M. **Idylls of Fishermen.** 1914. 9.50. AMS Pr.

Hardy, Arthur E. **Beginner's Guide to Coarse Fishing.** (Illus.). 1973. 8.75. Transatlantic.

Hawk, Dave. **One Hundred Years on Bass.** (Illus.). 1970. 6.00. Naylor.

Helm, Thomas. **Fishing Southern Salt Waters.** (Illus.). 1972. 10.00 Dodd.

Hill, W. M. **Coarse Fishing for New Anglers.** (Illus.). 1975. 9.95. David & Charles.

Hilton, Jack. **Quest for Carp.** (Illus.). 1972. 9.95. Transatlantic.

Holm, Don. **Fishing the Pacific.** (Illus.). 1972. 6.95. Winchester Pr.

Hoyt, Murray. **Fish in My Life.** 1964. 3.95. Crown.

Hughes, Stephen O. **Tight Lines & Dragonflies.** (Illus.). 1972. 5.95. Lippincott.

Janes, E. C. **Fresh Water Fishing Complete.** (Illus.). 1961. 4.95. HR&W.

Janes, Edward C. **Fishing with Lee Wulff.** (Illus.). 1972. 8.95. Knopf.

Jenkins, J. Geraint. **Nets & Coracles.** (Illus.). 1974. 18.95. David & Charles.

Johnson, et al. **Outdoor Tips: A Remington Sportsmen's Library Bk.** pap. 2.95. Benjamin Co.

The Joy of Fishing. 1974. pap. 3.95. Rand.

Kelly, Florence F. **Flowing Stream.** 34.95. Gordon Pr.

Klust, Gerhard. **Netting Materials for Fishing Gear.** (Illus.). 1974. pap. 6.50. (FAO). Unipub.

Knap, Jerome & Richey, David. **Getting Hooked on Fishing: An Angler's Handbook.** (Illus.). 1974. 7.95. Scribner.

Kostyunin, Yu N. & Nokonorou. I. V. **Trawling & New Methods of Continuous Fishing.** (Illus.). 1973. 16.00. Intl Schol Bk Serv.

Kreh, Lefty & Kessler. Hermann. **Fly Casting with Lefty Kreh.** (Illus.). 1974. 8.95. Lippincott.

Lamb, Dana S. **Where the Pools Are Bright & Deep.** (Illus.). 1973. 8.95; limited ed. 15.00. Winchester Pr.

Lane, Billy & Graham, Colin. **Billy Lanes Encyclopaedia of Float Fishing.** (Illus.). 1971. 7.50. Transatlantic.

Laycock, George. **The Field & Stream Guide**

to Fishing. 1973. pap. 1.25. Popular Lib.
Livingston, A. D. **Fishing for Bass: Modern Tactics & Tackle.** 1974. 8.95. Lippincott.
Lyman, Henry. **Successful Bluefishing.** (Illus.). 1974. 10.00. Intl Marine.
Lyman, Henry & Woolner, Frank. **Complete Book of Weakfishing.** (Illus.). 1973. 5.95. A S Barnes.
Lyons, Nick. **Seasonable Angler.** 1970. 5.95. Funk & W.
Lyons, Nick, ed. **Fisherman's Bounty: Treasury of Fascinating Lore & the Finest Stories from the World of Angling.** 1970. 6.95. Crown.
McClane, A. J. **McClane's Standard Fishing Encyclopedia.** (Illus.). 19.95. Reel Trophy.
McClane, Albert J. **Field & Stream International Fishing Guide.** (Illus.). 1971. 8.95; pap. 4.95. HR&W.
McClane, Albert J. **American Angler.** (Illus.). 1954. 5.00. HR&W.
— — **McClane's New Standard Fishing Encyclopedia & International Angling Guide** rev. ed. (Illus.). 1974. 40.00. HR&W.
McCristal, Vic. **Freshwater Fighting Fish.** (Illus.). 12.50. Soccer.
McDonald, John. **Quill Gordon.** 1972. 10.95. Knopf.
McGrail, William & McGrail, Joie. **Catch & the Feast.** (Illus.). 1969. 20.00. Weybright.
McInturff, Roy A. **Wilderness Fishing for Salmon & Steelhead.** 1974. 8.95. A S Barnes.
McNally, Tom. **Tom McNally's Fishermen's Bible.** 3rd ed. (Illus.). 1975. pap. 9.95. O'Hara.
Major, Harlan. **Basic Fishing.** (Illus.). 1968. pap. 1.95. Funk & W.
Michaelson, John. **Tackle Angling.** rev. ed. Harris, Brian, ed. (Illus.). 1975. 5.25. Soccer.
Mitchell, John. **Better Fishing, Freshwater.** 1968. 5.00. Intl Pubns Serv.
Moe, Martin. **Florida Fishing Grounds.** Orig. Title: Off Shore Coastal Fishing: Florida. pap. 1.95. Great Outdoors.
Mohan, Peter. **Carp for Everyone.** (Illus.). 1972. 8.95. David & Charles.
Moore, Ed. **Fresh Water Fishing.** (Illus.). 1965. pap. 0.95. Macmillan.
Morris, Dan & Strung, Norman. **Fisherman's Almanac.** (Illus.). 1970. 5.95. Macmillan.
Moss, Frank, ed. **The Lore of Sport Fishing.** (Illus.). 1975. 25.00. Crown.
Moss, Frank T. **Successful Striped Bass Fishing.** (Illus.). 1974. 12.50. Assn. Pr.
— — **Successful Striped Bass Fishing.** (Illus.). 1974. 12.50. Intl Marine.
Nadaud, J. **Peche.** (Illus., Fr.). 20.50. Larousse.
Netherby, Steve, ed. **The Experts' Book of Freshwater Fishing.** 1974. 9.95. S&S.
Nibler, C. W. **Goodbye Mr. Trout.** 1973. 3.75. Vantage.
Norton, Mortimer, ed. **Angling Success, by Leading Outdoor Writers.** facs. ed. 1935. 12.75. Bks for Libs.
Ormond, Clyde. **Outdoorsman's Handbook.** 1975. pap. 1.95. Berkley Pub.
Otter Board Design & Performance. (Illus.). 1975. pap. 4.50. (FAO). Unipub.
Outdoor Life Editors. **Tacklebox Library.** 5 vols. (Illus.). 1971. Set. 6.95. Har-Row.
Ovington, Ray. **Fresh Water Fishing.** 1973. 5.95. Hawthorn.
— — **Introduction to Bait Fishing.** 1975. pap. 3.95. Stackpole.
Parsons, P. A. **Complete Book of Fresh Water Fishing.** (Illus.). 1962. 8.95. Times Mirror Mag.
Parsons, P. Allen. **Complete Book of Fresh Water Fishing.** (Illus.). 1963. 8.95. Har-Row.
Peper, Eric & Rakhoff, Jim, eds. **Fishing Moments of Truth.** 1973. 8.95. Winchester Pr.
— — **Hunting & Fishing Moments of Truth.** 1973. limited ed. 25.00. Winchester Pr.
Pritchard, Michael. **Sea Angling.** National Federation of Sea Anglers, ed. (Illus.). 1976. pap. 2.50. British Bk Ctr.
Piper, John. **All About Angling.** 1971. 7.50.

Transatlantic.
Pobst, Richard. **Fish the Impossible Places.** (Illus.). 1974. 9.95. Freshet Pr.
Power, John & Brown, Jeremy. **Fisherman's Handbook.** 1972. 7.95. Scribner.
Perry, E. L. **Spoon Plugging.** 1974. pap. 9.95. O'Hara.
Puddepha, D. N. **Coarse Fishing Is Easy.** (Illus.). 1970. 8.95. David & Charles.
Radcliffe, W. **Fishing from the Earliest Time.** 1974. 15.00. Ares.
Radcliffe, William. **Fishing from the Earliest Times.** 1969. Repr. of 1921 ed. 16.95. B Franklin
Randolph, J. W. **World of Wood, Field & Stream.** 1962. 3.95. HR&W.
Raymond, Steve. **Year of the Angler.** 1973. 10.00. Winchester Pr.
Reiger, George, ed. **Zane Grey: Outdoorsman.** (Illus.). 1972. 9.95. P-H.
Reinfelder, Al. **Bait Tail Fishing.** (Illus.). 1969. 6.95. A S Barnes.
Ritz, Charles. **A Fly Fisher's Life.** 1973. 7.50. Crown.
Rosko, Milt. **Salt Water Fishing from Boats.** 1972. pap. 2.45. Macmillan.
Sams, Jonathan C. **Reflections of a Fishing Parson.** 1973. 2.95. Abingdon.
Samson, Jack. **Line Down: The Special World of Big Game Fishing.** 1973. 12.50. Winchester Pr.
Sawyer, Frank. **Nymphs & the Trout.** 1973. 5.95. Crown.
Schaldach, William J. **Coverts & Casts & Currents & Eddies.** 2 vols. (Illus.). boxed 25.00. Freshet Pr.
Schwiebert, Ernest. **Remembrances of Rivers Past.** (Illus.). 1972. 6.95. Macmillan.
Scott, Jack. **Greased Line Fishing.** (Illus.). 1970. boxed 10.75. Freshet Pr.
Seaman, Kenneth. **Big Fish from Small Waters.** (Illus.). 1973. 8.95. David & Charles.
Sharp, Hal. **Sportsman's Digest of Fishing.** 1963. pap. 1.75. B&N.
Sosin, Mark, ed. **Angler's Bible.** (Illus.) 1977. softbound. 7.95. Stoeger.
Sosin, Mark & Clark, John. **Through the Fish's Eye.** (Illus.). 1973. 8.95. Har-Row.
Sosin, Mark & Dance, Bill. **Practical Black Bass Fishing.** (Illus.). 1975. softbound. 5.95. Crown/Stoeger.
Sparano, Vin T. **The Complete Outdoors Encyclopedia.** (Illus.). 1973. 15.00. Har-Row.
Spiller, Burton L. **Fishin' Around.** 1974. 10.00. Winchester Pr.
Tacklebox Library. 5 bks. Incl. **Angler's Safety & First Aid.** Sosin, Mark J; **Freshwater Tackle.** Hall, Baird; **Fish Cookery.** Marshall, Mel; **Selecting Lures, Flies & Baits.** Rice, F. Philip, **Reading the Water.** Bates, Joseph D. (Illus.). pap. 6.95. slip case set. Har-Row.
Tapply, Horace G. **Sportsman's Notebook.** 1964. 7.95. HR&W.
Taylor, Fred J. **Fishing Here & There.** 1970. 8.75. Intl Pubns Serv.
Three Books on Fishings: Associated with the Complete Angler by Izaac Walton. 1962. Repr. of 1659 ed. 15.00. Schol Facsimiles.
Trench, Charles C. **The History of Angling.** (Illus.). 1974. 12.95. Follett.
Ulrich, Heinz. **How the Experts Catch Trophy Fish.** 1969. 6.95. A S Barnes.
Van De Water, Frederick F. **In Defense of Worms.** 1970. boxed 5.75. Freshet Pr.
Van Dyke, Henry. **Fisherman's Luck.** 1973. Repr. of 1900. ed. 5.50. R. West.
Von Brandt, Andres. **Fish Catching Methods of the World** rev. ed. (Illus.). 1972. 25.00. Heinman.
Walker, Richard. **Still Water Angling.** (Illus.). 1975. 12.00. David & Charles.
Wall, Roy. **Game & Fish: From Field to Table.** 1972. 5.95. Naylor.
Walton, Izaac & Cotton, Charles. **The Compleat Angler; or, the Contemplative Man's Recreation.** (Illus.). 1973. Repr. of 1962 ed. 7.50. Rowman.

Walton, Izaak. **Compleat Angler.** 3.95; pap. 2.95. Dutton.
Warner, Robert. **Don't Blame the Fish.** 1974. 8.95. Winchester Pr.
Waterman, Charles F. **The Fisherman's World.** 1972. 15.00. Random.
— — **Modern Fresh & Salt Water Fly Fishing.** (Illus.). 1974. pap. 3.95. Macmillan.
— — **The Part I Remember.** (Illus.). 1974. 8.95. Winchester.
Weeks, Edward. **Fresh Waters.** (Illus.). 1968. 7.95. Little.
Welle-Strand, E. **Angling in Norway.** (Illus.). 1971. pap. 4.00. Vanous.
Westman, James. **Secret of Why Fish Bite.** pap. 2.00. Wilshire.
Whitaker, Ralph R. **Song of the Outriggers: Big Game Fishing on the Ocean Surface.** Amos, William E., ed. (Illus.) 1972. 8.95. Green.
Willock, Colin, ed. **A B C of Fishing.** (Illus.). 1971. deluxe ed. 15.00. Transatlantic.
Wood, E. J. **Inshore Dinghy Fishing.** pap. 1.95. Transatlantic.
Wood, James. **Sport Fishing for Beginners.** 5.95. British Bk Ctr.
Wrangles, Alan, ed. **The Complete Guide to Coarse Fishing.** (Illus.). 1973. 12.50. David & Charles.
— — **The Complete Guide to Sea Angling.** (Illus.). 12.50. David & Charles.
Wright, D. Macer. **A Fish Will Rise.** (Illus.). 1972. 6.95. David Charles.
Wright, Leonard, Jr. **Thinking Man's Guide to Trout Angling.** 1972. 6.95. Dutton.
Zern, Ed. **A Fine Kettle of Fish Stories.** (Illus.). 1972. 5.95. Winchester Pr.
Zwirz, Bob. **A B C's of Fishing.** 1974. pap. 5.95. Digest Bks.

Fishing—Atlantic Ocean

Whitaker, Ralph R. **Song of the Outriggers: Big Game Fishing on the Ocean Surface.** Amos, William E., ed. (Illus.). 1972. 8.95. Green.

Fishing—Australia

Colwell, Max. **Whaling Around Australia.** (Illus.). 1969. 8.00. Verry.

Fishing—British Columbia

Haig-Brown, Roderick. **River Never Sleeps.** 1974. 7.50. Crown.

Fishing—British Honduras

Craig, Alan K. **Geography of Fishing in British Honduras & Adjacent Coastal Waters.** (Illus.). 1966. pap. 4.00. La State U Pr.

Fishing—Great Britain

Fysh, Hudson. **Round the Bend in the Stream.** (Illus.). 1968. 11.00. Verry.
Marston, A. N. **Encyclopedia of Angling.** 2nd ed. 1963. 15.00. Transatlantic.
Parsons, John. **Fisherman's Year.** (Illus.). 1975. 10.00. Intl Pubns Serv.
Willock, Colin, ed. **A B C of Fishing.** (Illus.). 1971. deluxe ed. 15.00. Transatlantic.

Fishing—Hawaii

Hosaka, Edward. **Shore Fishing in Hawaii.** pap. 4.95. Petroglyph.
Mackeller, Jean S. **Hawaii Goes Fishing.** (Illus.). 1968. Repr. of 1956 ed. 3.50. C E Tuttle.

Fishing—Japan

Fysh, Hudson. **Round the Bend in the Stream.** (Illus.). 1968. 11.00. Verry.

Fishing—New Zealand

Doogue, Raymond & Moreland, John. **New Zealand Sea Angler's Guide.** (Illus.). 1974. 8.50. Reed.

Ferris, George. **Fly Fishing in New Zealand.** 1972. 8.50. Intl Pubns Serv.

Fysh, Hudson. **Round the Bend in the Stream.** (Illus.). 1968. 11.00. Verry.

Parsons, John. **Fisherman's Year.** (Illus.). 1975. 10.00. Intl Pubns Serv.

Fishing—North America

Alaska Fishing Guide: 1974. (Illus.). 1974. pap. 3.95. Alaska Northwest.

Bradner, Enos. **Northwest Angling.** 2nd ed. (Illus.). 1969. 6.50. Binford.

Cramond, Michael. **Hunting & Fishing in North America.** (Illus.). 1953. 9.95. U of Okla Pr.

Evanoff, Vlad, ed. **Fresh-Water Fisherman's Bible.** (Illus.). 1964. pap. 2.50. Doubleday.

Herbert, Henry W. **Frank Forester's Fish & Fishing in the United States & British Provinces of North America.** (Illus.). 1970. Repr. of 1850 ed. 16.00. Arno.

Knap, Jerome. **Where to Fish & Hunt in North America: A Complete Sportsman's Guide.** (Illus.). 8.95. Pagurian.

McClane, Albert J. **American Angler.** (Illus.). 1954. 5.00. HR&W.

Matthiessen, Peter. **Wildlife in America.** (Illus.). 1964. pap. 2.95. Viking Pr.

Migdalski, Edward C. **Angler's Guide to the Fresh Water Sport Fishes of North America.** (Illus.). 1962. 9.50. Ronald.

Power, John & Brown, Jeremy. **Fisherman's Handbook.** 1972. 7.95. Scribner.

Rostlund, Erhard. **Freshwater Fish & Fishing in Native North America.** Repr. of 1952 ed. pap. 21.00. Johnson Repr.

Waterman, Charles F. **Fishing in America.** (Illus.). 1975. 19.95. HR&W.

Westman, James. **Why Fish Bite & Why They Don't.** 1961. 4.95. P-H.

Fishing—Pacific Ocean

Cannon, Raymond. **How to Fish the Pacific Coast.** 3rd ed. (Illus.). 1967. pap. 2.95. Lane.

Holm, Don. **Fishing the Pacific.** (Illus.). 1972. 6.95. Winchester Pr.

— — **Pacific North.** Orig. Title: Sport Fishing in the North Pacific. 1969. 12.50. Caxton.

Tracy, J. P. **Low Man on a Gill-Netter.** (Illus.). 1974. pap. 3.95. Alaska Northwest.

Fishing—United States

Alaska Fishing Guide 1975-76. rev. ed. (Illus.). 1975. pap. 3.95. Alaska Northwest.

Ames, Francis H. **Fishing the Oregon Country.** (Illus.). 1966. 7.95. Caxton.

Anderson, Tommy. **The Complete Guide to Florida Fishing.** (Illus.). 1973. 8.95. A S Barnes.

Babcock, Havilah. **My Health Is Better in November.** (Illus.). 1960. 5.95. HR&W.

Bascom, Dave. **How to Fish Good.** (Illus.). 1971. pap. 2.95. Winchester Pr.

Becker, A. C., Jr. **Gulf Coast Fishing.** 1970. 8.50. A S Barnes.

Dietz, Lew. **Touch of Wildness: A Maine Woods Journal.** 1970. 5.95. HR&W.

Donaldson, Ivan & Cramer, Frederick. **Fishwheels of the Columbia.** (Illus.). 1971. 10.00. Binford.

Duffy, M. **Hunting & Fishing in Louisiana.** 1969. 3.95. Pelican.

Dunaway, Vic. **Vic Dunaway's Fishing Guide to Florida - Fresh & Salt Water.** (Illus.). 9.95. pap. 6.95. O'Hara.

Elliot, Bob. **Bass Fishing in New England.** (Illus.). 1973. 6.50; pap. 3.50. Stone Wall Pr.

Fagerstrom, Stan. **Catch More Bass.** (Illus.). 1973. pap. 7.95. Caxton.

Fellegy, Joe, Jr. **Walleyes & Walleye Fishing.** (Illus.). 1973. 6.95. Dillon.

Freeman, Jim. **How to Catch California Trout.** (Illus.). 1972. pap. 1.95. Chronicle Bks.

— — **Lake Berryessa Fishing.** (Illus.). 1971. pap. 1.95. Chronicle Bks.

— — **North Sierra Trout Fishing.** (Illus.). 1972. pap. 1.95. Chronicle Bks.

Fysh, Hudson. **Round the Bend in the Stream.** (Illus.). 1968. 11.00. Verry.

Gallo, Philip S., Jr. **Guidebook to Saltwater Fishing in Southern California.** 1973. pap. 2.95. Ritchie.

Gilbert, De Witt, ed. **The Future of the Fishing Industry of the United States.** (Illus.). 1968. pap. 10.00. U of Wash Pr.

Gresham, Grits. **Fishes & Fishing in Louisiana.** 1965. 5.00; pap. 4.00. Claitors.

— — **Fishing & Boating in Louisiana.** pap. 2.00. Claitors.

— — **Fishing & Boating in Louisiana.** 1965. 4.00. Claitors.

Grey, Hugh, ed. **Field & Stream Treasury.** 1971. 12.95. HR&W.

Hayden, Mike. **Fishing the California Wilderness** (Illus.). 1974. pap. 2.95. Chronicle Bks.

Holm, Donald R. **One-Hundred One Best Fishing Spots in Oregon.** (Illus.). 1970. pap. 3.95. Caxton.

Klink, Jerry. **The Mighty Cortez Fish Trap.** (Illus.). 1973. 8.95. A S Barnes.

Konizeski, Dick. **The Montanans' Fishing Guide: Waters West of the Continental Divide.** Vol. 1. 2nd ed. (Illus.). 1975. pap. 4.95. Mountain Pr.

— — **The Montanans' Fishing Guide: Waters East of the Continental Divide.** Vol. 2. 1971. pap. 4.95. Mountain Pr.

Lewis, Gordon. **Florida Fishing: Fresh & Salt Water.** (Illus.). 1957. pap. 1.75. Great Outdoors.

McTeer, Ed. **Adventures in the Woods & Waters of the Low Country.** 4.95. Beaufort.

Morrison, Morie. **Fishing Western Waters.** rev. ed. Orig. Title: Fresh Water Fishing Illustrated. (Illus.). 1975. pap. 2.95. Chronicle Bks.

Murray, William H. **Adventures in the Wilderness.** Verner, William K., ed. (Illus.). 1970. Repr. 10.50. Syracuse U Pr.

Neasham, V. Aubrey. **Wild Legacy: California Hunting & Fishing Tales.** (Illus.). 1973. 6.50. Howell-North.

Rice, William. **Fishing the San Diego Bass Lakes.** (Illus.). 1972. pap. 1.95. Chronicle Bks.

Scharp, Hal. **Florida's Game Fish & How to Land Them.** (Illus.). 1968. 8.50. A S Barnes.

Schwind, Phil. **Striped Bass & Other Cape Cod Fish.** (Illus.). 1972. pap. 3.95. Chatham Pr.

Ulrich, Heinz. **America's Best Lake, Stream, & River Fishing.** 5.95. A S Barnes.

Wall, Roy. **An Angler Reflects: How to Catch the Wily Ones.** 1974. 7.95. Naylor.

Wharton, James. **Bounty of the Chesapeake: Fishing in Colonial Virginia.** 1957. pap. 1.25. U Pr of Va.

White, Donald J. **New England Fishing Industry: A Study in Price & Wage Setting.** (Illus.). 1954. 7.50. Harvard U Pr.

Wienecke, Lou & Peterson, John. **Guide to Far West Fishing.** (Illus.). 1973. pap. 3.50. P-H.

Wilcoxson, Kent H. **Angler's Guide to Fresh Water Fishing in New England.** (Illus.). 1973. pap. 4.50. Book Prod Serv.

Fishing Boats

Andrews, Ralph W. & Larssen, A.K. **Fish & Ships.** 7.95. Superior Pub.

Blair, Carvel H. & Ansel, William D. **Guide to Fishing Boats & Their Gear.** 1968. 6.00. Cornell Maritime.

Chapelle, Howard I. **The American Fishing Schooners: 1825-1935.** (Illus) 1973. 20.00. Norton.

Fishing Boats of the World-2. (Illus.). 1960. 22.00. (FAO). Unipub.

Fishing Boats of the World-3. (Illus.). 1967. 24.00. (FAO). Unipub.

Gillmer, Thomas C. **Working Watercraft.** (Illus.). 1972. 15.95. Intl Marine.

Silverton, Walter F. **Sport's-Fisherman Paradise: Adventures of a Sport's-Fisherman on Vancouver Island.** (Illus.). 9.95. Pageant-Poseidon.

Fishing Lures

Becker, A. C., Jr. **Lure Fishing.** (Illus.). 1970. 3.95. A S Barnes.

Evanoff, Vlad. **Make Your Own Fishing Lures.** (Illus.). 1975. 8.95. AS Barnes.

Reinfelder, Al. **Bait Tail Fishing.** (Illus.). 1969. 6.95. A S Barnes.

Fishing Stories

Brister, Bob. **Moss, Mallards & Mules: And Other Hunting & Fishing Stories.** 1973. 8.95. Winchester Pr.

Ford, Corey. **You Can Always Tell a Fisherman.** (Illus.). 1959. 2.95. HR&W.

Fox, Charles K., ed. **Armchair Adventure for the Angler.** 1970. 6.95. A S Barnes.

Gingrich, Arnold. **The Fishing in Print.** 1974. 12.95. Winchester Pr.

Gray, William B. **Fish Tales & Ocean Odd Balls.** (Illus.). 1970. 5.95; pap. 2.45. A S Barnes.

Humphrey, William. **Spawning Run.** (Illus.). 1970. 4.50. Knopf.

Lamb, Dana S. **Where the Pools Are Bright & Deep.** (Illus.). 1973. 8.95. Winchester Pr.

Lariar, Lawrence. **Fish & Be Damned.** 1953. 3.95. P-H.

Lyons, Nick, ed. **Fisherman's Bounty: Treasury of Fascinating Lore & the Finest Stories from the World of Angling.** 1970. 6.95. Crown.

Lyons, Nick. **Fishing Widows.** 1974. 5.95. Crown.

Selected Alaska Hunting & Fishing Tales. Vol. 3. (Illus.). 1974. pap. 3.95. Alaska Northwest.

Traver, Robert. **Trout Magic.** (Illus.). 1974. 7.50. Crown.

Woolner, Frank. **My New England.** (Illus.). 1972. 6.50. Stone Wall Pr.

Fishing Tackle

Adams, H. B. **Methods of Historical Study.** 1973. Repr. of 1884 ed. pap. 10.50. Johnson Repr.

Burrell, Leonard F. **Beginner's Guide to Home Course Tacklemaking.** (Illus.). 1973. 8.75. Transatlantic.

Clemens, Dale P. **Fiberglass Rod Making.** 1974. 10.00. Winchester Pr.

De Rohan-Csermak, Geza. **Sturgeon Hooks of Eurasia.** (Illus.). 1963. 8.50. Aldine.

Evanoff, Vlad. **Modern Fishing Tackle.** (Illus.). 1961. 6.95. A S Barnes

FAO Catalogue of Fishing Gear Designs. (Illus.). 1973. 13.00. (FAO). Unipub.

Graumont, Raoul & Wenstrom, Elmer. **Fisherman's Knots & Nets.** (Illus.). 1948. 5.00. Cornell Maritime.

Hoover, Robert L. **Chumash Fishing Equipment.** (Illus.). 1973. pap. 1.50. Ballena Pr.

Lewers, Dick. **Understanding Fishing Tackle.** (Illus.). 1972. 16.50. Reed.

McCristal, Vic. **Great Fishing with Lures.** (Illus.). 1972. 13.50. Soccer.

McNally, Tom. **Tom McNally's Complete Book of Fishermen's Knots.** (Illus.). 1974. 6.95; pap. 3.95. O'Hara.

Melner, Sam & Kessler, Herman. **Great Fishing Tackle Catalogs of the Golden Age.** (Illus.). 1972. 6.95. Crown.

Modern Fishing Gear of the World: 2. 1964. 22.00 (FAO). Unipub.

Pfeiffer, C. Boyd. **Tackle Craft.** (Illus.). 1975. softbound. 5.95. Crown/Stoeger.

Publications International Ltd. **The Complete**

Buying Guide to Fishing Equipment. 1973. pap. 1.95. PB.

Sosin, Mark & Kreh, Lefty. **Practical Fishing Knots.** (Illus.). 1975. softbound. 4.95. Crown/Stoeger.

Von Brandt, A. **Fish Catching Methods of the World.** rev. ed. (Illus.). 1972. 25.00. Heinman.

Wilson, James. **The Rod & the Gun.** (Illus.). 1973. Repr. of 1844 ed. 16.95. British Bk Ctr.

Fly Fishing

Annesley, Patrick, ed. **Hardy's Book of Fishing.** (Illus.). 1971. 13.95. Dutton.

Atherton, John. **The Fly & the Fish.** (Illus.). 1971. boxed 12.95. Freshet Pr.

Ball, John W. **Casting & Fishing the Artificial Fly.** (Illus.). 1972. pap. 3.95. Caxton.

Bates, Joseph D., Jr. **Streamer Fly Tying & Fishing.** (Illus.). 1966. 7.95. Stackpole.

Bay, Kenneth E. & Vinciguerra, Matthew M. **How to Tie Freshwater Flies.** 1974. 10.00. Winchester Pr.

Brooks, Joe. **Complete Book of Fly Fishing.** rev. ed. 1968. 5.95. A S Barnes.

Bucknall, Geoffrey. **Fly-Fishing Tactics on Rivers.** (Illus.). 1968. 5.25. Intl Pubns Serv.

Cairns, Bill. **Fly Casting with Bill Cairns.** (Illus.). 1974. 7.95. Scribner.

Collyer, David J. **Fly-Dressing.** (Illus.). 1975. 14.95. David & Charles.

Cross, Reuben. **The Completest Fly Tier.** (Illus.). 1971. 7.95. Freshet Pr.

Cullen, Anthony & Hemphill, Patrick. **Crash Strike.** (Illus.). 1971. pap. 8.75. Intl Pubns Serv.

Dick, Lenox. **Art & Science of Fly Fishing.** 2nd ed. (Illus.). 1972. 7.95. Winchester Pr.

Esquire, D. J. **Secrets of Angling.** 1970. boxed. 6.75. Freshet Pr.

Flick, Art, ed. **Art Flick's Master Fly-Tying Guide.** (Illus.). 1975. softbound. 5.95. Crown/Stoeger.

Gerlach, Rex. **Fly Fishing the Lakes.** (Illus.). 1972. 6.95. Winchester Pr.

Gingrich, Arnold. **The Joys of Trout.** (Illus.). 1973. 7.50. Crown.

Goldberg, Howard. **The Angler's Book on Fly-Tying & Fishing.** (Illus.). 1973. 9.95. Scribner.

Henkin, Harmon. **Fly Tackle—a Guide to the Tools of the Trade.** (Illus.). 1976. 9.95. Lippincott.

Hidy, V. S. **The Pleasures of Fly Fishing.** (Illus.). 1972. 10.00. Winchester Pr.

Hidy, Vernon S. & Sports Illustrated Editors. **Sports Illustrated Fly Fishing.** rev. ed. (Illus.). 1972. 4.95; pap. 1.95. Lippincott.

Hills, John W. **History of Fly Fishing for Trout.** 1971. boxed 8.95. Freshet Pr.

Ivens, T. C. **Still Water Fly Fishing: A Modern Guide to Angling in Reservoirs & Lakes.** 3rd ed. (Illus.). 1971. 12.50. Transatlantic.

Knight, John A. & Knight, Richard A. **Complete Book of Fly Casting.** (Illus.). 1963. 6.95. Putnam.

Koch, Ed. **Fishing the Midge.** (Illus.). 1973. 7.95. Freshet Pr.

Kreh, Bernard L. **Fly Fishing in Salt Water.** 1974. 9.95. Crown.

Latham, Roger, et al. **There's No Fishing Like Fly Rod Fishing.** (Illus.). 1972. 7.59. Rosen Pr.

Leisenring, James & Hidy, Vernon S. **The Art of Tying the Wet Fly & Fishing the Flymph.** (Illus.). 1971. 4.50. Crown.

Leiser, Eric. **Fly-Tying Materials.** (Illus.). 1973. 7.50. Crown.

Leonard, Edson. **Feather in the Breeze.** (Illus.). 1974. 7.95. Freshet Pr.

Lynde, John G. **Thirty-Four Ways to Cast a Fly.** (Illus.). 1969. 5.95. A S Barnes.

McClane, A. J. **The Practical Fly Fisherman.** (Illus.). 1975. 10.00. P-H.

McDonald, John. **Quill Gordon.** 1972. 10.95. Knopf.

Marinaro, Vincent C. **Modern Dry-Fly Code.** (Illus.). 1970. 10.00. Crown.

Mendoza, George. **Fishing the Morning Lonely.** (Illus.). 1974. 7.95. Freshet Pr.

Nix, Sam. **Salt-Water Fly-Fishing Handbook.** (Illus.). 1973. 6.95. Doubleday.

Orvis, Charles F. & Cheney, A. Nelson, eds. **Fishing with the Fly: Sketches by Lovers of the Art with Illustrations of Standard Flies.** (Illus.). 1967. Repr. 8.25. C E Tuttle.

Ovington, Roy. **Basic Fly Fishing & Fly Tying.** 1973. 6.95; pap. 3.95. Stackpole.

Peper, Eric & Rikhoff, Jim, eds. **Fishing Moments of Truth.** 1973. 8.95. Winchester Pr.

Puddepha, D. N. **Fly Fishing Is Easy.** (Illus.). 1973. 4.95. David & Charles.

Quick, James. **Fishing the Nymph.** (Illus.). 1960. 6.50. Ronald.

Reid, John. **Clyde-Style Flies & Their Dressings.** (Illus.). 1971. 6.95. David & Charles.

Sand, George X. **Salt Water Fly Fishing.** (Illus.). 1969. 10.95. Knopf.

Slaymaker, S. R., 2nd. **Simplified Fly Fishing.** (Illus.). 1969. 7.95. Har-Row.

Swisher, Doug & Richards, Carl. **Fly Fishing Strategy.** (Illus.). 1975. 10.00. Crown.

Veniard, John. **Fly Dresser's Guide.** (Illus.). 1973. 17.50. St. Martin.

Walker, Alf. **Fly Fishing Techniques: Basic Fundamentals & Championship Form.** (Illus.). 1975. 8.95. Pagurian.

Wallace, Bill. **Fly Fishing Digest.** 1973. pap. 4.95. Digest Bks.

Waterman, Charles F. **Modern Fresh & Salt Water Fly Fishing.** (Illus.). 1972. 8.95. Winchester Pr.

Whitlock, Dave & Boyle, Robert, eds. **Fly-Tyer's Almanac.** 1975. 10.00. Crown.

Wright. **Fishing the Dry Fly.** 1972. 6.95. Dutton.

Fossil Fishes

Herre, Albert. **Notes on Fishes in the Zoological Museum of Stanford University.** 1974. 6.95. N K Gregg.

Traquair, R. H. **Fishes of the Old Red Sandstone.** Pt. 2. Nos. 2-4. 1914. Set. pap. 14.75. Johnson Repr.

— —**Ganoid Fishes of British Carboniferous Formations.** Pt. 1. Nos. 2-7 1914. Set. pap. 31.50. Johnson Repr.

Woodward, A. Smith. **Wealden & Pubeck Fishes.** Pts. 1-3. 1916-19. Set. pap. 35.00. Johnson Repr.

Fresh Water Fishes

Branson, Branley A. & Batch, Donald A. **Fishes of the Red River Drainage, Eastern Kentucky.** (Illus.). 1974. pap. 4.00. U Pr of Ky.

Carlander, Kenneth D. **Handbook of Fresh-water Fishery Biology.** Vol. 1. 3rd ed. (Illus.). 1969. 15.00. Iowa St U Pr.

Eddy, Samuel. **How to Know the Freshwater Fishes.** 2nd ed. (Illus.). 1969. 6.50; pap. 5.00. Wm C Brown.

Evanoff, Vlad, ed. **Fresh-Water Fisherman's Bible.** (Illus.). 1964. pap. 2.50. Doubleday.

Everett, Charles. **Fresh Water Fishes.** (Illus.). pap. 1.00. Binford.

Hervey, George F. & Hems, Jack. **Illustrated Encyclopedia of Freshwater Fish.** (Illus.). 1973. 7.95. Doubleday.

Lagler, Karl F. **Freshwater Fishery Biology.** 1956. 9.95. Wm C Brown.

Lowe-McConnell, R. H. **Illustrated Key to Freshwater Fishes of the Volta Lake.** 1972. 6.00. Panther Hse.

Migdalski, Edward C. **Angler's Guide to the Fresh Water Sport Fishes of North America.** (Illus.). 1962. 9.50. Ronald.

Moore, Ed. **Fresh Water Fishing.** (Illus.). 1965. pap. 0.95. Macmillan.

Pet Library Ltd. **Know Your Bettas.** 1973. pap. 11.50. Doubleday.

Scott, W. B. **Freshwater Fishes of Eastern Canada.** 2nd ed. (Illus.). 1967. pap. U of Toronto Pr.

Sterba, Gunther. **Sterba-Freshwater Fishes.** 2 vols. (Illus.). 1974. pap. 16.95. TFH Pubns.

Ulrich, Heinz. **America's Best Lake, Stream, & River Fishing.** 5.95. A S Barnes.

Vostradovsky, J. **Freshwater Fishes.** (Illus.). 1974. 3.75. Transatlantic.

Walden, Howard T. **Familiar Fresh Water Fishes of America.** (Illus.). 1964. 7.37. Har-Row.

Walker, Braz. **Sharks & Loaches.** (Illus.). 1974. pap. 6.95. TFH Pubns.

Wilcoxson, Kent H. **Angler's Guide to Fresh Water Fishing in New York.** (Illus.). 1973. pap. 3.25. Book Prod Serv.

Flies

Harris, John R. **An Angler's Entomology.** (Illus.). 1973. 8.95. A S Barnes.

Schwiebert, Ernest G., Jr. **Matching the Hatch.** (Illus.). 1962. 7.50. Macmillan.

Harpoons

Mason, Otis T. **Aboriginal American Harpoons.** (Illus.). 1902. pap. 7.50. Shorey.

Indians of North America—Fishing

American Friends Service Committee. **Uncommon Controversy: Fishing Rights of the Muckleshoot, Puyallup & Nisqually Indians.** (Illus.). 1970. 5.95; pap. 2.95. U of Wash Pr.

Speck, F. G. **Catawba Hunting Trapping & Fishing.** (Illus.). 1946. softbound. 1.50. Univ Mus of U Pa.

Lobsters

Carrick, Carol. **The Blue Lobster.** (Illus.). 1975. 4.95. Dial.

Cook, Joseph J. **Nocturnal World of the Lobster.** (Illus.). 1971. 4.50. Dodd.

Dueland, Joy. **The Book of the Lobster.** (Illus.). 1973. pap. 4.95. NH Pub Co.

Johnson, Martin W. **The Palinurid & Scyllarid Lobster Larvae of the Tropical Eastern Pacific & Their Distribution As Related to the Prevailing Hydrography.** 1971. pap. 2.00. U of Cal Pr.

Prudden, T. M. **About Lobsters.** (Illus.). 1973. pap. 4.95. Wheelwright.

Taylor, Herb. **The Lobster: Its Life Cycle.** (Illus.). 1975. 5.95. Sterling.

Lobster Fisheries

Doliber, Earl. **Lobstering Inshore & Offshore.** 1973. 5.95. Intl Marine.

Dueland, Joy V. **The Book of the Lobster.** (Illus.). 1973. pap. 4.95. NH Pub Co.

Marine Biology

Agassiz, Elizabeth & Agassiz, Alexander. **Seaside Studies in Natural History: Marine Animals of Massachusetts Bay.** (Illus.). 1970. Repr. of 1865 ed. 10.00. Arno.

Arbuckle, Wanda R., et al. **Learning to Move & Moving to Learn: Book 3—Aquatic Animals.** 1973. 7.95. Merrill.

Atlas of the Living Resources of the Seas. 3rd ed. (Illus.). 1973. 12.00. (FAO). Unipub.

Baiardi, John C. & Ruggieri, George D., eds. **Aquatic Sciences.** 1974. 10.00. NY Acad Sci.

Barnes, Harold. **Oceanography & Marine Biology.** Vol. 12. 1974. 36.95. Hafner.

Barnes, Harold, ed. **Oceanography & Marine Biology: An Annual Review.** 11 vols. Incl. Vol. 1. 12.00; Vol. 2. 1973 ed. 32.95; 1964 ed. 12.00; Vol. 3. Vol. .5. 20.00; Vol. 6. 22.00; Vol. 8. 22.00; Vol. 9. 25.00; Vol. 10. 29.95; Vol. 11. 32.95; 1963-74. Hafner.

Berrill, N. J. **Life of the Ocean.** 1966. 5.50; by subscription 3.95. McGraw.
Boehme, Eckart, ed. **From the Law of the Sea Towards an Ocean Space Regime: Practical & Legal Implications of the Marine Revolution.** 1972. pap. 15.00. Intl Pubns Serv.
Boolootian, R. A. & Thomas. **Marine Biology.** 1967. pap. 2.48. HR&W.
Bush, Eric W., ed. **Flowers of the Sea.** 1970. 8.50. Naval Inst. Pr.
Carson, Rachel. **Under the Sea Wind: A Naturalist's Picture of Ocean Life.** 1952. 8.95. Oxford U Pr.
Carson, Rachel L. **Under the Sea Wind.** pap. 1.25. NAL.
Cavanaugh, G., et al. **Formulae & Methods V.** 1964. 3.50. Marine Bio.
Clarke, Arthur C. **Challenge of the Sea.** (Illus.). 1960. 4.59. HR&W.
Coker, Robert E. **This Great & Wide Sea: An Introduction to Oceanography & Marine Biology.** (Illus.). pap. 2.95. Har-Row.
Cousteau, Jacques & Dumas, Frederic. **The Silent World.** 1973. pap. 2.00. Ballantine.
Cousteau, Jacques, intro. by. **The Adventure of Life.** Vol. 14. (Illus.). 1975. 7.95. Abrams.
— — **Challenge of the Sea.** Vol. 18. (Illus.). 1975. 7.95. Abrams.
— — **Guide to the Sea.** Vol. 20. (Illus.). 1975. 7.95. Abrams.
— — **The Whitecaps.** Vol. 16. (Illus.). 1975. 7.95. Abrams.
Cousteau, Jacques Y. **Oasis in Space.** (Illus.). 1972. 7.95. Abrams.
Cousteau, Jacques-Yves & Dugan, James. **Living Sea.** (Illus.). 1963. 12.50. Har-Row.
— — **The Living Sea.** (Illus.). 1975. pap. 1.95. Ballantine.
Cousteau, Jacques-Yves & Dumas, Frederic. **Silent World.** 1953. 10.95. Har-Row.
— — **Silent World.** (Illus.). 1965. pap. 0.95. Har-Row.
Cox, Graham F. **Tropical Marine Aquaria.** rev. ed. (Illus.). 1974. Repr. 5.95. G&D.
Crane, Jules M. **Introduction to Marine Biology.** 1973. pap. 7.95. Merrill.
Crowder, William. **Seashore Life Between the Tides.** (Illus.). 1975. pap. 5.00. Dover.
Deacon, Margaret. **Scientists & the Sea, 1650-1900: A History of Marine Science.** 1971. 17.25. Acad Pr.
Drozhilova, L. I., ed. **General Ecology-Biocenology-Hydrobiology.** Vol. 1. (Illus.). 1975. 21.00. GK Hall.
Dunbar, Maxwell J., ed. **Marine Distributions.** (Illus.). 1963. 6.00. U of Toronto Pr.
Emery, K. O. **Coastal Pond-Studied by Oceanographic Methods.** 1969. 7.50. Am Elsevier.
European Marine Biology Symposium, 4th Proceedings. Crisp. D. J., ed. (Illus.). 1971. 47.50. Cambridge U Pr.
— — **Proceedings.** Crisp, D. J., ed. 39.50. Cambridge U Pr.
Evans, Idrisyn O. **Observer's Book of the Sea & Seashore.** (Illus.). 1962. 2.50. Warne.
Falconer, William. **Falconer's Marine Dictionary.** Repr. of 1780 ed. 25.00. David & Charles.
Fell, Barry. **Introduction to Marine Biology.** 1975. 10.95. Har-Row.
Friedrich, Hermann. **Marine Biology: An Introduction to Its Problems & Results.** (Illus.). 1970. 9.50. U of Wash Pr.
Galbraith, Robert & Boehler, Ted. **Subtidal Biology of California.** (Illus.). 1974. 7.50; pap. 4.50. Naturegraph.
Hardy, Alister. **Open Sea: Its Natural History.** 1971. 20.00. HM.
Harvey, Hildebrande W. **Chemistry & Fertility of Sea Waters.** 2nd ed. 1957. 17.95. Cambridge U Pr.
Hass, Hans. **Challenging the Deep: Thirty Years of Undersea Adventure.** Osers, Ewald, tr. from Ger. (Illus.). 1972. 11.95. Morrow.
Humm, Harold & Lane, Charles E., eds. **Bioactive Compounds from the Sea.** 1974. 18.75. Dekker.

Idyll, C. P. **Abyss: The Deep Sea & the Creatures That Live in It.** rev. ed. (Illus.). 1971. 8.95. T Y Crowell.
Johnson, Alexander B. **Deep Sea Soundings & Explorations of the Bottom.** 1861. Repr. 7.00. Greenwood.
Kyle, Harry M. **Biology of Fishes.** 1971. 12.95. TFH Pubns.
Lucas, Joseph. **Life in the Oceans.** 1974. 7.95. Dutton.
McConnaughey, Bayard H. **Introduction to Marine Biology.** 2nd ed. (Illus.). 1974. 13.95. Mosby.
Macdonald, A. G. **Physiological Aspects of Deep Sea Biology.** (Illus.). 1975. 35.00. Cambridge U Pr
Malins, D. C. & Sargent, J. R. **Biochemical & Biophysical Perspectives in Marine Biology.** 1974. 23.25. Acad Pr.
Marine Biological Laboratory. Serial Publications. 5.00. Marine Bio.
Marine Biological Laboratory & Woods Hole Oceanographic Institution. **Catalog of the Library of the Marine Biological Laboratory & the Woods Hole Oceanographic Institution.** 12 vols. 1971. 980.00. set. G K Hall.
Marine Biology. Vol. 2. Phytoplanviton. International Interdisciplinary Conference, 2nd. Oppenheimer, H. C., ed. 1966. 18.50; **Vol. 3. Ecology of Intertebrates. International Interdisciplinary Conference, 3rd.** Edmondson, W. T., ed. 1966. 16.25; **Vol. 4. Unresolved Problems in Marine Microbiology. International Interdisciplinary Conference. 4th.** Oppenheimer, C. H., ed. 1968. 25.25; **Vol. 5. International Interdisciplinary Conference, 5th.** Costlow, John D., Jr., ed. 1969. 52.25; pap. 21.00. Gordon.
National ISA Marine Science Instrumentation Symposium, 5th Proceedings. Murdock, L.C., ed. 1973. 9.00. Instru Soc.
Platt, Rutherford. **Water: The Wonder of Life.** 1971. 8.95. P-H.
Polikarpov, G. G. **Radio-Ecology of Aquatic Organisms.** 1966. 18.50. Van Nos Reinhold.
R. V. Pillsbury. **Deep-Sea Biological Expedition to the Gulf of Guinea, 1964-1965, Pt. 2.** (Illus.). 1970. pap. 7.95. U of Miami Pr.
Ray, Carleton & Ciampi, Elgin. **Underwater Guide to Marine Life.** (Illus.). 6.98. A S Barnes.
Raymont, J. E. **Plankton & Productivity in the Oceans.** 1963. 21.00. Pergamon.
Reish, Donald J. **Biology of the Oceans.** 1969. pap. 8.65. Dickenson.
Remane, Adolf & Schlieper, Carl. **Biology of Brackish Water.** 1973. 21.75. Halsted Pr.
Rheinheimer. Gerhard. **Aquatic Microbiology.** 1974. price not set. Wiley.
Robbins, Sarah F. & Yentsch, Clarice M. **The Sea Is All About Us.** (Illus.). 1973. 5.95. U Pr of New Eng.
Russell, F. S., ed. **Advances in Marine Biology.** Incl. Vol. 1. 1963. 15.50; Vol. 2. 1964. 13.50; Vol. 3. 1965. 19.00; Vol. 4. 1966. 16.50; Vol. 5. 1967. 22.00; Vol. 6. Russell, F. S. & Yonge, Maurice, eds. 1968. 21.00; Vol. 7. 1969. 21.00; Vol. 8. 1970. 24.00; Vol. 9. 1971. 24.50; Vol. 10. 1972. 29.00. Acad Pr.
— — **Advances in Marine Biology, Vol. 11,** 1973. 19.75. Acad Pr.
Russell, Findlay E. **Poisonous Marine Animals.** (Illus.). 1972. 8.95. TFH Pubns.
Russell-Hunter, W.D. **Aquatic Productivity: An Introduction to Some Basic Aspects of Biological Oceanography & Limnology.** (Illus.). 1970. 5.95. Macmillan.
Shilling, Charles W. & Werts, Margaret F. **Underwater Medicine & Related Sciences: A Guide to the Literature.** 1973. 37.50. IFI Plenum.
Smith, Bertie W. **The World Under Sea: A Concise Account of the Marine World.** 1940. Repr. 13.00. Finch Pr.
Society for Experimental Biology - 26th Symposium. **Effects of Pressure on Organisms.** 24.50. Acad. Pr.

Steele, J. H., ed. **Marine Food Chains.** (Illus.). 1973. Repr. of 1970 ed. 54.00. Hafner Serv.
Storr, John F. **Ecology & Oceanography of the Coral-Reef Tract, Abaco Island, Bahamas.** (Illus.). 1964. pap. 4.00. Geol Soc.
Ward, Ritchie. **Into the Ocean World.** 1974. 10.00. Knopf.
Wilber, Charles G. **Biological Aspects of Water Pollution.** (Illus.). 1971. 23.75. C C Thomas.
Yentsch, A., et al. **Marine & Estuarine Environments Organisms & Geology of the Cape Cod Region 1665-1965.** 1966. 6.00. Marine Bio.
Zeitzschel, B., ed. **The Biology of the Indian Ocean.** (Illus.). 1973. 50.50. Springer-Verlag.
Zenkevitch, L. **Biology of the Seas of the U.S.S.R.** Botcharskaya, S., tr. (Illus.). 1963. 26.75. Hafner.
Zoological Society Of London - 19th Symposium. **Aspects of Marine Zoology.** Marshall, N. B., ed. 1967. 14.00. Acad Pr.

Marine Biology—Antarctic Regions

Biology of the Antarctic Seas II. 1965. 12.00. Am Geophysical.
Biology of the Antarctic Seas III. 1967. 13.50. Am Geophysical.
Llano, George A. & Wallen, I. Eugene, eds. **Biology of the Antarctic Seas Four.** (Illus.). 1971. 30.00. Am Geophysical.
Reid, Joseph L., ed. **Antarctic Oceanology One.** 1971. 22.00. Am Geophysical.

Marine Biology—Atlantic Ocean

Butler, James N., et al. **Pelagic Tar from Bermuda & the Sargasso Sea.** (Illus.). pap. 5.00. Harvard Eng.
Morris, Byron F. & Mogelberg, Deborah D. **Identification Manual to the Pelagic Sargassum Fauna.** 1973. pap. 2.00. Harvard Eng.
Morris, Byron F. & Schroeder, Elizabeth. **Hydrographic Observations in the Sargasso Sea of Bermuda: 1967-1973.** 1973. pap. 2.00. Harvard Eng.
Murray, John & Hjort, J. **Depths of the Ocean.** (Illus.). 1964. Repr. of 1912 ed. 52.50. Hafner Service.
Pocklington, Roger. **Variability in the Ocean off Bermuda.** 1972. 2.00. Harvard Eng.
R. V. Pillsbury. **Deep-Sea Biological Expedition to the Gulf of Guinea, 1964-1965.** (Illus.). 1966. pap. 5.00. U of Miami Pr.
Taylor, William R. & Bernatowicz, Albert J. **Distribution of Marine Algae About Bermuda.** (Illus.). 1969. pap. 3.00. Harvard Eng.

Marine Biology—Pacific Ocean

Biology Colloquium, 33rd, Apr. 1972. **The Biology of the Oceanic Pacific: Proceedings.** Miller, Charles, ed. (Illus.). 1974. 6.00. Oreg St U Pr.
Committee On Oceanography. **Scientific Exploration of the South Pacific.** 1970. 10.50. Natl Acad Sci.
De Sylva, Donald P. **The Alfred C. Glassell Jr. University of Miami Argosy Expedition to Ecuador, Pt. 1: Introduction & Narrative.** (Illus.). 1972. 6.95. U of Miami Pr.
Galtsoff, P. S. **Pearl & Hermes Reef, Hawaii, Hydrographical & Biographical Observations.** Repr. of 1933 ed. pap. 5.00. Kraus Repr.
Johnson, Myrtle E. & Snook, Harry J. **Seashore Animals of the Pacific Coast.** (Illus.). pap. 5.95. Dover.
Marine Planktonic Diatoms of the Northern Pacific Coast. (Illus.). Date not set. Price not set. Mad River.
Pillay, T. V., ed. **Coastal Aquaculture in the Indo-Pacific Region.** (Illus.). 1974. 25.00. Unipub.

Marine Ecology

Arnov, Boris, Jr. **Homes Beneath the Sea: An Introduction to Ocean Ecology.** (Illus.). 1969. 4.95. Little.

Costlow, John D., ed. **Fertility of the Sea.** 2 vols. (Illus.). 1971. Vol. 1. 32.00; Vol. 2. 32.00; set. 59.00. Gordon.

Cousteau, Jacques. **The Sea in Danger.** (Illus.). 1975. 7.95. Abrams.

Cushing, D. H. **Marine Ecology & Fisheries.** (Illus.). 1975. 27.50; pap. 9.95. Cambridge U Pr.

Dunbar, Maxwell J., ed. **Marine Distributions.** (Illus.). 1963. 6.00. U of Toronto Pr.

Fay, Rimmon C. **Southern California's Deteriorating Marine Environment: An Evaluation of the Health of the Benthic Marine Biota of Ventura, Los Angeles & Orange Counties.** (Illus.). 1972. pap. 4.50. Ctr Calif Public.

Galtsoff, Paul S., ed. **Bibliography of Oysters & Other Marine Organisms Associated with Oyster Bottoms & Estuarine Ecology.** 1972. 74.00. G K Hall.

Green, J. **Biology of Estuarine Animals.** 1968. 9.50. U of Wash Pr.

Hedgpeth, Joel W. & Ladd, Harry S., eds. **Treatise on Marine Ecology & Paleoecology.** 2 vols. 1963. 1957. Vol. 1. 32.50; Vol. 2. 32.00; set. 55.00. Geol Soc.

Kaill, Michael & Frey, John. **Environments in Profile: An Aquatic Approach.** (Illus.). 1973. pap. 5.95. Canfield Pr.

Kinne, O. **Marine Ecology.** Vol. 1. 1970. Pt. 1. 41.00; Pt. 2. 41.00; Pt. 3. 39.50. Wiley.
— — **Marine Ecology.** Vol. 2. 1975. Pt. 1. 44.00; Pt. 2. 49.50. Wiley.
— — **Marine Ecology.** Vol. 3. Date not set. Price not set.

McLusky, Donald S. **Ecology of Estuaries.** (Illus.). 1972. 6.00. Hillary.

Menzies, Robert J., et al. **Abyssal Environment & Ecology of the World Oceans.** 1973. 30.25. Wiley.

Moore, Hilary B. **Marine Ecology.** (Illus.). 1958. 18.25. Wiley.

Nelson-Smith, A. **Oil Pollution & Marine Ecology.** 1973. 14.50. Plenum Pub.

Nybakken, James W. **Readings in Marine Ecology.** 1971. pap. 11.95. Har-Row.

Olsen, T. & Burgess, F. **Pollution & Marine Ecology.** 1967. 18.50. Wiley.

Radakov, D. V. **Schooling in the Ecology of Fish.** Mills, H. tr. from Rus. (Illus.). 1973. 19.75. Halsted Pr.

Reid, George K. **Ecology of Inland Waters & Estuaries.** (Illus.). 1961. 11.65. Van Nos Reinhold.

Sokolov, V. E. & Chapskii, K. K. eds. **Morphology & Ecology of Marine Mammals: Seals, Dolphins, Porpoises.** 1973. 24.00. Halsted Pr.

Steele, John H. **The Structure of Marine Ecosystems.** 1974. 7.95. Harvard U Pr.

Stephens, William. **Life in the Open Sea.** (Illus.). 1972. 4.33. McGraw.

Stevenson, L. Harold & Colwell, R. R., eds. **Estuarine Microbial Ecology.** (Illus.). 1973. 27.50. U of SC Pr.

Storr, John F. **Ecology & Oceanography of the Coral-Reef Tract, Abaco Island, Bahamas.** (Illus.). 1964. pap. 5.50. Geol Soc.

Tait, E. V. **Elements of Marine Ecology.** (Illus.). 1973. 12.80. Springer-Verlag.

Thorson, Gunner. **Life in the Sea.** (Illus.). 1971. 4.95; pap. 2.95. McGraw.

Vernberg, W. B. & Vernberg, F. J. **Environmental Physiology of Marine Animals.** (Illus.). 1972. 22.80. Springer-Verlag.

Vernberga, Winon, ed. **Symbiosis in the Sea.** 1974. 27.50. U of SC Pr.

Yentsch, A., et al. **Marine & Estuarine Environments Organisms & Geology of the Cape Cod Region 1665-1965.** 1966. 6.00. Marine Bio.

Zottoli, Robert. **Introduction to Marine**

Environments. (Illus.). 1973. pap. 5.95. Mosby.

Marine Fauna

Arnold, Augusta F. **Sea-Beach at Ebb-Tide.** (Illus.). 1968. pap. 4.00. Dover.

Barnard, J. Laurens, et al. **Abyssal Crustacea.** 1962. 15.00. Columbia U Pr.

Baslow, M. H. **Marine Pharmacology.** 1969. 19.75. Williams & Wilkins.

Briggs, John C. **Marine Zoogeography.** (Illus.). 1974. 27.50. McGraw.

Christiansen, Marit E. **Crustacea Decapoda Brachyura.** (Illus.). 1969. 10.00. Universitet.

Clark, A. H. **Ophiuroidea of the Hawaiian Islands.** Repr. of 1949 ed. pap. 11.00. Kraus Repr.

Clark, Ailsa. **Echinodermata Crinoidea.** 1971. 10.00. Universitet.

Costello, D. P. **Methods for Obtaining & Handling Marine Eggs & Embryos.** 1971. 8.00. Marine Bio.

Edmondson, C. H., et al. **Marine Zoology of Tropical Central Pacific.** Repr. of 1925 ed. pap. 11.00. Kraus Repr.

Ely, C. A. **Shallow-Water Asteroidea & Ophiuroidea of Hawaii.** Repr. of 1942 ed. pap. 7.00. Kraus Repr.

Fowler, H. W. & Ball, S. C. **Fishes of Hawaii, Johnston Island, & Wake Island.** Repr. of 1925 ed. pap. 4.00. Kraus Repr.

Gosner, Kenneth L. **Guide to Identification of Marine & Estuarine Invertebrates: Cape Hatteras to the Bay of Fundy.** 1971. 34.75. Wiley.

Gotto, R. V. **Marine Animals.** 1969. 5.95. Am Elsevier.

Gray, William B. **Fish Tales & Ocean Odd Balls.** (Illus.). 1970. 5.95; pap. 2.45. A S Barnes.

Great Britain Challenger Office. **Report on the Scientific Results of the Voyage of H. M. S. Challenger During the Years 1873-1876.** 50 Vols. (Illus.). 1880-1895. Set. 3850.00. Johnson Repr.

Green, J. **Biology of Estuarine Animals.** (Illus.). 1968. 9.50. U of Wash Pr.

Gulland, John A. **The Management of Marine Fisheries.** (Illus.). 1974. 16.50. U of Wash Pr.

Holly, M. **Polychaeta from Hawaii.** Repr. of 1935 ed. pap. 4.00. Kraus Repr.

Howell, A. Brazier. **Aquatic Mammals: Their Adaptations to Life in the Water.** (Illus.). 6.50. Peter Smith.

Jorgensen, C. B. **Biology of Suspension Feeding.** (Illus.). 1965. 17.00. Pergamon.

Krogh, August. **Osmotic Regulation in Aquatic Animals.** (Illus.). pap. 3.00. Dover.
— — **Osmotic Regulation in Aquatic Animals.** 6.00. Peter Smith.

Liburdi, Joe & Truitt, Harry. **Guide to Our Underwater World.** 5.95. Superior Pub.

MacGintie, G. E. & MacGintie, N. **Natural History of Marine Animals.** 2nd ed. 1968. 15.95. McGraw.

Millar, R. H. **British Ascidians.** 1970. 3.50. Acad Pr.

Miner, Roy W. **Field Book of Seashore Life.** (Illus.). 1950. 9.75. Putnam.

Newell, R. C. **Biology of Intertidal Animals.** 1970. 25.75. Am Elsevier.

Pequegnat, Willis E. & Chance, Fenner A., Jr., eds. **Contributions on the Biology of the Gulf of Mexico.** (Illus.). 1970. 17.95. Gulf Pub.

Ravensdale, T. **Coral Fishes: Their Care & Maintenance.** (Illus.). 1973. 7.95. Great Outdoors.

Ricketts, Edward F. & Calvin, Jack. **Between Pacific Tides.** 4th ed. Hedgpeth, Joel W., ed. (Illus.). 1968. 10.95. Stanford U Pr.

Smith, Lynwood. **Common Seashore Life of the Pacific Northwest.** (Illus.). 1962. 5.25; pap. 2.25. Na²uregraph.

Smith, R. I., et al. **Keys to Marine Invertebrates of the Woods Hole Region.** (Illus.). 1964. 5.00. Marine Bio.

Stephen, A. C. & Edmonds, S. J. **The Phyla Sipuncula & Echiura.** (Illus.). 1975. 35.00. British Bk Ctr.

Straughan, Robert P. **The Marine Collector's Guide.** (Illus.). 1973. 17.50. A S Barnes.

Sweeney, James B. **Pictorial History of Sea Monsters & Other Dangerous Marine Life.** 1972. 12.95. Crown.

Vernberg, W. B. & Vernberg, F. J. **Environmental Physiology of Marine Animals.** (Illus.). 1972. 22.80. Springer-Verlag.

Winberg, G. G. **Methods for the Estimation of Production of Aquatic Animals.** 1971. 9.00. Acad Pr.

Winn, H. E. & Olla, B. L. **Behavior of Marine Animals, Vol. 1: Invertebrates.** 1972. 16.00. Plenum Pub.

Marine Fauna—Atlantic Ocean

Schroeder, Robert. **Something Rich & Strange.** 1965. 5.95. Har-Row.

Marine Fauna—Pacific Ocean

Braun, Earnest & Brown, Vinson. **Exploring Pacific Coast Tide Pools.** (Illus.). 1966. 6.95; pap. 3.95. Naturegraph.

Burgess, Warren E. & Axelrod, Herbert R. **Pacific Marine Fishes, Bk. 3.** (Illus.). 1973. 20.00. TFH Pubns.

Fitch, John E. & Lavenberg, Robert J. **Marine Food & Game Fishes of California.** (Illus.). 1971. pap. 2.35. U of Cal Pr.

Guberlet, Muriel L. **Animals of the Seashore.** 3rd ed. (Illus.). 1962. 7.50. Binfords.

Kozloff, Eugene N., et al. **Keys to the Marine Invertebrates of Puget Sound, the San Juan Archipelago, & Adjacent Regions.** (Illus.). 1974. 12.00. U of Wash Pr.

Ricketts, Edward F. & Calvin, Jack. **Beween Pacific Tides.** 4th ed. Hedgpeth, Joel W., ed. (Illus.). 1968. 10.95. Stanford U Pr.

Smith, Lynwood. **Seashore Life of the Pacific Northwest.** (Illus.). 1962. 5.25; pap. 2.25. Naturegraph.

Steinbeck, John. **Log from the Sea of Cortez.** 1962. pap. 2.25. Viking Pr.

Marine Fauna—Red Sea

Cousteau, Jacques-Yves. **World Without Sun.** Dugan, James, ed. (Illus.). 1965. 15.00. Har-Row.

Marine Flora

Arber, A. **Water Plants: Study of Aquatic Angiosperms.** (Illus.). 1963. Repr. of 1920 ed. 12.40. Hafner Service.

Arnold, Augusta F. **Sea-Beach at Ebb-Tide.** (Illus.). 1968. pap. 4.00. Dover.

Baslow, M. H. **Marine Pharmacology.** 1969. 19.75. Williams & Wilkins.

Boney, A. D. **Biology of Marine Algae.** (Illus.). 1966. pap. 4.75. Hillary.

Church, Arthur H. **Thalassiophyta & the Subaerial Transmigration.** 1968. Repr. of 1919 ed. 6.95. Hafner.

Coker, W. C. & Couch, J. N. **Stipitate Hyndums of the Eastern U.S.** 1970. Repr. of 1951 ed. 22.40. Stechert.

Dawson, E. Yale. **Seashore Plants of Northern California.** 1966. pap. 2.45. U of Cal Pr.
— — **Seashore Plants of Southern California.** 1966. pap. 1.75. U of Cal Pr.

Dawson, Elmer Y. **Marine Botany: An Introduction.** 1966. 13.95. HR&W.

Fitch, John E. & Lavenberg, Robert J. **Marine Food & Game Fishes of California.** (Illus.). 1971. pap. 2.35. U of Cal Pr.

Johnson, T. W. & Sparrow, F. K. **Fungi in Oceans & Estuaries.** (Illus.). 1970. pap. 27.50. Stechert.

Kuznetsov, S. I. **Microflora of Lakes & Its Geochemical Activity.** Oppenheimer, Carl, tr. from Rus. (Illus.). 1975. 19.95. U of Tex Pr.

Sculthorpe, C. Duncan. **Biology of Aquatic Vascular Plants.** (Illus.). 1967. 35.00. St. Martin.

Marine Microbology

Colewell, R. **Marine & Estuarine Microbiology Laboratory Manual.** 1974. 9.50. Univ Park.

Droop, M. & Wood, F., eds. **Advances in Microbiology of the Sea.** Vol. 1. 1968. 11.00. Acad Pr.

Oppenheimer, Carl H., ed. **Symposium on Marine Microbiology Proceedings.** (Illus.). 1963. 22.50. CC Thomas.

Rodina, A. G. **Methods in Aquatic Microbiology.** (Illus.). 1972. 14.50. Univ Park.

Sieburth, John M. **Microbial Seascapes: A Pictorial Essay on Marine Microorganisms & Their Environments.** (Illus.). 1975. 9.50. Univ Park.

Stevenson, L. Harold & Colwell, R. R., eds. **Estuarine Microbial Ecology.** (Illus.). 1973. 27.50. U of SC Pr.

Wood, E. Ferguson. **Microbiology of Oceans & Estuaries.** 1967. 31.25. Am Elsevier.

Marine Pollution

Barros, James & Johnston, Douglas M. **International Law of Pollution.** 1974. 14.95. Free Pr.

Gamble, John K. & Pontecorvo, Giulio. **Law of the Sea: Emerging Regime of the Oceans.** 1974. 15.00. Ballinger Pub.

Hood, Donald W., ed. **Impingement of Man on the Oceans.** 1971. 33.25. Wiley.

International Congress, 2nd, San Remo, December 17-21, 1973. **Marine Pollution & Marine Waste Disposal: Proceedings.** Pearson, Erman A., et al, eds. (Illus.). 1975. 60.00. Pergamon.

Marx, Wesley. **Protected Ocean: How to Keep the Seas Alive.** (Illus.). 1972. 4.99. Coward.

Michelson, David R., & Science Book Associates, eds. **The Oceans in Tomorrow's World: How Can We Use & Protect Them?** (Illus.). 1972. 5.29. Messner.

Moorcraft, Colin. **Must the Seas Die?** (Illus.). 1973. 6.95. Gambit.

Nash, A. E., et al. **Oil Pollution & the Public Interest: A Study of the Santa Barbara Oil Spill.** (Illus.). 1972. pap. 3.75. Inst Gov Stud Berk.

Shinn, Robert A. **The International Politics of Marine Pollution Control.** (Illus.). 1974. 16.50. Praeger.

Skinner, Brian J. & Turekian, Karl K. **Man & the Ocean.** (Illus.). 1973. 7.95; pap. 2.95. P-H.

Marlin

Howard, John K. & Ueyanagi, Shoji. **Distribution - Relative Abundance of the Billfishes (Istiophoridae) Pacific Ocean.** (Illus., Atlas). 1965. Set. pap. 5.50. U of Miami Pr.

Primitive Fishing

Rau, Charles. **Prehistoric Fishing in Europe & North America.** 1884. 61.00. AMS Pr.

Titcomb, Margaret. **Native Use in Hawaii.** 1972. 7.00. U Pr of Hawaii.

Salmon

Agricultural Board. **Nutrient Requirements of Trout, Salmon & Catfish.** (Illus.). 1973. pap. 3.25. Natl Acad Sci.

Burgner, Robert L., ed. **Further Studies of Alaska Sockeye Salmon.** 1968. pap. 3.60. U of Wash Pr.

Caras, Roger. **Sockeye: The Life of a Pacific Salmon.** 1975. 6.95. Dial.

Jordan, David S. **Trout & Salmon of the Pacific Coast.** facs. ed. pap. 1.25. Shorey.

Koo, Ted S., ed. **Studies of Alaska Red Salmon.** (Illus.). 1962. 8.50. U of Wash Pr.

McClung, Robert M. **Leaper, the Story of an Atlantic Salmon.** (Illus.). 1957. 4.59. Morrow.

Netboy, Anthony. **Atlantic Salmon: A Vanishing Species.** (Illus.). 1968. 6.95. HM.

— — **The Salmon: Their Fight for Survival.** (Illus.). 1974. 15.00. HM.

— — **Salmon of the Pacific Northwest.** (Illus.). 5.50. Binford.

Schwiebert, Ernest. **Salmon of the World.** (Illus.). 1970. 100.00. Winchester Pr.

Salmon Fisheries

Crutchfield, James A. & Pontecorvo, Giulio. **Pacific Salmon Fisheries: A Study of Irrational Conservation.** (Illus.). 1969. 8.50. Johns Hopkins.

Dodds, Gordon B. **Salmon King of Oregon: R. D. Hume & the Pacific Fisheries.** 1963. 6.95. U of NC Pr.

Donaldson, Ivan & Cramer, Frederick. **Fishwheels of the Columbia.** (Illus.). 1971. 10.00. Binford.

Koo, Ted S., ed. **Studies of Alaska Red Salmon.** (Illus.). 1962. 8.50. U of Wash Pr.

Netboy, Anthony. **Atlantic Salmon: A Vanishing Species.** (Illus.). 1968. 6.95. HM.

Salmon Fishing

Bates, Joseph C., Jr. **Atlantic Salmon Flies & Fishing.** (Illus.). 1970. 14.95. Stackpole.

Holm, Don. **Pacific North.** Orig. Title: Sport Fishing in the North Pacific. 1969. 12.50. Caxton.

Humphrey, William. **Spawning Run.** (Illus.). 1970. 4.50. Knopf.

Royce, William F., et al. **Salmon Gear Limitations in Northern Washington Waters. Management of the High Seas Fisheries of the Northeastrn Pacific.** 1963. pap. 3.50. U of Wash Pr.

Wulf, Lee. **Atlantic Salmon.** (Illus.). 12.00. A S Barnes.

Salt Water Fishing

Allyn, Charles F. **Salt Water Fishing Methods in Florida.** (Illus.). 1975. pap. 1.95. Great Outdoors.

Bauer, Erwin A. **Salt-Water Fisherman's Bible.** (Illus.). pap. 2.50. Doubleday.

Becker, A. C., Jr. **Gulf Coast Fishing.** (Illus.). 1970. 8.50. A S Barnes.

Benedict, J. Nelson, et al. **Successful Ocean Game Fishing.** Moss, Frank T., ed. (Illus.). 1971. 12.50. Intl Marine.

Brooks, Joe. **Saltwater Game Fishing.** (Illus.). 1968. 10.95. Har-Row.

Cadieux, Charles E. **Introduction to Ocean Fishing.** (Illus.). 1972. 6.95. Stackpole.

Cannon, Raymond. **How to Fish the Pacific Coast.** 3rd ed. (Illus.). 1967. pap. 2.95. Lane.

Dunaway, Vic. **Modern Saltwater Fishing.** (Illus.). 1975. softbound. 5.95. Stoeger.

Evanoff, Vlad. **How to Fish in Salt Water.** (Illus.). 1962. 6.95. A S Barnes.

— — **How to Fish in Salt Water.** (Illus.). 1973. pap. 1.95. B&N.

— — **Surf Fishing.** (Illus.). 1974. 6.95. Har-Row.

Fallon, Jack. **All About Surf Fishing.** (Illus.). 1977. softbound. 5.95. Stoeger.

Farrington, S. Kip. **Fishing with Hemingway & Glassel.** 5.95. Yankee Peddler.

Goadby, Peter. **Big Fish & Blue Water.** 1972. 14.95. HR&W.

Holm, Don. **Pacific North.** Orig. Title: Sport Fishing in the North Pacific. 1969. 12.50. Caxton.

Kreh, Bernard L. **Fly Fishing in Salt Water.** 1974. 9.95. Crown.

Lyman, Henry & Woolner, Frank. **Tackle Talk.** 1971. 8.95. A S Barnes.

March, Edgar J. **Sailing Trawlers: The Story of Deep-Sea Fishing with Longline & Trawl.** 1970. 25.00. Intl Marine.

Migdalski, Edward C. **Angler's Guide to the Salt Water Game Fishes: Atlantic & Pacific.** (Illus.). 1958. 10.95. Ronald.

Mitchell, John. **Better Fishing: Saltwater.** (Illus.). 1971. 5.00. Intl Pubns Serv.

Nix, Sam. **Salt-Water Fly-Fishing Handbook.** (Illus.). 1973. 6.95. Doubleday.

Reiger, George. **Profiles in Salt Water Angling.** (Illus.). 1973. 14.95. P-H.

Rosko, Milt. **Fishing from Boats.** (Illus.). 1968. 6.95. Macmillan.

Sand, George X. **Salt Water Fly Fishing.** (Illus.). 1969. 10.95. Knopf.

Scharff, Robert. **Standard Handbook of Salt-Water Fishing.** rev. ed. (Illus.). 1966. 9.95. T Y. Crowell.

Schwind, Phil. **Striped Bass & Other Cape Cod Fish.** (Illus.). 1972. pap. 3.95. Chatham Pr.

Turnill, Gordon. **Sea Fishing.** (Illus.). pap. 2.75. (SpS). Soccer.

Wilcoxson, Kent H. **Angler's Guide to Salt Water Fishing in the Northeast.** 1975. pap. 4.95. Book Prod Serv.

Wisner, Bill. **How to Catch Saltwater Fish.** (Illus.). 1973. 8.95. Doubleday.

Woolner, Frank. **Modern Saltwater Sport Fishing.** (Illus.). 1972. 8.95. Crown.

Wrangles, Alan. **Inshore Sport Fishing.** (Illus.). 1973. 8.95. Beekman Pubs.

Seafood Processing

Gilles, M. T. **Fish & Shellfish Processing.** (Illus.). 1975. 36.00. Noyes.

Seafood

Blair, Eulilia C. **Fish & Seafood for Food-service Menu Planning.** 1975. price not set. Cahners.

Castle, Molly. **Health & Beauty from the Sea.** 1971. 5.95. Mason Charter.

Gibbons, Euell. **Stalking the Blue-Eyed Scallop.** 1964. 7.95; pap. 3.95. McKay.

Sea Turtles

Bustard, Robert. **Sea Turtles: Their Natural History & Conservation.** (Illus.). 1973. 11.95. Taplinger.

Carr, Archie. **So Excellent a Fishe: A Natural History of Sea Turtles.** (Illus.). 1973. pap. 2.95. Doubleday.

Carr, Archie F. **So Excellent a Fishe: A Natural History of Sea Turtles.** (Illus.). 1967. 5.95. Natural Hist.

Jacobs, Francine. **Sea Turtles.** (Illus.). 1972. 4.32. Morrow.

Rebel, Thomas P. **Sea Turtles & the Turtle Industry of the West Indies, Florida, & the Gulf of Mexico.** 1974. 10.00. U of Miami Pr.

Sea Water

Feld, Bernard T. **The Future of the Sea-Based Deterrent.** 1974. 12.50; pap. 3.95. MIT Pr.

Goodman, Joe & Thompson, Thomas G. **Characteristics of the Waters in Sections from Dutch Harbor, Alaska, to the Strait of Juan De Fuca & from the Strait of Juan De Fuca to Hawaii.** 1940. pap. 1.50. U of Wash Pr.

Harvey, Hildebrande W. **Chemistry & Fertility of Sea Waters.** 2nd ed. 1957. 17.95. Cambridge U Pr.

Levine, Sumner N, ed. **Selected Papers on Desalination & Ocean Technology.** (Illus.). 1967. pap. 4.50. Dover.

Martin, Dean F. **Marine Chemistry.** Vol. 1. 2nd rev ed. 1972. 11.50. Dekker.

— — **Marine Chemistry, Vol 2: Theory & Applications.** 1970. 11.50. Dekker.

Tyler, J. E. & Smith, R. C. **Measurements of Spectral Irradiation Underwater.** 1970. 28.25. Gordon.

Sharks

Ashley, Laurence M. **Laboratory Anatomy of the Shark.** 2nd ed. (Illus.). 1969. pap. 2.95. Wm C Brown.

Baldridge, H. David. **Shark Attack.** 1975. pap. 1.25. Berkeley Pub.

Brown, Theo W. **Sharks: The Silent Savages.** 1975. 7.95. Little.

Budker, Paul. **Life of Sharks.** Whitehead, Peter, tr. (Illus.). 1971. 12.50; pap. 3.95. Columbia U Pr.

Burgess, Robert F. **Sharks.** (Illus.). 1971. 4.95. Doubleday.

Clark, Eugenie. **Lady & the Sharks.** (Illus.). 1969. 6.95. Har-Row.

Cook, Joseph & Wisner, William L. **Nightmare World of the Shark.** (Illus.). 1968. 4.50. Dodd.

Cousteau, Jacques-Yves & Cousteau, Philippe. **Shark: Splendid Savage of the Sea.** (Illus.). 1970. 9.95. Doubleday.

Eddy, Samuel, et al. **Guide to the Study of the Anatomy of the Shark, Necturus, & the Cat.** 3rd ed. 1960. 4.50. Wiley.

Gans, Carl & Parsons, Thomas S. **Photographic Atlas of Shark Anatomy: The Gross Morphology of Squalus Acanithias.** 1964. 4.50. Acad Pr.

Helm, Thomas **Shark.** 1963. pap. 1.50. Macmillan.

Lineaweaver, Thomas H., III & Backus, Richard H. **The Natural History of Sharks.** (Illus.). 1973. pap. 2.50. Doubleday.

Lineaweaver, Thomas H., 3rd & Backus, Richard H. **Natural History of Sharks.** (Illus.). 1970. 7.95. Lippincott.

Pope, Patricia. **Dictionary of Sharks.** (Illus.). 1973. pap. 1.95. Great Outdoors.

Riedman, Sarah R. & Gustafson, Elton T. **Focus on Sharks.** (Illus.). 1969. 5.95. Abelard.

Scharp, Hal. **Shark Safari.** 1975. 9.95. A S Barnes.

Tinker, Spencer W. & DuLuca, Charles J. **Sharks & Rays: A Handbook of the Sharks & Rays of Hawaii & the Central Pacific Ocean.** 1973. 7.25. C E Tuttle.

Shark Fishing

Cropp, Ben. **Shark Hunters.** 1971. 7.50. Macmillan.

Helm, Thomas. **Shark.** 1963. pap. 1.50. Macmillan.

Housby, Trevor. **The Rubby-Dubby Trail: Shark Fishing in British Waters.** (Illus.). 1974. 11.50. Intl Pubns Serv.

Joseph, S. **Shark Bites Back.** 1970. 2.20. McGraw.

Pope, Patricia. **Dictionary of Sharks.** (Illus.). 1973. pap. 1.95. Great Outdoors.

Scharp, Hal. **Shark Safari.** (Illus.). 1975. 9.95. A S Barnes.

Wisner, Bill & Mundus, Frank. **Sportfishing for Sharks.** (Illus.). 1971. 10.95. Macmillan.

Shellfish

Gibbons, Euell. **Stalking the Blue-Eyed Scallop.** (Illus.). 1964. 7.95; pap. 3.95. McKay

Mason, Phillip. **Shellfish Cookbook.** (Illus.). 1974. 8.95. Drake Pubs.

Sinderman, C. J. **Principal Diseases of Marine Fish & Shellfish** 1970. 26.00. Acad Pr.

Spin Fishing

Evanoff, Vlad. **Spin Fishing.** (Illus.). 6.95. A S Barnes.

Michalak, David. **Spinfishing for Beginners.** (Illus.). 1973. 8.95. A S Barnes.

Strung, Norman & Rosko, Milt. **Spin-Fishing: The System That Does It All.** (Illus.). 1973. 8.95. Macmillan.

Striped Bass

Karas, Nicholas. **The Complete Book of the Striped Bass.** (Illus.). 1975. softbound. 5.95. Stoeger.

Lyman, Henry & Woolner, Frank. **Complete Book of Striped Bass Fishing.** (Illus.). 1954. 5.95. A S Barnes.

Trawls and Trawling

Piper, Steven. **The North Ships: The Life of a Trawlerman** 1974. 12.50. David & Charles.

Trout

Agricultural Board. **Nutrient Requirements of Trout, Salmon & Catfish.** (Illus.). 1973. pap. 3.25. Natl Acad Sci.

Bergman, Ray & Janes, Edward C. **Trout.** 1975. 15.00. Knopf.

Brooks, Charles E. **The Trout & the Stream.** 1974. 7.95. Crown.

Frost, W. E. & Brown, M. E. **The Trout.** (Illus.). Date not set. 8.50. Collins-World.

Heacox, Cecil E. **The Compleat Brown Trout.** 1974. 12.50. Winchester Pr.

Jordan, David S. **Trout & Salmon of the Pacific Coast.** facs. ed. 1906. pap. 1.25. Shorey.

Needham, Paul R. **Trout Streams: Conditions That Determine Their Productivity & Suggestions for Stream & Lake Management.** Bond, Carl E., ed. (Illus.). 1969. 11.95. Holden-Day.

Ripper, Charles L. **Trout.** (Illus.). 1966. 4.95. Morrow.

Schwiebert, Ernest. **Trout.** 1975. 35.00. Weybright.

Sedgwick, S. Drummond. **Trout Farming Handbook.** (Illus.). 1974. 10.75. Scholium Intl.

Swisher, Doug & Richards, Carl. **Selective Trout.** (Illus.). 1975. softbound. 5.95. Crown/Stoeger.

Van Gytenbeek, G. P. **The Way of a Trout.** (Illus.). 1972. 8.95. Lippincott.

Trout Fishing

Bashline, L. James. **Night Fishing for Trout.** (Illus.). 1973. 7.95. Freshet Pr.

Bigelow, Ogden. **Mulberry Trout.** (Illus.). 1969. 5.50. C E Tuttle.

Blaisdell, Harold F. **Trout Fishing in New England.** (Illus.). 1973. 6.50; pap. 3.50. Stone Wall Pr.

Bradford, Charles. **The Brook Trout & the Determined Angler.** (Illus.). 1970. boxed 6.75. Freshet Pr.

Brooks, Charles E. **Larger Trout for the Western Fly Fisherman.** (Illus.). 1970. 9.50. A S Barnes.

Brooks, Joe. **Trout Fishing.** (Illus.). 1972. 10.00. Har-Row.

— — **Trout Fishing.** (Illus.). 1972. 10.00. Har-Row.

Dickey, Charley & Moses, Fred. **Trout Fishing.** (Illus.). 1975. pap. 2.95. Oxmoor Hse.

Fox, Charles K. **This Wonderful World of Trout.** 1971. 9.95; leather special ed. 35.00. Freshet Pr.

Freeman, James **Practical Steelhead Fishing.** (Illus.). 1966. 7.95. A S Barnes.

Gingrich, Arnold. **The Joys of Trout.** (Illus.). 1973. 7.50. Crown.

Gordon, Theodore, et al. **American Trout Fishing.** Gingrich, Arnold, ed. (Illus.). 1966. 6.95. Knopf.

Grove, Alvin R., Jr. **The Lure & Lore of Trout Fishing.** (Illus.). 1971. boxed 9.95. Freshet Pr.

Haldane, A. R. **By River, Stream & Loch: Thirty Years with a Trout Rod.** 8.95. David & Charles.

Hills, John W. **History of Fly Fishing for Trout.** 1971. boxed 8.95. Freshet Pr.

Holland, Dan. **Trout Fisherman's Bible.** (Illus.). pap. 2.50. Doubleday.

Janes, Edward C. **Salmon Fishing in the Northeast.** (Illus.). 1973. 6.50; pap. 3.50. Stone Wall Pr.

Jennings, Preston. **Book of Trout Flies.** Lyons, Nick, ed. (Illus.). 1970. 7.50. Crown.

MacDougall, Arthur R. **Trout Fisherman's Bedside Book.** 1963. 5.00. S&S.

McInturff, Roy A. **Wilderness Fishing for Salmon & Steelhead.** (Illus.). 1974. 8.95. A S Barnes.

Mansfield, Kenneth, ed. **Trout & How to Catch Them.** (Illus.). 1972. 6.50. St. Martin.

Marinaro, Vincent C. **Modern Dry-Fly Code.** (Illus.). 1970. 10.00. Crown.

Nibler, C. W. **Goodbye Mr. Trout.** 1973. 3.75. Vantage.

Orman, Tony. **Trout with Nymph.** (Illus.). 1974. 9.50. Intl Pubns Serv.

Ovington, Ray. **How to Take Trout on Wet Flies & Nymphs.** 1974. 9.95. Freshet Pr.

— — **Tactics on Trout.** (Illus.). 1969. 10.95. Knopf.

Quick, James. **Fishing the Nymph.** (Illus.). 1960. 6.50. Ronald.

Raymond, Steve. **Kamloops: An Angler's Study of the Kamloops Trout.** (Illus.). 1971. 12.50. Winchester Pr.

Schwiebert, Ernest G., Jr. **Matching the Hatch.** (Illus.). 1962. 7.50. Macmillan.

Shingleton, John D. **Trout, the Whole Trout, & Nothing but the Trout: Solemnly Sworn Testimony on America's No. 1 Gamefish & How to Hook Him.** (Illus.). 1974. 5.95. Winchester Pr.

Talleur, Richard W. **Fly Fishing for Trout: A Guide for Adult Beginners.** (Illus.). 1977. softbound. 5.95. Stoeger.

Traver, Robert. **Trout Madness.** 1960. 8.95. St. Martin.

— — **Trout Magic.** 1974. 7.50. Crown.

Ure, James. **Bait for Trout: Being the Confessions of an Unorthodox Angler.** (Illus.). 1973. 5.95. Regnery.

Magazines and Periodicals of Interest to the Angler

All Outdoors Magazine (M)
Established 1947
Circulation: 60,000
Ralph Dice, Editor
All Outdoors, Inc.
P.O. Box 700
Denison, Texas 75020
(214) 463-2440

American Field (W)
Established 1874
Circulation: 15,000
W. F. Brown, Editor
American Field Publishing Co.
222 West Adams Street
Chicago, Illinois 60606
(312) 372-1383

Angler's News (W)
Established 1963
Circulation: 15,000
Charley Zaimes, Managing Editor
Jersey Angler Publishing Co., Inc.
Route 36 West
Atlantic Highlands, N.J. 07716
(201) 872-0888

Argosy (M)
Established 1882
Circulation: 626,000
Liz Sahadi, Editor
Popular Publications, Inc.
420 Lexington Avenue, Suite 2540
New York, N.Y. 10017
(212) 687-1234

Bassmaster Magazine (BM)
Established 1968
Circulation: 260,000
Bob Cobb, Editor
Bass Anglers Sportsman
  Society of America, Inc.
P.O. Box 3044
Montgomery, Alabama 36109
(205) 272-9530

Field & Stream (M)
Established 1895
Circulation: 2,000,000
Jack Samson, Editor
CBS Publications
383 Madison Avenue
New York, N.Y. 10017
(212) 688-9100

Fin & Feathers (M)
Established 1972
Circulation: 80,000
Ken Neudahl, Editor
Fin & Feathers, Inc.
P.O. Box 8595
White Bear Lake, Minnesota 55110
(612) 770-1401

The Fishermen's News (SM)
Established 1945
Circulation: 8,000
Walt Kisner, Jr., Editor
The Fishermen's News, Inc.
Fishermen's Terminal, Building C-3
Seattle, Washington 98119
(206) 282-7545

Fishing Gazette (M)
Established 1879
Circulation: 19,000
Robert J. Burns, Editor
Fishing Gazette Publishing Corp.
461 Eighth Avenue
New York, N.Y. 10001
(212) 563-3430

Fishing and Hunting News (W)
Established 1944
Circulation: 108,000
Vence Malernee, Editor
Outdoor Empire Publishing, Inc.
511 Eastlake Avenue E.
Seattle, Washington 98109
(206) 624-3845

Fishing Facts (M)
Established 1963
Circulation: 195,000
George Pazik, Editor
Northwoods Publishing Co., Inc.
P.O. Box 609
Menomonee Falls, Wisconsin 53051
(414) 255-4800

Fishing Tackle Trade News (M)
Established 1952
Circulation: 17,000
Clem Dippel, Editor
Fishing Tackle Trade News, Inc.
P.O. Box 70
Wilmette, Illinois 60091
(312) 256-0650

Fishing World (BM)
Established 1955
Circulation: 217,000
Keith Gardner, Editor
Allsport Publishing Co.
51 Atlantic Avenue
Floral Park, L.I., N.Y. 11001
(516) 352-9700

Florida Sportsman (BM)
Established 1969
Circulation: 74,000
Bill Halstrom, Editor
Wickstrom Publishers, Inc.
2701 South Bayshore Drive
Miami, Florida 33133
(305) 858-3546

Fly Fisherman (7 x yr.)
Established 1969
Circulation: 59,000
Donald D. Zahner, Editor
Fly Fisherman Magazine, Inc.
Dorset, Vermont 05251
(802) 867-5951

Fur-Fish-Game (Harding's Magazine) (M)
Established 1905
Circulation: 176,000
A. R. Harding, Editor
A. R. Harding Publishing Co.
2878 East Main Street
Columbus, Ohio 43209
(614) 231-9585

Great Lakes Sportsman (BM)
Established 1970
Circulation: 150,000
Tobin M. Wells, Editor
Sportsman Publications, Inc.
31360 Northwestern Highway
Farmington Hills, Michigan 48018
(313) 855-1424

Michigan Out-of-Doors (M)
Established 1947
Circulation: 120,000
Kenneth Lowe, Editor
Michigan United Conservation Clubs, Inc.
P.O. Box 30235
Lansing, Michigan 48909
(517) 371-1041

New England Sportsman (BM)
Established 1973
Circulation: 80,000
Frank Kepler, Editor
Sportsman Publications, Inc.
31360 Northwestern Highway
Farmington Hills, Michigan 48018
(313) 855-1424

Outdoor Arizona (M)
Established 1928
Circulation: 38,000
Manya Winsted, Editor
Phoenix Publishing, Inc.
4707 N. 12 Street
Phoenix, Arizona 85014
(602) 248-8900

Outdoor Life (M)
Established 1898
Circulation: 1,901,000
John Fry, Editor
Times Mirror Magazines, Inc.
380 Madison Avenue
New York, N.Y. 10017
(212) 687-3000

Outdoor Press (W)
Established 1966
Circulation: 49,000
Fred L. Peterson, Editor
The Outdoor Press, Inc.
N. 2012 Ruby Street
Spokane, Washington 99207
(509) 328-9392

Outdoors Today (W)
Established 1970
Circulation: 93,000
Harry Dotson, Editor
Outdoors Today, Inc.
P.O. Box 6852
St. Louis, Missouri 63144
(314) 727-2722

Pennsylvania Angler (M)
Established 1931
Circulation: 46,000
James F. Yoder, Editor
Pennsylvania Fish Commission
3532 Walnut Street
Harrisburg, Pennsylvania 17109
(717) 238-0441

Pennsylvania's Outdoor People (M)
Established 1959
Circulation: 133,000
Dennis A. Dardanell, Editor
Dardanell Publications, Inc.
610 Beatty Road
Monroeville, Pennsylvania 15146
(412) 373-7900

Popular Mechanics (M)
Established 1902
Circulation: 1,800,000
John A. Linkletter, Editor
The Hearst Corp.
224 West 57th Street
New York, N.Y. 10019
(212) 262-5700

Popular Science (M)
Established 1872
Circulation: 1,799,000
Hubert P. Luckett, Editor
Times Mirror Magazines, Inc.
380 Madison Avenue
New York, N.Y. 10017
(212) 687-3000

Saga (M)
Established 1950
Circulation: 142,000
Martin M. Singer, Editor
Gambi Publishing Corp.
333 Johnson Avenue
Brooklyn, N.Y. 11206
(212) 456-8600

Salt Water Sportsman (M)
Established 1939
Circulation: 102,000
Frank Woolner, Editor
Salt Water Sportsman, Inc.
10 High Street
Boston, Massachusetts 02110
(617) 426-4074

The Southern Lunker (BM)
Established 1975
Circulation: 50,000
Lee Mills, Editor
The Southern Lunker Magazine, Inc.
P.O. Box 6115
Monroe, Louisiana 71201
(318) 343-6238

Southern Outdoors (BM)
Established 1953
Circulation: 135,000
Bob Cobb, Editor
Bass Anglers Sportsman
  Society of America, Inc.
P.O. Box 3044
Montgomery, Alabama 36109
(205) 272-9530

Sporting Goods Business (M)
Established 1968
Circulation: 23,000
Robert Carr, Editor
Giralla Publications, Inc.
1515 Broadway
New York, N.Y. 10036
(212) 869-1300

Sports Afield with Rod & Gun (M)
Established 1887
Circulation: 1,400,000
Lamar Underwood, Editor
The Hearst Corp.
250 West 55th Street
New York, N.Y. 10019
(212) 262-8852

Sports and Recreation (BM)
Established 1946
Circulation: 43,000
Robert Bushnell, Editor
Nystrom Publishing Co., Inc.
9100 Cottonwood Lane
Maple Grove, Minnesota 55369
(612) 425-7900

Texas Sportsman (M)
Established 1971
Circulation: 53,000
John Kollman, Editor
Neptune Publishing Co.
P.O. Box 10411
San Antonio, Texas 78210
(512) 533-8991

Trout (Q)
Established 1960
Circulation: 24,000
Alvin R. Grove, Jr., Editor
Trout Unlimited
4260 East Evans Avenue
Denver, Colorado 80222
(303) 757-7144

Western Outdoor News (W)
Established 1953
Circulation: 80,000
Bill Rice, Editor
Western Outdoors Publications
3939 Birch Street
Newport Beach, California 92660
(714) 546-4370

Western Outdoors (M)
Established 1960
Circulation: 132,000
Burt Twiligar, Editor
Western Outdoors Publications
3939 Birch Street
Newport Beach, California 92660
(714) 546-4370

West Virginia Hills and Streams (M)
Established 1970
Circulation: 3,000
Leo Young, Editor
West Virginia Hills and Streams, Inc.
Box 38
Durbin, West Virginia 26264
(304) 456-4366

Canadian Periodicals

B.C. Outdoors (BM)
Established 1945
Circulation: 26,000
A. G. Downs, Editor
Northwest Digest, Ltd.
Box 900, Station A
Surrey, British Columbia V3S 4P4
(604) 574-5211

Fish and Game Sportsman (Q)
Established 1969
Circulation: 13,000
J. B. Wilkinson, Editor
Nimrod Publications, Ltd.
P.O. Box 1654
Regina, Saskatchewan S4P 3C4
(306) 523-8384

Northwest Sportsman (6 x yr.)
Established 1946
Circulation: 9,800
Jim Railton, Editor
Railton Publications, Ltd.
125 Talisman Avenue
Vancouver, British Columbia V5Y 2L6
(604) 876-3535

Ontario Fisherman & Hunter (M)
Established 1969
Circulation: 29,000
Burton J. Meyers, Editor
Daniel J. Thomey, Publisher
7 Guardsman Road
Thornhill, Ontario L3T 2A1
(416) 881-1033

Sporting Goods Trade (BM)
Established 1973
Circulation: 10,000
Douglas Alexander, Editor
Page Publications
380 Wellington Street West
Toronto, Ontario M5V 1E3
(416) 366-4608

Quebec Chasse et Pêche (M) (French)
Established 1971
Circulation: 19,000
Henri Poupart, Editor
Les Publications Plein Air, Inc.
3335 Desmarteau Street
Montreal, Quebec H1L 492
(514) 376-5910

Western Fish and Wildlife (BM)
Established 1965
Circulation: 10,000
J. L. Grundle, Editor and Publisher
1020 Horby Street
Vancouver, British Columbia V6Z 1V6
(604) 980-5821

Wildlife Crusader (M)
Established 1944
Circulation: 39,000
Paul F. Murphy, Editor
Manitoba Wildlife Federation
365 Bannatyne Avenue
Winnipeg, Manitoba R3A 0E5
(204) 774-2926

Explanation of Symbols: (M) Monthly; (BM) Bi-monthly; (SM) Semi-monthly; (W) Weekly; (Q) Quarterly

Directory of Organizations and Associations

AMERICAN ASSOCIATION FOR CONSERVATION INFORMATION

c/o Ronald E. Shay   Phone: (503) 229-5425
Oregon Game Commission
Portland, Oregon 97208
Ronald E. Shay, Pres.
Founded: 1938
Members: 68

Professional society of officials of state and provincial conservation agencies. Sponsors annual awards program whereby winners in various categories of conservation education work are selected by a panel of judges. Publications: (1) *Balance Wheel*, bimonthly; (2) *Yearbook*. Convention/Meeting: Annual — always June.

AMERICAN BASS FISHERMAN

P.O. Box 908   Phone: (305) 783-5271
Cocoa Beach, Florida 32931
George H. Oates, Pres.

AMERICAN CASTING ASSOCIATION

P.O. Box 158   Phone: (606) 666-5121
Picnic Hill
Jackson, Kentucky 41339
William B. Burke, Exec. Sec.
Founded: 1906
Members: 2500
Staff: 1

Federation of 45 local clubs, five state associations, and seven regional groups of amateur tournament fly and bait casters; also includes colleges and universities teaching angling and casting. Promotes casting and angling as a recreational activity. Coordinates, regulates, and establishes rules for sanctioned tournaments; sponsors competitions; works to develop improved fishing tackle; provides instruction in workshops and clinics; compiles statistics. Committees: Youth Activities; Conservation. Publication: *Creel*, quarterly. Formerly: (1940) National Association of Scientific Angling Clubs; (1961) National Association of Angling and Casting Clubs. Convention/Meeting: Annual.

AMERICAN COMMITTEE FOR INTERNATIONAL CONSERVATION

c/o The Wildlife Society   Phone: (301) 986-8700
7101 Wisconsin Avenue, N.W., Suite 611
Washington, D.C. 20014
Fred G. Evenden, Sec.-Treas.
Founded: 1930
Members: 55

Persons interested in conservation and preservation of wildlife and other natural resources of the world; stimulate, promote and finance research into status and ecology of threatened species; lend assistance to national and international organizations concerned with wildlife conservation, outside the U.S.

AMERICAN FISHERIES SOCIETY

5400 Grosvener Lane   Phone: (301) 897-8616
Bethesda, Maryland 20014
Carl R. Sullivan, Exec. Dir.
Founded: 1870
Members: 7000
Regional groups: 4

Fish culturists, fish biologists, commercial fishermen, hatcherymen, fish technologists, limnologists, and oceanographers. To promote the development of all branches of fishery science and practice, and the conservation, development, and wise utilization of fisheries, both recreational and commercial. Committees: Awards; Board of Professional Certification; Editorial; Educa-
tion; Endangered Species; Fish Disease; Fish Policy; International Fisheries; Metric Systems Study; Names of Fishes; Pollution — Water Quality; Student Affairs. Publications: (1) AFS Bulletin *Fisheries*, bimonthly; (2) *Journal of Ichthyology* (English edition of a publication of the Academy of Sciences of the U.S.S.R.), bimonthly; (3) *Hydrobiological Journal* (English edition of a publication of the Academy of Sciences of the U.S.S.R.), bimonthly; (4) *Transactions*, bimonthly; (5) *Membership Directory*, biennial; also publishes career guidance booklets. Convention/meeting: Annual.

AMERICAN FISHING TACKLE MANUFACTURERS ASSOCIATION

20 North Wacker Drive, Suite 2014   Phone: (312) 236-0565
Chicago, Ill. 60606
Thomas R. Schedler, Exec. V. Pres.
Founded: 1933
Members: 400
Staff: 10

Manufacturers of fishing tackle and allied products. Sponsors annual trade show. Publication: *News-Bulletin*, monthly. Formerly: Associated Fishing Tackle Manufacturers. Convention/Meeting: Semiannual — always May and Nov.

AMERICAN INSTITUTE OF BIOLOGICAL SCIENCES

1401 Wilson Boulevard   Phone: (703) 527-6776
Arlington, Virginia 22209
Richard Trumball, Exec. Dir.
Founded: 1948
Members: 11,851

Federation of professional biological associations and individuals with an interest in the life sciences. To promote unity and effectiveness of effort among persons engaged in biological research, teaching or application of biological data; to further the relationships of biological sciences to other sciences, the arts, and industries. Conducts symposium series; arranges for prominent biologists to lecture at small liberal arts colleges and radiation biologists to visit certain medical schools; provides advisory committees and other services to a number of government agencies and foundations, including the Environmental Protection Agency, the National Science Foundation, Office of Naval Research, National Aeronautics and Space Administration, Food and Drug Administration and Energy Research and Development Administration. Publications: (1) *BioScience*, monthly; (2) *Education Review*, quarterly. Convention/Meeting: Annual.

AMERICAN INSTITUTE OF FISHERY RESEARCH BIOLOGISTS

1226 Skyline Drive
Edmonds, Wash. 98020
F. Heward Bell, Sec.-Treas.
Founded: 1956
Members: 950

Professional society of biologists engaged in fishery research.

AMERICAN LEAGUE OF ANGLERS

810 18th Street, N.W.   Phone: (202) 347-7475
Washington, D.C. 20006
Otto Teller, President
Founded: 1973
Members: 2500

Persons interested in fishing and in defending the interests of fishermen. Proposes, supports and promotes legislation vital to sport fishing conservation and the rights of anglers to enjoy their sport free of unjust charges and restriction. Fights legislation that would destroy or damage fresh and salt water resources or infringe upon rights of sport fishermen. Monitors the performance of elected and appointed officials. Demands vigorous enforcement of existing laws which protect sport fishing and natural resources. Works to strengthen other national, state and local anglers organizations. Promotes good fisheries conservation practices.

AMERICAN LITTORAL SOCIETY
Sandy Hook   Phone: (201) 291-0055
Highlands, N.J. 07732
D. W. Bennett, Exec. Dir.
Founded: 1961
Encourages the underwater study of shore life by direct observation of the occurrence and ways of fishes and other marine animals; disseminates records of observations; assists in the solving of problems of scientific study, identification, and description; and fosters public interest in shore life and the need for conservation. Publication: *Underwater Naturalist,* quarterly. Convention/Meeting: Annual.

AMERICAN MEDICAL FLY FISHING ASSOCIATION
447 S. Main   Phone: (217) 532-6172
Hillsboro, Ill. 62049
Clinton Pace, M.D., Sec.
Founded: 1969
Members: 200
Offers physicians interested in conservation, environmental and ecological problems an opportunity to work toward achieving a better environment. Publication: *Newsletter,* irregular. Holds annual meeting.

AMERICAN RIVERS CONSERVATION COUNCIL
317 Pennsylvania Avenue, S.E.   Phone: (202) 547-6900
Washington, D.C. 20003
Bill Painter, Exec. Dir.
Founded: 1973
Members: 1000
Conservationists, fishermen, boaters and scientists interested in the protection of remaining wild and scenic free-flowing rivers. Promotes legislation aimed at river conservation. Works against destructive dams, channelization, and other wasteful water projects. Convention/Meeting: Annual.

ASSOCIATION OF MIDWEST FISH AND WILDLIFE COMMISSIONERS
c/o Chuck Post   Phone: (605) 224-3485
Department of Game, Fish and Parks
Sigurd Anderson Building
Pierre, South Dakota 57501
Chuck Post, Secretary
Founded: 1934
Members: 18
Fish and game commissioners and directors of 15 midwestern states and 3 Canadian provinces. Promotes conservation of wildlife and outdoor recreation. Sponsors Midwest Pheasant Council; Dove Committee. Committees: Federal-State Relations; Federal Aid; Legislation; Federal Farm Program; Wetlands. Publications: *Proceedings,* annual. Convention/Meeting: Annual.

ATLANTIC ESTUARINE RESEARCH SOCIETY
c/o Dr. Donald W. Lear, Jr.   Phone: (301) 268-5038
EPA Annapolis Field Office
Annapolis Science Center
Annapolis, Md. 21403
Donald W. Lear, Jr., Exec. Sec.
Founded: 1949
Members: 380
Persons actively engaged in biological, hydrographic, or related investigations of estuarine problems, particularly in the Chesapeake Bay-Carolina area. Convention/Meeting: Semiannual.

ATLANTIC SALMON ASSOCIATION
1405 Peel Street, Room 200   Phone: (514) 282-0007
Montreal, Canada H3A 1S5
Kenneth Reardon, Exec. Dir.
Founded: 1948
Members: 2300
Staff: 4
Dedicated to the conservation and preservation of the Atlantic Salmon. Non-profit organization. Publications: (1) *Atlantic Salmon Journal,* quarterly. Convention/Meeting: Annual.

ATLANTIC SEA RUN SALMON COMMISSION
State Of Maine   Phone: (207) 947-8627
Bldg. 34, Idaho Ave.
Bangor, Maine 04401
Maynard F. Marsh, Chm.
Founded: 1948
Members: 3
Staff: 6
A cooperative agreement among the University of Maine, the U.S. Bureau of Sport Fisheries and Wildlife, and the State of Maine, united for the restoration and management of Atlantic Salmon. Represents the U.S. at international meetings concerning Atlantic salmon.

BASS ANGLERS SPORTSMAN SOCIETY
1 Bell Road   Phone: (205) 272-9530
Montgomery, Alabama 36109
Ray W. Scott, Jr., President
Founded: 1968
Members: 250,000
Regional Groups: 33 state federations; 1465 local affiliated B.A.S.S. chapters
Staff: 120
For-profit organization publishing *Bassmaster Magazine* for persons interested in the sport of bass fishing. Publications: *Bassmaster Magazine,* bi-monthly; *Bassmaster Fishing Annual; Bass Fishing Guide.*

BOAT MANUFACTURERS ASSOCIATION
401 North Michigan Ave.   Phone: (312) 329-0590
Chicago, Ill. 60601
Matt J. Kaufman, Administrator
Founded: 1945
Members: 270
Manufacturers of boats. Staff services provided by parent body, Boating Industry Associations. Publications: (1) *Monday Morning Report,* weekly; (2) *Monthly Statistical Report;* (3) *Legislative Ledger,* monthly. Formerly: Outboard Boat Manufacturers Association. Convention/Meeting: Annual — always early fall, Chicago, Illinois.

BROTHERHOOD OF THE JUNGLE COCK
10 East Fayette St.
Baltimore, Md. 21202
Fred Wright, Exec. V. Pres.
Founded: 1939
Members: 250
"Anglers dedicated to conserve game fish and teach angling technique and good sportsmanship." Convention/Meeting: Annual, always third weekend in May.

CITIZENS COMMITTEE ON NATURAL RESOURCES
1346 Connecticut Ave., N.W.   Phone: (202) 785-1261
Washington, D.C. 20036
Spencer M. Smith, Jr., Sec.
Founded: 1954
Directors: 50
Staff: 2
Individuals interested in lobbying in behalf of conservation program dealing with government departments.

CLEAN WATER ACTION PROJECT

P.O. Box 19312 Phone: (202) 833-3404
Washington, D.C. 20036
David Zwick, Dir.

Research group affiliated with Ralph Nader. Research and advocacy for ending water pollution and drinking water contamination. Uses teams which employ scientists, lawyers and other professionals to work for clean water before the courts and administrative agencies and to push for stronger legislation at the state and national levels. Convention/Meetings: Annual — always held on the first Tuesday after the first Monday in June.

CONSERVATION AND RESEARCH FOUNDATION

Department of Botany Phone: (203) 442-5391 x306
Connecticut College
New London, Conn. 06320
Richard H. Goodwin, Pres.
Founded: 1953

Not a membership organization. To encourage biological research and promote conservation of renewable natural resources. Makes research grants; offers Jeanette Siron Pelton Award for outstanding published contributions in experimental plant morphology. Publishes *A Ten Year Report* (last one in 1963). Convention/ Meeting: Annual.

CONSERVATION EDUCATION ASSOCIATION

c/o Dr. Robert S. Cook Phone: (414) 465-2427
Office of Dean of Colleges
Univ. of Wisconsin — Green Bay
Green Bay, Wisconsin 54302
Dr. Robert S. Cook, Sec.-Treas.
Founded: 1947
Members: 950

Conservationists, educators and others interested in improving conservation education in public schools, teacher training institutions, and organization programs. Outstanding state, local and organizational conservation publications, especially those of normally limited distribution, are circulated bimonthly to members. Publications: (1) *Newsletter,* bimonthly; (2) *Proceedings,* annual. Formerly: (1953) National Committee on Policies in Conservation Education. Convention/Meeting: Annual — always August.

CONSERVATION FOUNDATION

1717 Massachusetts Ave., N.W. Phone: (202) 265-8882
Washington, D.C. 20036
William K. Reilly, Pres.
Founded: 1948
Staff: 40

Not a membership organization. Conducts research, education and information programs to develop knowledge, improve techniques, and stimulate public and private decision-making and action to improve the quality of the environment. Carries out environmental studies, demonstration planning programs, and offers a variety of conservation services at home and abroad. Publication: *CF Letter,* monthly; also publishes books, pamphlets, studies.

DEFENDERS OF WILDLIFE

1244 19th Street, N.W. Phone: (202) 659-9510
Washington, D.C. 20036
Dr. John W. Grady, Exec. Vice Pres.
Founded: 1925
Members: 35,000

Persons interested in wildlife and conservation. To promote, through education and research, the protection and humane treatment of all mammals, birds, fish and other wildlife, and the elimination of painful methods of trapping, capturing and killing wildlife. Publications: *Defenders of Wildlife Magazine,* bi-

monthly; alerts, press releases, etc. issued as necessary. Formerly: Anti-Steel-Trap League; Defenders of Furbearers. Convention/ Meeting: Annual.

EMERGENCY COMMITTEE TO SAVE AMERICA'S MARINE RESOURCES

110 Charlotte Pl. Phone: (201) 569-9511
Englewood Cliffs, N.J. 07632
Allan J. Ristori, Chm.
Founded: 1972

Founded to establish 200-mile fisheries limit to preserve, control and maintain natural marine resources in American waters. With passage of 200 mile legislation (HR 200), the committee will now concentrate on monitoring its implementation (as of March 1, 1977) and continue to review fisheries plans and treaties submitted by the Departments of Commerce and State. Maintains contact with both Congress and Federal Agencies. Testifies at Congressional hearings. Cooperates with American League of Anglers and National Coalition for Marine Conservation.

FEDERATION OF FLY FISHERMEN

Membership Service Office Phone: (213) 322-6441
519 Main Street
El Segundo, California 90245

To promote fly fishing as the most enjoyable and sportsmanlike method of fishing and as the method most consistent with the preservation and conservation of fishing waters and game fish. 158 affiliated clubs in United States, Canada, France, New Zealand and Chile.

FEDERATION OF WESTERN OUTDOOR CLUBS

4534½ University Way, N.E. Phone: (206) 632-6157
Seattle, Washington 98105
Robert Winkam, Pres.
Founded: 1932
Members: 1341

Outdoor clubs (41) in western United States with combined membership of 48,000, associate members 1300. Promotes conservation of forests, wildlife, and natural features. Publication: *Western Outdoor Quarterly.* Convention/Meeting: Annual — always Labor Day weekend.

FRIENDS OF NATURE, INC.

Brooksville, Me. 04617
Martin R. Haase, Exec. Sec.
Founded: 1953

Conservationists "dedicated to maintaining the balance of nature for the mutual benefit of man and his plant and animal friends." Carries on educational work and maintains several nature sanctuaries. Holds annual meeting.

FRIENDS OF THE EARTH

529 Commercial St. Phone: (415) 391-4270
San Francisco, Calif. 94111
David Brower, Founder, President
Founded: 1969

International conservation organization which concentrates on legislative and political activities in this field.

FRIENDS OF THE WILDERNESS

3515 East Fourth St. Phone: (218) 724-7227
Duluth, Minn. 55804
William H. Magie, Exec. Sec.
Founded: 1949
Members: 17,364

Persons interested in preservation of the Boundary Water Canoe Area of Minnesota, the wilderness canoe country of the Superior National Forest. Maintains library of 400 volumes pertaining to the area. Holds annual meeting.

FRUGAL BRUGAL SOCIETY
Claybrook Rd.
Dover, Massachusetts 02030
Frederick N. Blodgett, Pres.
Founded: 1932
Members: 100
Sportsmen from four countries, primarily those interested in fishing and shooting. (A Frugal Brugal is a drink made with unsweetened grapefruit juice and Brugal rum.) Purposes are: promotion of conviviality and camaraderie among fellow sportsmen; conservation of woodcock, partridge and ducks by strict adherence to game laws and the ability to cope therewith; improvement of game habitats in selected areas. Convention/ Meeting: Annual — always Oct.

GULF AND CARIBBEAN FISHERIES INSTITUTE
Rosenstiel School of Marine and   Phone: (305) 350-7533
Atmospheric Science
University of Miami
4600 Rickenbacker Causeway
Miami, Fla. 33149
James B. Higman, Exec. Dir.
Founded: 1948
Members: 500
Principally fishermen, fishery scientists and administrators. "To provide a means for exchange of information on research progress in fisheries among scientists and between scientists, industry and administrators." Publication: *Proceedings,* annual. Convention/Meeting: Annual — October or November, Miami Beach, Florida.

HUDSON RIVER FISHERMEN'S ASSOCIATION, INC.
Route 9D   Phone: (914) 265-3119
Garrison, New York 10524
David M. Seymour, President
Founded: 1966
Members: 400 in H.R.F.A.; another 400 in Chapters
Sport fishermen, commercial fishermen, writers, businessmen, lawyers, policemen and anyone interested in protecting the entire Hudson River and its drainage. To insure proper land use (including agriculture and all building) and to see that the river's resources are wisely managed.

INTERNATIONAL ASSOCIATION FOR GREAT LAKES RESEARCH
c/o State University College   Phone: (716) 862-5422
Buffalo, New York 14222
R. A. Sweeney, Treas.
Founded: 1967
Members: 550
Scientists, engineers, and others in the U.S. and Canada actively interested in research on the Great Lakes and their basins, or in research directly applicable to the understanding or management of large lakes. Presents Chandler Misener Award annually for best paper at annual conference. Publications: (1) *Lakes Letter,* quarterly; (2) *Proceedings of Annual Conference on Great Lakes Research.* Convention/Meeting (Conference on Great Lakes Research): Annual.

INTERNATIONAL ASSOCIATION OF GAME, FISH AND CONSERVATION COMMISSIONERS
1412 16th Street, N.W.   Phone: (202) 232-1652
Washington, D.C. 20036
John S. Gottschalk, Exec. V. Pres.
Founded: 1902
Members: 384

State and provincial game, fish and conservation departments (61) and officials (316). To educate the public to the economic importance of conserving natural resources and managing wildlife properly as a source of recreation and a food supply; to seek better conservation legislation, administration and enforcement. Publications: (1) *Proceedings,* annual; (2) *Newsletter,* bimonthly. Formerly: (1917) National Association of Game Commissioners and Wardens. Convention/Meeting: Annual — always second Monday in September.

INTERNATIONAL ATLANTIC SALMON FOUNDATION
P.O. Box 429   Phone: (506) 529-3818
St. Andrews, New Brunswick EOG 2XO (Canada)
or
425 Park Avenue   Phone: (212) 758-2800
New York, N.Y. 10022
Wilfred M. Carter, Exec. Dir. & Vice Pres.
Founded: 1968
Members: 900
Conservationists, scientists, government personnel, salmon anglers. Objective is the preservation and wise management of Atlantic salmon stocks. Program includes wide-range projects in four areas — education, management, research and international cooperation. Recent projects include: New England Atlantic Salmon Restoration Conference; construction of North American Salmon Research Center ($1.4 million research project); grant to Iceland for fish farming studies; production of an educational filmstrip on Atlantic salmon. Bestows grants and scholarships. Maintains library and aquarium exhibits. Publishes educational material. Committees: International Advisory Group, International Programs; NE States Restoration; Scientific Advisory Group. Publications: (1) *Newsletter,* bimonthly; (2) *Special Publication Series,* occasionally.

INTERNATIONAL COMMISSION FOR THE NORTHWEST ATLANTIC FISHERIES
P.O. Box 638   Phone: (902) 469-9105(6)
Dartmouth, Nova Scotia, Canada
L. R. Day, Exec. Sec.
Founded: 1949
Members: 18
Staff: 14
Contracting governments united for investigation, protection and conservation of fisheries of the Northwest Atlantic Ocean in order to provide a maximum sustained catch from these fisheries. Committees: International Control; Regulatory Measures; Research and Statistics. Publications: (1) *Proceedings,* annual; (2) *Research Bulletin,* annual; (3) *Statistical Bulletin,* annual; (4) *Special Publications,* irregular; also publishes a handbook. Convention/Meeting: Annual.

INTERNATIONAL GAME FISH ASSOCIATION
3000 E. Las Olas Blvd.   Phone: (305) 467-0161
Fort Lauderdale, Fla. 33316
Elwood K. Harry, Pres.
Founded: 1939
Members: 10,000
A nonprofit, tax-deductible organization which maintains and promotes ethical international angling regulations and compiles world marine fish records for 58 species. Also represent and inform marine recreational fishermen regarding research, conservation and legislative developments related to their sport. Encourage and support game fish tagging programs and other scientific data collection efforts. 100 international representatives. Membership opened to interested persons and organizations in May 1973. Publications: *The International Marine Angler,* bimonthly; *World Record Marine Fishes,* annual. Convention/Meeting: Annual.

INTERNATIONAL LIGHT TACKLE TOURNAMENT ASSOCIATION

2044 Federal Ave.
Costa Mesa, Calif. 92627   Phone: (714) 548-4273
Helen R. Smith, Exec. Sec.
Founded: 1945
Members: 78
Staff: 1

Angling clubs which are members of International Game Fish Association. Sponsors tournaments in which only light tackle is used and fish which are taken are later released. Publication: *Bulletin*, quarterly. Holds International Billfish Tournaments.

INTERNATIONAL NORTH PACIFIC FISHERIES COMMISSION, UNITED STATES SECTION

Uganik Bay
Kodiak, Alaska
Alfred Owen, Chairman
Founded: 1954
Members: 20

Intergovernmental organization of fishing industry and association representatives, state administrators, lawyers, and others interested in development of fisheries in the Pacific Northwest. INPFC, established by convention between the U.S., Canada, and Japan, works to promote and coordinate conservation programs to secure maximum sustainable production from the fisheries of the North Pacific Study Group, which recently formed a North Pacific Task Force to initiate reports on various problems. Offers guidance to U.S. commissioners to INPFC and advises federal and state government agencies and other institutions on research activities. Meets annually, prior to INPFC meetings.

INTERNATIONAL OCEANOGRAPHIC FOUNDATION

3979 Rickenbacker Causeway   Phone: (305) 361-5786
Virginia Key, Miami, Fla. 33149
F. G. Walton Smith, Pres.
Founded: 1953
Members: 65,000
Staff: 31

Scientists and laymen interested in the sea. Encourages scientific study and exploration of the oceans in all their aspects, including game and food fishes and other creatures of sea and shore; ocean currents; geology, chemistry, and physics of the sea and sea floor; submarine detection; and industrial applications of oceanography. Gives financial aid to research institutions to support scientific investigations. Gives Gold Medal Award. Operates unique permanent ocean science exposition, PLANET OCEAN, with 7 theaters under one roof. Publications: (1) *Sea Secrets* (question and answer series), 6/year; (2) *Sea Frontiers* (magazine), bimonthly; also publishes young people's booklet, *Training and Careers in Marine Science*, which is free to members and 50 cents to nonmembers. Members receive advisory service, book discount service, film rental service, and reduced admission to PLANET OCEAN.

INTERNATIONAL PACIFIC HALIBUT COMMISSION

P.O. Box 5009, University Station   Phone: (206) 634-1838
Seattle, Wash. 98105
Bernard E. Skud, Director
Founded: 1923
Members: 6
Staff: 24

Intergovernmental organization of Commissioners appointed by the United States (3) and Canada (3) to be responsible for management of the halibut fishery in the North Pacific and Bering Sea. Seeks to develop stocks of Pacific halibut to levels that will permit maximum sustained yield and to maintain stocks at those levels. Applies specific types of regulation and scientific investigations. Publications: (1) *Annual Report;* (2) *Scientific Reports,* irregular; (3) *Technical Reports,* irregular. Formerly: (1954) International Fisheries Commission. Convention/Meeting: Annual.

INTERNATIONAL PACIFIC SALMON FISHERIES COMMISSION

P.O. Box 30   Phone: (604) 521-3771
New Westminster, British Columbia V3L 4X9, Canada
A. C. Cooper, Dir.
Founded: 1937
Commissioners: 6
Advisors: 12
Staff: 55

To protect, preserve, and extend the sockeye and pink salmon fisheries of the Fraser River, which flows in British Columbia passing near the United States border. Publications: (1) *Annual Report;* (2) *Bulletins,* periodically; (3) *Progress Reports,* periodically. Meets several times a year and weekly during the fishing season.

INTERNATIONAL SPIN FISHING ASSOCIATION

P.O. Box 81
Downey, Calif. 90241
Richard Ream, Exec. Sec.
Founded: 1953

Sportsmen's clubs and individuals interested in spin fishing. Registers fresh and salt water records made on spin tackle on line classes ranging from 2- through 12-pound test; promotes conservation.

INTERNATIONAL UNION FOR CONSERVATION OF NATURE AND NATURAL RESOURCES

1110 Morges, Switzerland   Phone: (703) 280-4086
Dr. Gerardo Budowski, Dir. Gen.
Founded: 1948
Members: 414

International federation of national governments (38) and national and international organizations (326) in 95 countries. Seeks to maintain and enhance the diversity of the biosphere by promoting rational management of the earth's resources; to halt the destruction of our natural environment; to promote the conservation of wild places and wild animals and plants in their natural environments. Continuously reviews and assesses world environmental problems, and promotes research relating to their solution. Maintains close working relations with the United Nations System; cooperates with Council of Europe, Organization of African Unity, Organization of American States, and other intergovernmental bodies collaborates with International Council for Bird Preservation, International Council of Scientific Unions, and other non-governmental groups. Presents John Phillips Memorial Medal triennially for distinguished service in international conservation. Maintains library of 2500 volumes on nature conservation and wildlife management; IUCN Environmental Law Centre in Bonn, Federal Republic of Germany. Technical Commissions: Conservation Education; Ecology; Environmental Policy, Law, and Administration; Landscape Planning; Law and Administration; National Parks; Survival Service. Publications: (1) *IUCN Bulletin,* monthly; (2) Yearbook. General Assembly/Technical Meeting: Triennial.

INTERNATIONAL WOMEN'S FISHING ASSOCIATION

P.O. Box 2025   Phone: (305) 833-5310
Palm Beach, Fla. 33480
Mrs. Robert Boomhower, Pres.
Founded: 1955
Members: 450
Staff: 1

Sportfisherwomen. Promotes angling competition among women

anglers; encourages conservation; fosters fishing tournaments of all kinds. Gives monthly and yearly awards for outstanding fishing accomplishments. Has established a scholarship trust to help graduate students further their education in the field of the marine sciences. Publications: (1) *Hooks and Lines,* monthly; (2) *IWFA Yearbook.* Convention/Meeting: Annual — always Apr., Palm Beach, Fla.

IZAAK WALTON LEAGUE OF AMERICA

1800 N. Kent St., Suite 806   Phone: (703) 528-1818
Arlington, Va. 22209
Jack Lorenz, Exec. Dir.
Founded: 1922
Members: 50,000
Staff: 16
State divisions: 22
Local chapters: 600
Promotes means and opportunities for educating the public to conserve, maintain, protect and restore the soil, forest, water and other natural resources of the U.S. and promotes the enjoyment and wholesome utilization of those resources. Committees: Air Quality; Clean Water; Conservation Education; Public Lands. Publications: *League Leader, Outdoor America.* Convention/ Meeting: Annual.

J. N. "DING" DARLING FOUNDATION

3663 Grand Ave.   Phone: (515) 255-7860
Des Moines, Iowa 50312
Mr. Sherry R. Fisher, Chm.
Founded: 1962
Trustees: 50
"To initiate plans and to coordinate, guide and expedite programs, research and education which will bring about conservation and sound management of water, woods and soil; to restore and preserve historical sites; to create and assist in wildlife management plans; to improve and assure outdoor recreational opportunities for present and future generations." Established 1700-acre wildlife and waterfowl sanctuary on Sanibel Island, off the west coast of Florida. Awards scholarships at Iowa State University for wildlife management students. Named for the late J. N. "Ding" Darling, a professional cartoonist long active in conservation activities. Holds annual meeting.

LEAGUE TO SAVE LAKE TAHOE

1176 Emerson St.   Phone: (415) 328-5313
Palo Alto, California 94301
Steven C. Brandt, Pres.
Staff: 1
Membership comprised of individuals and organizations who give financial support to the League. Purpose is to "do all things and to perform all acts necessary to keep Lake Tahoe blue and to protect and preserve the natural beauty and grandeur of the Lake Tahoe area of California and Nevada; to promote and encourage the concept that all developments, improvements and man-made changes of any kind, which may be required to accommodate the proper and desirable growth of the area and provide the maximum recreational values, should place primary emphasis on preserving the natural beauty of the lake." Publication: *Newsletter,* quarterly. Convention/Meeting: Annual.

NATIONAL COALITION FOR MARINE CONSERVATION, INC.

P.O. Box 5131   Phone: (912) 234-8062
Savannah, Georgia 31403
Dr. Frank Carlton, President
Christopher M. Weld, Secretary
Founded: 1972
Members: 25,000
Recreational and commercial fishermen; fisheries scientists; fed-

eral and state administrators interested in the promotion of national policies and legislation affecting fisheries. Publication: *Right Rigger!,* monthly newsletter. Convention/Meeting: annual members' seminar.

NATIONAL FISHERIES INSTITUTE

1730 Pennsylvania Avenue, N.W.   Phone: (202) 785-0500
Suite 1150
Washington, D.C. 20006
Thomas E. Coller, Jr., Exec. Sec.
Founded: 1945
Members: 500
Producers (boat owners), distributors, processors, wholesalers, importers and canners of fish and shellfish. Divisions: National Fish Meal and Oil Association. Publications: (1) *Flashes,* weekly; (2) *Bluebook,* annual. Convention/Meeting: Annual — always Apr.

NATIONAL WATERSHED CONGRESS

1025 Vermont Ave., N.W.   Phone: (202) 347-5995
Washington, D.C. 20005
David G. Unger, Chairman, Steering Committee
Founded: 1954
Members: 30
National conservation, farm, civic and business organizations interested in fostering discussion and advancement of natural resources conservation and development through upstream watershed programs. (A watershed is the drainage area usually associated with a river or lake and divided from other watersheds by ridges or other characteristics of the terrain.) Holds annual conference (Congress) planned and conducted by a steering committee chosen by the participating organizations. The Congress "does not propagandize, adopt resolutions, promote projects, or take any action" — it acts as a forum for discussion of ways and means of expediting and broadening local watershed programs. Though the first Congresses were concerned primarily with water control and soil erosion, in recent years the Congress has dealt with river basin planning, regional interstate river compacts, and national water policy in general. Publication: *Proceedings,* annual. Holds annual Congress.

NATIONAL WILDLIFE FEDERATION

1412 16th St., N.W.   Phone: (202) 797-6800
Washington, D.C. 20036
Thomas L. Kimball, Exec. V. Pres.
Founded: 1936
State affiliate members: 53
Associate members: 700,000
Staff: 400
Local chapters: 7921
Federation of 3.5 million members and supporters. To encourage the intelligent management of the life-sustaining resources of the earth, and to promote a greater appreciation of these resources, their community relationship and wise use.

NATURAL RESOURCES COUNCIL OF AMERICA

1025 Connecticut Ave., N.W.   Phone: (202) 293-3200
Suite 914
Washington, D.C. 20036
Hamilton K. Pyles, Exec. Sec.
Founded: 1946
Members: 45
Federation of national and regional conservation organizations and scientific societies interested in conservation of natural resources. Sponsors special natural resource studies and surveys. Committee: Scientific Advisory. Publications: (1) *Legislative News Service* (actions taken by Congress on natural resources), weekly; (2) *Executive News Service* (actions taken by Executive Branch on natural resources), weekly; also publishes books on

selected natural resource topics. Convention/Meeting: Semi-annual—always held with North American Wildlife and Natural Resources Conference.

NEW ENGLAND ADVISORY BOARD
FOR FISH AND GAME PROBLEMS
115 Summit Avenue   Phone: (401) 821-9096
West Warwick, Rhode Island 02839
Theodore Boyer, Sec.
Founded: 1951
Members: 102
Sportsmen. To promote and improve conservation, hunting, fishing and recreation in New England. All New England states affiliated. Convention/Meeting: 3/year.

NORTH AMERICAN WILDLIFE FOUNDATION
709 Wire Bldg.   Phone: (202) 347-1774
1000 Vermont Avenue, N.W.
Washington, D.C. 20005
L. R. Jahn, Sec.
Founded: 1911
Contributing members: 400
Trustees: 30
"To insure, through financial support, the continuity of practical and systematic investigation into management practices and techniques throughout North America, to the end that the latest, most effective local, national, and international programs for wildlife and other natural resources will be adopted in the public interest." Foundation is not an action organization and does not attempt the actual mechanics of wildlife restoration; works through cooperating agencies, organizations, institutions. Owns Delta Waterfowl Research Station in Manitoba, Canada. Maintains library of over 500 volumes on natural science subjects and wildlife restoration and management.

OUTDOOR RECREATION INSTITUTE
5005 Wapakoneta
Washington, D.C. 20016
Dr. Frederick D. Sisler, Pres.
To advance outdoor recreational interests at all levels — family, local, state, and national; to emphasize recreational objectives of natural resource conservation, through technical research and educational activities. Provides information service on recreational equipment; answers technical inquiries; gives talks to groups on recreation, nutrition, foods, camping, etc.; conducts research in biology, pollution, recreational equipment, and other topics. Divisions: Research; Educational; Consulting. Sale of Namar fuel connecting kits for outboard motors.

OUTDOOR WRITERS ASSOCIATION OF AMERICA
4141 W. Bradley Rd.   Phone: (414) 354-9690
Milwaukee, Wis. 53209
Edwin W. Hanson, Exec. Dir.
Founded: 1927
Members: 1400
Staff: 3
Professional organization of newspaper, magazine, radio, television, and motion picture writers and photographers (both staff and free-lance) on outdoor recreation and conservation. Gives awards for outstanding writing and films in the field; conducts surveys for educational and industrial organizations; compiles market data for writer members, and offers liaison aid in writer assignments. Committees: Awards; Educational and Scholarship; Ethics; Youth Program. Publications: (1) *Outdoors Unlimited,* monthly; (2) *Spotlight,* quarterly; (3) *National Directory of Outdoor Writers,* annual; (4) *Standard Check List of Common Names for Principal American Sport Fishes,* revised periodically; (5) *Communicating the Outdoor Experience;* also publishes a youth education manual. Convention/Meeting: Annual.

OUTBOARD BOATING CLUB OF AMERICA
401 North Michigan Ave.   Phone: (312) 329-0590
Chicago, Ill. 60611
Matt Kaufman, Exec. Dir.
Founded: 1928
Boating Clubs. Provides members with information on current legislative problems; cruising and boating information. OBC is a consumer arm of International Expositions, Inc. Publishes directories, guidebooks, copies of laws and a number of leaflets and pamphlets relating to waterways and outboard boating.

PISCES SOCIETY OF AMERICA
61 Carthage Rd.   Phone: (914) 725-2880
Scarsdale, N.Y. 10583
J. S. Burrows, Pres.
Founded: 1965
Members: 86
Persons interested in fishing; conservationists, writers, ichthyologists, librarians, curators; clubs, lodges, publications, and business firms whose products are allied with fishing and conservation. "To educate, support, and promote angling sportsmanship, conservation, and the preservation of our wildlife and natural resources." Records outstanding catches of its fisherman-members, and offers a fishing certificate to members and others to document their catches. Presently inactive.

RESOURCES FOR THE FUTURE
1755 Massachusetts Ave., N.W.   Phone: (202) 462-4400
Washington, D.C. 20036
John E. Herbert, Sec.
Founded: 1952
Staff: 40
Foundation for research and education in conservation and development of natural resources. Publication: *Resources,* 3/year.

RESTORATION OF ATLANTIC SALMON
IN AMERICA, INC.
Box 164   Phone: (603) 525-3355, 3324
Hancock, N.H. 03499
Richard A. Buck, Chairman
Founded: 1973
Members: 350
Foundations, individuals, and national, regional and state conservation organizations interested in restoring Atlantic salmon to abundance in the waters of New England, and to protect these stocks wherever they may be found. Publication: *Newsletters.*

SCENIC HUDSON PRESERVATION CONFERENCE
545 Madison Avenue   Phone: (212) 755-3082
New York, N.Y. 10022
Judithe Melton, Exec. Dir.
Founded: 1963
Members: 22,000
Garden, civic, environmental, conservation and sportsmen groups (60); various towns, villages and municipalities; and individuals who espouse "a general concern for the natural resources of the Hudson River with particular emphasis on the preservation of the Hudson River Gorge and its attendant Highlands as an irreplaceable natural area of wilderness quality." Publications: *Bulletins,* irregular; and *Newsletters,* quarterly.

SIERRA CLUB
1050 Mills Tower   Phone: (415) 981-8634
San Francisco, California 94104
Michael McCloskey, Exec. Dir.
Members: 140,000
Staff: 90
Regional chapters: 48
All who feel the need to know more of nature, and know that

this need is basic to man. "To protect and conserve the natural resources of the Sierra Nevada, the United States and the World; to undertake and publish scientific and educational studies concerning all aspects of man's environment and the natural ecosystems of the World; and to educate the people of the United States and the World to the need to preserve and restore the quality of that environment and the integrity of those ecosystems." Works on urgent campaigns to save threatened areas, wildlife, and resources; conducts annual environmental workshops for educators; schedules wilderness outings; presents awards; maintains library. Chapters and committees schedule talks, films, exhibits, and conferences. Committees: Economics; Energy; Environmental Education; Environmental Research; Forest Practices; International Environment; Mountaineering; National Land Use; National Water Resources; Native American Issues; Outings; Population; Wilderness; Wildlife and Endangered Species. Departments: Conservation; Outings. Publications: (1) *National News Report,* weekly; (2) *Sierra Club Bulletin,* monthly; (3) *Ascent,* Sierra Club mountaineering journal, annual; also publishes books and produces films, posters, and exhibits. Member of: United Nations (with non-government organization status). Convention/Meeting (Wilderness Conference): Biennial.

SOUTHEASTERN ASSOCIATION OF GAME AND FISH COMMISSIONERS

c/o Arnold L. Mitchell   Phone: (502) 564-3400
Dept. of Fish and Wildlife Resources
Capital Plaza Tower, 4th Floor
Frankfort, Ky. 40601
Arnold L. Mitchell, Sec.-Treas.
Founded: 1947
Members: 16
Directors of state game and fish commissions in 16 southern states and Commonwealth of Puerto Rico. To protect the right of jurisdiction of southeastern states over their wildlife resources on public and private lands; study state and federal wildlife legislation and regulations as they affect the area; consult with and make recommendations to federal wildlife and public land agencies on federal management programs and programs involving federal aid to southeastern states; serve as a clearing house for exchange of ideas on wildlife management and research techniques. Sponsors statistical studies at North Carolina.

SPORT FISHERY RESEARCH FOUNDATION

608 13th Street, N.W., Suite 801   Phone: (202) 737-2145
Washington, D.C. 20005
Robert G. Martin, Sec.
Founded: 1962
Members: 5000
Individuals and organizations interested in improving sport fishing. Sole objective and activity is to help finance the graduate-level training of promising fishery scientists and to support research in the sport fishery resources field. Presents annual fellowship awards to promising graduate students in Fishery Science at selected universities throughout North America. Occasionally presents special research grants to established scientists. Affiliated with: Sport Fishing Institute. Holds annual meeting.

SPORT FISHING INSTITUTE

608 13th Street, N.W.   Phone: (202) 737-0668
Washington, D.C. 20005
Richard H. Stroud, Exec. V. Pres.
Founded: 1949
Members: 25,000
Staff: 9
Sport fish conservation agency supported by manufacturers of fishing tackle, outboard motors, boats, sporting goods, petroleum, and other related products. Provides research grants. Publishes periodic reviews of sport fish conservation activities carried on by government and private agencies; has compiled bibliography of unpublished theses on fishery biology. Publication: *SFI Bulletin,* monthly; also issues occasional special reports.

TROUT UNLIMITED

4260 E. Evans   Phone: (303) 757-7144
Denver. Colo. 80222
Esther Simon, Exec. Off.
Founded: 1959
Members: 21,000
Staff: 8
Chapters: 285
To conserve and preserve the natural habitat of the trout by influencing the activities and programs of governmental agencies, and keeping the public informed on water management problems. Emphasizes the sport in fishing. Maintains offices in Clay, New York, Woodland, Washington, and Portland. Bestows annual Trout Conservation Award. Conducts many research and education programs. Committees: Field Project; Pollution; Water Quality; Water Resources; Wild Rivers. Publications: (1) *Trout Magazine,* quarterly; (2) *Action Line Newspaper,* semi-annually; also publishes newsletters for several state councils. Convention/Meeting: Annual.

TRUSTEES FOR CONSERVATION

c/o Hilary Crawford, Jr.   Phone: (415) 362-2691
Mills Tower
220 Bush Street
San Francisco, California 94104
William J. Losh, Exec. Sec.
Founded: 1954
To secure the support of the people and the government in the preservation of national parks and monuments, wildlife and wilderness areas through legislative activities. Convention/Meeting: annual, always in December.

UNITED STATES TROUT FARMERS ASSOCIATION

Box 681   Phone: (801) 255-0228
Buhl, Idaho 83316
Gary Wright, Exec. Dir.
Founded: 1952
Members: 1100
Trout farmers and pay pond operators. To promote the sale of United States trout. Conducts research through state and federal agencies and colleges. Publication: *U.S. Trout News,* bimonthly; also publishes *Handbook of Trout Cookery, Tackle Talk and Trout* and a variety of sales and promotional aids for use by members. Holds annual meeting.

WESTERN ASSOCIATION OF STATE GAME AND FISH COMMISSIONERS

c/o Robert L. Salter   Phone: (208) 344-3772
Box 25
600 S. Walnut St.
Boise, Idaho 83707
Robert L. Salter, Sec.-Treas.
Founded: 1920
Members: 16
Officials of state and provincial game and fish agencies of western states and provinces. Promotes fish and game conservation in West. Publication: *Proceedings of WASGFC,* annual. Convention/Meeting: Annual.

WILDERNESS SOCIETY

1901 Pennsylvania Avenue, N.W.   Phone: (202) 293-2732
Washington, D.C. 20006
Stewart M. Brandborg, Exec. Dir.
Founded: 1935
Members: 110,000
Staff: 35

Persons interested in preserving wilderness through educational programs, scientific studies, and cooperation with local and state citizen organizations in resisting the destruction of wildland resources and wildlife. Conducts leadership training programs for citizen conservationists. Sponsors book award program for young people. Sponsors "A Way to the Wilderness" trip program. Publication: *Living Wilderness,* quarterly; also publishes *Wilderness Reports,* notices, and conservation alerts on critical conservation issues. Convention/Meeting: Annual.

WILDLIFE MANAGEMENT INSTITUTE
709 Wire Bldg.   Phone: (202) 347-1774
Washington, D.C. 20005
Daniel A. Poole, Pres.
Founded: 1946
Staff: 22

To promote better management and wise utilization of all renewable natural resources in the public interest. Sponsors annual North American Wildlife and Natural Resources Conference for government conservation administrators, technicians, scientists, educators and others interested in wildlife conservation. Publications: (1) *Outdoor News Bulletin,* biweekly; (2) *Transactions of Annual North American Wildlife and Natural Resources Conference* (and cumulative index); also publishes various books and monographs. Holds annual conference.

WILDLIFE SOCIETY
7101 Wisconsin Avenue, Suite 611   Phone: (301) 986-8700
Washington, D.C. 20014
Dr. Fred G. Evenden, Exec. Dir.
Founded: 1936
Members: 7300
Sectional groups: 7

Professional society of wildlife biologists and others interested in resource conservation and wildlife management on a sound biological basis. Publications: (1) *Journal of Wildlife Management,* quarterly; (2) *Wildlife Society Bulletin,* quarterly; (3) *Wildlife Monographs,* irregular. Formerly: (1937) Society of Wildlife Specialists. Convention/Meeting: Annual—held with North American Wildlife and Natural Resources Conference.

WORLD WILDLIFE FUND-U.S. APPEAL
1319 18th Street, N.W.   Phone: (202) 466-2160
Washington, D.C. 20036
Godfrey A. Rockefeller, Exec. Dir.
Founded: 1961
Staff: 15

Supported by contributions from individuals, funds, corporations, and foundations with a concern for conservation of wildlife and its habitat. Emphasizes preservation of endangered and vanishing species of wildlife anywhere in the world. Programs include public education, promoting law enforcement, initiating ecological and biological research, providing data on endangered species, buying land for nature reserves, and propagating threatened species in captivity. Support is given existing conservation societies, agencies, and governments to carry out projects and services. Maintains small library. Committee: Scientific Advisory. Affiliated with: World Wildlife Fund-International, and International Union for Conservation of Nature and Natural Resources, both headquartered at Morges, Switzerland. Holds board meetings.

(NOTE: Organizations and associations which are national in scope and who desire to be listed in this directory should send detailed information about themselves in the format shown here. Address: The Editor, ANGLER'S BIBLE, 55 Ruta Court, South Hackensack, N.J. 07606.)

Directory of Federal, State and Provincial Agencies Concerned with Fish Protection and Exploitation

FEDERAL GOVERNMENT

Bureau of Sport Fisheries and Wildlife
Fish and Wildlife Service
Department of the Interior
18th and C Streets, N.W.
Washington, D.C. 20240

Corps of Engineers
Department of Defense
Forrestal Building
Washington, D.C. 20314

Environmental Protection Agency
401 M Street, S.W.
Washington, D.C. 20460

Forest Service
Department of Agriculture
Building E
Rosslyn Plaza
Rosslyn, Virginia 22209

National Marine Fisheries Service
Department of Commerce
Page Building No. 2
3300 Whitehaven Parkway
Washington, D.C. 20235

STATE GOVERNMENTS

ALABAMA
Game and Fish Division
Department of Conservation and
  Natural Resources
64 North Union Street
Montgomery, Alabama 36104

ALASKA
Department of Fish and Game
Subport Building
Juneau, Alaska 99801

ARIZONA
Game and Fish Department
2222 West Greenway Road
Phoenix, Arizona 85203

ARKANSAS
Game and Fish Commission
Game and Fish Commission Building
2 Capitol Mall
Little Rock, Arkansas 72201

CALIFORNIA
Department of Fish and Game
Resources Agency
1416 Ninth Street
Sacramento, California 95814

Wildlife Conservation Board
Resources Agency
1416 Ninth Street
Sacramento, California 95814

COLORADO
Division of Wildlife
Department of Natural Resources
6060 Broadway
Denver, Colorado 80216

CONNECTICUT
Fish and Wildlife Unit
Department of Environmental
  Protection
State Office Building
165 Capitol Avenue
Hartford, Connecticut 06115

DELAWARE
Division of Fish and Wildlife
Department of Natural Resources and
  Environmental Control
Tatnall Building
Legislative Avenue and D Street
Dover, Delaware 19901

DISTRICT OF COLUMBIA
Department of Environmental Services
1875 Connecticut Avenue, N.W.
Washington, D.C. 20009

FLORIDA
Game and Fresh Water Fish
  Commission
Farris Bryant Building
620 South Meridian Street
Tallahassee, Florida 32304

GEORGIA
Game and Fish Division
Department of Natural Resources
270 Washington Street, S.W.
Atlanta, Georgia 30334

HAWAII
Fish and Game Division
Department of Land and Natural
  Resources
1179 Punchbowl Street
Honolulu, Hawaii 96813

IDAHO
Fish and Game Department
600 South Walnut
P.O. Box 25
Boise, Idaho 83707

ILLINOIS
Division of Fisheries
Department of Conservation
605 State Office Building
400 South Spring Street
Springfield, Illinois 62706

INDIANA
Fish and Wildlife Division
Department of Natural Resources
607 State Office Building
Indianapolis, Indiana 46204

Land, Forests and Wildlife
Resources Advisory Council
Department of Natural Resources
607 State Office Building
Indianapolis, Indiana 46204

IOWA
Fish and Wildlife Division
Conservation Commission
300 Fourth Street
Des Moines, Iowa 50319

KANSAS
Forestry, Fish and Game Commission
P.O. Box 1028
Pratt, Kansas 67124

KENTUCKY
Department of Fish and Wildlife
  Resources
4th floor
Capital Plaza Tower
Frankfort, Kentucky 40601

LOUISIANA
Fish Division
Wildlife and Fisheries Commission
Box 44095
Capitol Station
Baton Rouge, Louisiana 70804

MAINE
Department of Inland Fisheries
  and Game
284 State Street
Augusta, Maine 04330

Department of Marine Resources
State House Annex
Augusta, Maine 04330

MARYLAND
Department of Natural Resources
Tawes State Office Building
580 Taylor Avenue
Annapolis, Maryland 21401

MASSACHUSETTS
Department of Natural Resources
Leverett Saltonstall Building
100 Cambridge Street
Boston, Massachusetts 02202

MICHIGAN
Department of Natural Resources
Mason Building
Lansing, Michigan 48926

MINNESOTA
Game and Fish Division
Department of Natural Resources
Centennial Office Building
St. Paul, Minnesota 55155

MISSISSIPPI
Game and Fish Commission
Game and Fish Building
402 High Street
P.O. Box 451
Jackson, Mississippi 39205

MISSOURI
Game and Fish Commission
Department of Conservation
2901 North Ten Mile Drive
P.O. Box 180
Jefferson City, Missouri 65101

MONTANA
Department of Fish and Game
Helena, Montana 59601

NEBRASKA
Game and Parks Commission
2200 North 33rd Street
P.O. Box 30370
Lincoln, Nebraska 68503

NEVADA
Department of Fish and Game
P.O. Box 10678
Reno, Nevada 89510

NEW HAMPSHIRE
Department of Fish and Game
34 Bridge Street
Concord, New Hampshire 03301

NEW JERSEY
Fish, Game and Shellfisheries Division
Department of Environmental
   Protection
Labor and Industry Building
P.O. Box 1809
Trenton, New Jersey 08625

NEW MEXICO
Department of Game and Fish
State Capitol
Sante Fe, New Mexico 87503

NEW YORK
Division of Fish and Wildlife
Department of Environmental
   Conservation
50 Wolf Road
Albany, New York 12233

NORTH CAROLINA
Wildlife Resources Commission
Albermarle Building
325 North Salisbury Street
P.O. Box 27687
Raleigh, North Carolina 27611

NORTH DAKOTA
Department of Game and Fish
2121 Lovett Avenue
Bismarck, North Dakota 58505

OHIO
Department of Natural Resources
Fountain Square
Columbus, Ohio 43224

OKLAHOMA
Department of Wildlife Conservation
1801 North Lincoln Boulevard
P.O. Box 53465
Oklahoma City, Oklahoma 73105

OREGON
Fish Commission
307 State Office Building
Portland, Oregon 97201

Wildlife Commission
1634 Southwest Alder Street
P.O. Box 3503
Portland, Oregon 97208

PENNSYLVANIA
Fish Commission
P.O. Box 1673
Harrisburg, Pennsylvania 17120

RHODE ISLAND
Division of Fish and Wildlife
Department of Natural Resources
Veterans' Memorial Building
83 Park Street
Providence, Rhode Island 02903

SOUTH CAROLINA
Wildlife and Marine
   Resources Department
1015 Main Street
P.O. Box 167
Columbia, South Carolina 29202

SOUTH DAKOTA
Department of Game, Fish and Parks
State Office Building No. 1
Pierre, South Dakota 57501

TENNESSEE
Game and Fish Commission
Ellington Agricultural Center
P.O. Box 40747
Nashville, Tennessee 37220

TEXAS
Fish and Wildlife Division
Parks and Wildlife Department
John H. Reagan State Office Building
Austin, Texas 78701

UTAH
Division of Wildlife Resources
Department of Natural Resources
1596 West North Temple
Salt Lake City, Utah 84116

VERMONT
Department of Fish and Game
Agency of Environmental Conservation
Montpelier, Vermont 05602

VIRGINIA
Commission of Game and Inland
   Fisheries
4010 West Broad Street
P.O. Box 11104
Richmond, Virginia 23230

Marine Resources Commission
P.O. Box 756
Newport News, Virginia 23607

WASHINGTON
Department of Game
600 North Capitol Way
Olympia, Washington 98504

WEST VIRGINIA
Division of Wildlife Resources
Department of Natural Resources
1800 Washington Street, East
Charleston, West Virginia 25305

WISCONSIN
Forestry, Wildlife and Recreation
   Division
Department of Natural Resources
P.O. Box 450
Madison, Wisconsin 53701

WYOMING
Game and Fish Department
P.O. Box 1589
Cheyenne, Wyoming 82001

CANADA

ALBERTA
Alberta Fish and Wildlife Division
Natural Resources Building
9833 - 109th Street
Edmonton, Alberta T5K 2E1

BRITISH COLUMBIA
Fish and Wildlife Branch
Environment and Land Use
   Commission
Parliament Building
Victoria, British Columbia V8V 1X4

Department of Land, Forest and
   Water Resources
Parliament Building
Victoria, British Columbia V8V 1X4

MANITOBA
Department of Lands, Forests and
   Wildlife Resources
Fisheries Programs
9-989 Century Street
Winnipeg, Manitoba R3H 0W4

Manitoba Government Travel
200 Vaughan Street
Winnipeg, Manitoba R3C OP8

NEWFOUNDLAND
Canadian Wildlife Service
Sir Humphrey Gilbert Building
Duckworth Street
St. Johns, Newfoundland A1C 1G4

Department of Tourism
Wildlife Division
Confederation Building, 5th Floor
St. John's, Newfoundland A1C 5X1

Environment Canada, Fisheries and
   Marine Service
Building 302
Pleasantville
St. John's, Newfoundland A1C 5X1

NORTHWEST TERRITORIES
Game Management Branch
Government of the Northwest
   Territories
Yellowknife, Northwest Territories
   X0E 1H0

NOVA SCOTIA
Department of Environment
Box 2107
Halifax, Nova Scotia B3J 3B7

Department of Land and Forests
Dennis Building
Granville Street
Halifax, Nova Scotia B3J 3C4

ONTARIO
Sport Fisheries Branch
Ministry of Natural Resources
Whitney Building
Toronto, Ontario M7A 1W3

PRINCE EDWARD ISLAND
Department of Fish and Wildlife
Environmental Control Commission
Box 2000
Charlottetown, Prince Edward Island
   C1A 7N8

QUEBEC
Department of Tourism, Fish and
   Game
150 St. Cyrille East - 15th Floor
Quebec, Quebec G1R 4Y3

SASKATCHEWAN
Department of Natural Resources
Fisheries and Wildlife Branch
Administrative Building
Regina, Saskatchewan S4S 0B1

YUKON TERRITORY
Game Branch
Government of the Yukon Territory
Whitehorse, Yukon Territory Y1A 2C6

Directory of Manufacturers of Fishing Equipment

Tony Accetta & Son, Inc.
932 Avenue "E"
Riviera Beach, Florida   33404

Acme Tackle Company
69 Bucklin Street
Providence, Rhode Island   02907

Aftco
(See Axelson Fishing Tackle
Mfg. Co., Inc.)

Allan Tackle Mfg. Co., Inc.
325 Duffy Avenue
Hicksville, New York   11801

Allied Sports Company
P.O. Box 251
Eufala, Alabama   36027

Al's Goldfish Lure Co.
Indian Orchard, Massachusetts 01051

America's Cup
1443 Portero Avenue
South El Monte, California   91733

Ande, Inc.
1500 53rd Street
W. Palm Beach, Florida   33407

Angler Products, Inc.
210 Spring Street
Butler, Pennsylvania   16001

Anglers Manufacturing Corp.
7729 N. Eastlake Terrace
Chicago, Illinois   60626

Fred Arbogast Co., Inc.
313 W. North Street
Akron, Ohio   44303

Arnold Tackle Corp.
100 Commercial Avenue
Paw Paw, Michigan   49079

Axelson Fishing Tackle Mfg. Co., Inc.
1559 Placentia Avenue
Newport Beach, California   92660

Jim Bagley Bait Co., Inc.
Spirit Lake Road and Recker Highway
Winter Haven, Florida   33880

Bass-Buster, Inc.
Box 118
Amsterdam, Missouri   64723

Bead Chain Co.
110 Mountain Grove Street
Bridgeport, Connecticut   06605

L.L. Bean, Inc.
Freeport, Maine   04032

Bear Paw Tackle Co.
Route 2
Bellaire, Michigan   49615

Berkley & Company
Spirit Lake, Iowa   51360

Bevin-Wilcox Line Co.
Moodus, Connecticut   06469

Big Jon, Inc.
14393 Peninsula Drive
Traverse City, Michigan   49684

Biscayne Rod Mfg., Inc.
3321 N.W. 7th Avenue
Miami, Florida   33127

Blakemore Sales Corp.
North Highway 65
Branson, Missouri   65616

Bomber Bait Company
326 Lindsay
Gainesville, Texas   76240

Boone Bait Company, Inc.
P.O. Box 4009
Winter Park, Florida   32793

Browning
Route 1
Morgan, Utah   84050

Brownwell & Co., Inc.
(See Bevin-Wilcox Line Co.)

Buck Knives
1717 No. Magnolia Avenue
El Cajon, California   92022

Burke Flexo-Products
1969 So. Airport Road
Traverse City, Michigan   49684

Byrd Industries, Inc.
201 Rock Industries Park Road
Bridgeton, Missouri   63044

Bystrom Brothers, Inc.
2200 Snelling Avenue
So. Minneapolis, Minnesota   55404

C & G Tackle Mfg. Co.
1343 North 108 East Avenue
Tulsa, Oklahoma   74116

Camillus Cutlery Co.
Camillus, New York   13031

W.R. Case & Sons Cutlery Co.
Bradford, Pennsylvania   16701

Lew Childre & Sons, Inc.
P.O. Box 535
Foley, Alabama   36535

Colorado Tent & Awning Co.
3333 E. 52nd Avenue Cook Street
Denver, Colorado   80216

Continental Arms Corp.
697 5th Avenue
New York, New York   10022

Converse Rubber Co.
55 Fordham Road
Wilmington, Massachusetts   01887

Cordell Tackle, Inc.
P.O. Box 2020
Hot Springs, Arkansas   71901

Cortland Line Company
Cortland, New York   13045

Cosom
6030 Wayzata Boulevard
Minneapolis, Minnesota   55416

**Mel Cox Baits and Lures
Manufacturing Co.**
Box 1432
Fort Worth, Texas   76101

Creek Chub Bait Co.
113 Keyser Street
Garrett, Indiana   46738

Creme Lure Company
P.O. Box 87
Tyler, Texas   75701

Cuba Specialty Mfg. Co., Inc.
3 S. River Road
Houghton, New York   14744

J. Lee Cuddy Associates, Inc.
450 N.E. 79th Street
Miami, Florida   33138

Daiwa Corporation
14011 So. Normandie Avenue
Gardena, California   90247

Dardevle
(See Lou J. Eppinger Mfg. Co.)

Dart Mfg. Co.
1724 Cockrell Avenue
Dallas, Texas   75215

Data Sport, Inc.
5636 Abbott Avenue South
Edina, Minnesota   55410

Les Davis Fishing Tackle Co.
1565 Center Street
Tacoma, Washington   98409

Dorbo Mfg. Co.
1914 Dana Avenue
Cincinnati, Ohio   45207

Dragon Fly Company, Inc.
823 Broad Street
Sumter, South Carolina   29150

E.I. Du Pont de Nemours & Co., Inc.
1007 Market Street
Wilmington, Delaware   19898

Eagle Claw Fishing Tackle
(see Wright & McGill Co.)

Earlybird Co.
P.O. Box 1485
Boise, Idaho   83701

Emco Specialties, Inc.
P.O. Box 864
Des Moines, Iowa   50304

Lou J. Eppinger Mfg. Co.
6340 Schaefer Highway
Dearborn, Michigan   48126

Eska Company
2400 Kerper Boulevard
Dubuque, Iowa   52001

Factory Distributors
500 No. 7th Street
Fort Smith, Arkansas   72901

Featherweight Prods.
3454-8 Ocean View Boulevard
Glendale, California   91208

Fenwick
14799 Chestnut Street
Westminster, California   92683

Feurer Bros., Inc.
77 Lafayette Avenue
No. White Plains, New York   10603

Fin-Nor
(See Tycoon/Fin-Nor Corp.)

Fish It
P.O. Box 1033
Torrington, Connecticut   06790

Fishmaster Products, Inc.
P.O. Box 9635
Tulsa, Oklahoma   74107

Flambeau Products Corp.
801 Lynn Avenue
Baraboo, Wisconsin   53913

Isaac Franklin Co., Inc.
630 No. Pulaski Street
Baltimore, Maryland   21217

The Gaines Company
Box 35
Gaines, Pennsylvania   16921

Gapen Tackle Co.
Big Lake, Minnesota   55309

The Garcia Corporation
329 Alfred Avenue
Teaneck, New Jersey   07666

Gaunt Industries
6217 Northwest Highway
Chicago, Illinois   60631

Generic Systems, Inc.
P.O. Box 256
Rockaway, New Jersey   07866

Gentex Corp.
P.O. Box 315
Carbondale, Pennsylvania   18407

Gladding Corporation
441 Stuart Street
Boston, Massachusetts   02116

Glas-Lite
Walkerton, Indiana   46574

Gott Mfg. Co., Inc.
1608 Wheat Road
Winfield, Kansas   67156

Gudebrod Bros. Silk Co., Inc.
Fishing Tackle Division
12 South 12th Street
Philadelphia, Pennsylvania   19107

Hardy Brothers
(See Harrington & Richardson)

Harrington & Richardson
Industrial Row
Gardner, Massachusetts   01440

James Heddon's Sons
414 West Street
Dowagiac, Michigan   49047

Helin Tackle Co.
4099 Beaufait Avenue
Detroit, Michigan   48207

John J. Hildebrandt Corp.
817 High Street
Loganport, Indiana   46947

Hopkins Fishing Lure Co., Inc.
1130 Boissevain Avenue
Norfolk, Virginia   23507

IPCO
331 Lake Hazeltine Drive
Chaska, Minnesota   55318

Ideal Products, Inc.
101 W. DuBois Avenue
DuBois, Pennsylvania   15801

International Hook & Tackle
1830 So. Acoma Street
Denver, Colorado   80223

Ray Jefferson
Main & Cotton Streets
Philadelphia, Pennsylvania   19127

Luhr Jensen & Sons, Inc.
P.O. Box 297
Hood River, Oregon   97031

Jet-Aer Corp.
100 6th Avenue
Paterson, New Jersey   07524

Louis Johnson Co.
1547 Old Deerfield Road
Highland Park, Illinois   60035

Johnson Reels Co.
1531 Madison Avenue
Mankato, Minnesota   56001

Jorgensen Bros.
4225 Stanley Boulevard
Pleasanton, California   94566

Klamerus & Co.
4557 West 59th Street
Chicago, Illinois   60629

Knotmaster Industries, Inc.
P.O. Box 23201
San Diego, California   92123

Kodiak Corp.
P.O. Box 467
Ironwood, Michigan   49938

John C. Kremer
542 13th Street
West Palm Beach, Florida   33401

L&S Bait Co., Inc.
1500 East Bay Drive
Largo, Florida 33540

Lakeland Industries
Isle, Minnesota   56342

Lamiglas Corporation
716 West Meeker Street
Kent, Washington   98031

Lazy Ike Corp.
P.O. Box 1177
Fort Dodge, Iowa   50501

H.L. Leonard Rod Co.
25 Cottage Street
Midland Park, New Jersey   07432

Lindy/Little Joe
(See Ray-O-Vac)

Lisk Fly Mfg. Co.
P.O. Box 5126
Greensboro, North Carolina   27403

Lowrance Electronics, Inc.
12000 East Skelly Drive
Tulsa, Oklahoma   74128

Mac-Jac Manufacturing Co.
1590 Creston Street
Muskegon, Michigan   49443

Mann's Bait Co.
State Docks Road
Eufaula, Alabama   36027

Marathon Rubber Products Co.
510 Sherman Street
Wausau, Wisconsin   54401

Jerry Martin Co.
4411 Grand Avenue
Gurnee, Illinois   60031

Martin Reel Company
30 East Main Street
Mohawk, New York   13407

**Martin Tackle & Manufacturing
   Company**
512 Minor Avenue North
Seattle, Washington   98109

Mason Tackle Company
Otisville, Michigan   48463

Joseph Mennen Co., Inc.
192 Vincent Avenue
Lynbrook, New York   11563

Mepps
(See Sheldon's, Inc.)

Mighty-Mac, Inc.
Gloucester, Massachusetts   01930

Mildrum Manufacturing Co.
East Berlin, Connecticut   06023

Minn Kota Manufacturing Co.
201 No. 17th Street
Moorhead, Minnesota   56560

Mirrolure
(See L & S Bait Co., Inc.)

Bruce B. Mises, Inc.
1122 South Robertson Boulevard
Los Angeles, California   90035

Mister Twister, Inc.
200 Commerse Street
Minden, Louisiana   71055

Miya Epoch U.S.A., Inc.
2075 Palos Verdes Drive North
Lomita, California   90717

O. Mustad & Son, Inc.
185 Clark Street
Auburn, New York   13021

F.J. Neil Co., Inc.
345 Hillside Avenue
Williston Park, New York   11596

Norman Manufacturing Co., Inc.
Highway 96 East
Greenwood, Arkansas   72936

Normark Corp.
1710 E. 78th Street
(Highway 494 & Cedar Avenue)
Minneapolis, Minnesota   55423

Nova Products, Inc.
220 Avenue C
Carrollton, Georgia   30117

Nylon Net Co.
7 Vance Avenue
Memphis, Tennessee   38101

Oberlin Canteen Co.
212 Sumner Street
Oberlin, Ohio   44074

OLM International Corporation
145 Sylvester Road
South San Francisco, California   94080

Old Pal
(See Woodstream Corporation)

Olsen Knife Co., Inc.
Howard City, Michigan   49329

Optronics
350 North Wheeler Street
Fort Gibson, Oklahoma   74434

The Orvis Company, Inc.
Manchester, Vermont   05254

Outers Laboratories, Inc.
Onalaska, Wisconsin   54650

Padre Island Co.
2617 N. Zarzamora
San Antonio, Texas   78201

Paulin Products Co.
30520 Lakeland Boulevard
Willowick, Ohio   44094

Penguin Industries, Inc.
P.O. Box 97
Parkersburg, Pennsylvania   19365

Penn Fishing Tackle Mfg. Co.
3028 W. Hunting Park Avenue
Philadelphia, Pennsylvania   19132

Pequea Fishing Tackle, Inc.
Strasburg, Pennsylvania   17579

Pezon et Michel
(See Stoeger Industries)

Pflueger
P.O. Box 185
Columbia, South Carolina   29202

Phillips Fly & Tackle Co.
P.O. Box 188
Alexandria, Pennsylvania   16611

Phillipson
(See 3M Company)

Pico Lures
(See Padre Island Co.)

Plano Molding Company
113 South Center Avenue
Plano, Illinois   60545

J.R. Plasters Co.
111 No. Denver
Kansas City, Missouri   64123

**Plastics Research and Development
   Corporation**
3601 Jenny Lind
Fort Smith, Arkansas   72901

Plastilite Corp.
4909 North 45th Street
Omaha, Nebraska   68112

Pompanette, Inc.
1515 S.E. 16th Street
Fort Lauderdale, Florida   33316

Powerscopic Corp.
25 East Union Avenue
East Rutherford, New Jersey   07073

Quick Corporation of America
620 Terminal Way
Costa Mesa, California   92627

Ray-O-Vac
Box 488
Brainerd, Minnesota   56401

Rebel
(See Plastics Research and Development
   Corporation)

Rectack of America
4982 Firestone Boulevard
South Gate, California   90280

Reece Enterprises
P.O. Box 496
Columbus, Nebraska   68601

Riviera Manufacturing, Inc.
3859 Roger Chaffee Boulevard, S.E.
Grand Rapids, Michigan   49508

Hank Roberts
1033 Walnut Street
Boulder, Colorado   80302

Rod Caddy Corp.
920 W. Cullerton Street
Chicago, Illinois   60608

Rogers World Champion Lures
(See Silvertrol)

H.S. Ross
347 Buchanan Street
Twin Falls, Idaho   83301

Ruff'N Ready Manufacturing Co.
6 Andrews Street
Greenville, South Carolina   29601

St. Croix Corporation
9909 So. Shore Drive
Minneapolis, Minnesota   55441

Sampo, Inc.
Barneveld, New York   13304

Sargent & Co.
100 Sargent Drive
New Haven, Connecticut   06509

Saunders Archery Co.
Box 476
Industrial Site
Columbus, Nebraska   68601

Scientific Anglers/3M Company
P.O. Box 2007
Midland, Michigan   48640

Schaper
(See St. Croix Corporation)

Shakespeare Company
P.O. Box 246
Columbia, South Carolina   29202

Shannon Lure Co.
3654 W. Montrose Avenue
Chicago, Illinois   60618

Sheldon's, Inc.
P.O. Box 508
Antigo, Wisconsin   54409

Siberian Salmon Egg Co.
4660 E. Marginal Way South
Seattle, Washington   98134

Silvertrol
Purdy, Missouri   65734

Skyline Industries
4900 N.E. Parkway
Fort Worth, Texas   76101

Jim Smith Bass Trap Lure Co.
(See Gapen Tackle Co.)

Jack K. Smithwick & Son
P.O. Box 1205
Shreveport, Louisiana   71163

Southern Tackle Distributors, Inc.
(See Spinmaster)

Spinmaster
5800 Miami Lakes Drive East
Miami Lakes, Florida   33014

Sportsmen's Lab, Inc.
Box 732
Anoka, Minnesota   55303

Stearns Manufacturing Co.
P.O. Box 1498
St. Cloud, Minnesota   56301

Stembridge Products, Inc.
2941 Central Avenue
East Point, Georgia   30344

Stoeger Industries
55 Ruta Court
South Hackensack, New Jersey   07606

Storm Manufacturing Co.
P.O. Box 265
Norman, Oklahoma   73069

Stratton & Terstegge Co.
P.O. Box 1859
Louisville, Kentucky   40201

Strike King Lure Co.
2850 Sanderwood
Memphis, Tennessee   38118

Strike Master, Inc.
411 Washington Avenue
Minneapolis, Minnesota   55401

Subria Corp.
P.O. Box 113
Montclair, New Jersey   07042

Suick Lure Manufacturing Co.
Highway 45 North
Antigo, Wisconsin   54409

Sunset Line & Twine Company
Jefferson & Erwin Streets
Petaluma, California   94952

Syl-Mark Enterprises
P.O. Box 806
Northridge, California   91324

Taylor Instrument
Arden, North Carolina   28704

Telisons International Corp.
7075½ Vineland Avenue
No. Hollywood, California   91605

Tempo Products Co.
6200 Cochran Road
Cleveland, Ohio   44139

ThinFin
(See Storm Manufacturing Co.)

3M Company
(See Scientific Anglers/3M Company)

**Tri Fin Fishing Tackle Manufacturing
Corp.**
(See Storm Manufacturing Co.)

Trimarc Corp.
High Point Plaza
Hillside, Illinois   60162

True Temper Corp.
1623 Euclid Avenue
Cleveland, Ohio   44115

Tru-Nord
204 No. Ninth Street
Brainerd, Minnesota   56401

Tucker Duck & Rubber Co.
2701 Kelley Highway
Fort Smith, Arkansas   72901

Tycoon/Fin-Nor Corp.
7447 N.W. 12th Street
Miami, Florida   33126

Umco
P.O. Box 608
Watertown, New Mexico   55388

Uncle Josh Bait Company
524 Clarence Street
Fort Atkinson, Wisconsin   53538

Uniroyal Consumer Products
Naugatuck Footwear Plant
58 Maple Street
Naugatuck, Connecticut   06770

Universal Vise Company
22 Main Street
Westfield, Massachusetts   01085

Varmac Mfg. Co.
4201 Redwood Avenue
Los Angeles, California   90066

Vexilar, Inc.
9345 Penn Avenue S.
Minneapolis, Minnesota   55431

Vlchek Plastics Co.
15981 Valplast Road
Middlefield, Ohio   44062

Fritz von Schlegell
1407 Santa Fe Avenue
Los Angeles, California   90021

Waller Corp.
4220 Waller Drive
Crystal Lake, Illinois   60014

Weber Tackle Company
Stevens Point, Wisconsin   54481

Erwin Weller Co.
2105 Clark Street
Sioux City, Iowa   51104

Western Cutlery Co.
5311 Western Avenue
Boulder, Colorado   80302

Whopper Stopper, Inc.
P.O. Box 1111
Sherman, Texas   75090

Woodstream Corp.
Lititz, Pennsylvania   17543

Worth Fishing Tackle Company
P.O. Box 88
Stevens Point, Wisconsin   54481

Wright & McGill Co.
4245 E. 46th Avenue
Denver, Colorado   80216

Zebco
6101 East Apache
Tulsa, Oklahoma   74101

Specifications: Rods

All about Fishing Rods

Selecting the Right Rod

In most kinds of fishing, rod "action" is highly important. "Action" is the flex of a rod, which depends upon the rod-building material, its taper and length.

Most rods are rated as having actions that are light, medium-light, medium, heavy, medium heavy, or extra-heavy. A rod with medium-light action would be proper for casting light lures for small fish; a rod with heavy action would be suited to casting large lures for big fish.

A rod should be chosen first of all for its action. Quality rods are properly tapered for the best action. They are of the correct weight for their size, and for the type of fishing for which they are primarily designed. Finally, quality rods have snug ferrules; comfortable, well-designed handles; smooth working, positive-locking reel seats; a suitable number of long-wearing guides.

In many ways, fishing rods are like other merchandise; you get what you pay for. There are inexpensive rods on the market that have excellent actions and offer value for the price, but usually it is wise to purchase the best rod you can afford. "Brand name" rods are recommended. Manufacturers having a widely recognized, widely accepted "name" got their reputations by marketing quality rods, at fair prices, and then standing behind their products.

Rod Nomenclature

All rods are made up of about the same components. They may differ in design, size and actions, but all have handles, shafts, guides, reel seals.

Tips, Guides and Ferrules

Tips, guides and ferrules are important "hardware" on a rod. If a rod's tip-top or guides are not of quality material or well designed, they will wear quickly and cut a line...causing the loss of lures or hooked fish.

Tungsten carbide is a popular material for guides and tops. It is super hard, hence long-wearing, and is corrosion resistant. Guides and tops with ceramic inserts also fall into this category.

Stainless steel guides and tops are good, as are guides/tops of other metals when heavily chrome-plated.

The best kind of tip-top for rods other than fly rods is one having supporting bars. These supports help keep the tip ring from breaking loose and, moreover, aid in preventing the line from wrapping around the tip.

Roller tip-tops have rollers within the guide which are mounted on oilless bushings, or on greased but sealed ball bearings, to reduce friction.

Guides for spinning, spin-casting, and bait casting rods fundamentally are similar in design. The guides on a spinning rod are very large because line spirals off a spinning reel. They should be only slightly smaller on a spin-cast rod, since line also spirals—although less so—off a spin-cast reel. The guides on bait casting rods are smaller because line does not spiral.

Good ferrules should fit tightly; any new rod whose ferrules fit loosely is to be avoided. There are many rods available that are manufacturered with fiberglass ferrules. Some are self-ferruled with the smaller section(s) of the rod fitting directly into the larger section. Such rods are strong, light and have good actions.

Handles and Reel Seats

A rod handle must be comfortable, strong, and accept the reel in an easily adjustable, secure reel seat.

The handles and reel seats on spin-cast and bait casting rods are basically similar. Usually they are "offset" with the handle recessed where the reel is mounted. They may, however, be of the "double offset" type which means that not only is the handle recessed where the reel is mounted, but the grip, too, is at an "off" angle, instead of being in a straight line.

The handles of all spinning rods are straight, but the shapes of the main handle, and of the foregrip, may vary slightly. What's important is that the handle be comfortable. The handles on salt water spinning rods are usually quite long, 15 in. or more, so that two-handed casting can be done.

Long strong handles are the rule on surf fishing rods because two-handed casting is necessary. Boat, pier and deep sea rods also have long, sturdy handles because two hands are needed in using them. Also, the handles of such rods frequently are placed in rod-holding sand spikes, boat rod-holders, or in the sockets of harnesses or belts.

Hardwood handles are preferred on many heavy-duty rods because they are rugged and withstand years of use.

The best fixed reel seats are double screw-locking; next best, single screw-locking. Sliding bands, of metal or plastic, are used to secure reels on some spinning and fly rods. The primary advantage of sliding bands is that they are light.

Rod reel seats may be made of tough plastic, chrome-plated brass, or of anodized aluminum. All are satisfactory.

Tips, guides and ferrules are important "hardware" on a rod. If a rod's tip-top or guides are not of quality material or well designed, they will wear quickly and cut a line...causing the loss of lures or hooked fish.

Spin-cast reels mount higher on a rod's reel seat than do bait casting reels. For that reason some spin-cast rods have low-profile reel seats... which puts the spin-cast reel's push-button within easy reach of the caster's thumb. Too, monofilament line tends to balloon a bit when leaving a spin-cast reel, so the guides on a good spin-cast rod are larger than the guides on a typical bait casting rod. There should be enough guides on the rod to permit uniform bending, and they should be properly spaced.

Bait Casting Rods

The bait casting rod is used with a revolving spool reel, usually one having a level-wind mechanism that spools the line evenly onto the reel. A long, light, whippy bait casting rod is best for fishing with light line and light lures; a shorter, fairly stiff, "heavy-action" rod best handles heavy line and lures.

Bait casting rods and reels provide

great casting accuracy, allow very good "feel" in working lures, and are excellent in fighting hooked fish.

Many tackle companies make bait casting rods expressly designed for fishing with plastic worms. Such rods are fairly stout, with actions ranging from "medium" to "medium heavy," and popular lengths are 5½ or 6 ft.

A light bait casting outfit would consist of a fast, free-spool type reel on a 6 or 6½ ft., light-tip action rod, and best line would be 6 to 10 lb. test. A medium outfit, for use with lures around ⅝ oz., would include a rod 5½ or 6 ft., of either "medium" or "medium heavy" action. Matching line would test 12 to 18 lbs. A heavy outfit, for lures up to 2 oz., would be a stiff, "heavy" action bait casting rod of 5 or 5½ ft., and line testing 15 to 25 lbs.

Ferrules or "joints" alter the normal action of a single-piece rod shaft, so—where action is concerned—the fewer pieces the better; also, the more ferrules the more a rod weighs. However, the bait casting rod that breaks down into at least two pieces is readily portable.

A good bait casting rod has a reliable means of locking the reel to the reel seat. The bait casting reel should readily fit into the rod's reel seat, and it should be possible to quickly, easily, and solidly lock the reel into place on the rod handle.

Spin-Cast Rods

Spin-cast rods are very similar in style, etc. to bait casting rods, but there are differences.

While a spin-cast rod may be used with a bait casting reel, and a bait casting reel may be used on a spin-cast rod, a spin-cast reel operates best on a spin-cast rod.

Spin-cast reels mount higher on a rod's reel seat than do bait casting reels. For that reason some spin-cast rods have low-profile reel seats... which puts the spin-cast reel's push-button within easy reach of the caster's thumb. Too, monofilament line tends to balloon a bit when leaving a spin-cast reel, so the guides on a good spin-cast rod are larger than the guides on a typical bait casting rod. There should be enough guides on the rod to permit uniform bending, and they should be properly spaced.

Fairly long, whippy spin-cast rods are generally preferred because they perform best with light lines and lures used most often in spin-casting. Popular lengths are 6 and 6½ ft.

The important thing in selecting a spin-cast rod for its action is to consider the weight of the lures to be cast. If the rod is to flex and "work" it must be limber enough to respond to the weight of the lure and provide maximum momentum at the instant the lure is delivered, or "cast."

Spinning Rods

All spinning rods have a few things in common: the reel seats are near the center of the handle, guides are oversized, and the rod shaft is usually long and whippy. Spinning rod lengths may range from a minimum of 4½ ft. up to 14 ft. Weight may be 1½ to 30 ounces. Spinning rod actions range from ultra-light to extra heavy.

Spinning rods may be of one- or multiple-piece design. For the ultimate in casting, a one-piece rod is best since it has no ferrules to interfere with the natural flexing of the rod's shaft. For transportation convenience the sectional rods, whether two-, three-piece or more pieces, are best.

Guides are of particular importance on spinning rods because line pours from open-face fixed-spool spinning reels in large spirals. The first, and largest guide, chokes down part of this whirl and passes the line onto the next guide, which further reduces the size of the spiral. If the rod guides are correctly sized and spaced, the line will be moving without any spirals by the time it reaches the end of the spinning rod.

Spinning rod guides also should be elevated from the rod's shaft. The butt guide will be highest from the shaft, the other guides decreasing gradually in elevation. This elevation of guides is to reduce "line slap," which occurs when the line whirls off the reel spool.

Fly Rods

Fly rods are available in one-, two- and three-piece construction; two-piece models are most popular. Extra tip sections are available with some rods, but add to the price.

Some fly rods have extension butts, most being removable. An extension butt adds three or four inches to the handle, and may be used as a second rod grip or pressed against the angler's belly to provide leverage when fighting large fish.

Fly rods made of tubular fiberglass are the most popular. Custom-grade bamboo rods, which have smooth actions, are preferred by many trout fishermen. Solid glass fly rods generally are not up to the quality of most fiberglass rods, and tend to be heavier.

All guides on a fly rod should be of adequate size, especially the butt or first guide, so the fly line will pass through freely with the least resistance or friction.

In a sense fly rods are "sized," and must be selected for length, weight, "action," weight of line to be used, and the kind of fishing to be done.

A fly rod for all-around fishing would be 8 or 8½ ft., weighing 4 to 5 oz., and taking a No. 7 or 8 weight line. For very light dry fly fishing, a rod measuring 6 to 7½ ft., weighing 2½ to 3½ oz., and taking a No. 5 or 6 line would be appropriate. For heavy fishing the fly rod should be 8½ to 9½ ft., weigh 4½ oz. or more, and balance with a No. 8 to 11 weight line.

Most fly rods are marked by the manufacturer as to the weight (number) of fly line that is suited to the rod.

Surf Rods

Tubular fiberglass is generally considered the best possible material for surf rods. Typical surf rods, even the shortest and lightest, are comparatively heavy, so those made of the lightest materials are in demand.

The most popular surf rods are big spinning "sticks," but some anglers still prefer to do their surf casting with revolving spool reels, so there are actually two kinds of surf rods—long, two-handed spinning rods, and powerful, lengthy, "conventional" surf rods.

One-piece surf rods are preferred by most beach veterans, since they have smoother casting action and are lighter, but when transportation is a problem, two-piece rods are necessary. Some surf rods are available with one-piece shafts, but with detachable handles.

Surf rods are available in lengths 7 to 14 ft., but the conventional type is most popular in lengths of 8 to 10 ft., measuring from the butt to tip-top. The action of such rods is designed to handle lures weighing 2 to 4 oz.

The heavy surf spinning rod runs 10 to 14 ft., and while the butt action may be quite powerful, the most serviceable of these rods have tips light enough to handle a wide range of lure weights, and also reduce the fatigue factor in casting.

The guides on a surf spinning rod are larger than the guides on other spinning rods. The butt guide, in particular, is giant size, and necessarily so to gather the looping monofilament line as it leaves the spinning reel spool. Always check the surf spinning rod to be certain the butt, or first guide, is sufficiently large.

Boat and Bay Rods

Boat and bay rods, which might also be called pier or trolling rods, encompass an unbelievably vast variety of rods. They are meant primarily for salt water fishing, but many are used in fresh water for deep trolling or heavy fresh water game fish.

Most of these rods are uniquely short, have stiff, powerful actions, large reel seats built to accept the larger salt water revolving spool reels, and long, husky, two-handed handles.

The exact model or type of boat or bay rod to be selected depends upon personal preference. Many boat-bay rods may be considered "workhorses" or powerful rods by which to put fish into the boat.

One must decide for himself, or with the assistance of an experienced angler or qualified tackle store clerk, on the length, weight, and degree of "heaviness" in the boat-bay rod he needs. The longer rods are best for bridge or pier fishing, because their extra length enables a fisherman to reach well away from bridge structure—to better control his bait, and also to keep hooked fish from fouling line in bridge or pier supports. For boat trolling, shorter rods will do, as they are easier to handle in the confines of a boat.

A rod with a "soft" or sensitive tip is useful in fishing for wary or easy-biting fish because the rod's light tip will aid the angler in detecting short bites. When fishing from a party boat crowded with fishermen, and it's necessary to boat hooked fish quickly to avoid tangled lines, short, extra-stiff boat rods are best.

Class Rods

The big game fish, deep sea rod must be more solidly built and more dependable than any other fishing rod.

When a prized fish of 130 pounds leaps over the surface, or an 800 pounder sounds to the bottom, are not times for a rod handle to split, or for guides to rip off.

Most manufacturers grade their deep sea rods according to line test classifications; in other words, to take a fish that would be eligible for record purposes in the "under 30 pound line test classification," one should purchase a rod rated as a "30 pound class" or less rod. Such classification of rods really is just another way of identifying their actions from "light" to "medium" to "heavy." In this vein, rods usually are listed as 30, 50, or 80 pound class.

However, if records or fishing contests are unimportant, it should be remembered that the longer the rod the more easily and quickly large fish can be boated.

Quality construction is essential in big game fish rods. The handles, ferrules, reel seats and guides must be top grade. Guides are especially important. They should be heavy-duty, well-supported, and of roller type. The roller guides on the big game fish rod should have self-lubricating bearings.
—Courtesy of the American Fishing Tackle Manufacturers Association.

A complete list of graphite rods available can be found in the specifications section.

1977 Product Preview Rods

Graphite continues to capture the attention of both manufacturers and fishermen for 1977. Those companies that have marketed models made from this miracle material in the past few years have expanded their lines considerably. Another clue to the growth of graphite as a rod-building material can be found in the number of companies that are selling graphite for the first time this year.

Considerable research and development effort has been given to making fiberglass better. Several rod makers are unveiling glass models with subtle improvements and refinements. Blanks are getting lighter and stronger each season, and the addition of ceramic guides and tip tops adds to the appeal of many rods.

Shakespeare's Ugly Stiks open a new area for composites in which

Shakespeare Ugly Stik Rods.

graphite and glass are blended to produce rugged rods that are reported to be unbreakable under normal fishing conditions. In fact, the new rods are covered by both a 30-day refund and a 5-year free-replacement warranty from Shakespeare. There are twelve rods in the series, including five spinning, one spin-cast and two bait-cast Ugly Stiks. Salt water anglers can find a 7-foot spinning rod, a 6-foot-6-inch trolling rod, an 8-foot-6-inch special rod for downriggers and a 9-foot fly rod that handles a No. 11 fly line.

Using the Howald Process to produce 100-percent-graphite rods, Shakespeare has added seven new models to bring the total number of graphite rods in the line to fourteen. Spinning rods range in length from a 5-foot ultralight to a 7-foot all-purpose design and a 10-foot-6-inch graphite surf rod. Fly rods start with a 4½-footer for a 5-weight line and go up to a 9-foot model for a 10-weight line.

Fenwick is introducing a new, higher-modulus fiberglass material called Fenglass. It retains many of the qualities of conventional fiber-glass, but it is somewhat lighter, feels a little stiffer and has a sensitivity that is unique for the material. After two years of experimentation, Fenglass has been fashioned into a series of casting rods called the Lunkerstik 2000 series.

Another addition to the 2000 series is the Grip-lok pistol grip handle made of lightweight synthetic material. It totally eliminates the need for a butt ferrule of any type, and no adapters are necessary. The blank simply slips into the grip. These bait-casting rods are available in several models ranging from ultralight actions to power actions and in length from 5½ to 6 feet.

Bass fishermen are beginning to perfect the technique of flipping, in which a lure is tossed into the shallows or some type of structure by means of a long rod. Fenwick's Flippin'Stik is 7½ feet long, will handle lures from 3/8-ounce to 2 ounces, and lines from 15- to 30-pound test. The tip is extra stiff to enable anglers to set a hook faster, and the distance between the reel seat and the first guide has been extended to permit re-casting without touching the reel.

The line of Fenwick HMG graphite rods is even more complete this year in all categories, and the company offers as many fly rod options as any other manufacturer, including new 10½-foot models to handle an 8-weight line and an 11-weight line. There has been renewed interest in the Voyageur travel rods that offer a combination spinning-fly option; this series includes a new graphite model that handles 2- to 6-pound monofilament and a 6-weight fly line.

Daiwa has added new models to all its series of rods. There are eight additions to the VIP series which is the best of the fiberglass line. These rods have glass-to-glass ferrules, ceramic guides on some models and a tricolor triple-diamond wrap.

The attention-getter from Daiwa this year is a series of ultralight rods tailored to fit the new Minicast and Minispin Systems. On the Minispin System, the reel is built right into the Neoprene handle and there are two rod models: a 4½-foot two-piece and a 5-foot five-piece. Each ultralight rod is built

Shakespeare Graflite Graphite Rods.

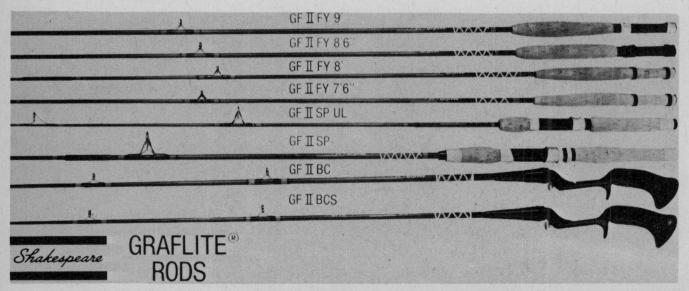

GF II FY 9'
GF II FY 8'6"
GF II FY 8'
GF II FY 7'6"
GF II SP UL
GF II SP
GF II BC
GF II BCS

Shakespeare GRAFLITE® RODS

Fenwick Voyageur fly/spin combination.

Daiwa Mini-Spin combination.

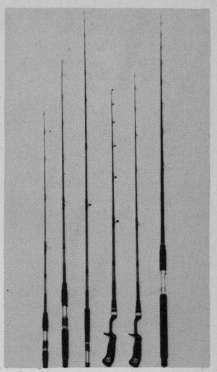

The Daiwa VIP Series.

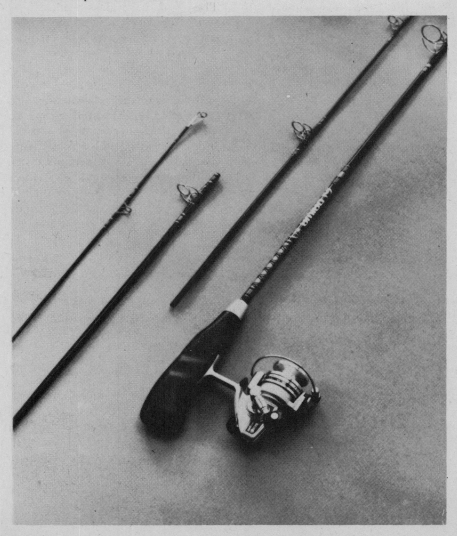

for a specific reel to produce balanced action.

Seven new System G graphite fly rods manufactured by Scientific Anglers/3M made their appearance in the marketplace. Using 3M's Oriented Filament technology, the rods are 100-percent graphite in a rich, translucent maroon color. Ferrules are the new 3M low-profile internal-metal design that reduces line slap and transmits a smooth flow of power. Reel seats are reversed to prevent the locking nut from backing off. The System G fly rods are available for line sizes 4 through 10, and each model in graphite is slightly longer than the corresponding rod in fiberglass because the material is lighter and stronger.

Scientific Anglers/3M has also unveiled an 8-foot-1-inch pack rod that disassembles into five pieces. The 4-ounce rod, balanced with a 6-weight fly line, is the company's

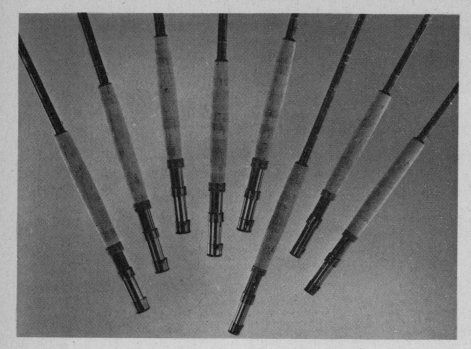

Scientific Anglers/3M System Fly Rods.

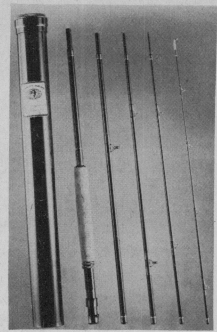

System 6 Pack Rod by Scientific Anglers/3M.

Lamiglas computer-engineered graphite fishing rods.

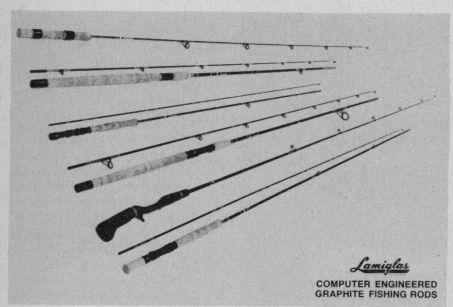

Lamiglas
COMPUTER ENGINEERED
GRAPHITE FISHING RODS

first entry into the pack rod field.

The Lamiglas line-up of computer-engineered graphite fishing rods and blanks now stands at 115, with 6 new fly, mooching and worm-spin rods. There's a new 7¼-ounce, 9-foot fly rod that will handle a 12 or 13 fly line and is strong enough to wrestle the toughest fish that swim. Salmon fishermen will find new sensitivity in the S86SAC mooching rod, built for line weights from 10 to 30 pounds and lures from 1½ to 4 ounces.

Spinning enthusiasts will enjoy the S56 model, which is 5½ feet long, weighs 2½ ounces and can handle lines from 6- to 8-pound test. There are also a 6½-footer and a 7-footer (S66M and S70M) that are designed for 8- to 12-pound test line and lures weighing 1/4 to 3/8 ounce. For the sock-it-to-'em fisherman, Lamiglas has a 5-foot-8-inch worm spin rod which has a double-locking reel seat and is capable of handling lures from 1/4 to 5/8 ounce and line tests from 8 to 17 pounds.

The heart of the Lamiglas graphite engineering is in the design of the graphite-to-graphite ferrule. Based on computer readouts, the ferruling system allows virtually the same action and telegraphing sensitivity as a one-piece rod, because the ferrules are designed and manufactured as an integral part of the total rod.

For the do-it-yourself enthusi-

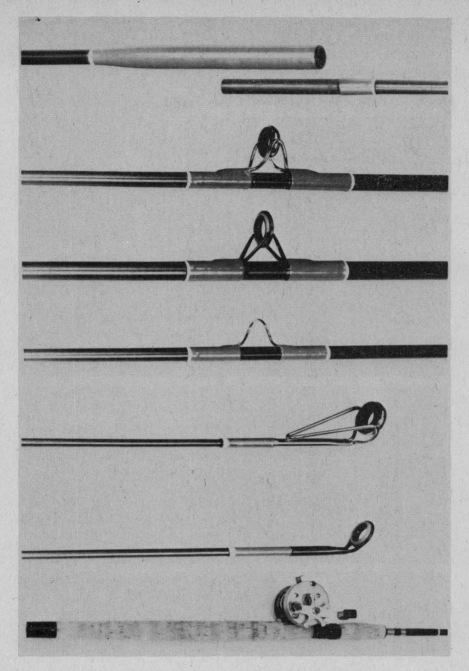

Specially engineered graphite ferrules and quality components are features of Lamiglas rods.

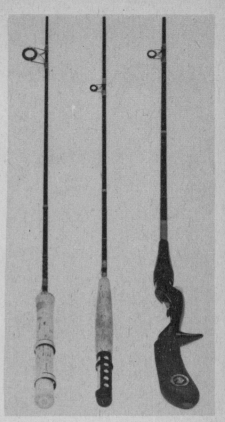

Berkley graphite rods.

ast, Lamiglas markets an extensive line of both graphite and fiberglass fishing-rod blanks for every rod style imaginable.

Berkley & Co. has entered the graphite-rod business by introducing nine models made from 96-per-cent - graphite - reinforced fibers. The rods feature all-aluminum-oxide tip top and stripper guides for the fly models and all-aluminum oxide on the spinning and bait-casting designs (with the exception of ultralight spin). There are five fly rods, from a 7-footer for a 4-weight line to a 9-footer for 8- or 9-weight line.

Graphite spinning sticks include a 5-foot ultralight that weighs 2 ounces and handles 4-to 10-pound line and a 6½-footer that only weighs 1/2 ounce more and can be used with lines up to 12-pound test. Bait-casting rods feature a medium-light and a medium model, the former 5 feet 2 inches and the latter 5½ feet. The lighter bait-casting rod handles lures up to 3/8 ounce, while the huskier design works with lures up to 1/2 ounce.

For the bargain-conscious angler, Berkley has introduced its new Gray Series of glass rods in six models. All have ceramic guides and tip tops, and annodized-aluminum reel seats, and the spinning rods have specie cork grips. There

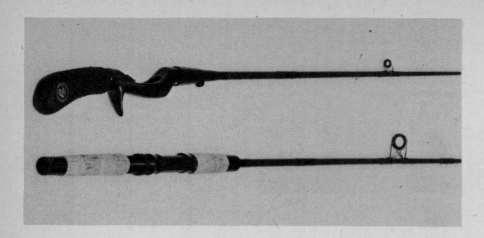

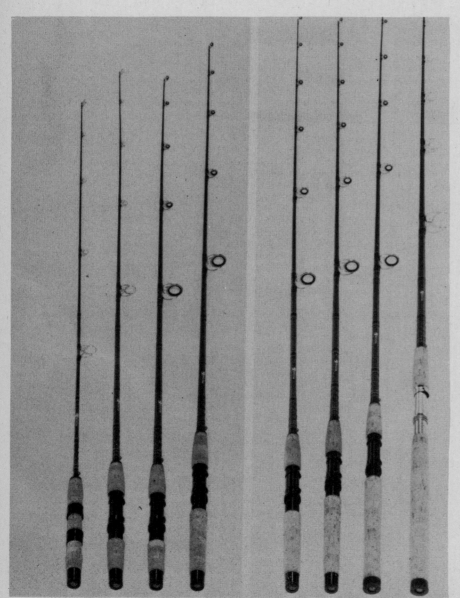

The new line of Garcia Mitchell

are two bait-casting designs, 5 feet 2 inches and 5½ feet, a 6-foot spin-cast rod, a 5-foot-3-inch Powerlite, and 6½-foot and 7-foot spinning rods.

The serious spin fisherman now has an even greater choice of high-quality Garcia Conolon rods with the recently introduced Mitchell spinning rod line. The eleven models, ranging from 5 feet to 7½ feet cover the waterfront from ultralight to heavy fresh water/light salt water use. These lightweight powerful spinning rods feature structural fiberglass ferrules, hand-wound guides, select-grade specie cork grips, and Conoguard long-life finish.

Seven new fly rods just announced by Garcia range from 6 feet to 9 feet. This Conolon series covers a wide span of fishing assignments from small brushy streams to steelhead and Atlantic salmon waters. Each rod comes with a protective plastic tube and fitted cap.

Meeting all pertinent I.G.F.A. class specifications, the rods in the Garcia Conolon Big Game series now feature a new aluminum butt section in addition to a detachable butt design with a self-aligning ferrule. There is a PVC plastic bushing located between the chromed-brass reel seats and the new aluminum butt sections to prevent the electrolysis that has plagued other rods with aluminum butts. Other features include Varmac reel seats and Aftco and Mildrum roller guides.

Transa-Coil naturally spiraled blanks, Slipstream guides, cushion butt and comfort grips, plus a double-locking reel seat system, mark the Zebco Pro Staff rods. These are tailored for the serious angler and are available in spinning, spin-casting, bait-casting and fly series.

Skyline Industries has added to its 100-percent-graphite fishing rods with the introduction of its

Saturn line as a companion to the Apollo series. The Saturns are similar to the Apollo blanks except that the ridges have not been buffed down. All Skyline graphite rods are hand-crafted, using a spiral technique of arranging the fibers for power, flex pattern and sensitivity.

The new 1977 products also include a two-piece 7-foot spinning rod made specifically for West Coast fishing and capable of handling a 1/16-ounce lure with 4-pound test line. On the stronger side, the Doodle-Soc'N rod is also a 7-footer, but this model is made for vertical jigging with an extra strong butt and tip. Planned for salt water fishermen is a new 7-foot Pop In rod designed with a light, sensitive tip and plenty of backbone.

Two new spinning rods for walleye fishing and live bait work in Northern lakes round out the Skyline additions. The 5½-foot and 6-foot models work with 1/4- to 3/4-ounce lures and 10- to 17-pound test line. Their outstanding features are sensitive tips and strong butts for working the weeds of cold-water lakes, but they are finding favor as worm rods with anglers below the Mason-Dixon line.

The Orvis Company of Manchester, Vermont, is adding to its line of thirteen specially designed graphite fly rods and five spinning rods. At the same time, the company is refining its graphite series to incorporate subtleties that make excellent rods even better. The big news from Orvis is its entry into the graphite-blank business. For the first time, customers will be able to buy blanks. Until now, Orvis graphite was reserved solely for Orvis rods finished by Orvis.

Leading the list of new rods for 1977 from Wright & McGill is the Eagle Claw Granger Graphite Blue Diamond series constructed from

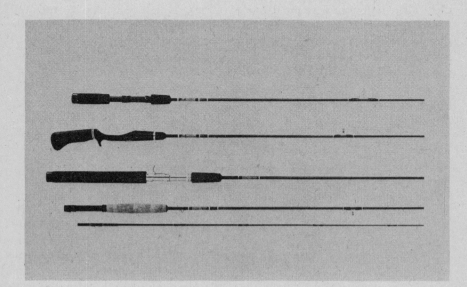

1977 additions to the Skyline 100-percent graphite series.

Eagle Claw's Blue Diamond Graphite.

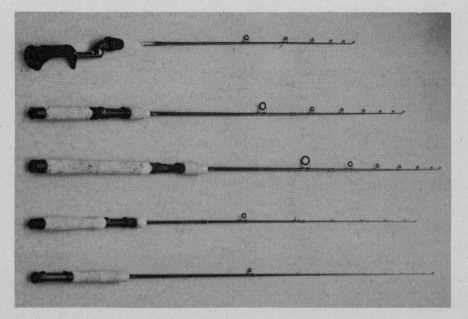

3M brand graphite-oriented filaments. Specially engineered miniature steel ferrules bring out the best performance in two-piece models. This top-of-the-line series features finest-quality components, such as ceramic guides (hard-chromed snake guides in fly rods), lightweight magnesium handles on casting models, high-quality specie cork grips, nickel silver hook keepers, and the Sealflex 100 finish on the wraps. There are seventeen models including fly rods for line sizes 4 through 10 and a combination spin/fly pack rod that breaks down into four pieces and has a suede case.

Graphite combination spin/fly pack rod by Eagle Claw.

Advances in the design of fiberglass produced the new Water Seal line for Eagle Claw. Available in fifteen models for fly fishing, spinning, and bait casting, this series features unique unilateral filaments, mini-ferrules that eliminate the stiff spot in two-piece construction and ceramic guides.

A special Granger series of rods has been designed for the steelhead and salmon fisherman of the Northwest and the Great Lakes. These rods are long and strong, with sensitive tips and the power to stop a running fish.

Bass pro Tom Mann has added his signature to another series of rods that he personally designed for largemouth fanciers. Anyone

who has fished with Tom knows he prefers spinning tackle for bass fishing; that is why his signature series contain one casting model and nine spinning rods, from a 5-foot model to a pair of husky 7-footers.

Billed as the newest thing in fishing rods, Pflueger's Graph-Glass combines the light weight and strength of graphite with the durability of fiberglass to make one of the strongest and most sensitive fishing rods yet produced. It will be available in eight fresh water models and seven salt water and specialty rods. The series will include deluxe handles and ceramic guides.

Rod designers at Heddon have worked overtime to introduce new model rods in several series, plus additions to existing lines. Mark Graphite boasts top quality in this new material at an affordable price. There are presently five models, with more to be added later. These include two spinning rods (one a 5-foot ultralight), a pair of bait-casting rods and an 8-foot fly rod. The guides are the best ceramic on the market.

Bass anglers should get excited over the Slickstick series of jet-black rods that run the gamut of spinning, fly and bait casting.

Heddon Mark steelhead-tarpon-bonefish fly rod.

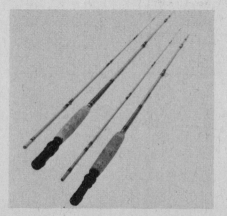

There are a dozen models in the series including many with quick tip worm action. All have hard, smooth, long-lasting aluminum-oxide guides, and the fly rods deliver a small loop of line on every cast.

The new Mark Legacy series has the look of pewter and is rated by Heddon as its best line of rods. Four casting models, five spinning and four fly rods round out this series, which contains a rod to cover most of the popular fishing assignments. On the casting rods, handles are specially designed Gatorhide. Spinning sticks boast positive-lock reel seats.

Almost all series of Olympic rods boast new models for 1977. There is now a 9-foot fly rod for a 10- or 11-weight line in the 9000 Carbon Fiber Rods, as well as a pair of medium surf rods measuring 9 and 10 feet. A pair of 5½- and 6-foot two-piece spin-casting worm rods completes the 8000 and 6000 series, while a 6½-foot spinning rod has been added to the 7000 series. The popular 3000 series now features Fuji ceramic guides instead of the older style of guides. Rod actions in this series have not changed.

At Browning the modestly priced STD series complements the Silaflex line. Eight models (two fly rods, two casting rods, two spinning rods and two salt water rods) constitute the initial entry of this series. Blanks are dark brown in color with an attractive orange-and-white wrap. Flexible fiberglass ferrules prevent dead spots in the action of the two-piece rods and ceramic guides are used on the casting rods. Other models have hard-chromed steel guides.

The rods for 1977 show more sophistication than ever before, and anglers have an extensive choice in graphite designs as well as in the more familiar fiberglass. It makes one wonder where we go from here.

Berkley

Fresh Water Spinning Rods

Model No.: P30
Length: 6½', 7'
No. Pieces: 2
No. Guides: 4 chrome-plated stainless steel and 1 aluminum oxide
Tip Top: Aluminum oxide
Rec. Lure Wt.: ⅛-¾ oz.
Action: Magnum light
Handle: Double locking ring reel seat — anodized aluminum; coated cork grips.

Model No.: C30
Length: 6½', 7'
No. Pieces: 2
No. Guides: 4 chrome-plated stainless steel
Tip Top: Chrome-plated stainless steel
Rec. Lure Wt.: ³⁄₁₆-½ oz.
Action: Medium-light
Handle: Red anodized aluminum reel seat with tapered specie cork grips.

Model No.: C32. Same as Model C30 except:
Rec. Lure Wt.: ⅛-½ oz.

Model No.: B30
Length: 6½', 7'
No. Pieces: 2
No. Guides: 4 chrome-plated stainless steel
Tip Top: Chrome-plated steel
Rec. Lure Wt.: ⅛-⅜ oz.
Action: Light
Handle: Brown anodized aluminum reel seat with specie cork grips.

Ultralight & Powerlite Spinning Rods

Model No.: P20
Length: 5½'
No. Pieces: 1
No. Guides: 4 chrome-plated stainless steel
Tip Top: Chrome-plated stainless steel
Rec. Lure Wt.: ¹⁄₃₂-⅜ oz.
Action: Ultralight
Handle: Double locking ring anodized aluminum reel seat with textured walnut inlay.

Model No.: P21. Same as Model No. P20 except:
No. Pieces: 2
Rec. Lure Wt.: ¹⁄₁₆-⅜ oz.

Model No.: P24. Same as Model No. P20 except:
Length: 5'3"
Rec. Lure Wt.: ⅛-½ oz.
Action: Powerlite

Model No.: P25
Length: 5'3"
No. Pieces: 1
No. Guides: 4 aluminum oxide
Tip Top: Aluminum oxide
Rec. Lure Wt.: ⅛-½ oz.
Action: Powerlite

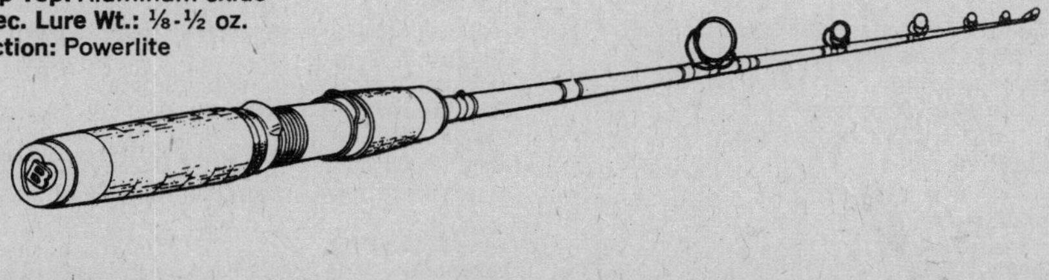

Model No.: C20
Length: 5'
No. Pieces: 1
No. Guides: 3 chrome-plated stainless steel
Tip Top: Chrome-plated steel
Rec. Lure Wt.: ¹⁄₃₂-⅛ oz.
Action: Ultralight

Model No.: C21
Length: 5', 5½'
No. Pieces: 2
No. Guides: 5' rods: 3; 5½' rods: 4; chrome-plated stainless steel
Tip Top: Chrome-plated stainless steel
Rec. Lure Wt.: ¹⁄₁₆-⅜ oz.
Action: Ultralight
Handle: Anodized aluminum reel seat with specie cork grips.

Model No.: C24
Length: 5'3"
No. Pieces: 1
No. Guides: 4 chrome-plated stainless steel
Tip Top: Chrome-plated steel
Rec. Lure Wt.: ⅛-½ oz.
Action: Powerlite

Model No.: C26. Same as Model C21 except:
Length: 5'9"
No. Guides: 4
Rec. Lure Wt.: ⅛-¾ oz.
Action: Powerlite

Model No.: B20
Length: 4'9"
No. Pieces: 1
No. Guides: 3 chrome-plated stainless steel
Tip Top: Chrome-plated steel
Rec. Lure Wt.: ¹⁄₃₂-⅛ oz.
Action: Ultralight

Model No.: B21
Length: 5½'
No. Pieces: 2
No. Guides: 3 chrome-plated stainless steel
Tip Top: Chrome-plated steel
Rec. Lure Wt.: ¹⁄₁₆-⅜ oz.
Action: Ultralight
Handle: Brown anodized aluminum reel seat with specie cork grips.

Spin-Casting Rods

Model No.: P10
Length: 6', 6½'
No. Pieces: 2
No. Guides: 4 chrome-plated stainless steel and 1 aluminum oxide
Tip Top: Aluminum oxide
Rec. Lure Wt.: ¹⁄₁₆-½ oz.
Action: Medium-light
Handle: Live action nylon/fiberglass handle with anodized aluminum reel lock.

Model No.: C10
Length: 6', 6½'
No. Pieces: 2
No. Guides: 4 chrome-plated stainless steel
Tip Top: Chrome-plated stainless steel
Rec. Lure Wt.: ¹⁄₁₆-½ oz.
Action: Medium-light
Handle: Fast taper tubular glass fresh water handle with specie cork grips.

Model No.: B10
Length: 6', 6½'
No. Pieces: 2
No. Guides: 4 chrome-plated stainless steel
Tip Top: Chrome-plated steel
Rec. Lure Wt.: ⅛-⅜ oz.
Action: Light
Handle: Live action handle with specie cork grips.

Bait-Casting Rods

Model No.: P12ML
Length: 5'2"
No. Pieces: 1
No. Guides: 5 aluminum oxide
Tip Top: Aluminum oxide
Rec. Lure Wt.: ³⁄₁₆-⅝ oz.
Action: Medium-light

Model No.: P16M
Length: 5½', 6'
No. Pieces: 1
No. Guides: 6 aluminum oxide
Tip Top: Aluminum oxide
Rec. Lure Wt.: ¼-¾ oz.
Action: Medium
Handle: Detachable pistol grip.

Model No.: P16MH. Same as Model No. P16M except:
Length: 5½'
Rec. Lure Wt. ¼-1 oz.
Action: Medium-heavy

Model No.: C12ML
Length: 5½'
No. Pieces: 1
No. Guides: 5 chrome-plated stainless steel
Tip Top: Aluminum oxide
Rec. Lure Wt.: ³⁄₁₆-⅝ oz.
Action: Medium-light
Handle: Pistol grip.

Model No.: C12MLC. Same as Model No. C12ML except:
No. Guides: 5 aluminum oxide

Model No.: C16M
Length: 5½'
No. Pieces: 1
No. Guides: 5 chrome-plated stainless steel
Tip Top: Aluminum oxide
Rec. Lure Wt.: ¼-¾ oz.
Action: Medium

Model No.: C16MC. Same as Model No. C16M except:
No. Guides: 5 aluminum oxide

Model No.: C16MH. Same as Model No. C116M except:
No. Guides: 5 aluminum oxide
Rec. Lure Wt.: ¼-1 oz.
Action: Medium-heavy

Model No.: C19
Length: 5'10"
No. Pieces: 1
No. Guides: 4 chrome-plated stainless steel

Model No. C30

Berkley (con't.)

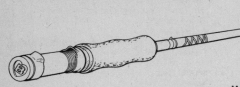

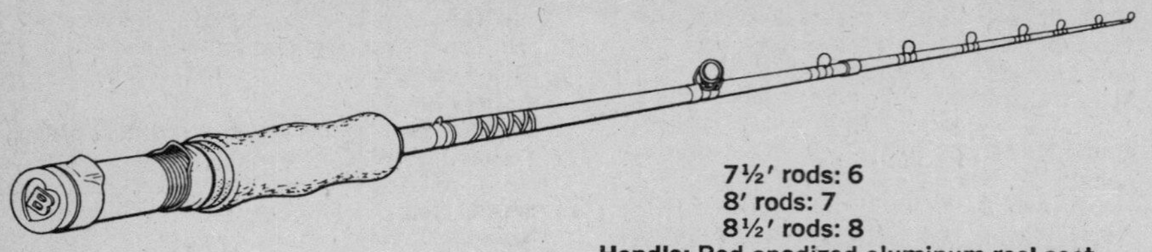

Model No. P40

Tip Top: Chrome-plated steel
Rec. Lure Wt.: ½-1¼ oz.
Action: Muskie
Handle: Specie cork foregrips and grips.

Model No.: B12ML
Length: 5′2″
No. Pieces: 1
No. Guides: 4 chrome-plated stainless steel
Tip Top: Chrome-plated steel
Rec. Lure Wt.: ³⁄₁₆-⅝ oz.
Action: Medium-light
Handle: Nylon fiberglass with molded pistol grip.

Model No.: B16M
Length: 5½′
No. Pieces: 1
No. Guides: 4 chrome-plated stainless steel
Tip Top: Chrome-plated steel
Rec. Lure Wt.: ¼-¾ oz.
Action: Medium
Model No.: B16MH. Same as Model No. B16M except:
Rec. Lure Wt.: ¼-1 oz.
Action: Medium-heavy

Fly Rods

Model No.: P40
Length: 6′3″, 7′, 7½′, 8′, 8½′
No. Pieces: 2
No. Guides: 6′3″ rods: 5; 7′, 7½′, 8′ rods: 6; 8½′ rods: 7; all stainless steel snake guides and one aluminum oxide
Tip Top: Chrome-plated stainless steel
Rec. Line: 6′3″ rods: 4
        7′ rods: 5
        7½′ rods: 6
        8′ rods: 7
        8½′ rods: 8
Handle: Double locking anodized aluminum fixed reel seat.

Model No.: C40
Length: 7½′, 8′, 8½′
No. Pieces: 2
No. Guides: 7½′, 8′ rods: 5; 8½′ rods: 6; all stainless steel snake guides and one chrome-plated stainless steel
Tip Top: Chrome-plated stainless steel
Rec. Line: 7½′ rods: 6
        8′ rods: 7
        8½′ rods: 8
Handle: Specie cork foregrip.

Model No.: C40
Length: 7½′, 8′, 8½′
No. Pieces: 2
No. Guides: 7½′, 8′ rods: 5; 8½′ rods: 6; all stainless steel snake guides and one chrome-plated stainless steel
Tip Top: Chrome-plated stainless steel
Rec. Line: 7′ rods: 5

        7½′ rods: 6
        8′ rods: 7
        8½′ rods: 8
Handle: Red anodized aluminum reel seat with specie cork foregrip.

Model No.: B40
Length: 7½′, 8′, 8½′
No. Pieces: 2
No. Guides: 7½′, 8′ rods: 4; 8½′ rods: 5; all stainless steel snake guides and one chrome-plated stainless steel guide
Tip Top: Chrome-plated stainless steel
Rec. Line: 7½′ rods: 6
        8′ rods: 7
        8½′ rods: 8
Handle: Gold and brown anodized aluminum fixed reel seat with specie cork foregrip.

Salt Water Spinning Rods

Model No.: B90
Length: 6½′, 7′, 8′, 8½′, 9′, 10½′, 12′
No. Pieces: 2
No. Guides: 6½′, 7′ rods: 4; 8′, 8½′, 9′, 10½′ rods: 5; 12′ rods: 6; all chrome-plated stainless steel
Tip Top: Chrome-plated steel
Rec. Lure Wt.: 6½′ rods: ½ oz.
        7′ rods: 2-3 oz.
        8′ rods: 1-2½ oz.
        8½′ rods: 1-1⅔ oz.
        9′ rods: 2-3 oz.
        10½′ rods: 2½-4 oz.
        12′ rods: 3-4¼ oz.
Action: Medium

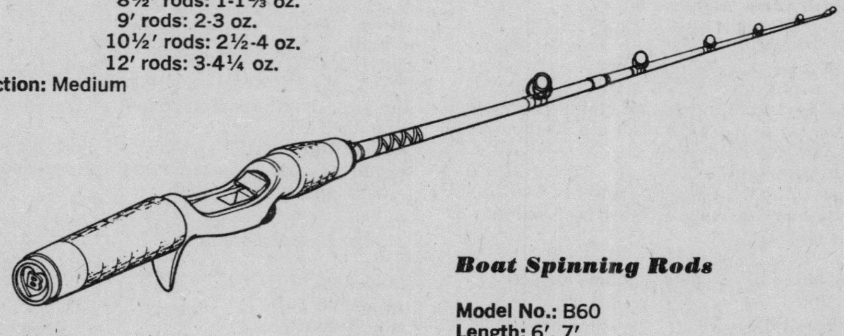

Model No. P10

Model No.: B95
Length: 7½′
No. Pieces: 2
No. Guides: 5 chrome-plated stainless steel
Tip Top: Chrome-plated steel
Rec. Lure Wt.: 1-2 oz.
Action: Medium

Model No.: B98
Length: 10′, 11½′
No. Pieces: 2
No. Guides: 10′ rods: 5; 11½′ rods: 6; all chrome-plated statinless steel
Tip Top: Carbology
Rec. Lure Wt.: 10′ rods: 5-6 oz.
           11½′ rods: 6-8 oz.
Action: Medium

Boat Rods

Model No.: B70
Length: 6′, 6½′, 7′, 8′

No. Pieces: 1
No. Guides: 6′, 6½′ rods: 3; 7′, 8′: 4; all chrome-plated stainless steel
Tip Top: Chrome-plated steel
Action: 6′, 6½′, 8′: medium; 7′ rods: medium-heavy
Handle: Boat handle with chrome-plated or anodized aluminum reel seat and specie cork foregrip.

Model No.: B74. Same as Model B70 except:
Length: 6½′
Action: Medium-light

Model No.: B75. Same as Model B70 except:
Length: 7½′
No. Pieces: 2
No. Guides: 4

Model No.: B72. Same as Model B70 except:
Length: 6′

Model No.: B106. Same as Model No. B70 except:
Length: 6′4″
No. Guides: 7
Action: Fast tip

Model No.: B108. Same as Model No. B70 except:
Length: 6′11″
No. Guides: 8
Action: Fast tip

Boat Spinning Rods

Model No.: B60
Length: 6′, 7′
No. Pieces: 1
No. Guides: 6′ rods: 3; 7′ rods: 4; all chrome-plated stainless steel
Tip Top: 6′ rods: chrome-plated stainless steel; 7′ rods: chrome-plated stainless steel
Rec. Lure Wt.: 7′ rods: ⅜-¾ oz.
Action: Medium
Handle: Chrome or anodized aluminum reel seat with specie cork foregrips.

Model No.: B62
Length: 6½′, 7′
No. Pieces: 2
No. Guides: 4 chrome-plated stainless steel
Tip Top: 6½′ rods: chrome-plated stainless steel; 7′ rods: chrome-plated steel
Rec. Lure Wt.: ⅜-¾ oz.
Action: Medium
Handle: Chrome or anodized aluminum reel seat with specie cork foregrips.

Model No.: B73
Length: 6′, 7′
No. Pieces: 1

Berkley (con't.)

No. Guides: 6' rods: 3
7' rods: 5
Tip Top: Chrome-plated stainless steel
Action: Medium
Handle: Brown anodized aluminum reel seat with specie cork foregrips.

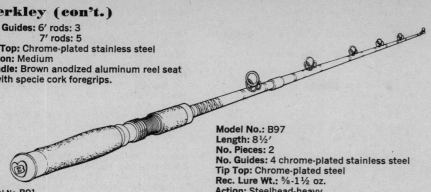

Model No. P91

Mooching Rod

Model No.: P91
Length: 8½'
No. Pieces: 2
No. Guides: 6 chrome-plated stainless steel
Tip Top: Chrome-plated stainless steel
Action: Medium-mooching
Handle: Double locking ring anodized aluminum reel seat with specie cork grips.

Popping Rod

Model No.: B50
Length: 7'
No. Pieces: 1
No. Guides: 4 chrome-plated stainless steel
Tip Top: Chrome-plated steel
Rec. Lure Wt.: ½-1 oz.
Action: Medium
Handle: Chrome trigger reel seat with double locking rings and specie cork grips.

Steelhead Rods

Model No.: P92
Length: 8' casting
No. Pieces: 2
No. Guides: 7 aluminum oxide
Tip Top: Aluminum oxide
Rec. Lure Wt.: ⅜-¾ oz.
Action: Steelhead
Handle: Double locking ring anodized aluminum reel seat with specie cork grips.

Model No.: P94. Same as Model P92 except:
Length: 8'
No. Guides: 7 chrome-plated stainless steel and 1 aluminum oxide

Model No.: C94
Length: 8'
No. Pieces: 2
No. Guides: 6 chrome-plated stainless steel
Tip Top: Chrome-plated steel
Rec. Lure Wt.: ⅜-¾ oz.
Action: Steelhead
Handle: Red anodized aluminum reel seat with specie cork grips.

Model No.: B94
Length: 8'
No. Pieces: 2
No. Guides: 5 chrome-plated stainless steel
Tip Top: Chrome-plated steel
Rec. Lure Wt.: ⅜-¾ oz.
Action: Steelhead
Handle: Brown anodized aluminum reel seat with specie cork grips.

Model No.: B97
Length: 8½'
No. Pieces: 2
No. Guides: 4 chrome-plated stainless steel
Tip Top: Chrome-plated steel
Rec. Lure Wt.: ⅝-1½ oz.
Action: Steelhead-heavy
Handle: Brown anodized aluminum reel seat with specie cork grips.

Browning

Spinning Rods

Model No.: 332904
Length: 4½'
No. Pieces: 1
No. Guides: 3 chrome-plated stainless steel
Tip Top: Carboloy
Rec. Lure Wt.: 1/16-3/16 oz.
Action: Ultralight
Handle: Overall 8" with spin rings reel seat.

Model No.: 332955. Same as Model No. 332904 except:
Length: 5½'
No. Pieces: 2
No. Guides: 5 chrome-plated stainless steel
Rec. Lure Wt.: 1/12-¼ oz.

Model No.: 332905
Length: 6'
No. Pieces: 2
No. Guides: 5 chrome-plated stainless steel
Tip Top: Carboloy
Rec. Lure Wt.: ⅛-⅜ oz.
Action: Ultralight
Handle: Overall 9½"; all cork with reel seat.

Model No.: 332906. Same as Model 332905 except:
Handle: Overall 9½"; fixed reel seat.

Model No.: 332910
Length: 6'
No. Pieces: 2
No. Guides: 5 ceramic
Tip Top: Ceramic
Rec. Lure Wt.: ½-1¼ oz.
Action: Medium-heavy freshwater; light saltwater
Handle: Overall 12¾"; fixed reel seat.

Model No.: 332912
Length: 5½'
No. Pieces: 1
No. Guides: 5 ceramic
Tip Top: Ceramic
Rec. Lure Wt.: ¾-2 oz.
Action: Heavy
Handle: Overall 12¾"; fixed reel seat.

Model No.: 332914
Length: 6½'
No. Pieces: 2
No. Guides: 5 chrome-plated stainless steel
Tip Top: Carboloy
Rec. Lure Wt.: ⅛-⅜ oz.

Action: Light
Handle: Overall 9½"; all cork with spin rings reel seat.

Model No.: 332915
Length: 6½'
No. Pieces: 2
No. Guides: 5 chrome-plated stainless steel
Tip Top: Carboloy
Rec. Lure Wt.: 3/16-¾ oz.
Action: Casts a wide range from a delicate minnow to a ⅝ ounce bass plug
Handle: Overall 12¾"; fixed reel seat.

Model No.: 332970
Length: 7'
No. Pieces: 2
No. Guides: 5 chrome-plated stainless steel
Tip Top: Carboloy
Rec. Lure Wt.: ¼-¾ oz.
Action: Medium (for bass, pike, muskie and coho)
Handle: Overall 16"; fixed reel seat.

Model No.: 332971
Length: 7'
No. Pieces: 5 (including handle)
No. Guides: 6 (foul-proof for either spinning or fly line)
Tip Top: Carboloy
Rec. Lure Wt.: ⅛-⅜ oz.
Action: Accommodates either spinning or fly reels
Handle: Overall 13¼"; fixed reel seat.

Model No.: 332990
Length: 9'
No. Pieces: 2
No. Guides: 7 (foul-proof)
Tip Top: Carbology
Rec. Lure Wt.: 1/16-1 oz.
Action: Accommodates spin, fly, spin cast or bait casting reels
Handle: Sliding multipurpose reel seat.

Casting Rods

Model No.: 312900
Length: 5½'
No. Pieces: 1
No. Guides: 5 carboloy
Tip Top: Carboloy
Rec. Lure Wt.: ⅝-1 oz.
Action: Husky (for bass and muskie)
Handle: Detachable.

Model No.: 412900. Same as Model No. 312900 except:
No. Guides: 5 ceramic
Tip Top: Ceramic

Model No.: 312903
Length: 5½'
No. Pieces: 1
No. Guides: 5 carboloy
Tip Top: Carboloy
Rec. Lure Wt.: ⅜-⅝ oz.
Action: For bass
Handle: Detachable.

Model No.: 412903. Same as Model No. 312903 except:
No. Guides: 5 ceramic
Tip Top: Ceramic

Model No.: 312906
Length: 6'
No. Pieces: 1
No. Guides: 6 carboloy
Tip Top: Carboloy

Browning (con't.)

Rec. Lure Wt.: ⅝-1 oz.
Action: Suited to handle spinners, spoons, poppers and other lures
Handle: Detachable.

Model No.: 412906. Same as Model No. 312906 except:
No. Guides: 6 ceramic
Tip Top: Ceramic

Model No.: 312910
Length: 6'
No. Pieces: 2 (3 with detachable handle)
No. Guides: 6 carboloy
Tip Top: Carboloy
Rec. Lure Wt.: ¼-⅝ oz.
Action: Light
Handle: Detachable.

Model No.: 412910. Same as Model No. 312910 except:
No. Guides: 6 ceramic
Tip Top: Ceramic

Model No.: 312920
Length: 6'
No. Pieces: 2 (3 with detachable handle)
No. Guides: 6 carboloy
Tip Top: Carboloy
Rec. Lure Wt.: ⅜-1 oz.
Action: Light
Handle: Detachable.

Model No.: 412920. Same as Model No. 312920 except:
No. Guides: 6 ceramic
Tip Top: Ceramic

Model No.: 312930
Length: 6½'
No. Pieces: 2 (3 with detachable handle)
No. Guides: 6 carboloy
Tip Top: Carboloy
Rec. Lure Wt.: ¼-1 oz.
Action: Suited for drifting or bottom fishing live bait
Handle: Detachable.

Fly Rods

Model No.: 322960
Length: 6'
No. Pieces: 2
No. Guides: 1 stripping; 5 snake; all deep chromed stainless steel
Tip Top: Chrome-plated stainless steel
Rec. Line: 5 wt.
Handle: Overall 9¾"; hand shaped grip of 6X super specie cork. Reel seats are bronze anodized. Reel is secured by a contoured hood plus double lock nuts.

Model No.: 322970. Same as Model No. 322960 except:
Length: 7'
Rec. Line: 6 wt.

Model No.: 322975
Length: 7½'
No. Pieces: 2
No. Guides: 1 stripping; 5 snake; all deep chromed stainless steel
Tip Top: Chrome-plated stainless steel
Rec. Line: 6 wt.
Handle: Overall 9¾".

Model No.: 322980. Same as Model No. 322960 except:
Length: 8'

No. Guides: 1 stripping; 6 snake
Rec. Line: 6, 7 wt.
Handle: Overall 10¾".

Model No.: 322985. Same as Model No. 322960 except:
Length: 8½'
No. Guides: 1 stripping; 6 snake
Rec. Line: 6, 7 wt.
Handle: Overall 10¾".

Model No.: 322986. Same as Model No. 322960 except:
Length: 8½'
No. Guides: 1 stripping; 6 snake
Rec. Line: 8, 9 wt.
Handle: Overall 10¾".

Model No.: 322990. Same as Model No. 322960 except:
Length: 9'
No. Guides: 1 stripping; 6 snake
Rec. Line: 8 wt.
Handle: Overall 10¾".

Model No.: 322991. Same as Model No. 322960 except:
Length: 9'
No. Guides: 1 stripping; 6 snake
Rec. Line: 9, 10 wt.
Handle: Overall 10¾"; 6" gaspe butt available.

Salt Water and Heavy Fresh Water Rods

Model No.: 142961 (Spinning)
Length: 7'1½"
No. Pieces: 2
No. Guides: 6 spinning, hard chromed stainless steel
Tip Top: Carboloy
Rec. Lure Wt.: ⅜-2 oz.
Action: Salt water light to medium
Handle: Overall 22"; 6X super specie cork; fixed bronze anodized alloy reel seat with machined double screw locks.

Model No.: 142957. Same as Model No. 142961 except:
Length: 6'9"
No. Pieces: 1
Rec. Lure Wt.: ½-2 oz.
Handle: Overall 15½".

Model No.: 142968. Same as Model No. 142961 except:
Length: 7'6"
Rec. Lure Wt.: ⅝-4 oz.
Action: Surf and jetty casting
Handle: Overall 24¾".

Model No.: 142971. Same as Model No. 142961 except:
Length: 8'¾"
No. Guides: 7 spinning
Rec. Lure Wt.: ⅞-5 oz.
Action: Medium to heavy salt water
Handle: Overall 24¾".

Model No.: 172900 (Spin-Cast)
Length: 5'6½"
No. Pieces: 1
No. Guides: 5 ceramic casting
Tip Top: Ceramic
Rec. Lure Wt.: ¾-2 oz.
Action: Jigging and trolling
Handle: Overall 17"; 6X super specie cork; fixed bronze anodized alloy reel seat with machined double screw locks.

Model No.: 172905. Same as Model No. 172900 except:
Length: 6½'
No. Guides: 6 ceramic
Rec. Lure Wt.: ⅝-2 oz.
Action: Popping rod for salt water
Handle: Overall 17¾".

Model No.: 172906 (Spinning)
Length: 6½'
No. Pieces: 1
No. Guides: 6 spinning, hard chromed stainless steel
Tip Top: Carboloy
Rec. Lure Wt.: ⅝-2 oz.
Action: For both boat and jetty salt water
Handle: Overall 17¾"; 6X super specie cork; fixed bronze anodized alloy reel seat with machined double screw locks.

Model No.: 172970 (Casting)
Length: 7'
No. Pieces: 1
No. Guides: 5 ceramic casting
Tip Top: Ceramic
Rec. Lure Wt.: ⅝-4 oz.
Action: Popping and trolling
Handle: Overall 17¾"; 6X super specie cork; fixed bronze anodized alloy reel seat with machined double screw locks.

Model No.: 172971 (Trolling)
Length: 7'
No. Pieces: 2
No. Guides: 5 carboloy
Tip Top: Carboloy
Rec. Lure Wt.: ⅞-5 oz.
Action: Light salt water
Handle: Overall 19"; 6X super specie cork; fixed bronze anodized alloy reel seat with machined double screw locks.

River and Surf Rods

Model No.: 342908
Length: 8'
No. Pieces: 2
No. Guides: 6 spinning, polished hard-chromed, stainless steel
Tip Top: Carboloy
Rec. Lure Wt.: ⅝-2½ oz.
Action: For steelhead and salmon casting on big rivers
Handle: Overall 24"; 6X specie cork; anodized reel seat with double screw locks.

Model No.: 342918. Same as Model No. 342908 except:
No. Guides: 6 spincast, chromed stainless steel

Model No.: 342909. Same as Model No. 342908 except:
Length: 9'
No. Guides: 6 spinning, polished hard-chromed, stainless steel
Rec. Lure Wt.: ¾-3 oz.
Handle: Overall 24¾".

Model No.: 342919. Same as Model No. 342908 except:
Length: 9'
No. Guides: 6 spincast, chromed stainless steel
Rec. Lure Wt.: ¾-3 oz.
Handle: Overall 24¾".

Model No.: 342911
Length: 11'
No. Pieces: 2

Browning (con't.)

No. Guides: 7 spinning, polished hard-chromed, stainless steel
Tip Top: Carboloy
Rec. Lure Wt.: 2-7 oz.
Action: Heavy surf
Handle: Overall 28½"; anodized reel seat with double screw locks.

Trolling Rods

Regulation IGFA Class Rods

Model No.: 162920
Length: 6'8"
No. Pieces: 2
No. Guides: 6 AFTCO roller
Tip Top: AFTCO roller
Action: 12 lb.
Handle: Overall 26⅝"; polished rosewood; chromed double lock reel seat and chromed two-way gimbal nock.

Model No.: 162930. Same as Model No. 162920 except:
Action: 20 lb.

Model No.: 152910. Same as Model No. 162920 except:
Action: 30 lb.
Handle: Overall 29½".

Model No.: 152915. Same as Model No. 162920 except:
No. Guides: 5 AFTCO roller
Action: 50 lb.
Handle: Overall 30½".

STD Rods

Model No.: 012903 (Casting)
Length: 5½'
No. Pieces: 1 (nondetachable handle)
No. Guides: 5 ceramic
Tip Top: Ceramic
Rec. Lure Wt.: ⅜-⅝ oz.
Handle: Optional slip on pistol grip; locking reel seat.

Model No.: 012920 (Casting)
Length: 6'
No. Pieces: 2 (nondetachable handle)
No. Guides: 5 ceramic
Tip Top: Ceramic
Rec. Lure Wt.: ⅜-1 oz.
Action: Casting
Handle: Optional slip on pistol grip; locking reel seat.

Model No.: 022975 (Fly)
Length: 7½'
No. Pieces: 2
No. Guides: 1 stripping, 5 snake; all chromed stainless steel
Action: Lightweight
Handle: Overall 9¾"; specie cork with fixed metal reel seat.

Model No.: 022985 (Fly). Same as Model No. 022975 except:
Length: 8½'
No. Guides: 1 stripping, 6 snake; all chromed stainless steel
Handle: Overall 10¾"; specie cork with fixed metal reel seat.

Model No.: 032906 (Spinning)
Length: 6'
No. Pieces: 2

No. Guides: 5 light spin; chromed stainless steel
Rec. Lure Wt.: ⅛-⅜ oz.
Action: Lightweight
Handle: Overall 12⅞"; specie cork with fixed metal reel seat.

Model No.: 032915 (Spinning)
Length: 6½'
No. Pieces: 2
No. Guides: 5 chromed stainless steel
Rec. Lure Wt.: 3/16-¾ oz.
Handle: Overall 12¾"; specie cork with fixed metal reel seat.

Model No.: 072906 (Salt water)
Length: 6½'
No. Pieces: 1
No. Guides: 6 spinning
Rec. Lure Wt.: ⅝-2 oz.
Action: Salt water
Handle: Overall 17¾"; specie cork with fixed metal reel seat.

Model No.: 042957 (Salt water)
Length: 6'9"
No. Pieces: 1
No. Guides: 6 spinning
Rec. Lure Wt.: ½-2 oz.
Handle: Overall 15½"; specie cork with fixed reel seat.

Model No.: 072970 (Salt water)
Length: 7'
No. Pieces: 1
No. Guides: 5 casting
Rec. Lure Wt.: ⅝-4 oz.
Handle: Overall 17¾"; specie cork with fixed metal reel seat.

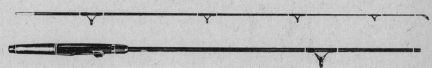

Model No. IL-26HSL

Lew Childre

Spinning Rods

Model No.: IL-16HSL
Length: 6'
No. Pieces: 1
No. Guides: 5 Fuji speed guides
Tip Top: Fuji speed tip top
Rec. Lure Wt.: ⅛-½ oz.
Action: Extra light
Handle: Spinning, light.

Model No.: 1-16HSL. Same as Model 1L-16HSL except:
Rec. Lure Wt.: ⅜-⅝ oz.
Action: Light

Model No.: 4-16HSML. Same as Model 1L-16HSL except:
Rec. Lure Wt.: ⅜-1 oz.
Action: Medium
Handle: Spinning, medium-light.

Model No.: 1L-26HSL
Length: 6'
No. Pieces: 2
No. Guides: 5 Fuji speed guides

Tip Top: Fuji tip top
Rec. Lure Wt.: ⅛-½ oz.
Action: Spinning light
Handle: 6' rod: spinning, light.

Model No.: 1-26HSL, 1-27HSML. Same as Model 1L-26HSL except:
Length: 6', 7'
Rec. Lure Wt.: ⅜-⅝ oz.
Action: Light
Handle: 6' rod: spinning, light
7' rod: spinning, medium-light.

Model No.: 4-266HSML. Same as Model 1L-26HSL except:
Length: 6½'
Rec. Lure Wt.: ⅜-1 oz.
Action: Medium
Handle: Spinning, medium-light.

Model No.: EIL-286S
Length: 8'6"
No. Pieces: 2
No. Guides: 5 Fuji speed guides
Tip Top: Fuji speed tip top
Rec. Lure Wt.: Salmon eggs; live bait
Action: Medium
Handle: Blank through handle construction.

Model No.: EI-279S. Same as Model EIL-286S except:
Length: 7'9"
Rec. Lure Wt.: Lightweight lures; live bait

Model No.: E6-279S. Same as Model EIL-286S except:
Length: 7'9"
Rec. Lure Wt.: Heavy lures and leads
Action: Heavy

Model No.: IL-16SSL
Length: 6'
No. Pieces: 1
No. Guides: 5 slip-on hard rings
Tip Top: Stainless steel
Rec. Lure Wt.: ⅛-½ oz.
Action: Extra light
Handle: Spinning ultra-light; spinning, light; spinning medium-light.

Model No.: I-16SSL. Same as Model IL-16SSL except:
Rec. Lure Wt.: ⅜-⅝ oz.
Action: Light

Model No.: 4-16SSML. Same as Model IL-16SSL except:
Length: 6'
No. Pieces: 1
Rec. Lure Wt.: ⅜-1 oz.
Action: Medium

Model No.: IL-26SSL
Length: 6'
No. Pieces: 2
No. Guides: 5 slip-on hard rings

Lew Childre (con't.)

Tip Top: Stainless steel
Rec. Lure Wt.: ⅛-½ oz.
Action: Extra Light
Handle: Spinning ultra-light; spinning, light; spinning medium-light.

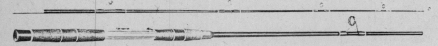

Model No. EIL-286S

Model No.: I-26SSL. Same as Model IL-26SSL except:
Rec. Lure Wt.: ⅜-⅝ oz.
Action: Light

Model No.: IL-266SSML
Length: 6½'
No. Pieces: 2
No. Guides: 5 slip-on hard rings
Tip Top: Stainless steel
Rec. Lure Wt.: ⅛-½ oz.
Action: Extra light
Handle: Spinning ultra-light; spinning, light; spinning medium-light.

Model No.: I-266SSML. Same as Model IL-266SSML except:
Rec. Lure Wt.: ⅜-⅝ oz.
Action: Light

Model No.: 4-266SSML. Same as Model IL-266SSML except:
Rec. Lure Wt.: ⅜-1 oz.
Action: Medium

Model No.: I-27SSML
Length: 7'
No. Pieces: 2
No. Guides: 5 slip-on hard rings
Tip Top: Stainless steel
Rec. Lure Wt.: ⅜-⅝ oz.
Action: Light
Handle: Spinning ultra-light; spinning, light; spinning medium-light.

Bait-Casting Rods

Model No.: IL-16HO
Length: 6'
No. Pieces: 1
No. Guides: 6 Fuji speed rings
Tip Top: Fuji tip top
Rec. Lure Wt.: ⅛-½ oz.
Action: Extra light
Handle: Offset.

Model No.: I-16HO. Same as Model IL-16HO except:
Rec. Lure Wt.: ⅜-⅝ oz.
Action: Light

Model No.: 4-16HO. Same as Model IL-16HO except:
Rec. Lure Wt.: ⅜-1 oz.
Action: Medium

Model No.: 6-16HO. Same as Model IL-16HO except:
Rec. Lure Wt.: ½-1¼ oz.
Action: Heavy

Model No.: I-152HO
Length: 5'2"
No. Pieces: 1

No. Guides: 6 Fuji speed rings
Tip Top: Fuji tip top
Rec. Lure Wt.: ⅜-⅝ oz.
Action: Light
Handle: Offset.

Model No.: I-156HO. Same as Model I-152HO except:
Length: 5'6"

Model No.: 4-156HO. Same as Model I-152HO except:
Length: 5½'
Action: Medium

Model No.: I-159HO
Length: 5'9"
No. Pieces: 1
No. Guides: 6 Fuji speed rings
Tip Top: Fuji tip top
Rec. Lure Wt.: ⅜-⅝ oz.
Action: Light
Handle: Offset.

Model No.: 6-158HO
Length: 5'8"
No. Pieces: 1
No. Guides: 6 Fuji speed rings
Tip Top: Fuji tip top
Rec. Lure Wt.: ½-1¼ oz.
Action: Heavy
Handle: Offset.

Model No.: IL-16SO
Length: 6'
No. Pieces: 1
No. Guides: 6 slip-on hard rings
Tip Top: Stainless steel
Rec. Lure Wt.: ⅛-½ oz.
Action: Extra Light
Handle: #0 offset; #02HC two-handed offset; #OBB; black bass #OCB custom.

Model No.: I-16SO. Same as Model IL-16SO except:
Rec. Lure Wt.: ½-1¼ oz.
Action: Light

Model No.: 4-16SO. Same as Model IL-16SO except:
Rec. Lure Wt.: ⅜-1 oz.
Action: Medium

Model No.: 6-16SO. Same as Model IL-16SO except:
Rec. Lure Wt.: ½-1¼ oz.
Action: Heavy

Model No.: I-156SO
Length: 5½'
No. Pieces: 1
No. Guides: 6 slip-on hard rings
Tip Top: Stainless steel
Rec. Lure Wt.: ⅜-⅝ oz.
Action: Light
Handle: #0 offset; #02HC two-handed offset; #OBB; black bass #OCB custom bass.

Model No.: I-159SO. Same as Model I-156SO except:
Length: 5'9".

Model No.: 4-156SO. Same as Model

I-156SO except:
Length: 5½'
Rec. Lure Wt.: ⅜-1 oz.
Action: Medium

Model No.: 6-158SO. Same as Model I-156SO except:
Length: 5'8"
Rec. Lure Wt. ½-1¼ oz.
Action: Heavy

Cortland

Spinning Rods

Model No.: SR2000M
Length: 6½', 7', 7½'
No. Guides: 5
Action: Medium
Handle: Specie cork grips; anodized double-locking reel seat.

Model No.: UL2000
Length: 5', 5½'
No. Guides: 4 chrome-plated stainless steel
Action: Ultra-light
Handle: 5½' rods: aluminum fixed reel seat.

Fly Rods

Model: C-G-graphite
Length: 7', 7½', 8', 8½', 9'
No. Guides: 7 aluminum oxide
Rec. Line: 7' rods: 4 or 5
7½' rods: 5 or 6
8' rods: 6 or 7
8½' rods: 7 or 8
9' rods: 8 or 9

Model: Pro-Crest
Length: 6½', 7', 7½', 8', 8½'
No. Guides: 5
Rec. Line: 6½', 7' rods: 5 or 6
7½', 8' rods: 6 or 7
8½' rods: 7 or 8
Handle: Aluminum reel seat.

Model No.: FR2000
Length: 6½', 7', 7½', 8', 8½'
No. Guides: 8 stainless steel
Rec. Line: 6½', 7', 7½' rods: 5 or 6
8' rods: 6 or 7
8½' rods: 7 or 8
Handle: Specie cork grips; anodized double-locking reel seat; rubber tipped butt cap.

Daiwa

Fresh Water Spinning Rods

Model No.: VIP10
Length: 5½'
No. Pieces: 2
No. Guides: 5 chrome-plated stainless steel
Tip Top: Stainless steel
Rec. Lure Wt.: Not specified
Action: Ultra-light
Handle: Fixed anodized aluminum reel seat.

Model No.: VIP11. Same as Model No. VIP10 except:
Length: 6'
Action: Light

Model No.: VIP19. Same as Model No. VIP10 except:
Length: 5'

Daiwa (con't.)

Model No.: VIP12
Length: 6½'
No. Pieces: 2
No. Guides: 5 chrome-plated stainless steel
Tip Top: Stainless steel
Rec. Lure Wt.: Not specified
Action: Medium-light
Handle: Fixed anodized aluminum reel seat.

Model No.: VIP13. Same as Model No. VIP12 except:
Length: 7'

Model No.: VIP82. Same as Model No. VIP12 except:
Action: Medium

Model No.: VIP83. Same as Model No. VIP12 except:
Length: 7'
Action: Medium

Model No.: 1019
Length: 5'
No. Pieces: 2
No. Guides: 3 chrome-plated
Tip Top: Chrome-plated
Rec. Lure Wt.: Not specified
Action: Ultra-light
Handle: Specie cork grip with fixed anodized aluminum reel seat.

Model No.: 1012. Same as Model No. 1019 except:
Length: 6½', 7'
Action: Medium-light

Model No.: 1310
Length: 5½'
No. Pieces: 2
No. Guides: 3 chrome-plated
Tip Top: Chrome-plated
Action: Ultra-light
Handle: Specie cork grips with anodized aluminum reel seat.

Model No.: 1312. Same as Model No. 1310 except:
Length: 6½'
No. Guides: 4
Action: Medium-light

Model No.: 1313. Same as Model No. 1312 except:
Length: 7'

Model No.: 1325
Length: 8'
No. Pieces: 2
No. Guides: 4 chrome-plated
Tip-Top: Chrome-plated
Action: Medium
Handle: Specie cork grips with chrome-plated brass reel seat.

Model No.: 1327. Same as Model No. 1325 except:
Length: 9'

Model No.: 1510
Length: 5½'
No. Pieces: 2
No. Guides: 3 V-shaped wire; chrome-plated
Tip Top: Chrome-plated
Action: Ultra-light
Handle: Hooded double-locking anodized aluminum.

Model No.: 1511. Same as Model No. 1510 except:
Length: 6'
No. Guides: 4
Action: Light

Model No.: 1512. Same as Model No. 1511 except:
Length: 6½'
Action: Medium-light

Model No.: 1513. Same as Model No. 1512 except:
Length: 7'

Model No.: 1582. Same as Model No. 1512 except:
Length: 6½'
Action: Medium

Model No.: 5012 Regal
Length: 6½'
No. Pieces: 2
No. Guides: 5 chrome-plated stainless steel
Tip-Top: Chrome-plated stainless steel
Action: Medium-light
Handle: Hooded double locking anodized aluminum reel seat.

Model No.: 5019 Regal. Same as Model No. 5012 except:
Length: 5'
No. Guides: 4
Action: Ultra-light

Model No.: 5310 Regal. Same as Model No. 5012 Regal except:
Length: 5½'
No. Guides: 4
Action: Light

Model No.: 5313 Regal. Same as Model No. 5012 Regal except:
Length: 7'
Action: Medium-heavy

Model No.: 5313D Regal. Same as Model No. 5012 Regal except:
Length: 7'
No. Guides: Dialoy
Tip Top: Dialoy
Action: Medium-heavy

Spin — Casting Rods

Model No.: VIP31P
Length: 6'
No. Pieces: 2
No. Guides: 5 chrome-plated stainless steel
Tip Top: Chrome-plated stainless steel
Action: Medium-light
Handle: Neoprene pistol grips with reinforced fiberglass offset handles of ABS plastic.

Model No.: VIP91DP. Same as Model No. VIP31P except:
No. Guides: Dialoy
Tip Top: Dialoy
Action: Medium

Model No.: 1031
Length: 6'
No. Pieces: 2
No. Guides: 4 chrome-plated
Tip Top: Chrome-plated
Action: Medium-light
Handle: Specie cork grips with ABS plastic offset handle.

Model No.: 1331P
Length: 6'
No. Pieces: 2
No. Guides: 4 chrome-plated
Tip Top: Chrome-plated
Action: Medium-light
Handle: Die cast aluminum reel seat with offset pistol grips.

Model No.: 1531P
Length: 6'
No. Pieces: 2
No. Guides: 4 chrome-plated
Tip Top: Chrome-plated
Action: Light
Handle: Fiberglass reinforced offset pistol grips.

Model No.: 5031P Regal
Length: 6'
No. Pieces: 2
No. Guides: Chrome-plated stainless steel
Tip Top: Chrome-plated stainless steel
Rec. Lure Wt.: Not specified
Action: Medium-light
Handle: Neoprene pistol grips with reinforced fiberglass reel seat of anodized aluminum.

Fly Rods

Model No.: VIP 43
Length: 7'
No. Pieces: 2
No. Guides: 6 chrome-plated stainless steel
Tip Top: Chrome-plated stainless steel
Rec. Line: #5-6
Handle: Duracork grips with hooded anodized aluminum reel seat.

Model No.: VIP 45. Same as Model No. VIP 43 except:
Length: 8'
No. Guides: 7
Rec. Line: #7-8

Model No.: VIP 47. Same as Model No. VIP 43 except:
Length: 9'
No. Guides: 8
Rec. Line: #11-12

Model No.: 1345
Length: 8'
No. Pieces: 2
No. Guides: 7 chrome-plated
Tip Top: Chrome-plated
Rec. Line: AFTMA #7-8
Handle: Specie cork grips with hooded anodized aluminum reel seat.

Model No. 5344 Regal
Length: 7½'
No. Pieces: 2
No. Guides: 6 snake guides with stainless steel stripping guide
Tip Top: Chrome-plated stainless steel
Rec. Line: AFTMA #6
Handle: Specie cork grip with anodized aluminum reel seat.

Model No.: 5345 Regal. Same as Model No. 5344 Regal except:
Length: 8'
Rec. Line: AFTMA #7

Model No.: 5347 Regal. Same as Model No. 5344 Regal except:
Length: 9'
Rec. Line: AFTMA #8

Daiwa (con't.)

Salt Water Spinning Rods

Model No.: VIP 23
Length: 7'
No. Pieces: 2
No. Guides: 7 chrome-plated stainless steel
Tip Top: Chrome-plated stainless steel
Action: Medium
Handle: Hooded double locking chrome-plated brass reel seat with cellite grips.

Model No.: VIP 25. Same as Model No. VIP 23 except:
Length: 8'
No. Guides: 8

Model No.: VIP 73D
Length: 7'
No. Pieces: 1
No. Guides: 5 dialoy
Tip Top: Dialoy
Action: Medium boat & jetty
Handle: Hooded double locking anodized aluminum reel seat with duracork grips.

Model No.: 1027
Length: 9'
No. Pieces: 2
No. Guides: 4 chrome-plated
Tip Top: Chrome-plated
Action: Medium
Handle: Specie cork grips with anodized aluminum reel seat.

Model No.: 1524
Length: 7½'
No. Pieces: 2
No. Guides: 7 chrome-plated
Tip Top: Chrome-plated
Rec. Lure Wt.: Not specified
Action: Medium
Handle: Cork grip with double locking anodized aluminum reel seat.

Model No.: 1525. Same as Model No. 1524 except:
Length: 8'

Model No.: 1571
Length: 6'
No. Pieces: 1
No. Guides: 4 chrome-plated stainless steel
Tip Top: Chrome-plated stainless steel
Action: Heavy
Handle: Hooded double locking anodized aluminum reel seat.

Model No.: 1571RT. Same as Model No. 1571 except:
Tip Top: Roller

Model No.: 1573. Same as Model No. 1571 except:
Length: 7'

Model No.: 1595. Same as Model No. 1524 except:
Length: 8'
No. Guides: 4
Action: Medium-heavy

Model No.: 1599. Same as Model No. 1595 except:
Length: 10'

Model No.: 5324 Regal

Length: 7½'
No. Pieces: 2
No. Guides: 4 chrome-plated stainless steel
Tip Top: Chrome-plated stainless steel
Rec. Lure Wt.: Not specified
Action: Medium-heavy
Handle: Specie cork grip with double locking brass chrome-plated reel seat.

Model No.: 5327 Regal. Same as Model No. 5324 Regal except:
Lenght: 9'
No. Guides: 3

Model No.: 5329 Regal. Same as Model No. 5324 Regal except:
Length: 10'
No. Guides: 3

Model No.: 5463 Regal. Same as Model No. 5324 Regal except:
Length: 7'
No. Pieces: 1
No. Guides: 5

Model No.: 5622 Regal. Same as Model No. 5324 Regal except:
Length: 6½'
No. Pieces: 1
No. Guides: 4
Action: Medium-heavy boating

Model No.: 5624 Regal. Same as Model No. 5324 Regal except:
Length: 7½'
No. Pieces: 1
No. Guides: 3
Action: Medium-heavy boating

Salt Water Rods

Model No.: S-12
Length: 11½'
No. Pieces: 2
No. Guides: 4 chrome-plated stainless steel
Tip Top: Stainless steel
Action: Extra-heavy
Handle: Hypalon grips with chrome-plated brass reel seat.

Model No.: 708DX
Length: 8'
No. Pieces: 2
No. Guides: 4 chrome bridged stainless steel
Tip Top: Dialoy
Action: Heavy
Handle: Hypalon grips with chrome-plated brass reel seat.

Model No.: 710DX. Same as Model No. 708DX except:
Length: 10'

Model No.: 811DX. Same as Model No. 708DX except:
Length: 11½'
Action: Extra-heavy

Model No.: 813DX. Same as Model No. 811DX except:
Length: 13'
No. Guides: 5

Model No.: 621
Length: 11', 13', 15'
No. Pieces: 3 (except 15' rod: 4)
No. Guides: 11', 13' rods: 3; 15' rods: 4; all chrome-plated stainless steel
Tip Top: Chrome-plated stainless steel
Rec. Lure Wt.: Not specified

Action: Heavy
Handle: Double locking brass chrome reel seat with nylon cord grips.

Regulation IGFA Class Rods

Model No.: 9083-20
Length: 6'8"
No. Pieces: 1
No. Guides: 5 roller
Tip Top: Roller
Action: 20 lb. trolling
Handle: Not specified.

Model No.: 9083-30. Same as Model No. 9083-20 except:
Action: 30 lb. trolling

Model No.: 9083-50. Same as Model No. 9083-20 except:
Action: 50 lb. trolling

Model No.: 9083-80. Same as Model No. 9083-20 except:
Action: 80 lb. trolling

Model No.: 9083-130. Same as Model No. 9083-except:
No. Guides: 5 mildrum
Tip Top: Mildrum
Action: 130 lb. trolling

Model No. 9083-U. Same as Model No. 9083-130 except:
Action: Unlimited class

Bait-Casting Rods

Model No. VIP 50DP
Length: 5½'
No. Pieces: 1
No. Guides: 5 dialoy
Tip Top: Dialoy
Action: Medium-heavy
Handle: Neoprene pistol grips with reinforced fiberglass handle.

Model No.: VIP 60DP. Same as Model No. 50DP except:
Action: Medium

Model No.: 1340P
Length: 5½'
No. Pieces: 1
No. Guides: 4 chrome-plated
Tip Top: Chrome-plated
Action: Medium
Handle: Die cast aluminum reel seat with offset pistol grips.

Model No.: 1591P
Length: 6'
No. Pieces: 2
No. Guides: 4 chrome-plated
Tip Top: Chrome-plated
Action: Medium-heavy
Handle: Neoprene pistol grips.

Model No.: 5331P Regal
Length: 6'
No. Pieces: 2
No. Guides: 5 chrome-plated stainless steel
Tip Top: Chrome-plated stainless steel
Action: Medium
Handle: Neoprene pistol grips with fiberglass reinforced ABS reel seat.

Model No.: 5431P Regal. Same as Model No.

Daiwa (con't.)

5331P Regal except:
No. Pieces: 1

Model No.: 5430DP Regal
Length: 5½'
No. Pieces: 1
No. Guides: 5 dialoy
Tip Top: Dialoy
Rec. Lure Wt.: Worm and jigging
Action: Medium
Handle: Neoprene pistol grips with fiberglass reinforced ABS reel seat.

Model No.: 5331DP Regal. Same as Model No. 5430DP Regal except:
Length: 6'
No. Pieces: 2

Model No.: 5431DP Regal. Same as Model No. 5430DP Regal except:
Length: 6'

Ocean Rods

Model No.: TTW 100
Length: 6'
No. Pieces: 1
No. Guides: 5 dialoy
Tip Top: Dialoy
Action: Casting
Handle: Cellite grips with chrome-plated brass reel seat.

Model No.: TTW 200
Length: 6¾'
No. Pieces: 1
No. Guides: 5 dialoy
Tip Top: Dialoy
Action: Spinning
Handle: Cellite grips with stainless steel reel seat.

Model No.: TTW 300. Same as Model No. TTW 200 except:
Length: 7'
Action: Spin trolling

Model No.: TTW 400
Length: 6⅔'
No. Pieces: 1
No. Guides: 5 roller
Tip Top: Roller
Action: Trolling

Model No.: TTW 500. Same as Model No. TTW 200 except:
Length: 8'

Eagle Claw

Spinning Rods

Model No.: WS Water Seal
Length: 5½', 6½', 7'
No. Pieces: 2
No. Guides: 5
Tip Top: Ceramic
Rec. Line: 5½' rods: 2-6
6½', 7' rods: 6-10
Action: 5½' rods: light
6½' rods: medium
7 rods: medium and power
Handle: Standard cork.

Model No.: GS Graphite
Length: 7', 8½', 9'
No. Pieces: 2
No. Guides: 5
Tip Top: Ceramic
Rec. Line: 7' rods: 4-12
8½' rods: 10-20
9' rods: 15-25
Action: 7' rods: light, medium
8½' rods: medium
9' rods: power
Handle: Standard cork.

Model No.: MB865
Length: 7'
No. Pieces: 2
No. Guides: 6 chromed
Tip Top: Chromed
Rec. Lure Wt.: Not specified
Action: Parabolic
Handle: Cork with fixed reel seat.

Model No.: MB865M. Same as Model MB865 except:
Action: Modified impact

Model No.: MB965F
Length: 6½'
No. Pieces: 2
No. Guides: 6 chromed carbon steel
Tip Top: Chromed carbon steel
Rec. Lure Wt.: Not specified
Action: Medium parabolic
Handle: Cork with fixed anodized aluminum reel seat.

Model No.: MB970F. Same as Model No. MB965F except:
Length: 7'

Model No.: MB980F. Same as Model No.

MB965F except:
Length: 8'

Model No.: MB985F. Same as Model No. MB965F except:
Length: 8½'

Model No.: MB965FM. Same as Model MB965F except:
Length: 6½', 7'
Action: Modified impact action

Model No.: MBFLX. Same as Model MB965F except:
Length: 6½', 7'
Action: Heavier
Handle: Lighter reel seat.

Model No.: MJCF
Length: 6½', 7'
No. Pieces: 2
No. Guides: 6 chromed stainless steel
Tip Top: Chromed stainless steel
Rec. Lure Wt.: Not specified
Action: Parabolic
Handle: Not specified.

Model No.: MJCF
Length: 8'
No. Pieces: 2
No. Guides: 6 chromed stainless steel
Tip Top: Chromed stainless steel
Rec. Lure Wt.: Heavy lures and bait
Action: Heavy
Handle: Not specified.

Model No.: MJCFM. Same as Model MJCF except:
Length: 6½', 7'
Action: Modified impact

Model No.: M4465F
Length: 6½', 7'
No. Pieces: 2
No. Guides: 6 hard chromed stainless steel
Tip Top: Tungsten carbide
Rec. Lure Wt.: Not specified
Action: Impact
Handle: Cork with fixed anodized aluminum reel seat and double locking rings.

Model No.: MSDS
Length: 6½', 7'
No. Pieces: 2
No. Guides: 6 tungsten carbide
Tip Top: Tungsten carbide
Rec. Lure Wt.: Not specified
Action: Modified impact
Handle: Cork with fixed anodized aluminum reel seat and double locking rings.

Model No.: MA2L
Length: 6½', 7'
No. Pieces: 2
No. Guides: 6 chromed stainless steel
Tip Top: Tungsten carbide
Rec. Lure Wt.: Not specified
Action: Ultra-light
Handle: Cork with fixed anodized aluminum reel seat.

Model No.: MLWL
Length: 5', 5½', 6', 6½'
No. Pieces: 2
No. Guides: 7 chromed stainless steel
Tip Top: Chromed stainless steel
Rec. Lure Wt.: Not specified
Action: Ultra-light
Handle: Cork with fixed anodized aluminum reel seat and double locking rings.

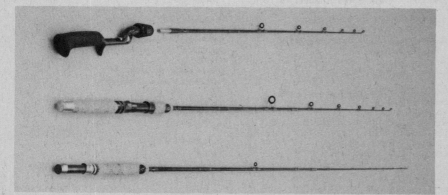

Water Seal Series

Eagle Claw (con't.)

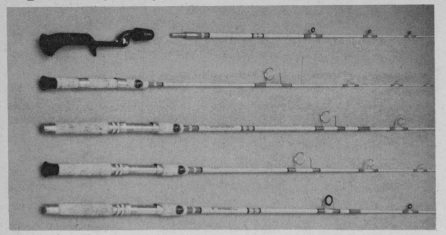

MTM

Model No.: LWLX. Same as Model MLWL except:
Length: 4½', 5', 5½'
No. Pieces: 1

Model No.: MLW
Length: 5', 6', 6½'
No. Pieces: 2
No. Guides: 4 chromed stainless steel
Tip Top: Chromed stainless steel
Rec. Lure Wt.: Not specified
Action: Light parabolic
Handle: Specie cork reel seat with sliding rings.

Model No.: LWLW
Length: 5'4", 5'8"
No. Pieces: 2
No. Guides: 4 chromed stainless steel
Tip Top: Chromed stainless steel
Rec. Lure Wt.: Plastic worm
Action: Pro-action
Handle: Cork with fixed anodized aluminum reel seat and double locking rings.

Model No.: MPLL
Length: 7'
No. Pieces: 2
No. Guides: 6 hard chromed stainless steel
Tip Top: Chromed stainless steel
Rec. Lure Wt.: Eggs, grubs and other light baits
Action: Fly rod
Handle: Cork with anodized aluminum reel seat and chromed hood and sleeve.

Model No.: MPLS
Length: 7½', 8', 8½', 9'
No. Pieces: 2
No. Guides: 5 hard chromed stainless steel
Tip Top: Chromed stainless steel
Rec. Lure Wt.: 7½' rods: bait or trolling with light lures; 8' rods: light lead or weighted flies; 8½' rods: ⅜ oz.
Action: Light
Handle: Cork with fixed reel seat.

Model No.: MPLX
Length: 6½', 7'
No. Pieces: 1
No. Guides: 5 hard chromed stainless steel
Tip Top: Chromed stainless steel
Rec. Lure Wt.: Not specified

Action: Worm rod
Handle: Cork with fixed reel seat.

Model No.: MPLMC. Same as Model MPLX except:
Length: 10'
Action: Mooching rod

Model No.: MPLFX. Same as Model MPLX except:
Length: 8'3", 9'
Action: Spinning steelhead; salmon

Model No.: MBNWS
Length: 8', 8½'
No. Pieces: 1
No. Guides: 5 chromed stainless steel
Tip Top: Chromed stainless steel
Rec. Lure Wt.: Not specified
Action: Heavy
Handle: Cork with fixed reel seat.

Model No.: MB877. Same as Model MBNWS except:
Length: 7'7"
Handle: Lighter weight reel seat.

Model No.: M8480
Length: 8', 8½'
No. Pieces: 2
No. Guides: 5 hard chromed stainless steel
Tip Top: Chromed stainless steel
Rec. Lure Wt.: Not specified
Action: Impact, heavy duty
Handle: Cork with fixed anodized aluminum reel seat and double locking rings.

Model No.: M60DLS. Same as Model M8480 except:
Length: 8½'
Action: Full parabolic

Model No.: MB9SH
Length: 9'
No. Pieces: 2
No. Guides: 5 hard chromed stainless steel
Tip Top: Chromed
Rec. Lure Wt.: Not specified
Action: Heavy, salt water
Handle: Cork with fixed anodized aluminum reel seat and double locking rings.

Model No.: MSEA. Same as Model MB9SH except:

Length: 7½', 8'
Action: Light, salt water

Model No.: JRM
Length: 7'3"
No. Pieces: 2
No. Guides: 6 chrome stainless steel
Tip Top: Chrome stainless steel
Rec. Lure Wt.: Not specified
Action: Heavy
Handle: Detachable specie cork with chromed reel seat.

Model No.: MOS
Length: 6½', 7', 7½', 8', 8½', 9'
No. Pieces: 2
No. Guides: 5 hard chromed stainless steel
Tip Top: Chromed stainless steel
Rec. Lure Wt.: Not specified
Action: Ocean (for fishing Coho and Chinook Salmon)
Handle: Cork with fixed reel seat.

Model No.: MOSS
Length: 10'
No. Pieces: 2
No. Guides: 5 hard chromed stainless steel
Tip Top: Chromed stainless steel
Rec. Lure Wt.: Not specified
Action: Ocean surf
Handle: Cork with fixed reel seat; longer handle for surf spinning.

Model No.: 8770SP
Length: 7'
No. Pieces: 1
No. Guides: 5 hard chromed stainless steel (extra heavy duty)
Tip Top: Stainless steel
Rec. Lure Wt.: Not specified
Action: All-purpose
Handle: Cork with fixed reel seat.

Model No.: M4LWL
Length: 5½'
No. Pieces: 4
No. Guides: 4 chromed stainless steel
Tip Top: Chromed stainless steel
Rec. Lure Wt.: Not specified
Action: Light
Handle: Cork with fixed anodized aluminum reel seat.

Model No.: M6TMS
Length: 6'9"
No. Pieces: 6
No. Guides: 5 stainless steel
Tip Top: Chromed
Rec. Lure Wt.: Not specified
Action: Light
Handle: Cork with fixed anodized aluminum reel seat.

Model No.: LWLFD
Length: 6½'
No. Pieces: 1
No. Guides: 4 foul-proof
Tip Top: Tungsten carbide
Rec. Lure Wt.: Worm
Action: Light
Handle: Specie cork with fixed anodized reel seat.

Model No.: MPLSX
Length: 7½'
No. Pieces: 2
No. Guides: 5 hard chromed stainless steel
Tip Top: Chromed stainless steel
Rec. Lure Wt.: Worm
Action: Light

Eagle Claw (con't.)

Handle: Cork with fixed anodized aluminum reel seat, chromed hood and sleeve.

Model No.: MB960FML
Length: 6', 6½', 7'
No. Pieces: 2
No. Guides: 6 chromed carbon steel
Tip Top: Chromed carbon steel
Rec. Lure Wt.: Not specified
Action: Medium parabolic
Handle: Cork with fixed anodized aluminum reel seat.

Model No.: M5565
Length: 6½'
No. Pieces: 2
No. Guides: 6 hard chromed stainless steel
Tip Top: Tungsten carbide
Rec. Lure Wt.: Worm
Action: Impact
Handle: Cork with fixed anodized aluminum reel seat and double locking rings.

Model No.: SWBC
Length: 8', 9'
No. Pieces: 1
No. Guides: 5 hard chromed stainless steel (extra heavy duty)
Tip Top: Chromed stainless steel
Rec. Lure Wt.: Not specified
Action: Ocean surf
Handle: Cork with fixed chromed reel seat.

Model No.: MSTS
Length: 6', 6½', 7'
No. Pieces: 2
No. Guides: 6 hard chromed stainless steel (extra heavy duty)
Tip Top: Chromed stainless steel
Rec. Lure Wt.: Not specified
Action: All-purpose
Handle: Cork with fixed chrome reel seat.

Model No.: CPLW
Length: 5'4", 5'8"
No. Pieces: 1
No. Guides: 5 ceramic
Tip Top: Ceramic
Rec. Lure Wt.: Not specified
Action: Ultra-light
Handle: Cork with fixed reel seat.

Model No.: PLW. Same as Model CPLW except:
No. Guides: 5 carbide
Tip Top: Carbide

Model No.: CPWDS
Length: 6½'
No. Pieces: 1
No. Guides: 5 ceramic
Tip Top: Ceramic
Rec. Lure Wt.: Not specified
Action: Not specified
Handle: Detachable; cork with fixed reel seat.

Model No.: PWDS. Same as Model CPWDS except:
No. Guides: 5 carbide
Tip Top: Carbide

Model No.: MCPWS
Length: 6½', 7'
No. Pieces: 2
No. Guides: 5 ceramic
Tip Top: Ceramic
Rec. Lure Wt.: Not specified
Action: Not specified

Handle: Specie cork pistol grip; handle is fitted with 26/64 female ferrule; also comes with a 26/64 male ferrule for attaching to rod blade.

Model No.: MPWS. Same as Model MCPWS except:
No. Guides: 5 carbide
Tip Top: Carbide

Model No.: MTM
Length: 6½', 7'
No. Pieces: 2
No. Guides: 6
Tip Top: Not specified
Rec. Lure Wt.: Plastic worm
Action: Worm
Handle: Cork with fixed reel seat.

Spin-Casting Rods

Model No.: CMGCJM
Length: 6', 6½'
No. Pieces: 2
No. Guides: 4
Tip Top: Ceramic
Rec. Line: 6' rods: 6-10
        6½' rods: 8-12
Handle: Double offset aluminum reel seat and standard cork grips.

Model No.: CM2RC
Length: 6', 6½'
No. Pieces: 2
No. Guides: 6
Tip Top: Ceramic
Rec. Line: 6' rods: 6-8
        6½' rods: 8-12
Handle: Straight magnesium reel seat and pistol comfort grips.

Model No.: WC Water Seal
Length: 5', 5½'
No. Pieces: 1
No. Guides: 5
Tip Top: Ceramic
Rec. Line: 5' rods: 8-10
        5½' rods: 8-10, 10-15, 15-25
Action: 5' rods: light
        5½' rods: medium and power
Handle: Pistol comfort grips.

Model No.: GC Graphite
Length: 5½'
No. Pieces: 1
No. Guides: 5 wire-frame ceramic
Tip Top: Ceramic
Rec. Line: 10-12, 8-12
Action: Light or ultra-light
Handle: Pistol comfort grips.

Model No.: MB1360
Length: 6', 6½'
No. Pieces: 2
No. Guides: 6 chrome-plated
Tip Top: Chrome-plated
Rec. Lure Wt.: Not specified
Action: Parabolic
Handle: Cork with baked enamel die-cast aluminum reel seat.

Model No.: MB1360M. Same as Model MB1360 except:
Action: Modified impact

Model No.: B1350W
Length: 5', 5½', 6', 6½'
No. Pieces: 2
No. Guides: 6 chrome-plated
Tip-Top: Chrome-plated

Rec. Lure Wt.: Not specified
Action: Pro-action
Handle: Cork with fixed baked enamel die-cast aluminum reel seat.

Model No.: MB1360X. Same as Model B1350W except:
Length: 6'
No. Pieces: 2

Model No.: MB2360. Same as Model MB2370 except:
Length: 6', 6½'
Action: Modified impact

Model No.: MGCJM
Length: 6', 6½'
No. Pieces: 2
No. Guides: 6 chromed stainless steel
Tip Top: Chromed stainless steel
Rec. Lure Wt.: Not specified
Action: Modified impact
Handle: Cork with baked enamel die-cast aluminum reel seat.

Model No.: MDRC
Length: 6', 6½', 7'
No. Pieces: 2
No. Guides: 6 hard chromed stainless steel
Tip Top: Tungsten carbide
Rec. Lure Wt.: Not specified
Action: Impact
Handle: Cork with baked die-cast aluminum reel seat.

Model No.: DHC
Length: 5', 5½', 6'
No. Pieces: 1
No. Guides: 6 hard-chromed stainless steel
Tip Top: Chromed stainless steel
Rec. Lure Wt.: Not specified
Action: Pro-action
Handle: Cork with baked enamel die-cast aluminum reel seat.

Model No.: DHCC. Same as Model DHC except:
Handle: Ferruled detachable comfort grip.

Model No.: MDHC
Length: 5½', 6', 6½'
No. Pieces: 2
No. Guides: 6
Handle: Cork with fixed reel seat.

Model No.: MSDC
Length: 6', 6½'
No. Pieces: 2
No. Guides: 6 tungsten carbide
Tip Top: Tungsten carbide
Rec. Lure Wt.: Not specified
Action: Impact action
Handle: Cork with fixed baked enamel die-cast aluminum reel seat.

Model No.: SDC
Length: 5', 5½', 6'
No. Pieces: 1
No. Guides: 6 tungsten carbide
Tip Top: Tungsten carbide
Rec. Lure Wt.: Not specified
Action: Pro-action
Handle: Cork with detachable baked enamel die-cast aluminum reel seat.

Model No.: SDCC. Same as Model SDC except:
Length: 5½', 6'
Handle: Ferruled detachable comfort grip.

Eagle Claw (con't.)

Model No.: M2RC
Length: 7'
No. Pieces: 2
No. Guides: 6 hard-chromed stainless steel
Tip Top: Tungsten carbide
Rec. Lure Wt.: Not specified
Action: Impact
Handle: Cork with baked die-cast aluminum reel seat.

Model No.: 2RCH
Length: 5½', 6'
No. Pieces: 1
No. Guides: 6
Tip Top: Not specified
Rec. Lure Wt.: Not specified
Action: Worm
Handle: Detachable.

Model No.: MLWC
Length: 6', 6½'
No. Pieces: 2
No. Guides: 6 chromed stainless steel
Tip Top: Chromed stainless steel
Rec. Lure Wt.: Not specified
Action: Light parabolic
Handle: Cork with baked enamel die-cast aluminum reel seat.

Model No.: MDWM
Length: 7'8"
No. Pieces: 2
No. Guides: Not specified; hard-chromed stainless steel
Tip Top: Chromed stainless steel
Rec. Lure Wt.: Not specified
Action: Light
Handle: Cork with baked enamel die-cast aluminum reel seat.

Model No.: MDW. Same as Model MDWM except:
Length: 6'
Action: Worm and muskie

Model No.: DWX. Same as Model MDWM except:
Length: 6'
No. Pieces: 1
Action: Heavy
Handle: Detachable ferruled.

Model No.: MB1355M
Length: 5½'
No. Pieces: 2
No. Guides: 4 chrome-plated
Tip Top: Chrome-plated
Rec. Lure Wt.: Not specified
Action: Modified impact
Handle: Cork with baked enamel die-cast aluminum reel seat.

Model No.: CDHC5
Length: 5', 5½', 6'
No. Pieces: 1
No. Guides: 5 ceramic
Tip Top: Ceramic
Rec. Lure Wt.: Not specified
Action: Full impact
Handle: Detachable with fixed reel seat.

Model No.: LWLWC
Length: 5'4"
No. Pieces: 1
No. Guides: 4 chromed stainless steel
Tip Top: Chromed stainless steel
Rec. Lure Wt.: Not specified
Action: Light

Handle: Cork with fixed reel seat.

Model No.: LWLWD. Same as Model LWLWC except:
Length: 6½'
Handle: Detachable ferruled handle.

Casting Rods

Model No.: MOSC
Length: 8½', 9'
No. Pieces: 2
No. Guides: 5 hard-chromed stainless steel casting
Tip Top: Braced
Rec. Lure Wt.: Not specified
Action: Standard
Handle: Brass chrome-plated reel seat with double locking rings.

Model No.: MPLC
Length: 8', 8½'
No. Pieces: 2
No. Guides: 6 hard-chromed stainless steel casting
Tip Top: Braced chromed stainless steel
Rec. Lure Wt.: Not specified
Action: Heavy
Handle: Anodized aluminum reel seat; extra length specie cork grip.

Salt Water Casting Rods

Model No.: MA9SH
Length: 9'
No. Pieces: 2
No. Guides: Not specified; hard-chromed stainless steel casting
Tip Top: Braced
Action: Heavy
Handle: Fixed anodized aluminum reel seat with double locking rings.

Model No.: M8480R. Same as Model MA9SH except:
Length: 8'
Action: Impact

Boat Casting Rods

Model No.: MDF
Length: 8½'
No. Pieces: 2
No. Guides: Not specified; hard-chromed stainless steel
Tip Top: Braced
Rec. Lure Wt.: Not specified
Action: Heavy
Handle: Fixed anodized aluminum reel seat with double locking rings.

Mooching Rods

Model No.: MPLMC
Length: 10'
No. Pieces: 2
No. Guides: Not specified; hard-chromed stainless steel
Tip Top: Braced
Rec. Lure Wt.: Not specified
Action: Heavy
Handle: Anodized aluminum reel seat with double locking rings.

Popping Rods

Model No.: 8765
Length: 6½'
No. Pieces: 2
No. Guides: Not specified; hard-chromed

stainless steel extra heavy duty spinning
Tip Top: Braced hard-chromed
Action: Not specified
Handle: Chromed reel seat with finger trigger.

Model No. AFS. Same as Model 8765 except:
Length: 7'

Model No.: CAFS7
Length: 7'
No. Pieces: 2
No. Guides: 5 ceramic
Tip Top: Ceramic
Rec. Lure Wt.: Not specified
Action: Not specified
Handle: Chromed reel seat with finger trigger.

Model No.: C8765
Length: 6½'
No. Pieces: 1
No. Guides: 5
Tip Top: Ceramic
Rec. Line: 15-20
Handle: Brass chrome-plated reel seat with finger trigger.

Trolling Rods

Model No.: MTR
Length: 6½', 7', 7½', 8'
No. Pieces: 2
No. Guides: 4 chrome-plated stainless steel
Tip Top: Chrome-plated stainless steel
Rec. Lure Wt.: Not specified
Action: Light
Handle: Hardwood handle with cork foregrip.

Model No.: MTRL. Same as Model MTR except:
Tip Top: Light sensitive tip for fresh water

Model No.: MPLT
Length: 8'
No. Pieces: 2
No. Guides: 5 hard-chromed stainless steel
Rec. Lure Wt.: Not specified
Action: Light
Handle: Hardwood with cork foregrip and anodized reel seat.

Model No.: MBNWT
Length: 7'4"
No. Pieces: 2
No. Guides: 4 chromed stainless steel
Tip Top: Chromed stainless steel
Rec. Lure Wt.: Not specified
Action: Heavy
Handle: Chromed reel seat with finger trigger, hardwood rear grip, and cork foregrip.

Model No.: M8485TR
Length: 8½'
No. Pieces: 2
No. Guides: 6 hard-chromed stainless steel casting
Tip Top: Braced
Rec. Lure Wt.: Not specified
Action: Heavy
Handle: Anodized aluminum double locking rings, hardwood handle, and cork foregrip.

Model No.: GTRT
Length: 7½'
No. Pieces: 2
No. Guides: 4 chromed stainless steel casting

Eagle Claw (con't.)

Tip Top: Steel roller
Rec. Lure Wt.: Not specified
Action: Ocean trolling
Handle: Detachable hardwood handle with cork foregrip and rubber butt cap.

Worm Rods

Model No.: CMBFLX
Length: 6½', 7'
No. Pieces: 2
No. Guides: 5
Tip Top: Ceramic
Rec. Line: 12-17
Handle: Fixed single nut reel seat and standard cork grips.

Model No.: CPWR
Length: 5½', 6', 6½'
No. Pieces: 2
No. Guides: 5 ceramic
Tip Top: Ceramic
Rec. Lure Wt.: Not specified
Action: Worm
Handle: Spin cast comfort grip, detachable handle.

Fly Rods

Model No.: WF Water Seal
Length: 6½', 7', 7½', 8', 8½'
No. Pieces: 2
No. Guides: 6 snake and 1 wire-frame ceramic
Tip Top: Ceramic
Rec. Line: 6½' rods: 4
7' rods: 5
7½' rods: 6-7
8', 8½' rods: 7
Handle: Screw fed aluminum reel seat and standard cork grips.

Model No.: GF Graphite
Length: 7', 7½', 8', 8½', 9'
No. Pieces: 2
No. Guides: 7', 7½', 8' rods: 6 snake and 1 wire frame; 9' rods: 7 snake and 1 wire frame; all ceramic
Tip Top: Ceramic
Rec. Line: 7' rods: 5
7½' rods: 6
8' rods: 4, 5, 6, 7
8½' rods: 8
9' rods: 10
Handle: Extended cork handle.

Model No.: MLWFF5, MLWFF5½
Length: 5', 5½'
No. Pieces: 2
No. Guides: 5 stainless steel snake guides plus one chromed stainless steel stripper guide
Tip Top: Chromed
Rec. Line: Not specified
Handle: Anodized reel seat of lightweight aluminum.

Model No.: M8599
Length: 9'
No. Pieces: 2
No. Guides: 7 stainless steel and one chromed stripper guide
Tip Top: Hand chrome-plated
Rec. Line: 10 wt.
Handle: Anodized aluminum reel seat, specie cork grip.

Model No.: MPFLS-9
Length: 9'
No. Pieces: 2
No. Guides: 6 chromed stainless steel spinning
Tip Top: Chromed
Rec. Line: 10 wt.
Handle: Special extension butt, anodized aluminum reel seat, specie cork grip.

Model No.: MLWFF
Length: 6', 6½', 7'
No. Pieces: 2
No. Guides: 5 stainless steel snake plus one chromed stainless steel stripper
Tip Top: Chromed
Rec. Line: 6 wt.
Handle: Anodized reel seat of lightweight aluminum.

Model No.: M2A
Length: 7½', 8', 8½', 9'
No. Pieces: 2
No. Guides: 7 gold finished stainless steel plus one hard-chromed stripper
Tip Top: Hard-chromed
Rec. Line: 7' rods: 6 wt.
7½', 8', 8½' rods: 7 wt.
9' rods: 9 wt.
Handle: Anodized aluminum reel seat.

Model No.: MB8A
Length: 7', 7½', 8', 8½', 9'
No. Pieces: 2
No. Guides: Chromed stripper guide
Tip Top: Not specified
Rec. Line: 7' rods: 6 wt.
7½', 8', 8½' rods: 7 wt.
9' rods: 9 wt.
Handle: Aluminum reel seat, specie cork grip.

Model No.: M3A
Length: 7½', 8', 8½', 9'
No. Pieces: 2
No. Guides: 6 stainless steel snake guides plus one chromed stripper guide
Tip Top: Chromed
Rec. Line: 7½', 8', 8½' rods: 7 wt.
9' rods: 9 wt.
Handle: Specie cork grip.

Model No.: M4A
Length: 8', 8½'
No. Pieces: 2
No. Guides: 7 chromed stainless steel
Tip Top: Chromed stainless steel
Rec. Line: 7 wt.
Handle: Anodized reel seat of lightweight aluminum.

Model No.: MB2580
Length: 8'
No. Pieces: Not specified
No. Guides: Chromed stainless steel stripper
Tip Top: Chromed
Rec. Line: 7 wt.
Handle: Anodized aluminum reel seat.

Model No.: MB2585. Same as Model MB2580 except:
Length: 8½'

Spin/Fly Rods

Model No.: M4TMU
Length: 7½'
No. Pieces: 4
No. Guides: 5 stainless steel
Tip Top: Chromed stainless steel
Rec. Line: 7 wt.

Rec. Lure Wt.: Not specified
Action: Medium parabolic
Handle: Reversible handle with screw lock anodized aluminum reel seat, specie cork grip.

Model No.: M4TMUL. Same as Model M4TMU except:
Length: 6½'
Rec. Lure Wt.: Up to ¼ oz.

Model No.: M4PLP
Length: 7½'
No. Pieces: 4
No. Guides: 5 stainless steel snake plus one spinning butt stripper
Tip Top: Chromed stainless steel
Rec. Line: Not specified
Handle: Anodized aluminum reel seat and gold-plated sliding rings on cork foregrip.

All-Purpose Travel Rods

Model No.: VM8TM—sets up as 5 different rods
Length: 5', 6'9"
No. Pieces: 8
No. Guides: 5 chromed stainless steel
Tip Top: Chromed stainless steel
Rec. Lure Wt.: Not specified
Action: Not specified
Handle: Reversible with specie cork grips.

Fenwick

Spinning Rods

Model No.: 953
Length: 5'3"
No. Pieces: 1
No. Guides: Aluminum oxide guides
Tip Top: Aluminum oxide
Rec. Line: 1-4
Rec. Lure Wt.: ⅛-⅝ oz.
Action: Ultra-light
Handle: Double locking aluminum reel seat, cork grip.

Model No.: G-953-graphite. Same as Model No. 953 except:
Rec. Line: 6-12

Model No.: 960
Length: 6'
No. Pieces: 1
No. Guides: Ceramic
Tip Top: Ceramic
Rec. Lure Wt.: ½-1 oz.
Action: Heavy
Handle: Double locking aluminum reel seat, cork grip.

Model No.: 965
Length: 6½'
No. Pieces: 1
No. Guides: Ceramic
Tip Top: Ceramic
Rec. Lure Wt.: ½-1 oz.
Action: Heavy
Handle: Double locking aluminum reel seat, cork grip.

Model No.: PLS61
Length: 6'
No. Pieces: 2
No. Guides: Aluminum oxide
Tip Top: Carbide
Rec. Lure Wt.: ⅜-⅝ oz.

Fenwick (con't.)

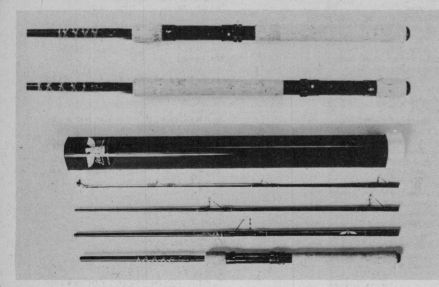

Model No. SF74-4 Model No. SF75-5

Action: Medium
Handle: Double locking aluminum reel seat, cork grip.

Model No.: PLS615. Same as Model PLS61 except:
No. Guides: Ceramic
Tip Top: Ceramic

Model No.: PLS65
Length: 6½'
No. Pieces: 2
No. Guides: Aluminum oxide
Tip Top: Carbide
Rec. Lure Wt.: ¼-⅝ oz.
Action: Medium
Handle: Double locking aluminum reel seat, cork grip.

Model No.: PLS66
Length: 6½'
No. Pieces: 2
No. Guides: Ceramic
Tip Top: Ceramic
Rec. Lure Wt.: ½-1 oz.
Action: Heavy
Handle: Double locking aluminum reel seat, cork grip.

Model No.: PLS70
Length: 7'
No. Pieces: 2
No. Guides: Aluminum oxide
Tip Top: Carbide
Rec. Lure Wt.: ¼-⅝ oz.
Action: Medium
Handle: Double locking aluminum reel seat, cork grip.

Model No.: PLS70S. Same as Model PLS70 except:
No. Guides: Not specified; ceramic
Tip Top: Ceramic

Model No.: PLS72
Length: 7'
No. Pieces: 2
No. Guides: Not specified; ceramic
Tip Top: Ceramic

Rec. Lure Wt.: ½-1 oz.
Action: Heavy
Handle: Double locking aluminum reel seat, cork grip.

Model No.: PLS75
Length: 7½'
No. Pieces: 2
No. Guides: Not specified; hard-chrome braced spinning
Tip Top: Aluminum oxide
Rec. Lure Wt.: ¼-⅝ oz.
Action: Light
Handle: Double locking aluminum or chrome-plated brass reel seat, cork grip with butt cap and winding check.

Model No.: FS83. Same as Model PLS75 except:
Length: 8'3"

Model No.: FS50
Length: 5'
No. Pieces: 2
No. Guides: Aluminum oxide
Tip Top: Carbide
Rec. Lure Wt.: ⅟₁₆-¼ oz.
Action: Ultra-light
Handle: Cork grip with sliding rings.

Model No.: FS55
Length: 5½'
No. Pieces: 2
No. Guides: Aluminum oxide

Tip Top: Carbide
Rec. Lure Wt.: ⅟₁₆-¼ oz.
Action: Ultra-light
Handle: Cork grip with sliding rings.

Model No.: FS60
Length: 6'
No. Pieces: 2
No. Guides: Not specified; chrome-plated stainless steel
Tip Top: Carbide
Rec. Lure Wt.: ⅟₁₆-¼ oz.
Action: Ultra-light
Handle: Cork grip with sliding rings.

Model No.: FS61. Same as Model FS60 except:
Handle: Double locking aluminum reel seat, cork grip.

Model No.: FS65
Length: 6½'
No. Pieces: 2
No. Guides: Aluminum oxide
Tip Top: Carbide
Rec. Lure Wt.: ⅛-½ oz.
Action: Light
Handle: Fixed double locking reel seat, cork grip.

Model No.: FS65-4. Same as Model FS65 except:
No. Pieces: 4
Rec. Lure Wt.: ⅛-⅜ oz.

Model No.: FS70
Length: 7'
No. Pieces: 2
No. Guides: Chrome-plated stainless steel
Tip Top: Carbide
Rec. Lure Wt.: ¼-½ oz.
Action: Light
Handle: Double locking aluminum reel seat, cork grip.

Model No.: FS70-4. Same as Model FS70 except:
No. Pieces: 4
Rec. Line: 4 to 8
Rec. Lure Wt.: ⅛-½ oz.

Model No.: FS75
Length: 7½'
No. Pieces: 2
No. Guides: Not specified; chrome-plated stainless steel
Tip Top: Carbide
Rec. Lure Wt.: ¼-½ oz.
Action: Light
Handle: Double locking aluminum reel seat, cork grip.

Model No.: FS80
Length: 8'
No. Pieces: 2
No. Guides: Hard-chrome braced spinning

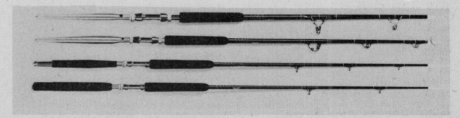

Model No. 610 Model No. 670

Fenwick (con't.)

Tip Top: Aluminum oxide
Rec. Line: 8-20
Rec. Lure Wt.: ⅜-1 oz.
Action: Medium-light
Handle: Double locking aluminum or chrome-plated brass reel seat, cork grip with butt cap and winding check.

Model No.: FS85. Same as Model FS80 except:
Length: 8½'

Model No.: FS90. Same as Model FS80 except:
Length: 9'

Model No.: FS86
Length: 8½'
No. Pieces: 2
No. Guides: Braced aluminum
Tip Top: Aluminum oxide
Rec. Line: 10-25
Rec. Lure Wt.: ⅝-1½ oz.
Action: Medium
Handle: Double locking aluminum reel seat, cork grip with butt cap and winding check.

Model No.: FS88. Same as Model FS86

Model No.: GFS70-graphite
Length: 7'
No. Guides: Foul-proof
Tip Top: Ceramic
Rec. Lure Wt.: ¼-½ oz.
Action: Light
Handle: Cork body reel seat; cork grip.

Model No.: GFS83-graphite
Length: 8'3"
No. Pieces: 2
No. Guides: Ceramic
Tip Top: Carbide
Rec. Lure Wt.: ¼-⅝ oz.
Action: Light
Handle Cork body reel seat.

Model No.: FS67-4
Length: 5'9"
No. Pieces: 4
No. Guides: Foul-proof fly-guides
Tip Top: Ceramic
Rec. Lure Wt.: ¹⁄₁₆-⅜ oz.
Action: Ultra-light
Handle: Cork grip with aluminum sliding rings.

Model No.: 140
Length: 4½'
No. Pieces: 1
No. Guides: Aluminum oxide
Tip Top: Carbide
Rec. Lure Wt.: ¹⁄₁₆-¼ oz.
Action: Ultra-light
Handle: Cork grip with sliding rings.

Model No.: G145-graphite
Length: 4½'
No. Pieces: 1
No. Guides: Aluminum oxide
Tip Top: Aluminum oxide
Rec. Line: 1-4
Rec. Lure Wt.: ¹⁄₁₆-¼ oz.
Action: Ultra-light
Handle: Cork grip with sliding rings.

Salt Water Spinning Rods

Model No.: PS90

Length: 9'
No. Pieces: 2
No. Guides: Not specified; hard-chrome braced
Tip Top: Carbide
Rec. Line: 10-20
Rec. Lure Wt.: 1-4 oz.
Action: Heavy
Handle: Double locking reel seat, cork grip.

Model No.: PS105. Same as Model PS90 except:
Length: 10½'
Rec. Line: 15-30
Rec. Lure Wt.: 3-6 oz.

Model No.: PS100. Same as Model PS90 except:
Length: 10'
Rec. Line: 18-40
Rec. Lure Wt.: 4-10 oz.

Model No.: PS120. Same as Model PS90 except:
Length: 12'
Rec. Line: 15-30
Rec. Lure Wt.: 3-6 oz.

Spin-Casting Rods

Model No.: FC60
Length: 6'
No. Pieces: 2
No. Guides: Aluminum oxide
Rec. Line: 6-12
Rec. Lure Wt.: ¼-⅝ oz.
Action: Ultra-light
Handle: Hypalon foregrips with rear cork grips and heavy duty tempered aluminum notched butt ferrules. Detachable soft plastic butt cap.

Model No.: FC65. Same as Model FC60 except:
Length: 6½'
Rec. Lure Wt.: ⅜-⅝ oz.

Model No.: GFC554-graphite.
Length: 5½'
No. Pieces: 1
No. Guides: Ceramic
Rec. Line: 8-15
Tip Top: Carbide
Action: Medium

Bait-Casting Rods

Model No.: PLC60
Length: 6'
No. Pieces: 2
No. Guides: Aluminum oxide
Tip Top: Aluminum oxide
Rec. Lure Wt.: ½-1 oz.
Action: Medium

Model No.: 1255. Same as Model PLC60 except:
Length: 5½'
No. Pieces: 1
No. Guides: Not specified; carbide
Tip Top: Carbide

Model No.: 1260. Same as Model PLC60 except:
No. Pieces: 1
No. Guides: Not specified; carbide
Tip Top: Carbide

Model No.: 1450. Same as Model PLC60 except:

Length: 5'
No. Pieces: 1

Model No.: 1455. Same as Model PLC60 except:
Length: 5½'
No. Pieces: 1

Model No.: 1460. Same as Model PLC60 except:
No. Pieces: 1

Model No.: GFC555-graphite. Same as Model PLC60 except:
Length: 5½'
No. Pieces: 1

Model No.: GFC605-graphite. Same as Model PLC60 except:
No. Pieces: 1

Model No.: 1457
Length: 5½'
No. Pieces: 1
No. Guides: Ceramic
Tip Top: Ceramic
Rec. Lure Wt.: ⅝-1⅝ oz.
Action: Fast tip; extra power
Handle: Hypalon foregrip with cork rear grips and heavy duty notched tempered aluminum butt ferrules. Detachable soft plastic butt cap.

Model No.: GFC557-graphite. Same as Model 1457 except graphite

Model No.: 1465
Length: 6½'
No. Pieces: 1
No. Guides: Ceramic
Tip Top: Ceramic
Rec. Lure Wt.: ½-1 oz.
Action: Extra power
Handle: Hypalon foregrips with cork rear grips and heavy duty notched tempered aluminum butt ferrules. Detachable soft plastic butt cap.

Model No.: 1256. Same as Model 1465 except:
Length: 5½'
No. Guides: Not specified; carbide
Tip Top: Carbide
Rec. Lure Wt.: ⅝-1¼ oz.

Model No.: 1261. Same as Model 1465 except:
No. Guides: Not specified; carbide
Tip Top: Carbide
Rec. Lure Wt.: ⅝-1¼ oz.

Model No.: 1456. Same as Model 1465 except:
Length: 5½'
Rec. Lure Wt.: ⅝-1¼ oz.

Model No.: 1461. Same as Model 1465 except:
Rec. Lure Wt.: ⅝-1¼ oz.

Model No.: GFC556-graphite. Same as Model 1465 except:
Length: 5½'
Rec. Lure Wt.: ⅝-1¼ oz.

Model No.: FS110
Length: 9'
No. Pieces: 2
No. Guides: Foul-proof flex
Tip Top: Aluminum oxide

Fenwick (con't.)

Rec. Lure Wt.: ⅜-¾ oz.
Action: Casting rod
Handle: Double locking aluminum or chrome-plated brass reel seats, cork grip with butt cap and winding check.

Salt Water Bait-Casting Rods

Model No.: PLB70C
Length: 7'
No. Pieces: 2
No. Guides: Not specified; hard-chrome braced spin
Tip Top: Carbide
Rec. Lure Wt.: Trolling
Action: Medium
Handle: Double locking reel seats, cork grips.

Model No.: PLB79. Same as Model PLB70C except:
Length: 7'9"
Rec. Lure Wt.: ⅝-1½ oz.

Model No.: PLB83. Same as Model PLB70C except:
Length: 8'3"
Rec. Lure Wt.: ¾-2 oz.

Model No.: PLB90. Same as Model PLB70C except:
Length: 9'
Rec. Lure Wt.: 1-3 oz.

Steelhead-Casting Rods

Model No.: FS79C
Length: 7'9"
No. Pieces: 2
No. Guides: Aluminum oxide
Tip Top: Aluminum oxide
Rec. Lure Wt.: ¼-⅝ oz.
Action: Steelhead
Handle: Cork body reel seat.

Model No.: FS80C. Same as Model FS79C except:
Length: 8'
Rec. Lure Wt.: ⅜-1 oz.

Model No.: FS83C. Same as Model FS79C except:
Length: 8'3"

Model No.: FS85C. Same as Model FS79C except:
Length: 8½'
Rec. Lure Wt.: ⅜-1 oz.

Model No.: GFS83C-graphite. Same as Model FS79C except:
Length: 8'3"
Rec. Line: 8-20

Fly Rods

Model No.: FF605
Length: 6'
No. Pieces: 2
No. Guides: Hand-chromed snake
Tip Top: Aluminum oxide
Rec. Line: 5
Action: Ultra-light

Model No.: FF705
Length: 7'
No. Pieces: 2
No. Guides: Hard-chromed snake
Tip Top: Aluminum oxide
Rec. Line: 5
Action: Light

Model No.: FF755
Length: 7½'
No. Pieces: 2
No. Guides: Hard-chromed snake
Tip Top: Aluminum oxide
Rec. Line: 5
Action: Light

Model No.: FF805
Length: 8'
No. Pieces: 2
No. Guides: Hard-chromed snake
Tip Top: Aluminum oxide
Rec. Line: 5

Model No.: FF706
Length: 7'
No. Pieces: 2
No. Guides: Hard
Tip Top: Aluminum oxide
Rec. Line: 6

Model No.: FF756
Length: 7½'
No. Pieces: 2
No. Guides: Hard-chromed snake
Tip Top: Aluminum oxide
Rec. Line: 6

Model No.: FF806
Length: 8'
No. Pieces: 2
No. Guides: Hard-chromed snake
Tip Top: Aluminum oxide
Rec. Line: 6

Model No. FF856
Length: 8½'
No. Pieces: 2
No. Guides: Hard-chromed snake
Tip Top: Aluminum oxide
Rec. Line: 6

Model No.: FF807
Length: 8'
No. Pieces: 2
No. Guides: Hard-chromed snake
Tip Top: Aluminum oxide
Rec. Line: 7

Model No.: FF857
Length: 8½'
No. Pieces: 2
No. Guides: Hard-chromed snake
Tip Top: Aluminum oxide
Rec. Line: 7

Model No.: FF858
Length: 8½'
No. Pieces: 2
No. Guides: Hard-chromed snake
Tip Top: Aluminum oxide
Rec. Line: 8

Model No.: FF909
Length: 9'
No. Pieces: 2
No. Guides: Hard-chromed snake
Tip Top: Aluminum oxide
Rec. Line: 9

Model No.: FF9010
Length: 9'
No. Pieces: 2
No. Guides: Hard-chromed snake
Tip Top: Aluminum oxide
Rec. Line: 10

Model No.: GFF-634-graphite
Length: 6½'
No. Pieces: 2
No. Guides: Hard-chromed snake
Rec. Line: 4
Handle: Cork body reel seat.

Model No.: GFF-704-graphite
Length: 7'
No. Pieces: 2
No. Guides: Ceramic stripping and chrome-plated snake
Rec. Line: 4
Handle: Cork body reel seat.

Model No.: GFF-755-graphite
Length: 7½'
No. Pieces: 2
No. Guides: Ceramic stripping and chrome-plated snake
Rec. Line: 4 or 5
Handle: Cork body reel seat.

Model No.: GFF-805-graphite. Same as Model No. GFF-634 except:
Length: 8'
Rec. Line: 5

Model No.: GFF-905-graphite. Same as Model No. GFF-634 except:
Length: 9'
Rec. Line: 5

Model No.: GFF-756-graphite. Same as Model No. GFF-634 except:
Length: 7½'
Rec. Line: 6

Model No.: GFF-806-graphite. Same as Model No. GFF-634 except:
Length: 8'
Rec. Line: 6

Model No.: GFF-856-graphite. Same as Model No. GFF-634 except:
Length: 8½'
Rec. Line: 6

Model No.: GFF-857-graphite. Same as Model No. GFF-634 except:
Length: 8½'
Rec. Line: 7

Model No.: GFF-858-graphite. Same as Model No. GFF-634 except:
Length: 8½'
Rec. Line: 8

Model No.: GFF-908-graphite. Same as Model No. GFF-634 except:
Length: 9'
Rec. Line: 8
Handle: Detachable extension butt.

Model No.: GFF-1058-graphite. Same as Model No. GFF-634 except:
Length: 10½'
Rec. Line: 8
Handle: 6" detachable extension butt.

Model No.: GFF-9010-graphite. Same as Model No. GFF-634 except:
Length: 9'
Rec. Line: 10
Handle: 6" detachable extension butt.

Model No.: GFF-10511-graphite. Same as Model No. GFF-634 except:
Length: 10½'
Rec. Line: 11

Fenwick (con't.)

Handle: 6″ detachable extension butt.

Model No.: GFF-9012-graphite. Same as Model No. GFF-634 except:
Length: 9′
Rec. Line: 12
Handle: 2″ fixed extension butt.

Model No.: GFF-806-4 Graphite Voyageur
Length: 8′
No. Pieces: 4
Rec. Line: 6
Action: Light
Handle: Shaped cork with aluminum reel seat and double-locking nuts.

Model No.: GFF-857-4 Graphite Voyageur
Length: 8½′
No. Pieces: 4
Rec. Line: 7
Action: Light
Handle: Shaped cork with aluminum reel seat and double-locking nuts.

Mooching Rods

Model No.: GFS-91C-graphite
Length: 9′
No. Pieces: 2
Rec. Lure Wt.: 1-2½ oz.
Action: Heavy

Model No.: FS88C
Length: 8½′
No. Pieces: 2
No. Guides: Aluminum oxide
Tip Top: Aluminum oxide
Rec. Lure Wt.: ⅝-1½ oz.
Action: Heavy
Handle: Chrome-plated double locking brass reel seat, cork grip.

Model No.: FS89C. Same as Model FS88C except:
Length: 8′10″
Rec. Lure Wt.: 1-2½ oz.

Popping, Musky and Deep Jigging Rods

Model No.: PLP83
Length: 8′3″
No. Pieces: 2
No. Guides: Ceramic
Tip Top: Ceramic
Rec. Lure Wt.: ¼-⅝ oz.
Handle: Cork handle with 3″ foregrip and 10″ rear grip.

Model No.: 760
Length: 6′
No. Guides: Aluminum oxide
Tip Top: Aluminum oxide
Rec. Lure Wt.: 1-3 oz.
Handle: Cork.

Model No.: 770
Length: 7′
No. Pieces: 1
No. Guides: Ceramic
Tip Top: Ceramic
Rec. Lure Wt.: ½-1 oz.
Action: Heavy
Handle: Double locking chrome-plated reel seat, cork grip.

Model No.: 771
Length: 7′

No. Pieces: 1
No. Guides: Not specified; ceramic
Tip Top: Ceramic
Rec. Lure Wt.: ¾-3 oz.
Action: Heavy
Handle: Double locking chrome-plated reel seat, cork grip.

Model No.: PLP65
Length: 6½′
No. Pieces: 2
No. Guides: Not specified; ceramic
Tip Top: Ceramic
Rec. Lure Wt.: ½-1 oz.
Action: Heavy
Handle: Double locking chrome-plated reel seat, cork grip.

Model No.: PLP71
Length: 7′
No. Pieces: 2
No. Guides: Not specified; ceramic
Tip Top: Ceramic
Rec. Lure Wt.: ½-1 oz.
Action: Heavy
Handle: Double locking chrome-plated reel seat, cork grip.

Model No.: GPLP-71-graphite
Length: 7′
No. Pieces: 2
No. Guides: Aluminum oxide
Tip Top: Aluminum oxide
Rec. Lure Wt.: ½-1 oz.
Action: Light

Trolling Rods

Model No.: 610 (Deluxe)
Length: 6′9″
No. Pieces: 2
No. Guides: 5 Aftco roller
Tip Top: Aftco roller
Rec. Lure Wt.: Not specified
Action: Trolling rod
Line Class: 12 lb.
Handle: Hypalon covered stainless steel with gimbal nock.

Model No.: 620. Same as Model 610 except:
Line Class: 20 lb.

Model No.: 630. Same as Model 610 except:
Line Class: 30 lb.

Model No.: 640. Same as Model 610 except:
Length: 6′10″
Line Class: 50 lb.

Model No.: 660. Same as Model 610 except:
Length: 7′1″
No. Guides: 5 Mildrum double roller
Tip Top: Mildrum double roller
Line Class: 80 lb.

Model No.: 670. Same as Model 610 except:
Length: 7′1″
No. Guides: 5 Mildrum double roller
Tip Top: Mildrum double roller
Line Class: 130 lb.

Model No.: 522 (Boat)
Length: 7′3″
No. Pieces: 2
No. Guides: Stainless steel
Tip Top: Roller
Rec. Lure Wt.: Not specified
Action: Trolling rod
Line Class: 18-25 lb.

Handle: Hypalon with rubber butt cap and chrome-plated double locking reel seat.

Model No.: 532. Same as Model 522 except:
Line Class: 25-40 lb.

Model No.: 821
Length: 6′9″
No. Pieces: 1
No. Guides: Carbide
Tip Top: Carbide
Action: Trolling
Handle: Synthetic foam with gimbal nock.

Model No.: 841 (Standard)
Length: 6′10″
No. Pieces: 1
No. Guides: Carbide
Tip Top: Carbide
Action: Trolling
Handle: Synthetic foam with gimbal nock.

Model No.: G-610, G-620, G-630 (graphite)
Length: 6′9″
No. Pieces: 1
No. Guides: Aftco double roller
Tip Top: Aftco roller
Action: Trolling
Handle: Stainless steel with gimbal nock.

Model No.: G-640, G-650, G-660 (graphite)
Length: 6′10″
No. Pieces: 1
No. Guides: Aftco double roller
Tip Top: Aftco roller
Action: Trolling
Handle: Stainless steel with gimbal nock.

Fly/Spin Combo Rods

Model No.: SF74-4
Length: 7′
No. Pieces: 4
No. Guides: Not specified; chrome-plated
Tip Top: Chrome-plated
Rec. Line: 6 wt.
Handle: Cork grip; combination fly and spin handle.

Model No.: SF75-5. Same as Model SF74-4 except:
Length: 7½′
No. Pieces: 5

Combo Trolling/Jig Rod

Model No.: PT809
Length: 6′8″
No. Pieces: 1
No. Guides: 6 braced conventional
Tip Top: Roller tip
Rec. Lure Wt.: 2-10 oz.
Action: Heavy
Handle: Double locking reel seat, cork grip.

Live Bait and Jig Rods

Model No.: PB60C
Length: 6′
No. Pieces: 1
No. Guides: Not specified; braced
Tip Top: Carbide
Rec. Lure Wt.: ½-1½ oz.
Action: Fast power
Handle: Double locking reel seat, cork grip.

Model No.: JB65C. Same as Model PB60C except:

Fenwick (con't.)

Length: 6½'
Rec. Lure Wt.: ½-2 oz.

Model No.: PB71C
Length: 7'
No. Pieces: 2
No. Guides: Braced
Tip Top: Carbide
Rec. Lure Wt.: ¾-2 oz.
Action: Fast
Handle: Chrome-plated seat.

Model No.: PB72
Length: 7'
No. Pieces: 2
No. Guides: Hard-chrome braced
Tip Top: Carbide
Rec. Lure Wt.: 1-2½ oz.

Model No.: PB74
Length: 7½'
No. Pieces: 1
No. Guides: Chrome braced
Tip Top: Carbide
Rec. Lure Wt.: ¾-1½ oz.

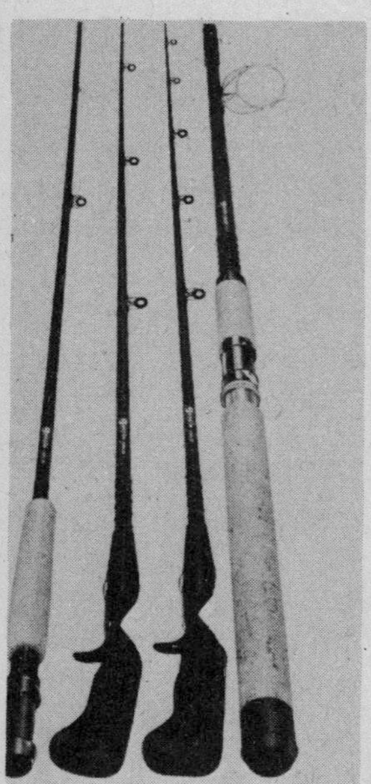

Deluxe Series

Garcia

Spinning Rods

Model No.: B551 (Brown Series)
Length: 7'2"
No. Pieces: 2
No. Guides: 7 hard-chromed guides plus one
    braced stripping guide
Tip Top: Tungsten carbide
Rec. Lure Wt.: ⅜-3 oz.
Action: Light-medium; ultra-fast taper
Handle: Not specified.

Model No.: B552. Same as Model B551
    except:
Length: 7½'
Rec. Lure Wt.: ⅝-4 oz.

Model No.: B546
Length: 6½'
No. Pieces: 4
No. Guides: 4 chrome-plated
Tip Top: Chrome-plated
Rec. Lure Wt.: ¼-½ oz.
Action: Light
Handle: Not specified.

Freshwater Spinning Rods

Model No.: 2110 (Deluxe Series)
Length: 6½'
No. Pieces: 2
No. Guides: 5 genuine agate
Tip Top: Genuine agate
Rec. Lure Wt.: ¼-½ oz.
Action: Light
Handle: Not specified.

Model No.: 2111 (Deluxe Series)
Length: 7'
No. Pieces: 2
No. Guides: 5 genuine agate
Tip Top: Genuine agate
Rec. Lure Wt.: ¼-⅝ oz.
Action: Medium
Handle: Not specified.

Model No.: 2112 (Deluxe Series)
Length: 7'
No. Pieces: 2
No. Guides: 5 genuine agate
Tip Top: Genuine agate
Rec. Lure Wt.: ⅝-1¼ oz.
Action: Heavy; fast taper
Handle: Not specified.

Model No.: B112. Same as Model 2112
    except:
No. Guides: Not specified; carbide

Model No.: B122 (Deluxe Series)
Length: 6½'
No. Pieces: 2
No. Guides: 5 carbide
Tip Top: Carbide
Rec. Lure Wt.: ⅜-¾ oz.
Action: Medium
Handle: Not specified.

Model No.: B123. Same as Model B122
    except:
Length: 7'
Rec. Lure Wt.: ⅜-1 oz.

Model No.: 2121 (Deluxe Series)
Length: 5'
No. Pieces: 2
No. Guides: 4 hard-chromed stainless steel
    guides plus one braced stripper
Tip Top: Hard-chromed stainless steel
Rec. Lure Wt.: 1/16-¼ oz.
Action: Ultra-light
Handle: Not specified.

Model No.: 2132 (Deluxe Series)
Length: 5½'
No. Pieces: 2
No. Guides: 4 hard-chromed stainless steel
    guides plus one braced stripper
Tip Top: Hard-chromed stainless steel
Rec. Lure Wt.: ⅛-½ oz.
Action: Light; fast taper
Handle: Not specified.

Model No.: 2134 (Deluxe Series)
Length: 6'
No. Pieces: 2

No. Guides: 4 hard-chromed stainless steel
    guides plus one braced stripper
Tip Top: Hard-chromed stainless steel
Rec. Lure Wt.: ¼-⅝ oz.
Action: Light; fast taper
Handle: Not specified.

Model No.: 2133. Same as Model 2134
    except:
Length: 7'
No. Guides: 5
Rec. Lure Wt.: ¼-½ oz.

Model No.: 2135. Same as Model 2134
    except:
Length: 6½'
No. Guides: 5
Rec. Lure Wt.: ¼-½ oz.

Model No.: B501 (Brown Series)
Length: 5½'
No. Pieces: 2
No. Guides: 4 hard-chromed stainless steel
Tip Top: Hard-chromed stainless steel
Rec. Lure Wt.: ⅛-½ oz.
Action: Light; fast taper
Handle: Not specified.

Brown Series: Surf, Popping, Boat, Fly

Model No.: 2500. Same as Model B501
    except:
Length: 5'
Rec. Lure Wt.: 1/16-¼ oz.
Action: Ultra-light

Model No.: 2503. Same as Model B501
    except:
Length: 6'
No. Pieces: 2
Rec. Lure Wt.: 1/16-¼ oz.
Action: Ultra-light

Model No.: 2505 (Brown Series)
Length: 6½'
No. Pieces: 2
No. Guides: 4 hard-chromed stainless steel
Tip Top: Hard-chromed stainless steel
Rec. Lure Wt.: ¼-½ oz.

Garcia (con't.)

Action: Light
Handle: Not specified.

Model No.: B508. Same as Model 2505 except:
No. Guides: 5 carbide
Tip Top: Carbide
Action: Light; fast taper

Model No.: 2502. Same as Model 2505 except:
Length: 6′
Rec. Lure Wt.: ¼-⅝ oz.
Action: Light; fast taper

Model No.: 2507. Same as Model 2505 except:
Length: 7′
No. Guides: 5

Model No.: 2508. Same as Model 2505 except:
No. Guides: 5
Action: Light; fast taper

Model No.: 2510. Same as Model 2505 except:
Length: 7′
Rec. Lure Wt.: ¼-½ oz.
Action: Light; fast taper

Model No.: 2512 (Brown Series)
Length: 6½′
No. Pieces: 2
No. Guides: 5 hard-chromed stainless steel
Tip Top: Hard-chromed stainless steel
Rec. Lure Wt.: ⅜-¾ oz.
Action: Medium
Handle: Not specified.

Model No.: 2513. Same as Model 2512 except:
Length: 7′
Rec. Lure Wt.: ⅜-1 oz.

Model No.: 2601 (Blue Series)
Length: 5′
No. Pieces: 2
No. Guides: 4 hard-chromed
Tip Top: Hard-chromed
Rec. Lure Wt.: ¹⁄₁₆-¼ oz.
Action: Ultra-light
Handle: Cork handle with sliding rings.

Model No.: B601. Same as Model 2601 except:
Length: 5½′
Action: Light
Handle: Fixed reel seat.

Model No.: 2604 (Blue Series)
Length: 6½′
No. Pieces: 2
No. Guides: 4 hard-chromed
Tip Top: Hard-chromed
Rec. Lure Wt.: ¼-½ oz.
Action: Light
Handle: Not specified.

Model No.: 2605 (Blue Series)
Length: 7′
No. Pieces: 2
No. Guides: 4 hard-chromed
Tip Top: Hard-chromed
Rec. Lure Wt.: ¼-½ oz.
Action: Light
Handle: Not specified.

Model No.: 2606 (Blue Series)
Length: 7′
No. Pieces: 2
No. Guides: 4 hard-chromed stainless steel
Tip Top: Hard-chromed stainless steel
Rec. Lure Wt.: ⅜-¾ oz.
Action: Medium
Handle: Not specified.

Model No.: 2609 (Blue Series)
Length: 6½′
No. Pieces: 2
No. Guides: 4 hard-chromed
Tip Top: Hard-chromed
Rec. Lure Wt.: ¼-⅝ oz.
Action: Light; fast taper
Handle: Not specified.

Model No.: 2610 (Blue Series)
Length: 7′
No. Pieces: 2
No. Guides: 4 hard-chromed

Avocado Series: Fly, Boat & Saltwater

Tip Top: Hard-chromed
Rec. Lure Wt.: ¼-½ oz.
Action: Light; fast taper
Handle: Not specified.

Model No.: 8201 (Avocado Series)
Length: 5½′
No. Pieces: 2
No. Guides: 4 hard-chromed stainless steel
Tip Top: Hard-chromed stainless steel
Rec. Lure Wt.: ⅛-½ oz.
Action: Light; fast taper
Handle: Not specified.

Model No.: 8208 (Avocado Series)
Length: 6½′
No. Pieces: 2
No. Guides: 5 hard-chromed stainless steel
Tip Top: Hard-chromed stainless steel
Rec. Lure Wt.: ¼-½ oz.
Action: Light; fast taper
Handle: Not specified.

Model No.: 8210 (Avocado Series)
Length: 7′
No. Pieces: 2

No. Guides: 5 hard-chromed stainless steel
Tip Top: Hard-chromed stainless steel
Rec. Lure Wt.: ¼-½ oz.
Action: Light; fast taper
Handle: Not specified.

Model No.: 8212 (Avocado Series)
Length: 6½′
No. Pieces: 2
No. Guides: 5 hard-chromed stainless steel
Tip Top: Hard-chromed stainless steel
Rec. Lure Wt.: ⅜-¾ oz.
Action: Medium
Handle: Not specified.

Saltwater Spinning Rods

Model No.: 2154 (Deluxe Series)
Length: 10′
No. Pieces: 2
No. Guides: 7 hard-chromed stainless steel
Tip Top: Tungsten carbide
Rec. Lure Wt.: 1-4½ oz.
Action: Medium; fast taper
Handle: Not specified.

Model No.: 2553 (Brown Series)
Length: 9½′
No. Pieces: 2
No. Guides: 6 hard-chromed guides plus one braced stripping guide
Tip Top: Tungsten carbide
Rec. Lure Wt.: 1-4½ oz.
Action: Medium; fast taper
Handle: Not specified.

Model No.: 2554. Same as Model 2553 except:
Length: 10′
No. Guides: 7

Model No.: 2571. Same as Model 2553 except:
Length: 9′
No. Guides: 7
Rec. Lure Wt.: 1-4 oz.

Model No.: 2573. Same as Model 2553 except:
Length: 11′4″
No. Guides: 8
Rec. Lure Wt.: 2-5 oz.
Action: Heavy

Model No.: 2653 (Blue Series)
Length: 7′5″
No. Pieces: 1
No. Guides: 4 hard-chromed stainless steel
Tip Top: Hard-chromed stainless steel
Rec. Lure Wt.: 1-4 oz.
Action: Medium
Handle: Detachable hardwood handle, chrome-plated reel seat, neoprene foregrip.

Model No.: 2654 (Blue Series)
Length: 10′
No. Pieces: 2
No. Guides: 6 hard-chromed stainless steel
Tip Top: Hard-chromed stainless steel
Rec. Lure Wt.: 1-4½ oz.
Action: Medium; fast taper
Handle: Not specified.

Model No.: 8255 (Avocado Series)
Length: 7½′
No. Pieces: 2
No. Guides: 6 varmac hard-chromed stainless steel guides plus one braced stripper
Tip Top: Hard-chromed stainless steel
Rec. Lure Wt.: ⅝-4 oz.

Garcia (con't.)

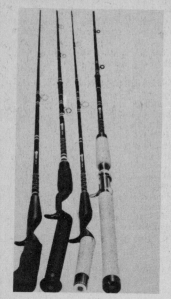

Brown Series: Surf, Popping, Boat, Fly

Action: Light-medium; fast taper
Handle: Not specified.

Model No.: 8271 (Avocado Series)
Length: 9'
No. Pieces: 2
No. Guides: 6 hard-chromed varmac guides plus one braced stripping guide
Tip Top: Hard-chromed stainless steel
Rec. Lure Wt.: 1-4 oz.
Action: Medium; fast taper
Handle: Not specified.

Steelhead and Saltwater Spinning Rods

Model No.: 2506 (Brown Series)
Length: 7'
No. Pieces: 2
No. Guides: 5 hard-chromed guides plus one braced stripping guide
Tip Top: Tungsten carbide
Rec. Lure Wt.: ⅝-1 oz.
Action: Fast taper; light for saltwater, medium-heavy for freshwater
Handle: Not specified.

Model No.: 2509 (Brown Series)
Length: 7'
No. Pieces: 1
No. Guides: 7 hard-chromed guides plus one braced stripping guide
Tip Top: Tungsten carbide
Rec. Lure Wt.: ½-1½ oz.
Action: Light; fast taper
Handle: Not specified.

Model No.: 2551 (Brown Series)
Length: 8'
No. Pieces: 2
No. Guides: 5 hard-chromed guides plus one braced stripping guide
Tip Top: Tungsten carbide
Rec. Lure Wt.: ⅝-2½ oz.
Action: Medium; fast taper
Handle: Not specified.

Model No.: 2552. Same as Model 2551 except:
Length: 8½'

Model No.: 2650 (Blue Series)
Length: 8'
No. Pieces: 2
No. Guides: 5 hard-chromed stainless steel
Tip Top: Hard-chromed stainless steel
Rec. Lure Wt.: ⅝-1¼ oz.
Action: Light
Handle: Not specified.

Model No.: 2651 (Blue Series)
Length: 8½'
No. Pieces: 2
No. Guides: 5 hard-chromed stainless steel
Tip Top: Hard-chromed stainless steel
Rec. Lure Wt.: ⅝-1½ oz.
Action: Light-medium
Handle: Not specified.

Model No.: 2652 (Blue Series)
Length: 9'
No. Pieces: 2
No. Guides: 5 hard-chromed stainless steel
Tip Top: Hard-chromed stainless steel
Rec. Lure Wt.: 1-3 oz.
Action: Medium
Handle: Not specified.

Model No.: 2655 (Blue Series)
Length: 9½'
No. Pieces: 2
No. Guides: 6 hard-chromed stainless steel
Tip Top: Hard-chromed stainless steel
Rec. Lure Wt.: 1-3 oz.
Action: Medium
Handle: Not specified.

Model No.: 8206 (Avocado Series)
Length: 7'
No. Pieces: 2
No. Guides: 5 hard-chromed stainless steel guides plus one braced stripper
Tip Top: Hard-chromed stainless steel
Rec. Lure Wt.: ⅝-1 oz.
Action: Fast taper; light for saltwater, medium-heavy for freshwater
Handle: Not specified.

Model No.: 8252 (Avocado Series)
Length: 8½'
No. Pieces: 2
No. Guides: 5 varmac hard-chromed stainless steel guides plus one braced stripper
Tip Top: Hard-chromed stainless steel
Rec. Lure Wt.: ⅝-2½ oz.
Action: Medium; fast taper
Handle: Not specified.

Model No.: 8267 (Avocado Series)
Length: 8'
No. Pieces: 2
No. Guides: 5 hard-chromed stainless steel guides plus one braced stripper
Tip Top: Hard-chromed stainless steel
Rec. Lure Wt.: ⅝-1¼ oz.
Action: Light-medium
Handle: Not specified.

Spincasting and Baitcasting Rods

Model No.: 2218
Length: 6½'
No. Pieces: 2
No. Guides: 5 hard-chromed stainless steel guides plus one braced stripper
Tip Top: Tungsten carbide
Rec. Lure Wt.: ⅜-⅝ oz.

Action: Medium; fast taper
Handle: Not specified.

Model No.: 2521 (Brown Series)
Length: 6'
No. Pieces: 2
No. Guides: 4 hard-chromed stainless steel
Tip Top: Hard-chromed stainless steel
Rec. Lure Wt.: ½-¾ oz.
Action: Medium
Handle: Not specified.

Model No.: 2522
Length: 6½'
No. Pieces: 2
No. Guides: 5 hard-chromed stainless steel
Tip Top: Hard-chromed stainless steel
Rec. Lure Wt.: ¼-⅝ oz.
Action: Light
Handle: Not specified.

Model No.: 2524 (Brown Series)
Length: 6'
No. Pieces: 1
No. Guides: 5 hard-chromed stainless steel
Tip Top: Hard-chromed stainless steel
Rec. Lure Wt.: ¼-⅝ oz.
Action: Light; fast taper
Handle: Not specified.

Model No.: 2526 (Brown Series)
Length: 6½'
No. Pieces: 2
No. Guides: 5 hard-chromed stainless steel
Tip Top: Hard-chromed stainless steel
Rec. Lure Wt.: ⅜-⅝ oz.
Action: Medium; fast taper
Handle: Not specified.

Model No.: 2525. Same as Model 2526 except:
Length: 7'
Rec. Lure Wt.: ⅜-¾ oz.
Handle: Two-hand handle.

Model No.: 2528. Same as Model 2526 except:
Length: 6'
Rec. Lure Wt.: ⅜-¾ oz.

Model No.: 2621 (Blue Series)
Length: 6½'
No. Pieces: 2
No. Guides: 5 hard-chromed
Tip Top: Hard-chromed
Rec. Lure Wt.: ¼-⅝ oz.
Action: Light
Handle: Not specified.

Model No.: 2622 (Blue Series)
Length: 6'
No. Pieces: 2
No. Guides: 4 hard-chromed
Tip Top: Hard-chromed
Rec. Lure Wt.: ¼-½ oz.
Action: Light
Handle: Not specified.

Model No.: 2629 (Blue Series)
Length: 5'8"
No. Pieces: 1
No. Guides: 4 hard-chromed
Tip Top: Hard-chromed
Rec. Lure Wt.: ¼-⅝ oz.
Action: Medium; fast taper
Handle: Not specified.

Model No.: 2628 (Blue Series)
Length: 6'
No. Pieces: 2

Garcia (con't.)

No. Guides: 4 hard-chromed
Tip Top: Hard-chromed
Rec. Lure Wt.: ¼-⅝ oz.
Action: Light; fast taper
Handle: Not specified.

Model No.: 8226 (Avocado Series)
Length: 6½'
No. Pieces: 2
No. Guides: 5 hard-chromed stainless steel
Tip Top: Hard-chromed stainless steel
Rec. Lure Wt.: ⅜-⅝ oz.
Action: Medium; fast taper
Handle: Not specified.

Model No.: 8228 (Avocado Series)
Length: 6'
No. Pieces: 2
No. Guides: 5 hard-chromed stainless steel
Tip Top: Hard-chromed stainless steel
Rec. Lure Wt.: ⅜-¾ oz.
Action: Medium; fast taper
Handle: Not specified.

Saltwater Rods

Model No.: B572 (Brown Series)
Length: 6'10"
No. Pieces: 2
No. Guides: 6 hard-chromed stainless steel plus one braced stripper
Tip Top: Hard-chromed stainless steel
Rec. Lure Wt.: 1-2½ oz.
Action: Medium; fast taper
Handle: Brass reel seat with two locking rings, neoprene handle and foregrip.

Model No.: B573 (Brown Series)
Length: 6'4"
No. Pieces: 1
No. Guides: 5 hard-chromed stainless steel guides plus one braced stripper
Tip Top: Hard-chromed stainless steel
Rec. Lure Wt.: 1-2½ oz.
Action: Medium; fast taper
Handle: Brass reel seat with two locking rings, neoprene handle and foregrip.

Model No.: B574. Same as Model B573 except:
Length: 6'10"
No. Guides: 6 hard-chromed
Rec. Lure Wt.: 1-3 oz.

Model No.: B575 (Brown Series)
Length: 7'
No. Pieces: 1
No. Guides: 6 hard-chromed plus one braced stripper
Tip Top: Hard-chromed
Rec. Lure Wt.: 1½-4 oz.
Action: Medium; fast taper
Handle: Brass reel seat with two locking rings, neoprene handle and foregrip.

Model No.: B576 (Brown Series)
Length: 8'
No. Pieces: 1
No. Guides: 7 hard-chromed varmac stainless steel guides plus one braced stripper
Tip Top: Hard-chromed varmac stainless steel
Rec. Lure Wt.: 1½-4 oz.
Action: Medium; fast taper
Handle: Brass reel seat with two locking rings, neoprene handle and foregrip.

Boat Rods

Model No.: 2532 (Brown Series)

Length: 7'
No. Pieces: 1
No. Guides: 4 hard-chromed stainless steel
Tip Top: Tungsten carbide
Rec. Lure Wt.: 3-5 oz.
Action: Heavy; fast taper
Handle: Neoprene foregrips, detachable hardwood butt.

Model No: 2559 (Brown Series)
Length: 7'8"
No. Pieces: 1
No. Guides: 4 hard-chromed guides plus one braced stripping guide
Tip Top: Tungsten carbide
Rec. Lure Wt.: 1-4 oz.
Action: Medium
Handle: Detachable hardwood butt, neoprene foregrip.

Model No.: 2662 (Blue Series)
Length: 6½'
No. Pieces: 1
No. Guides: 4 hard-chromed carbon steel
Tip Top: Hard-chromed carbon steel
Rec. Lure Wt.: Not specified
Action: Heavy
Handle: Detachable wood handle, neoprene foregrip, heavily-chromed, front locking reel seat.

Model No.: 2663 (Blue Series)
Length: 7'
No. Pieces: 1
No. Guides: 4 hard-chromed carbon steel
Tip Top: Hard-chromed carbon steel
Rec. Lure Wt.: 1¼-3 oz.
Action: Medium
Handle: Detachable wood handle, neoprene foregrip, front locking reel seat.

Model No.: 2565 (Brown Series)
Length: 6'8"
No. Pieces: 1
No. Guides: 6 tungsten carbide
Tip Top: Tungsten carbide
Handle: Neoprene foregrip, detachable hardwood butt. Gimbal shape handle with rubber butt cap.

Model No.: 2668 (Blue Series)
Length: 6½'
No. Pieces: 1
No. Guides: 4 bridged hard-chromed stainless steel
Tip Top: Roller
Rec. Lure Wt.: Not specified
Action: Heavy
Handle: Detachable hardwood butt with gimbal taper.

Model No.: 2877 (Black Series)
Length: 5½'
No. Pieces: 1
No. Guides: 3 hard-chromed stainless steel spinning
Tip Top: Hard-chromed stainless steel
Rec. Lure Wt.: 1¾-3½ oz.
Action: Light-medium
Handle: Detachable butt.

Model No.: 2891 (Black Series)
Length: 5½'
No. Pieces: 1
No. Guides: 3 hard-chromed carbon steel conventional
Tip Top: Hard-chromed carbon steel
Rec. Lure Wt.: 2½-4 oz.
Action: Light
Handle: Detachable butt.

Model No.: 8293 (Avocado Series)
Length: 6½'
No. Pieces: 1
No. Guides: 4 hard-chromed stainless steel
Tip Top: Hard-chromed stainless steel
Rec. Lure Wt.: 1¾-3½ oz.
Action: Medium
Handle: Detachable hardwood butt.

Model No.: 8294 (Avocado Series)
Length: 6½'
No. Pieces: 1
No. Guides: 4 hard-chromed
Tip Top: Hard-chromed
Rec. Lure Wt.: 1¾-3½ oz.
Action: Light-medium
Handle: Detachable butt.

Model No.: 8297 (Avocado Series)
Length: 6½'
No. Pieces: 1
No. Guides: 4 hard-chromed
Tip Top: Hard-chromed
Rec. Lure Wt.: 2½-5 oz.
Action: Medium
Handle: Detachable butt.

Boat and Trolling Rods

Model No.: 2878 (Black Series)
Length: 6'
No. Pieces: 1
No. Guides: 4 hard-chromed carbon steel
Tip Top: Hard-chromed carbon steel
Rec. Lure Wt.: Not specified
Action: Heavy
Handle: Glass shaft continuing through cork butt.

Model No.: 2879 (Black Series)
Length: 6½'
No. Pieces: 1
No. Guides: 4 hard-chromed carbon steel
Tip Top: Roller
Rec. Lure Wt.: Not specified
Action: Heavy
Handle: Shaft continuing through hardwood butt.

Model No.: 2889 (Black Series)
Length: 6½'
No. Pieces: 1
No. Guides: 4 hard-chromed stainless steel roller
Tip Top: Hard-chromed stainless steel roller
Rec. Lure Wt.: Not specified
Action: Heavy
Handle: Detachable butt.

Model No.: 2892 (Black Series)
Length: 6½'
No. Pieces: 1
No. Guides: 4 hard-chromed carbon steel
Tip Top: Hard-chromed carbon steel
Rec. Lure Wt.: 1-2½ oz.
Action: Light
Handle: Detachable butt.

Model No.: 2894 (Black Series)
Length: 6½'
No. Pieces: 1
No. Guides: 4 hard-chromed carbon steel
Tip Top: Hard-chromed carbon steel
Rec. Lure Wt.: 1¾-3½ oz.
Action: Light-medium
Handle: Detachable butt.

Model No.: 2897 (Black Series)
Length: 6½'
No. Pieces: 1

Garcia (con't.)

No. Guides: 4 hard-chromed carbon steel
Tip Top: Hard-chromed carbon steel
Rec. Lure Wt.: 2½-5 oz.
Action: Medium
Handle: Detachable butt.

Model No.: 2898 (Black Series)
Length: 6'5"
No. Pieces: 1
No. Guides: 4 hard-chromed carbon steel
Tip Top: Hard-chromed carbon steel
Rec. Lure Wt.: Not specified
Action: Heavy
Handle: Detachable butt.

Model No.: 2899 (Black Series)
Length: 6'5"
No. Pieces: 1
No. Guides: 4 hard-chromed carbon steel
Tip Top: Roller
Rec. Lure Wt.: Not specified
Action: Heavy
Handle: Detachable butt.

Saltwater Trolling Rods

Model No.: B570 (Brown Series)
Length: 7'
No. Pieces: 1
No. Guides: 5 varmac hard-chromed
  stainless steel
Tip Top: Aftco roller
Rec. Lure Wt.: Not specified
Action: Heavy
Handle: Brass reel seat with two locking
  rings, neoprene handle and foregrip.
  Double-slotted gimbal nock and removable
  rubber butt cap.

Model No.: 2565 (Big Game Series)
Length: 6'8"
No. Pieces: 1
No. Guides: 6 tungsten carbide
Tip Top: Tungsten carbide
Handle: Hypalon foregrip; detachable butt
  with gimbal nock.

Model No.: 2566. Same as Model No.
  2565 except:
Length: 6'
No. Guides: 4 tungsten carbide

Model No.: R590
No. Guides: 5 Aftco roller
Tip Top: Aftco roller
Action: 3-thread
Handle: Detachable butt with self-aligning
  ferrule; Varmac double-locking reel seat.

Model No.: R596. Same as Model No.
  R590 except:
Rec. Line: 6-thread

Model No.: R597. Same as Model No. R590
  except:
Rec. Line: 9-thread

Model No.: R599. Same as Model No.
  R590 except:
No. Guides: 4 Mildrum roller
Tip Top: Mildrum double roller
Rec. Line: 24-thread

Spinning and Trolling Rod

Model No.: 2888 (Black Series)
Length: 7'5"

No. Pieces: 1
No. Guides: 4 hard-chromed stainless steel
Tip Top: Hard-chromed stainless steel
Rec. Lure Wt.: 1-3 oz.
Action: Medium
Handle: Detachable butt.

Worm Rods

Model No.: 2154 (Brown Series)
Length: 5½'
No. Pieces: 1
No. Guides: 5 hard-chromed stainless steel
Tip Top: Hard-chromed stainless steel
Rec. Lure Wt.: ⅜-1 oz.
Action: Heavy
Handle: Not specified.

Model No.: 2516 (Brown Series)
Length: 6'
No. Pieces: 1
No. Guides: 6 hard-chromed stainless steel
  guides plus one braced stripper
Tip Top: Hard-chromed stainless steel
Rec. Lure Wt.: ⅜-¾ oz.
Action: Medium; fast taper
Handle: Not specified.

Model No.: 2529. Same as Model 2516
  except:
Length: 5'8"
No. Guides: 4

Model No.: B529. Same as Model 2529
  except:
No. Pieces: 2
No. Guides: 4

Model No.: 8225 (Avocado Series)
Length: 5'
No. Pieces: 1
No. Guides: 5 hard-chromed stainless steel
  guides plus one braced stripper
Tip Top: Hard-chromed stainless steel
Rec. Lure Wt.: ½-1 oz.
Action: Medium-stiff
Handle: Not specified.

Model No.: 8229 (Avocado Series)
Length: 5'8"
No. Pieces: 1
No. Guides: 4 hard-chromed stainless steel
Tip Top: Hard-chromed stainless steel
Rec. Lure Wt.: ⅜-¾ oz.
Action: Medium; fast taper
Handle: Not specified.

Model No.: 8315 (Ambassadeur Series)
Length: 5'
No. Pieces: 1
No. Guides: 5 ceramic
Tip Top: Ceramic
Rec. Lure Wt.: ½-1 oz.
Action: Medium-stiff
Handle: Not specified.

Model No.: 8316 (Ambassadeur Series)
Length: 5½'
No. Pieces: 1
No. Guides: 6 ceramic
Tip Top: Ceramic
Rec. Lure Wt.: ½-1 oz.
Action: Medium-soft
Handle: Cushion-foam foregrip.

Model No.: 8317 (Ambassadeur Series)
Length: 5½'
No. Pieces: 1
No. Guides: 6 ceramic
Tip Top: Ceramic

Rec. Lure Wt.: ⅝-1¼ oz.
Action: Medium-light
Handle: Not specified.

Model No.: 8318 (Ambassadeur Series)
Length: 5½'
No. Pieces: 1
No. Guides: 6 ceramic
Tip Top: Ceramic
Rec. Lure Wt.: ⅝-1¼ oz.
Action: Medium-stiff
Handle: Not specified.

Model No.: 8319 (Ambassadeur Series)
Length: 6'
No. Pieces: 1
No. Guides: 6 tungsten carbide
Tip Top: Tungsten carbide
Rec. Lure Wt.: ½-1 oz.
Action: Medium-soft
Handle: Not specified.

Model No.: 8321 (Ambassadeur Series)
Length: 6'
No. Pieces: 1
No. Guides: 6 ceramic
Tip Top: Ceramic
Rec. Lure Wt.: ⅝-1¼ oz.
Action: Medium-light
Handle: Not specified.

Model No.: 8322 (Ambassadeur Series)
Length: 6'
No. Pieces: 1
No. Guides: 6 ceramic
Tip Top: Ceramic
Rec. Lure Wt.: ⅜-1 oz.
Action: Medium
Handle: Not specified.

Model No.: 8324 (Ambassadeur Series)
Length: 6½'
No. Pieces: 2
No. Guides: 6 ceramic
Tip Top: Ceramic
Rec. Lure Wt.: ½-1 oz.
Action: Medium-soft
Handle: Not specified.

Model No.: 8326 (Ambassadeur Series)
Length: 6'
No. Pieces: 2
No. Guides: 6 ceramic
Tip Top: Ceramic
Rec. Lure Wt.: ⅝-1¼ oz.
Action: Medium-light
Handle: Cushion-foam foregrip.

Model No.: 2212 (Deluxe Series)
Length: 5½'
No. Pieces: 1
No. Guides: 6 hard-chromed stainless steel
  plus one braced stripper
Tip Top: Tungsten carbide
Rec. Lure Wt.: ½-1 oz.
Action: Medium-soft

Model No.: 2213. Same as Model No. 2212
  except:
Rec. Lure Wt.: ⅝-1¼ oz.
Action: Medium-stiff

Model No.: 2214. Same as Model No. 2212
  except:
Length: 6'
Rec. Lure Wt.: ⅜-1 oz.
Action: Medium

Model No.: 2229 (Deluxe Series)
Length: 5½'

Garcia (con't.)

No. Pieces: 1
No. Guides: 6 carbide
Tip Top: Carbide
Rec. Lure Wt.: ⅜-¾ oz.
Action: Medium; fast taper

Worm Spinning Rods

Model No.: D503
Length: 4½'
No. Pieces: 1
No. Guides: 4 stainless steel
Tip Top: Stainless steel
Rec. Lure Wt. ⅛-⅜ oz.
Action: Medium

Model No.: 8216 (Avocado Series)
Length: 6'
No. Pieces: 1
No. Guides: 6 hard-chromed stainless steel
    guides plus one braced stripper
Tip Top: Hard-chromed stainless steel
Rec. Lure Wt.: ⅜-¾ oz.
Action: Medium; fast taper
Handle: Not specified.

Model No.: 8217 (Avocado Series)
Length: 5½'
No. Pieces: 2
No. Guides: 5 hard-chromed stainless steel
    guides plus one braced stripper
Tip Top: Hard-chromed stainless steel
Rec. Lure Wt.: ⅜-¾ oz.
Action: Medium; fast taper
Handle: Not specified.

Worm Musky Rod

Model No.: 8220 (Avocado Series)
Length: 5½'
No. Pieces: 1
No. Guides: 4 hard-chromed
Tip Top: Hard-chromed stainless steel
Rec. Lure Wt.: 1¾-6 oz.
Action: Very heavy
Handle: Not specified.

Fly Rods

Model No.: B534 (Brown Series)
Length: 7'
No. Pieces: 2
No. Guides: 5 stainless steel snake
Tip Top: Hard-chromed
Rec. Line: 6 or 7

Model No.: B535. Same as Model No. B534
    except:
Length: 7½'
Rec. Line: 7

Model No.: B536. Same as Model No. B534
    except:
Length: 8'
Rec. Line: 7

Model No.: 2402 (Deluxe Series)—dry fly
    action
Length: 7'
No. Pieces: 2
No. Guides: 5 stainless steel snake guides
    plus one genuine agate stripping guide
Tip Top: Stainless steel
Rec. Line: 6 wt.
Handle: Not specified.

Model No.: 2404. Same as Model 2402
    except:
Length: 8'

Model No.: 2405. Same as Model 2402
    except:
Length: 8½'
No. Guides: 6
Rec. Line: 7 wt.

Model No.: 2536 (Brown Series)
Length: 7'10"
No. Pieces: 2
No. Guides: 5 stainless steel snake guides
    plus one stainless steel stripping guide
Tip Top: Hard-chromed
Rec. Line: 7 wt.
Handle: Not specified.

Model No.: 2537. Same as Model 2536
    except:
Length: 8½'
Rec. Line: 9 wt.

Model No.: 2636 (Blue Series)
Length: 7'3"
No. Pieces: 2
No. Guides: 5 stainless steel snake guides
    plus one hard-chromed stripping guide
Tip Top: Hard-chromed
Rec. Line: 6 wt.
Handle: Not specified.

Model No.: 2637 (Blue Series)
Length: 8'
No. Pieces: 2
No. Guides: 4 stainless steel snake guides
    plus one hard-chromed stripping guide
Tip Top: Hard-chromed
Rec. Line: 6 wt.
Handle: Not specified.

Model No.: 2638 (Blue Series)
Length: 8½'
No. Pieces: 2
No. Guides: 5 stainless steel snake guides
    plus one hard-chromed stripping guide
Tip Top: Hard-chromed
Rec. Line: 7 wt.
Handle: Not specified.

Model No.: 2639 (Blue Series)
Length: 9'
No. Pieces: 2
No. Guides: 6 stainless steel snake guides
    plus one hard-chromed stripping guide
Tip Top: Hard-chromed
Rec. Line: 8
Handle: Not specified.

Model No.: 8237 (Avocado Series)
Length: 8'
No. Pieces: 2
No. Guides: 5 stainless steel snake guides
    plus one hard-chromed stripping guide
Tip Top: Hard-chromed
Rec. Line: 6 wt.
Handle: Not specified.

Model No.: N547—dry-fly action
Length: 7½'
No. Pieces: 5
No. Guides: 4 stainless steel snake guides
    plus one chrome-plated carbon steel
    stripper guide
Tip Top: Hard-chromed stainless steel
Rec. Line: 9
Handle: Not specified.

Popping Rods

Model No.: 2233
Length: 7'
No. Pieces: 2
No. Guides: 6 ceramic
Tip Top: Ceramic
Rec. Lure Wt.: ½-1 oz.
Action: Medium-light

Model No.: 2533 (Brown Series)
Length: 7'
No. Pieces: 1
No. Guides: 6 hard-chromed stainless steel
    stripping
Tip Top: Tungsten carbide
Rec. Lure Wt.: ¼-¾ oz.
Action: Medium

Model No.: 8233 (Avocado Series)
Length: 7'
No. Pieces: 1
No. Guides: 6 stainless steel
Tip Top: Hard-chromed stainless steel
Rec. Lure Wt.: ¼-¾ oz.
Action: Medium

Model No.: 2887 (Black Series)
Length: 7'
No. Pieces: 1
No. Guides: 5 hard-chromed carbon steel
Tip Top: Hard-chromed carbon steel
Rec. Lure Wt.: ½-1½ oz.
Action: Light
Handle: Detachable butt; trigger reel seat.

Model No.: 8333 (Ambassadeur Series)
Length: 7'
No. Pieces: 1
No. Guides: 5 ceramic
Tip Top: Ceramic
Rec. Lure Wt.: ½-¾ oz.
Action: Light; fast taper
Handle: Not specified.

Gladding

Spinning Rods

Model No.: 1-246-150 (Classic IV Series)
Length: 5'
No. Pieces: Not specified
No. Guides: 4 stainless steel
Tip Top: Carboloy
Rec. Lure Wt.: Not specified
Action: Ultra-light
Handle: Die-cast aluminum offset handle,
    rubber-protected, epoxy-coated aluminum
    butt cap and forecap. Specie cork grip
    with anodized aluminum fixed reel seat
    with "duoloc" reel hoods.

Model No.: 1-204-260
Length: 6'
No. Pieces: 2
No. Guides: 3 chromed
Tip Top: Chromed
Rec. Lure Wt.: Not specified
Action: Spinning rod
Handle: Specie cork fore and rear grips,
    aluminum reel seat with sliding hood and
    locking ring.

Model No.: 1-212-260
Length: 6'
No. Pieces: 2
No. Guides: 3 hard chrome-plated
Tip Top: Chrome-plated

Gladding (con't.)

Rec. Lure Wt.: Not specified
Action: Medium
Handle: Man-size handle with cork fore and rear grips, fixed reel seat, locking ring hoods of ABS.

Model No.: 1-220-266
Length: 6½'
No. Pieces: 2
No. Guides: 3 chrome
Tip Top: Chrome
Rec. Lure Wt.: Not specified
Action: Spinning rod
Handle: Specie cork fore and rear grips, anodized aluminum fixed reel seat with sliding hood and locking ring.

Model No.: 1-223-380
Length: 8'
No. Pieces: 2
No. Guides: 4 stainless steel
Tip Top: Stainless steel
Rec. Lure Wt.: Not specified
Action: Medium
Handle: Full-size cork grips, chrome-on-brass reel seat.

Model No.: 1-223-310. Same as Model 1-223-380 except:
Length: 10'
No. Guides: Not specified; stainless steel

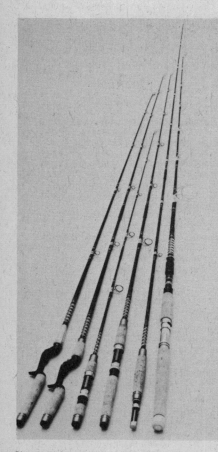

Classic III Series

Model No.: 1-223-390. Same as Model 1-223-380 except:
Length: 9'
No. Guides: Not specified; stainless steel

Model No.: 1-223-466 (Stripper Special)
Length: 6½'
No. Pieces: 2
No. Guides: 4 stainless steel
Tip Top: Stainless steel
Rec. Lure Wt.: Not specified
Action: Spinning rod
Handle: Not specified.

Model No.: 1-223-460. Same as Model 1-233-466 except:
Length: 6'

Model No.: 1-224-868 (All Carbide Guide Series)
Length: 6'8"
No. Pieces: 2
No. Guides: 4 carbide
Tip Top: Carbide
Rec. Lure Wt.: Not specified
Action: Medium
Handle: Specie cork fore and rear grips, non-rusting anodized aluminum handle with fixed reel seat.

Model No.: 1-228-266 (White Knight Series)
Length: 6½'
No. Pieces: 2
No. Guides: 4 chrome-plated
Tip Top: Chrome-plated
Rec. Lure Wt.: Not specified
Action: Medium
Handle: Cork grips, anodized aluminum reel seat.

Model No.: 1-228-270. Same as Model 1-228-266 except:
Length: 7'

Model No.: 1-230-250 (Forester Series)
Length: 5'
No. Pieces: 2
No. Guides: 4 hard-chromed "V" frame
Tip Top: Not specified
Rec. Lure Wt.: Not specified
Action: Light
Handle: Cork fore and rear grips, anodized locking reel seat.

Model No.: 1-230-866 (Forester Series)
Length: 6½'
No. Pieces: 2
No. Guides: 4 hard-chromed "V" frame
Tip Top: Not specified
Rec. Lure Wt.: Not specified
Action: Medium
Handle: Full-size handle with cork rear and fore grips, anodized locking reel seat.

Model No.: 1-232-050 (Outdoorsman Series)
Length: 5'
No. Pieces: 2
No. Guides: 4 hard chrome-plated
Tip Top: Hard chrome-plated
Rec. Lure Wt.: Not specified
Action: Ultra-light
Handle: Cork rear and fore grips, anodized aluminum fixed reel seat, spinning handle with locking ring.

Model No.: 1-232-056. Same as Model 1-232-050 except:
Length: 5½'

Model No.: 1-232-266 (Outdoorsman Series)

Length: 6½'
No. Pieces: 2
No. Guides: Not specified; hard-chrome
Tip Top: Hard-chrome
Rec. Lure Wt.: Not specified
Action: Fast taper
Handle: Metal casting handle with drive reel lock, anodized aluminum fixed seat, spinning handle with locking ring.

Model No.: 1-232-270. Same as Model 1-232-266 except:
Length: 7'

Model No.: 1-233-470 (Outdoorsman Saltwater Rod Series)
Length: 7'
No. Pieces: 2
No. Guides: 4
Tip Top: Not specified
Rec. Lure Wt.: Not specified
Action: Medium
Handle: Handle has heavy-chromed brass reel seat with double-locking rings, extra-long cork fore and rear grips with rubber butt cap.

Model No.: 1-233-410. Same as Model 1-233-470 except:
Length: 10'

Model No.: 1-233-480. Same as Model 1-233-470 except:
Length: 8'

Model No.: 1-233-490. Same as Model 1-233-470 except:
Length: 9'

Model No.: 1-233-870. Same as Model 1-233-470 except:
Action: Fast taper

Model No.: 1-233-876. Same as Model 1-233-470 except:
Length: 7½'
Action: Fast taper

Model No.: 1-233-880. Same as Model 1-233-470 except:
Length: 8'
Action: Fast taper

Model No.: 1-236-866 (Classic I Series)
Length: 6½'
No. Pieces: 2
No. Guides: 5 stainless steel
Tip Top: Carbide
Rec. Lure Wt.: Not specified
Action: Vari-flex
Handle: Full cork grips, anodized fixed reel seat with locking ring, aluminum casting handle with epoxy finish. Rubber-protected metal butt cap and forecap.

Model No.: 1-236-970. Same as Model 1-236-866 except:
Length: 7'
Action: Power-flex

Model No.: 1-242-050 (Classic III Series)
Length: 5'
No. Pieces: 2
No. Guides: 4 carbide
Tip Top: Carbide
Rec. Lure Wt.: Not specified
Action: Ultra-light
Handle: Not specified

Model No.: 1-242-866. Same as Model

Gladding (con't.)

1-242-050 except:
Length: 6½'
No. Guides: 5 carbide
Action: Vari-flex

Model No.: 1-242-970. Same as Model
1-242-050 except:
Length: 7'
No. Guides: Not specified; carbide
Action: Power-flex

Model No.: 1-246-866 (Classic IV Series)
Length: 6½'
No. Pieces: Not specified
No. Guides: 5 stainless steel
Tip Top: Carboloy
Rec. Lure Wt.: Not specified
Action: Uni-flex
Handle: Die-cast aluminum offset handle,
rubber-protected, epoxy-coated aluminum
butt cap and forecap. Specie cork grip
with anodized aluminum fixed reel seat
with "duoloc" reel hoods.

Model No.: 1-246-970. Same as Model
1-246-866 except:
Length: 7'

Model No.: 1-332-966 (Bassin' Man Series)
Length: 6½'
No. Pieces: 1
No. Guides: 5 stainless steel
Tip Top: Stainless steel
Rec. Lure Wt.: Not specified
Action: Medium-heavy
Handle: Handle has specie cork fore and rear
grips, anodized aluminum fixed reel seat.

Model No.: 1-334-050
Length: 5'
No. Pieces: 1
No. Guides: 3 chrome
Tip Top: Chrome
Rec. Lure Wt.: Not specified
Action: Ultra-light
Handle: Specie cork fore and rear grips,
anodized fixed reel seat with sliding hood
and locking ring.

Saltwater Spinning Rods

Model No.: 1-229-370 (White Knight Series)
Length: 7'
No. of Pieces: 2
No. Guides: 4 stainless steel flex
Tip Top: Stainless
Rec. Lure Wt.: Not specified
Action: Medium
Handle: Saltwater size cork grips, corrosion-
resistant reel seat.

Model No.: 1-229-376. Same as Model
1-229-370 except:
Length: 7½'

Model No.: 1-229-380. Same as Model
1-229-370 except:
Length: 8'

Model No.: 1-229-390. Same as Model
1-229-370 except:
Length: 9'
No. Guides: 5

Model No.: 1-243-870 (Classic III Series)
Length: 7'
No. Pieces: 2

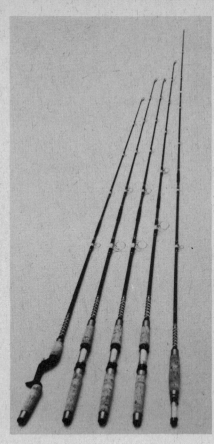

Classic I Series

No. Guides: 6 stainless steel
Tip Top: Carbide
Rec. Lure Wt.: Not specified
Action: Fast taper
Handle: Specie cork fore-grip, oversize rear
grip with rubber butt cap. Heavy chromed
brass reel seat with double-locking rings.

Model No.: 1-243-876. Same as Model
1-243-870 except:
Length: 7½'
No. Guides: Not specified; stainless steel

Model No.: 1-243-880. Same as Model
1-243-870 except:
Length: 8'
No. Guides: Not specified; stainless steel

Model No.: 1-243-890. Same as Model
1-243-870 except:
Length: 9'
No. Guides: Not specified; stainless steel

Casting Rods

Model No.: 1-004-250
Length: 5'
No. Pieces: 1
No. Guides: 2 chromed
Tip Top: Chromed
Rec. Lure Wt.: Not specified
Action: Not specified
Handle: Die-cast aluminum handle, specie
cork grip, positive-locking reel fastener.

Spin Cast Rods

Model No.: 1-104-256
Length: 5½'
No. Pieces: 2
No. Guides: 2 chromed
Tip Top: Chromed
Rec. Lure Wt.: Not specified
Action: Not specified
Handle: Die-cast aluminum handle, specie
cork grip, positive-locking reel fastener.

Model No.: 1-130-860 (Forester Series)
Length: 6'
No. Pieces: 2
No. Guides: 4 hard-chromed "V" frame
Tip Top: Not specified
Rec. Lure Wt.: Not specified
Action: Medium
Handle: Genuine cork grip, simplified reel
seat fastener.

Model No.: 1-132-260 (Outdoorsman Series)
Length: 6'
No. Pieces: 2
No. Guides: 5 hard chrome-plated
Tip Top: Hard chrome-plated
Rec. Lure Wt.: Not specified
Action: Medium
Handle: Cork fore and rear grips, spiral drive
reel seat fastener, metal casting handle
with spiral drive reel lock, anodized
aluminum fixed seat spinning handle with
locking ring.

Model No.: 1-132-266. Same as Model
1-132-260 except:
Length: 6½'

Model No.: 1-136-860 (Classic I Series)
Length: 6'
No. Pieces: 2
No. Guides: 4 stainless steel
Tip Top: Carbide
Rec. Lure Wt.: Not specified
Action: Vari-flex
Handle: Rubber-protected metal butt cap
and forecap, epoxy finished. Contoured
specie cork grips. Die-cast aluminum
casting handles with epoxy finish,
aluminum fixed seat spinning handle with
locking ring.

Model No.: 1-142-860
Length: 6'
No. Pieces: 2
No. Guides: 5 Carbide
Tip Top: Carbide
Rec. Lure Wt.: Not specified
Action: Vari-flex
Handle: Super strength.

Model No.: 1-142-460. Same as Model
1-142-860 except:
Action: Power-flex

Model No.: 1-146-860 (Classic IV Series)
Length: 6'
No. Pieces: Not specified
No. Guides: 5 stainless steel
Tip Top: Carboloy
Rec. Lure Wt.: Not specified
Action: Uniflex flex
Handle: Die-cast aluminum offset handle,
rubber-protected, epoxy-coated aluminum
butt cap and forecap. Specie cork grips
with anodized aluminum fixed reel seat
with "duoloc" reel hoods.

Gladding (con't.)

Freshwater Spin Cast Rods

Model No.: 1-120-000
Length: 6'
No. Pieces: 2
No. Guides: 3 chrome
Tip Top: Chrome
Rec. Lure Wt.: Not specified
Action: Not specified
Handle: Die-cast aluminum handle, specie cork grip, positive-locking reel seat.

Model No.: 1-124-860 (All Carbide Guide Series)
Length: 6'
No. Pieces: 2
No. Guides: 4 carbide
Tip Top: Carbide
Rec. Lure Wt.: Not specified
Action: Medium
Handle: Specie cork fore and rear grips, non-rusting die cast aluminum handle with chip-resistant finish.

Model No.: 1-128-260 (White Knight Series)
Length: 6'
No. Pieces: 2
No. Guides: 4 chrome-plated
Tip Top: Chrome-plated
Rec. Lure Wt.: Not specified
Action: Medium
Handle: Die-cast handle, genuine cork grips, high-strength metal reel seats.

Bait-Casting Rods

Model No.: 1-032-461 (Bassin' Man Series)
Length: 6'
No. Pieces: 1
No. Guides: 5 stainless steel
Tip Top: Stainless steel
Rec. Lure Wt.: Not specified
Action: Medium
Handle: Die-cast aluminum offset handle coated with chip resistant epoxy, contour fitting pistol grip of non-slip material.

Model No.: 1-032-561. Same as Model 1-032-461 except:
Action: Medium-heavy

Model No.: 1-042-461 (Bassin' Man Series)
Length: 6'
No. Pieces: 1
No. Guides: 5 speed
Tip Top: Not specified
Rec. Lure Wt.: Not specified
Action: Medium
Handle: Die-cast aluminum offset handle coated with epoxy, contoured rear pistol grip of non-slip material. Cork fore grip and positive-locking reel seat fastener.

Model No.: 1-042-561. Same as Model 1-042-461 except:
Action: Medium-heavy

Model No.: 1-060-557 (Bassin' Man Series)
Length: 5½'
No. Pieces: 1
No. Guides: 6 speed
Tip Top: Not specified
Rec. Lure Wt.: Not specified
Action: Medium-heavy
Handle: Die-cast aluminum with epoxy coating, specie cork fore grip, contoured pistol rear grip of non-slip material. Reel seat fastener locks swiftly and securely.

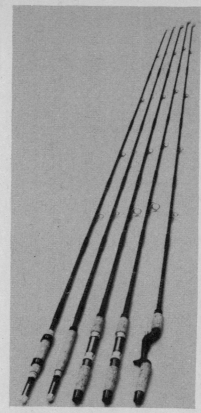

Pack Rods

Model No.: 1-060-561. Same as Model 1-060-557 except:
Length: 6'
Action: Medium-heavy

Casting/Spin Cast Rods

Model No.: 1-042-460 (Classic III Series)
Length: 6'
No. Pieces: 1
No. Guides: 4 carbide
Tip Top: Carbide
Action: Power-flex
Handle: Detachable handle with self-aligning fore-grip chuck, specie cork grip, spiral-drive reel seat fastener.

Model No.: 1-112-260
Length: 6'
No. Pieces: 2
No. Guides: 3 hard chrome-plated
Tip Top: Hard chrome-plated
Rec. Lure Wt.: Not specified
Action: Medium
Handle: Super strength die cast metal handle with cork grip, simplified reel fastener.

Spin Cast Wormin' Rods

Model No.: 1-024-456 (All Carbide Guide Series)
Length: 5½'
No. Pieces: 1
No. Guides: 4 carbide
Tip Top: Carbide

Rec. Lure Wt.: Large lures
Action: Bass/worm
Handle: Non-rusting die cast aluminum handle, specie cork fore and rear grips.

Model No.: 1-024-460. Same as Model 1-024-456 except:
Length: 6'

Surf Casting Rods

Model No.: 1-033-692 (Outdoorsman Saltwater Rod Series)
Length: 9½'
No. Pieces: 2
No. Guides: 3 stainless steel saltwater casting rings
Tip Top: Not specified
Rec. Lure Wt.: Not specified
Action: Heavy
Handle: Double locking chromed brass reel seat, 4½' cork fore grip, detachable wood rear grip, cushioned butt cap.

Boat Rods

Model No.: 1-503-356
Length: 5½'
No. Pieces: 1
No. Guides: 2
Tip Top: Not specified
Rec. Lure Wt.: Not specified
Action: Medium-light
Handle: Detachable wood butt, chrome-on-brass reel seat, cork forward grip.

Model No.: 1-511-250
Length: 5'
No. Pieces: 1
No. Guides: 3 stainless steel saltwater
Tip Top: Stainless steel
Rec. Lure Wt.: Not specified
Action: Light
Handle: Chromed brass double-locking reel seat.

Model No.: 1-511-256. Same as Model 1-511-250 except:
Length: 5½'

Model No.: 1-511-359. Same as Model 1-511-250 except:
Length: 5'10"
Action: Medium

Model No.: 1-511-370. Same as Model 1-511-250 except:
Length: 7'
No. Guides: 4 stainless steel
Action: Medium

Model No.: 1-511-560. Same as Model 1-511-250 except:
Length: 6'
Action: Heavy

Model No.: 1-511-660 (Forester Series)
Length: 6'
No. Pieces: 1
No. Guides: 2 stainless steel heavy-duty salt water
Tip Top: Stainless steel
Rec. Lure Wt.: Not specified
Action: Extra-heavy
Handle: Extra-sturdy handle has fiberglass shaft extending from wood rear grip to butt.

Gladding   (con't.)

Model No.: 1-011-660. Same as Model
  1-511-660 except:
Tip Top: Roller

IGFA Class Boat Rods

Model No.: 1-609-305 (Forester Series)
Length: Not specified
No. Pieces: 1
No. Guides: 3 stainless steel guides plus one
  roller butt guide
Tip Top: Roller
Rec. Lure Wt.: Not specified
Action: 30-50 lb.
Handle: Detachable handle has loc-top,
  chromed brass gimbal butt, double-locking
  reel seat, hardwood handle, cork fore grip.

Model No.: 1-611-203 (Forester Series)
Length: Not specified
No. Pieces: 1
No. Guides: AFTCO roller
Tip Top: Not specified
Rec. Lure Wt.: Not specified
Action: 20-30 lb.
Handle: Not specified.

Model No.: 1-611-305. Same as Model
  1-611-203 except:
Action: 30-50 lb.

Model No.: 1-611-508. Same as Model
  1-611-203 except:
Action: 50-80 lb.

Boat Spinning Rods

Model No.: 1-811-366 (Forester Series)
Length: 6½'
No.Pieces: 1
No. Guides: 4 stainless steel "V" frame
Tip Top: Stainless
Rec. Lure Wt.: Not specified
Action: Medium
Handle: Not specified.

Model No.: 1-811-370. Same as Model
  1-811-366 except:
Length: 7'

Model No.: 1-833-276
Length: 7½'
No. Pieces: 1
No. Guides: 4 stainless steel guides plus one
  40mm "V" frame stripper guide
Tip Top: Not specified
Rec. Lure Wt.: Not specified
Action: Fast tip
Handle: Heavy-chromed brass reel seat, cork
  fore grip, detachable wood rear grip.

Boating and Trolling Rods

Model No.: 1-533-366 (Outdoorsman
  Saltwater Rod Series)
Length: 6½'
No. Pieces: 1
No. Guides: 4 hard chrome-plated
Tip Top: Hard chrome-plated
Rec. Lure Wt.: Not specified
Action: Medium-heavy
Handle: Heavy-chromed brass reel seat,
  detachable wood rear grip, 4½" cork
  fore grip.

Model No.: 1-803-366
Length: 6½'
No. Pieces: 1
No. Guides: 3 stainless steel
Tip Top: Stainless steel
Rec. Lure Wt.: Not specified
Action: Not specified
Handle: Detachable wood butt, chrome-on-
  brass reel seat.

IGFA Saltwater Trolling Rods

Model No.: 1-667-300
Length: 7'
No. Pieces: 1
No. Guides: 4 stainless steel
Tip Top: Roller
Rec. Lure Wt.: Not specified
Action: 30 lb. light
Handle: Hardwood handles, "Nuevo"
  fore grip, brass reel seat, trolling butts.

Model No.: 1-667-400. Same as Model
  1-667-300 except:
Action: 40 lb. medium

Model No.: 1-667-500. Same as Model
  1-667-300 except:
Action: 50 lb. medium-heavy

Model No.: 1-667-600. Same as Model
  1-667-300 except:
Action: 60 lb. heavy

Model No.: 1-965-200
Length: 7'1"
No. Pieces: 1
No. Guides: 5 "AFTCO" roller
Tip Top: Roller
Rec. Lure Wt.: Not specified
Action: 20 lb. light
Handle: "Nuevo" fore grips, detachable
  hardwood handles, brass chromed reel
  seats.

Model No.: 1-965-000. Same as Model
  1-965-200 except:
Action: Unlimited lb. heavy

Model No.: 1-965-130. Same as Model
  1-965-200 except:
Action: 130 lb. heavy

Model No.: 1-965-300. Same as Model
  1-965-200 except:
Action: 30 lb.

Model No.: 1-965-500. Same as Model
  1-965-200 except:
Action: 50 lb. medium

Model No.: 1-965-800. Same as Model
  1-965-200 except:
Action: 80 lb. heavy

Model No.: 1-967-200 Royal II (Royal
  Custom Series)
Length: 6'9"
No. Pieces: 1
No. Guides: 7 hard-chromed stainless steel
  saltwater
Tip Top: Roller
Rec. Lure Wt.: Not specified
Action: 20 lb.
Handle: "Nuevo" fore grip, hardwood
  handles, locktop chrome reel seats,
  chrome gimbal nocks.

Model No.: 1-967-300 Royal III. Same as
  Model 1-967-200 except:

No. Guides: 6 "AFTCO" roller
Action: 30 lb.

Model No.: 1-967-000 Royal VII. Same as
  Model 1-967-200 except:
No. Guides: 5 Mildrum roller
Action: Unlimited

Model No.: 1-967-130 Royal VI. Same as
  Model 1-967-200 except:
No. Guides: 5 Mildrum roller
Action: 130 lb.

Model No.: 1-967-500 Royal IV. Same as
  Model 1-967-200 except:
No. Guides: 6 "AFTCO" roller
Action: 50 lb.

Model No.: 1-967-800 Royal V. Same as
  Model 1-967-200 except:
No. Guides: 5 "AFTCO" roller
Action: 80 lb.

Trolling, Boat and Pier Rods

Model No.: 1-665-259
Length: 5'10"
No. Pieces: 1
No. Guides: 3 stainless steel
Tip Top: Carboloy
Rec. Lure Wt.: Not specified
Action: 20 lb. light
Handle: "Nuevo" fore grip, detachable boat
  butt with brass chrome reel seat.

Model No.: 1-665-363. Same as Model
  1-665-259 except:
Length: 6'3"
Action: 40 lb. medium

Model No.: 1-665-376. Same as Model
  1-665-259 except:
Length: 7'6"
Action: 25 lb. medium

Model No.: 1-665-380. Same as Model
  1-665-259 except:
Length: 8'
Action: 30 lb. medium

Fly Rods

Model No.: 1-412-270
Length: 7'
No. Pieces: 2
No. Guides: 3 snake guides plus one hard
  chrome-plated stripper guide
Tip Top: Not specified
Rec. Line: 6 wt.
Handle: Not specified.

Model No.: 1-428-280 (White Knight Series)
  Medium Action
Length: 8'
No. Pieces: 2
No. Guides: 3 snake guides plus one hard
  chrome-plated stripper guide
Tip Top: Hard chrome-plated
Rec. Line: 7 wt.
Handle: Genuine cork grip, ABS reel seats.

Model No.: 1-432-280
Length: 8'
No. Guides: 5 snake plus one stripper
Rec. Line: 7 wt.
Handle: Specie cork grip, anodized aluminum
  reel seat, full-wrapped ferrule.

Model No.: 1-432-286. Same as Model
  1-432-280 except:

Gladding (con't.)

Length: 8½'
Rec. Line: 8 wt.

Model No.: 1-436-280 (Classic I Series)
Length: 8'
No. Pieces: 2
No. Guides: 5 snakes guides plus one stripper guide
Tip Top: Carbide
Rec. Line: 7 wt.
Handle: Tapered cork grip handle, two-tone anodized reel seat with locking ring. Die-cast aluminum casting handle with epoxy finish. Rubber-protected metal butt cap and forecap, epoxy finish.

Model No.: 1-436-286. Same as Model 1-436-280 except:
Length: 8½'
Rec. Line: 8 wt.

Model No.: 1-442-280 (Classic III Series)
Length: 8'
No. Pieces: 2
No. Guides: 6 stainless steel snake guides plus one carbide stripper guide
Tip Top: Not specified
Rec. Line: 7 wt.
Handle: Handle has "duoloc" anodized reel seat.

Model No.: 1-446-170 (Classic IV Series)
Length: 7'
No. Pieces: Not specified
No. Guides: 6 stainless steel snake guides plus one stripper guide
Tip Top: Stainless steel
Rec. Line: 6 wt.
Handle: Die-cast aluminum offset handle, rubber-protected, epoxy-coated aluminum butt cap and forecap. Specie cork grip with anodized aluminum fixed reel with "duoloc" reel hoods.

Model No.: 1-446-176. Same as Model 1-446-270 except:
Length: 7½'
No. Guides: 7 stainless steel snake guides plus one stripper guide

Model No.: 1-446-180. Same as Model 1-446-270 except:
Length: 8'
No. Guides: 7 stainless steel snake guides plus one stripper guide
Rec. Line: 7 wt.

Model No.: 1-446-186. Same as Model 1-446-270 except:
Length: 8½'
No. Guides: 7 stainless steel snake guides plus one stripper guide
Rec. Line: 7 wt.

Model No.: 1-446-493. Same as Model 1-446-270 except:
Length: 9'3"
No. Guides: 7 stainless steel snake guides plus two stripper guides
Rec. Line: 9 or 10

Saltwater Spinning & Surf Rods

Model No.: 1-267-380
Length: 8'
No. Pieces: 2
No. Guides: 5 stainless steel

Tip Top: Carboloy
Rec. Lure Wt.: Not specified
Action: Medium; multiple taper
Handle: "Nuevo" grips.

Model No.: 1-267-310. Same as Model 1-267-380 except:
Length: 10'

Model No.: 1-267-390. Same as Model 1-267-380 except:
Length: 9'

Model No.: 1-267-410. Same as Model 1-267-380 except:
Length: 10'
Action: Heavy

Model No.: 1-267-412. Same as Model 1-267-380 except:
Length: 12'
Action: Heavy

Model No.: 1-267-490. Same as Model 1-267-380 except:
Length: 9'
Action: Heavy

Popping Rod

Model No.: 1-033-270 (Outdoorsman Saltwater Rod Series)
Length: 7'
No. Pieces: 1
No. Guides: 4 stainless steel
Tip Top: Stainless steel
Rec. Lure Wt.: Not specified
Action: Popping
Handle: Straight handle has chromed brass reel seat with barrel trigger and double lock, cork fore and rear grips.

Hardy Brothers

Spinning Rods

Model: Fibalite Spinning
Length: 6½', 7', 8', 8½', 9½', 10'
No. Pieces: 2
No. Guides: Hard chrome plate
Tip Top: Hard Sintox ceramic
Handle: Cork.

Model: B.C. Ten-Ten
Length: 10'10"
No. Pieces: 2
No. Guides: Hard chrome fullopen intermediate
Tip Top: Sintox
Handle: Solid cork with mushroom top.

Fly Rods

Model: Palakona Super Light Cane
Length: 6', 6'8", 7'2"
No. Pieces: 2
No. Guides: Not specified; agatipe
Tip Top: Stainless steel
Rec. Line: 5 wt.
Handle: Shaped solid cork, skeletal reel seat and sliding ring, capped butt.

Model No.: Same as Palakona Super Light Cane except:
Length: 7'6"
Rec. Line: 6 wt.

Model: Palakona Medium Action Cane
Length: 8', 8½', 8'9"
No. Pieces: 2
No. Guides: 2; agatipe
Tip Top: Stainless steel
Rec. Line: 7, 8 wt.
Handle: Solid cork, shaped to hand, fixed screw grip and cork covered housing.

Model: Smuggler
Length: 8'
No. Pieces: 4
No. Guides: Chrome
Rec. Line: #6
Action: Medium
Handle: Shaped solid cork.

Model: Salmon
Length: 12½', 14'
No. Pieces: 3
Tip Top: Agatipe
Rec. Line: #9 - #10
Handle: Solid cork, shaped with mushroom top.

Model: Invincible
Length: 10½'
No. Pieces: 2
Rec. Line: 7
Handle: Solid cork, shaped to hand.

Reservoir Rods

Model: Dick Walker Little Lake
Length: 9'
No. Pieces: 2
No. Guides: Chrome snake
Rec. Line: #7
Handle: Shaped solid cork with mushroom thumb grip.

Model: Dick Walker Superlite
Length: 9'3"
No. Pieces: 2
No. Guides: Tungsten carbide
Rec. Line: #7-#8

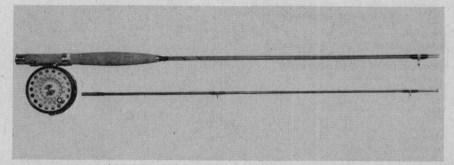

Palakona Super Light Cane

Hardy Brothers (con't.)

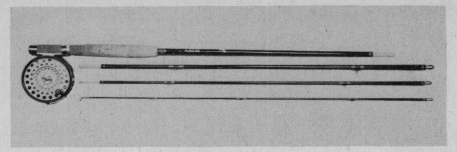

Smuggler
Handle: Solid cork with mushroom thumb grip.

Coarse Rods

Model: The Hardy Swing Tip
Length: 8'9", 9½'
No. Pieces: 2
No. Guides: Hard chrome
Rec. Lure Wt.: ¾ oz.
Handle: Slim parallel, finest specie cork.

Model: The Hardy Swim Feeder
Length: 8'9", 9'6"
No. Pieces: 2
No. Guides: Hard chrome
Handle: Slim parallel, finest specie cork.

James Heddon's Sons

Spinning Rods

Model No.: 3670 solid fiberglass
Length: 6'
No. Pieces: 2
No. Guides: 3 chromed finish
Tip Top: Not specified
Rec. Line: #4-12
Rec. Lure Wt.: ¼-½ oz.
Action: Medium-light
Handle: Not specified.

Model No.: 4565. Same as Model 3670 except: tubular
Length: 6'9"

Model No.: 3771 Starcast
Length: 6'
No. Pieces: 2
No. Guides: 3 chromed "V" frame
Tip Top: Chrome
Rec. Lure Wt.: ¼-⅝ oz.
Action: Medium
Handle: Natural-tone aluminum fixed reel seat, specie cork fore and rear grips.

Model No.: 4018
Length: 7'
No. Pieces: 1
No. Guides: 4 chrome
Tip Top: Chrome
Rec. Line: #6-#10
Rec. Lure Wt.: ⅜-⅝ oz.
Action: Medium

Model No.: 4663
Length: 6½'
No. Pieces: 2
No. Guides: 4 chromed "V" frames
Tip Top: Chrome

Rec. Line: #6-15
Rec. Lure Wt. ⅜-⅝ oz.
Action: Medium
Handle: Aluminum fixed reel seat, specie cork rear and fore grips.

Model No.: 4665. Same as Model 4663 except:
Length: 7'

Model No.: 5011
Length: 5'7
No. Pieces: 1
No. Guides: 4 aluminum oxide
Tip Top: Aluminum oxide
Rec. Line: #6-#12
Rec. Lure Wt.: ¼-⅝ oz.
Action: Medium
Handle: Specie cork grip.

Model No.: 5018
Length: 7'
No. Pieces: 2
No. Guides: 5 ceramic
Tip Top: Ceramic
Rec. Line: #6-#12
Rec. Lure Wt.: ¼-⅝ oz.
Action: Medium
Handle: Specie cork grip.

Model No.: 6015
Length: 6'3"
No. Pieces: 1
No. Guides: 5 carbide
Tip Top: Carbide
Rec. Line: #8-#20
Rec. Lure Wt.: ⅜-1 oz.
Action: Medium-heavy
Handle: Specie cork plus posi-lock reel seat.

Model No.: 6018
Length: 7'
No. Pieces: 2
No. Guides: 5 carbide
Tip Top: Carbide
Rec. Line: #6-#12
Rec. Lure Wt.: ¼-⅝ oz.
Action: Medium-light
Handle: Specie cork plus posi-lock reel seat.

Model No.: 7012
Length: 6'
No. Pieces: 2
No. Guides: 5 aluminum oxide
Tip Top: Aluminum oxide
Rec. Line: #2-#8
Rec. Lure Wt.: ¼-½ oz.
Action: Light
Handle: Posi-lock reel seat.

Model No.: 7018
Length: 7'
No. Pieces: 2
No. Guides: 6 aluminum oxide
Tip Top: Aluminum oxide
Rec. Line: #6-#12
Rec. Lure Wt.: ¼-⅝ oz.
Action: Medium-light
Handle: Posi-lock reel seat.

Model No.: 7444
Length: 6'3"
No. Pieces: 1
No. Guides: 5
Tip Top: Carbide
Rec. Lure Wt.: ⅜-1 oz.
Action: Worm rod; medium-heavy
Handle: Not specified.

Model No.: 8016-graphite
Length: 5'8"
No. Pieces: 1
No. Guides: 5 aluminum oxide
Tip Top: Aluminum oxide
Rec. Line: #6-#20
Rec. Lure Wt.: ⅜-⅝ oz.
Action: Medium

Model No.: 9912
Length: 9'
No. Pieces: 2
No. Guides: 8
Tip Top: Aluminum oxide
Rec. Line: #6-#40
Rec. Lure Wt.: ¼-⅝ oz.
Action: Medium-light

Model No.: 9916
Length: 8½'
No. Pieces: 2
No. Guides: 6 stainless steel
Tip Top: Aluminum oxide
Rec. Line: #6 - #40
Rec. Lure Wt.: ¼-⅝ oz.
Action: Medium-light

Model No.: 845
Length: 6'
No. Pieces: 2
No. Guides: 4 gold plated
Tip Top: Chromed
Rec. Line: #6-#12
Rec. Lure Wt.: ¼-⅝ oz.
Action: ML
Handle: Deluxe mark handles, specie cork grips, anodized reel seats.

Model No.: 846. Same as Model 845 except:
Length: 6½'

Model No.: 848. Same as Model 845 except:
Length: 7'

Casting Rods

Model No.: 3335
Length: 5½'
No. Pieces: 1
No. Guides: 3 chromed "V" frame
Tip Top: Chrome
Rec. Lure Wt.: ¼-⅝ oz.
Action: Medium
Handle: Detachable offset handle, "speed-grip" reel holder, specie cork grip.

Model No.: 5001
Length: 5½'
No. Pieces: 1
No. Guides: 5 aluminum oxide

Heddon's (con't.)

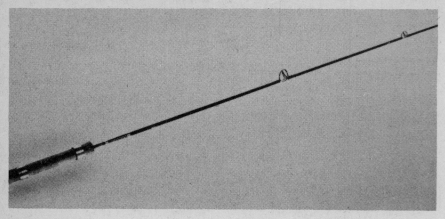

Ultra Light Spinning Rod

Tip Top: Aluminum oxide
Rec. Line: #6-#20
Rec. Lure Wt.: ¼-⅝ oz.
Action: Medium-light
Handle: Modern.

Model No.: 5006. Same as Model No. 5001
except:
Length: 6'
Rec. Lure Wt.: ⅜-⅝ oz.
Action: Medium

Model No.: 6002
Length: 5½'
No. Pieces: 1
No. Guides: 5 carbide
Tip Top: Carbide
Rec. Line: #6-#20
Rec. Lure Wt.: ¼-⅝ oz.
Action: Medium-light
Handle: Specie cork grip.

Model No.: 6006
Length: 6'
No. Pieces: 1
No. Guides: 5 carbide
Tip Top: Carbide
Rec. Line: #8-#20
Rec. Lure Wt.: ½-1 oz.
Action: Medium-heavy
Handle: Detachable; specie cork grip.

Model No.: 7002
Length: 5½'
No. Pieces: 1
No. Guides: 6 aluminum oxide
Tip Top: Aluminum oxide
Rec. Line: #6-#20
Rec. Lure Wt.: ¼-⅝ oz.
Action: Medium-light
Handle: Low profile; gatorhide finish.

Model No.: 8002-graphite
Length: 5½'
No. Pieces: 1
No. Guides: 5 aluminum oxide
Tip Top: Aluminum oxide
Rec. Line: #8-#25
Rec. Lure Wt.: ⅜-⅝ oz.
Action: Medium
Handle: Modern.

Model No.: 8004-graphite. Same as Model
No. 8002 except:

Rec. Lure Wt.: ⅜-1 oz.
Action: Medium-heavy

Model No.: 9918
Length: 9'
No. Pieces: 2
No. Guides: 8 ceramic casting
Tip Top: Ceramic
Rec. Line: #6-#4
Rec. Lure Wt.: ¼-⅝ oz.
Action: Medium-light

Model No.: 9919
Length: 7'
No. Pieces: 2
No. Guides: 6 stainless steel
Tip Top: Carbide
Rec. Line: #8-#20
Rec. Lure Wt.: ⅜-⅞ oz.
Action: Medium

Spin-Casting Rods

Model No.: 3450
Length: 5½'
No. Pieces: 2
No. Guides: 3
Tip Top: Chrome
Rec. Lure Wt.: ¼-½ oz.
Action: Medium-light

Model No.: 4243. Same as Model 3450
except: tubular
Length: 6'3"

Model No.: 3551
Length: 5½'
No. Pieces: 2
No. Guides: 3 chromed "V" frame
Tip Top: Chrome
Rec. Line: #6-#12
Rec. Lure Wt.: ¼-⅝ oz.
Action: Medium
Handle: Fixed aluminum handle, "speed-grip" reel holders, specie cork grip.

Model No.: 3553. Same as Model 3551
except:
Length: 6'

Model No.: 4002
Length: 5½'
No. Pieces: 1
No. Guides: 4 chrome
Tip Top: Chrome
Rec. Line: #6-#10
Rec. Lure Wt.: ⅜-⅝ oz.
Action: Medium

Model No.: 4443
Length: 6'
No. Pieces: 2
No. Guides: 4 chromed "V" frame
Tip Top: Chrome
Rec. Line: #6-#15
Rec. Lure Wt.: ⅜-⅝ oz.
Action: Medium
Handle: Fixed aluminum handle, "speed-grip" reel holder, specie cork grips.

Model No.: 4446. Same as Model 4443
except:
Length: 6½'

Model No.: 5008
Length: 6½'
No. Pieces: 2
No. Guides: 5 aluminum oxide
Tip Top: Aluminum oxide
Rec. Line: #6-#15
Rec. Lure Wt.: ⅜-⅝ oz.
Action: Medium
Handle: Traditional.

Model No.: 6008
Length: 6½'
No. Pieces: 2
No. Guides: 5 carbide
Tip Top: Carbide
Rec. Line: #6-#15
Rec. Lure Wt.: ⅜-⅝ oz.
Action: Medium
Handle: Specie cork grip.

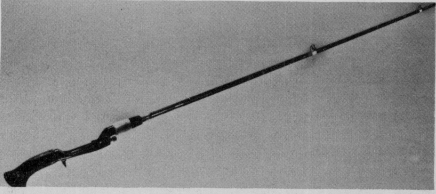

Worm Rod

Heddon's (con't.)

Model No.: 6275
Length: 5'8"
No. Pieces: 2
No. Guides: 5
Tip Top: Carbide
Rec. Lure Wt.: ⅜-1 oz.
Action: Medium-heavy
Handle: Not specified.

Model No.: 9917
Length: 7'
No. Pieces: 2
No. Guides: 6 stainless steel
Tip Top: Carbide
Rec. Line: #8-#25
Rec. Lure Wt.: ½-1 oz.
Action- Medium-heavy

Fresh Water Spin-Casting Rods

Model No.: 816
Length: 6'
No. Pieces: 2
No. Guides: 5 gold-plated
Tip Top: Gold-plated
Rec. Lure Wt.: ¼-⅝ oz.
Action: Medium-light
Handle: Deluxe mark handles, specie cork grips, anodized reel seats.

Model No.: 818. Same as Model 816 except:
Length: 6½'

Fly Rods

Model No.: 876
Length: 8'
No. Pieces: 2
No. Guides: 7 gold-plated
Tip Top: Gold-plated
Rec. Line: #7
Handle: Deluxe mark handles, specie cork grips, anodized reel seats.

Model No.: 8026
Length: 8'
No. Pieces: 2
No. Guides: 7 snake guides; aluminum oxide stripper
Rec. Line: #6-#7
Action: Medium

Fly/Spinning Rod

Model No.: 6460
Length: 6½'
No. Pieces: 6
No. Guides: 5 stainless steel
Tip Top: Carbide
Rec. Line: #4-#20 spin; #6-#7 fly
Rec. Lure Wt.: ¼-⅝ oz.
Action: Medium-light
Handle: Reversible for spin or fly; 15" case.

Ultra Light Spinning Rods

Model No.: 6725
Length: 4½'
No. Pieces: 1
No. Guides: 4 stainless steel
Tip Top: Stainless steel
Rec. Line: #2-#6
Rec. Lure Wt.: ⅟₁₆-⅜ oz.
Action: Ultra-light
Handle: Light streamlined.

Model No.: 878. Same as Model 876 except:
Length: 8'6"
Rec. Line: #8

Model No.: 4023
Length: 7½'
No. Pieces: 1
No. Guides: 4 chrome
Tip Top: Chrome
Rec. Line: #8
Action: Light

Model No.: 4887
Length: 8½'
No. Pieces: 2
No. Guides: 5 chrome
Tip Top: Chrome
Rec. Line: 8
Action: Medium

Model No.: 5028
Length: 8½'
No. Pieces: 2
No. Guides: 7 snake
Tip Top: Chrome
Rec. Line: #8
Action: Medium
Handle: Specie cork grip; hook keeper.

Model No.: 6026
Length: 8'
No. Pieces: 2
No. Guides: 6 stainless steel plus carbide stripper
Tip Top: Hard chrome
Rec. Line: #7-#8
Action: Medium
Handle: Specie cork grip; hook keeper.

Model No.: 7024
Length: 7½'
No. Pieces: 2
No. Guides: 5 stainless steel snake; aluminum oxide stripper
Tip Top: Chrome
Rec. Line: #7
Action: Medium
Handle: Posi-lock reel seat.

Model No.: 7026
Length: 8'
No. Pieces: 2
No. Guides: 6 stainless steel snake; 1 aluminum oxide stripper
Rec. Line: #7-#8

Action: Medium
Handle: Posi-lock reel seat.

Model No.: 7028. Same as Model No. 7026 except:
Length: 8½'
Rec. Line: #8

Model No.: 7029. Same as Model No. 7026 except:
Length: 9'
No. Guides: 7
Rec. Line: #9

Model No.: 8020
Length: 5'
No. Pieces: 1
No. Guides: 4 spiral
Tip Top: Carbide
Rec. Line: #2-#6
Rec. Lure Wt.: ⅟₁₆-¼ oz.
Action: Ultra-light

Boat/Bay/Pier Rods

Model No.: 9050
Length: 5½'
No. Pieces: 1
No. Guides: 2 chrome
Tip Top: Not specified
Action: Medium
Handle: American hardwood handles. Butt .375.

Model No.: 9051. Same as Model 9050 except:
Action: Medium-heavy
Handle: Butt .450.

Model No.: 9052. Same as Model 9050 except:
Length: 6'
Action: Medium-heavy
Handle: Butt .450.

Lamiglas

Freshwater Spinning Rods

Model No.: S46UL-graphite
Length: 4½'
No. Pieces: 2
No. Guides: Stainless bridged

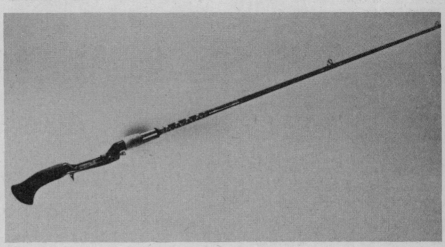

Worm Rod

Lamiglas (con't.)

Tip Top: Aluminum oxide
Rec. Line: 2-6
Rec. Lure Wt.: 1⁄16-1⁄4 oz.
Action: Ultra-light
Handle: Specie cork; lightweight sliding lock rings.

Model No.: S56UL-graphite
Length: 5½'
No. Pieces: 2
No. Guides: Stainless bridged
Rec. Line: 4-8
Rec. Lure Wt.: ¼-⅜ oz.
Action: Ultra-light
Handle: Specie cork; lightweight sliding lock rings.

Model No.: S66L-graphite
Length: 6½'
No. Pieces: 2
No. Guides: Stainless bridged
Rec. Line: 4-10
Rec. Lure Wt.: ⅛-¼ oz.
Action: Light
Handle: Specie cork.

Model No.: S66M-graphite
Length: 6½'
No. Guides: Lightweight stainless bridged; aluminum oxide cores
Tip Top: Aluminum oxide
Rec. Line: 8-12
Rec. Lure Wt.: ¼-⅜ oz.

Model No.: S701-graphite. Same as Model No. S66-graphite except:
Length: 7'

Model No.: S701-graphite
Length: 7'
No. Pieces: 2
No. Guides: Stainless bridged
Tip Top: Aluminum oxide
Rec. Line: 4-10
Rec. Lure Wt.: ⅛-¼ oz.
Action: Light

Model No.: WS68ML-graphite
Length: 5'8"
Rec. Line: 8-17
Rec. Lure Wt.: ¼-⅝ oz.
Action: Worm

Fly Rods

Model No.: F702-graphite
Length: 7'
No. Pieces: 2
No. Guides: Hard-chromed stainless steel
Tip Top: Aluminum oxide
Rec. Line: 2-3
Handle: Specie cork; black anodized reel seat.

Model No.: F763-graphite. Sames as Model No. F702-graphite except:
Length: 7½'
Rec. Line: 3-4

Model No.: F804-graphite. Same as Model No. F702-graphite except:
Length: 8'
Rec. Line: 4-5

Model No.: F865-graphite. Same as Model No. F702-graphite except:

Length: 8½'
Rec. Line: 5-6

Model No.: F906-graphite. Same as Model No. F702-graphite except:
Length: 9'
Rec. Line: 6-7

Model No.: F912T-graphite. Same as Model No. F702-graphite except:
Length: 9'
Rec. Line: 12-13

Model No.: F968-graphite. Same as Model No. F702-graphite except:
Length: 9½'
Rec. Line: 8-9

Model No.: F1008-graphite. Same as Model No. F702-graphite except:
Length: 10'
Rec. Line: 8-9

Model No.: F1068-graphite. Same as Model No. F702-graphite except:
Length: 10½'
Rec. Line: 8-9

Steelhead/Salmon/Saltwater Rods

Model No.: S80LS-graphite
Length: 8'
No. Guides: Lightweight stainless steel
Tip Top: Aluminum oxide
Rec. Line: 6-10
Rec. Lure Wt.: ¼-⅜ oz.
Action: Light
Handle: Cork under reel.

Model No.: S80MS-graphite
Length: 8'
No. Guides: Lightweight stainless steel
Tip Top: Aluminum oxide
Rec. Line: 8-12
Rec. Lure Wt.: ⅜-¾ oz.

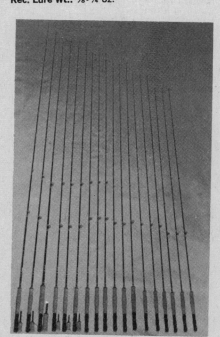

Lamiglas Fly Rods

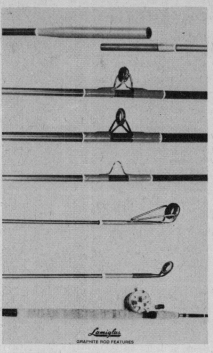

Lamiglas Graphite Rod Features

Action: Medium
Handle: Cork under reel.

Model No.: S80MHC-graphite
Length: 8'
No. Guides: Lightweight stainless steel
Tip Top: Aluminum oxide
Rec. Line: 10-20
Rec. Lure Wt.: ½-1½ oz.
Action: Medium-heavy
Handle: Cork under reel.

Model No.: S86LS-graphite
Length: 8½'
No. Guides: Lightweight stainless steel
Tip Top: Aluminum oxide
Rec. Line: 6-10
Rec. Lure Wt.: ¼-⅜ oz.
Action: Light
Handle: Cork under reel.

Model No.: S86MC-graphite
Length: 8½'
No. Guides: Lightweight stainless steel
Tip Top: Aluminum oxide
Rec. Line: 8-12
Rec. Lure Wt.: ⅜-¾ oz.
Action: Medium
Handle: Cork under reel.

Model No.: S86MHS-graphite
Length: 8½'
No. Guides: Lightweight stainless steel
Tip Top: Aluminum oxide
Rec. Line: 10-20
Rec. Lure Wt.: ½-1½ oz.
Action: Medium-heavy; spinning
Handle: Cork under reel.

Model No.: S86MHC-graphite. Same as Model No. S86MHS-graphite except:
Action: Medium-heavy; casting

Model No.: S86SAC-graphite

Lamiglas (con't.)

Length: 8½'
No. Guides: Lightweight stainless steel
Tip Top: Aluminum oxide
Rec. Line: 10-30
Rec. Lure Wt.: 1½-4 oz.
Action: Medium-heavy; mooching
Handle: Cork under reel.

Model No.: S90MHC-graphite
Length: 9'
No. Guides: Lightweight stainless steel
Tip Top: Aluminum oxide
Rec. Line: 10-20
Rec. Lure Wt.: ¾-2½ oz.
Action: Medium-heavy
Handle: Cork under reel.

Spin Cast Rods

Model No.: SC56-graphite
Length: 5½'
No. Guides: Lightweight stainless steel
Tip Top: Aluminum oxide
Rec. Line: 8-10
Rec. Lure Wt.: ¼-⅜ oz.
Action: Light
Handle: Vinyl pistol grips.

Model No.: SC501-graphite. Same as Model
No. SC56-graphite except:
Length: 5'10"

Worm Rods

Model No.: W56L-graphite
Length: 5½'
No. Guides: Hard chromed stainless steel;
aluminum oxide cores
Tip Top: Aluminum oxide
Rec. Line: 10-20
Rec. Lure Wt.: ¼-⅝ oz.
Action: Light
Handle: Vinyl pistol grips.

Model No.: W56MM-graphite
Length: 5½'
No. Guides: Hard chromed stainless steel;
aluminum oxide cores
Tip Top: Aluminum oxide
Rec. Line: 12-25
Rec. Lure Wt.: ⅝-1¼ oz.
Action: Medium-heavy
Handle: Vinyl pistol grips.

Model No.: W60L-graphite. Same as Model
No. W56L-graphite except:
Length: 6'

Model No.: W60MH-graphite. Same as Model
No. W56MH-graphite except:
Length: 6'

Martin

Spinning Rods

Model No.: 1-016 (Midnight Series)
Length: 6'
No. Pieces: 2
No. Guides: 3 chromed steel
Tip Top: Chromed
Rec. Lure Wt.: Not specified
Action: Spinning rod
Handle: Specie cork grips with clear anodized
aluminum fixed reel seat.

Model No.: 1-017 (Midnight Series)
Length: 16½'
No. Pieces: 2
No. Guides: 4 chromed steel
Tip Top: Chromed
Rec. Lure Wt.: Not specified
Action: Spinning rod
Handle: Clear anodized aluminum fixed reel
seat with specie cork grips.

Model No.: 1-027 (Tuffy Series)
Length: 6½'
No. Pieces: 2
No. Guides: 4 stainless
Tip Top: Stainless
Rec. Lure Wt.: Not specified
Action: Spinning rod
Handle: Anodized aluminum reel seat with
specie cork grips.

Model No.: 1-028 (Tuffy Series)
Length: 7'
No. Pieces: 2
No. Guides: 5 stainless
Tip Top: Stainless
Rec. Lure Wt.: Not specified
Action: Spinning rod
Handle: Anodized aluminum reel seat with
specie cork grips.

Model No.: 1-125 (Fly Wate Series)
Length: 5½'
No. Pieces: 2
No. Guides: 4 stainless foulproof
Tip Top: Ovallan
Rec. Lure Wt.: Not specified
Action: Spinning rod
Handle: Anodized reel seat with specie
cork grip.

Model No.: 1-127 (Fly Wate Series)
Length: 6½'
No. Pieces: 2
No. Guides: 4 Ovallan stainless wire frame
Tip Top: Ovallan stainless wire frame
Rec. Lure Wt.: Not specified
Action: Spinning rod
Handle: Anodized reel seat with specie
cork grip.

Model No.: 1-128. Same as Model 1-127
except:
Length: 7'
No. Guides: 5 Ovallan

Model No.: 1-129 (Fly Wate Series)
Length: 9'
No. Pieces: 2
No. Guides: 6 stainless wire frame Ovallan
Tip Top: Carboloy
Rec. Lure Wt.: Not specified
Action: Spinning rod
Handle: Chrome-plated brass reel seat.

Model No.: 1-666 (Portage Rod)
Length: 6½'
No. Pieces: 6
No. Guides: 4 stainless steel
Tip Top: Stainless steel
Rec. Lure Wt.: Not specified
Action: Spinning rod
Handle: Not specified.

Model No.: 1-915
Length: 5½'
No. Guides: 3 stainless steel
Tip Top: Stainless steel
Action: Light-medium
Handle: Detachable wood; chromed
brass reel seats.

Model No.: 81-715 (Blue Chip Series)
Length: 5½'
No. Pieces: 2
No. Guides: 4 stainless foulproof
Tip Top: Carboloy
Rec. Lure Wt.: Not specified
Action: Spinning rod
Handle: Specie cork with gold anodized rings.

Model No.: 81-716. Same as Model 81-715
except:
Length: 6'
No. Guides: 5 stainless foulproof

Model No.: 81-717 (Blue Chip Series)
Length: 6½'
No. Pieces: 2
No. Guides: 5 stainless wire frame plus one
carboloy gathering guide
Tip Top: Carboloy
Rec. Lure Wt.: Not specified
Action: Spinning rod
Handle: Brown and gold anodized reel seat
with gold double lock rings. Specie cork
grips, gold anodized caps.

Model No.: 81-718. Same as Model 81-717
except:
Length: 7'

Model No.: 81-777. Same as Model 81-717
except:
Length: 6½'

Model No. 85-757

Martin (con't.)

No. Pieces: 2
Action: Medium-heavy

Spin Casting Rods

Model No.: 5-001 (Ivory Series)
Length: 5½′
No. Pieces: 2
No. Guides: 4 chromed steel
Tip Top: Chromed
Rec. Lure Wt.: Not specified
Action: Casting
Handle: Specie cork grip and ABS reel seat.

Model No. **5-011**

Model No.: 5-011 (Midnight Series)
Length: 5½′
No. Pieces: 2
No. Guides: 3 chromed steel
Tip Top: Chromed
Rec. Lure Wt.: Not specified
Action: Fast tip
Handle: Specie cork grip with cast aluminum reel seat.

Model No.: 5-012 (Midnight Series)
Length: 6′
No. Pieces: 2
No. Guides: 4 chromed steel
Tip Top: Chromed
Rec. Lure Wt.: Not specified
Action: Fast tip
Handle: Cast aluminum reel seat and specie cork grip.

Model No.: 5-036 (Tuffy Series)
Length: 6′
No. Pieces: 2
No. Guides: 3 chromed steel
Tip Top: Chromed
Rec. Lure Wt.: Not specified
Action: Casting
Handle: Cast aluminum handle with specie cork grips.

Model No.: 5-037 (Tuffy Series)
Length: 6½′
No. Pieces: 2
No. Guides: 4 chromed steel
Tip Top: Chromed
Rec. Lure Wt.: Not specified
Action: Casting
Handle: Cast aluminum handle with specie cork grips.

Model No.: 5-135 (Fly Wate Series)
Length: 5½′
No. Pieces: 2
No. Guides: 3 stainless wire frame Ovallan
Tip Top: Ovallan
Rec. Lure Wt.: Not specified
Action: Casting
Handle: Specie cork grip with cast aluminum fast locking reel seat.

Model No.: 5-136. Same as Model 5-135 except:
Length: 6′

Model No.: 5-137. Same as Model 5-135 except:
Length: 6½′
No. Guides: 4 stainless wire frame Ovallan

Model No.: 5-545 (Ivory Series)
Length: 4½′
No. Pieces: 1
No. Guides: 2 chromed steel
Tip Top: Chromed
Rec. Lure Wt.: Not specified
Action: Casting
Handle: Specie cork grip and ABS reel seat.

Model No.: 5-550 (Ivory Series)
Length: 5′
No. Pieces: 1
No. Guides: 3 chromed steel
Tip Top: Chromed
Rec. Lure Wt.: Not specified
Action: Casting
Handle: Specie cork grip and ABS reel seat.

Model No.: 5-555 (Ivory Series)
Length: 5½′
No. Pieces: 1
No. Guides: 3 chromed steel
Tip Top: Chromed
Rec. Lure Wt.: Not specified
Action: Casting
Handle: Specie cork grip and ABS reel seat.

Model No.: 5-666 (Portage Rods)
Length: 5½′
No. Pieces: 5
No. Guides: 4 chromed steel
Tip Top: Not specified
Rec. Lure Wt.: Not specified
Action: Casting
Handle: Not specified.

Model No.: 85-756 (Blue Chip Series)
Length: 6′
No. Pieces: 2
No. Guides: 4 stainless wire frame plus one carboloy gathering guide
Tip Top: Carboloy
Rec. Lure Wt.: Not specified
Action: Casting
Handle: Specie cork grips. Fast locking cast aluminum reel seat. Gold-plated butt and foregrip caps.

Model No.: 85-757. Same as Model 85-756 except:
Length: 6½′
No. Guides: 5 stainless

Fly Rods

Model No.: 3-015 (Tuffy Series)
Length: 7½′
No. Pieces: 2
No. Guides: 4 snake guides plus one chromed steel stripper
Tip Top: Chromed steel
Rec. Line: 7 wt.

Handle: Specie cork grip with aluminum reel seat.

Model No.: 3-016 (Tuffy Series)
Length: 8′
No. Pieces: 2
No. Guides: 4 snake guides plus one chromed steel stripper
Tip Top: Chromed steel
Rec. Line: 7 wt.
Handle: Specie cork grip with aluminum reel seat.

Model No.: 3-175 (Fly Wate Series)
Length: 7½′
No. Pieces: 2
No. Guides: 4 stainless snake guides plus one carboloy stripper
Tip Top: Stainless
Rec. Line: 5 wt.
Handle: Anodized reel seat with double lock rings. Specie cork grip.

Model No.: 3-176. Same as Model 3-175 except:
Length: 8′
No. Guides: 5 stainless snake guides plus one carboloy stripper
Rec. Line: 8 wt.

Model No.: 3-177. Same as Model 3-175 except:
Length: 8½′
No. Guides: 6 stainless snake guides plus one carboloy stripper
Rec. Line: 8 wt.

Model No.: 3-666 (Portage Rod)
Length: 6½′
No. Pieces: 6
No. Guides: 4
Tip Top: Not specified
Rec. Line: 7 wt.
Handle: Not specified.

Model No.: 73-434 (Bass Pro)
Length: 7′
No. Pieces: 2
No. Guides: 4 chromed stainless plus one carboloy stripper
Tip Top: Stainless
Rec. Line: 10 wt.
Handle: Specie cork grip. Brown and gold anodized reel seat with gold double lock rings.

Saltwater Fly Rods

Model No.: 3-178 (Fly Wate Series)
Length: 9′
No. Pieces: 2
No. Guides: 7 stainless snake guides plus one carboloy stripper
Tip Top: Stainless
Rec. Line: 11 wt.
Handle: Chrome-plated brass reel seat with detachable fighting butt.

Martin (con't.)

Fly Casting Fly Rod

Model No.: 83-734 (Blue Chip Series)
Length: 7'
No. Pieces: 2
No. Guides: 4 stainless guides plus one carboloy stripper
Tip Top: Not specified
Rec. Line: 8
Handle: Specie cork and gold anodized lock rings, specie cork grip.

Spin and Fly Rod

Model No.: 31-666 (Portage Rod)
Length: 6½'
No. Pieces: 6
No. Guides: 4 stainless steel
Tip Top: Not specified
Rec. Line: 6, 7 wt.
Handle: Fixed reel seat.

Popping Rod

Model No.: 2-257 (Fly Wate Series)
Length: 7'
No. Pieces: 2
No. Guides: 4 stainless wire frame
Tip Top: Stainless braced
Rec. Lure Wt.: Not specified
Action: Popping rod
Handle: Finger grip chrome-plated brass reel seat, specie cork grips.

Boat-Bay-Pier Rods

Model No.: 6-016 (Tuffy Series)
Length: 6'
No. Pieces: 1
No. Guides: 3 heavy duty chromed
Tip Top: Chromed
Rec. Lure Wt.: Not specified
Action: Boat rod
Handle: Detachable wood handle, specie cork foregrip with chrome-plated brass reel seat.

Model No.: 6-106 (Ivory Series)
Length: 6'
No. Pieces: 1
No. Guides: 3 chrome-plated stainless
Tip Top: Chrome-plated
Rec. Lure Wt.: Not specified
Action: Medium
Handle: Detachable wood handle, chrome-plated brass reel seat with wood foregrip.

Fresh/Saltwater Rods

Model No.: 65-157
Length: 5½'
No. Pieces: 1
No. Guides: 2 stainless steel
Tip Top: Stainless steel
Action: Heavy
Handle: Detachable wood; chromed brass ferrules and hoods.

Model No.: 65-170
Length: 7'
No. Pieces: 1
No. Guides: 3 stainless steel
Tip Top: Stainless steel
Action: Medium
Handle: Detachable wood; chromed brass ferrules and hoods.

Casting/Trolling Rods

Model No.: 66-955
Length: 5½'
No. Pieces: 1
No. Guides: 3 stainless wire frame
Action: Light
Handle: Detachable; chromed brass reel seat with double lock rings.

Model No.: 66-970
Length: 7'
No. Pieces: 1
No. Guides: 4 stainless wire frame
Action: Medium
Handle: Detachable; chromed brass reel seat with double lock rings.

Model No.: 67-765R
Length: 6½'
No. Guides: 3 stainless steel
Tip Top: Stainless steel roller
Action: Heavy; trolling
Handle: Chromed brass reel seat with double lock rings.

Model No.: 67-770R
Length: 7'
No. Guides: 4 stainless steel
Tip Top: Stainless steel; roller
Action: Extra heavy; trolling
Handle: Chromed brass reel seat with double lock rings.

Casting Worm Rods

Model No.: 84-005 (Blue Chip Series)
Length: 5'
No. Pieces: 1
No. Guides: 4 carboloy
Tip Top: Carboloy
Rec. Lure Wt.: Not specified
Action: Worm rod
Handle: Anodized fast-lock reel seat, specie cork grips with gold anodized butt and foregrip caps.

Model No.: 4-145 (Fly Wate Series)
Length: 5½'
No. Pieces: 1
No. Guides: 4 Ovallan stainless
Tip Top: Stainless
Rec. Lure Wt.: Not specified
Action: Heavy
Handle: Fast locking anodized aluminum reel seat, 7" specie cork butt grip with bumper.

OLM

Fresh Water Spinning Rods

Model No.: 1065
Length: 6½'
No. Pieces: 2
No. Guides: 4 stainless steel bridge
Action: Light
Handle: Powdered cork; black aluminum reel seat.

Model No.: 2060
Length: 6'
No. Pieces: 2
No. Guides: 4 stainless steel wire
Action: Light
Handle: Contoured specie cork.

Model No.: 3055-FG
Length: 5½'
No. Pieces: 2
No. Guides: 4 ceramic
Action: Medium
Handle: "Eva" rubber grip.

Model No.: 3065-FG. Same as Model No. 3055-FG except:
Length: 6½'

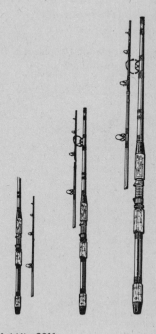

Model No. 2011

Model No.: 3070
Length: 7'
No. Pieces: 2
No. Guides: 5 supported stripper
Action: Medium
Handle: "Eva" rubber grip; aluminum BS reel seat.

Model No.: 3070-FG
Length: 7'
No. Pieces: 2
No. Guides: 5 ceramic
Action: Medium
Handle: "Eva" rubber grip.

Model No.: 7055
Length: 5½'
No. Pieces: 2
No. Guides: 4 stainless steel
Action: Medium
Handle: "Eva" rubber grip.

Model No.: 7070
Length: 7'
No. Pieces: 2
No. Guides: 5 stainless steel wire bridge
Action: Medium
Handle: "Eva" rubber grip.

Model No.: 9055
Length: 5½'
No. Pieces: 2
No. Guides: 4 ceramic
Tip Top: Ceramic
Action: Medium
Handle: Custom cork.

OLM (con't.)

Model No.: 9090
Length: 9'
No. Pieces: 2
No. Guides: 5 ceramic
Tip Top: Ceramic
Action: Medium

Salt Water Spinning Rods

Model No.: 8-90
Length: 9'
No. Pieces: 2
No. Guides: 7 supported stripper
Action: Medium-light
Handle: Cork; aluminum reel seat.

Model No.: 9-90
Length: 9'
No. Pieces: 2
No. Guides: 7 stainless steel wire bridge
Action: Medium-light
Handle: Contoured specie cork.

Model No.: 1011
Length: 11'
No. Pieces: 2
No. Guides: 6 stainless steel bridge
Action: Heavy
Handle: Powdered cord; black aluminum
   reel seat.

Model No.: 1080
Length: 8'
No. Pieces: 2
No. Guides: 5 stainless steel bridge
Action: Medium
Handle: Powdered cork; black aluminum
   reel seat.

Model No.: 2011
Length: 11'
No. Pieces: 2
No. Guides: 6 stainless steel wire
Action: Heavy
Handle: Contoured specie cork; double
   locking aluminum BS reel seat.

Model No.: 2080
Length: 8'
No. Pieces: 2
No. Guides: 5 stainless steel wire
Action: Medium
Handle: Contoured specie cork; double
   locking aluminum BS reel seat.

Model No.: 3011
Length: 11'
No. Pieces: 2
No. Guides: 4 supported stripper
Action: Extra heavy
Handle: "Eva" rubber grip; aluminum BS
   reel seat.

Model No.: 9010
Length: 10'
No. Pieces: 2
No. Guides: 5 ceramic
Tip Top: Ceramic
Action: Medium

Spin Cast Rods

Model No.: 1260
Length: 6'
No. Pieces: 2
No. Guides: 4 stainless steel bridge

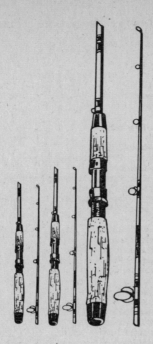

Model No. 2060

Action: Light
Handle: Contoured specie cork; aluminum
   reel seat.

Model No.: 2260. Same as Model No. 1260
   except:
No. Guides: 4 stainless steel wire bridge

Model No.: 2260 PR. Same as Model No.
   1260 except:
No. Guides: 3 chromed stainless steel bridge
Handle: Powdered cork.

Model No.: 2265. Same as Model No. 1260
   except:
Length: 6½'
No. Guides: 5 stainless steel wire bridge

Model No.: 2570X
Length: 7'
No. Pieces: 4
No. Guides: 5 stainless steel wire bridge
Action: Light
Handle: Contoured specie cork; aluminum
   reel seat.

Model No.: 3260
Length: 6'
No. Pieces: 2
No. Guides: 4 supported stripper
Action: Medium
Handle: Rubber grip; aluminum reel seat.

Model No.: 7260
Length: 6'
No. Pieces: 2
No. Guides: 4 stainless steel bridge
Action: Medium
Handle: "Eva" rubber grip.

Model No.: 9255
Length: 5½'
No. Pieces: 2
No. Guides: 5 ceramic
Action: Medium

Worm Rods

Model No.: 2455
Length: 5½'
No. Pieces: 1
No. Guides: 4 Fuji
Action: Medium (spin cast)

Model No.: 2460. Same as Model No.2455
   except:
Length: 6'

Model No.: 6255-2MF
Length: 5½'
No. Pieces: 2
No. Guides: 5 ceramic
Action: Medium (spin cast)
Handle: Spring reel lock; reel keeper;
   no-twist chuck.

Model No.: 6260-2MF. Same as Model No.
   6255-2MF except:
Length: 6'

Model No.: 8255
Length: 5½'
No. Pieces: 1
No. Guides: 5 ceramic
Action: Medium (spin cast)
Handle: Casting.

Model No.: 8260. Same as Model No. 8255
   except:
Length: 6'

Model No.: 9355
Length: 5½'
No. Pieces: 1
No. Guides: 5 ceramic
Action: Medium

Live Bait Rods

Model No.: 3065-IS
Length: 6½'
No. Pieces: 1
No. Guides: 5 ceramic
Action: Medium
Handle: Rubber grip; chrome plated reel seat.

Model No.: 3070-ILB
Length: 7'
No. Pieces: 1
No. Guides: 9 ceramic
Action: Medium-heavy
Handle: Rubber grip; chrome plated reel seat.

Fly Rods

Model No.: 1180
Length: 8'
No. Pieces: 2
No. Guides: 7 stainless steel bridge
Action: Medium
Handle: Powdered cork; black aluminum
   reel seat.

Model No.: 2175
Length: 7½'
No. Pieces: 2
No. Guides: 5 stainless steel wire bridge
Action: Medium
Handle: Contoured specie cork.

Model No.: 2190. Same as Model No. 2175
   except:
Length: 9'
No. Guides: 7

Model No.: 3180

OLM (con't.)

Length: 8'
No. Pieces: 2
No. Guides: 7 supported stripper
Action: Medium
Handle: "Eva" rubber grip; aluminum reel seat.

Model No.: 7180
Length: 8'
No. Pieces: 2
No. Guides: 7 stainless steel wire bridge
Action: Medium
Handle: Aluminum BS seat.

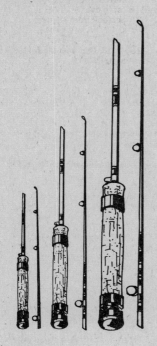

Model No. 1180

Model No.: 9170
Length: 7'
No. Pieces: 2
No. Guides: 7 ceramic
Tip Top: Fuji ceramic
Rec. Line: 6-7
Action: Light
Handle: Stream-line grip.

Model No.: 9190
Length: 9'
No. Pieces: 2
No. Guides: 10 ceramic
Tip Top: Fuji ceramic
Rec. Line: 10-11
Action: Medium
Handle: Stream-line grip.

Surf Casting Rods

Model No.: 12-3
Length: 12'
No. Pieces: 3
No. Guides: 4 stainless steel wire bridge plus 1 folding
Action: Heavy
Handle: Wooden or rubber grip; chrome-plated reel seat.

Model No.: 13-2. Same as Model No. 12-3 except:
Length: 13'
No. Pieces: 2
Action: Extra heavy

Model No.: 14-3. Same as Model No. 12-3 except:
Length: 14'

Mooching Rods

Model No.: 2080M
Length: 8'
No. Pieces: 2
No. Guides: 5 stainless steel wire bridge
Action: Light
Handle: Contoured specie cork; aluminum reel seat.

Model No.: 2085MC. Same as Model No. 2080M except:
Length: 8½'
No. Guides: 5 conventional
Handle: Contoured specie cork.

Telescopic Rods

Model No.: 123
Length: 12'
No. Pieces: 3
Action: Medium

Model No.: 163
Length: 16'
No. Pieces: 4
Action: Medium

Model No.: 563-T (spinning)
Length: 6½'
No. Pieces: 6
No. Guides: 3 chromed stainless bridge
Action: Medium
Handle: Powdered cork.

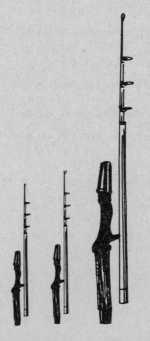

Model No. 660T

Model No.: 660-T (spin-cast)
Length: 6'
No. Pieces: 6
No. Guides: 3 chromed stainless bridge
Action: Medium
Handle: Powdered cork.

Big Game Trolling & Tournament Rods

Model No.: 3577-RH
Length: 7'3"
No. Pieces: 1
No. Guides: 6 Mildrum roller
Action: Medium-heavy
Handle: Neoprene foregrip.

Model No.: 3578-S
Length: 7½'
No. Pieces: 1
No. Guides: 8 carboloy
Action: Medium
Handle: Contoured specie cork.

Model No.: 3830
Length: 6'9"
No. Pieces: 1
No. Guides: 5 double wrapped stainless steel
Action: 30 lb. class
Handle: Wooden power grip.

Orvis

Spinning Rods

Model No.: M9251-1-graphite
Length: 5'
Tip Top: Ceramic
Rec. Line: 2 wt.
Rec. Lure Wt.: 1/16-1/4 oz.
Handle: Cork.

Model No.: M9267-1-graphite
Length: 6½'
Tip Top: Ceramic
Rec. Line: 6 wt.
Rec. Lure Wt.: 3/16-5/8 oz.
Handle: Cork.

Model No.: M9272-1-graphite
Length: 7'
Tip Top: Ceramic
Rec. Line: 12 wt.
Rec. Lure Wt.: ½-2 oz.
Handle: Cork.

Model No.: M9355-1
Length: 7'
No. Guides: Chromed stainless steel
Rec. Line: 6 wt.
Rec. Lure Wt.: 1/8-½ oz.
Action: Medium

Model No.: M9356-2
Length: 7'
Rec. Lure Wt.: 1/8-1/4 oz.; 1/4-½ oz.
Action: Light; medium

Model No.: M9504-1
Length: 5'9"
No. Guides: Chromed stainless steel
Rec. Line: 2 wt.
Rec. Lure Wt.: 1/16-1/4 oz.
Action: Ultra-light

Model No.: M9601-1
Length: 6'
No. Guides: Chromed stainless steel

Orvis (con't.)

Rec. Line: 4 wt.
Rec. Lure Wt.: 1/16-1/4 oz.
Action: Super-light

Model No.: M9655-1. Same as Model No. M9355-1 except:
Length: 6½′
Action: Light

Model No.: M9761-1
Length: 7½′
No. Guides: Chromed stainless steel
Rec. Line: 10 wt.
Rec. Lure Wt. ½-⅝ oz.
Action: Heavy

Model No.: M9950-1
Length: 5′
No. Guides: Chrome
Rec. Line: 4 wt.
Rec. Lure Wt.: ⅛-¼ oz.
Action: Ultra-light

Model No.: M9955-1
Length: 6½′
No. Guides: Chrome
Rec. Line: 6 wt.
Rec. Lure Wt.: ¼-½ oz.
Action: Medium

Model No.: M9960-1
Length: 8′
No. Guides: Chrome
Rec. Line: 10 wt.
Rec. Lure Wt.: ½-¾ oz.
Action: Heavy

Fly Rods

Model No.: M9069-1
Length: 6½′
Rec. Line: 4 wt.
Action: Ultra-light
Handle: Superfine reel seat.

Model No.: M9079-1
Length: 8½′
Rec. Line: 9 wt.
Handle: Walnut reel seat.

Model No.: M9081-1
Length: 8′9″
Rec. Line: 11 wt.
Action: Heavy
Handle: Chromed metal reel seat.

Model No.: M9270-1-graphite
Length: 7′
No. Guides: Aluminum oxide ceramic
Rec. Line: 5 wt.

Model No.: M9279-1-graphite
Length: 7′9″
Rec. Line: 5 wt.
Handle: Cork locking reel seat.

Model No.: M9280-11-graphite
Length: 8′
No. Guides: Aluminum oxide ceramic
Rec. Line: 6 wt.
Handle: Cork locking reel seat.

Model No.: M9283-1-graphite
Length: 8′3″
Rec. Line: 7 wt.
Handle: Cork locking reel seat.

Model No.: M9290-11-graphite
Length: 9′
No. Guides: Aluminum oxide ceramic
Rec. Line: 9 wt.
Handle: Metal reel seat; choice of 2″ or 6″ butt extension.

Model No.: M9650-1
Length: 6½′
No. Pieces: 2
Rec. Line: 6 wt.
Handle: Cork grip.

Model No.: M9764-2
Length: 7½′
No. Pieces: 3
Rec. Line: 5 wt.
Handle: Cork.

Model No.: M9801-1
Length: 8′
No. Pieces: 2
Rec. Line: 8 wt.
Handle: Cork.

Model No.: M9812-2
Length: 8½
No. Pieces: 2
Rec. Line: 6 wt.
Action: Slow
Handle: Cork.

Model No.: M9908-1
Length: 7′
No. Pieces: 2
No. Guides: Chrome-plated stainless steel
Tip Top: Chrome-plated stainless steel
Handle: Black locking reel seat.

Model No.: M9918-1
Length: 8′
No. Pieces: 2
Rec. Line: 7 wt.

Model No.: M9921-1. Same as Model No. M9908-1 except:
Length: 8½′

Model No.: M9922-1
Length: 8½′
No. Pieces: 2
Rec. Line: 9 wt.

Salmon/Steelhead/Saltwater Rod

Model No.: M9815-2
Length: 8′9″
No. Pieces: 2
Rec. Line: 10 wt.

Pezon et Michel

Fly Rods

Model No.: CS222
Length: 6′10″, 7′4″, 7′9″, 8′3″, 8′8″, 9′3″
No. Pieces: 2
Rec. Line: 6′10″, 7′4″, 7′9″, 8′3″ rods: AFTMA #5
8′8″ rods: AFTMA #7
9′3″ rods: AFTMA #9
Handle: Shaped handle with screw fitting reel seat.

Model No.: CS224
Length: 6′10″, 7′4″, 7′9″, 8′3″
No. Pieces: 2
Rec. Line: AFTMA # 5
Handle: Cigar handle with butt cap and sliding ring reel seat.

Model: Super Parabolic PPP
Length: 7′2″, 7′5″, 7′7″, 7′7½″, 7′11½″, 8′1″, 8′3″, 8′5″
No. Pieces: 2
Rec. Line: 8′1″ rods: AFTMA #4-5
7′2″, 7′5″, 7′7″ rods: AFTMA #5
7′7½″, 8′3″ rods: AFTMA #5-6
7′11½″, 8′5″ rods: AFTMA #6
8′3″ rods: AFTMA #6-7
Handle: Shaped handle with screw fitting reel seat.

Model: Parabolic Extra
Length: 8′2″, 8′5″, 8′10″, 9½′
No. Pieces: 2
Rec. Line: 8′2″ rods: AFTMA #5
8′2″, 8′5″, 9½′ rods: AFTMA #5-6
8′10″ rods: AFTMA #6
Handle: Shaped handle with screw fitting reel seat.

Model: Parabolic Prima
Length: 8′, 8½′, 9′
No. Pieces: 2
Rec. Line: 8′ rods: AFTMA #4-5
8½′ rods: AFTMA #5-6
9′ rods: AFTMA #6-7
Handle: Shaped handle with screw fitting reel seat.

Model: Parabolic Graphite CCC—Light
Length: 7½′, 8′, 8½′, 9′
No. Pieces: 2
Rec. Line: 8′, 9′ rods: AFTMA #5
7½′, 8½′ rods: AFTMA #6
Handle: Shaped contour cork handle with 1 ring set and 1 sliding ring reel seat.

Model: Parabolic Graphite CCC—Strong
Length: 8½′, 9′, 10½′, 11′
No. Pieces: 2
Rec. Line: 8½′, 9′ rods: AFTMA #8
10½′, 11′ rods: AFTMA #9
Action: Strong
Handle: Shaped contour cork handle with 1 ring set and 1 sliding ring reel seat.

Model: Parabolic Mirage Riccardi
Length: 6½′
No. Pieces: 2
Action: Casting
Handle: Cigar handle with 2 sliding rings reel seat.

Model: Parabolic Royale Super
Length: 6′10″, 7′4″, 7′9″, 8′3″
No. Pieces: 2
Action: Casting
Handle: Solid cork cigar shaped grip with walnut root screw fitting reel seat.

Model: Parabolic HF
Length: 7½′, 8′, 8½′, 9′
Rec. Line: 7½′, 8′ rods: AFTMA #5
8½′, 9′ rods: AFTMA #6
Handle: Shaped contour handle with 1 ring set and 1 sliding reel seat.

Model: Parabolic Saumon
Length: 10½′, 12′, 14′
No. Pieces: 10½′ rods: 2; 12′, 14′ rods: 3
Rec. Line: 10½′ rods: AFTMA #7
12′ rods: AFTMA #10
14′ rods: AFTMA #11-12
Handle: Light, shaped cork handle with

Pezon et Michel (con't.)

screw fitting reel seat.

Model: Parabolic Saumon Graphite CCC
Length: 14'
No. Pieces: 3
Rec. Line: AFTMA #11-12
Handle: Chrome-plated butt and end rings.

Model: Parabolic Saumon HF
Length: 12½', 14'
No. Pieces: 3
Rec. Line: 12½' rods: AFTMA #9-10
        14' rods: AFTMA #10-12
Handle: 1 ring set on cork handle; 1 sliding ring reel seat.

Casting Rods

Model: Luxor Luxe
Length: 7'3"
No. Pieces: 2
Action: Extra-light to medium
Handle: Cork.

Model: Luxor Luxe-Extra Light
Length: 6'7"
No. Pieces: 2
Action: Extra-light
Handle: Cork.

Model: Luxor Luxe-Wading
Length: 3½'
No. Pieces: 1
Action: Extra-light
Handle: Cork.

Model: Luxor Luxe HF
Length: 5', 5½', 6', 6½', 7', 8½', 9'
No. Pieces: 2
Action: Extra-light to medium-heavy
Handle: Cork.

Model: Telebolic
Length: 5½', 6'
No. Pieces: 2
Action: Extra-light to light
Handle: Cork.

Model: Telebolic Saumon
Length: 9'10", 10½'
No. Pieces: 2
Action: Multicone
Handle: Cork.

Trolling Rod

Model: Super Oceanic
Length: 6'10"
No. Pieces: 2
Action: 30 lb., 50 lb., 80 lb.
Handle: Cork upper section and wood lower section with chrome-plated reel seat.

Pflueger

Freshwater Spinning Rods

Model No.: G110S—graphite
Length: 5' 6½'
No. Pieces: 2
No. Guides: 5' rods: 4 stainless steel; 6½' rods: 5 ceramic
Tip Top: 5' rods: stainless steel; 6½' rods: ceramic
Action: 5' rods: ultra-light
        6½' rods: medium

Model No. 115F

Handle: Specie cork grip; aluminum locking rings.

Model No.: 1155 (Graph-Glass)
Length: 5', 6½'; 7'
No. Pieces: 2
No. Guides: 5' rods: 4 stainless steel; 6½', 7' rods: 5 ceramic
Tip Top: 5' rods: stainless steel; 6½', 7' rods: ceramic
Action: 5' rods: ultra-light
        6½', 7' rods: medium
Handle: Cork grips.

Model No.: 315SP
Length: 5', 6½', 7'
No. Pieces: 2
No. Guides: 5' rods: 4 stainless steel; 6½', 7' rods: 5 ceramic
Tip Top: 5' rods: stainless steel; 6½', 7' rods: ceramic
Handle: Standard cork grips.

Model No.: 415SP
Length: 5', 6½', 7'
No. Pieces: 2
No. Guides: 5' rods: 4 stainless steel; 6½', 7' rods: 1 ceramic lead, 3 stainless steel
Tip Top: 5' rods: stainless steel; 6½', 7' rods: ceramic
Action: 5' rods: ultra-light
        6½', 7' rods: medium
Handle: Standard cork grips.

Model No.: 515SP
Length: 5', 6½'
No. Pieces: 2
No. Guides: 4 stainless steel
Tip Top: stainless steel
Action: 5' rods: ultra-light
        6½' rods: medium
Handle: Cork grips.

Salt Water Spinning Rod

Model No.: 115SWSP (Graph-Glass)
Length: 6½', 7½'
No. Pieces: 1
No. Guides: 6½' rods: 5 ceramic; 7½' rods: 6 foul proof
Tip Top: Ceramic
Action: Medium
Handle: Cork grips.

Spin-Casting Rod

Model No.: 104PB
Length: 6', 6'6"
No. Pieces: 2
No. Guides: 5 Fuji hard

Tip Top: Fuji hard-speed
Rec. Lure Wt.: Not specified
Action: Medium

Bait-Casting Rods

Model No.: G110B-graphite
Length: 5'8"
No. Pieces: 1
No. Guides: 5 ceramic
Tip Top: Ceramic
Action: Medium
Handle: Pistol grip detachable.

Model No.: 115B (Graph-Glass)
Length: 5'8", 6'
No. Pieces: 1
No. Guides: 5 ceramic
Tip Top: Ceramic
Action: Medium
Handle: Deluxe detachable.

Model No.: 315BC
Length: 5½'
No. Pieces: 1
No. Guides: 5 ceramic
Tip Top: Ceramic
Action: Medium
Handle: Pistol grip.

Model No.: 515BC
Length: 5½'
No. Pieces: 1
No. Guides: 4 stainless steel
Tip Top: Stainless steel
Action: Medium
Handle: Standard cork grips.

Push Button Rods

Model No.: 315PB
Length: 6'
No. Pieces: 2
No. Guides: 5 ceramic
Tip Top: Ceramic
Action: Medium
Handle: Deluxe.

Model No.: 415PB
Length: 6'
No. Pieces: 2
No. Guides: 1 ceramic lead, 3 stainless steel
Tip Top: Ceramic
Action: Medium
Handle: Standard cork grips.

Model No.: 515PB
Length: 6'
No. Pieces: 2
No. Guides: 4 stainless steel

Model No. 115 S W

Pflueger (con't.)

Tip Top: Stainless steel
Action: Medium
Handle: Standard cork grips.

Fly Rods

Model No.: G110F—graphite
Length: 7½', 8, 8½', 9'
No. Pieces: 2
No. Guides: 1 ceramic stripper, 4 stainless
  steel
Tip Top: Stainless steel
Action: Light to medium
Handle: Standard cork grips.

Model No.: 115F (Graph-Glass)
Length: 8', 8½'
No. Pieces: 2
No. Guides: 1 ceramic, 4 stainless steel
Tip Top: Stainless steel
Action: Medium
Handle: Standard cork grips.

Model No.: 515FY
Length: 8'
No. Pieces: 2
No. Guides: 4 stainless steel snake
Tip Top: Stainless steel
Action: Medium
Handle: Fly grips.

Salt Water Surf Rods

Model No.: 115SW (Graph-Glass)
Length: 8', 9', 10'
No. Pieces: 2
No. Guides: 5 stainless steel wire frame
Tip Top: Carboloy
Action: Medium
Handle: Deluxe.

Model No.: 1015
Length: 8', 9', 10'
No. Pieces: 2
No. Guides: 5 stainless steel wire frame
Tip Top: Stainless steel
Action: Medium
Handle: Surf.

Quick

Spinning Rods

Model No.: 6055
Length: 5½'
No. Pieces: 1
No. Guides: Not specified; polygon
Tip Top: Not specified
Rec. Lure Wt.: Not specified
Action: Light
Handle: Neo-grip.

Model No.: 6065
Length: 6½'
No. Pieces: 2
No. Guides: Not specified
Tip Top: Not specified
Rec. Lure Wt.: Not specified
Action: Fast taper
Handle: Neo-grip.

Model No.: 6060. Same as Model 6065
  except:
Length: 6'
Action: Medium-heavy

Model No.: 6066. Same as Model 6065
  except:

Action: Medium-heavy

Model No.: 6070. Same as Model 6065
  except:
Length: 7'

Model No.: 6071. Same as Model 6065
  except:
Length: 7'
Action: Medium-heavy

Model No.: UL6056R
Length: 5½'
No. Pieces: 2
No. Guides: Not specified
Tip Top: Not specified
Rec. Lure Wt.: Not specified
Action: Ultra-light
Handle: Cork grip.

Model No.: UL6056. Same as Model UL6056R
  except:
Length: 6'
Handle: Neo-grip.

Model No.: FS65
Length: 6½'
No. Pieces: 1
No. Guides: Not specified; polygon
Tip Top: Tungsten carbide
Rec. Lure Wt.: Not specified
Action: Powerful
Handle: Not specified.

Model No.: FS70. Same as Model FS65
  except:
Length: 7'

Fresh Water Spinning Rods

Model No.: 6065R
Length: 6½'
No. Pieces: 2
No. Guides: Not specified
Tip Top: Not specified
Rec. Lure Wt.: Not specified
Action: Fast taper
Handle: Cork grip.

Model No.: 6070R
Length: 7'
No. Pieces: 2
No. Guides: Not specified
Tip Top: Not specified
Rec. Lure Wt.: Not specified
Action: Fast taper
Handle: Cork grip.

Salt Water Spinning Rods

Model No.: 6077R
Length: 7'
No. Pieces: 2
No. Guides: Not specified
Tip Top: Not specified
Rec. Lure Wt.: Not specified
Action: Light
Handle: Cork grip.

Model No.: 6088R
Length: 8'
No. Pieces: 2
No. Guides: Not specified
Tip Top: Not specified
Rec. Lure Wt.: Not specified
Action: Fast taper
Handle: Not specified.

Model No.: 6090R. Same as Model 6088R
  except:
Length: 9'

Model No.: CS70
Length: 7'
No. Pieces: 1
No. Guides: Not specified; polygon
Tip Top: Tungsten carbide
Rec. Lure Wt.: Not specified
Action: Fast tip
Handle: Not specified.

Bait-Casting Rods

Model No.: CS60
Length: 6'
No. Pieces: 1
No. Guides: Not specified; polygon
Tip Top: Carbide
Rec. Lure Wt.: Not specified
Action: Power
Handle: Cork grip.

Model No.: CS75
Length: 7'
No. Pieces: 1
No. Guides: 7 heavy duty conventional
  guide or 7 Polygon Spinning
Tip Top: Tungsten carbide
Rec. Lure Wt.: Not specified
Action: Heavy
Handle: Not specified.

Model No.: FC56
Length: 5½'
No. Pieces: 1
No. Guides: Not specified; carboloy
Tip Top: Carboloy
Rec. Lure Wt.: Not specified
Action: Medium-stiff
Handle: Detachable offset casting, positive
  locking, and self aligning.

Model No.: FC58. Same as Model FC56
  except:
Length: 5'9"

Model No.: FC59. Same as Model FC56
  except:
Length: 5'9"
Action: Medium-light

Model No.: FC60. Same as Model FC56
  except:
Length: 6'
Action: Medium

Fly Rods

Model No.: 6176
Length: 7½'
No. Pieces: 2
No. Guides: Not specified
Tip Top: Not specified
Rec. Line: Light weights
Handle: Not specified.

Model No.: 6180
Length: 8'
No. Pieces: 2
No. Guides: Not specified
Tip Top: Not specified
Rec. Line: Not specified
Handle: Not specified.

Model No.: 6186. Same as Model 6180
  except:
Length: 8½'

Mooching Rod.

Model No.: 6086
Length: 8½'
No. Pieces: Not specified

Quick (con't.)

No. Guides: Not specified
Tip Top: Not specified
Rec. Lure Wt.: Not specified
Action: Light
Handle: Not specified.

Steelhead Rods

Model No.: 6080
Length: 8′
No. Pieces: 2
No. Guides: Not specified
Tip Top: Not specified
Rec. Lure Wt.: Not specified
Action: Light
Handle: Neo-grip.

Model No.: 6080R
Length: 8′
No. Pieces: 2
No. Guides: Not specified
Tip Top: Not specified
Rec. Lure Wt.: Not specified
Action: Light
Handle: Cork grip.

Model No.: 6081
Length: 8′
No. Pieces: Not specified
No. Guides: Not specified
Tip Top: Not specified
Rec. Lure Wt.: Not specified
Action: Light
Handle: Not specified.

Model No. 25SP-70ML

St. Croix

Spinning Rods

Model No.: 02SP-50LT
Length: 5′
No. Pieces: 1
No. Guides: 2 coil
Tip Top: Coil
Rec. Lure Wt.: ⅛-⅜ oz.
Action: Light
Handle: Aluminum rings, cork grip.

Model No.: 24SP-70ML
Length: 7′
No. Pieces: 2
No. Guides: 5 stainless steel
Tip Top: Carboloy
Rec. Lure Wt.: ¼-⅝ oz.
Action: Medium-light
Handle: Double locking nuts, chrome butt
and foregrips.

Model No.: 19SP-59ML-SH
Length: 5′9″
No. Pieces: 1
No. Guides: 4 stainless steel
Tip Top: Stainless steel
Rec. Lure Wt.: ¼-½ oz.
Action: Medium-light
Handle: Specie cork handle.

Model No.: 19SP-59ML

Length: 5′9″
No. Pieces: 1
No. Guides: 4 stainless steel
Tip Top: Stainless steel
Rec. Lure Wt.: ¼-½ oz.
Action: Medium-light
Handle: Black reel seat.

Model No.: 09SP-56UL
Length: 5½′
No. Pieces: 2
No. Guides: 3 mono-loop
Tip Top: Chromed-steel
Rec. Lure Wt.: ⅛-¼ oz.
Action: Ultralight
Handle: Anodized reel seat.

Model No.: 09SP-66ML Same as Model
No. 09SP-56UL except:
Length: 6½′
Action: Medium-light

Model No.: 09SP-70ML. Same as Model
No. 09SP-56UL except:
Length: 7′
Action: Medium-light

Model No.: 12SP-66ML
Length: 6½′
No. Pieces: 2
No. Guides: 4 chromed-steel
Tip Top: Chromed-steel
Rec. Lure Wt.: ¼-⅝ oz.
Action: Medium-light
Handle: Reel seat with double locking ring.

Model No.: 12SP-70ML. Same as Model
No. 12SP-66ML except:
Length: 7′

Model No.: 12SP-56UL
Length: 5½′
No. Pieces: 2
No. Guides: 3 chrome-plated
Tip Top: Chrome-plated
Rec. Lure Wt.: ⅛-¼ oz.
Action: Ultra light
Handle: Cork grip.

Model No.: 15SP-66MD
Length: 6½′
No. Pieces: 2
No. Guides: 4 chrome-plated
Tip Top: Chrome-plated
Rec. Lure Wt.: ⅛-¾ oz.
Action: Medium
Handle: Brown anodized reel seat, brown
fore and butt caps.

Model No.: 08SP-66ML
Length: 6½′
No. Pieces: 2
No. Guides: 3 gold-plated
Tip Top: Gold-plated
Rec. Lure Wt.: ¼-⅝ oz.
Action: Medium-light
Handle: Anodized reel seat.

Model No.: 25SP-70ML
Length: 7′
No. Pieces: 2
No. Guides: 5 stainless steel
Tip Top: Carboloy
Rec. Lure Wt.: ¼-⅝ oz.
Action: Medium-light
Handle: Chrome reel seat with double locking
rings.

Model No.: 29SP-UL
Length: 5′, 5½′, 6′
No. Pieces: 5′ rods: 1; 5½′, 6′ rods: 2
No. Guides: 4 foul proof
Tip Top: Carboloy
Rec Lure Wt.: ¹⁄₁₆-¼ oz.
Action: Ultralight
Handle: Diamond butt wrap.

Model No.: 29SP-ML
Length: 6½′, 7′, 7½′
No. Pieces: 2
No. Guides: 5 stainless steel
Tip Top: Carboloy
Rec. Lure Wt.: ¼-⅝ oz.
Action: Medium-light
Handle: Brown reel seat with gold hoods
and double lock nuts.

Model No.: 25SP-66MD
Length: 6½′
No. Guides: 5 carboloy
Tip Top: Carboloy
Rec. Lure Wt.: ⅜-¾ oz.
Action: Medium
Handle: Black reel seat with chrome hoods
and double lock nuts.

Salt Water Rods

Model No.: 09SW-80MD
Length: 8′
No. Pieces: 2
No. Guides: 4 stainless steel
Tip Top: Stainless steel
Rec. Lure Wt.: ½-1½ oz.
Action: Medium
Handle: Anodized reel seat.

Model No.: 12SW-90MH
Length: 9′
No. Pieces: 2
No. Guides: 4 stainless steel
Tip Top: Stainless steel
Rec. Lure Wt.: ¾-3 oz.
Action: Medium-heavy
Handle: Brass chrome reel seat.

Model No.: 19SW-76MD

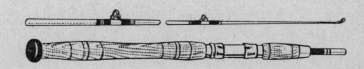

Model No. 13BT-60XH-1

St. Croix (con't.)

Length: 7½'
No. Pieces: 2
No. Guides: 5 stainless steel
Tip Top: Stainless steel
Rec. Lure Wt.: ½-1½ oz.
Action: Medium
Handle: Brass chrome reel seat.

Model No.: 19SW-86MH. Same as Model No. 19SW-76MD except:
Length: 8½'
Rec. Lure Wt.: ¾-3 oz.
Action: Medium-heavy

Model No.: 24SW-80MD-1
Length: 8'
No. Pieces: 1
No. Guides: 5 stainless steel foul proof
Tip Top: Stainless steel
Rec. Lure Wt.: ¾-2 oz.
Action: Medium
Handle: Chrome reel seat and double locking rings.

Model No.: 24SW-70MD-1. Same as Model No. 24SW-80MD-1 except:
Length: 7'
No. Guides: 4

Model No.: 24SW-70MD-2. Same as Model No. 24SW-80MD-1 except:
Length: 7'
No. Pieces: 2
No. Guides: 4

Model No.: 24SW-76MD-1. Same as Model No. 24SW-80MD-1 except:
Length: 7½'
No. Guides: 4

Model No.: 24SW-66-ML-1. Same as Model No. 24SW-80MD-1 except:
Length: 6½'
No. Guides: 4
Rec. Lure Wt.: ⅜-¾ oz.
Action: Medium-light

Model No.: 24SW-80MD-2. Same as Model No. 24SW-80MD-1 except:
No. Pieces: 2

Model No.: 24SW-100XH-2. Same as Model No. 24SW-80MD-1 except:
Length: 10'
No. Pieces: 2
Rec. Lure Wt.: 5-10 oz.
Action: Extra-heavy

Spin-Casting Rods

Model No.: 09SC-60ML
Length: 6'
No. Pieces: 2
No. Guides: 3 mono-loop
Tip Top: Chrome-plated
Rec. Lure Wt.: ¼-½ oz.
Action: Medium-light
Handle: Black offset handle with cork butt grip.

Model No.: 01SC-46LT
Length: 4½'
No. Pieces: 1
No. Guides: 2 coil
Tip Top: Coil
Rec. Lure Wt.: ⅛-⅜ oz.

Action: Light
Handle: Black cycoloc handle.

Model No.: 02SC-50LT
Length: 5'
No. Pieces: 1
No. Guides: 2 coil
Tip Top: Coil
Rec. Lure Wt.: ⅛-⅜ oz.
Action: Light
Handle: Black metal handle with cork grips.

Model No.: 08SC-60ML
Length: 6'
No. Pieces: 2
No. Guides: 3 gold-plated
Tip Top: Gold-plated
Rec. Lure Wt.: ¼-⅝ oz.
Action: Medium-light
Handle: Brown offset handle with cork grip.

Model No.: 08SC-56ML. Same as Model No. 08SC-60ML except:
Length: 5½'
No. Pieces: 1

Model No.: 19SC-60ML
Length: 6'
No. Pieces: 2
No. Guides: 4 stainless steel
Tip Top: Stainless steel
Rec. Lure Wt.: ¼-⅝ oz.
Action: Medium-light
Handle: Non-detachable black action handle

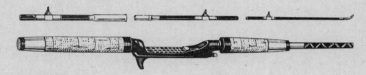

Model No. 25SC-66MD

Model No.: 12SC-60ML
Length: 6'
No. Pieces: 2
No. Guides: 4 chromed-steel
Tip Top: Chromed-steel
Rec. Lure Wt.: ¼-⅝ oz.
Action: Medium-light
Handle: Brown butt with brown reel seat.

Model No.: 05SC-26HV
Length: 2½'
No. Pieces: 1
No. Guides: 1 mono-loop
Tip Top: Chrome-plated
Rec. Lure Wt.: ½-1½ oz.
Action: Heavy
Handle: Black metal handle with grips.

Model No.: 05SC-30HV
Length: 3'
No. Pieces: 1
No. Guides: 2 mono-loop
Tip Top: Chrome-plated
Rec. Lure Wt.: ½-1½ oz.
Action: Heavy
Handle: Black metal handle with cork grips.

Model No.: 15SC-66MD
Length: 6½'
No. Pieces: 2
No. Guides: 4 stainless steel
Tip Top: Chromed-steel
Rec. Lure Wt.: ⅜-¾ oz.

Action: Medium
Handle: Brown action handles with cork butt.

Model No.: 25SC-66MD
Length: 6½'
No. Pieces: 2
No. Guides: 5 carboloy
Tip Top: Carboloy
Rec. Lure Wt.: ⅜-¾ oz.
Action: Medium
Handle: Black non-detachable handle with cork grips.

Model No.: 25SC-60ML
Length: 6'
No. Pieces: 2
No. Guides: 5 carboloy
Tip Top: Carboloy
Rec. Lure Wt.: ¼-⅝ oz.
Action: Medium-light
Handle: Black non-detachable handle with cork grips.

Bait-Casting Rods

Model No.: 05BC
Length: 4½', 5½'
No. Pieces: 1
No. Guides: 4½' rods: 2 mono-loop; 5½' rods: 3 conventional
Tip Top: Chrome-plated
Rec. Lure Wt.: ½-1½ oz.
Action: Heavy
Handle: Black metal handles with cork grips.

Model No.: 12BC
Length: 5½', 6'
No. Pieces: 1
No. Guides: 4 chromed-steel
Tip Top: Chromed-steel
Rec. Lure Wt.: ⅜-⅝ oz.
Action: Medium-light
Handle: Brown offset handle with cork grips.

Model No.: 19BC
Length: 5½', 6'
No. Pieces: 5½' rods: 1 or 2; 6' rods: 1
No. Guides: 4 stainless steel
Tip Top: Stainless steel
Rec. Lure Wt.: 5½' rods: ⅜-⅝ oz., ½-1 oz.
6' rods: ⅜-⅝ oz.
Action: 5½' rods: medium-light or medium-heavy
6' rods: medium-light
Handle: Non-detachable black handle with black pistol grips.

Model No.: 25BC
Length: 5'2", 5½', 6', 6½'
No. Pieces: 1
No. Guides: 5'2" rods: 5; 5½' rods: 4 or 5; 6' rods: 5; all carboloy
Tip Top: Carboloy
Rec. Lure Wt.: 5'2" rods: ⅜-⅝ oz., ½-1 oz.
5½' rods: ⅜-⅝ oz., ½-1 oz., ⅝-1½ oz., 1-3 oz.
6' rods: ⅜-⅝ oz.
6½' rods: ⅝-1½ oz., 1-3 oz.

St. Croix (con't.)

Action: 5'2" rods: medium-light or medium-heavy
5½' rods: medium-light, medium-heavy or heavy
6' rods: medium-light
6½' rods: medium-heavy or heavy
Handle: Detachable handle with pistol grip.

Model No.: 29BC
Length: 5'2", 5½', 5'9", 6'
No. Pieces: 1
No. Guides: 5 aluminum oxide
Tip Top: Aluminum oxide
Rec. Lure Wt.: 5'2" rods: ⅜-⅝ oz., ½-1 oz.
5½' rods: ⅜-⅝ oz., ½-1 oz.
5'9" rods: ⅜-¾ oz., ½-1¼ oz., ⅝-1½ oz,
6' rods: ⅜-⅝ oz.
Action: 5'2" rods: medium-light or medium-heavy
5½' rods: medium-light or medium-heavy
5' 9" rods: medium-light, medium or medium-heavy
6' rods: medium-light
Handle: Brown detachable handle with pistol grip.

Boat Rods

Model No.: 13BT-60MD-D
Length: 6'
No. Pieces: 1
No. Guides: 3 stainless steel
Tip Top: Stainless steel
Rec. Line: 10-30 lb.
Action: Medium
Handle: Detachable butt with brass chrome reel seat.

Model No.: 04BT-50ML-1
Length: 5'
No. Pieces: 1
No. Guides: 2 conventional
Tip Top: Conventional
Rec. Lure Wt.: Not specified
Action: Medium-light
Handle: Non-detachable wooden handles and foregrips, aluminum reel seats

Model No.: 13BT-60XH-1
Length: 6'
No. Pieces: 1
No. Guides: 2 stainless steel
Tip Top: Stainless steel
Rec. Line: 30-80 lb.
Action: Extra-heavy
Handle: Non-detachable wooden handle with chrome-plated brass reel seat.

Model No.: 12BT-66MD-D
Length: 6½'
No. Pieces: 1
No. Guides: 3 stainless steel
Tip Top: Stainless steel
Rec. Line: 15-30 lb.
Action: Medium
Handle: Chrome-plated brass reel seat, detachable wooden handle, rubber butt caps.

Model No.: 12BT-66MH-DRT. Same as Model No. 12BT-66MD-D except:
Tip Top: Roller
Rec. Line: 25-40 lb.
Action: Medium-heavy

Model No.: 23BT-66HV-D
Length: 6½'
No. Pieces: 1
No. Guides: 4 stainless steel
Tip Top: Stainless steel
Rec. Line: 20-50 lb.
Action: Heavy
Handle: Chrome-plated brass reel seat, detachable wooden handle, hardwood butt cap and foregrip.

Model No.: 23BT-66HV-DRT. Same as Model No. 23BT-66HV except:
Tip Top: Mildrum roller

Model No.: 23BT-70MH-D
Length: 7'
No. Pieces: 1
No. Guides: 4 stainless steel
Tip Top: Stainless steel
Rec. Line: 15-40 lb.
Action: Medium-heavy
Handle: Chrome-plated brass reel seat, detachable handle, hardwood butt and foregrip.

Model No.: 13BT-60XH-1RT
Length: 6'
No. Pieces: 1
No. Guides: 2 stainless steel
Tip Top: Roller
Rec. Line: 30-80 lb.
Action: Extra-heavy
Handle: Hardwood handle with brass/chrome reel seat.

Model No.: 13BT-66HV-DRT
Length: 6½'
No. Pieces: 1
No. Guides: 3 stainless steel
Tip Top: Roller
Rec. Line: 20-50 lb.
Action: Heavy
Handle: Brass/chrome reel seat and detachable dense wood handle.

Model No.: 23 Regulation
Length: 6½'
No. Pieces: 1
No. Guides: 4 Aftco roller
Tip Top: Aftco roller
Rec. Line: 20 lb., 30 lb., 50 lb., 80 lb.
Handle: Heavy duty brass/chrome reel seat, hardwood butt.

Fly Rods

Model No.: 09FF
Length: 8'
No. Pieces: 2
No. Guides: 3 stainless steel snake plus 1 mono-loop stripper
Tip Top: Fly
Rec. Line: 6-7
Action: Medium-light
Handle: Anodized reel seat, tapered cork handle.

Model No.: 12FF
Length: 8', 8½'
No. Pieces: 2
No. Guides: 4 stainless steel snake plus 1 chromed steel stripper
Tip Top: Fly
Rec. Line: 8' rods: 6-7
8½' rods: 7-8
Action: 8' rods: medium-light
8½' rods: medium
Handle: Tapered cork grips with brown forecaps.

Model No.: 19FF
Length: 7½', 8', 8½'
No. Pieces: 2
No. Guides: 7½' rods: 4 snake plus 1 stripper; 8' rods: 5 snake plus 1 stripper; 8½' rods: 4 snake plus 2 stripper; all aluminum
Tip Top: Fly
Rec. Line: 7½', 8' rods: 6-7
8½' rods: 7-8
Action: 7½', 8' rods: medium-light
8½' rods: medium
Handle: Tapered cork grip, black forecap.

Model No.: 29FF-LT
Length: 6½', 7'
No. Pieces: 2
No. Guides: 6½' rods: 4 snake plus 1 aluminum oxide stripper; 7' rods: 5 snake plus 1 aluminum oxide
Tip Top: Fly
Rec. Line: 5-6
Action: Light
Handle: Light cork handle.

Model No.: 29FF-90
Length: 9'
No. Pieces: 2
No. Guides: 8 stainless steel snake plus 2 aluminum oxide stripper
Tip Top: Fly
Rec. Line: 8-9 or 10-11
Action: Medium-heavy or heavy
Handle: Brown reel seat, detachable fighting butt.

Salmon/Steelhead Rods

Model No.: 12SS
Length: 8', 8½'
No. Pieces: 2
No. Guides: 5 steel
Tip Top: Chromed steel
Rec. Lure Wt.: 8' rods: ¼-⅝ oz.
8½' rods: ¼-⅝ oz. or ⅜-1 oz.
Action: 8' rods: medium-light
8½' rods: medium-light or medium-heavy
Handle: Cork butt grips.

Model No.: 19SS
Length: 7½', 8', 8½', 9'
No. Pieces: 2

Model No. 19SU

St. Croix (con't.)

No. Guides: 7½' rods: 5; 8', 8½', 9' rods: 6;
all stainless steel
Tip Top: Stainless steel
Rec. Lure Wt.: ¼-⅝ oz.
Action: Medium-light
Handle: Cork butt grips.

Surf Rods

Model No.: 12SU
Length: 7', 8', 9'
No. Pieces: 1
No. Guides: 4 stainless steel
Tip Top: Stainless steel
Rec. Lure Wt.: 7', 8' rods: 1-3 oz.
9' rods: 1½-4 oz.
Action: Medium
Handle: Brass/chrome reel seat; one piece
cork butt grips.

Model No.: 19SU
Length: 7', 8', 9'
No. Pieces: 1
No. Guides: 4 stainless steel
Tip Top: Carboloy
Rec. Line: 7', 8' rods: 1-3 oz.
9' rods: 1½-4 oz.
Action: Medium
Handle: Brass/chrome reel seat; one piece
cork butt grips.

Model No.: 25SU
Length: 9½'
No. Pieces: 1
No. Guides: 3 stainless steel
Tip Top: Stainless steel
Rec. Lure Wt.: 3-8 oz.
Action: Extra-heavy
Handle: Wood spring butt; brass/chrome
reel seat.

IGFA Regulation Rods

Model No.: 26RG-12
Length: 6'9"
No. Pieces: 1
No. Guides: 5 Aftco roller; 4 Varmac plus 1
Aftco stripper
Tip Top: Aftco roller
Action: 12 lb. class
Handle: Wood.

Model No.: 26RG-20
Length: 6'9"
No. Pieces: 1
No. Guides: 5 Aftco roller; 4 Varmac plus 1
Aftco
Tip Top: Aftco roller
Action: 20 lb. class
Handle: Wood.

Model No.: 26RG-50
Length: 6'9"
No. Pieces: 1
No. Guides: 5 Aftco roller; 4 Varmac plus 1
Aftco Stripper
Tip Top: Aftco roller
Action: 50 lb. class
Handle: Wood or aluminum

Model No.: 26RG-80
Length: 6'9"
No. Pieces: 1
No. Guides: 5 Mildrum roller; 4 Varmac
plus 1 Aftco stripper
Tip Top: Mildrum roller
Action: 80 lb. class

Handle: Wood or aluminum.

Model No.: 26RG-130
Length: 6'9"
No. Pieces: 1
No. Guides: 5 Mildrum roller; 4 Varmac plus
1 Mildrum stripper
Tip Top: Mildrum roller
Action: 130 lb. class
Handle: Wood or aluminum.

Model No.: 26RG-180
Length: 6'9"
No. Pieces: 1
No. Guides: 5 Mildrum roller; 4 Varmac plus
1 Mildrum stripper
Tip Top: Mildrum roller
Action: 180 lb. class
Handle: Wood or aluminum.

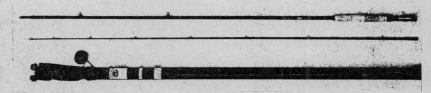

Fiberglass Series

Scientific Anglers/3M

Fiberglass Fly Rods

Model No.: System 4
Length: 7'2"
No. Pieces: 2
No. Guides: Not specified; hand chrome-
plated stainless steel guides plus one
carboloy stripping guide
Tip Top: Hard chrome-plated stainless steel
Rec. Line: 4 wt.
Handle: Lightweight anodized aluminum
reel seat, double lock rings, specie cork
comfort grip.

Model No.: System 5. Same as Model System
4 except:
Length: 7'7"
Rec. Line: 5 wt.

Model No.: System 6. Same as Model System
4 except:
Length: 8'1"
Rec. Line: 6 wt.

Model No.: System 7. Same as Model System
4 except:
Length: 8'5"
Rec. Line: 7 wt.

Model No.: System 8. Same as Model System
4 except:
Length: 8'8"
Rec. Line: 8 wt.

Model No.: System 9. Same as Model System
4 except:
Length: 8'11"
Rec. Line: 9 wt.

Model No.: System 10. Same as Model
System 4 except:
Length: 9'1"
Rec. Line: 10 wt.

Model No.: System 11. Same as Model

System 4 except:
Length: 9'3"
Rec. Line: 11 wt.

Graphite Fly Rods

Model No.: System G4
Length: 7'11"
No. Pieces: 2
Tip Top: Chrome-plated stainless steel
Rec. Line: 4

Model No.: System G5. Same as Model No.
System G4 except:
Length: 8'3"
Rec. Line: 5

Model No.: System G6. Same as Model No.
System G4 except:
Length: 8'7"
Rec. Line: 6

Model No.: System G7. Same as Model No.
System G4 except:
Length: 8'4"
Rec. Line: 7

Model No.: System G8. Same as Model No.
System G4 except:
Length: 8'9"
Rec. Line: 8

Model No.: System G9. Same as Model No.
System G4 except:
Length: 9'4"
Rec. Line: 9

Model No.: System G10. Same as Model No.
System G4 except:
Length: 9'5"
Rec. Line: 10

Shakespeare

Spinning Rods

Model No.: SP200
Length: 5½', 6½', 7'
No. Guides: 5 aluminum oxide
Tip Top: Aluminum oxide
Rec. Lure Wt.: 5½' rods: ¼-⅝ oz.
6½', 7' rods: ⅛-⅜ oz.
Action: 5½' rods: medium
6½', 7' rods: all purpose

Model No.: GF II—Graflite
Length: 5'
No. Guides: 4 stainless steel
Tip Top: Stainless steel
Action: Ultra-light
Handle: Anodized aluminum reel seats;
sliding hoods with locking ring.

Model No.: SP 508 UL
Length: 5'

Shakespeare (con't.)

No. Pieces: 2
No. Guides: 4 gold plated
Tip Top: Gold plated
Rec. Lure Wt.: ¹⁄₁₆-¼ oz.
Action: Ultra-light

Model No.: SP608
Length: 6½', 7'0"
No. Pieces: 2
No. Guides: 5 gold-plated, stainless steel,
  wire frame
Tip Top: Carbide
Rec. Lure Wt.: ⅛-⅜ oz.
Action: All purpose
Handle: Cork grip with plastic forecap and
  butt cap.

Model No.: SP708
Length: 6½', 7'0"
No. Pieces: 2
No. Guides: 5 carbide ring, wire frame,
  Mildrum
Tip Top: Carbide ring, wire frame
Rec. Lure Wt.: ⅛-⅜ oz.
Action: All purpose
Handle: Reel seat—black barrel, natural
  hoods and two locking rings, specie cork
  grip with plastic forecap and butt cap.

Model No.: SP 860
Length: 8½'
No. Guides: 7
Rec. Lure Wt.: ¼-⅝ oz.
Action: Medium

Model No.: BWS 555
Length: 9'
No. Pieces: 2
No. Guides: 5 stainless steel
Tip Top: Carbide
Action: Heavy
Handle: Cork foregrip and reargrip chrome
  brass reel seat with two locking rings.

Model No.: BWS 595
Length: 6', 6½', 7'
No. Pieces: 2
No. Guides: 6', 6½' rods: 4; 7' rods: 5
  stainless steel
Tip Top: Carbide
Action: Medium
Handle: Cork foregrip; reel seat.

Model No.: SS 745
Length: 8'
No. Pieces: 2
No. Guides: 4 stainless steel wire frame
Tip Top: Stainless steel
Action: Universal
Handle: Cork reargrip and foregrip; two
  locking rings; sliding hood reel seat.

Model No.: PRC 70
Length: 7'
No. Pieces: 4
No. Guides: 4 wire framed stainless steel
Tip Top: Wire framed stainless steel
Rec. Lure Wt.: ⅛-⅜ oz.
Action: All purpose
Handle: Convertible for spinning or fly reel.

Bait-Casting Rods

Model No.: BC 200
Length: 5½', 6'
No. Pieces: 1
No. Guides: 5 aluminum oxide

Tip Top: Aluminum oxide
Rec. Lure Wt.: ⅜-⅝ oz.
Action: Medium
Handle: Pistol grip.

Model No.: GF II BC—Graflite
Length: 5'8"
No. Guides: 5 aluminum oxide
Tip Top: Aluminum oxide
Action: Heavy
Handle: Double offset-pistol grip.

Model No.: BC 708
Length: 5½', 6'
No. Guides: 5 aluminum oxide
Tip Top: Aluminum oxide
Rec. Lure Wt.: ⅜-⅝ oz.
Action: Medium
Handle: Detachable pistol grip.

Model No.: BC 11
Length: 3', 4', 5'
No. Guides: 3' rods: 1; 4', 5' rods: 2; all
  chromed stainless steel
Tip Top: Chromed stainless steel
Rec. Lure Wt.: 3', 4' rods: ¼-¾ oz.
              5 rods: ⅜-⅝ oz.
Action: 3' rods: heavy
        4' rods: medium heavy
        5' rods: medium

Model No.: PB160
Length: 6'
No. Pieces: 2
No. Guides: 3 chrome-plated steel, stamped
  frame
Tip Top: Chrome-plated steel, stamped frame
Rce. Lure Wt.: ⅛-⅜ oz.
Action: All purpose
Handle: Double offset non-detachable
  handle with black butt cap, specie cork
  grip.

Model No.: PB408
Length. 6', 6½'
No. Pieces: 2
No. Guides: 4 stamped frame, chrome-plated
Tip Top: Stamped frame, chrome-plated
Rec. Lure Wt.: ⅛-⅜ oz.
Action: All purpose
Handle: Non-detachable, double offset,
  Reel-Tyte-Lock, cork grip, black plastic
  butt cap.

Model No.: PB508
Length. 6', 6½'
No. Pieces: 2
No. Guides: 5 stamped frame, stainless steel,
  gold-plated
Tip Top: Stamped frame, stainless steel,
  gold-plated
Rec. Lure Wt.: ⅛-⅜ oz.
Action: All purpose
Handle: Specie cork grip, black plastic
  fore cap and butt cap.

Fly Rods

Model No.: GF II FY—Graflite
Length: 7½', 8' 8½', 9'
No. Pieces: 2
No. Guides: 7½', 8', 8½' rods: 7; 9' rods: 8;
  all stainless steel snake
Tip Top: Stainless steel
Rec. Line: 7½' rods: 5
           8' rods: 6
           8½' rods: 8
           9' rods: 9
Rec. Lure Wt.: 7½' rods: 1⅝ oz.
               8' rods: 1¾ oz.

  8½' rods: 3⅞ oz.
  9' rods: 4 oz.
Handle: Specie cork grip.

Model No.: FTP 8
Length: 8'
No. Pieces: 6
No. Guides: 6
Rec. Line: #7

Model No.: FY708
Length: 7'6", 8'0", 8'6"
No. Pieces: 2
No. Guides: 7½' rods: 6; 8½' rods: 7; all
  stainless steel snake guides plus one wire
  frame stainless stripper guide
Tip Top: Stainless steel
Rec. Line: 7½' rods: 6; 8½' rods: 7
Handle: Cork grip, black barrel reel seat
  with single lock ring.

Model No.: FY 608
Length: 8', 8½', 9'
No. Pieces: 2
No. Guides: 8' rods: 6; 8½', 9' rods: 7;
  gold-plated stainless steel
Tip Top: Gold-plated stainless steel
Rec. Line: 8' rod: 7
           8½' rod: 8
           9' rod: 9
Handle: Reel seat with gold hood and lock
  ring.

Model No.: FY200
Length: 7½', 8½'
No. Pieces: Not specified
No. Guides: 7½' rods: 6; 8½' rods: 7; all
  aluminum oxide stripper
Tip Top: Not specified
Rec. Line: 8
Handle: Specie cork grip.

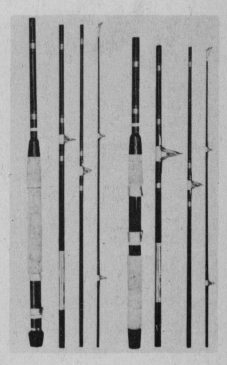

Model No. PRC 70   Model No. PRC 66

Shakespeare (con't.)

Popping Rods

Model No.: BWC 160
Length: 7'
No. Pieces: 1
No. Guides: 5 stainless steel wire frame
Tip Top: Carbide
Action: Light
Handle: Specie cork reargrip and foregrip;
   sliding hood reel seat.

Model No.: SS 166
Length: 7½'
No. Pieces: 1
No. Guides: 5 ceramic
Tip Top: Ceramic
Action: Light

Sportfishing Rods

Model No.: BWC 615
Length: 6'
No. Pieces: 1
No. Guides: 7 hard-crome wire frame
Tip Top: Hard-chrome wire frame
Handle: Hypalon fore and reargrip; two
   locking rings.

Model No.: BWS 617. Same as Model BWC
   615 except:
Length: 7'
No. Guides: 7 stainless steel spinning
Tip Top: Carbide

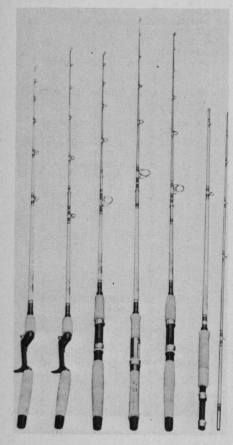

508 Series

Salmon/Steelhead Rods

Model No.: BWC 610
Length: 8'3"
No. Guides: 7 conventional stainless steel
Tip Top: Carbide
Handle: Reversed reel seat with two locking
   rings; cork fore and reargrips.

Model No.: BWS 611. Same as Model BWC
   610 except:
No. Guides: Stainless steel spinning

Telescopic Rod

Model No.: STP 6
Length: 6'
No. Pieces: 6
No. Guides: 3
Rec. Lure Wt.: ⅛-⅜ oz.
Action: All purpose
Handle: Specie cork.

Skyline

Spinning Rods

Model No.: SKS5502-graphite
Length: 5½'
Guides: Stainless steel
Tip Top: Ceramic
Rec. Line: 4-10
Rec. Lure Wt.: ¹⁄₁₆-¼ oz.
Action: Extra light
Handle: Fuji; reel locks.

Model No.: SKS5505-graphite
Length: 5½'
Guides: Stainless steel
Tip Top: Ceramic
Rec. Line: 8-14
Rec. Lure Wt.: ⅛-⅜ oz.
Action: Medium
Handle: Fuji; reel locks.

Model No.: SKS6503-graphite
Length: 6½'
Guides: Stainless steel
Tip Top: Ceramic
Rec. Line: 6-17
Rec. Lure Wt.: ⅛-½ oz.
Action: Light
Handle: Fuji; reel locks.

Model No.: SKHS8505-graphite (steelhead)
Length: 8½'
Guides: Stainless steel
Tip Top: Ceramic
Rec. Line: 8-30
Rec. Lure Wt.: ¼-1¾ oz.
Action: Medium
Handle: Fuji; reel seats and locks.

Casting Rods

Model No.: SKC5508-graphite
Length: 5½'
Rec. Line: 12-30
Rec. Lure Wt.: ¼-1⅝ oz.
Action: Medium

Model No.: SKC5512-graphite
Length: 5½'
No. Pieces: 1
Guides: Ceramic
Rec. Line: 14-30
Rec. Lure Wt.: ⅜-1¾ oz.

Action: Heavy
Handle: Fuji; reel locks.

Model No.: SKC6004-graphite
Length: 6'
No. Pieces: 1
Guides: Ceramic
Rec. Line: 8-20
Rec. Lure Wt.: ¼-¾ oz.
Action: Light
Handle: Fuji; reel locks.

Fly Rods

Model No.: SKF7005-graphite
Length: 7'
No. Pieces: 2
Guides: Ceramic stripper and snake
Rec. Line: 4-6
Action: Power
Handle: Cork; reel seats and locks.

Model No.: SKF8007-graphite. Same as Model
   No. SKF7005-graphite except:
Length: 8'
Rec. Line: 5-8
Action: Light tip

Model No.: SKF8508-graphite. Same as Model
   No. SKF7005-graphite except:
Length: 8½'
Rec. Line: 6-9
Action: Full

Model No.: SKF9010-graphite. Same as Model
   No. SKF7005 except:
Length: 9'
Rec. Line: 10-11

Spinmaster

Spinning Rods

Model: C31
Length: 6½'
No. Pieces: 1
Guides: 5 stainless steel flex
Action: Medium-light
Handle: Cork; chrome reel seat with double
   locking nuts.

Model No.: C34. Same as Model No. C31
   except:
Length: 7'
No. Pieces: 2
Action: Medium

Model No.: SP-5
Length: 7½'
No. Pieces: 2
No. Guides: 4 stainless steel flex
Action: Medium-heavy
Handle: Cork butt and foregrip; anodized
   aluminum reel seat.

Model No.: 1000-1B
Length: 5½'
No. Pieces: 2
No. Guides: Chrome plated glass bridge
Action: Ultra-light
Handle: Cork butt and foregrip; anodized
   aluminum or chrome over brass reel seat.

Model No.: 6606-F
Length: 6½'
No. Pieces: 1
No. Guides: 4 Fuji Speed ring
Action. Medium

Spinmaster (con't.)

Handle: Chrome over brass double locking reel seats.

Model No.: 204B
Length: 6½'
No. Pieces: 2
No. Guides: Chrome over brass braced
Action: Light
Handle: Anodized aluminum reel seats.

Model No.: 211. Same as Model No. 204B except:
No. Pieces: 1
No. Guides: 4 stainless steel flex
Action: Medium-light

Model No.: 216B
Length: 7'
No. Pieces: 2
No. Guides: 5 chrome over brass braced
Action: Medium
Handle: Anodized aluminum reel seats.

Model No.: 244. Same as Model No. 216B except:
Length: 8'
No. Guides: Stainless steel flex
Action: Heavy

Spincast Rods

Model No.: 3400
Length: 6'
No. Pieces: 2
Action: Light
Handle: Chrome over brass reel seat.

Model No.: 6055-F
Length: 5½'
No. Pieces. 1
No. Guides: 6 Fuji Speed ring
Action: Worm
Handle: Featherweight with rubber grip.

Model No.: 8000-B
Length: 6½'
No. Pieces: 2
No. Guides: 4 chrome-plated brass bridge
Action: Medium
Handle: Cork butt and foregrip; anodized aluminum reel seats.

Surfing Rods

Model No.: 248B
Length: 9'
No. Pieces: 2
No. Guides: Chrome over brass braced
Action: Medium
Handle: Anodized aluminum reel seats.

Model No.: 274
Length: 11½'
No. Pieces: 2
No. Guides: 4 stainless steel flex
Action: Heavy
Handle: Chrome over brass reel seat.

Model No.: 5000-5B
Length: 8½'
No. Pieces: 2
No. Guides: 4 chrome plated brass bridge
Action: Heavy
Handle: Cork butt and foregrip; chrome over brass reel seats.

Trolling Rods

Model No.: 6/0 STD
Length: 6½'
No. Pieces: 2
No. Guides: 4 SE boat rod
Tip Top: Roller
Action: 20-30 lb.
Handle: Chrome over brass reel seat; gimbal butt.

Model No.: 9/0 DX. Same as Model No. 6/0 STD except:
No. Guides: 4 stainless steel roller
Action: 50-80 lb.

Model No.: 30-50
Length: 6½'
No. Guides: 4 Tycoon roller
Tip Top: Tycoon roller
Action: 30-50 lb.
Handle: Chrome over brass reel seat; gimbal butt.

Model No.: VT-80
No. Guides: 5 Tycoon-Fin-nor aluminum frame roller
Tip Top: Roller
Handle: Varmac locking reel seat; aluminum butt; naugahyde foregrip.

Boat Rods

Model No.: D14
Length: 6'
No. Pieces: 2
No. Guides: SE boat rod
Action: Light
Handle: Chrome over brass reel seat.

Model No.: D22GC. Same as Model No. D14 except:
Length: 6½'
Action: Medium
Handle: Gimbal butt.

Popping Rod

Model No.: 270
Length: 7'
No. Pieces: 1
No. Guides: 5 stainless steel flex
Action: Heavy
Handle: Chrome over brass reel seat.

Tycoon/Fin-Nor

Spinning Rods

Model No.: HRH Light
No. Pieces: 1 or 2
No. Guides: 5 perfection ring
Tip Top: Stainless perfection ring
Handle: Cork; screw-locking seats.

Model No.: HRH Medium-Heavy
No. Pieces: 1 or 2
No. Guides: 5 perfection ring
Tip Top: Stainless steel perfection ring
Handle: Cork; screw-locking seats.

Trolling Rods

Model No.: HRH #12
No. Guides: 5 Aftco roller
Tip Top: Stainless roller
Handle: Aluminum butt.

Model No.: HRH #20
No. Guides: 5 nylon roller
Tip Top: Stainless roller
Handle: Aluminum butt.

Model No.: HRH #30, #50
No. Guides: 5 nylon roller
Tip Top: Stainless roller
Handle: Aluminum butt or curved aluminum butt.

Model No.: HRH #80, #130
No. Guides: 5 aluminum roller
Tip Top: Aluminum roller
Handle: Aluminum butt or curved aluminum butt.

Model No.: Regal #20, #30, #50, #80
No. Guides: 5 roller
Tip Top: Stainless steel roller

Zebco

Spinning Rods

Model No.: 4443
Length: 4'10"
No. Pieces: 3
No. Guides: 3 chrome-plated stainless steel
Tip Top: Chrome-plated stainless steel
Action: Light (for light freshwater)
Handle: Specie cork butt and foregrip; aluminum reel seat, hoods and locking ring.

Model No.: 4470. Same as Model No. 4443 except:
Length: 6'
No. Pieces: 2
Action: Medium (for medium-freshwater fishing)

Model No.: 7050 (Sundowner rod series)
Length: 5½'
No. Pieces: 2
No. Guides: 4 hard crome-plated stainless steel
Tip Top: Hard chrome-plated stainless steel
Rec. Lure Wt.: Not specified
Action: Light (for light freshwater)
Handle: Permanent ABS butt caps; flared for greater cushioning.

Model No.: 7400. Same as Model 7050 except:
Length: 6½'
Action: Medium (for all-around freshwater fishing)

Model No.: 7500
Length: 7'
No. Pieces: 2
No. Guides: 5 chrome-plated stainless steel
Tip Top: Chrome-plated stainless steel
Action: Medium-heavy (for light saltwater/heavy freshwater)
Handle: Specie cork butt and foregrip; anodized aluminum reel seat; chromed brass hoods and double locking rings.

Model No.: 7900. Same as model 7050 except:
Length: 9'
Action: Heavy-action surf

Model No.: 7051. Centennial rod series
Length: 5½'
No. Pieces: 2

Zebco (con't.)

No. Guides: 4 hard-chrome-plated stainless steel
Tip Top: Hard chrome-plated stainless steel
Rec. Lure Wt.: Not specified
Action: Light (for light freshwater)
Handle: Aluminum, with butt grips and foregrips of specie cork.

Model No.: 7101. Same as Model 7051 except:
Length: 6'
No. Guides: 3
Action: Medium (for medium-light freshwater fishing)

Model No.: PS20 (Pro Staff series)
Length: 5½'
No. Pieces: 2
No. Guides: 4 aluminum oxide slipstream
Tip Top: Aluminum oxide
Rec. Lure Wt.: Not specified
Action: Light
Handle: Burnt cork; flared butt molded into the rod handle.

Model No.: PS21. Same as Model PS20 except:
Length: 6½'
Action: Light-medium

Model No.: PS24. Same as Model PS20 except:
Length: 7'
Action: Medium-heavy

Model No.: PS81
Length: 8'
No. Pieces: 1
No. Guides: 5 stainless steel (3 bridged)
Tip Top: Carbide
Action: Heavy (for medium-to-heavy saltwater fishing)
Handle: Specie cork butt and foregrip; chromed brass reel seat; hoods and double lock rings.

Spin-Casting Rods

Model No.: 6300. Deluxe, 6200. (Sundowner rod series)
Length: 6'
No. Pieces: 2
No. Guides: 5 hard gold-plated stainless steel
Tip Top: Hard gold-plated stainless steel
Rec. Lure Wt.: Not specified
Action: Medium (for all freshwater fishing)
Handle: Permanent ABS butt caps; flared for greater cushioning.

Model No.: 8900. Same as Model 6200 except:
Length: 7'
Guides: Chrome-plated stainless steel
Tip Top: Carbide
Action: Heavy (for heavy freshwater; light saltwater fishing)
Handle: Specie cork.

Model No.: 8900. Same as Model 6200 except:
Length: 5½'
No. Pieces: 1
Action: Heavy (for bass fishing)

Model No.: 4002
Length: 30"
No. Pieces: 1
No. Guides: 1 chrome plated stainless steel
Tip Top: Chrome plated stainless steel
Action: Light (for crappie fishing)
Handle: Offset with clip and screw reel lock; cork butt grip and plastic butt cap.

Model No.: 4044
Length: 5'
No. Pieces: 2
No. Guides: 2 chrome plated stainless steel
Tip Top: Chrome plated stainless steel
Action: Extra-heavy (for pier, boat and jetty fishing)
Handle: Aluminum reel seat, hoods and locking ring; plastic forecap; protective rubber butt cushion.

Model No.: 4060 (Centennial rod series)
Length: 5½'
No. Pieces: 2
No. Guides: 3 hard chrome-plated stainless steel
Tip Top: Hard chrome-plated stainless steel
Rec. Lure Wt.: Not specified
Action: Medium (for medium freshwater fishing)
Handle: Cork butt and foregrip.

Model No.: 4076
Length: 4½'
No. Pieces: 1
No. Guides: 2 chromed wire
Tip Top: Chromed wire
Action: Light (for light freshwater fishing)
Handle: Offset with clip and screw reel lock; cork butt grip.

Model No.: 8406. Same as Model 4060 except:
Length: 5½'
Action: Worm (for worm fishing; deep jigging)

Model No.: 8800. Same as Model 4060 except:

Length: 6'
No. Guides: 4
Action: Heavy (for medium-heavy freshwater fishing)

Model No.: 8965. Same as Model 8800 except:
Length: 6½'
Action: Heavy (for light saltwater; heavy freshwater fishing)

Model No.: 6100. Same as Model 8800 except:
Action: Medium (for medium-light freshwater fishing)

Model No.: 6104
Length: 6'
No. Pieces: 4
No. Guides: 4 chrome plated stainless steel
Tip Top: Chrome plated stainless steel
Action: Medium (for all freshwater fishing)
Handle: Aluminum offset with plunger screw and clip reel lock; specie cork butt and foregrip.

Model No.: PS10 (Pro Staff series)
Length: 6'
No. Pieces: 2
No. Guides: 5 slipstream
Tip Top: Aluminum oxide
Rec. Lure Wt.: Not specified
Action: Medium
Handle: Burnt cork; flared butt molded into the rod handle.

Model No.: PS30. Same as Model PS10 except:
Length: 5'
No. Guides: 4
Action: Worm-action

Fly Rods

Model No.: PS40 (Pro Staff series)
Length: 8'
No. Pieces: 2
No. Guides: 5 hard-chromed stainless steel
Tip Top: Aluminum oxide
Rec. Line: #6-#7
Action: Trout
Handle: Anodized aluminum reel seat, hoods and double locking rings; burnt cork butt grip; ABS shock ring inserts.

Model No.: PS42. Same as Model No. PS40 except:
Length: 8½'
Rec. Line: #8
Action: Bass

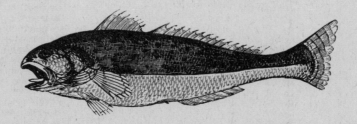

Graphite Rods

Spinning Rods

Mfr.: Eagle Claw
Model No.: GS
Length: 7′, 8½′, 9′
No. Pieces: 2
No. Guides: 5
Tip Top: Ceramic
Rec. Line: 7′ rods: 4-12
8½′ rods: 10-20
9′ rods: 15-25
Action: 7′ rods: light, medium
8½′ rods: medium
9′ rods: power
Handle: Standard cork.

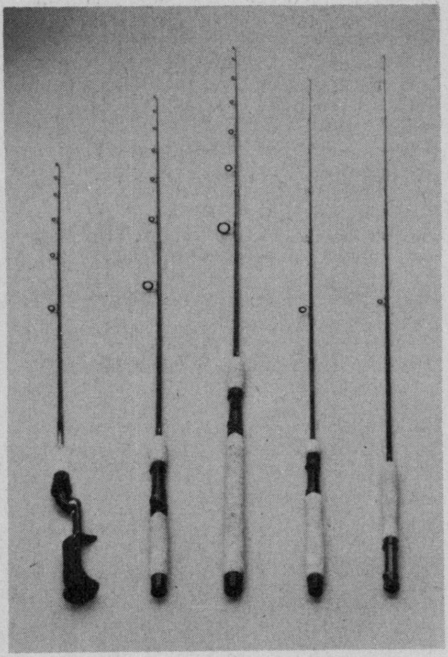

Eagle Claw Blue Diamond Graphite Rods

Mfr.: Fenwick
Model No.: GFS70
Length: 7′
No. Guides: Foul-proof
Tip Top: Ceramic
Rec. Lure Wt.: ¼-½ oz.
Action: Light
Handle: Cork body reel seat; cork grip.

Mfr.: Fenwick
Model No.: GFS83
Length: 8′3″
No. Pieces: 2
No. Guides: Ceramic
Tip Top: Carbide
Rec. Lure Wt.: ¼-⅝ oz.
Action: Light
Handle: Cork body reel seats.

Mfr.: Fenwick
Model No.: G145
Length: 4½′
No. Pieces: 1
No. Guides: Aluminum oxide

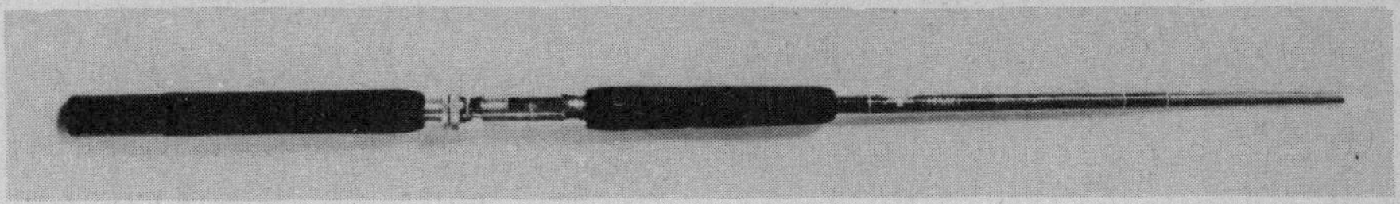

Fenwick Trolling Graphite Rod

Tip Top: Aluminum oxide
Rec. Line: 1-4
Rec. Lure Wt.: 1⁄16-¼ oz.
Action: Ultra-light
Handle: Cork grip with sliding rings.

Mfr.: James Heddon's Sons
Model No.: 8016
Length: 5′8″
No. Pieces: 1
No. Guides: 5 aluminum oxide
Tip Top: Aluminum oxide
Rec. Line: #6-#20
Rec. Lure Wt.: ⅜-⅝ oz.
Action: Medium

Mfr.: Orvis
Model No.: M9251-1
Length: 5′
Tip Top: Ceramic
Rec. Line: 2 wt.
Rec. Lure Wt.: 1⁄16-¼ oz.
Handle: Cork.

Mfr.: Orvis
Model No.: M9267-1
Length: 6½′
Tip Top: Ceramic
Rec. Line: 6 wt.
Rec. Lure Wt.: 3⁄16-⅝ oz.
Handle: Cork.

Mfr.: Orvis
Model No.: M9272-1
Length: 7′
Tip Top: Ceramic
Rec. Line: 12 wt.
Rec. Lure Wt.: ½-2 oz.
Handle: Cork.

Mfr.: Shakespeare
Model No.: GF II
Length: 5′
No. Guides: 4 stainless steel
Tip Top: Stainless steel
Action: Ultra-light
Handle: Anodized aluminum reel seats; sliding hoods with locking ring.

Mfr.: Skyline
Model No.: SKS5502
Length: 5½′
Guides: Stainless steel
Tip Top: Ceramic
Rec. Line: 4-10
Rec. Lure Wt.: 1⁄16-¼ oz.
Action: Extra light
Handle: Fuji; reel locks.

Mfr.: Skyline
Model No.: SKS5505
Length: 5½′
Guides: Stainless steel
Top Top: Ceramic
Rec. Line: 8-14
Rec. Lure Wt.: ⅛-⅜ oz.
Action: Medium
Handle: Fuji; reel locks.

Mfr.: Skyline
Model No.: SKS6503
Length: 6½′
Guides: Stainless steel
Tip Top: Ceramic
Rec. Line: 6-17
Rec. Lure Wt.: ⅛-½ oz.
Action: Light
Handle: Fuji; reel locks.

Mfr.: Skyline
Model No.: SKHS8505
Length: 8½′
No. Guides: Stainless steel
Tip Top: Ceramic
Rec. Line: 8-30
Rec. Lure Wt.: ¼-1¾ oz.
Action: Medium
Handle: Fuji; reel seats and locks.

Fresh Water Spinning Rods

Mfr.: James Heddon's Sons
Model No.: 8002
Length: 5½′
No. Pieces: 1
No. Guides: 5 aluminum oxide
Tip Top: Aluminum oxide
Rec. Line: #8-#25
Rec. Lure Wt.: ⅜-⅝ oz.
Action: Medium
Handle: Modern.

Mfr.: James Heddon's Sons
Model No.: 8004. Same as Model No. 8002 except:
Rec. Lure Wt.: ⅜-1 oz.
Action: Medium-heavy

Mfr.: Lamiglas
Model No.: S46UL
Length: 4½′
No. Pieces: 2
No. Guides: Stainless bridged
Tip Top: Aluminum oxide
Rec. Line: 2-6
Rec. Lure Wt.: 1⁄16-¼ oz.
Action: Ultra-light
Handle: Specie cork; lightweight sliding lock rings.

Mfr.: Lamiglas
Model No.: S56UL
Length: 5½′
No. Pieces: 2
No. Guides: Stainless bridged
Rec. Line: 4-8
Rec. Lure Wt.: ¼-⅜ oz.
Action: Ultra-light
Handle: Specie cork; lightweight sliding lock rings.

Mfr.: Lamiglas
Model No.: S66L
Length: 6½′
No. Pieces: 2
No. Guides: Stainless bridged
Rec. Line: 4-10

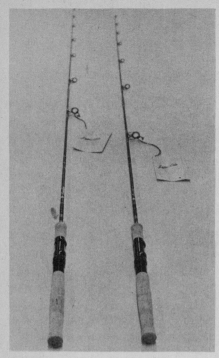

Lamiglas Fresh Water Spinning Rods

Rec. Lure Wt.: ⅛-¼ oz.
Action: Light
Handle: Specie cork.

Mfr.: Lamiglas
Model No.: S66M
Length: 6½'
No. Guides: Lightweight stainless bridged; aluminum oxide cores
Tip Top: Aluminum oxide
Rec. Line: 8-12
Rec. Lure Wt.: ¼-⅜ oz.

Mfr.: Lamiglas
Model No.: S701. Same as Model No. S66 except:
Length: 7'

Mfr.: Lamiglas
Model No.: S70L
Length: 7'
No. Pieces: 2
No. Guides: Stainless bridged
Tip Top: Aluminum oxide
Rec. Line: 4-10
Rec. Lure Wt.: ⅛-¼ oz.
Action: Light

Mfr.: Lamiglas
Model No.: WS68ML
Length: 5'8"
Rec. Line: 8-17
Rec. Lure Wt.: ¼-⅝ oz.
Action: Worm

Mfr.: Pflueger
Model No.: G11OS
Length: 5', 6½'
No. Pieces: 2
No. Guides: 5' rods: 4 stainless steel; 6½' rods: 5 ceramic
Tip Top: 5' rods: stainless steel; 6½' rods: ceramic
Action: 5' rods: ultralight

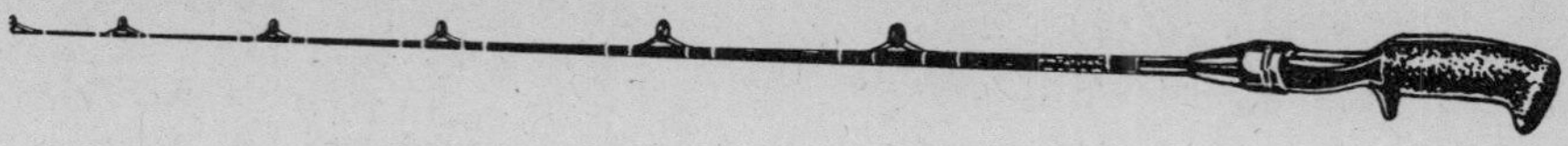

Pflueger G110B

6½' rods: medium
Handle: Specie cork grips; aluminum locking rings.

Mfr.: Skyline
Model No.: SKC5512
Length: 5½'
No. Pieces: 1
Guides: Ceramic
Rec. Line: 14-30
Rec. Lure Wt.: ⅜-1¾ oz.
Action: Heavy
Handle: Fuji; reel locks.

Mfr.: Skyline
Model No.: SKC5508. Same as Model No. SK5512 except:
Rec. Line: 12-30
Rec. Lure Wt.: ¼-1⅝ oz.
Action: Medium

Mfr.: Skyline
Model No.: SKC6004
Length: 6'
No. Pieces: 1
Guides: Ceramic
Rec. Line: 8-20
Rec. Lure Wt.: ¼-¾ oz.
Action: Light
Handle: Fuji; reel locks.

Spin Casting Rods

Mfr.: Eagle Claw
Model No.: GC
Length: 5½'
No. Pieces: 1
No. Guides: 5 wire-frame ceramic
Tip Top: Ceramic
Rec. Line: 10-12, 8-12
Action: Light; ultra-light
Handle: Pistol comfort grips.

Mfgr.: Fenwick
Model No.: GFC554
Length: 5½'
No. Pieces: 1
No. Guides: Ceramic
Rec. Line: 8-15
Action: Medium

Mfr.: Lamiglas
Model No.: SC56
Length: 5½'
No. Guides: Lightweight stainless steel
Tip Top: Aluminum oxide
Rec. Line: 8-10
Rec. Lure Wt.: ¼-⅜ oz.
Action: Light
Handle: Vinyl pistol grips.

Mfr.: Lamiglas
Model No.: SC501. Same as Model No. SC56 except:
Length: 5'10"

Bait Casting

Mfr.: Fenwick

Model No.: GFC555
Length: 5½'
No. Pieces: 1
No. Guides: Aluminum oxide
Tip Top: Aluminum oxide
Rec. Lure Wt.: ½-1 oz.
Action: Medium

Mfr.: Fenwick
Model No.: GFC605
Length: 6'
No. Pieces: 1
No. Guides: Aluminum oxide
Tip Top: Aluminum oxide
Rec. Lure Wt.: ½-1 oz.
Action: Medium

Mfr.: Fenwick
Model No.: GFC557
Length: 5½'
No. Pieces: 1
No. Guides: Ceramic
Tip Top: Ceramic
Rec. Lure Wt.: ⅝-1⅝ oz.
Action: Fast tip; extra power
Handle: Hypalon foregrip with cork rear grips and heavy duty notched tempered aluminum butt ferrules. Detachable soft plastic butt cap.

Mfr.: Fenwick
Model No.: GFC556
Length: 5½'
No. Pieces: 1
No. Guides: Ceramic
Tip Top: Ceramic
Rec. Lure Wt.: ⅝-1¼ oz.
Action: Extra-power
Handle: Hypalon foregrips with cork rear grips and heavy duty notched tempered aluminum butt ferrules. Detachable soft plastic butt cap.

Mfr.: Pflueger
Model No.: G110B
Length: 5'8"
No. Pieces: 1
No. Guides: 5 ceramic
Tip Top: Ceramic
Action: Medium
Handle: Pistol grip detachable.

Mfr.: Shakespeare
Model No.: GF II BC
Length: 5'8"
No. Guides: 5 aluminum oxide
Tip Top: Aluminum oxide
Action: Heavy
Handle: Double offset-pistol grip.

Steelhead Casting Rod

Mfr.: Fenwick
Model No.: GFS83C
Length: 8'3"
No. Pieces: 2
No. Guides: Aluminum oxide

Tip Top: Aluminum oxide
Rec. Line: 8-20
Rec. Lure Wt.: ¼-⅝ oz.
Action: Steelhead
Handle: Cork body reel seat.

Fly Rods

Mfr.: Cortland
Model: C-G
Length: 7', 7½', 8', 8½', 9'
No. Guides: 7 aluminum oxide
Rec. Line: 7' rods: 4 or 5
      7½' rods: 5 or 6
      8' rods: 6 or 7
      8½' rods: 7 or 8
      9' rods: 8 or 9

Mfr.: Eagle Claw
Model No.: GF
Length: 7', 7½', 8', 8½', 9'
No. Pieces: 2
No. Guides: 7', 7½', 8' rods: 6 snake and 1
wire frame ceramic; 9' rods: 7 snake and
1 wire frame ceramic
Tip Top: Ceramic
Rec. Line: 7' rods: 5
      7½' rods: 6
      8' rods: 4, 5, 6, 7
      8½' rods: 8
      9' rods: 10
Handle: Extended cork handle.

Mfr.: Fenwick
Model No.: GFF-634
Length: 6½'
No. Pieces: 2
No. Guides: Hard-chromed snake
Rec. Line: 4
Handle: Cork body reel seat.

Mfr.: Fenwick
Model No.: GFF-704
Length: 7'
No. Pieces: 2
No. Guides: Ceramic stripping and chrome-
plated snake
Rec. Line: 4
Handle: Cork body reel seat.

Mfr.: Fenwick
Model No.: GFF-755
Length: 7½'
No. Pieces: 2
No. Guides: Ceramic stripping and
chrome-plated snake
Rec. Line: 4 or 5
Handle: Cork body reel seat.

Mfr.: Fenwick
Model No.: GFF-805. Same as Model No.
GFF-634 except:
Length: 8'
Rec. Line: 5

Mfr.: Fenwick
Model No.: GFF-905. Same as Model No.
GFF-634 except:
Length: 9'
Rec. Line: 5

Mfr.: Fenwick
Model No.: GFF-756. Same as Model No.
GFF-634 except:
Length: 7½'
Rec. Line: 6

Mfr.: Fenwick
Model No.: GFF-806. Same as Model No.

GFF-634 except:
Length: 8'
Rec. Line: 6

Mfr.: Fenwick
Model No.: GFF-856. Same as Model No.
GFF-634 except:
Length: 8½'
Rec. Line: 6

Mfr.: Fenwick
Model No.: GFF-857. Same as Model No.
GFF-634 except:
Length: 8½'
Rec. Line: 7

Mfr.: Fenwick
Model No.: GFF-858. Same as Model No.
GFF-634 except:
Length: 8½'
Rec. Line: 8

Mfr.: Fenwick
Model No.: GFF-908. Same as Model No.
GFF-634 except:
Length: 9'
Rec. Line: 8
Handle: Detachable extension butt.

Mfr.: Fenwick
Model No.: GFF-1058. Same as Model No.
GFF-634 except:
Length: 10½'
Rec. Line: 8
Handle: 6" detachable extension butt.

Mfr.: Fenwick
Model No.: GFF-9010. Same as Model No.
GFF-634 except:
Length: 9'
Rec. Line: 10
Handle: 6" detachable extension butt.

Mfr.: Fenwick
Model No.: GFF-10511. Same as Model No.
GFF-634 except:
Length: 10½'
Rec. Line: 11
Handle: 6" detachable extension butt.

Mfr.: Fenwick
Model No.: GFF-9012. Same as Model No.
GFF-634 except:
Length: 9'
Rec. Line: 12
Handle: 2" fixed extension butt.

Mfr.: Fenwick
Model No.: GFF-806-4 Graphite Voyageur
Length: 8'
No. Pieces: 4
Rec. Line: 6
Action: Light
Handle: Shaped cork with aluminum reel
seat and double-locking nuts.

Mfr.: Fenwick
Model No.: GFF-857-4 Graphite Voyageur
Length: 8½'
No. Pieces: 4
Rec. Line: 7
Action: Light
Handle: Shaped cork with aluminum reel
seat and double-locking nuts.

Mfr.: Lamiglas
Model No.: F702
Length: 7'
No. Pieces: 2

No. Guides: Hard-chromed stainless steel
Tip Top: Aluminum oxide
Rec. Line: 2-3
Handle: Specie Cork; black anodized
reel seat.

Mfr.: Lamiglas
Model No.: F763. Same as Model No. F702
except:
Length: 7½'
Rec. Line: 3-4

Mfr.: Lamiglas
Model No.: F804. Same as Model No. F702
except:
Length: 8'
Rec. Line: 4-5

Mfr.: Lamiglas
Model No.: F865. Same as Model No. F702
except:
Length: 8½'
Rec. Line: 5-6

Mfr.: Lamiglas
Model No.: F906. Same as Model No. F702
except:
Length: 9'
Rec. Line: 6-7

Mfr.: Lamiglas
Model No.: F912. Same as Model No. F702
except:
Length: 9'
Rec. Line: 12-13

Mfr.: Lamiglas
Model No.: F968. Same as Model No. F702
except:
Length: 9½'
Rec. Line: 8-9

Mfr.: Lamiglas
Model No.: F1008. Same as Model No.
F702 except:
Length: 10'
Rec. Line: 8-9

Mfr.: Lamiglas
Model No.: F1068. Same as Model No.
F702 except:
Length: 10½'
Rec. Line: 8-9

Mfr.: Orvis
Model No.: M9270-1
Length: 7'
No. Guides: Aluminum oxide ceramic
Rec. Line: 5 wt.

Mfr.: Orvis
Model No.: M9279-1
Length: 7'9"
Rec. Line: 5 wt.
Handle: Cork locking reel seat.

Mfr.: Orvis
Model No.: M9280-11
Length: 8'
No. Guides: Aluminum oxide ceramic
Rec. Line: 6 wt.
Handle: Cork locking reel seat.

Mfr.: Orvis
Model No.: M9283-1
Length: 8'3"
Rec. Line: 7 wt.
Handle: Cork locking reel seat.

Mfr.: Orvis
Model No.: M9290-11
Length: 9'
No. Guides: Aluminum oxide ceramic
Rec. Line: 9 wt.
Handle: Metal reel seat; choice of 2" or 6" butt extension.

Mfr.: Pezon et Michel
Model: Parabolic CCC-Light
Length: 7½', 8', 8½', 9'
No. Pieces: 2
Rec. Line: 8', 9' rods: AFTMA #5
7½', 8½' rods: AFTMA #6
Handle: Shaped contour cork handle with 1 ring set and 1 sliding ring reel seat.

Mfr.: Pezon et Michel
Model: Parabolic CCC-Strong
Length: 8½', 9', 10½', 11'
No. Pieces: 2
Rec. Line: 8½', 9' rods: AFTMA #8
10½', 11' rods: AFTMA #9
Action: Strong
Handle: Shaped contour cork handle with 1 ring set and 1 sliding ring reel seat.

Mfr.: Pezon et Michel
Model: Parabolic Saumon CCC
Length: 14'
No. Pieces: 3
Rec. Line: AFTMA #11-12
Handle: Chrome-plated butt and end rings.

Scientific Anglers/3M Graphite Rods

Mfr.: Scientific Anglers/3M
Model No.: System G8. Same as Model No. System G4 except:
Length: 8'9"
Rec. Line: 8

Mfr.: Scientific Anglers/3M
Model No.: System G9. Same as Model No. System G4 except:
Length: 9'4"
Rec. Line: 9

Mfr.: Scientific Anglers/3M
Model No.: System G10. Same as Model No. System G4 except:

Pflueger G110F

Mfr.: Pflueger
Model No.: G110F
Length: 7½', 8', 8½', 9'
No. Pieces: 2
No. Guides: 1 ceramic stripper, 4 stainless steel
Tip Top: Stainless steel
Action: Light to medium
Handle: Standard cork grips.

Mfr.: Scientific Anglers/3M
Model No.: System G4
Length: 7'11"
No. Pieces: 2
Tip Top: Chrome-plated stainless steel
Rec. Line: 4

Mfr.: Scientific Anglers/3M
Model No.: System G5. Same as Model No. System G4 except:
Length: 8'3"
Rec. Line: 5

Mfr.: Scientific Anglers/3M
Model No.: System G6. Same as Model No. System G4 except:
Length: 8'7"
Rec. Line: 6

Mfr.: Scientific Anglers/3M
Model No.: System G7. Same as Model No. System G4 except:
Length: 8'4"
Rec. Line: 7

Length: 9'5"
Rec. Line: 10

Mfr.: Shakespeare
Model No.: GF II FY
Length: 7½', 8', 8½', 9'
No. Pieces: 2
No. of Guides: 7½', 8', 8½' rods: 7; 9' rods: 8; all stainless steel snake
Tip Top: Stainless steel
Rec. Line: 7½' rods: 5
8' rods: 6
8½' rods: 8
9' rods: 9
Rec. Lure Wt.: 7½' rods: 1⅝ oz.
8' rods: 1¾ oz.
8½' rods: 3⅞ oz.
9' rods: 4 oz.
Handle: Specie cork grip.

Mfr.: Skyline
Model No.: SKF7005
Length: 7'
No. Pieces: 2
Guides: Ceramic stripper and snake
Rec. Line: 4-6
Action: Power action
Handle: Cork; reel seats and locks.

Mfr.: Skyline
Model No.: SKF8007. Same as Model No. SKF7005 except:
Length: 8'
Rec. Line: 5-8

Action: Light tip

Mfr.: Skyline
Model No.: SKF8508. Same as Model No. SKF7005 except:
Length: 8½'
Rec. Line: 6-9
Action: Full action

Mfr.: Skyline
Model No.: SKF9010. Same as Model No. SKF7005 except:
Length: 9'
Rec. Line: 10-11

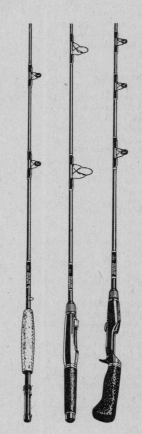

Skyline Graphite Rods

Mooching Rod

Mfr.: Fenwick
Model No.: GFS-91C
Length: 9'
No. Pieces: 2
Rec. Lure Wt.: 1-2½ oz.
Action: Heavy

Steelhead/Salmon/Saltwater Rods

Mfr.: Lamiglas
Model No.: S80LS
Length: 8'
No. Guides: Lightweight stainless steel
Tip Top: Aluminum oxide
Rec. Line: 6-10
Rec. Lure Wt.: ¼-⅜ oz.
Action: Light
Handle: Cork under reel.

Mfr.: Lamiglas
Model No.: S80MS
Length: 8'
No. Guides: Lightweight stainless steel
Tip Top: Aluminum oxide
Rec. Line: 8-12
Rec. Lure Wt.: ⅜-¾ oz.
Action: Medium
Handle: Cork under reel.

Mfr.: Lamiglas
Model No.: S80MHC
Length: 8'
No. Guides: Lightweight stainless steel
Tip Top: Aluminum oxide
Rec. Line: 10-20
Rec. Lure Wt.: ½-1½ oz.
Action: Medium-heavy
Handle: Cork under reel.

Mfr.: Lamiglas
Model No.: S86LS
Length: 8½'
No. Guides: Lightweight stainless steel
Tip Top: Aluminum oxide
Rec. Line: 6-10
Rec. Lure Wt.: ¼-⅜ oz.
Action: Light
Handle: Cork under reel.

Mfr.: Lamiglas
Model No.: S86MC
Length: 8½'
No. Guides: Lightweight stainless steel
Tip Top: Aluminum oxide
Rec. Line: 8-12
Rec. Lure Wt.: ⅜-¾ oz.
Action: Medium
Handle: Cork under reel.

Mfr.: Lamiglas
Model No.: S86MHS
Length: 8½'
No. Guides: Lightweight stainless steel
Tip Top: Aluminum oxide
Rec. Line: 10-20
Rec. Lure Wt.: ½-1½ oz.
Action: Medium-heavy; spinning
Handle: Cork under reel.

Mfr.: Lamiglas
Model No.: S86MHC. Same as Model No.
 S86MHS except:
Action: Medium-heavy; casting

Mfr.: Lamiglas
Model No.: S86SAC
Length: 8½'
No. Guides: Lightweight stainless steel

Tip Top: Aluminum oxide
Rec. Line: 10-30
Rec. Lure Wt.: 1½-4 oz.
Action: Medium-heavy; mooching
Handle: Cork under reel.

Mfr.: Lamiglas
Model No.: S90MHC
Length: 9'
No. Guides: Lightweight stainless steel
Tip Top: Aluminum oxide
Rec. Line: 10-20
Rec. Lure Wt.: ¾-2½ oz.
Action: Medium-heavy
Handle: Cork under reel.

Trolling Rods

Mfr.: Fenwick
Model No.: G-610, G-620, G-630
Length: 6'9"
No. Pieces: 1
No. Guides: Aftco double roller
Tip Top: Aftco roller
Action: Trolling
Handle: Stainless steel with gimbal nock.

Mfr.: Fenwick
Model No.: G-640, G-650, G-660
Length: 6'10"
No. Pieces: 1
No. Guides: Aftco double roller
Tip Top: Aftco roller
Action: Trolling
Handle: Stainless steel with gimbal nock.

Worm Rods

Mfr.: Lamiglas
Model No.: W56L
Length: 5½'
No. Guides: Hard chromed stainless steel;
 aluminum oxide cores
Tip Top: Aluminum oxide
Rec. Line: 10-20
Rec. Lure Wt.: ¼-⅝ oz.
Action: Light
Handle: Vinyl pistol grips.

Mfr.: Lamiglas
Model No.: W56MH
Length: 5½
No. Guides: Hard chromed stainless steel;
 aluminum oxide cores
Tip Top: Aluminum oxide
Rec. Line: 12-25
Rec. Lure Wt.: ⅝-1¼ oz.
Action: Medium-heavy
Handle: Vinyl pistol grips.

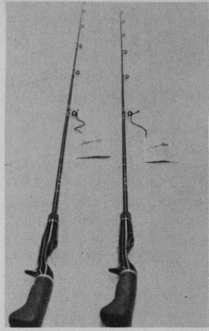

Lamiglas Graphite Worm Rods

Mfr.: Lamiglas
Model No.: W60L. Same as Model No.
 W56L except:
Length: 6'

Mfr.: Lamiglas
Model No.: W60MH. Same as Model No.
 W56MH except:
Length: 6'

Popping, Musky and Deep Jigging Rod

Mfr.: Fenwick
Model No.: GPLP-71
Length: 7'
No. Pieces: 2
No. Guides: Aluminum oxide
Tip Top: Aluminum oxide
Rec. Lure Wt.: ½-1 oz.
Action: Light

See "Putting Graphite in Perspective" by Mark Sosin, pages 34–41.

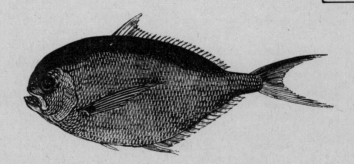

Specifications: Reels

All about Fishing Reels

Types

In general there are six kinds of reels; bait-casting, spinning, spin-casting, fly, salt water and "specials."

Bait-casting reels are used primarily in fresh water, but also in salt water. They are available in a variety of designs, sizes and price ranges, and all mount on the top of a rod handle. They all have revolving spools.

The spinning reel is often referred to as an "open face reel," since the line and spool are exposed at the front of the reel. The spinning reel's spool is stationary on both the cast and the retrieve. It is the momentum of the cast lure which pulls line from the spool.

Spinning reels are properly mounted under the rod and, like other reels are available in various designs, line capacities, quality. Open-face spinning reels are extremely popular and perform equally well in fresh or salt water fishing.

A spin-casting reel may be described as a "closed-face spinning reel." It has a "nose cone" or "hood" (front cover) that houses the line and stationary spool. On the cast, after the line has been first released from the spool by depressing a lever or "pushbutton" (or "trigger") with the thumb, the line passes from the spool through a hole in the front of the cone.

Spin-casting reels are designed chiefly to be mounted on the top of a standard bait-casting or spin-casting rod, but they can be used with other kinds of rods and even be mounted under a rod handle.

The fly reel is used chiefly to store bulky fly line and there are two general types; single-action and automatic models. With a single-action reel, the angler must turn the reel handle to retrieve line; with an automatic reel, he merely trips a trigger which releases spring tension that revolves the reel spool and swiftly re-spools the line.

There are many kinds of salt water reels, ranging from boat and pier reels to surf reels and heavy-duty, deep-sea trolling reels. Prices vary according to type, size and over-all quality; while some salt water reels may be purchased for less than $10 others sell for well over $1,000.

"Specialty" reels would include those designed for trolling with wire line, built-in reels that are an integral part of the rod, reels designed for still-fishing and ice fishing, and spin-casting reels made especially for under-the-rod use.

Bait Casting Reels

In its simplest form, a bait-casting reel comprises inter-locking gears, hubs, side plates, screws, nuts, a handle and a "foot" (stand) by which it is secured to a rod handle. When a cast is made, the momentum of the lure (or bait) pulls line from the reel by rotating the spool; line is re-spooled when the angler turns the reel handle.

Simply designed bait-casting reels are best suited to still-fishing or light trolling—fishing that does not require casting. If casting is to be done, better quality bait-casting reels are preferred since they give almost complete trouble-free casting performance.

Most bait-casting reels have brakes, level-winds, anti-backlash devices, free-spool arrangements and adjustable drags.

The level-wind on a reel is a guide which, when the reel's handle is turned, moves back-and-forth to re-spool line evenly on the spool. Level-winds may be of varying shapes and sizes, but all serve the same purpose—controlling and spooling line evenly.

Manufacturers have different names for anti-backlash devices they build into their reels, but all perform the same basic function: slowing the reel spool during the cast. Many bait casting reels have "centrifugal" brakes to control the spool.

This "braking" of the swiftly turning reel spool prevents annoying line tangles called "backlashes" or "overruns." The amount of pressure or braking exerted by an anti-backlash mechanism is knob-adjustable, and should be varied according to the weight of the lure or bait cast.

Most modern bait-casting reels are "free-spool" type, and some "total free-spool." Free-spool means that a clutch-like system disengages everything during the cast except the level-wind, reduces friction, and allows smoother, longer casts.

A reel with total free-spool also disengages the level-wind, which remains stationary on the cast and further reduces friction, while only the spool turns to pay out line. By turning the handle of a free-spool or total free-spool reel, the clutch automatically re-engages gears to begin the retrieve.

Drags on bait-casting reels apply tension to the spool so that line will pay out under pressure. The amount of pressure or "drag" is adjustable by turning a knurled knob or "star" drag control. Drags are valuable in fighting strong fish and in trolling.

The fisherman who will do serious bait-casting should buy the best reel he can afford. The best-built, best-designed reels are the more expensive models; casting ease and efficiency are in direct proportion to the quality of the reel.

Spinning Reels

A spinning reel is a simplified casting machine in that the line, pulled by the lure or bait, merely unfurls from the reel's stationary spool. Since the spool does not revolve, there is little friction, minimum possibility of backlash; smooth, long casts with light lures are routine.

Spinning reels have anti-reverse locks, which prevent the crank handle from turning backward. The anti-reverse lock is useful when playing hooked fish, and when trolling or still fishing since it will prevent line from paying out except against the tension of the pre-set drag.

Spinning reels are designed to be used chiefly with monofilament line. The reels are mounted under the rod, which keeps the cast line from slapping against the rod.

Spinning reels have three kinds of line pick-up mechanisms: bail, manual and automatic. The bail type, which is most popular, is a wire ring with a roller which catches the line and circles the spool when the handle is turned, thus re-spooling line. The bail must be flipped downward, or "opened" by the angler to free the line prior to casting.

Spinning reels with manual pick-ups have no bail but, instead, a simple roller mounted on the spool housing. The angler uses the tip of his forefinger to lift line from the roller and free it for a cast, replacing line to the roller the same way to pick up and retrieve line.

Automatic pick-ups are small, curved metal "arms" on the spool housing which catch and secure the line.

To cast, the fisherman lifts line from the abbreviated pick-up, thus freeing it. To re-spool line, the handle is cranked forward and the miniature pick-up automatically contacts and spools the line.

Most spinning reels have the handle mounted on the left side, which means that the right-handed caster casts with his right hand and then retrieves with his left. A left-handed caster will cast with his left, switch the rod to his right hand, and crank the reel with his left hand.

To give fishermen the opportunity to handle a spinning rod any way they like, some reels are offered in either right or left-hand models; some are so built that the handle is interchangeable and can be mounted on either the left or right side.

A quick, easy spool release is important. Many spinning reels have a depressible button on the spool face which, when pressed, instantly releases the spool. Other designs require the spool knot to be screwed counter-clockwise to be released.

Interchangeable spools provide the advantage of changing lines conveniently—from a light line to heavier line, for example, or to replace a worn or lost line.

The drags on most spinning reels are pressure discs located on the face of the line spool. Some reels, however, have drag adjustment knobs at the back or bottom of the reel. The best drags are easy to reach, reliable and smooth with no "catches" or hesitation.

Spin Casting Reels

The main components of a standard spin-casting or "push-button" reel are the body or gear housing, nose cone (front cover), foot, push-button (trigger or thumb release), drag adjustment knob, handle and anti-reverse.

All spin-casting reels are similar in their basic operation. The monofilament line is stored on a stationary spool contained within a nose cone, and is released for the cast when the push-button is depressed to withdraw the spool's pick-up pin(s) from line-holding position. On the cast, the freed line is pulled by the lure (or bait) off the spool through a hole in the nose cone.

A forward turn of the reel handle returns the pin(s) to the line pick-up position, and continued turning of the handle causes them to rotate around the spool and thus re-spool the line.

There is some short delay in pick-up of the line on spin-casting reels having only one pin; surer and quicker line retrieve is possible with reels which have more than one.

Since a spin-casting reel's pick-up pin(s) work constantly, they should be well-made of hard material, not unduly subject to wear or breakage. A faulty or broken pin makes a spin-casting reel inoperative.

The push-button of a spin-casting reel should be shaped and located for casting comfort. Most manufacturers build reels with push-buttons on top, and these are most popular, but some reels have release buttons on the side.

The majority of spin-casting reels have single-knob handles; some have double knobs. Other than comfort, handle design contributes little to a reel's performance so, as with type of push-buttons, single or double handles is a matter of personal preference.

As with spinning reels, some spin-casting reels are available with cranks on either the left or right side of the reel and some have handles that are interchangeable. These factors are important to the fisherman who will cast with his left hand and retrieve with his right.

Anti-reverse mechanisms are useful, preventing handles from turning backwards. Some reels have built-in, permanent anti-reverses; others are engaged by levers. The latter models should have the levers located out-of-the-way yet easy to reach.

All quality spin-casting reels have quickly adjustable drags with a wide range of tensions. "Star" drags, mounted on the handle are popular, but some reels have drag knobs top-mounted for handling ease. Other drags are adjusted by turning nose-cone rings.

One of the most important considerations in selecting a spin-casting reel is that it properly fit the rod to be used. All spin-casting reels will not mount well on all bait-casting or spin-casting rods. It is wise to test the reel on the rod to be used to be certain it is held securely in the reel seat and at a comfortable height.

Fly Reels

The simplest single-action fly reel is merely a spool within a frame connected by posts. It may not have a drag, or at best a modest one, but will likely have a light brake or "click."

Size of the reel is important. Small fly reels with small line capacity match light fly rods taking light (small diameter) fly lines. For heavier fishing with longer and heavier rods, requiring larger size lines, larger reels are obviously needed.

The size of a reel has nothing to do with its quality. A small reel can be expensive, a large one lower-priced. While higher-priced reels may not be necessary, they most likely will not jam, drop screws, loosen, or otherwise perform badly. Moreover, a good grade of fly reel will last indefinitely if cared for.

Single-action fly reels are lighter than most automatic models and have fewer moving parts so less can go wrong with them. They also have greater line capacity and are available with interchangeable spools. Better single-action reels also have serviceable drags.

Single-action reels with quickly interchangeable spools are desirable so fly lines can be switched readily. A spool with a fresh, dry line may replace a soaked, dirty line.

The best single-action reels have a drag sufficiently strong so that when the angler strips line from the reel for a quick cast the reel spool will not over-run and tangle line.

Modern automatic fly reels are precision machines. There are two basic types; those that mount vertically on the rod and those that mount horizontally. There are no technical advantages or disadvantages to either style; choice being a matter of individual preference.

A folding trigger, or release bar, is desirable in an automatic just so long as it can be out-of-the-way when the reel is stored and not subject to damage. A safety lock is useful, too, since it can prevent the trigger from being ripped accidentally.

Other good features in the automatic fly reel include quick, no-tool take-down; maximum line capacity; silent wind mechanism; and all-around dependability.

Many quality fly reels, both automatic and single-action, have stripping guides, usually of hard metal. These are mounted in the reel frame in the front and provide a smooth, protective passage for the fly line, reducing line wear.

The heavy-duty fly reel—used chiefly in salt water fly fishing—must be sturdily made, with a minimum of parts, have a great line capacity, and a powerful drag.

Salt Water Reels

There is a wide range of reels designed specifically for salt water fishing. They differ in design, size, etc. according to the primary purpose for which they are to be used.

There are reels for surf fishing; reels for bay, boat and pier fishing; reels for light trolling in bay or ocean; reels with wide spools; and ones with narrow spools; and, finally, there are deep-sea or "big game" ocean trolling reels.

Salt water reels of all types have a few things in common. They usually are sturdily built, corrosion resistant, have strong drags, and hold hundreds of yards of heavy-test line.

Surf reels are either open-face spinning or revolving spool type, the latter with or without level-wind. Both types have good line capacity, accommodating at least 200 yards of 20 pound test line.

Reels intended for light bay, boat or pier fishing (sometimes called "service" reels) look like over-sized bait-casting reels; some models have level-winds. They should hold at least 150 yards of line, have brass, aluminum, or tough plastic spools, strong star drags, and side-plates.

The light ocean-bay trolling reel should have a smooth drag, fast speed of retrieve, and good line capacity.

Salt water reels with wide spools have greater line capacity than those with narrow spools. Narrow spool reels are generally preferred when fishing wire line, since the larger spool diameter will not be likely to cause kinks in the wire. Many fishermen prefer narrow spool reels when fishing lead-core lines, for the same reason.

Deep-sea, or "big game" reels are the workhorses among anglers. More than any other kind of reel, these must be strongly made. Powerful and large ocean game-fish often fight for several hours, causing extreme stress and wear to a reel. Only the best reels will hold up under such abuse, fish after fish, season after season.

The spools of deep-sea reels are especially important, and they should be of one-piece construction, either aluminum, bronze, stainless steel or other equally strong material.

Many of the larger deep-sea reels have harness lugs built into the top of the reel so that the fisherman can snap on his "fighting harness" when playing a fish. Some also have rod clamps which are used to screw the reel tightly to the rod handle, giving added assurance that the reel will not loosen on the rod's reel seat.

Over-all construction, line capacity, retrieve ratio, and quality of drag all are to be considered in the salt water reel. Drags that can be pre-set and controlled by a lever are desirable on the larger reels.

—Courtesy of the American
Fishing Tackle Manufacturers Association.

1977 Product Preview
Reels

The trend in spinning reels is toward full-skirted models, both for practical and cosmetic reasons. By extending the skirt of the spool beyond the reel housing, designers are masking the area behind the spool from dirt and also from line falling behind it. This is particularly important when anglers carelessly let a reel rest in the bottom of a boat or drop it in soft sand or dirt.

There are, of course, new entries in bait-casting reels, but another apparent design direction is in miniature reels. Anglers are moving toward lighter and lighter gear, and a growing number now enjoy fishing with fine lines and equally delicate tackle.

Zebco has introduced the 4-ounce Omega 113 that is 25 percent lighter than any other ultralight spin-cast reel. It has a 4.1:1 gear

Zebco Omega 113 Ultralight.

ratio and comes equipped with 65 yards of 6-pound test Stren. Other features include a stainless-steel cover, silent selective antireverse, top-mounted ultra-smooth drag and distinctive Omega styling. There are two other reels in the Omega series: the Omega One and the Omega 33. The former is the heavy-duty model capable of handling line sizes from 14 to 20 pounds, while the 33 works best with lines from 8 to 12 pounds.

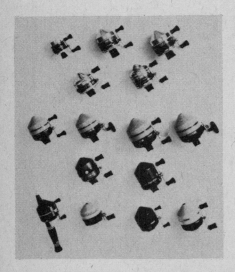

Zebco has redesigned its line of closed-face reels.

The entire line of Zebco spin-cast reels has undergone a styling change. The Omega series features power handles and a colorful information band that provides a line-capacity chart. On the 800 series, the information band has been added, as well as distinctive new colors. The 808 and 800 will have power handles and the 888 and 802 will continue to offer the option of a counterbalanced handle and torpedo grip.

Daiwa has a brand-new Silvercast series of spin-casting reels for 1977, with three models, all boasting a fast 4.1:1 retrieve ratio. The 208RL holds 75 yards of 8-pound

The Silvercast Series by Daiwa.

test; the 210RL has a capacity of 80 yards of 10-pound test; and the 212RL requires 100 yards of 12-pound test to fill the spool. Each reel has both left-hand and right-hand retrieve, a calibrated drag system, positive pin line pickup and quick-change aluminum spool.

In the ultralight class, Daiwa engineers have designed rod and reel combinations that go together. These are packaged in a special case that holds both rod and reel. The Minicast-Gold reel is a precision innovation that weighs less than 6 ounces and has a unique and

Daiwa's Minicast-Gold Big Wheel.

patented drag system. The built-in drag can be preset just like a conventional spin-cast reel. Or, if the angler prefers, he can rely solely on the thumb wheel mounted on the side of the reel; drag is applied with the thumb. Another alternative permits a combination of the two. The Minicast-Gold has 4.1:1 retrieve, positive pin pickup and on/off antireverse and can handle 65 yards of 6-pound line.

There is also a Minispin reel (model MS-1) that is open-faced spinning, has a retrieve ratio of 4.4:1 and a line capacity of 110 yards of 4-pound test. In the Minispin system, the reel is built right into the handle of a specially designed five-piece pack rod.

Daiwa GS-6 gold-skirted spool spinning reel.

The Daiwa GS-6 gold-skirted spool reel offers a large handle, left-hand or right-hand retrieve, fully skirted spool and a positive lock handle release for compact storage. The retrieve is 4.7:1, gears are precision machined for smooth performance and the drive has stainless-steel ball bearings. The drag is Teflon and the angler has the choice of closing the bail manually or by cranking the handle. This reel complements the other models in the series.

A new ceramic line guide and pickup pin have been added to most of the spin-cast reels in the Johnson Reel line to reduce fric-

Johnson Reels Guide 155.

tion and contribute to longer line life. The reels are being loaded at the factory with Stren line in the appropriate test for the specific reel. There is a new Johnson Guide 165 that features a precision ball-bearing retrieve, rugged Teflon-coated gears and an oscillating spool to crosswind line. The Guide 155 is basically the same reel in a smaller size with reduced line capacity.

Johnson is also introducing a Laker II Model 140C with a 3:1 gear ratio, die-cast metal spool and flash-fired Permalloy gears. This year, Johnson is marketing rod-and-reel combinations to help anglers put the right rod with a Johnson reel.

From Orvis comes word that its famous C.F.O. fly reels in sizes III, IV and V will be available with a multiplying gear ratio as well as the traditional one-to-one retrieve. Orvis will also market two new heavy-duty fly reels with superb drags for salmon, steelhead, bone-

fish, tarpon and other heavy-weights. The standard version is called the Marquesas and the salmon and steelhead model the Umpqua. The reels have already been field-tested by top fishing experts and rated among the best.

Shakespeare's 1980 President II bait-casting reel carries the state of the art a giant step forward. It has been designed for the angler who wants longer, more accurate casts without backlash and for the fisherman who needs rugged power to

control big fish in fresh and salt water. The drag is a multistage design that is smooth from the moment it comes out of the box. A new centrifugal braking system comes with three sets of weights for a full range of lures. Shakespeare's exclusive Hydro-Film cast control takes over to apply pressure as the spool slows down. There is a 5:1 gear ratio, a power handle, dual ball bearings and even a retainer ring around the crankshaft nut to prevent it from coming loose. Line capacity is rated at 200 yards of 15-pound test monofilament and 135 yards of 20-pound test. An anodized-gunmetal black frame with eagle medallion and distinctive engravings give the reel a classic but rugged look.

New spinning reels are the latest addition to the line at Penn Reels. The Philadelphia-based company is marketing a fully skirted spool model that is gold-anodized and designed for hard use. The company has recently introduced a pair of smaller spinning reels, the 714 and the smaller 716. Both feature a 5.1:1 gear ratio, push-button removable spool, a Teflon drag and a stainless steel bail. The 714 has a capacity of 200 yards of 6-pound test and the 716 holds 225 yards of 4-pound test.

Available in five sizes, from ultralight to heavy-duty salt water, the Eagle Claw Blue Pacific skirted-spool spinning reel series has

The 1980 President II by Shakespeare.

Blue Pacific Series from Eagle Claw.

just been unveiled by Wright & McGill. These reels feature fully automatic bail systems that trip the bail mechanism internally, eliminating the typical loud knock of other reels when the handle comes around. There's a 6-element, multi-disk drag system for increased smoothness, helical gearing and a folding reversible handle for left-hand or right-hand retrieve.

Childre Speed Spool.

Eagle Claw's Blue Pacific Trolling Reel.

A Blue Pacific series of trolling reels is being offered by Eagle Claw with seven models, three of which are level wind. The other four reels in this series are the equivalent of 1/0, 2/0, 3/0 and 4/0 trolling reels. They all feature full-range star drags, spool and bearing tension adjustments, chrome-plated brass spools and stainless reinforced side plates. Gear ratios are 3:1 on the smaller models and 2.4:1 on the 3/0 and 4/0.

Two new, popularly priced, open-faced spinning reels are being offered by Berkley and Company. Model 625 has an interchangeable handle for left-hand or right-hand retrieve, and the handle folds down for storage. The smooth, helical-cut gears have a fast ratio of 4.2:1. The 625 is spooled at the factory with 330 yards of 8-pound Trilene XL.

Model 620 has left-hand retrieve,

a fold-down handle, ball-bearing action and a helical-cut pinion and is also factory-spooled with 330 yards of 8-pound Trilene XL.

Lew Childre and Sons has entered the reel business with the Speed Spool: a bait-casting reel made expressly for black bass and light salt water fishing. It is shaped so that it can be cupped in the rod hand easily, and the paddle-shaped grips on the power handle make it comfortable to crank. The level wind has a Fuji diamond-polished hard speed guide that won't groove and extends the life of the line by reducing wear. The spool has purposely been made narrow so that the angle to the line guide is minimal. The level wind disengages on the cast and engages by turning the handle forward when the gears mesh. This is a new concept in bait-casting reels that has to be fished to be appreciated.

Heddon's new bait-casting reel (Model 3200) has a level wind that disengages during the cast for extra distance and more accuracy. Preci-

sion steel ball bearings insure smooth operation, and helical gears give the reel a fast 4.1:1 gear ratio. It has a power handle, automatic centrifugal drag system and patented clutch, and the line capacity is 150 yards of 12-pound test.

Heddon has added three new models to its spin-cast line—a husky salt water model, a popular fresh water size and a light fresh water reel. There's also a new Ultracast for light-tackle fishing, which has a 4:1 gear ratio and

Heddon 3200 Bait-casting Reel.

on/off antireverse and comes with prewound 4-pound test line.

Pflueger has announced the addition of a new free-spool baitcasting reel known as the 2800 Series. The reel includes such features as automatic re-engagement of the reel by turning the crank, power handle with star drag, hydro thumb anti-backlash control and a 4.7:1 gear ratio. The frame is anodized aluminum, drive gears are precision cut, pinions are corrosion-resistant and there are two stainless-steel ball bearings. The built-up aluminum spool holds 250 yards of 12-pound test or 200 yards of 15-pound test.

Following the trend toward skirted-spool spinning reels, Pflueger has developed the 800 Series which includes four deluxe models with fully skirted spools. Each has a six-disk adjustable drag, right-hand or left-hand retrieve, Teflon line roller, aluminum frame and spool, and ball bearings. The four sizes range from ultra-light and standard fresh water to a heavy fresh water/light salt water model and a heavy salt water reel.

With today's bait casters requiring more sophisticated equipment, the Garcia Corporation is introducing the Ambassadeur 5600C and 6600C with ThumBar free-spool control. ThumBar lets the angler put the reel into free spool while his thumb lies on the line, giving him perfect one-hand control for casting.

In addition, these Ambassadeurs contain every other feature that is characteristic of Ambassadeur. The 4.7:1 retrieve is fast; there are stainless-steel ball bearings, dual anti-backlash brakes and no-tool takedown. A 5600 CDL in a handsome teak case with a silver engraving plate is available for presentations.

The high-speed Ambassadeur 5500 is now being marketed in a narrow-spool version designated the 5500CN. This is lighter in weight and more compact than the standard model but has all the same features.

Garcia Abu-Matic 330.

Garcia's new Abu-Matic 330 and 350 spin-casting reels have a unique brake button that allows the angler to apply extra drag pressure whenever necessary. When the back-up drag is released, the preset drag tension automatically returns to operation. Both models have an extra-large orifice for ease and accuracy in casting, and they have Positive-Drive, a direct drive retrieve that goes into effect the instant pressure is applied.

For blue-water trolling, Garcia has introduced the solidly engineered yet moderately priced Ambassadeur 20 and 30 Big Game Trolling reels. The 20 is comparable to a 2½/0, while the 30 is a powerful 4/0 reel. Spools are made of heavily chromed solid brass and run on stainless-steel ball bearings. The frames are brush-finished stainless steel and are extremely rigid one-piece units. The lever drag swings from free spool to full drag over a wide arc, providing micro-fine adjustments.

A series of seven Kingfisher GK

Garcia Ambassadeur 5600C with ThumBar.

trolling reels is now being marketed for the salt water angler and the big-lake fisherman. All reels in the series feature stainless-steel spools and side plates as well as stainless-steel pinions and master gears. The free spool levers are large and conveniently located. The three smaller models also have a level wind to spool line evenly.

Olympic has proudly announced a new deluxe series of skirted spool reels called the LG-DX Series. These are available in four models, tailored for heavy fresh water action and for salt water. The housing is made from alumite, an aluminum alloy that won't rust or pit. Handles are interchangeable for right-hand or left-hand retrieve, and they fold down for storage with a touch of a single lever. A noiseless stopper system on the lower part of the main housing eliminates antireverse noise, and the pawl engages only when the

reel is antireversed. This saves drag wear on the ratchet and the anti-reverse dog. A helicon gear system provides fast retrieve ratios that are just under 5:1. Line capacity varies from 270 yards of 12-pound test on LG-DX 4 to 270 yards of 20-pound test on LG-DX 1.

The 250 VO is the newest and smallest member of the LG-VO series of skirted-spool spinning reels. It has a gear ratio of 4.56:1, line capacity of 270 yards of 10-pound test and a patented helicon gear system and is made from forged aluminum. There are eight washers in the disk drag system and slow level winding with three reduction gears.

Three smaller models—the 1500 VO, 1800 VO and 2000 VO—have been added to the skirted-spool Spark Series of spinning reels. Based on 10-pound test line, capacities are 185 yards for the 1500, 230 yards for the 1800 and 260 yards for

the 2000.

A new miniature spin-casting reel called the Olympet 1000 has also been introduced. With a gear ratio of 4.25:1 and a line capacity of 98 yards of 4-pound test, it is designed for ultralight work and features an extra long nonslip handle. The push lever is strategically located so that the thumb reaches it easily and pushes it forward to put the reel in free spool.

Skirted spools, miniaturization and more sophisticated bait-casting reels are the pace setters for 1977. If you're in the market for a new reel, you will do well to consider the direction that reel manufacturers believe the industry will take. With a crystal ball, one could probably predict that there will be more of the same for 1978, but those reels are on the drawing boards right now.

Berkley

Spinning Reels

Model No.: 420
Line Capacity: 375 yds. 8 lb. Trilene XL
Gear Ratio: 3.2 to 1

Model No.: 446
Line Capacity: 275 yds. 6 lb. Trilene XL
Gear Ratio: 4.1 to 1
Drag System: Disc
Ball Bearings: Yes

Model No.: 604
Line Capacity: 200 yds. 4 lb. Trilene XL
Gear Ratio: 3.6 to 1

Model No. 604

Model No.: 612
Line Capacity: 250 yds. 8 lb. Trilene XL
Gear Ratio: 3.6 to 1

Model No.: 4201
Line Capacity: 375 yds. 8 lb. Trilene XL
Gear Ratio: 4.5 to 1
Ball Bearings: Yes

Model No.: 870
Line Capacity: 200 yds. 17 lb. Trilene Tensimatic
Gear Ratio: 4 to 1
Ball Bearings: Yes

Model No.: 680
Line Capacity: 250 yds. 17 lb. Trilene Tensimatic
Gear Ratio: 3.6 to 1
Drag System: Disc

Model No.: 690
Line Capacity: 300 yds. 20 lb. Trilene Tensimatic
Gear Ratio: 3.6 to 1
Drag System: Disc
Spool Material: Magnum

Model No.: 725
Line Capacity: 330 yds. 8 lb. Trilene XL
Gear Ratio: 4.2 to 1
Features: Ball bearing; stainless steel bail; left/right handle.

Model No.: 612
Line Capacity: 250 yds. 8 lb. Trilene XL
Gear Ratio: 3.6 to 1
Features: Cam operated bail system; lightweight.

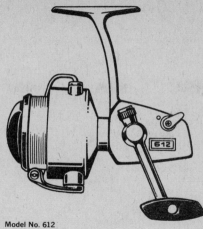

Model No. 612

Model No.: 604
Line Capacity: 200 yds. 4 lb. Trilene XL
Gear Ratio: 3.6 to 1
Features: Cam operated bail system; folding handle; removable side plate; die cast face gear; anti-foul drag knob.

Spin-Casting Reels

Model No.: 300
Line Capacity: 125 yds. 8 lb. Trilene XL
Gear Ratio: 3 to 1
Drag System: Star

Model No. 300

Model No.: 870
Line Capacity: 200 yds. 17 lb. Trilene Tensimatic
Gear Ratio: 4 to 1
Features: Ball bearing action; machine-cut helical gears; aluminum die cast construction.

Fly Reels

Model No.: 500
Line Capacity: 25 yds. flyline; 50 yds. braided or mono

Model No.: 510
Line Capacity: 30 yds. Berkley floating fly line
Drag System: Adjustable

Model No.: 1056
Line Capacity: 45 yds. 18 lb. dacron backing
Features: Press out spool; comes with tool kit; lever bar drag.

Model No.: 556
Line Capacity: 80 yds. 18 lb. dacron backing
Features: Removable spool; interchangeable handle; comes with tool kit.

Browning

Spinning Reels

Model No.: 1330
Line Capacity: 210 yds. 6 lb. test mono
Gear Ratio: 4.2 to 1
Weight: 8 oz.
Drag System: Multi-disc
Ball Bearings: Yes

Model No.: 5330
Line Capacity: 240 yds. 8 lb. test mono
Gear Ratio: 4.1 to 1
Weight: 12 oz.
Drag System: Multi-disc
Ball Bearings: Yes

Model No.: 5430
Line Capacity: 130 yds. 20 lb. test mono
Gear Ratio: 3.8 to 1
Weight: 15 oz.
Drag System: 6 disc system
Ball Bearings: Yes

Spin Casting Reels

Model No.: 1130
Line Capacity: 100 yds. 10 lb. test mono
Gear Ratio: 2.71 to 1
Weight: 8.4 oz.
Drag System: Star Multi-disc
Ball Bearings: Yes

Model No.: 5130
Line Capacity: 90 yds. 12 lb. test mono
Gear Ratio: 3.6 to 1
Weight: 12.5 oz.
Drag System: Star Multi-disc
Ball Bearings: Yes

Fly Reels

Model No.: 1230
Line Capacity: 25 yds. 15 lb. test braided mono
Weight: 4 oz.
Spool Material: Aluminum

Model No.: 5230
Line Capacity: 50 yds. 15 lb. test braided mono
Weight: 5 oz.

Continental

Spinning Reels

Model No.: Alcedo Mark IV
Line Capacity: 700 yds. 14 lb. test
Ball Bearings: Yes

Alcedo 2 C/S

Continental (con't.)

Model No.: Alcedo Mark V
Line Capacity: 600 yds. 20 lb. test
Ball Bearings: Yes

Model No.: Alcedo 2 C/S
Line Capacity: 350 yds. 6 lb. mono
Gear Ratio: 4 to 1
Weight: 11½ oz.
Ball Bearings: Yes
Spool Material: Duraluminum

Model No.: Alcedo Micron
Line Capacity: 260 yds. 4 lb. test mono
Gear Ratio: 5¼ to 1
Weight: 6⅓ oz.
Ball Bearings: Yes
Spool Material: Duraluminum

Cortland

Graphite Fly Reels

Model No.: C-6 Graphite Fly Reel I
Weight: 2½ oz.
Spool Size: 2⅞"
Features: Self lubricating; gears and other internal parts made of high density graphite material.

Cortland Fly Reels

Model No.: Crown Rim Control
Line Capacity: 3¼": 90 yds. 20 lb. backing; 3½": 120 yds. 20 lb. backing; 3⅝": 170 yds. 20 lb. backing
Drag System: Rim control
Spool Size: 3¼"; 3½"; 3⅝
Features: One-piece frame; quick change spool.

Daiwa

Spinning Reels

Model No.: 2500
Line Capacity: 275 yds. 12 lb. mono
Gear Ratio: 4.8 to 1
Weight: 15 oz.
Ball Bearings: Yes
Spool Material: Aluminum, skirted

Model No.: 4000
Line Capacity: 300 yds. 15 lb. mono
Gear Ratio: 4.7 to 1
Weight: 17 oz.
Ball Bearings: Yes
Spool Material: Aluminum, skirted

Model No.: 7000
Line Capacity: 200 yds. 25 lb. mono
Gear Ratio: 4.4 to 1
Weight: 23 oz.
Ball Bearings: Yes
Spool Material: Aluminum, skirted

Model No.: 7450 HRL
Line Capacity: 315 yds. 10 lb. mono; 280 yds. 12 lb. mono
Gear Ratio: 4.1 to 1
Weight: 13 oz.
Drag System: Spring loaded
Ball Bearings: Yes

Model No.: 7650 HRL
Line Capacity: 420 yds. 12 lb. mono; 265 yds. 15 lb. mono
Gear Ratio: 4.1 to 1
Weight: 17.6 oz.
Drag System: Spring loaded
Ball Bearings: Yes

Model No.: SS4000
Line Capacity: 200 yds. 20 lb. mono
Gear Ratio: 4.3 to 1
Weight: 23 oz.
Features: Sealed ball bearings; six-element drag system; silent optional anti-reverse; manual or automatic bail.

Model No.: GS-9
Line Capacity: 225 yds. 30 lb. mono
Gear Ratio: 3.3 to 1
Weight: 28 oz.
Features: Sealed ball bearing drive; six-element drag system; optional anti-reverse; machine-cut drive and pinion gears.

Model No.: 7000C
Line Capacity: 250 yds. 20 lb. mono
Gear Ratio: 4.7 to 1
Weight: 25 oz.
Features: Ball bearings and bushings; six-element drag system; anodized aluminum skirted spool; machine-cut drive and pinion gears.

Model No.: B400
Line Capacity: 200 yds. 20 lb. mono
Gear Ratio: 4.2 to 1
Weight: 22 oz.
Features: Brass bushings; drive and pinion gears; six-element drag system; folding handle.

Model No.: 406
Line Capacity: 420 yds. 12 lb. mono; 265 yds. 15 lb. mono

Model No. GS-9

Gear Ratio: 3.5 to 1
Weight: 15 oz.
Features: All metal gears; quick-change spool; adjustable drag system; automatic bail arm; optional on/off anti-reverse.

Spin Casting Reels

Model No.: 2100
Line Capacity: 85 yds. 8 lb. mono
Gear Ratio: 2.1 to1
Weight: 6 oz.
Drag System: Star

Model No.: 2200
Line Capacity: 85 yds. 8 lb. mono
Gear Ratio: 2.3 to 1
Weight: 6.3 oz.
Drag System: Star

Model No.: 212RL
Line Capacity: 120 yds. 10 lb. mono; 100 yds. 12 lb. mono
Gear Ratio: 4.1 to 1
Weight: 11.1 oz.
Features: Calibrated dial drag system; right or left hand retrieve; high speed retrieve; positive pin pickup; quick change aluminum spool.

Model No.: 28
Line Capacity: 115 yds. 12 lb. mono; 100 yds. 15 lb. mono
Gear Ratio: 3.1 to 1
Weight: 12 oz.
Features: Carbon steel pin pickup; all aluminum gears; four disc star drag system; stainless steel line guard.

Model No.: 9300
Line Capacity: 80 yds. 8 lb. mono
Gear Ratio: 2.5 to 1
Weight: 7 oz.

Fly Reels

Model No.: 731
Weight: 5.3 oz.
Features: One direction single click system; chrom-plated line guard; anodized aluminum spool.

Model No.: 734
Weight: 7 oz.
Features: One direction single click mechanism; chrome-plated line guard; anodized silver spool.

Daiwa (con't.)

Bait Casting Reels

Model No.: 3H
Line Capacity: 198 yds. 12 lb. mono
Gear Ratio: 5 to 1
Weight: 10.5 oz.
Features: Sealed ball bearings; star drag; automatic level wind; calibrated bearing break; centrifugal anti-backlash control; power handle; free spool mechanism.

Model No.: 5H
Line Capacity: 198 yds. 12 lb. mono
Gear Ratio: 5 to 1
Weight: 11.9 oz.

Model No.: 6H
Line Capacity: 240 yds. 12 lb. mono; 220 yds. 15 lb. mono
Gear Ratio: 5 to 1
Weight: 12.3 oz.

Eagle Claw

Spinning Reels

Model No.: Blue Pacific 125 Ultra Light
Gear Ratio: 4.1 to 1
Weight: 8.5 oz.
Drag System: Multi-disc
Ball Bearings: Yes

Model No.: Blue Pacific 225 Light Fresh Water
Gear Ratio: 3.4 to 1
Weight: 10 oz.

Model No.: Blue Pacific 425 Medium Fresh Water
Gear Ratio: 3.5 to 1
Weight: 16.5 oz.

Model No.: Blue Pacific 525 Light Surf
Gear Ratio: 3.5 to 1
Weight: 20.5 oz.

Model No.: Blue Pacific 625 Heavy Salt Water
Gear Ratio: 3.5 to 1
Weight: 24 oz.

Spin Casting Reels

Model No.: 102 Light Weight Push Button
Drag System: Star

Model No.: 103 Light to Medium Lures Push Button
Drag System: Star

Model No.: 104 Medium to Heavy Lures Push Button (Oscillating Spool)

Fly Reels

Model No.: EC10
Weight: 3½ oz.

Model No.: EC-11 Medium Single Action
Weight: 4 oz

Model No.: EC-12 Large Single Action
Weight: 4½ oz.

Model No.: ECD
Spool Material: Aluminum

Garcia

Spinning Reels

Model No.: GK10
Line Capacity: 200 yds. 8 lb. test mono
Gear Ratio: 3.8 to 1
Weight: 10 oz.
Drag System: Multi-disc
Ball Bearings: Yes

Model No.: GK22
Line Capacity: 180 yds. 6 lb. test mono
Gear Ratio: 4 to 1
Weight: 9 oz.
Drag System: Adjustable
Ball Bearings: Yes

Model No. GK22

Model No.: GK24
Line Capacity: 200 yds. 10 lb. test mono
Gear Ratio: 4 to 1
Drag System: Adjustable
Ball Bearings: Yes

Model No.: GK26
Line Capacity: 280 yds. 15 lb. test mono
Gear Ratio: 4 to 1
Drag System: Adjustable
Ball Bearings: Yes, carbon steel

Model No.: 300
Line Capacity: 300 yds. 8 lb. test mono
Gear Ratio: 3.7 to 1
Weight: 11.25 oz.
Drag System: Teflon
Ball Bearings: Yes
Spool Material: Aluminum

Model No.: 300C
Line Capacity: 300 yds. 8 lb. test mono
Gear Ratio: 3.7 to 1
Weight: 11.25 oz.
Drag System: Teflon
Ball Bearings: Yes
Spool Material: Aluminum

Model No.: 300DL
Line Capacity: 300 yds. 8 lb. test mono
Gear Ratio: 3.7 to 1
Weight: 11.25 oz.
Drag System: Teflon
Ball Bearings: Yes
Spool Material: Aluminum

Model No.: 306
Line Capacity: 400 yds. 10 lb. test mono
Gear Ratio: 3.9 to 1
Weight: 14.4 oz.
Drag System: Fiber friction disc
Ball Bearings: Yes
Spool Material: Teflon

Model No.: 308
Line Capacity: 300 yds. 4 lb. test mono
Gear Ratio: 4.6 to 1
Weight: 7.4 oz.
Ball Bearings: Yes
Spool Material: Aluminum

Model No.: 320
Line Capacity: 225 yds. 6 lb. test mono
Gear Ratio: 3.6 to 1
Weight: 9.9 oz.
Drag System: Fiber friction disc
Ball Bearings: Yes

Model No.: 330
Line Capacity: 200 yds. 4 lb. test mono
Gear Ratio: 3.7 to 1
Weight: 11.3 oz.
Drag System: Teflon
Ball Bearings: Yes
Spool Material: Aluminum

Model No.: 406
Line Capacity: 150 yds. 12 lb. test mono
Gear Ratio: 4.5 to 1
Weight: 19.4 oz.
Drag System: Teflon
Ball Bearings: Yes
Spool Material: Aluminum

Model No.: 408
Line Capacity: 300 yds. 4 lb. test mono
Gear Ratio: 5.5 to 1
Weight: 7.8 oz.
Drag System: Teflon
Ball Bearings: Yes
Spool Material: Aluminum

Model No.: 410
Line Capacity: 300 yds. 8 lb. mono
Gear Ratio: 4.8 to 1
Weight: 11.5 oz.
Drag System: Teflon
Ball Bearings: Yes
Spool Material: Aluminum

Model No.: 440
Line Capacity: 200 yds. 4 lb. test mono
Gear Ratio: 4.8 to 1
Weight: 11.8 oz.
Drag System: Teflon
Ball Bearings: Yes
Spool Material: Aluminum

Spin Casting Reels

Model No.: Abu-Matic 170
Line Capacity: 165 yds. 15 lb. royal bonnyl
Gear Ratio: 3 to 1
Weight: 11 oz.
Features: Syncro drag; star wheel drag.

Model No. GK32

Garcia (con't.)

Model No.: Abu-Matic 150
Line Capacity: 180 yds. 12 lb. royal bonnyl
Weight: 11 oz.
Gear Ratio: 3 to 1
Features: Pre-set drag.

Model No.: Abu-Matic 120
Line Capacity: 125 yds. 8 lb. royal bonnyl
Weight: 9 oz.
Gear Ratio: 3 to 1
Features: Pre-set drag.

Model No.: GK32
Line Capacity: 100 yds. 8 lb. test mono
Gear Ratio: 2.7 to 1
Weight: 8 oz.
Drag System: Dial

Model No. GK34

Model No.: GK34
Line Capacity: 100 yds. 10 lb. test mono
Gear Ratio: 3½ to 1
Drag System: Star
Ball Bearings: Yes

Bait Casting Reels

Model No.: 6500C
Line Capacity: 275 yds. 15 lb. test
Gear Ratio: 4.7 to 1
Drag System: Adjustable star
Ball Bearings: Stainless steel

Model No.: 1750
Line Capacity: 130 yds. 12 lb. test mono
Gear Ratio: 3.3 to 1
Weight: 6.3 oz.

Model No.: 2500C
Line Capacity: 120 yds. 12 lb. royal bonnyl
Weight: 8.6 oz.
Gear Ratio: 4.7 to 1
Features: Adjustable star drag; stainless
   steel ball bearings.

Model No. 5000

Model No.: 5000
Line Capacity: 210 yds. 15 lb. royal bonnyl
Gear Ratio: 3.6 to 1
Weight: 8.5 oz.
Drag System: Adjustable star

Model No.: 5000B
Line Capacity: 220 yds. 15 lb. royal bonnyl
Gear Ratio: 3.6 to 1
Weight: 8.5 oz.
Drag System: Star

Model No.: 5000C
Line Capacity: 165 yds. 15 lb. test mono
Gear Ratio: 3.6 to 1
Weight: 10.7 oz.
Drag System: Multi-disc star
Ball Bearings: Yes

Model No.: 5000D
Line Capacity: 130 yds. 15 lb. test mono
Gear Ratio: 3.6 to 1
Weight: 8.5 oz.
Drag System: Adjustable

Model No.: 5001C
Line Capacity: 165 yds. 15 lb. test mono
Gear Ratio: 3.6 to 1
Weight: 10.7 oz.
Drag System: Multi-disc star
Ball Bearings: Yes

Model No.: 5500C
Line Capacity: 225 yds. 10 lb. test mono
Gear Ratio: 4.7 to 1
Weight: 10.3 oz.
Drag System: Adjustable
Ball Bearings: Yes

Model No.: 6000
Line Capacity: 220 yds. 15 lb test mono
Gear Ratio: 3.6 to 1
Weight: 9.7 oz.
Drag System: Star

Model No.: 6000C
Line Capacity: 220 yds. 15 lb. test mono
Gear Ratio: 3.6 to 1
Weight: 11.9 oz.
Drag System: Multi-disc star
Ball Bearings: Yes

Fly Reels

Model No.: 754
Line Capacity: DT #6 plus 100 yds. 15 lb.
   backing
Gear Ratio: 1 to 1
Weight: 5.7 oz.
Drag System: Adjustable

Model No.: 758
Line Capacity: WF #9 plus 150 yds. 20 lb.
   backing
Gear Ratio: 1 to 1
Weight: 6.4 oz.
Features: Adjustable drag.

Model No.: GK42
Line Capacity: #6 plus 50 yds. backing
Weight: 4½ oz.
Drag System: Adjustable shoe type

Model No.: GK44
Line Capacity: #6 plus 100 yds. backing
Weight: 5 oz.
Features: Chromed line guard; adjustable
   shoe-type drag.

Model No.: GK50
Line Capacity: 35 yds. 6 wt.

Model No. GK44

Saltwater Reels

Model No.: 302
Line Capacity: 575 yds. 15 lb. royal bonnyl
Gear Ratio: 3.9 to 1
Weight: 20 oz.
Drag System: Multi-disc
Ball Bearings: Yes
Spool Material: Aluminum

Model No.: 402
Line Capacity: 420 yds. 15 lb. test mono
Gear Ratio: 4.5 to 1
Weight: 21.7 oz.
Drag System: Pressure washers with Teflon
Ball Bearings: Yes
Spool Material: Aluminum

Model No.: 440
Line Capacity: 330 yds. 12 lb. test mono
Gear Ratio: 4.8 to 1
Weight: 11.8 oz.
Drag System: Teflon friction disc
Ball Bearings: Yes

Model No.: 486
Line Capacity: 420 yds. 15 lb. test mono
Gear Ratio: 4.1 to 1
Weight: 24 oz.
Drag System: Ferodo friction disc
Ball Bearings: Yes
Spool Material: Aluminum

Model No.: 488
Line Capacity: 400 yds. 20 lb. test mono
Gear Ratio: 4.1 to 1
Weight: 26.5 oz.
Drag System: Ferodo friction disc
Ball Bearings: Yes
Spool Material: Aluminum

Model No. 600A

Garcia (con't.)

Model No.: 600A
Line Capacity: 400 yds. 30 lb. test royal bonnyl
Gear Ratio: 3 to 1
Weight: 19.7 oz.
Drag System: Star
Spool Material: Metal

Model No.: 9000
Line Capacity: 375 yds. 30 lb. royal bonnyl #11
Gear Ratio: 4.2 to 1
Weight: 15.4 oz.
Drag System: Adjustable star
Ball Bearings: Yes

Model No.: 10,000C
Line Capacity: 475 yds. 30 lb. royal bonnyl #11
Gear Ratio: 4.2 to 1
Weight: 16.1 oz.
Drag System: Adjustable star
Ball Bearings: Yes

Gladding

Spinning Reels

Model No.: 610
Line Capacity: 150 yds. 8 lb. test mono
Drag System: Adjustable disc
Spool Material: Plastic

Model No.: 630
Line Capacity: 190 yds. 8 lb. test mono
Drag System: Adjustable
Spool Material: Plastic

Model No.: 730A Freshwater
Line Capacity: 225 yds. 8 lb. test
Gear Ratio: 3.5 to 1

Model No.: 725A Ultralight
Line Capacity: 200 yds. 4 lb. test
Gear Ratio: 4.2 to 1

Model No.: 750A Heavy Duty
Line Capacity: 250 yds. 15 lb. test
Gear Ratio: 3.5 to 1

Model No.: 760A Saltwater
Line Capacity: 250 yds. 25 lb. test mono
Gear Ratio: 3.7 to 1

Classic 925 Ultralight

Model No.: Classic 925 Ultralight
Line Capacity: 220 yds. 6 lb. test
Gear Ratio: 4.75 to 1

Model No.: Classic 930 Freshwater
Line Capacity: 250 yds. 8 lb. test
Gear Ratio: 3.7 to 1

Model No.: Classic 935 Freshwater Saltwater
Line Capacity: 265 yds. 10 lb. test mono
Gear Ratio: 3.7 to 1

Classic 960 Heavy Saltwater

Model No.: Classic 960 Heavy Saltwater
Line Capacity: 250 yds. 20 lb. test
Gear Ratio: 3.5 to 1

Model No.: 880 Salt Water
Line Capacity: 250 yds. 25 lb. test mono
Gear Ratio: 3.7 to 1

Model No.: 870 Freshwater—Saltwater
Line Capacity: 250 yds. 15 lb. test mono
Gear Ratio: 3.5 to 1

Model No.: 840 Freshwater
Line Capacity: 250 yds. 8 lb. test mono
Gear Ratio: 3.5 to 1

Model No.: 820 Ultra-Light
Line Capacity: 200 yds. 4 lb. test mono
Gear Ratio: 4.2 to 1

Spin Cast Reels

Model No.: Spin Cast 30A
Line Capacity: 100 yds. 8 lb. test mono

Model No.: Spin Cast 40
Line Capacity: 100 yds. 8 lb. test mono

Model No.: Spin Cast 125
Line Capacity: 100 yds. 8 lb. test mono
Features: Metal gears; chromed multi-point pick-up; star drag.

Model No.: Spin Cast 165
Line Capacity: 100 yds. 8 lb. test mono
Features: Die-cast aluminum housing; aluminum nose cone; plastic spool; adjustable star drag.

Model No.: Thumber 135
Line Capacity: 100 yds. 8 lb. mono
Features: Star drag; all aluminum nose cone; thumb control push button.

Bassin Man 195

Model No.: Bassin Man 195
Line Capacity: 150 yds. 15 lb. test mono
Gear Ratio: 3.5 to 1
Features: Double ball-bearing drive; star drag.

Bait Casting Reels

Model No.: 3 Casting Reel
Line Capacity: 100 yds. 15 lb. test
Gear Ratio: 4 to 1

Fly Reels

Model No.: 1033 Lightweight Gladding-South Bend Gear Fly Reel
Line Capacity: 75 yds. HEH; 100 yds. HDF

Model No.: 1044 Regular Gladding-South Bend Gear Fly Reel
Line Capacity: 100 yds. HDH; 125 yds. HCF
Gear Ratio: 2.66 to 1

Model No.: 1055 Kingsize Gladding-South Bend Gear Fly Reel
Line Capacity: 100 yds. GBC; 125 yds. GAF
Gear Ratio: 2.66 to 1

Model No.: 1122 Single Action Finalist
Line Capacity: 35 yds. #5 fly line
Spool Diameter: 2½"

Model No.: 1130 Oreno-Matic
Line Capacity: 25 yds. #6 fly line
Weight: 8.5 oz.

Model No.: 1140 Oreno-Matic
Line Capacity: 35 yds. #6 fly line
Weight: 9.5 oz.

Model No.: 1180 Flat-Mounting Automatic
Line Capacity: 35 yds. #6 fly line
Weight: 9 oz.

Model No.: 1190 Oreno-Matic
Line Capacity: 35 yds. #6 fly line
Weight: 9.5 oz.

Hardy Brothers

Fly Reels

Model No.: Featherweight
Gear Ratio: 1⅔ to 1
Weight: 3 oz.

The Husky

Model No.: The Husky
Gear Ratio: 1⅔ to 1
Weight: 7¾ oz.

Hardy Brothers (con't.)

Model No.: The Princess
Gear Ratio: 1⅔ to 1
Weight: 4¾ oz.

Model No.: Zenith
Gear Ratio: 1⅔ to 1
Weight: 7¼ oz.

Model No.: L.R.H. Lightweight
Gear Ratio: 1⅔ to 1
Weight: 3¾ oz.

James Heddon's Sons

Spinning Reels

Model No.: 212
Line Capacity: 200 yds. 15 lb. test mono
Weight: 15 oz.
Drag System: Multi-disc
Spool Material: Metal

Model No.: 222
Line Capacity: 200 yds. 8 lb. test mono
Weight: 12 oz.
Drag System: Multi-disc
Spool Material: Metal

Model No.: 281
Line Capacity: 100 yds. 6 lb. test mono
Gear Ratio: 4.5 to 1
Drag System: Multi-disc
Ball Bearings: Yes
Spool Material: Metal

Model No.: 282
Line Capacity: 200 yds. 8 lb. test mono
Gear Ratio: 4.5 to 1
Drag System: Multi-disc
Ball Bearings: Yes
Spool Material: Metal

Model No.: 283
Line Capacity: 200 yds. 15 lb. test mono
Gear Ratio: 4.5 to 1
Drag System: Multi-disc
Ball Bearings: Yes
Spool Material: Metal

Model No.: 284
Line Capacity: 200 yds. 20 lb. test mono
Gear Ratio: 4.5 to 1
Drag System: Multi-disc
Ball Bearings: Yes
Spool Material: Metal

Spin Casting Reels

Model No.: 112
Line Capacity: 100 yds. 6 lb. test mono
Weight: 7 oz.
Drag System: Adjustable drag

Model No.: 152
Line Capacity: 100 yds. 8 lb. test mono
Weight: 10 oz.
Drag System: Star

Model No.: 185
Gear Ratio: 4 to 1
Weight: 11 oz.
Drag System: Star
Ball Bearings: Yes

Saltwater Trolling Reels

Model No.: 409
Line Capacity: 300 yds. 20 lb. test mono

Gear Ratio: 3 to 1
Weight: 20 oz.
Drag System: Star
Spool Material: Metal
Spool Size: 3 1/16" plate diameter, 2⅛" width

Model No.: 421
Line Capacity: 225 yds. 30 lbs. test dacron
or mono
Gear Ratio: 3 to 1
Weight: 18 oz.
Drag System: Star
Spool Material: Metal
Spool Size: 3¼" plate diameter, 2½" width

Model No.: 422
Line Capacity: 275 yds. 30 lb. dacron
Gear Ratio: 2½ to 1
Weight: 22 oz.
Drag System: Star
Spool Material: Metal
Spool Size: 3¾" plate diameter, 2½" width

Model No.: 445
Line Capacity: 300 yds. 20 lb. test
Gear Ratio: 3 to 1
Weight: 20 oz.
Drag System: Star
Spool Material: Metal
Spool Size: 3 1/16" plate diameter, 2⅛" width

Model No.: 450
Line Capacity: 200 yds. 36 lb. test
Weight: 19 oz.
Drag System: Star
Spool Material: Metal
Spool Size: 2⅝" plate diameter, 2½" width

Model No.: 499
Line Capacity: 250 yds. 15 lb. test mono
Gear Ratio: 3 to 1
Weight: 14 oz.
Drag System: Star
Spool Size: 2⅝" plate diameter, 1¾" width

Johnson

Spin Casting Reels

Model No.: 088A
Line Capacity: 240 ft. 10 lb. test mono.
Handles 6 lb. to 12 lb. test
Gear Ratio: 3 to 1
Weight: 8 oz.
Drag System: Star

Model No.: 100B
Line Capacity: 230 ft. 10 lb. test stren.
Handles 6 lb. to 10 lb. test
Weight: 9 oz.
Drag System: Multiple shoe
Ball Bearings: Bronze

Model No.: 110B
Line Capacity: 450 ft. 10 lb. test stren.
Handles 8 lb. to 15 lb. test
Weight: 11½ oz.
Drag System: Multiple shoe
Ball Bearings: Yes

Model No.: 125
Line Capacity: 240 ft. 10 lb. test mono.
Handles 6 lb. to 12 lb. test
Gear Ratio: 3 to 1
Weight: 10 oz.
Drag System: Adjustable audible

Model No.: 130B
Line Capacity: 405 ft. 10 lb. test stren.

Handles 285 ft. 20 lb. test
Weight: 15 oz.
Drag System: Automatic fish-tiring drag
Ball Bearings: Bronze

Model. No.: 140C
Line Capacity: 230 ft. 10 lb. test stren.
Handles 4 lb. to 12 lb. test
Gear Ratio: 3 to 1
Features: Die cast metal spool; Permalloy
gears; safety lock; audible adjustable drag.

Martin

Spinning Reels

Model No.: Ultra Light 104
Line Capacity: 200 yds. 4 lb. test
Gear Ratio: 5 to 1
Weight: 9 oz.
Drag System: Spring loaded
Ball Bearings: Yes

Model No.: 207A
Line Capacity: 200 yds. 6 lb. test
Weight: 10 oz.
Ball Bearings: Yes

Model No.: 400
Line Capacity: 200 yds. 6 lb. test
Gear Ratio: 3.8 to 1
Weight: 11 oz.
Drag System: Multi-disc
Ball Bearings: Yes

Model No.: 807
Line Capacity: 175 yds. 20 lb. test
Gear Ratio: 4 to 1
Weight: 12 oz.
Drag System: Multi-disc
Ball Bearings: Yes

Spin Casting Reels

Model No.: 220
Line Capacity: 80 yds. 6 lb. test mono
Drag System: Star

Model No.: 500
Line Capacity: 100 yds. 8 lb. test mono
Weight: 9 oz.
Drag System: Star

Model No.: 700
Line Capacity: 100 yds. 8 lb. Martin "Tuffy"
mono
Weight: 9 oz.
Drag System: Star

Fly Reels

Model No.: 6
Line Capacity: 30 yds. DT6F
Weight: 9¼ oz.

Model No.: 8
Line Capacity: 30 yds. DT6F

Model No.: 38G
Line Capacity: 30 yds. DT6F
Weight: 8¾ oz.

Model No.: 47
Line Capacity: Designed for 8 lb. test mono
Weight: 8½ oz.

Model No.: 48
Line Capacity: 30 yds. DT6F
Weight: 9 oz.

Martin (con't.)

Model No. 47

Model No.: Fly-Wate 49
Line Capacity: 30 yds. DT8F; 35 yds. WF8F
Weight: 9¼ oz.

Model No.: 60
Line Capacity: 30 yds. DT6F
Weight: 3½ oz.

Model No.: 61
Line Capacity: 35 yds. WF8F
Weight: 3¾ oz.

Model No.: 62
Line Capacity: 30 yds. DT6F
Weight: 3½ oz.

Model No.: 63
Line Capacity: 35 yds. WF8F
Weight: 3¾ oz.

Model No.: 64
Line Capacity: 35 yds. WF9F plus 150 yds.
18 lb. test dacron backing
Weight: 6¼ oz.
Drag System: Adjustable

Model No.: 65
Line Capacity: 35 yds. WF9F plus 130 yds. 18
lb. test braided dacron backing
Weight: 5 oz.

Model No.: 66
Line Capacity: 35 yds. WF9F plus 130 yds.
18 lb. test dacron backing
Weight: 5½ oz.

Model No.: Martin Model 68
Line Capacity: 35 yds. WF9F plus 150 yds. 18
lb. test
Gear Ratio: 3 to 1
Weight: 7 oz.

Model No. 81

Model No.: 81
Line Capacity: 30 yds. DT8F; 35 yds. WF8F
Weight: 9 oz.

Model No.: 83
Line Capacity: 30 yds. DT8F; 35 yds. WF8F
Weight: 9¼ oz.

Model No.: 94
Line Capacity: 30 yds. DT6F
Weight: 8¾ oz.

Trolling Reels

Model No.: Sovereign 23 AXL
Line Capacity: 100 yds. 14 lb. test mono
plus 230 yds. 18 lb. test dacron backing;
30 yds. DT6F
Weight: 10 oz.

Model No.: Trol-O-Matic 35A
Line Capacity: 35 yds. WF9F plus 150 yds.
18 lb. test backing
Weight: 15¾ oz.

OLM

Spinning Reels

Model No.: LG—DX No. 1
Line Capacity: 270 yds. 20 lb. mono
Gear Ratio: 4.78 to 1
Weight: 26.9 oz.
Features: All alumite housing; bail return
shock absorber; helicon gear system;
convertible handle; two piece stainless
steel ball bearings; double-locking handle
screw; noiseless stopper system.

Model No.: 250 VO
Line Capacity: 270 yds. 10 lb. mono
Gear Ratio: 4.56 to 1
Weight: 16.2 oz.
Features: Sealed ball bearing; solid nylon
brushing; folding handle; disc drag system.

Model No.: 500 VO
Line Capacity: 270 yds. 18 lb. mono
Gear Ratio: 4.78 to 1
Weight: 22.1 oz.
Features: Convertible handle; helicon gear;
alumite-treated anti-corrosive anodized
alloy spool; anti-reverse; stainless ball
bearing moverment; reduction gear; folding
handle.

Model No.: 350 III
Line Capacity: 300 yds. 12 lb. mono
Gear Ratio: 5.13 to 1
Weight: 18 oz.
Features: Stainless steel ball bearing
movement; helicon gear; digital drag
system; detachable spools.

Model No.: 650 III
Line Capacity: 270 yds. 25 lb. mono
Gear Ratio: 3.55 to 1
Weight: 26.7 oz.
Features: Manual bails; detachable spools;
stainless steel ball bearings; helicon
gear; convertible hand retrieving; digital
drag adjustment; plastic handle arm grip.

Model No.: HM No. 1/0
Line Capacity: 400 yds. 8 lb. mono
Gear Ratio: 5.2 to 1
Weight: 13.6 oz.

Features: Squirted spool; helicon gear;
stainless ball bearing movement; dragging
system with seven washers and coil spring
center; all metal anti-reverse level.

Model No.: HM No. 2
Line Capacity: 440 yds. 4 lb. mono
Gear Ratio.: 5.1 to 1
Weight: 12 oz.
Features: Helicon gear; stainless ball bearing
movement; anti-reverse; drag system with
seven washers plus coil spring center;
converting handle.

Model No.: 1500 VO
Line Capacity: 185
Gear Ratio: 3.82 to 1
Weight: 13.9 oz.
Features: Pinion gear; stainless steel bail
arm; die-cast spool; cranked oscillator;
double lock handle.

Model No.: 2000 VO
Line Capacity: 260 yds. 10 lb. mono
Gear Ratio: 4.5 to 1
Weight: 15.9 oz.
Features: Convertible handle; double locking
handle screw; pinion gear.

Model No.: 3100 VO
Line Capacity: 260 yds. 8 lb. mono
Gear Ratio: 3.36 to 1
Weight: 8.8 oz.
Features: Left handle; manual full return
bail; available with ball bearing movement.

Model No.: 3200 VO
Line Capacity: 245 yds. 15 lb. mono
Gear Ratio: 4.5 to 1
Weight: 19.0 oz.
Features: Manual full return bail; available
with ball bearing movement; reduction
gear; stainless steel bail arm; left and right
convertible handle.

Model No.: Seiki 940
Line Capacity: 270 yds. 10 lb. mono
Gear Ratio: 5.13 to 1
Weight 11.6 oz.
Features: Sealed ball bearing; disc drag
system; helicon gear system; anti-reverse;
hi-aluminum spool.

Model No.: 510
Line Capacity: 160 yds. 6 lb. mono
Gear Ratio: 4.7 to 1
Weight: 9.9 oz.
Features: Convertible handle; anti-reverse;
multi-disc dragging system; convertible
folding handle.

Model No.: 530
Line Capacity: 200 yds. 15 lb. mono
Gear Ratio: 4.5 to 1
Weight: 15.3 oz.
Features: Ball bearing mechanism;
convertible folding handle; brass pinion;
helical gear; anti-reverse; multi-disc
dragging system.

Model No.: 2000
Line Capacity: 180 yds. 8 lb. mono
Gear Ratio: 3.18 to 1
Weight: 5.9 oz.
Features: Left handle; machine cut pinion
gear; stainless steel bail system; die-cast
housing.

Model No.: 2800
Line Capacity: 195 yds. 20 lb. mono

OLM (con't.)

Gear Ratio: 4.0 to 1
Weight: 21.5 oz.
Features: Ball bearing movement; stainless steel ball system; spiral gear; left handle.

Model No.: Auto No. 2
Line Capacity: 280 yds. 15 lb. mono
Gear Ratio: 5.1 to 1; 2.83 to 1
Weight: 24.7 oz.
Features: Multi-disc drag washer; two sealed ball bearings; automatic speed change system.

Spin Casting Reels

Model No.: 312
Line Capacity: 90 yds. 10 lb. mono
Gear Ratio: 3 to 1
Weight: 8 oz.
Features: All metal face; 6 point pick-up; star drag; side push button; free spool lever.

Model No.: 310
Line Capacity: 80 yds. 8 lb.
Gear Ratio: 2.65 to 1
Weight: 7.5 oz.
Features 6 point pick-up; star drag; side push button; all metal face.

Model No.: 1000-DX
Line Capacity: 98 yds. 4 lb. mono
Gear Ratio: 42.5 to 1
Features: Anti-reverse lever; non-slip long handle; twist proof dragging system.

Model No.: 110
Line Capacity: 75 yds. 10 lb. mono
Gear Ratio: 2.7to 1
Weight: 7.6 oz.
Features: Spool drag; cast gear and brass cut pinion gear; solid rubber line snapper.

Model No.: 125
Line Capacity: 130 yds. 8 lb. mono
Gear Ratio: 3.5 to 1
Drag System: 9.1 oz.
Features: Star drag; pinion gear; handle grip; stainless steel rotor; solid rubber line snapper.

Deep Sea Reels

Model No.: D.S. No. 2
Line Capacity: 435 yds. 25 lb. mono
Gear Ratio: 3.29 to 1
Weight: 29.2 oz.
Features: Rotating guide bar; large star drag; two sealed ball bearings; convertible.

Model No.: 606
Line Capacity: 350 yds. 12 lb. mono
Gear Ratio: 2.92 to 1
Weight: 13.3 oz.
Features: Anti-corrosive spool; star drag; double-end stainless plates.

Model No.: 615
Line Capacity: 300 yds. 35 lb. mono
Gear Ratio: 3.14 to 1
Weight: 29.1 oz.
Features: Double-end stainless plates; harness ring; oiling eye; plastic plate.

Model No.: 625
Line Capacity: 380 yds. 25 lb. mono
Gear Ratio: 3 to 1

Weight: 20.1 oz.
Features: Anti-corrosive heavy salt water resistant chrome; oiling eye; level winding system.

Model No.: 635 LW
Line Capacity: 300 yds. 35 lb. mono
Gear Ratio: 3 to 1
Weight: 23.5 oz.
Features: Anti-corrosive spool; star drag; double-end stainless plates.

Bait Casting Reels

Model No.: 7700
Line Capacity: 245 yd. 10 lb. mono
Gear Ratio: 4 to 1
Weight: 10.8 oz.
Features: Two sealed stainless ball bearings; non-slip handle grip; stainless spool shaft; machine cut main and pinion gear; star drag.

Model No.: 720A
Line Capacity: 100 yds. 15 lb. mono
Gear Ratio: 3.3 to 1
Weight: 6 oz.

Model No.: 737
Line Capacity: 100 yds. 15 lb. mono
Gear Ratio: 3.8 to 1
Weight: 5.6 oz.

Fly Reels

Model No.: 440
Line Capacity: AFTMA L-8-F 50 yds.
Weight: 7.1 oz.
Features: Adjustable disc brak drag; convertible line guard and pawls; quick spool release.

Model No.: 480
Line Capacity: AFTMA L-6-F 40 yds.
Weight: 9.5 oz.
Features: Free stripping tension release; folding retrieve lever; machine cut brass gears; adjustable disc brake drag.

Orvis

Fly Reels

Model No.: F 1695
Line Capacity: WF6F line plus 50 yds. backing
Weight: 3 oz.
Spool Size: 3"
Features: Exposed spool rim; lever-adjustable drag; comes in fleece-lined leather case.

Model No.: F1930
Line Capacity: WF8F line plus 50 yds. backing
Weight: 3.5 oz.
Spool Size: 3³⁄₁₆"
Features: Lever-adjustable drag; reversible for left and right hand wind; exposed spool rim.

Model No.: F1710-Battenkill III
Line Capacity: WF6F plus 75 yds. backing
Weight: 3¾ oz.
Spool Size: 3¼".

Model No.: F1712-Battenkill IV
Line Capacity: WF8F plus 100 yds. backing
Weight: 3¾ oz.
Spool Size: 3¼"

Model No.: F1714-Battenkill V
Line Capacity: WF9F plus 200 yds. backing
Weight: 5¼ oz.
Spool Size: 3⅞"

Model No.: F1618-Madison 4/5
Line Capacity: WF4F; WF5F
Weight: 4 oz.
Spool Size: 3"
Features: Drag not adjustable.

Model No.: F1622-Madison 8
Line Capacity: WF8F flyline plus 150 yds. backing
Weight: 6 oz.
Spool Size: 3⅝"
Features: Drag with 8 positive settings.

Model No.: F0802-Magnalite Multiplier
Line Capacity: WF8F plus 50 yds. backing
Weight: 6½ oz.
Spool Size: 3½"

Model No.: F1662
Line Capacity: WF9F line plus 200 yds. 20 lb. test dacron backing
Weight: 11 oz.
Spool Size: 1⅜ oz.

Model No.: F1667-Seamaster "Tarpon"
Line Capacity: WF11F plus 335 yds. 20 lb. test dacron backing
Weight: 12 oz.

Spinning Reels

Model No.: F1627-50A
Line Capacity: 140 yds. 4 lb. test
Gear Ratio: 5 to 1
Weight: 6½ oz.
Features: Adjustable drag; silent gearing.

Model No.: F1648-100S
Line Capacity: 240 yds. 8 lb. test
Gear Ratio: 3.65 to 1
Weight: 10 oz.
Features: Stainless steel ball bearings; non-corrosive parts.

Model No.: F1652-150S
Line Capacity: 240 yds. 8 lb. test mono
Weight: 13 oz.
Features: Stainless steel ball bearings.

Penn

Spinning Reels

Model No.: 716
Line Capacity: 225 yds. 4 lb. mono
Gear Ratio: 5.1 to 1
Weight: 8.5 oz.
Features: Ball bearings; push button locking spool with teflon and stainless steel multi-drag system.

Model No. 716

Penn (con't.)

Model No.: 714
Line Capacity: 200 yds. mono
Gear Ratio: 5.1 to 1
Features: Stainless steel gear and ball
  bearings.

Model No.: 722
Line Capacity: 200 yds. 6 lb. mono
Gear Ratio: 5 to 1
Weight: 9¾ oz.
Features: Ball bearing pinion gear; full teflon
  drag system; two spools; anodized solid
  aluminum spool; folding handle.

Model No. 712

Model No.: 712
Line Capacity: 190 yds. 8 lb. mono
Gear Ratio: 4.1 to 1
Weight: 12¾ oz.
Features: Stainless steel main shaft; shielded
  ball bearings; aluminum spool; multi-disc
  full range drag; heavy duty bail arm;
  stainless steel bail.

Model No.: 704
Line Capacity: 450 yds. 10 lb. mono
Gear Ratio: 3.8 to 1
Weight: 21 oz.
Features: Teflon drag; one-piece rotor cup;
  ball bearings; strong main gear; aluminum
  housing; rugged stainless bail.

Model No.: 710
Line Capacity: 200 yds. 12 lb. mono
Gear Ratio: 3.6 to 1
Weight: 16⅜ oz.
Features: Teflon drags; tungsten carbide line
  guide rollers; stainless steel components;
  standard left hand drive.

Bait Casting Reels

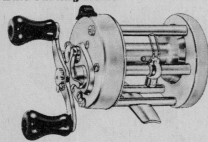

Model No. 940

Model No.: 940
Line Capacity: 225 yds. 12 lb. mono
Gear Ratio: 4 to 1

Weight: 11⅝ oz.
Features: Centrifugal spool; free spool clutch;
  multistage fighting drag system.

Model No.: 910
Line Capacity: 175 yds. 12 lb. mono
Gear Ratio: 4 to 1
Weight: 11 oz.
Features: Centrifugal spool drag; free spool
  clutch; multistage fighting drag system.

Level Wind Reels

Model No.: 9S
Line Capacity: 225 yds. 15 lb. mono
Gear Ratio: 3 to 1
Weight: 11 oz.
Features: Plastic spool; free spool action;
  spare pawl; star drag; torpedo handle.

Model No.: 209 MF
Line Capacity: 350 yds. 20 lb. mono
Gear Ratio: 3 to 1
Weight: 19.5 oz.
Features: Torpedo grip handle; star drag;
  spare pawl; full free spool action; metal
  or plastic spools.

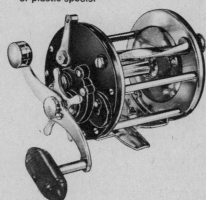

Model No. 350M

Model No.: 350 M
Line Capacity: 225 yds. 36 lb. nylon
Gear Ratio: 3 to 1
Weight: 20 oz.
Features: Brass metal spool; spiral bar.

Universal Reels

Model No.: 285
Line Capacity: 200 yds. 36 lb. nylon
Gear Ratio: 2.3 to 1
Weight: 17 oz.
Features: Reinforced plastic spool; torpedo
  handle; star drag.

Model No.: 85
Line Capacity: 200 yds. 36 lb. nylon
Gear Ratio: 2.3 to 1
Drag System: 16 oz.
Features: Reinforced plastic spool; free spool
  action; star drag; sliding click.

Trolling Reels

Model No.: 68
Line Capacity: 400 yds. 45 lb. nylon
Gear Ratio: 2.5 to 1
Weight: 29 oz.
Features: Rod clamps; chrome plated brass
  spools; moly-coated gears; torpedo
  handles; free spool action.

Model No.: 149
Line Capacity: 250 yds. 30 lb. dacron
Gear Ratio: 2.1 to 1
Weight: 24.5 oz.
Features: Fiberglas spool; torpedo handles;
  optional anti-reverse lever; one shot
  lubrication system.

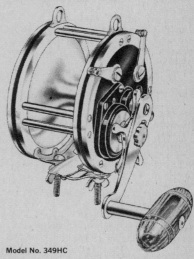

Model No. 349HC

Model No.: 349 HC
Line Capacity: 350 yds. 30 lb. dacron
Gear Ratio: 2⅓ to 1
Drag System: 37 oz.
Features: Solid bronze one cast metal spool;
  double leverage handle; optional
  anti-reverse lever; two lever control.

Pflueger

Spinning Reels

Model No.: 543
Line Capacity: 10 lb. mono
Gear Ratio: 3.5 to 1
Weight: 8 oz.
Features: 5-disc star drag; all metal gears
  and spool; ceramic pick-up pin.

Model No.: 222
Line Capacity: 180 yds. 6 lb. mono
Weight: 8 oz.
Features: Multi-disc drag; optional
  anti-reverse; folding bail and line roller.

Model No. 227

Pflueger (con't.)

Model No.: 227
Line Capacity: 240 yds. 8 lb. mono
Gear Ratio: 3.8 to 1
Weight: 10 oz.
Features: Multi-disc drag; folding steel bail; anti-reverse.

Model No.: 429
Line Capacity: 250 yds. 15 lb. mono
Gear Ratio: 3.4 to 1
Weight: 18 oz.
Features: Full race ball bearing; folding bail; optional anti-reverse; metal spool with pipe cleaner.

Model No.: 327
Line Capacity: 240 yds. 8 lb. mono
Gear Ratio: 3.8 to 1
Weight: 10 oz.
Features: Multi-disc drag; optional anti-reverse; ball-bearing mounted pinion.

Model No.: 643
Line Capacity: 250 yds. 20 lb. mono
Gear Ratio: 3.6 to 1
Weight: 22½ oz.
Features: Full race ball-bearing; stainless bail; adjustable drag range.

Bait Casting Reels

Model No.: 610 B
Line Capacity: 200 yds. 15 lb. mono
Weight: 9 oz.
Features: Stainless steel ball bearings; star drag; bronze & steel gears.

Model No.: 611 B
Line Capacity: 130 yds. 15 lb. mono
Weight: 8.7 oz.
Features: Stainless steel ball bearing; heat dissipating drag; optional anti-reverse.

Model No.: 1893 L
Line Capacity: 175 yds. 15 lb. braided
Gear Ratio: 4 to 1
Weight: 7¾ oz.
Features: Brass gears; bronze bushings; removable level-wind; anti-backlash; sliding click.

Model No. 1943

Model No.: 1943
Line Capacity: 175 yd. 15 lb. braided
Gear Ratio: 4 to 1
Weight: 7⅞ oz.
Features: Brass bearings; nylon and brass gears.

Fly Reels

Model No.: 1495
Weight: 6 oz.

Features: Adjustable drag; stainless steel line guide; instant take-apart spool release.

Model No.: 577
Line Capacity: L or T fly line + 250 yds. 15 lb. test mono backing
Weight: 10.5 oz.
Features: Adjustable drag; dual nylon bearings; solid aluminum spool.

Model No.: 1535
Weight: 6 oz.
Features: Adjustable drag; chromed pillars; line guards and crossplate.

Model No. 1535

St. Croix

Spinning Reels

Model No.: SL111
Line Capacity: 200 yds. 10 lb. test mono
Gear Ratio: 4 to 1
Weight: 12 oz.
Drag System: Multi-disc Teflon
Ball Bearings: Yes

Model No.: FS870
Line Capacity: 200 yds. 6 lb. mono
Gear Ratio: 3.48 to 1
Weight: 10 oz.

Model No.: FS880
Line Capacity: 200 yds. 8 lb. test mono
Gear Ratio: 3.5 to 1
Weight: 10 oz.
Drag System: Multi-disc
Ball Bearings: Yes

Model No. FS890

Model No.: FS890
Line Capacity: 300 yds. 20 lb. mono
Gear Ratio: 3.5 to 1
Weight: 12 oz.

Spin Casting Reels

Model No.: RF76
Line Capacity: 180 yds. 10 lb. test mono. Handles 6 lb. to 12 lb. test
Gear Ratio: 3 to 1
Drag System: Adjustable star

Model No. RF76

Model No.: 212
Line Capacity: 90 yds. 8 lb. test mono
Gear Ratio: 3 to 1
Weight: 6.7 oz.
Drag System: Long range pressure-type

Model No.: 238
Line Capacity: 90 yds. 8 lb. test
Gear Ratio: 3 to 1
Weight: 6.7 oz.
Drag System: Star

Model No.: 252
Line Capacity: 110 yds. 10 lb. test mono
Gear Ratio: 3 to 1
Weight: 10 oz.
Drag System: Pressure-type

Model No.: 268
Line Capacity: 100 yds. 10 lb. test
Gear Ratio: 3.5 to 1
Weight: 12.5 oz.

Bait Casting Reels

Model No.: 33
Line Capacity: 100 yds. 15 lb. braided line
Weight: 4 oz.
Drag System: Fingertip

Model No.: 44A
Line Capacity: 100 yds. 15 lb. test braided line
Weight: 6 oz.
Spool Material: Metal

Model No. 62

Model No.: 62
Line Capacity: 50 yds. 15 lb. test
Gear Ratio: 4 to 1
Weight: 5.5 oz.

St. Croix (con't.)

Fly Reels

Model No.: 25
Line Capacity: 30 yds. HCH taper; 25 yds. "C" level
Weight: 4½ oz.
Drag System: 2 position adjustable

Model No. 29

Model No.: 29
Line Capacity: 40 yds. "C" level line
Weight: 9½ oz.

Trolling Reels

Model No.: 5000
Line Capacity: 250 yds. 30 lb. test mono
Gear Ratio: 2.3 to 1
Weight: 17 oz.
Drag System: Star
Spool Material: Metal

Model No.: 6000
Line Capacity: 350 yds. 30 lb. test mono
Gear Ratio: 2.4 to 1
Weight: 20 oz.
Drag System: Multi-disc star

Model No.: 7000
Line Capacity: 300 yds. 35 lb. test
Gear Ratio: 2.4 to 1
Weight: 29.6 oz.
Spool Size: 2³¹⁄₆₄"

Model No. 7000

Scientific Anglers/3M

Fly Reels

Model No.: 9
Weight: 6¼ oz.
Spool Size: 3¾"
Features: Convertible handle; all metal spring latch; adjustable click-drag; corrosion-resistant components.

Model No.: 4
Weight: 3.5 oz.
Spool Size: 2¾"
Features: Convertible handle; all metal spring latch; adjustable click-drag.

Model No.: 5
Weight: 3¾ oz.
Spool Size: 3"
Features: One-piece spool; metal spring latch; adjustable click-drag.

Model No.: 7
Weight: 4½ oz.
Spool Size: 3⁷⁄₁₆"
Features: One-piece spool; all metal spring latch; adjustable click-drag.

Model No.: 10
Weight: 7½ oz.
Spool Size: 3⅞"
Features: Reels incorporate special corrosion-resistant components for saltwater use.

Scientific Anglers/3M Fly Reels

Model No.: 11
Weight: 8 oz.
Spool Size: 4"
Features: Reels incorporate special corrosion-resistant components for saltwater use.

Shakespeare

Spinning Reels

Model No.: 2540
Line Capacity: 250 yd. 12 lb. mono
Gear Ratio: 3.5 to 1
Features: Ball bearing for smooth retrieve; precision gears; one-piece foldaway crank with large grip and selective nonreverse.

Model No.: 2310
Line Capacity: 200 yds. 8 lb. mono
Gear Ratio: 3.3 to 1
Features: Selective non-reverse and precision gear.

Model No.: 1980
Gear Ratio: 5 to 1
Features: Stainless steel gear plate; aluminum spool; star drag; two stainless steel ball bearings.

Model No.: 2210 LH
Line Capacity: 270 yds. 6 lb. test mono; 180 yds. 8 lb. test mono
Gear Ratio: 3.7 to 1

Model No.: 2200 LH
Line Capacity: 170 yds. 6 lb. test mono
Gear Ratio: 5.2 to 1

Model No.: 1810
Line Capacity: 190 yds. 8 lb. test mono
Gear Ratio: 4 to 1

Model No.: 1756
Line Capacity: 145 yds. 8 lb. test mono
Gear Ratio: 4 to 1

Model No.: 2400
Line Capacity: 180 yds. 6 lb. test
Gear Ratio: 5.2 to 1

Model No.: 2410
Line Capacity: 270 yds. 8 lb. test mono
Gear Ratio: 4.5 to 1

Model No. 2430

Model No.: 2430
Line Capacity: 300 yds. 10 lb. test mono
Gear Ratio: 4.2 to 1

Model No.: 2450
Line Capacity: 400 yds. 12 lb. test mono
Gear Ratio: 4.1 to 1

Model No.: 2500
Line Capacity: 200 yds. 6 lb. mono
Gear Ratio: 4 to 1

Shakespeare (con't.)

Model No.: 2510
Line Capacity: 1200 yds. 8 lb. test mono
Gear Ratio: 3.8 to 1

Model No. 2510

Spin Casting Reels

Model No.: 1700 II
Gear Ratio: 4 to 1
Features: 4 unit; aluminum alloy construction; removable one piece spool; crank handle; stainless steel line guide.

Model No.: 1777 Level Wind Spin Cast
Line Capacity: 120 yds. 10 lb. mono
Gear Ratio: 4 to 1
Features: Aluminum alloy frame and side plates; smooth, hard ceramic pick-up pin; selective non-reverse.

Model No.: 7500
Line Capacity: 100 yds. 8 lb. mono
Gear Ratio: 4 to 1
Features: Stainless steel cone eyelet; permanent non-reverse.

Model No.: 7503
Line Capacity: 90 yds. 8 lb. test mono
Gear Ratio: 4 to 1

Model No.: 7504
Line Capacity: 85 yds. 20 lb. test mono
Gear Ratio: 4 to 1

Fly Reels

Model No.: 1822 O.K. Automatic
Line Capacity: Any L, WF or DT taper fly line up to No. 6
Weight: 8.5 oz.

Model No.: 1824
Line Capacity: Any L, WF or DT taper fly line up to No. 6
Weight: 8.9 oz.

Model No.: 1826
Line Capacity: Any L, WF or DT taper fly line up to No. 6
Weight: 9.4 oz.

Model No.: 1827
Line Capacity: Any L, WF or DT taper fly line up to No. 6
Weight: 9.4 oz.

Model No.: 7593
Line Capacity: Up to No. 6 wt. level
Weight: 4½ oz.
Spool Size: 2³⁄₁₆″ diameter; 1″ width

Model No.: 2530
Line Capacity: Up to No. 7 wt. level
Weight: 4⅞ oz.
Spool Size: ⅞″ width; 2½″ diameter

Model No.: 2531
Line Capacity: Up to No. 11 wt. level
Weight: 5½ oz.
Spool Size: 2″ diameter; ¹⁵⁄₁₆″ width

Model No.: 7594 Purist
Line Capacity: Up to 7 wt. level
Gear Ratio: 1 to 1
Weight: 4⅞ oz.
Drag System: 1 way drag can be set for right or left hand use
Spool Size: 2¹¹⁄₁₆″ diameter, ¹³⁄₁₆″ width

Model No.: 7595
Line Capacity: Up to 8 wt. level
Gear Ratio: 1 to 1
Weight: 5⅝ oz.
Spool Size: 2¹¹⁄₁₆″ diameter, 1″ width

Model No.: 7596
Line Capacity: Up to 11 wt. level
Gear Ratio: 1 to 1
Weight: 5⅝ oz.
Drag System: 1 way drag can be set for right or left hand use
Spool Size: 3¹⁄₁₆″ diameter, ¹³⁄₁₆″ width

Model No.: 7597
Line Capacity: Up to 12 wt. level
Gear Ratio: 1 to 1
Weight: 6⅜ oz.
Spool Size: 3¹⁄₁₆″ diameter, 1″ width

Bait Casting Reels

Model No.: 599
Line Capacity: 125 yds. 12½ lb. braided nylon; 100 yds. 15 lb. braided nylon
Weight: 3.9 oz.
Spool Size: 1⅜″ diameter

Model No.: 1924MS Direct Drive Reel
Line Capacity: 100 yds. 15 lb. braided nylon without arbor
Weight: 9.0 oz.
Ball Bearings: Yes
Spool Size: 1½″ diameter

Model No.: 1950 Direct Drive Level Wind
Line Capacity: 50 yds. 15 lb. braided nylon with arbor; 100 yds. 15 lb. braided nylon without arbor
Weight: 8.7 oz.

Model No.: 1973A Direct Drive Sportcast
Line Capacity: 50 yds. 12½ lb. braided line
Weight: 5.5 oz.
Ball Bearings: Yes, stainless steel

Spinmaster

Spinning Reels

Model No.: I
Line Capacity: 340 yds. 2 lb.
Gear Ratio: 4.9 to 1
Weight: 8.3 oz.
Features: Diamond cut gears; stainless steel full bail retrieve; free running line roller; 6-disc drag system; folding bail and handle; anti-reverse mechanism.

Model No.: II
Line Capacity: 420 yds. 4 lb.
Gear Ratio: 4.1 to 1
Weight: 12 oz.
Features: Diamond cut gears; stainless steel full bail retrieve; free running line roller; 6-disc drag system; folding bail and handle; anti-reverse mechanism.

Model No.: III
Line Capacity: 470 yds. 4 lb.
Gear Ratio: 4.1 to1
Weight: 13.9 oz.
Features: Diamond cut gears; stainless steel full bail retrieve; free running line roller; 6-disc drag system; folding bail and handle; anti-reverse mechanism.

Model No.: IV
Line Capacity: 580 yds. 6 lb.
Gear Ratio: 4.1 to 1
Weight: 17.3 oz.
Features: Diamond cut gears; stainless steel full bail retrieve; free running line roller; 6-disc drag system; folding bail and handle; anti-reverse mechanism.

Model No.: V
Line Capacity: 310 yds. 12 lb.
Gear Ratio: 3.6 to 1
Weight: 18 oz.
Features: Diamond cut gears; stainless steel full bail retrieve; free running line roller; 6-disc drag system; folding bail and handle; anti-reverse mechanism.

True Temper

Spinning Reels

Model No.: 507
Line Capacity: 200 yds. 8 lb. test mono
Gear Ratio: 3.5 to 1
Weight: 10 oz.
Drag System: Multiple
Ball Bearings: Yes
Spool Material: Aluminum

Model No.: 527
Line Capacity: 200 yds. 10 lb. test mono
Gear Ratio: 3.7 to 1
Weight: 12 oz.
Drag System: Multiple
Ball Bearings: Yes
Spool Material: Aluminum

Model No.: 537
Line Capacity: 200 yds. 15 lb. test mono
Gear Ratio: 3.87 to 1
Weight: 17 oz.
Drag System: Multiple
Ball Bearings: Yes
Spool Material: Aluminum

Model No.: 707
Line Capacity: 200 yds. 6 lb. test mono
Gear Ratio: 4.4 to 1
Weight: 7¾ oz.
Ball Bearings: Yes

Model No.: 727
Line Capacity: 200 yds. 10 lb. test mono
Gear Ratio: 4.1 to 1
Weight: 11½ oz.
Drag System: Adjustable
Ball Bearings: Yes
Spool Material: Aluminum

Model No.: 737
Line Capacity: 200 yds. 15 lb. test mono
Gear Ratio: 4.1 to 1
Weight: 13½ oz.
Ball Bearings: Yes

True Temper (con't.)

Model No.: 747
Line Capacity: 300 yds. 20 lb. test mono
Gear Ratio: 4.2 to 1
Weight: 21 oz.
Ball Bearings: Yes

Spin Casting Reels

Model No.: 327
Line Capacity: 100 yds. 10 lb. test mono
Gear Ratio: 3.2 to 1
Weight: 9½ oz.
Drag System: Wheel type
Spoon Material: Metal

Model No.: 337
Line Capacity: 100 yds. 15 lb. test mono
Gear Ratio: 3.5 to 1
Weight: 13 oz.
Drag System: Star
Ball Bearings: Yes

Tycoon/Fin-Nor

Spinning Reels

Model No.: Fin-Nor #3
Line Capacity: 300 yds. 8 lb. test; 225 yds.
    10 lb. test

Model No.: Fin-Nor #4
Line Capacity: 400 yds. 8 lb. test; 300 yds.
    15 lb. test

Fly Reels

Model No.: 1 "The Trout"
Line Capacity: 150 yds. 12 lb. test plus
    30 yds. #6
Weight: 6 oz.

Model No.: 2 "The Salmon"
Line Capacity: 200 yds. 15 lb. test plus
    40 yds. #9

Model No.: 3 "The Tarpon"
Line Capacity: 250 yds. 20 lb. test backing
    plus 40 yds. #10

Trolling Reels

Model No.: Big Game 12-20 lb. class
Line Capacity: 1200 yds. 12 lb. test;
    1000 yds. #20
Gear Ratio: 4 to 1
Size: 2½/0

Model No.: Big Game 30 lb. class
Gear Ratio: 4 to 1
Size: 4/0

Model No.: Big Game
Line Capacity: 800 yds. 50 lb.
Gear Ratio: 3 to 1
Spool Size: 6/0

Model No.: Big Game 50 lb. class
Line Capacity: 1200 yds. 50 lb.;
    650 yds. 80 lb.
Gear Ratio: 3 to 1
Size: 7½/0

Model No.: Big Game 80 lb. class reel
Line Capacity: 1000 yds. 80 lb.
Gear Ratio: 2¾ to 1, 1 to 1
Size: 9/0

Model No.: Big Game 50 lb. class
Line Capacity: 1000 yds. 130 lb. test
Gear Ratio: 1 to 1, 2 to 1, 3 to 1
Size: 12/0

Model No.: Golden Regal 20
Line Capacity: 1000 yds. 12 lb. test;
    800 yds. 20 lb. test

Model No.: Golden Regal 30
Line Capacity: 800 yds. 30 lb. test

Model No.: Golden Regal 50
Line Capacity: 800 yds. 50 lb. test

Zebco

Spinning Reels

Model No.: Cardinal 3
Line Capacity: 178 yds. 4 lb. test
Gear Ratio: 5 to 1
Drag System: Multi-disc
Ball Bearings: Yes

Model No.: Cardinal 6
Line Capacity: 1230 yds. 12 lb. mono
Gear Ratio: 3.5 to 1
Drag System: Multi-disc
Ball Bearings: Yes

Model No.: Cardinal 4
Line Capacity: 200 yds. 8 lb. test mono
Gear Ratio: 5 to 1
Drag System: Multi-disc
Ball Bearings: Yes

Model No.: Cardinal 7
Line Capacity: 220 yds. 17 lb. mono
Drag System: Multi-disc
Ball Bearings: Yes

Cardinal 6X and 7X

Model No.: Cardinal 6X
Line Capacity: 230 yds. 12 lb. mono
Gear Ratio: 5 to 1
Weight: 14.3 oz.
Features: Stainless ball bearings; stern-mounted drag; positive anti-reverse.

Model No.: Cardinal 7X
Line Capacity: 220 yds. 17 lb. mono
Gear Ratio: 5 to 1
Weight: 14.8 oz.
Features: Stern-mounted power drag; stainless steel ball bearings; stainless steel worm gear.

Model No.: 39XBL
Line Capacity: 200 yds. 8 lb. mono

Gear Ratio: 3.4 to 1
Drag System: Disc
Ball Bearings: Yes
Spool Material: Aluminum

Model No.: 95 XB
Line Capacity: 303 yds. 20 lb. mono
Gear Ratio: 3.4 to 1
Weight: 19.5 oz.
Features: Seven-disc drag; selective anti-reverse; zinc main and brass pinion gears.

Model No.: 80 XRL
Line Capacity: 300 yds. 15 lb. mono
Weight: 19.75 oz.
Features: Multiple-disc drag; torpedo knob; selective anti-reverse.

Model No.: 15 XRL
Line Capacity: 130 yds. 8 lb. mono
Gear Ratio: 3.4 to 1
Weight: 9.5 oz.
Features: Selective anti-reverse; multiple-disc drag; nickel-plated handle.

Model No.: 20 XR
Line Capacity: 160 yds. 8 lb. mono
Gear Ratio: 3.3 to 1
Weight: 8.5 oz.
Features: Multiple-disc drag; selective anti-reverse; heavy-duty gears.

Spin Casting Reels

Model No.: Omega One
Line Capacity: 105 yds. 14 lb. mono
Gear Ratio: 3 to 1
Weight: 11.25 oz.
Features: Stainless steel ball bearings; anti-reverse; star drag; removable spool.

Model No.: 33
Line Capacity: 100 yds. 10 lb. mono
Gear Ratio: 3 to 1
Weight: 8 oz.
Features: Stainless steel ball bearings; wide-range drag system; selective anti-reverse; interchangeable handle.

Model No.: Omega 113
Line Capacity: 65 yds. 6 lb. mono
Gear Ratio: 4.1 to 1
Weight: 4 oz.
Features: Hard chromed radial-edge spinner-head; thumb control; multi-disc drag; silent anti-reverse; corrosion-resistant.

Model No.: 888
Line Capacity: 100 yds. 20 lb. mono

Zebco (con't.)

Weight: 13.5 oz.
Features: Stainless steel gears; star drag; selective anti-reverse; torpedo knob.

Model No.: 800
Line Capacity: 50 yds. 14 lb. mono
Weight: 9 oz.
Features: Selective anti-reverse; multiple-disc drag system; stainless steel handle.

Model No.: 700
Line Capacity: 80 yds. 20 lb. mono
Weight: 8 oz.
Features: Selective anti-reverse; metal gears; stainless steel spinnerhead.

Model No.: 600
Line Capacity: 75 yds. 10 lb. mono
Weight: 7.5 oz.
Features: Radial-edge spinnerhead; aluminum covers; full-circle brake ring; adjustable drag system.

Model No.: 202
Line Capacity: 75 yds. 15 lb. mono
Weight: 6 oz.
Features: Stainless steel spinnerhead; ratchet drag system; aluminum handle.

Omega

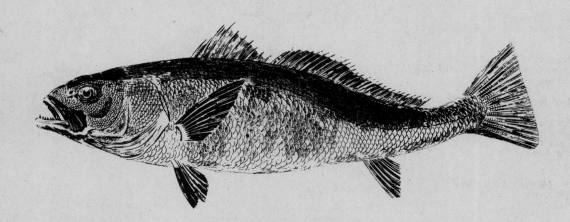

Specifications: Hooks and Lures

Hooks

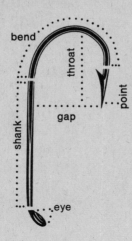

In the illustration at the left, the various parts of a fish hook are shown together with their names. The two important dimensions of the hook are made clear: its gap and its throat. The hook shown here is a Mustad-Viking hook. Note the width of the gap, the clearance between point and shank, and the depth of the throat of the hook. These generous dimensions make for a bigger bite, for deeper penetration of the point, and for better holding power. The weight of the fish is carried high up on the centre of the bend.

HOOK TERMINOLOGY

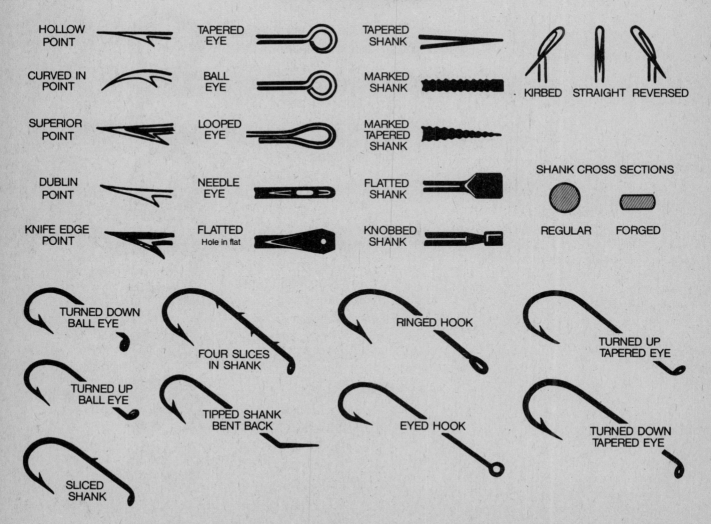

1977 Product Preview Lures

The array of artificial lures available today is staggering, yet manufacturers continue to market additions to their already crowded lines. When one considers how expensive it is to develop and manufacture a lure—any lure—the amount of fish-catching confidence exhibited in each creation is impressive.

Viewing the lure business in its entirety, there does not seem to be any major breakthroughs for 1977. Most of the work tends to be in subtle modifications of existing designs and in refinements that make a bait fish better than it did before. Some lure models will certainly be new for the company making them, but in many instances a similar bait had already been produced by another company.

Bass anglers continue to get most of the attention, and an increasing number of lures now have rattles in them. There have been improvements in spinner baits; soft plastics are molded into new and better shapes; and paint jobs on lures are more realistic than ever. Interestingly, many of these baits are being tested by anglers for other species, and the range of a given lure is being increased. In the artificial-lure business, the products are getting slicker and more sophisticated all the time. It makes one wonder what happened to last year's favorites.

The Jitterbug has been around for a long time, but Arbogast has just come out with a new version that is weedless. It's made in 3/8- and 5/8-ounce models and boasts a Hula Skirt for extra action. Speaking of skirts, Arbogast has a Quick Change Skirt that attaches to any lure with a specially designed wire

Arbogast's Weedless Jitterbug.

loop that is open on one end. These are available in three sizes, including an extra-husky one for salt water or big fresh water lures.

From Prescott Spinner comes word of a Buzzer-Spinner Worm that can be tossed into the heaviest cover and won't hang up. When retrieved quickly on the surface, it creates a buzzing disturbance that attracts bass, and it also turns fast

Quick Change Skirt by Arbogast.

Burke's Wig-Wag Minno.

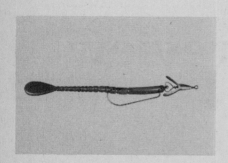

Prescott Buzzer-Spinner Worm.

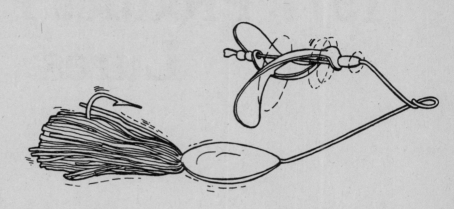

Skimmer Dedly Dudly from Burke.

Prescott Sea Gull.

Heddon Brush Popper.

on a slow retrieve. A salt water offering called the Sea Gull from Prescott is made from solid brass and plated with a mirror finish. It comes in seven sizes, from 1/8 ounce to 3 ounces, with a plain treble hook, a white bucktail treble or a single O'Shaughnessy with bucktail.

The Wig-Wag Minno, hot out of the molds of Burke Flexo-Products, will probably be copied by other lure manufacturers because it catches fish. Right now, it is

being made in four sizes, from a 1/8-ounce model to a 1¼ ounce. These lures have taken more than two dozen different salt water species and most fresh water gamefish. They can be cast, trolled or jigged. A flat head on Burke's Skimmer Dedly Dudly makes it a better buzzer by pushing the lure to the surface and making it stay there even at slow speeds. The flat head helps it to skim over grass, weeds and pads. Skimmer Dudly is made in 3/8- and 5/8-ounce sizes.

Several new lures have been included in the selection offered by James Heddon's Sons, starting with a deep-diving version of the traditional River Runt. A 1/4-ounce version of the Brush Popper has the same features as its 1/2-

ounce cousin, including the ability to slither over logs and through debris. It can also be used as a parachute bait and allowed to flutter to the bottom. Hi-Jacker, a new shad bait by Jack Davis, Heddon's master lure designer, is living up to

Heddon Hi-Jacker.

Super Liz by Mister Twister.

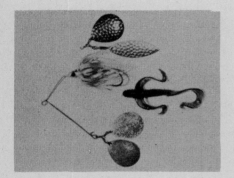

Mister Twister Twin-Sation.

its advance billing anywhere that shad form part of larger fishes' diet.

Soft plastics are the strong suit at Mister Twister, where innovation is the company's mainstay. A number of new items are featured for 1977, with the Sassy Shrimp heading the list. This plastic shrimp tail slips on a specially made leadhead, and in the water it looks like a real shrimp. The eight curly-tail legs on the imitation flutter in the water like those of a live shrimp. The color combinations are extensive and imaginative. Tails are made in 3-inch and 4-inch models and heads in four sizes, from 1/4 ounce to 1 ounce.

Two bass baits of particular interest are the Sassy Skirt and the Super Liz. The Skirt has six Mister Twister tails and can be fished alone or in conjunction with a plastic worm or a spinner bait; all

three can be combined if you prefer. The arms of the Sassy Skirt have a unique undulating action. It comes in 1½-inch, 2¼-inch and 3-inch lengths. The Super Liz differs from the regular Lizard in that the four legs on the new model are all Twister tails. It has a superior action in the water and promises to be a hot number for bass.

Mister Twister has a new line of spinner baits and a Groovy Grub with an extra-wide tail that is also available with a special grub head. The company has added both new shapes and new coloration to its worm line. Multi-color worms are now being made, in which the Twister tail is a different color from the body of the worm.

Fly fishermen know that hair bugs for bass and panfish are a thing of the past, but The Gaines Company of Gaines, Pennsylvania, is now tying these commercially and they are better than the ones

you can tie yourself. Some models are neatly trimmed, while others have the bushy appearance that has proved even more effective. Look at the Gaines Bush Bug, Stream Cleaner and Fuzz Bug. For panfish, the company has a new line of chenille-bodied bugs and sponge-bodied floaters, which it calls Softie Crickets.

In addition to some new poppers for 1977 that will increase its extensive topwater line for the fly fisherman, Gaines has introduced a series of Lead Bugs. Lead Bugs are hand-dressed lead-headed lures, including the effective shad dart-style head and several others that please a variety of fish species. Gaines seems to have items that are hard to find elsewhere because they involve so much hand labor; they are made in Pennsylvania.

Back in the 1830's Julio T. Buel of Whitehall, New York, invented and patented the first metal trolling lure. Not only was the Sagamore spoon an instant success; it revolutionized fishing and gained international acclaim. Over the years, fishermen forgot the first spoon, but the fish didn't. That's why Ed Eppinger of Dardevle has revived this old-time favorite and made it part of the famous Dardevle line. The Sagamore Flash is 13/32 ounce and tailored to be trolled with a fly. There is also a paper-thin Sagamore Spoon in 1/0, 2/0 and 3/0 sizes. Buel originated the Fluted Spinner 137 years ago

Gaines Hair Bugs.

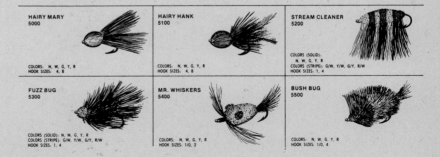

and Dardevle has brought it back for 1977 in three sizes: 1/0, 2/0 and 3/0.

On the salt water scene, Fenwick has made news by improving its existing line of trolling lures and incorporating new models and colors that should really do a job. The Cuttlefish 101 is a 4-inch imitation of a squid that works with everything from salmon and stripers to offshore fish. It can be rigged for trolling or casting and is available with 1/2-ounce and 1-ounce weights. There are nine color combinations, each with luminescent eyes and that all-important red slash. The Octopus 102 is a companion to the Cuttlefish 101 and one of the best salmon lures available. It is 4½ inches long and comes in ten two-color combinations, plus twenty single colors.

Fenwick has redesigned its Psychotails, those colored plastic strands that slip over a trolling bait or can be used for jigging with just a weight. Continued research has shown that the lures work better if the individual strands are softened and tapered. This gives the lure a better silhouette in the water and it catches more fish.

There's also a Bullethead that features plastic feathers. The plastic versions are far stronger than the chicken feathers traditionally used on this type of lure and reportedly produce their share of fish. The lure is available with a Flecto-Scale finish and a pearl finish and comes in three sizes and weights for trolling.

Designers at Strike King Lure Company have come up with a very deep running Scykoscout in the magnum size (3/8 ounce) and peanut size 1/4 ounce); both are

Hexhead from Fenwick.

available in countless color combinations. A sound chamber has been put in to create the rattle that is gaining in popularity among bass fishermen. The Big S and Little S have a baby brother in the Peanut S (1/4 ounce).

The new Buzz King spinner bait gives the angler the option of single, double or Tri-Spin Reflecto blades and is made specifically for fast topwater buzzing. Gold, chartreuse, fire orange or white blades are also available.

Particularly impressive is the new Timber King by Strike King. A perfectly balanced spoon with a double weed guard, it is dressed with a full tail skirt so that it will crawl over logs or glide over moss and lily pads. The hook is 5/0 and the spoon weighs 1/2 ounce for easy casting with the heavier lines necessary for fishing in cover.

A rip bait called the Stripe King (1/2 ounce), when jigged or bumped off the bottom, imitates a dying shad, creating sound waves heard by the fish. Strike King also has a new Diamond Back Shimmy Shad (3/8 ounce) that sends out vibrant pulsating waves.

Worth's Streamspin is an ideal casting or jigging lure that weighs 7/16 ounce and comes with either a single or a double blade. Adding to its versatility is the exclusive bead-lok fastening that permits quick changing of heads. The jig head has

Fenwick Squids.

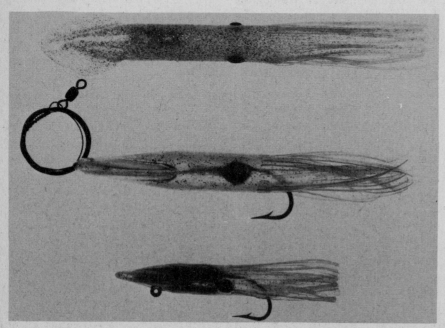

Worth Streamspin.

Worth Fishdevil.

a nonabsorbent plastic skirt which allows the angler to store the lure virtually dry in his tackle box and eliminates rust or corrosion.

Unlike most spoons, which tend to flatten horizontally on retrieve, Worth's Fishdevil is designed to stay vertically on edge. Its shape produces a lifelike action, while its elongated hook slot allows the hook to stay in line and clear of the lure at all times. Made of nonrusting material for use in both fresh and salt water, the Fishdevil comes in 3/4 ounce with a 1/0 treble and 2/3 ounce with a number 2 treble.

Worth's Musky Fin, a favorite since 1953, is now available in four smaller sizes for a variety of other species. The original weighs 1⅛ ounces, while the newest members of the family weigh 3/4 ounce, 1/3 ounce, 1/5 ounce and a tiny 1/9 ounce. Worth's patented offset shaft acts as a keel to prevent line

Musky Fin from Worth.

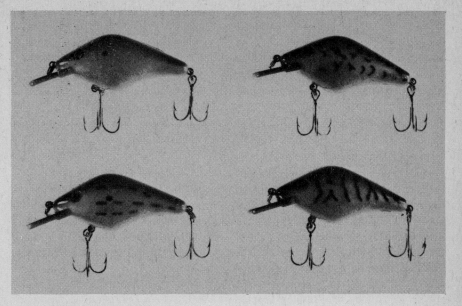

Tom Mann's Razor Back.

twist, while the flashing fluted nickel blade has a streak of red on the underside for added attraction.

The curly-tailed Jelly Waggler and the smaller grub-sized Jelly Wiggler are new from Mann's Bait Company. Jelly Wagglers are available with tails of the same color or in fluorescent shades. They are packed in several ways, including the new 25-pack that insures an adequate supply. There is a twin-bladed Little George and this popular lure is now being made in crawfish color as well as in the full range of other hues. Razor Backs are currently being manufactured in sizes from 1/8 ounce to 3/8 ounce and in both standard and deep-diving models.

Frog Mann is a topwater bait that contains BB shot inside dual sound chambers that give off supervibes as the lure is walked across the surface. It's made in two frog colors and four coach-dog shades. The Mann-O-Lure is a flat, all-metal lure tailored for salt water fishing but effective in fresh water as well. It comes in 1/2- and 1-ounce sizes in black, green,

brown, yellow and chartreuse combined with chrome and is worked as a jigging lure. There is also a Rabbit Spoon for structure jigging; it is made in 1/4-, 1/2- and 3/4-ounce models.

Spoons are the new item at Mepps. Imported by Sheldons', Inc., Mepps spinners have been famous for a long time, and the line continues to be improved with subtle variations. The spoons, however, have just been introduced. They are available in three sizes, weighing 1/5, 1/3 and 1/2 ounce. Colors are gold, silver, Rainbo scale and Redbo scale.

Colors are the big news at Rogers of Purdy, Missouri, and both the Craw Paps and the series of Big Jims, Middle Jims, Deep Jims and Little Jims come in a variety of new shades. Heading the list of colors is a red coach dog, chartreuse coach dog, white or white-and-black coach dog, and various shades with orange bellies which have increased in popularity.

The Les Davis Killer Diller combines swimming, squirming and gurgling actions to attract salmon,

Les Davis Killer Diller.

Les Davis Bang Tail Spinner.

trout, bass and other species. It can be cast or trolled and comes in four sizes: 1/12 ounce, 1/10 ounce, 1/4 ounce and 1/2 ounce. There are eleven color combinations. The Killer Diller is all metal with brazed rings and a channel through which the water flows, creating a sonic disturbance that attracts gamefish.

The Bang Tail spinner, in six sizes, from 1/16 ounce to 1/3 ounce, and in thirteen body colors, is another innovation from Les Davis. The flashing Scalelite blade

can be seen from great distances and it revolves easily. The smaller sizes are made for fly rod fishing and the larger models can be used with spinning or revolving spool tackle.

The Pt. Defiance Spoon from Les Davis has a special design that does not lose its action when bait is attached to the hook. Scalelite gives it flash and it is touted as a killer for salmon and trout when used in conjunction with a Herring Dodger and 18 inches of leader.

If you wonder what could possibly be new in pork rind, it's Ripple Rind, produced by Uncle Josh. Ripple Rind comes in several sizes and colors and has a unique swimming action because its shape is similar to that of a curly-tail worm. The pork rind, of course, is tough, and there's no way a fish is going to tear it off a hook. Ripple Rind can be used by itself or added to almost any lure to appeal to more fish.

Lure making is reaching a new degree of sophistication that improves on existing models and attempts to create new baits that are even better than the old. When you consider that every lure must catch the fisherman first and then the fish, it takes excellent design work to add a new lure to a line. From present signs, it is probably safe to bet that there will be a new breakthrough with different types of lures in the years ahead.

Lures

Fred Arbogast

Name: Weedless Jitterbug
Type: Plug
Color(s): 26 assorted
Length(s): 2″; 2½″
Weight(s): ⅜ oz.; ⅝ oz.
Material: Plastic

Name: Luminous Hula Popper
Type: Plug
Color(s): Natural
Weight(s): ¼ oz.; ⅜ oz.; ⅝ oz.
Material: Plastic

Name: Pug-Nose
Type: Pug
Color(s): 22 assorted
Length(s): 3¼″
Weight(s): ⅝ oz.

Name: Hammerhead
Type: Plug
Color(s): 7 assorted
Length(s): 5½″; 7½″
Weight(s): 1 oz.; 2½ oz.

Name: Jig Spinners (Prescott Style)
Type: Spinner
Color(s): Nickel; fluorescent red; gold;
  red & white
Length(s): ¾″; 1¼″

Pug-Nose

Name: Triton
Type: Plug
Color(s): 6 assorted
Weight(s): ¾ oz.; 1 oz.; 2 oz.

Name: The Whispy
Type: Spinner
Color(s): 5
Length(s): 1″; 1½″

Name: Jitterbug
Type: Plug
Color(s): 22 assorted
Length(s): 1¼″; 2″; 2½″; 3″
Weight(s): ⅛ oz.; ¼ oz.; ⅜ oz.; ⅝ oz.;
  1¼ oz.

Name: Tournament Hawaiian Wiggler
Type: Spinner
Color(s): Assorted
Length(s): 4″
Weight(s): ⅝ oz.; ¼ oz.

Name: Leadbelly
Type: Spoon
Color(s): 6 assorted
Weight(s): ⅝ oz.; ⅜ oz.; ⅛ oz.

Name: K-B 3 Dimensional Spoon
Type: Spoon
Color(s): Nickel; gold; copper; coho blue

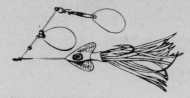

Tournament Hawaiian Wiggler

Length(s): 3½″; 4½″
Weight(s): 1 oz.; 1¾ oz.

Name: The Doctor Spoon
Type: Spoon
Color(s): 6 assorted
Length(s): 3¾″; 4½″
Weight(s): 1³⁄₁₆ oz.; ⅝ oz.
Material: Solid brass

Name: Wiggly-Eye
Type: Fin panfish
Color(s): Assorted
Length(s): ½″
Material: Nickel body

Name: Arbo-Gaster
Type: Spinner
Color(s): 31 assorted
Length(s): 1¾″; 2¼″; 2¾″
Weight(s): ⅛ oz.; ¼ oz.; ⅝ oz.

Weedless Jitterbug

Jim Bagley

Name: Hustle Bug
Type: Jig
Color(s): 8 assorted
Weight(s): ¹⁄₁₆ oz.; ⅛ oz.
Material: Plastic

Name: Regular Salty Dog
Type: Jig
Color(s): Assorted
Weight(s): ¼ oz.
Material: Lead, plastic

Name: Salty Dog Shrimp
Type: Jig
Color(s): Assorted
Weight(s): ⁵⁄₁₆ oz.; 1 oz.; 2 oz.
Material: Plastic

Name: Salty Dog Spoon
Type: Jig
Color(s): 5 assorted
Weight(s): 1 oz.; 2 oz.
Material: Lead body

Name: Bug Eye Shrimp
Type: Jig

Color(s): 8 assorted
Weight(s): 1 oz.; 2 oz.; 3 oz.

Name: Balsa Bang-O-Lure
Type: Plug
Color(s): 3
Length(s): 4¼″; 5¼″
Material: Balsa wood

Name: Dub'L-07 Fish Agent
Type: Plug
Color(s): 5
Length(s): 3½″; 5½″
Material: Balsa wood

Name: Switch Blade
Type: Spinner bait
Color(s): 7
Weight(s): ¼ oz.; ½ oz.

Name: Spinner Bug
Type: Spinner bait
Color(s): 7
Weight(s): ¼ oz.; ½ oz.

Name: Purty Bug
Type: Spinner bait
Color(s): Assorted
Weight(s): ⅛ oz.; ¼ oz.
Material: Plastic tail

Name: Submarine Shad
Type: Spinner bait
Color(s): 6 assorted
Weight(s): ⅛ oz.; ¼ oz.; ½ oz.; ¾ oz.

Name: Hardhead Baby Fly Worms
Type: Worm, rigged, non weedless
Color(s): 5
Length(s): 2½″; 4½″

Name: Medium 6″ Hardhead Worms
Type: Worm, rigged, weedless
Color(s): Assorted
Length(s): 6″
Material: Gold plated nonweedless hooks

Name: King Size 8″ Hardhead Worms
Type: Worm
Color(s): 6 assorted
Length(s): 8″
Material: 2 gold plated weedless hooks

Name: Ol' Monster 9″ Hardhead Worms
Type: Worm, rigged, weedless
Color(s): Assorted
Length(s): 9″

Name: King Size 8″ Eager Beaver
Type: Worm
Color(s): Black; purple; blue
Length(s): 8″

Name: 16″ Awful Worms
Type: Worm
Color(s): black; purple; blue
Length(s): 16″

Name: Spring Tail Worms
Type: Worm
Color(s): 7 assorted
Material: Plastic

Name: Spring Tail 9″ Mag-num Worms
Type: Worm
Color(s): Assorted

Length(s): 9″
Material: Plastic

Name: Flat Tail Molly
Type: Worm, rigged, weedless
Color(s): Assorted
Length(s): 8″

Name: Salt Water Eel
Type: Worm
Color(s): 6 assorted
Length(s): 10″
Material: Stainless steel chain; chrome-plated head

Bass Buster

Name: Worm Jig
Type: Jig
Color(s): Black; blue; purple; red
Length(s): 2″; 4″; 6″
Weight(s): ¼ oz.; ⅜ oz.
Material: Plastic

Name: Mini Twister
Type: Jig
Color(s): 8 assorted
Weight(s): ¼ oz.; ⅛ oz.; ¹⁄₃₂ oz.

Name: Maribou Jigs
Type: Jig
Color(s): 9 assorted
Weight(s): ¹⁄₆₄ oz.; ¹⁄₃₂ oz.; ¹⁄₁₆ oz.; ⅛ oz.; ¼ oz.; ⅜ oz.; ½ oz.; ⅝ oz.
Material: Gold plated hook; maribou body

Name: Bucktail Jig
Type: Jig
Color(s): 9 assorted
Weight(s): ⅛ oz.; ¼ oz.; ⅜ oz.; ½ oz.
Material: Gold plated hook; fiber guard

Name: Beetle
Type: Jig
Color(s): 19 assorted
Weight(s): ¼ oz.; ³⁄₁₆ oz.; ⅛ oz.; ¹⁄₁₆ oz.; ¹⁄₃₂ oz.; ¹⁄₆₄ oz.
Material: Gold plated hook; plastic body

Name: Crappie Buster Jigs
Type: Jig
Color(s): Assorted
Weight(s): ⅛ oz.; ¹⁄₁₆ oz.; ¹⁄₃₂ oz.
Material: Gold plated hook; chenille body

Name: Mini Twister Spin
Type: Spinner bait
Color(s): 8 assorted
Weight(s): ¼ oz.; ⅛ oz.; ¹⁄₃₂ oz.

Name: Tandem Spin
Type: 2 Blade spinner bait
Color(s): 11 assorted
Weight(s): ¼ oz.; ⅜ oz.; ½ oz.; ⅝ oz.
Material: Copper blades; nickel plated hook; vinyl skirt

Name: Scorpion
Type: Spinner bait
Color(s): 8 assorted
Weight(s): ½ oz.; ⅜ oz.; ¼ oz.; ⅛ oz.
Material: Chrome or copper spinner; nickel plated hook and plastic skirt

Name: Beetle spin
Type: Spinner bait
Color(s): 19 assorted
Weight(s): ¼ oz.; ⅛ oz.; ¹⁄₃₂ oz.; ³⁄₁₆ oz.
Material: Gold plated hook; chrome blade, plastic blade

Name: Tarantula
Type: Spinner bait
Color(s): Assorted
Weight(s): ½ oz.; ⅜ oz.; ¼ oz.
Material: Nickel plated hook; chrome blade

Name: Slinky Worm
Type: Worm
Color(s): Assorted
Length(s): 4″; 6″; 7½″; 9″
Material: Plastic

Mackerel Jigs

Bead Chain

Name: Mackerel Jigs
Type: Jig
Color(s): Metal finish
Length(s): Small; medium; large
Weight(s): ¾ oz.; ½ oz.; ⅜ oz.
Material: Metal finish

Name: Diamond Treble
Type: Jig
Color(s): Nickel finish
Weight(s): 1 oz.; 1⅝ oz.; 2 oz.; 3 oz.; 4 oz.; 6 oz.; 8 oz.; 10 oz.; 14 oz.; 16 oz.

Name: Diamond Squids
Type: Jig
Color(s): Polished nickel finish
Length(s): 2″; 3″; 4″; 5″
Weight(s): 1 oz.; 3 oz.; 4¾ oz.; 8 oz.
Material: Brass

Flat Diamond Lure

Name: Flat Diamond Lure
Type: Jig
Color(s): Nickel finish
Weight(s): ½ oz.; ¾ oz.; 1 oz.; 1¼ oz.; 1½ oz.; 2 oz.

Name: Small Diamond Jigs
Type: Jig
Color(s): Nickel finish
Weight(s): ¼ oz.; ⅓ oz.; ½ oz.

Blakemore

Name: Crappie's Delight
Type: Jig
Color(s): Assorted
Weight(s): ¹⁄₆₄ oz.; ¹⁄₃₂ oz.; ¹⁄₁₆ oz.; ⅛ oz.
Material: Marabou skirt

Name: Road Runner
Type: Jig
Color(s): Assorted
Weight(s): ¹⁄₁₆ oz.; ⅛ oz.; ¼ oz.

Name: Trout & Panfish Worm
Type: Worm
Color(s): Assorted
Length(s): 2″
Material: Plastic

Name: Cheese Treated Worm
Type: Worm
Color(s): White; red
Length(s): 3¼″
Material: Plastic

Name: Single-spin
Type: Spinner bait
Color(s): Fluorescent; standard
Weight(s): ¼ oz.; ⅜ oz.
Material: Nickel or copper blades

Name: Split Tail Spin
Type: Spinner bait
Color(s): Assorted
Weight(s): ¹⁄₁₆ oz.; ⅛ oz.

Name: Twister
Type: Spinner bait
Color(s): Assorted
Weight(s): ¾ oz.

Name: Crayfish
Type: Spinner
Color(s): 8 assorted
Length(s): 2⅞″; 3⅝″
Weight(s): ¼ oz.; ½ oz.

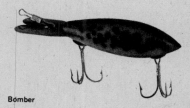

Bomber

Bomber

Name: Jig
Type: Jig
Color(s): Assorted
Length(s): 2¾″; 3″; 3¼″; 3½″
Weight(s): ¼ oz.; ½ oz.; ¾ oz.; 1 oz.

Name: Speed Shad

Type: Plug
Color(s): 33 assorted
Length(s): 2″; 2½″; 3″
Weight(s): ⅕ oz.; ⅓ oz.; ⅖ oz.

Name: Pinfish
Type: Plug
Color(s): Assorted
Length(s): 2″; 2½″; 3″
Weight(s): ¼ oz.; ⅜ oz.; ½ oz.

Name: Jerk Bait
Type: Jig
Color(s): 15 assorted
Length(s): 3″; 3½″; 4⅛″
Weight(s): ½ oz.; ⅝ oz.; ⅞ oz.

Name: Waterdog
Type: Plug
Color(s): 20 assorted
Length(s): 3½″; 4½″; 5½″
Weight(s): ¼ oz.; ½ oz.; ⅝ oz.

Pinfish

Name: The Bomber; Baby; Midget; Small;
Medium; Large
Type: Plug
Color(s): Assorted
Length(s): 2½″; 2¾″; 3¼″; 3¾″; 4¼″
Weights: ¼ oz.; ⅜ oz.; ½ oz.; ⅝ oz.; ¾ oz.

Name: Spinstick
Type: Spinner
Color(s): Assorted
Length(s): 2½″; 3½″
Weight(s): ¼ oz.; ⅜ oz.

Name: Bushwacker
Type: Spinner bait
Color(s): Assorted
Weight(s): ¼ oz.; ½ oz.

Name: Slab Spoon
Type: Spoon
Color(s): Assorted
Length(s): 1½″; 1¾″; 2⅛″
Weight(s): ⅝ oz.; ⅞ oz.; 1¼ oz.

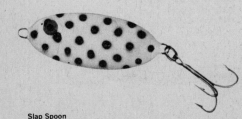

Slap Spoon

Boone

Name: Spinana
Type: Plug
Color(s): 6
Weight(s): ⅓ oz.; ½ oz.
Material: Plastic

Name: Needlefish
Type: Plug
Color(s): Green & white
Weight(s): ½ oz.
Material: Plastic

Name: Zig-Zagger
Type: Plug
Color(s): 5
Weight(s): ¾ oz.
Material: Plastic

Name: Queen Bee
Type: Popping bug
Color(s): Yellow & black
Material: Natural cork

Name: Shad Jigs
Type: Jigs
Color(s): 9 assorted
Weight(s): ⅛ oz.; ¼ oz.; ½ oz.; 1 oz.
Material: Bucktail; nylon

Name: Scuba-Du-Diva
Type: Jig
Color(s): 3
Weight(s): 1 oz.; 1½ oz.; 2 oz.; 3 oz.; 4 oz.

Name: Round Worms
Type: Worm
Color(s): 10
Length(s): 6¼″
Material: Plastic

Name: Teasers
Type: Teaser
Color(s): 4
Length(s): 12″; 15″
Material: Nylon

Burke

Name: Wig Wag Worm
Type: Worm
Color(s): Assorted
Length(s): 7″; 9″

Name: "Skimmer" Dedly Dudly
Type: Spinner
Color(s): Assorted
Weight(s): ⅜ oz.; ⅝ oz.

Name: Wig-Wag Minno
Type: Spinner
Color(s): Assorted
Weight(s): ⅛ oz.; ⅜ oz.; ⅝ oz.

Name: Jig-A-Do Worm
Type: Worm
Color(s): Assorted
Length(s): 4″; 7″
Weight(s): ⅓ oz.; ½ oz.
Material: Plastic

Name: Spin-Dance
Type: Spinner
Color(s): 10
Weight(s): ¼ oz.; ½ oz.

Name: Salt Water Wig-Wags
Type: Worm
Color(s): 14 assorted

Weight(s): ⅛ oz.; ¼ oz.; ⅜ oz.; ½ oz.
Material: Plastic

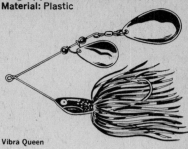

Vibra Queen

Cotton Cordell

Name: Big O
Type: Plug
Color(s): Assorted
Weight(s): ⅓ oz.; ⅜ oz.; ½ oz.; ⅝ oz.; 1 oz.
Material: Plastic

Name: Deep Big O
Type: Plug
Color(s): Assorted
Weight(s): ¼ oz.; ⅓ oz.; ⅜ oz.; ½ oz.; ⅝ oz.
Material: Plastic

Name: Gay Blade
Type: Plug
Color(s): Assorted
Weight(s): ⅛ oz.; ¼ oz.; ⅜ oz.; ¾ oz.
Material: Metal

Name: Super Shad
Type: Plug
Color(s): Assorted
Weight(s): ¼ oz.; ⅓ oz.; ⅜ oz.

Gay Blade

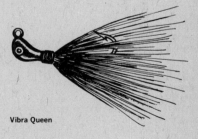

Vibra Queen

Name: Boy Howdy
Type: Spinner
Color(s): Assorted
Weight(s): ⅓ oz.; ⅜ oz.
Material: Plastic

Name: Near Nuthin'
Type: Plug
Color(s): 3
Weight(s): ½ oz.; ⅞ oz.; 2 oz.
Material: Plastic

Name: Vibra Queen
Type: Spinner
Color(s): Assorted
Weight(s): ¼ oz.; ⅜ oz.
Material: Rubber or vinyl skirts

Name: Banana Jig
Type: Jig
Color(s): Assorted
Weight(s): ⅛ oz.; ¼ oz.; ½ oz.
Material: Bucktail

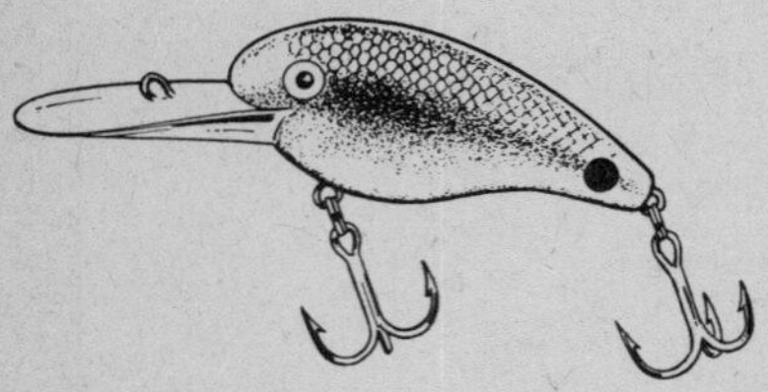

Deep Big O

Creek Chub

Name: Creek Chub Ding Bat
Type: Jig
Color(s): Assorted
Length(s): 2″
Weight(s): ¼ oz.
Material: Plastic

Name: Cheekie
Type: Spinner
Color(s): 6
Weight(s): ½ oz.

Name: Striper Strike
Type: Plug
Color(s): Assorted
Weight(s): ½ oz.; ¾ oz.; 1 oz.; 1½ oz.; 2¼ oz.
Material: Plastic

Name: Mouse
Type: Plug
Color(s): Assorted
Weight(s): ¼ oz.
Material: Plastic

Name: Darter
Type: Plug
Color(s): Assorted
Weight(s): ½ oz.
Material: Wood; plastic

Name: Plunker
Type: Plug
Color(s): Assorted
Length(s): 1⅝″; 2″; 2½″
Weight(s): ⅛ oz.; ¼ oz.; ⅜ oz.; ½ oz.
Material: Wood; plastic

Name: Nikie
Type: Plug
Color(s): Assorted
Weight(s): ¼ oz.; ⅛ oz.
Material: Plastic

Name: Creek Chub Mouse
Type: Plug
Color(s): Assorted
Length(s): 2¼″; 2½″; 2¾″
Weight(s): ¼ oz.; ⅜ oz.; ½ oz.
Material: Plastic

Name: Creek Chub Striper Strike
Type: Plug
Color(s): Amber
Length(s): 2½″; 3″; 4½″; 5¼″
Weight(s): ½ oz.; ¾ oz.; 1 oz.; 1½ oz.; 2¼ oz.
Material: Plastic

Name: Creek Chub Huskie Jointed Pikie
Type: Plug
Length(s): 6″
Weight(s): 1½ oz.
Material: Plastic; wood

Name: Creek Chub Giant Straight Pikie
Type: Plug
Length(s): 8″
Weight(s): 3½ oz.
Material: Wood

Name: Creek Chub Jointed Snook Pikie
Type: Plug
Length(s): 4⅞″
Weight(s): 1⅛ oz.
Material: Wood

Name: Creek Chub Wiggle Diver
Type: Plug
Color(s): 3
Length(s): 5″
Weight(s): 1½ oz.
Material: Plastic

Name: Creek Chub Super Pikie
Type: Plug
Length(s): 4⅞″
Weight(s): 1⅛ oz.

Name: Streeker
Type: Spinner
Color(s): 7
Weight(s): ⅜ oz.; 1 oz.
Material: Plastic

Name: Straight Pikie
Type: Spinner
Color(s): Assorted
Weight(s): ½ oz.; ¾ oz.; 1⅛ oz.; 1½ oz.; 3¼ oz.; 3½ oz.
Material: Plastic; wood

Name: Creek Chub Injured Minnow
Type: Spinner
Color(s): Assorted
Length(s): 1⅝″; 2″; 3¾″; 2¾
Weight(s): ⅛ oz.; ¼ oz.; ⅝ oz.; ½ oz.
Material: Plastic; wood

Name: Creek Chub Streeker
Type: Spinner
Color(s): Assorted
Length(s): 3″; 4½″
Weight(s): ⅜ oz.; 1 oz.
Material: Plastic

Name: Creek Chub Cohokie
Type: Spoon
Color(s): Assorted
Length(s): 2″; 2¾″
Weight(s): ¼ oz.; ½ oz.
Material: Metal

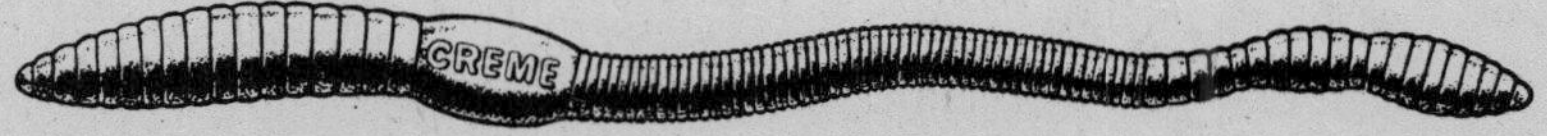

Scoundrel

Creme

Name: Caddis Fly
Type: Fly
Color(s): Brown; yellow

Name: Brown Frog
Type: Fly

Name: Bee
Type: Fly

Name: Sand Crab
Type: Fly

Name: Grasshopper
Type: Fly

Name: Spent Wing Salmon Fly
Type: Fly

Name: Ratlin' Grub
Type: Jig
Color(s): Assorted
Weight(s): ¼ oz.

Name: Soda Straw
Type: Worm
Color(s): Assorted
Length(s): 10″

Name: Scoundrel
Type: Worm
Color(s): Assorted
Length(s): 6″

Name: Shimmy Gal
Type: Worm
Color(s): Assorted
Length(s): 7¼″

Name: Scally-Wag
Type: Worm
Color(s): Assorted
Length(s): 4″; 6″
Material: Plastic

Dardevle

Name: Thindervle
Type: Spoon
Length(s): 3¼″ x ¾″
Weight(s): ⅓ oz.
Material: Metal

Name: Dardevle; Dardevlet; Dardevle Imp; Dardevle Spinnie; Dardevle Midget
Type: Spoon
Color(s): Not specified
Length(s): 3⅝″ x 1¼″; 2⅞″ x 1 3/16″; 2¼″ x ⅞″; 1¾″ x ¾″; 1⅜″ x ⅝″
Weight(s): 1 oz.; ⅗ oz.; ⅖ oz.; ¼ oz.; 3/16 oz.
Material: Metal

Name: Seadevle
Type: Spoon
Length(s): 5¾″ x 1⅛″
Weight(s): 3 oz.
Metal: Metal

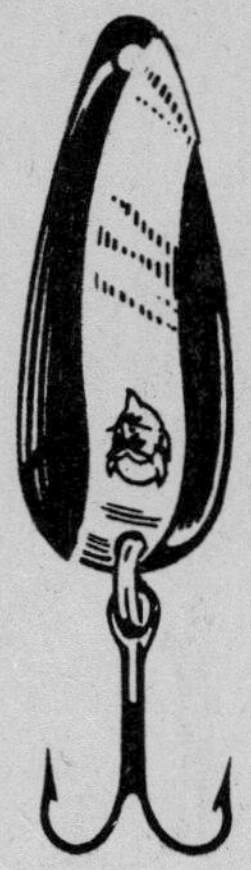

Dardevle Imp

Name: Rok't-Devle Imp
Type: Spoon
Length(s): 2¼" x ⅞"
Weight(s): ⅘ oz.
Material: Metal

Name: Dardevle Klincker
Type: Spinner
Color(s): Assorted
Length(s): 3⅝" x 1¼"
Weight(s): 1 oz.

Name: Fluted Spinner
Type: Spinner
Color(s): Assorted
Length(s): 3 sizes
Material: Metal

Name: Crystal Dardevles
Type: Spoon
Color(s): Silver; bronze; copper

Name: Sagamore Flash with Koho Fly
Type: Spoon
Color(s): 21
Length(s): 4⁵⁄₁₆"
Weight(s): ¹³⁄₃₂ oz.

Name: Huskie Devle
Type: Spoon
Color(s): 4
Length(s): 5⅜"
Weight(s): 3⅛ oz.

Name: Notangle
Type: Spinner
Color(s): Assorted
Weight(s): ⅛ oz.; ¼ oz.; ½ oz.

Les Davis

Name: Scalelite-Squid
Type: Spinner
Color(s): 8 assorted
Length(s): 3 sizes

Name: Scalelite North Star
Type: Spinner fly
Color(s): Green back; blue back; yellow back

Name: Witch Doctor
Type: Plug
Color(s): Assorted
Length(s): 2½"; 3"; 3⅝"
Weight(s): ¼ oz.; ⅓ oz.; ½ oz.
Material: Plastic

Name: Cutplug
Type: Plug
Color(s): Silver or gold scalelite; assorted
Length(s): 3"; 4"; 5"
Weight(s): ⅜ oz.; ¾ oz.; 1½ oz.
Material: Plastic

Name: Hotrod
Type: Spinner
Color(s): Assorted
Weight(s): ⅙ oz.; ¼ oz.; ⅜ oz.; ½ oz.
Material: Spring metal blade; solid brass

Name: Killer Diller
Type Spinner
Color(s): Assorted
Weight(s): ¹⁄₁₂ oz.; ⅒ oz.; ¼ oz.; ½ oz.
Material: Metal with brazed rings

Name: Bang Tail
Type: Spinner
Color(s): Assorted
Weight(s): ¹⁄₁₆ oz.; ¹⁄₁₂ oz.; ⅛ oz.; ⅙ oz.; ¼ oz.; ⅓ oz.

Dragon Fly

Name: Round Head Bucktail Jig
Type: Jig
Color(s): White; red & white; yellow
Weight(s): ¼ oz.; ⅜ oz.; ½ oz.; ¾ oz.; 1 oz.

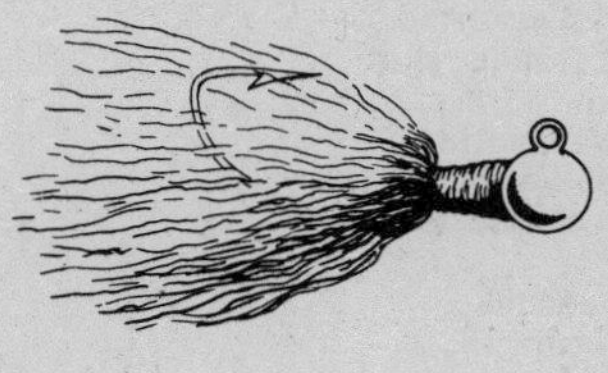

Round Head Bucktail Jig

Name: Three Eyed Devil
Type: Popper bug
Color(s): Yellow; white

Name: Shad Dart
Type: Jig
Color(s): Red head; white or yellow tail
Weight(s): ¹⁄₁₂ oz.; ⅛ oz.; ⅓ oz.

Name: Crappie Fly
Type: Jig
Color(s): Assorted
Weight(s): ¹⁄₁₆ oz.

Name: Striper Rock Bass Jig
Type: Jig
Color(s): Assorted
Weight(s): ⅛ oz.; ¼ oz.; ½ oz.; 1 oz.

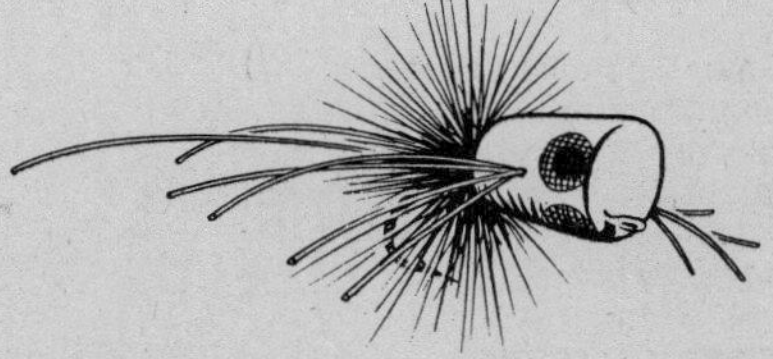

Three Eyed Devil

Name: Wiggle Tail Spin
Type: Spinner
Color(s): Assorted
Weight(s): ¼ oz.
Material: Nickel

Name: Propellor Plug
Type: Plug
Color(s): Assorted
Weight(s): ¼ oz.

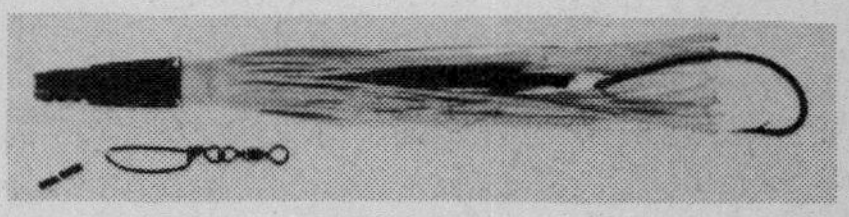

Psychobeads

Fenwick

Name: Knucklehead
Type: Jig on skirt
Length(s): 5"; 6"; 9½"; 12"; 16½"

Name: Bullethead
Type: Jig
Color(s): Assorted skirt colors
Length(s): 4½"; 5 ½"; 6½"
Weight(s): ½ oz.; 1 oz.
Material: Plastic feathers

Name: Psychotails
Type: Jig
Color(s): 20 assorted
Length(s): 4½"; 6½"; 8½"; 10½"; 11"; 12"; 14"
Material: Plastic

Name: Psychobeads
Type: Jig
Color(s): Assorted
Length(s): 11"; 12"
Weight(s): 2 oz.; 4 oz.; 6 oz.
Material: Clear plastic head or Flecto-scale metallic

Name: Psychosquid
Type: Jig
Color(s): Phosphorescent squid color
Length(s): 4"; 6"; 11"; 14"
Weight(s): 1 oz.
Material: Plastic

Name: Konahead
Type: Jig
Color(s): Assorted
Length(s): Transparent heads: 13"; 15½"
Solid Color head: 7¾"; 11"; 13"; 15½"
Weight(s): 5½ oz.; 7 ¾ oz.; 8½ oz.; 9½ oz.; 16 oz.; 17 oz.

Name: Cuttlefish 101
Type: Jig
Color(s): Assorted
Length(s): 4"
Weight(s): ½ oz.; 1 oz.

Name: Octopus 102
Type: Jig
Color(s): Assorted
Length(s): 4½"
Weight(s): ½ oz.; 1 oz.

Name: Psychohex
Type: Jig
Length(s): 18"

Name: Hexhead
Type: Jig
Length(s): 3¾"; 4½"; 5"; 7½"
Weight(s): ¾ oz.; 1 oz.; 2 oz.; 4 oz.

Gaines

Name: Bucktail Beau
Type: Bug
Color(s): Assorted
Weight(s): 1/32 oz.; 1/16 oz.; ⅛ oz.; ¼ oz.; ⅜ oz;. ½ oz.
Material: Lead

Name: Mr. Magic
Type: Bug
Color(s): Assorted
Material: Cork body; bucktail

Name: Helgrabug
Type: Bug
Color(s): 8 assorted
Material: Sponge body

Name: Marabou Miss 7600
Type: Bug
Color(s): Assorted
Material: Chenille

Name: Minnie — Pop 200
Type: Popper
Color(s): Standard color assortment

Name: Pan Popp 1100
Type: Popper
Color(s): Standard color assortment

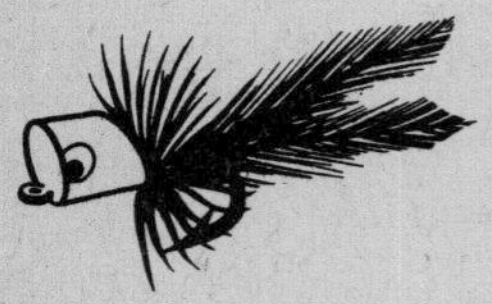

Gnat 3200

Name: Bee Bug 1700
Type: Popper
Color(s): Standard color assortment

Name: Gnat 3200
Type: Popper
Color(s): Standard color assortment

Name: Froggie
Type: Popper
Color(s): Standard color assortment

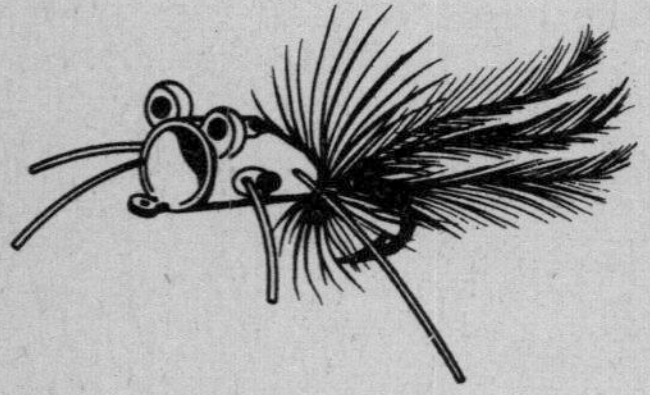

Froggie

Gapen

Name: Ripple Fish
Type: Spinner
Color(s): Assorted
Weight(s): ⅜ oz.; ⅝ oz.

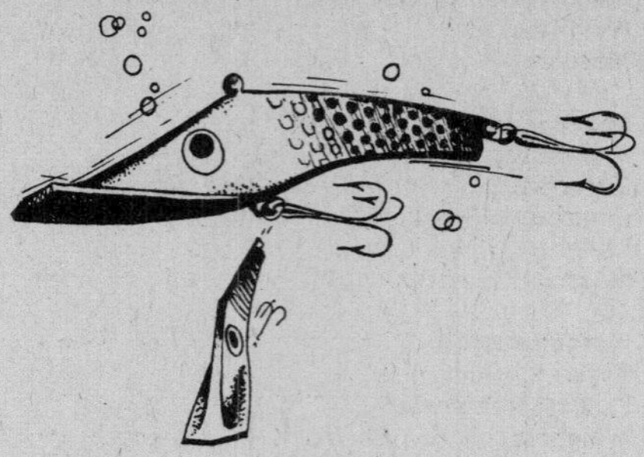

Shoveler

Name: De'Minnow
Type: Spinner
Color(s): Assorted
Weight(s): ⅜ oz.; ⅝ oz.

Name: Shoveler
Type: Spinner
Color(s): Assorted
Weight(s): ⅜ oz.; ⅝ oz.

Name: Crappie Bait
Type: Jig
Color(s): Assorted
Weight(s): 1/32 oz.
Material: Vinyl body; nickel-plated head

Name: Weedcutter I
Type: Spinner bait
Color(s): 5 assorted
Material: Rubber skirt

Name: Weedcutter III
Type: Spinner bait
Color(s): 5 assorted

Name: Leeches
Type: Worm
Color(s): Assorted
Length(s): 2"; 3½"
Material: Vinyl

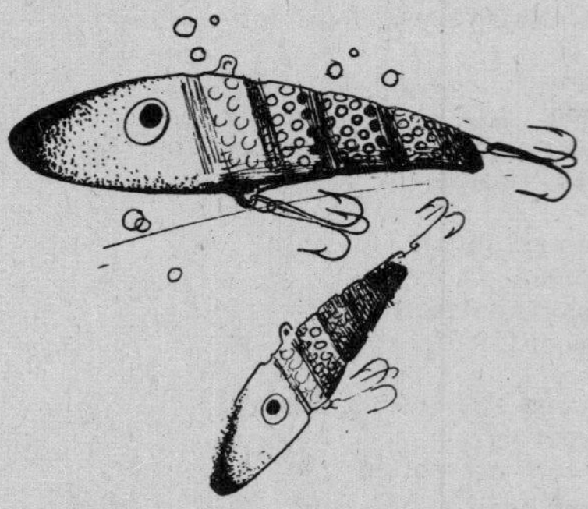

Ripple Fish

Gladding

Name: Flectolite Shyster
Type: Spinner
Color(s): 3 assorted
Weight(s): ⅛ oz.; ¼ oz.; ⅓ oz.; ½ oz.

Name: Safari
Type: Spinner
Color(s): Assorted
Weight(s): ⅝ oz.

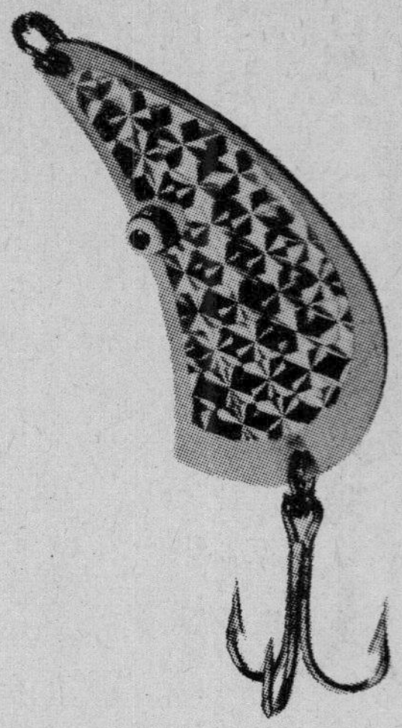

Cyclops

Name: Racketeer
Type: Spoon
Color(s): Red
Length(s): 1½"; 2"
Weight(s): ¼ oz.; ⅜ oz.

Name: Cyclops
Type: Spoon
Colors: Assorted
Weight(s): ¼ oz.; ½ oz.; ⅜ oz.; ⅝ oz.; 1 oz.

Name: Squirm Worm
Type: Worm
Color(s): Purple; black; strawberry
Length(s): 7"

Name: Shad Dart Jig Fly
Type: Jig
Color(s): Assorted
Weight(s): 1/16 oz.; 3/32 oz.; ⅛ oz.; 3/16 oz.

Name: Big Bug Eye
Type: Bug
Color(s): Yellow; white
Weight(s): 2 oz.; 3 oz.

Name: Tall Tale Shrimp
Type: Jig
Color(s): 8
Weight(s): ¼ oz.; ½ oz.; ¾ oz.; 1 oz.; 2 oz.
Material: Nickel head

Name: Skin Head
Type: Jig
Color(s): 5
Weight(s): ½ oz.; ¾ oz.; 1½ oz.; 2½ oz.
Material: Lead alloy head; feather jig

Gudebrod

Name: Sniper
Type: Jig
Color(s): 8 assorted
Length(s): 3⅜"; 2⅞"; 5¼"
Weight(s): ⅛ oz.; ½ oz.; 1⅛ oz.
Material: Plastic

Name: Bippie
Type: Plug
Color(s): Assorted
Length(s): 2¼"
Weight(s): ⅝ oz.

Name: Bassprin
Type: Plug
Color(s): 12 assorted
Weight(s): ⅛ oz.; ⅜ oz.; ½ oz.

Name: Firebacks
Type: Plug
Color(s): 3 fluorescent

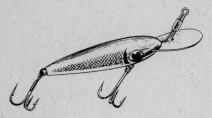

Bump "N" Grind

Name: Bump 'N' Grind
Type: Plug
Color(s): 3 fluorescent
Length(s): 2⅜"; 2⅞"; 5½"
Weight(s): ⅛ oz.; ½ oz.; 1⅛ oz.

Name: Maverick
Type: Plug
Color(s): 7 standard; 3 flourescent
Length(s): 3¼"; 4¼"
Weight(s): ¼ oz.; ⅜ oz.

Name: Goodie
Type: Plug
Color(s): 12 assorted
Length(s): 2⅞"
Weight(s): ¼ oz.

Name: Blabber Mouth
Type: Plug
Color(s): Assorted
Length(s): 1¾"; 3"
Weight(s): ⅛ oz.; ½ oz.

Name: Trouble Maker
Type: Plug
Color(s): 14 assorted
Length(s): 1½"; 2"; 2⅝"; 3¾"; 5¼"
Weight(s): ⅛ oz.; ¼ oz.; ½ oz.; 1¼ oz.; 1¾oz.

Name: Sinner Spinner
Type: Spinner
Color(s): 14 assorted
Length(s): 1¾"; 2⅞"
Weight(s): ½ oz.; ⅜ oz.

Name: Gudespoon
Type: Spoon
Color(s): Nickel
Length(s): 2½"; 3"; 3½"; 4¾"; 6"
Weight(s): 3⁄16 oz.; 5⁄16 oz.; ⅜ oz.; 1 oz.; 1½ oz.
Material: Brass; nickelchrome finish

Bippie

NO. 2, 1977 EDITION

James Heddon's Sons

Name: Surface lure 210
Type: Plug
Color(s): 8 assorted
Length(s): 3½"
Weight(s): ⅝ oz.
Material: Stainless steel fittings

Name: Crackleback
Type: Plug
Color(s): Assorted; crackle-textured finish
Length(s): 3⅞"; 4½"
Weight(s): ⅜ oz.; ⅝ oz.

Name: Southern Tadpolly
Type: Plug
Color(s): assorted
Length(s): 1¾"; 2⅞"; 3¾"
Weight(s): ½ oz.; ⅝ oz.; 1¼ oz.

Name: Big Bud 9410
Type: Plug
Length(s): 2¾"
Weight(s): ⅝ oz.

Name: Big Chugger Spook
Type: Plug
Color(s): Assorted

Name: Big Prowler
Type: Plug
Color(s): Assorted
Length(s): 6½"
Weight(s): 1⅝ oz.

Zara II

Name: Cousin 1
Type: Plug
Color(s): Assorted
Length(s): 4¾"
Weight(s): ½ oz.

Name: Prowler
Type: Plug
Color(s): 6 assorted
Length(s): 2⅝"; 3⅝"; 4⅝"
Weight(s): ¼ oz.; ⅜ oz.; ⅝ oz.

Name: Heddon Big Hedd
Type: Plug
Weight(s): ⅝ oz.

Name: Zara Spook
Type: Plug
Length(s): 2⅝"; 4½"
Weight(s): ⅜ oz.; ¾ oz.

Name: Brush Popper Model 5440
Type: Spinner
Color(s): 8 assorted
Weight(s): ½ oz.
Material: Epoxy finish; brass and stainless steel hardware

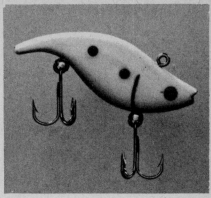

Hi-Jacker

Name: Smokey Joe
Type: Spinner
Color(s): Assorted
Weight(s): 3⁄16 oz.; ¼ oz.

Name: Wounded Spook
Type: Spinner
Length(s): 3⅛"
Weight(s): ⅝ oz.

Name: Zara II
Type: Plug
Color(s): 8
Length(s): 3⅝"
Weight(s): ⅝ oz.
Material: Plastic

Name: Hi-Jacker
Type: Plug
Color(s): 6
Length(s): 2¾"
Weight(s): ⅜ oz.
Material: Plastic

Name: Brush Popper 5430
Type: Spinner
Color(s): 5
Weight(s): ¼ oz.

Swimmerspoon

Helin

Name: Flatfish
Type: Plug
Color(s): 37 assorted
Length(s): 21 assorted
Material: Wood or plastic

Name: Fishcake
Type: Plug
Color(s): Assorted
Length(s): 1¾"; 2¼"; 2¾"
Weight(s): ¼ oz.; ⅜ oz.; ⅝ oz.

Name: Swimmerspoon
Type: Spoon
Color(s): 16 assorted
Length(s): Assorted

Hopkins

Name: Shorty Lures
Type: Jig
Color(s): Stainless steel finish
Length(s): Assorted
Weight(s): ⅛ oz.; ¼ oz.; ¾ oz.; 1½ oz.; 2¼ oz.
Material: Stainless steel

Name: No-Eql
Type: Jig
Color(s): Stainless steel finish
Length(s): Assorted
Weight(s): ⅓ oz.; ½ oz.; 1¼ oz.; 2 oz.; 2¾ oz.; 3¼ oz.
Material: Stainless steel

Name: Hammered Spoons
Type: Spoon
Color(s): All white; red/white; stainless steel
Length(s): 2⅜"; 3⅞"; 5½"
Weight(s): ¼ oz.; ¾ oz.; 1¾ oz.
Material: Stainless steel hardware

Name: "St" Lures
Type: Spoon
Color(s): 7
Length(s): 2"; 3"; 4"; 6"
Material: Chrome-plated heads; plastic tails

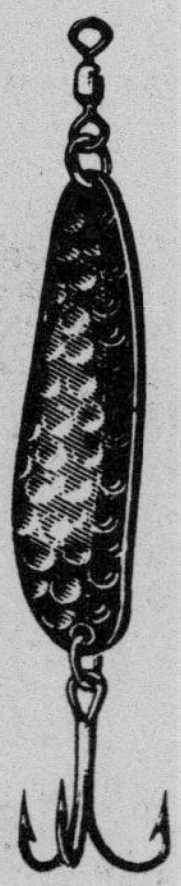

Krocodile

Luhr Jensen

Name: Rattlesnake
Type: Spoon
Color(s): Assorted
Length(s): 1⅞"; 2¼"; 2⅞"
Weight(s): ¼ oz.; ⅜ oz.; ⅝ oz.

Name: Krocodile
Type: Spoon
Color(s): Assorted
Length(s): 1 5/16"; 1 9/16"; 2⅛"; 2⅝"; 3⅜"; 4¼"; 5⅛"; 6⅛"
Weight(s): ⅙ oz.; 3/16 oz.; ¼ oz.; ⅜ oz.; ½ oz.; ⅝ oz.; ¾ oz.; 1 oz.; 1½ oz.; 1¾ oz.; 2¼ oz.; 3¼ oz.; 3¾ oz.; 5¼ oz.; 7 oz.

Name: Spinnin' Minny
Type: Spinner
Color(s): Silver; gold; green; blue
Length(s): 2½"; 3"; 4"; 5"
Weight(s): ⅛ oz.; ¼ oz.; ⅜ oz.; ⅝ oz.
Material: Clear plastic body

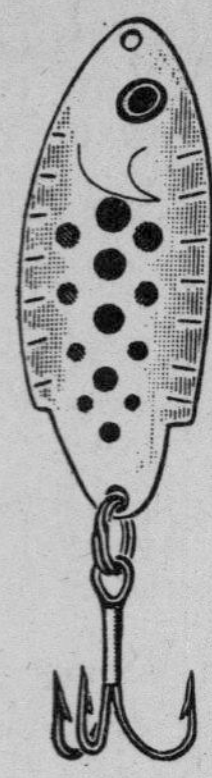

Bikini

Name: Prism-Lite Squid
Type: Plug
Color(s): Green; blue; pink; orange; chartreuse
Length(s): 3"; 4"; 5"
Material: Vinyl streamer

Name: Bikini
Type: Wobbler
Color(s): Assorted
Length(s): 1½"; 1¾"
Weight(s): ⅙ oz.; ¼ oz.
Material: Brass

Name: Mounti
Type: Spinner
Color(s): Assorted
Weight(s): 1/10 oz.; ⅙ oz.; ¼ oz.; ½ oz.; ⅝ oz.; ¾ oz.
Material: Plated brass blade

Name: Hog-Back Jig
Type: Jig
Color(s): 12
Weight(s): ¼ oz.; ⅜ oz.; ⅝ oz.
Material: Vinyl skirt

Name: Fishback
Type: Plug
Color(s): Assorted
Length(s): 2¼"; 2⅞"; 3¾"
Weight(s): ⅛ oz.; ⅜ oz.; ½ oz.; ⅝ oz.; ¾ oz.
Material: Plastic

Name: Fire-Plug
Type: Plug
Color(s): Assorted
Length(s): 1¾"; 2½"; 3"
Weight(s): 1/16 oz.; ⅛ oz.; 5/16 oz.
Material: Plastic

Name: Hot Shot
Type: Plug
Color(s): Assorted
Length(s): 1½"; 2¼"; 2⅝"; 3¼"; 3⅝"
Weight(s): 1/20 oz.; 1/10 oz.; ¼ oz.; ⅜ oz.; ⅝ oz.
Material: Plastic

Louis Johnson

Name: Silver Minnow Weedless
Type: Jig

Name: Lucky Lujon
Type: Jig
Material: Brass

Name: Silver Salmon Sprite

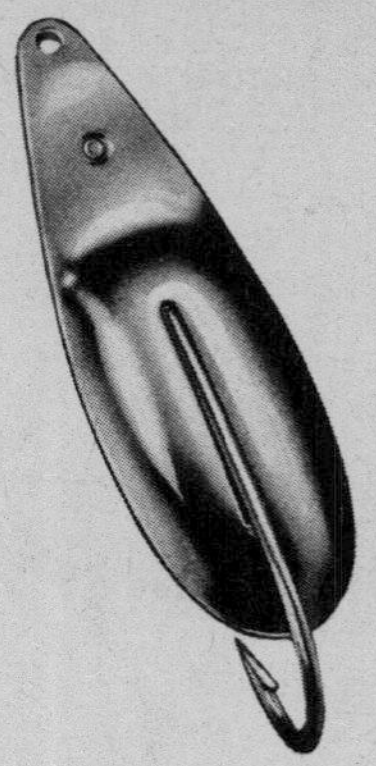

Caper

Type: Plug
Color(s): Trout like spots
Weight(s): ⅛ oz.; ¼ oz.; ½ oz.; ¾ oz.

Name: Sprite-Weedless and Non-Weedless
Type: Spoon
Weight(s): ⅛ oz.; ¼ oz.; ½ oz.; ¾ oz.

Name: Sea Silver Minnow Non-Weedless
Type: Spoon

Name: Caper
Type: Spoon with replaceable flared weed guard

Name: Bucktail Spoon
Type: Spoon
Color(s): 7
Weight(s): ⅛ oz.; ¼ oz.; ½ oz.; ¾ oz.; 1⅜ oz.

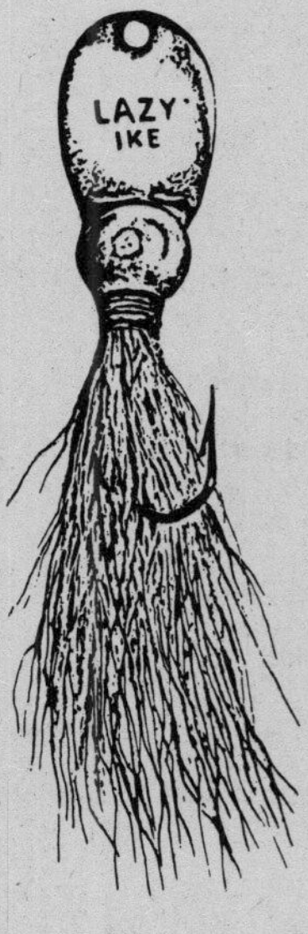

Wigly Jig

Lazy Ike

Name: Li'l Wigly
Type: Jig
Color(s): 6
Weight(s): ¼ oz.

Name: Wigly Jig
Type: Jig
Color(s): 4
Weight(s): ¼ oz.; ⅜ oz.; ¾ oz.

Name: Super Jigs
Type: Jig
Color(s): Assorted
Weight(s): 1/16 oz.; ⅛ oz.; ¼ oz.; ⅜ oz.; ½ oz.
Material: Bucktail hair; marabow feathers

Name: Wigly Crawler
Type: Jig-Semi-weedless
Color(s): 5
Weight(s): ¼ oz.; ⅜ oz.; ½ oz.; ¾ oz.

Name: Chug Ike
Type: Plug
Color(s): 6 standard; 6 metallic
Length(s): 2"; 3"
Weight(s): ¼ oz.; ½ oz.

Name: Sail Shark
Type: Plug
Color(s): 12 standard; 6 metallic
Length(s): 1⅝"
Weight(s): ¾ oz.

Name: Flex Ike
Type: Plug
Color(s): 12 standard; 12 metallic
Length(s): 2¾"; 3"
Weight(s): ⅙ oz.; ¼ oz.

Name: Snappertail
Type: Plug
Color(s): 6 standard; 6 metallic
Length(s): 3¼"
Weight(s): ½ oz.

Name: Snapper
Type: Plug
Color(s): 6 standard; 6 metallic
Length(s): 2¾"
Weight(s): ⅜ oz.
Material: Plastic

Name: Tail Shark
Type: Plug
Color(s): 6 standard; 6 metallic
Length(s): 2½"
Weight(s): ½ oz.

Name: Lazy Ike KL Series
Type: Plug
Color(s): Assorted combinations
Length(s): 1 1/16"; 1¾"; 2"; 2½"; 3"; 3½"
Weight(s): 1/32 oz.; 1/15 oz.; ⅛ oz.; ¼ oz.; ⅓ oz.; ⅝ oz.

Name: HS Hippy Spinners
Type: Spinner bait
Color(s): 6 assorted
Weight(s): ¼ oz.; ⅜ oz.; ½ oz.

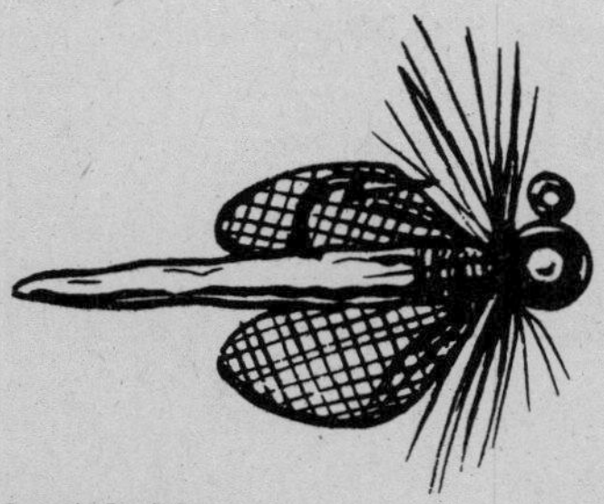

Crappie Do-Odie

Lindy/Little Joe

Name: Hot Tails
Type: Worm
Color(s): 6
Length(s): 4"; 6"; 7¼"; 9"
Material: Plastic

Name: Squirrel Spin
Type: Spinner
Color(s): Assorted
Weight(s): 1/16 oz.; ⅛ oz.; ¼ oz.; ⅜ oz.

Name: Sparkle Tandem Spin
Type: Spinner
Color(s): Assorted hot colored skirts
Weight(s): ¼ oz.; ⅜ oz.; ½ oz.
Material: Rubber or vinyl skirts

Name: Super Leech
Type: Worm
Color(s): 3
Length(s): 2"; 3"; 4"

Name: Crappie Do-Odle
Type: Plug
Color(s): Assorted
Weight(s): 1/16 oz.

Name: Little Joe
Type: Jig
Color(s): 6
Weight(s): ½ oz.; ¾ oz.; ⅞ oz.

Name: Lazy Dazy
Type: Plug
Color(s): 16
Weight(s): ¼ oz.; ⅜ oz.
Material: Plastic

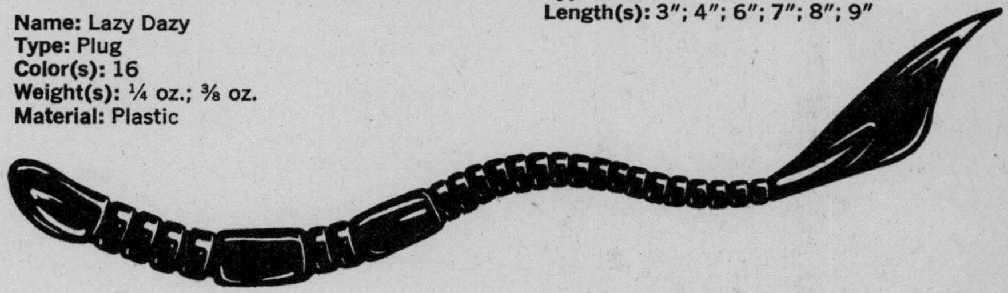

Hot Tails

Mann's

Name: Jelly Wiggler
Type: Worm
Color(s): Assorted
Length(s): 2"; 4"; 6"
Material: Plastic

Name: Deep Pig Razorback
Type: Plug
Color(s): Assorted
Weight(s): ⅛ oz.; ¼ oz.
Material: Plastic

Name: Little George
Type: Plug
Color(s): 17
Weight(s): ¼ oz.; ½ oz.; ¾ oz.; 1 oz.

Name: Jelly Worm Grub
Type: Jig
Weight(s): 1/16 oz.

Name: Fat Albert
Type: Plug
Color(s): Assorted
Weight(s): ⅜ oz.; ½ oz.

Name: Super George

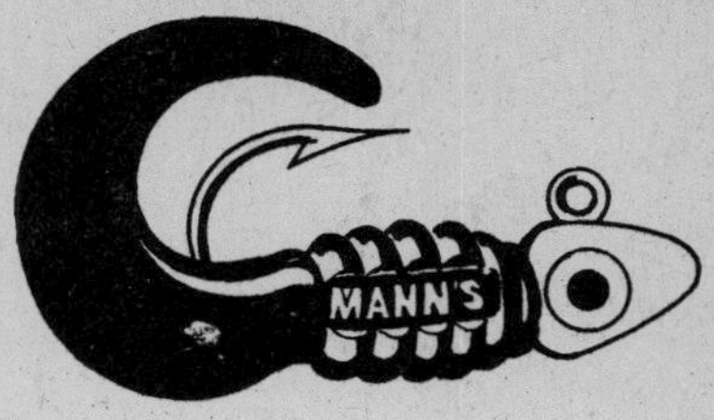

Jelly Wiggler

Type: Plug
Weight(s): ½ oz.
Material: Plastic body; nickle blade

Name: Little George
Type: Plug
Color(s): Pearl lustre

Name: Big George
Type: Plug
Color(s): Pearl lustre
Weight(s): ½ oz.
Material: Plastic

Name: Wally Bully
Type: Spinner bait
Color(s): 11 assorted

Name: Jelly Worm
Type: Worm
Length(s): 3"; 4"; 6"; 7"; 8"; 9"

Martin

Name: Candle Fish
Type: Trolling spoon
Color(s): Assorted
Length(s): 1⅛"; 2"; 3⅛"; 4½"
Material: Metal

Name: Gimpy
Type: Trolling spoon
Color(s): Assorted
Length(s): 1"
Material: Metal

Name: Seattle Six
Type: Spoon
Color(s): Assorted
Length(s): 4⅝"
Material: Metal

Name: Ottogator
Type: Spoon
Color(s): Assorted
Length(s): 2¾"; 3½"
Weight(s): ½ oz.; 1 oz.
Material: Steel

Name: Otto Special
Type: Spinner
Length(s): 1¾"; 2"; 2¼"; 2½"
Material: Metal

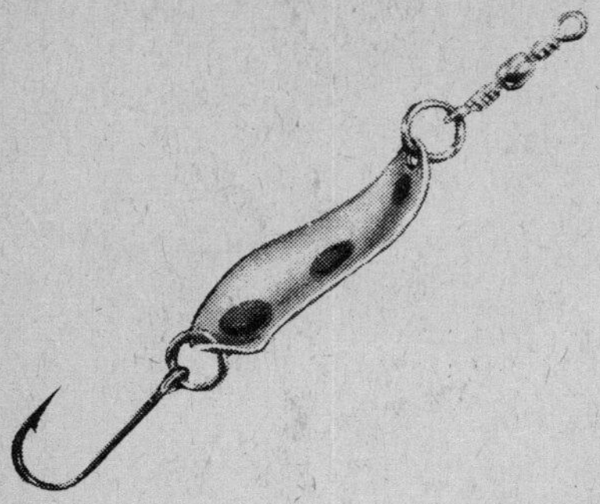

Gimpy

Name: Plastic Spoons
Type: Spoon
Length(s): 1½″; 1¾″; 2½″
Material: Plastic

Name: Sal Squidder
Type: Squid
Color(s): Assorted
Length(s): 4″
Material: Stainless steel shaft; plastic

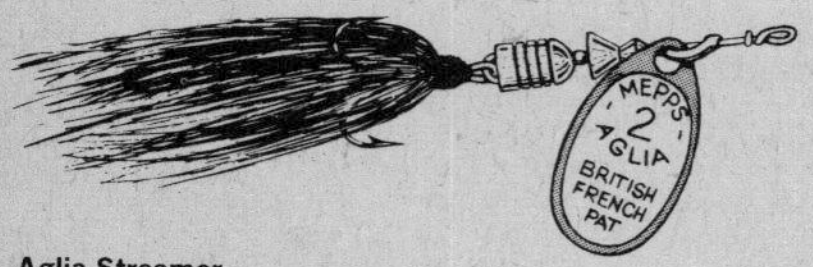

Aglia Streamer

Mepps

Name: Mepps Spoon
Type: Spoon
Color(s): Silver; gold
Weight(s): ⅕ oz.; ⅓ oz.; ½ oz.

Name: Giant Killer
Type: Spinner
Color(s): Assorted
Weight(s): 1½ oz.

Name: Musky Killer
Type: Spinner or jig
Color(s): Assorted
Weight(s): ½ oz.

Name: Giant Killer Mino
Type: Spinner
Color(s): Lifelike
Weight(s): 1 oz.; 1½ oz.

Name: Black Fury Plain
Type: Spinner
Color(s): 1
Weight(s): ⅛ oz.; ⅙ oz.; ¼ oz.; ⅓ oz.

Name: Aglia Long Mino
Type: Spinner
Length(s): 1⅞″; 2⅛″; 2⅝″ 2⅞″; 3⅜″; 4½″
Weight(s): ⅙ oz.; ⅕ oz.; ⅓ oz.; ½ oz.; ⅚ oz. 1 oz.

Name: Aglia
Type: Spinner
Color(s): Assorted standard and metallic
Weight(s): 1/12 oz.; ⅛ oz.; ⅙ oz.; ¼ oz.; ⅓ oz.; ½ oz.

Name: Aglia Long
Type: Spinner
Color(s): Assorted
Weight(s): ⅛ oz.; ⅙ oz.; ¼ oz.; ⅓ oz.; ½ oz.

Name: Aglia Streamer
Type: Spinner
Color(s): Assorted
Weight(s): 1/12 oz.; ⅛ oz.; ⅙ oz.; ¼ oz.; ⅓ oz.; ½ oz.

Name: Aglia Dressed
Type: Spinner
Color(s): Assorted
Weight(s): 1/12 oz.; ⅛ oz.; ⅙ oz.; ¼ oz.; ⅓ oz.; ½ oz.

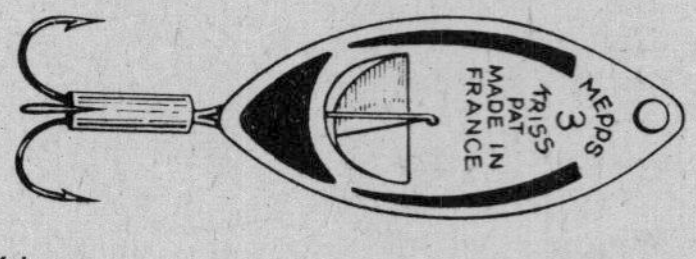

Kriss

Name: Comet Dressed
Type: Spinner
Color(s): Assorted
Weight(s): 1/10 oz.; ⅛ oz.; ⅕ oz.; ⅓ oz.; ⅜ oz.

Name: Aglia Mino-Spin
Type: Spinner bait
Color(s): 5
Weight(s): 3/16 oz.; ⅜ oz.; ⅞ oz.

Name: Kriss
Type: Spoon
Color(s): Gold or Silver
Weight(s): 1/10 oz.; 1/7 oz.; ¼ oz.

Mirrolure

Name: 52m Family
Type: Plug
Length(s): 3⅝″; 4¼″
Weight(s): ⅜ oz.; 9/16 oz.; ½ oz.; ⅝ oz.; ⅞ oz.; ⅝ oz.; ⅞ oz.; ⅝ oz.; ⅞ oz.; ¾ oz.; 1 oz.

Name: Tiny Trout Family
Type: Plug
Length(s): 2⅛″; 3⅝″
Weight(s): ¼ oz.; 9/16 oz.; ⅜ oz.

Name: Double Scat
Type: Spinner
Length(s): 3⅝″
Weight(s): ½ oz.

Name: Popular Spinner Models
Type: Spinner
Length(s): 3⅝″
Weight(s): ½ oz.; ⅝ oz.

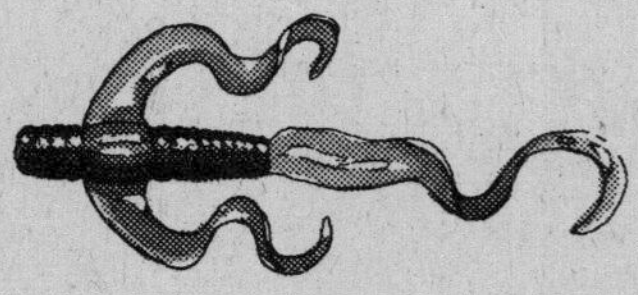

Sin-Sation

Mister Twister

Name: Sassy Skirt
Type: Plug
Color(s): Assorted
Length(s): 1½″; 2¼″; 3″
Material: Rubber skirt

Name: Sin-Sation
Type: Jig
Color(s): Assorted
Length(s): 3″; 4″; 6″

Name: Twin-Sation
Type: Spinner
Color(s): Assorted
Weight(s): ⅛ oz.; ⅜ oz.; ¾ oz.

Name: Meeny Spin
Type: Spinner
Color(s): Assorted
Length(s): 3″
Weight(s): ⅛ oz.; ¼ oz.

Name: Phenom
Type: Worm
Color(s): Assorted
Length(s): 6″

Name: Eee-Ill
Type: Worm
Color(s): 9
Length(s): 7″; 9″; 11″
Material: Vinyl

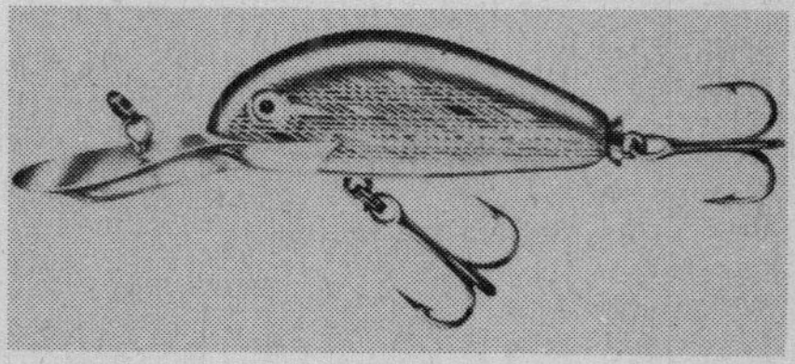

Little Scooper

Norman

Name: Flasher
Type: Plug
Length(s): 2″
Weight(s): ¼ oz.

Name: Chugger-Flash
Type: Plug
Length(s): 3¼″
Weight(s): ⅜ oz.

Name: Rat-Lur
Type: Plug
Length(s): 3¼″
Weight(s): ⅝ oz.

Name: Quarter-Back Deep Runner
Type: Plug
Length(s): 1¾″; 4½″; 5½″
Weight(s): ¼ oz.; ½ oz.; 1 oz.

Name: Jointed-Minnow Series
Type: Plug
Length(s): 2½″; 3½″; 4½″ 5½″
Weight(s): ⅛ oz.; ¼ oz.; ⅜ oz.; ⅝ oz.

Name: Linebacker Series
Type: Plug
Length(s): 2½″; 3½″; 4½″; 5½″; 7″
Weight(s): ⅛ oz.; ¼ oz.; ⅜ oz.; ⅝ oz.; 1 oz.

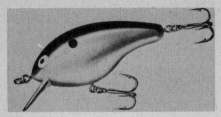

Little "N"

Name: Super Scooper
Type: Plug
Color(s): Assorted
Length(s): 2″
Weight(s): ⅜ oz.

Name: Little Scooper
Type: Plug
Color(s): Assorted
Length(s): 1¾″
Weight(s): ¼ oz.

Name: Baby N
Type: Plug
Color(s): Assorted
Length(s): 2″
Weight(s): ¼ oz.

Name: Little N #1900
Type: Plug
Color(s): Assorted
Length(s): 2½″
Weight(s): ⅜ oz.

Name: Big N
Type: Plug
Color(s): Assorted
Length(s): 3″
Weight(s): ⅝ oz.

Name: Woundedflash
Type: Spinner
Length(s): 2¼″; 3¼″
Weight(s): ¼ oz.; ½ oz.

Name: Spinnerbait
Type: Spinner bait
Color(s): 6
Weight(s): ⅜ oz.
Material: Nylon skirt; steel hook

Name: The Ranger Worm
Type: Worm
Color(s): 10 assorted
Length(s): 6″; 8″

Rapala Jigging Lure

Normark

Name: Countdown Sinking Models
Type: Jig
Color(s): Assorted
Length(s): 2″; 2¾″; 3½″; 4⅜″
Weight(s): ¼ oz.; ⅜ oz.; ½ oz.; ⅝ oz.

Name: Original Floating Models
Type: Plug
Color(s): Silver; gold; blue; fluorescent red
Length(s): 2″; 2¾″; 3½″; 4⅜″; 5¼″; 7″
Material: Balsa wood body, stainless steel
    wire

Name: Rapala Jigging Lure
Type: Plug
Color(s): Silver; gold; fluorescent red
Length(s): 1½″; 2″; 2¾″; 3½″
Weight(s): 3⁄16 oz.; 5⁄16 oz.; ½ oz.; ¾ oz.

Name: Jointed Rapala
Type: Plug
Color(s): Silver, gold; blue; fluorescent red
Length(s): 2¾″; 3½″; 4⅜″

Name: Rapala Deep Diver
Type: Plug
Color(s): Silver; gold; blue; fluorescent red
Length(s): 2¾″; 3½″
Weight(s): ⅜ oz.; ½ oz.

Name: Magnum Rapalas
Type: Plug
Color(s): Silver; gold; blue; fluorescent red
Length(s): 5¼″; 7″
Weight(s): ¾ oz.; ⅞ oz.; 1½ oz.; 2 oz.
Material: Odoum wood bodies

OLM

Name: Go-Getter
Type: Jig
Color(s): White; yellow; red & white

Name: Crappie Jig
Type: Jig
Color(s): White; yellow
Weight(s): 1⁄16 oz.

Name: Marble Spinner
Type: Spinner
Color(s): Assorted
Weight(s): ⅛ oz.; ¼ oz.

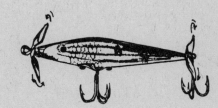

Pico Slasher

Padre Island

Name: Hondo Jig
Type: Jig
Color(s): Assorted
Weight(s): ⅜ oz.; ⅝ oz.

Name: Pico Super Pop
Type: Plug
Color(s): Assorted
Length(s): 3¼″
Weight(s): ½ oz.
Material: Plastic; bucktail

Name: Pico Deep Digger
Type: Plug
Color(s): Assorted
Length(s): 3½″

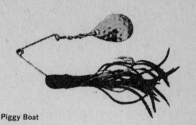

Piggy Boat

Weight(s): ½ oz.
Material: Plastic

Name: Pico Side-Shad
Type: Plug
Color(s): Assorted
Length(s): 2½″
Weight(s): ½ oz.

Name: Hot Pants
Type: Spinner bait
Color(s): Assorted
Weight(s): ½ oz.
Material: Wire; plastic

Name: Piggy Boat
Type: Spinner bait
Color(s): Assorted
Weight(s): ⅓ oz.
Material: Rubber; nickel

Name: Pico Slasher
Type: Spinner bait
Color(s): Assorted
Length(s): 4″
Weight(s): ½ oz.
Material: Plastic

Name: Jigging Spoon
Type: Spoon
Color(s): Silver
Weight(s): ⅝ oz.
Material: Silver

Name: Wild Card Worm
Type: Worm
Color(s): Assorted
Length(s): 4″; 5″; 6″

Name: Pico Grub
Type: Worm
Color(s): Assorted
Length(s): 3″

Rebel

Name: Minnows
Type: Plug
Color(s): Assorted
Length(s): 1½″—7″
Weight(s): 1⁄16 oz.; ⅛ oz.; ¼ oz.; ⅜ oz.;
    ½ oz.; 1 oz.; 2 oz.

Name: Super Minnow
Type: Plug
Color(s): Assorted
Length(s): 5½″; 7″
Weight(s): 1¼ oz.; 2 oz.

Name: Deep Runner-Spoonbill Minnow
Type: Plug
Color(s): Assorted
Length(s): 3½″; 4½″; 5½″; 7″
Weight(s): ¼ oz.; ⅜ oz.; ¾ oz.; 1 oz.

Humback

Name: Jointed "Broken Back" Minnow
Type: Plug
Color(s): Assorted
Length(s): 2½"; 3½"; 4½"; 5½"
Weight(s): ⅛ oz.; ¼ oz.; ⅜ oz.; ½ oz.

Name: "R" Series Floaters
Type: Plug
Color(s): Assorted
Length(s): 1⅝"; 2"; 2½"; 3"
Weight(s): ¼ oz.; ⅜ oz.; ½ oz.; ¾ oz.

Name: "R" Series Deep Runners
Type: Plug
Color(s): Assorted
Length(s): 1⅝"; 2"; 2½"; 3"
Weight(s): ⅜ oz.; ½ oz.; ¾ oz.; ⅞ oz.

Name: Super-R
Type: Plug
Color(s): Assorted
Length(s): 2½"
Weight(s): ⅜ oz.

Name: Humpback
Type: Plug
Color(s): Assorted
Length(s): 1¾"
Weight(s): ¼ oz.; ⅜ oz.

Name: Windcheater Popper
Type: Popper
Color(s): Assorted
Length(s): 3¾"; 5"; 5½"
Weight(s): ⅞ oz.; 2½ oz.; 3 oz.

Name: Pop-R
Type: Popper
Color(s): Assorted
Length(s): 2½"; 3"
Weight(s): ¼ oz.; ½ oz.

Name: Jumpin' Minnow
Type: Plug
Color(s): Assorted
Length(s): 3½"; 4½"
Weight(s): ⅜ oz.; ½ oz.

Name: Racket Shad
Type: Plug
Color(s): Assorted
Length(s): 2½"; 3"
Weight(s): ⅜ oz.; ⅝ oz.

Name: Shallow-R
Type: Plug
Color(s): Assorted
Length(s): 2"; 2½"
Weight(s): ⅜ oz.; ⅝ oz.

Wee-R

Name: Maxi-R
Type: Plug
Color(s): Assorted
Length(s): 3"
Weight(s): ⅞ oz.

Name: Wee-R
Type: Plug
Color(s): Assorted
Length(s): 2"
Weight(s): ⅜ oz.

Name: Teeny-R
Type: Plug
Color(s): Assorted
Length(s): 1⅝"
Weight(s): ⅜ oz.

Name: Ringworm
Type: Worm
Color(s): Assorted
Length(s): 4"; 6"; 7½"
Material: Plastic

Hank Roberts

Name: Bass Plug
Type: Plug
Color(s): 6
Material: Deer hair

Name: Woolly Worm
Type: Fly
Color(s): 6
Material: Wavy hackle

Name: Large Dixie Demon
Type: Popper
Color(s): 5
Material: Dylite

Name: Bass Bush Bugs
Type: Bug
Color(s): Assorted
Material: Deer hair

Rogers

Name: Hawg Hunter, Sr.
Type: Plug
Color(s): Assorted
Weight(s): ½ oz.

Name: Big Jim
Type: Plug
Color(s): Assorted
Weight(s): ⅜ oz.; ½ oz.

Name: Ambusher Single Spin
Type: Spinner
Color(s): Assorted
Weight(s): ⅛ oz.; ³⁄₁₆ oz.; ¼ oz.; ⅜ oz.; ½ oz.

Name: Super Craw-Pap
Type: Plug
Color(s): 17 assorted
Weight(s): ¾ oz.

Name: Craw Pap
Type: Plug
Color(s): 17 assorted
Weight(s): ½ oz.

Name: Spinwinder
Type: Spinner bait
Color(s): 15 assorted
Length(s): 1½"; 3"; 6"
Weight(s): ¹⁄₁₆ oz.; ⅛ oz.; ¼ oz.; ⅜ oz.

Name: Maribou Weedless Bass Jigs
Type: Jig
Color(s): 10
Weight(s): ⅛ oz.; ¼ oz.; ⅜ oz.; ½ oz.
Material: Bucktail or synthetic hair

Name: Gumbo Worms
Type: Worm
Color(s): 9 assorted
Length(s): 6"; 7¼"

Name: Hooktail
Type: Worm
Color(s): Assorted
Length(s): 1½"; 3"; 6"

Jack K. Smithwick & Son

Name: Tail Gater
Type: Jig
Weight(s): ¼ oz.

Name: Wood Chug
Type: Jig
Weight(s): ¼ oz.

Name: Rogue
Type: Plug
Length(s): 5½"
Weight(s): ½ oz.

Name: Devils Horse
Type: Spinner
Weight(s): ½ oz.

Name: Devils Horse
Type: Spinner
Weight(s): ⅜ oz.

Name: Chug Horse
Type: Spinner
Weight(s): ½ oz.

Name: Buck and Bawl
Type: Spinner
Weight(s): ⅜ oz.

Name: Buck and Bawl Jr.
Type: Spinner
Weight(s): ¼ oz.

Name: King Snipe
Type: Spinner
Weight(s): ⅜ oz.

Flip Tail Lizard

Stembridge

Name: Fuddlebug Regular, Fuddlebug Junior
Type: Worm
Color(s): 20 assorted
Length(s): 1¾"; 2¾"
Material: Plastic; stainless steel clip

Name: Fliptail Family: Daddy; Regular; Junior; Lizard; Baby
Type: Worm
Color(s): 20 assorted
Length(s): 2¼"; 5½"; 6¼"; 7¼"; 9¼"
Weight(s): ¹⁄₆₄ oz.; ³⁄₁₆ oz.; ¼ oz.; ⅜ oz.; ½ oz.
Material: Plastic

Name: Lizard
Type: Worm
Color(s): Assorted
Length(s): 6¼″
Weight(s): ⅜ oz.
Material: Plastic

Strike King

Name: Spence Scout
Type: Plug
Color(s): Assorted
Weight(s): ⅜ oz.
Material: Wood

Name: Big "S"
Type: Plug
Color(s): Assorted
Weight(s): ⅝ oz.
Material: Molded polystyrene

Name: Happy Hooker
Type: Spinner
Color(s): Assorted
Weight(s): ½ oz.

Name: Diamondback Shimmy Shad
Type: Spinner
Color(s): 12
Weight(s): ⅜ oz.

Name: Timber King
Type: Spoon
Color(s): Assorted
Weight(s): ½ oz.

Thin Fin

Name: Wiggle Wart
Type: Plug
Color(s): Assorted
Length(s): 3″
Weight(s): ⅜ oz.

Name: Bass Hog
Type: Spinner
Length(s): 2½″; 3″
Weight(s): ⅜ oz.; ⅝ oz.
Material: Solid lead head in plastic casing

Name: Whiz Bang
Type: Jig
Color(s): Assorted
Length(s): 2¼″
Weight(s): ⅓ oz.

Name: Fatso
Type: Jig
Color(s): Assorted
Length(s): 2½″; 3″; 3¾″
Weight(s): ⅓ oz.; ⅜ oz.; ⅝ oz.

Name: Hot 'N Tot
Type: Plug
Color(s): Assorted
Length(s): 3″; 3¾″
Weight(s): ¼ oz.; ½ oz.

Mr. Champ

Weber

Name: Blade Colorado Spinner
Type: Spinner
Color(s): Assorted
Material: Solid brass blade

Name: Mr. Champ
Type: Spoon
Color(s): Assorted
Weight(s): ⅛ oz.; ¼ oz.; ⅓ oz.; ½ oz.; ⅞ oz.; 1 oz.; 1¾ oz.
Material: Solid brass blades

Name: Weedless Mousie
Type: Plug
Color(s): Mouse-gray
Material: Deer hair

Name: Fire Nit-Wit
Type: Popper
Color(s): Assorted
Material: Dylite

Name: Jungle Eyes
Type: Streamer
Color(s): Assorted

Fire Nit-Wit

Whopper Stopper

Name: Hellbender
Type: Spinner
Color(s): Assorted
Weight(s): ¼ oz.; ½ oz.; ⅝ oz.; ⅞ oz.
Material: Plastic

Name: Bayou Boogie
Type: Plug
Color(s): Assorted
Weight(s): ¼ oz.; ⅓ oz.; ½ oz.; ¾ oz.
Material: Plastic

Name: Hellcat
Type: Plug
Color(s): Assorted
Weight(s): ¼ oz.; ⅜ oz.; ½ oz.
Material: Plastic

Hellcat

Name: Salty Boogie
Type: Plug
Color(s): Assorted
Length(s): 4½″
Weight(s): 3 oz.
Material: Plastic

Name: Whirlybird
Type: Spinner
Color(s): Assorted regular; hot colors
Length(s): 4″
Weight(s): ½ oz.
Material: Plastic skirt; brass blade

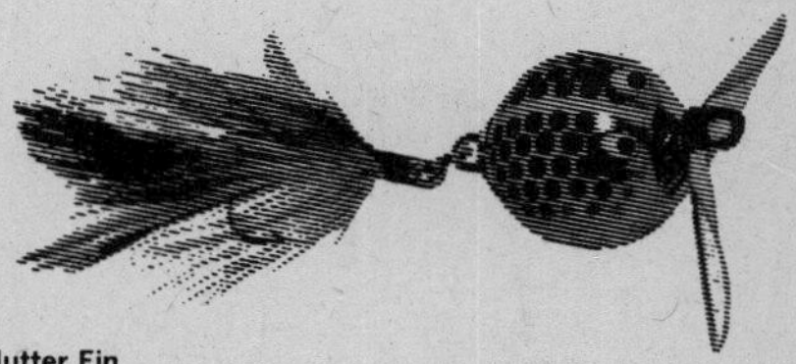

Flutter Fin

Worth

Name: Flutter-Fin
Type: Spinner
Color(s): 6
Weight(s): ¼ oz.
Material: Plastic

Name: Demon
Type: Spoon
Color(s): 6
Length(s): 10 different lengths
Weight(s): 10 different weights
Material: Solid brass

Name: Musky Fin
Type: Spinner
Color(s): Assorted
Weight(s): ⅙ oz.; ⅕ oz.; ⅓ oz.; ¾ oz.; 1⅛ oz.
Material: Nickel

Name: Fishdevil
Type: Spoon
Color(s): Assorted
Length(s): 2⅞″; 3¼″
Weight(s): ⅔ oz.; ¾ oz.

Name: Streamspin
Type: Jig spinner
Color(s): Assorted fluorescent
Weight(s): 7/16 oz.
Material: Plastic skirt

Specifications: Lines and Leaders

1977 Product Preview Lines

The Gladding Fishing Line Division has introduced a new Teflon-coated Invincible Fly Line that boasts a frictionless coating that the company claims is superior to conventional coatings. The Teflon enables the line to cast more smoothly, giving the angler greater distance and, because it reduces

Gladding Invincible Fly Line Kit

friction, the line has less wear on the guides. Millions of multiple-flotation spheres are sandwiched between the inner and outer skins of the line, making it float and giving it tremendous buoyancy.

Invincible Fly Lines are available in level lines, double tapers, weight-forward tapers, salt water tapers and tapered shooting heads. They are packaged with a can of line cleaner and a coil of tapered leader.

The Orvis Company, after five years of research, has developed a new Strike Indicator Fly Line. Ex-cellent visibility comes from an 18-inch blaze-orange tip that permits the angler to monitor the progress of the fly. The color change, however, does not affect the delicate tip that has been a trademark of Orvis fly lines. Strike Indicator lines will be marketed in sizes WF-3F through WF-9-F.

Mason Tackle, line specialists in Otisville, Michigan, has made a number of packaging changes in its line to make monofilament available in lengths to suit almost every angling need. New this year is an economical quality braided Da-cron line called Mason's Offshore Dacron. It is available in I.G.F.A. classes and is packaged both in connected spools and in bulk.

A new Soft Monofilament is being marketed by Olympic. Developed by Japan's Mitsubishi Chemical, the line uses 6- and 66-copolymer nylon 2030A and comes in green, light green and transparent. It is packaged in 110-yard spools, 550-yard spools and in bulk. Sizes range from 1-pound through 90-pound test with a wide assortment of breaking strengths.

Lines

Ande

Type: Tournament monofilament line
Breaking Strength (in lbs.): 2 to 400
Color(s): 4
Packaging: Not specified

Tournament Monofilament

Berkley

Type: Crusader braided canepole line
Breaking Strength (in lbs.): Assorted test
weights
Color(s): Assorted colors
Packaging: 10 yd. winders, 12 per box

Type: Spin Chief nylon filament line
Breaking Strength (in lbs.): 4; 6; 8; 10; 12;
15; 20; 25; 30; 40; 50; 60; 75; 100;
125; 150
Color(s): Mist blue
Packaging: 100 yds., 2, 6 or large capacity
bulks spools per box

Type: Depth-o-Matic nylon monofilament line
Breaking Strength (in lbs.): 15; 20; 25; 30; 40
Color(s): New color every 10 feet
Packaging: ¼ lb. spools; 1 lb. spools

Type: Mill Ends nylon monofilament line
Breaking Strength (in lbs.): 2; 4; 6; 8; 10; 12;
15; 20; 25; 30; 40; 50; 60
Color(s): Assorted colors
Packaging: Not specified

Type: Medallion braided nylon bait casting
line
Breaking Strength (in lbs.): 10; 12; 15; 20;
25; 30; 40; 50
Color(s): Black; camouflage
Packaging: 50 yd. spools, 2 per box

Type: Medallion dacron trolling and surfing
braided lines
Breaking Strength (in lbs.): 10; 18; 27; 45;
72; 117
Color(s): Green fleck
Packaging: 50 yd. spools, 6 per box; 100
yd. spools, 2 or 6 per box; 1000 yd. spools

Type: Crusader braided nylon bait casting
lines
Breaking Strength (in lbs.): 10; 12; 15; 20;
25; 30; 40; 50

Color(s): Black camouflage
Packaging: 50 yd. spools, 2 or 6 per box

Type: Crusader braided nylon squidding line
Breaking Strength (in lbs.): 18; 27; 36; 45
54; 63; 72; 90; 110
Color(s): Sand
Packaging: 50 yd. spools, 6 per box

Type: Dew Flex nylon monofilament line
Breaking Strength (in lbs.): 4; 6; 8; 10; 12;
15; 20; 25; 30; 40; 50; 60; 75; 100;
125; 150
Color(s): Mist blue
Packaging: 100 yd. spools; large capacity
bulk spools

Type: Trilene XL casting line
Breaking Strength (in lbs.): 2; 4; 6; 8; 10; 12;
14; 17; 20; 25; 30; 40; 50; 60; 80
Color(s): Clear; high visibility clear
Packaging: 110 yd. spools, 2 per box;
yardage spools; service spools; filler
spools

Trilene XL

Type: Trilene tensimatic heavy-duty line
Breaking Strength (in lbs.): 4; 6; 8; 10; 12;
14; 17; 20; 25; 30; 40; 50; 60; 80
Color(s): High visibility green
Packaging: 110 yd. spools, 2 per box;
yardage spools; filler spools

Type: Trilene Dura Tuff
Breaking Strength (in lbs.): 4; 6; 8; 10; 12;
14; 17; 20; 25; 30; 40; 50; 60; 80
Color(s): Copper; sea mist green
Packaging: Popular filler spools; 110 yd.
spools, 2 per box; yardage spools

Bevin-Wilcox

Type: Spin cast monofilament line
Breaking Strength (in lbs.): 4; 6; 8; 10; 12;
15; 20; 25; 30; 40; 50; 60
Color(s): Blue; green
Packaging: 100 yd. narrow spools, 12 per
box; 8 lb. spools; 4 lb. spools; 2 lb. spools;
1 lb. spools

Trilene XL

Type: BEV-flex monofilament line
Breaking Strength (in lbs.): 4; 6; 8; 10; 12;
15; 20; 25; 30; 40; 50; 60
Color(s): Blue; green; smoketone; clear
Packaging: 100 yd. wide spools, 2 per box;
100 yd. wide spools, 12 per box; 100 yd.
wide spools; 100 yd. wide spools, 6 per
box; 8 lb. spools; 4 lb. spools; 2 lb.
spools; 1 lb. spools

Type: Perflex monofilament line
Breaking Strength (in lbs.): 4; 6; 8; 10; 12;
15; 20; 25; 30; 40; 50
Color(s): Pearl gray
Packaging: 100 yd. wide spools, 2, 6 or 12
per box; 8 lb. spools; 4 lb. spools; 2 lb.
spools; 1 lb. spools

Type: Pilot dacron salt water surf and trolling
lines
Breaking Strength (in lbs.): 12; 20; 30; 40;
50; 60; 70; 80; 96; 130
Color(s): Greenspot; tan
Packaging: 50 yd. wide spools, 6 per box;
50 yd. wide spools, 12 per box; 100 yd.
wide spools, 6 per box; 200 yd.; 300 yd.;
500 yd.; 600 yd.; 800 yd.; 1000 yd.;
1200 yd. spools

Type: Cast-ezy casting lines
Breaking Strength (in lbs.): 10; 12; 15; 20;
25; 30; 35; 40; 50
Color(s): Black; camouflage
Packaging: 50 yd. wide spools, 1, 2, 6 or 12
per box

Cortland

Type: Premium monofilament imported
nylorfi line
Breaking Strength (in lbs.): 4; 6; 8; 10; 12;
15; 20; 25; 30
Color(s): Neutral grey
Packaging: 100 meter (109.3 yds.),
connected; large capacity bulk spools

Type: Cortland monowire solid wire deep
trolling line

Dacron Trolling

Breaking Strength (in lbs.): 10; 15; 20; 30; 40; 50
Color(s): Not specified
Packaging: 100 yd. spools, 2 connected

Type: Micron braided casting line
Breaking Strength (in lbs.): 10; 12; 15; 20; 25; 30; 40; 50
Color(s): Surgical white
Packaging: 50 yd. spools, 2 connected

Type: Wormer casting line blend of polyester fibers
Breaking Strength (in lbs.): 10 12; 15; 20; 25; 30; 35
Color(s): Two-tone green
Packaging: 50 yd. spools, 2 connected; 100 yd. spools, 2 connected

Type: Micron braided trolling line
Breaking Strength (in lbs.): 5½; 10; 27; 45; 72; 117
Color(s): Surgical white
Packaging: 100 yd. spools, 6 connected; 150 yd. spools, 6 connected; 500 yd., 800 yd., 1200 yd. or 2500 yd. spools

Type: Mono-worm flat monofilament casting line
Breaking Strength (in lbs.): 12; 15; 20; 25; 30; 35
Color(s): Two-tone green
Packaging: 100 yd. spools, 2 per box; 1000 yd. spools

Type: Cam-o-flage braided nylon casting line
Breaking Strength (in lbs.): 10; 12; 15; 18; 20; 25; 30; 35; 42; 50
Color(s): Camouflage
Packaging: 50 yd. spools, 2 per box; 1000 yd. spools

Mono-Worm

Type: Braided dacron trolling line
Breaking Strength (in lbs.); 10; 18; 27; 36; 45; 72; 117
Color(s): Greenspot
Packaging: 50 yd. spools, 6 per box; 100 yd. spools, 6 per box; 500 yd., 800 yd., 1200 yd. or 2500 yd. spools

Type: Kerplunk braided nylon over lead core deep trolling line
Breaking Strength (in lbs.): 18; 27; 36; 45; 60
Color(s): New color every 10 yards
Packaging: 100 yd. spools, 2 connected

Type: Salt water tournament grade monofilament line
Breaking Strength (in lbs.): 6; 12; 20; 30; 50; 80
Color(s): Mist green
Packaging: 600 yd. or 1200 yd. spools

Cam-o-flage

Dragon Fly

Type: Superior monofilament spinning line
Breaking Strength (in lbs.): 6; 8; 10; 12; 15; 20; 25; 30
Color(s): Mist, smoke
Packaging: 100 yd. spools, 2 connected

Type: Braided waterproofed nylon casting line
Breaking Strength (in lbs.): 15; 20; 25; 30; 35; 40; 50; 63; 72
Color(s): Black; camouflage
Packaging: 50 yd. spools, 2 connected

Type: Monofilament spinning line
Breaking Strength (in lbs.): 6; 8; 10; 12; 15; 20
Color(s): Mist; smoke
Packaging: 100 yds. spools, 12 connected 100 yd. spools connected

DuPont

Type: Stren monofilament line
Breaking Strength (in lbs.): 2 to 30
Color(s): Clear; blue fluorescent
Packaging: 220-350 yds. (depending on lb. test); 100 yd. spools, 2 connected

Type: Stren monofilament line
Breaking Strength (in lbs.): 2 to 30
Color(s): Golden fluorescent
Packaging: 220-350 yds. depending on lb. 100 yd. spools connected

Type: Stren monofilament line
Breaking Strength (in lbs.): 6 to 80
Color(s): Golden fluorescent
Packaging: 2,400 yd. spools; 4,800 yd. spools; 150 yd. spools

Type: Stren monofilament line
Breaking Strength (in lbs.): 2 to 40
Color(s): Clear; blue fluorescent
Packaging: 2,400 yd. spools; 4,800 yd. spools; 100 yd. spools, 6 connected or 2 connected

I.G.F.A. Dacron

Garcia

Type: Royal bonnyl II monofilament line
Breaking Strength (in lbs.): 2; 4; 6; 8; 10; 12; 15; 20; 25; 30; 40; 50
Color(s): Brown; yellow
Packaging: 100 yd. spools; long-length spools

Type: Braided casting sinking dacron line
Breaking Strength (in lbs.): 10; 12; 15; 20; 25; 30; 35; 40; 45; 50
Color(s): Green
Packaging: 50 yd. spools; 1,000 yd. spools

Type: Invisible monofilament line
Breaking Strength (in lbs.): 2; 4; 6; 8; 10; 12; 15; 20; 25; 30; 40; 50; 60
Color(s): Visible in air, invisible in water
Packaging: 100 yd. spools; long-length spools

Type: Braided casting floating nylon line with braided-in lubrication
Breaking Strength (in lbs.): 10; 12; 15; 20; 25; 30; 35; 40; 45; 50
Color(s): Camouflage; black
Packaging: 50 yd. spools; 1 000 yd. spools

Type: Lead core trolling line
Breaking Strength (in lbs.): 18; 25; 40; 60
Color(s): Color-coded every ten yards
Packaging: 50 yd. spools, 2 per box; 100 yd. coils, 2 per box

Type: Squidding line
Breaking Strength (in lbs.): 18; 27; 36; 45; 54; 63; 72

Color(s): Not specified
Packaging: 50 yd. spools, 2 or 6 connected; 1,000 yd. bulk spools

Type: Braided dacron trolling line
Breaking Strength (in lbs.): 6; 12; 20; 30; 50; 80; 130; 162
Color(s): Not specified
Packaging: 50 yds.; 500 yds.; 600 yds.; 800 yds.; 1000 yds.

Type: Starlon extra-strength monofilament line
Breaking Strength (in lbs.): 6; 12; 15; 20; 25; 30; 40; 50; 80
Color(s): Green
Packaging: Filler spools; 1000 yd., 1200 yd., 5000 yd. spools

Mark V Deep Trolling

Gladding

Type: Invincible braided floating nylon bait casting line
Breaking Strength (in lbs): 6; 9; 12; 15; 18; 20; 25; 30; 35; 40; 45; 50
Color(s): Black; white
Packaging: 50 yd. spools; 1,000 yd. spools

Type: Mercury ultra-soft monofilament
Breaking Strength (in lbs.): 2; 4; 6; 8; 10; 12; 15; 20; 25; 30; 35; 40
Color(s): Gunmetal
Packaging: 100 yd. spools, 2 per box

Type: Super monofilament spinning-casting line
Breaking Strength (in lbs.): 4; 6; 8; 10; 12; 15
Color(s): Mist green
Packaging: 100 yd. spools, 1 or 2 per box

Type: Gladyl monofilament siliconized finish
Breaking Strength (in lbs.): 2; 4; 6; 8; 10; 12; 15; 20; 25; 30; 40; 50
Color(s): Aqua mist
Packaging: 100 yd. spools, 2 per box

Type: Special Mark V braided dacron leadcore line
Breaking Strength (in lbs.): 20; 30; 45; 60
Color(s): New color every 10 yds.
Packaging: 100 yd. spools, 2 per box

Type: Clearon monofilament siliconized finish line
Breaking Strength (in lbs.): 4; 6; 8; 10; 12; 15; 20; 25
Color(s): Clear
Packaging: 100 yd. spools, 2 per box

Type: Champion monofilament line
Breaking Strength (in lbs.): 4; 6; 8; 10; 12; 15; 20; 25; 30; 40; 50
Color(s): Mist green
Packaging: 100 yd. spools

Type: Dreadnaught nylon braided casting line
Breaking Strength (in lbs.): 12; 15; 20; 25; 30
Color(s): Multicolor; black
Packaging: 50 yd. spools, 2 per box

Type: South Bend Black Oreno braided nylon casting trolling line
Breaking Strength (in lbs.): 10; 12; 15; 18; 20; 25; 30; 35; 40
Color(s): Midnight blue
Packaging: 50 yd. spool, 2 per box

Type: Super casting line
Breaking Strength (in lbs.): 12; 15; 20; 25
Color(s): Black
Packaging: 50 yd. spools, 1 or 2 per box

Type: Beachcomber braided nylon-sand line
Breaking Strength (in lbs.): 18; 27; 36; 45; 54; 63
Color(s): Sand
Packaging: 50 yd. spools, 12 connected; 150 yd. spools, 6 connected

Type: Trident braided greenspot dacron line
Breaking Strength (in lbs.): 5; 10; 18; 27; 36; 45; 72; 117
Color(s): Greenspot; black
Packaging: 150 yd. spools, 6 per box; 600 yd., 1000 yd., 1200 yd. spools

Type: Mark V—deep trolling nylon braided over leadcore line
Breaking Strength (in lbs.): 18; 25; 45; 60
Color(s): New color every 10 yds.
Packaging: 50 yd. spools, 2 per box; 100 yd. spools, 2 per box

Type: Snag King braided dacron line
Breaking Strength (in lbs.): 63; 72; 90; 108
Color(s): Ivory
Packaging: 100 yd. spools, 6 per box; 1000 yd. spools

Mercury Ultra-soft Monofilament

Type: Cor-Les dacron line
Breaking Strength (in lbs.): 20; 30; 45; 60
Color(s): New color every 10 yds.
Packaging: 100 yd. spools, 2 per box

Type: Bass in man "All Pro" magnum bass nylon monofilament line
Breaking Strength (in lbs.): 10; 12; 14; 18; 22
Color(s): Invisible smoke grey
Packaging: 300 yd. spools; 275 yd. spools; 250 yd. spools; 200 yds. spools; 150 yd. spools

Type: Gladding depth-finder monofilament line
Breaking Strength (in lbs.): 6; 8; 10; 12; 15; 20; 25; 30
Color(s): New color every 10 yds.
Packaging: 100 yd. spools; 200 yd. spools

Type: Gladding L-B nylon monofilament line
Breaking Strength (in lbs.): 4; 6; 8; 10; 12; 15; 20; 25; 30; 40; 50
Color(s): Water blue
Packaging: 100 yd. spools, 12 per box

Type: South Bend Mark II mono line
Breaking Strength (in lbs.): 6; 8; 10; 12; 15; 20; 25; 30; 40; 50; 60
Color(s): Low visibility green
Packaging: 100 yd. spools, 2 per box; ¼ lb. spools, 6 per box

Type: South Bend Mark II casting and trolling line
Breaking Strength (in lbs.): 12; 15; 20
Color(s): Black
Packaging: 50 yd. spools, 1 or 2 per box

Type: South Bend Mark II squidding line
Breaking Strength (in lbs.): 27; 36; 45
Color(s): Yellow
Packaging: 150 yd. spools

G-6 Dacron

Gudebrod

Type: G-6 trolling line
Breaking Strength (in lbs.): 6; 12; 20; 30; 50; 80;
Color(s): Bluespot; greenspot; white
Packaging: 100 yd. spools, 6 per box; 500 yd. spools; 1200 yd. spools

Type: G-T teflon coated casting line
Breaking Strength (in lbs.): 5; 10; 15; 20; 27; 36; 45; 72
Color(s): Greenspot; white
Packaging: 100 yd. spools 2 or 6 per box; 500 yd., 1200 yd. spools

Type: Bee line braided nylon casting line
Breaking Strength (in lbs.): 10; 15; 20; 25; 30; 35; 45; 63; 84; 108
Color(s): Black and white
Packaging: 50 yd. spools, 2 or 6 per box; 100 yd. spools, 6 per box; 1000 yd. spools

Type: Green Dart ultra limp monofilament line
Breaking Strength (in lbs.): 4; 6; 8; 10; 12; 15; 20; 25; 30; 40; 50
Color(s): Green
Packaging: 100 yd. spools, 2 or 6 per box; 500 yd. spools; ½ lb. and 1 lb. spools

Type: Metered lead core line
Breaking Strength (in lbs.): 18; 27; 36; 45
Color(s): New color every 10 yds.
Packaging: 100 yd. spools, 2 per box

Lakeland

Type: Nylon monofilament line
Breaking Strength (in lbs.): 8; 10; 15; 20; 30
Color(s): Not specified
Packaging: Not specified

Martin

Type: Depth-O-Meter nylon monofilament fishing line
Breaking Strength (in lbs.): 4; 6; 8; 10; 12; 15; 20; 25; 30; 40
Color(s): 25 ft. of each color: clear, yellow, red, blue. Repeated every 100 ft. throughout length of line
Packaging: 200 yd. spool

Mason

Type: Off-Shore dacron trolling and surfing line
Breaking Strength (in lbs.): 12; 20; 30; 50; 80; 130
Color(s): Natural
Packaging: 100 yd. spools, 6 per box; 300 yd., 500 yd. and large capacity bulk spools

Type: Super Soft monofilament line
Breaking Strength (in lbs.): 2; 4; 6; 8; 10; 12; 15; 20; 25; 30; 40; 50
Color(s): Clear; mist blue
Packaging: 100 yd. spools, 2 or 6 per box; 200 yd. spools

Type: Bass-On super bass line
Breaking Strength (in lbs.): 4; 6; 8; 10; 12; 15; 17; 20; 25; 30
Color(s): Charcoal brown
Packaging: 100 yd. spools, 2 or 6 per box; large capacity bulk spools

Type: Coho tournament grade spinning and trolling line
Breaking Strength (in lbs.): 12; 15; 20; 25; 30; 40
Color(s): Blue
Packaging: ⅛ lb. spools, ¼ lb. spools

Type: Braided nylon bait casting line
Breaking Strength (in lbs.): 10; 12; 15; 20; 25; 30; 40; 50

Color(s): Black; camouflage
Packaging: 50 yd. spools, 6 per box

Type: Silver Zephyr spinning and trolling line
Breaking Strength (in lbs.): 4; 6; 8; 10; 12; 15; 20; 25 30
Color(s): Gray mist
Packaging: 100 yd. spools, 2 or 6 per box

Mises

Type: Chameleon maxi-spool
Breaking Strength (in lbs.): 4; 6; 8; 10; 12; 15; 20; 25; 30; 40
Color(s): Not specified
Packaging: 660 yd. spools

Type: Foam green maxi-spool monoline
Breaking Strength (in lbs.): 4; 6; 8; 10; 12; 15; 20; 25; 30; 40; 50; 60
Color(s): Foam green
Packaging: 660 yd. spools

Type: Chameleon "one shot" filling spool
Breaking Strength (in lbs.): 2; 4; 6; 8; 10; 12; 15; 20; 25; 30; 40
Color(s): Color-changing
Packaging: 2 lb., 4 lb.: 280 yds.; 6 lb., 20 lb., 25 lb., 30 lb., 40 lb.: 250 yds.; 8 lb., 12 lb., 15 lb.: 220 yds.

Type: Blue mist mono line
Breaking Strength (in lbs.): 4; 6; 8; 10; 12; 15; 20; 25; 30; 40; 50; 60; 80
Color(s): Blue
Packaging: 4 lb., 6 lb., 8 lb., 10 lb., 12 lb.: 3,200 yds.; 15 lb., 20 lb., 25 lb., 30 lb., 40 lb.: 2,600 yds.; 50 lb. 60 lb.: 1,900 yds.; 80 lb.: 1,300 yds.

Type: Super soft "one shot" filling spool mono line
Breaking Strength: 2; 4; 6; 8; 10; 12; 15; 20; 25; 30; 40
Color(s): Not specified
Packaging: 2 lb., 4 lb.: 280 yds.; 6 lb., 20 lb., 25 lb., 30 lb., 40 lb.: 250 yds.; 8 lb., 10 lb., 12 lb., 15 lb.: 220 yds.

OLM

Type: Soft monofilament nylon line
Breaking Strength (in lbs.): 1; 2; 3; 4; 5; 6; 7; 8; 9; 10; 11; 12; 15; 20; 25
Color(s): Green; light green; transparent
Packaging: 110 yd. spools, 2 connected

Type: Soft monofilament nylon line
Breaking Strength (in lbs.): 2; 4; 6; 8; 10; 12; 15; 20; 25; 30; 35; 40; 45; 50; 60; 65; 75; 90
Color(s): Green; light green; transparent
Packaging: 110 yds. spools, 5 or 10 connected

Type: Soft monofilament nylon line
Breaking Strength (in lbs.): 8; 10; 12; 15; 20; 25; 30; 35; 40; 45; 50; 60; 65; 75; 90
Color(s): Green; light green; transparent
Packaging: ⅛ lb. and ¼ lb. spools

Shakespeare

Type: Super 7000 mono nylon
Breaking Strength (in lbs.): 2; 4; 6; 8; 10; 12; 15; 17; 20; 25; 30; 40; 50
Color(s): Water blue
Packaging: 110 yd. spools, 2 or 6 per box; large capacity bulk spools

Type: 6000 Saltwater nylon monofilament
Breaking Strength (in lbs.): 12; 15; 20; 25; 30; 40; 50; 60; 80; 100
Color(s): Green
Packaging: ¼ lb. spools, 6 per box

Type: 9000 Golden Eye-Crosser mono-filament
Breaking Strength (in lbs.): 6; 8; 10; 12; 15; 17; 20; 25; 30
Color(s): Gold
Packaging: 100 yd. spools, 2 per box

Type: 4499 braided dacron
Breaking Strength (in lbs.): 20; 30; 50; 80; 130
Color(s): White
Packaging: 100 yd. spools, 2 per box

Tycoon Fin-Nor

Type: Gold bond dacron
Breaking Strength (in lbs.): 20; 30; 50; 80; 130
Color(s): Gold
Packaging: 600 yds.; 800 yds.; 1,000 yds.; 1,200 yds.

Type: Tournament monofilament
Breaking Serength (in lbs.): 6; 12; 20; 30; 50; 80
Color(s): Not specified
Packaging: 600 yd. spools; 1,000 yd. spools

Weber

Type: Bulk limp nylon monofilament
Breaking Strength (in lbs.): 2; 4; 6; 8; 10; 12; 15; 20; 25; 30; 40; 50; 75; 90; 125; 150; 175; 200
Color(s): Camouflage; mist
Packaging: ⅛ lb. spools; ¼ lb. spools; ½ lb. spools; 1 lb. spools

Type: Redi-pak limp nylon
Breaking Strength (in lbs.): 1; 2; 3; 4; 5; 6; 8; 10; 12; 15; 20; 25; 30; 40; 60
Color(s): Camouflage mist
Packaging: 4 yd. spools; 5 yd. spools; 7 yd. spools; 8 yd. spools; 10 yd. spools; 15 yd. spools; 20 yd. spools; 30 yd. spools

Type: Limp nylon monofilament spinning
Breaking Strength (in lbs.): 2; 4; 6; 8; 10; 12; 15; 20
Color(s): Camouflage; mist
Packaging: 100 yd. spools, 2 connected

Type: Mill Ends nylon monofilament
Breaking Strength (in lbs.): 2; 4; 6; 8; 10; 12; 15; 20
Color(s): Camouflage
Packaging: 50 yd. spools, 12 per box

Fly Lines

Berkley

Type: Specialist sinking fly line
Length: L: 25 yds.; WF: 30 yds.; DT: 30 yds.; ST; 10 yds.
Color(s): High visibility yellow; bright white; brown
AFTMA Designation: L-5-S; L-6-S; L-7-S; L-8-S; L-9-S; WF-6-S; WF-7-S; WF-8-S; WF-9-S; WF-10-S; DT-5-S; DT-6-S; DT-7-S; DT-8-S; DT-9-S; DT-10-S; ST-7-S; ST-8-S; ST-9-S; ST-10-S; ST-11-S

Type: Specialist floating fly line
Length: L: 25 yds.; WF: 30 yds.; DT: 30 yds.
Color(s): High visibility yellow; bright white; light green; sky blue; cocoa brown; deep brown
AFTMA Designation: L-4-F; L-5-F; L-6-F; L-7-F; L-8-F; L-9-F; WF-4-F; WF-5-F; WF-6-F; WF-7-F; WF-8-F; WF-9-F; WF-F-10; WF-11-F; DT-3-F; DT-4-F; DT-5-F; DT-6-F; DT-7-F; DT-8-F; DT-9-F; DT-10-F

Type: Golden zephyr floating fly line
Length: L: 25 yds.; WF: 30 yds.; DT: 30 yds.
Color(s): Green
AFTMA Designation: L-4-F; L-5-F; L-6-F; L-7-F; WF-6-F; WF-7-F; WF-8-F; WF-9-F; WF-10-F; DT-4-F; DT-5-F; DT-6-F; DT-7-F

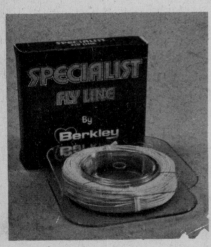

Specialist

Cortland

Type: 444 floating fly line
Length: 30 yd. coil
Color(s): Not specified
AFTMA Designation: DT-3-F; DT-4-F; DT-5-F; DT-6-F; DT-7-F; DT-8-F; DT-9-F; DT-10-F

Type: 444 floating fly line rocket tapers
Length: 35 yd. coils
Color(s): Yellow
AFTMA Designation: WF-4-F; WF-5-F; WF-6-F; WF-7-F; WF-8-F; WF-9-F; WF-10-F; WF-11-F

Type: 444 bug tapers
Length: 35 yd. coils
Color(s): Yellow
AFTMA Designation: WF-7-F; WF-8-F; WF-9-F; WF-10-F

444 Floating

Type: 444 salt water tapers
Length: 35 yd. coils
Color(s): Yellow
AFTMA Designation: WF-8-F; WF-9-F; WF-10-F; WF-11-F

Type: "333" floating fly line
Length: L: 25 yd. coil; DT: 30 yd. coil
Color(s): Mist green; dark amber; white
AFTMA Designation: L-3-F; L-4-F; L-5-F; L-6-F; L-7-F; L-8-F; L-9-F; DT-4-F; DT-5-F; DT-6-F; DT-7-F; DT-8-F; DT-9-F

Type: "333" bug tapers
Length: 35 yd. coils
Color(s): Mist green; dark amber; white
AFTMA Designation: WF-7-F; WF-8-F; WF-9-F; WF-10-F; WF-11-F

Type: "333" rocket tapers
Length: 35 yd. coils
Color(s): Mist green; dark amber; white
AFTMA Designation: WF-5-F; WF-6-F; WF-7-F; WF-8-F; WF-9-F; WF-10-F; WF-11-F

Type: "333" sink-tip tapers
Length: 35 yds.
Color(s): Dark green sink tip, light green balance
AFTMA Designation: WF-5-F/S; WF-6-F/S; WF-7-F/S; WF-8-F/S; WF-9-F/S; WF-10-F/S; WF-11-F/S

Type: 444 Sinking fly line
Length: DT: 30 yds.; WF: 35 yds.
AFTMA Designation: DT-5-S; DT-6-S; DT-7-S; DT-8-S; DT-9-S; WF-5-S; WF-6-S; WF-7-S; WF-8-S; WF-9-S; WF-10-S; WF-11-S

Type: 444 flourescent tournament floating fly line
Length: 30 yds.
Color(s): High visibility red
AFTMA Designation: DT-5-F; DT-6-F; DT-7-F; DT-8-F; DT-9-F; WF-5-F; WF-6-F; WF-7-F; WF-8-F; WF-9-F

Type: Nymph-tip taper floating fly line
Length: 35 yds.
Color(s): Yellow
AFTMA Designation: WF-4-F; WF-5-F; WF-6-F; WF-7-F; WF-8-F; WF-9-F

333 Floating

Garcia

Type: Lee Wulff long belly fly line
Length: 30 yds.
Color(s): Ivory; aqua; grey
AFTMA Designation: WF-5-S; WF-6-S; WF-7-S; WF-8-S; WF-9-S; WF-10-S; WF-5-F; WF-6-F; WF-7-F; WF-8-F; WF-9-F; WF-10-F; WF-5-F/S; WF-6-F/S; WF-7-F/S; WF-8-F/S; WF-9-F/S; WF-10-F/S

Type: Kingfisher floating fly line
Length: L: 25 yds.; WF: 30 yds.; DT: 30 yds.
Color(s): Not specified
AFTMA Designation: L-4-F; L-5-F; L-6-F; L-7-F; L-8-F; L-9-F; WF-4-F; WF-5-F; WF-6-F; WF-7-F; WF-8-F; WF-9-F; DT-4-F; DT-5-F; DT-6-F; DT-7-F; DT-8-F; DT-9-F

Type: Garcia sinking fly line
Length: L: 25 yds; WF: 37 yds.; WF-5-S: 30 yds.; DT: 30 yds.
Color(s): Mahogany; aqua
AFTMA Designation: L-3-S; L-4-S; L-5-S; L-6-S; L-7-S; WF-5-S; WF-6-S; WF-7-S; WF-8-S; DT-4-S; DT-5-S; DT-6-S; DT-7-S

Type: Garcia floating fly line
Length: L: 25 yds.; WF: 30 yds.; DT: 30 yds.
Color(s): Mahogany; aqua; ivory
AFTMA Designation: L-3-F; L-4-F; L-5-F; L-6-F; L-7-F; WF-5-F; WF-6-F; WF-7-F; WF-8-F; WF-9-F; WF-10-F; DT-4-F; DT-5-F; DT-6-F; DT-7-F

Garcia Dacron Sinking

Ideal

Gladding

Type: Magistrate
Length: L: 25 yd. coil; WF: 35 yd. coil; DT: 30 yd. coil
Color(s): Green
AFTMA Designation: L-1-F; L-2-F; L-3-F; L-5-F; L-6-F; L-7-F; L-8-F; WF-6-F; WF-7-F; WF-8-F; WF-9-F; DT-5-F; DT-6-F; DT-7-F; DT-8-F

Type: Super Aqua sink
Length: L: 25 yd. coil; WF: 35 yd. coil; DT: 30 yd. coil; ST: 11 yd. coil
Color(s): Dark green
AFTMA Designation: L-3-S; L-4-S; L-5-S; L-7-S; L-8-S; L-9-S; L-10-S; WF-5-S; WF-6-S; WF-7-S; WF-8-S; WF-9-S; WF-10-S; WF-11-S; DT-5-S; DT-6-S; DT-7-S; DT-8-S; DT-9-S; DT-10-S; ST-9-S; ST-11-S

Super Aerofloat

Type: Super-aerofloat
Length: L: 25 yd. coil; WF: 35 yd. coil; DT: 30 yd. coil; ST: 11 yd. coil
Color(s): White; green
AFTMA Designation: L-3-F; L-4-F; L-5-F; L-6-F; L-7-F; L-8-F; L-9-F; WF-6-F; WF-7-F; WF-8-F; WF-9-F; WF-10-F; DT-5-F; DT-6-F; DT-7-F; DT-8-F; DT-9-F; ST-9-F; ST-10-F

Type: Super-aerofloat salt water taper
Length: 40 yd. coil; 200 yds. with 18 lb. test backing
Color(s): White; green
AFTMA Designation: SWF-9-F; SWF-10-F; SWF-11-F

Type: Salmon taper
Length: 40 yd. coil, 200 yd. backing
Color(s): New color every 10 yds.
AFTMA Designation: WF-9-S; WF-10-S; WF-11-S; WF-12-S

Type: Super line levels

Length: 25 yd. coil
Color(s): Green
AFTMA Designation: L-5-F; L-6-F; L-7-F

Type: Super line double tapers
Length: 30 yd. coil
Color(s): Green
AFTMA Designation: DT-5-F; DT-6-F; DT-7-F

Type: Ideal fly line
Length: 25 yd. coil
Color(s): Dark green
AFTMA Designation: L-3-F; L-5-F; L-6-F; L-7-F

Type: South Bend Mark II fly line
Length: 30 yds.
Color(s): Green
AFTMA Designation: L-6-F; L-7-F; DT-6-F; DT-7-F

Magistrate

Gudebrod

Type: G-5 nylon floating fly line
Length: DT: 30 yds; WF: 30 yds.; L: 25 yds.
Color(s): Green; white
AFTMA Designation: DT-4-F; DT-5-F; DT-6-F; DT-7-F; DT-8-F; WF-5-F; WF-6-F; WF-7-F; WF-8-F; WF-9-F; L-4-F; L-5-F; L-6-F; L-7-F

Type: Hi-Spot floating fly line
Length: DT: 30 yds.; L: 25 yds.
Color(s): Green; amber
AFTMA Designation: DT-5-F; DT-6-F; DT-7-F; L-4-F; L-6-F; L-7-F; L-8-F

Type: Sink-R'-Dacron fly line
Length: DT: 30 yds. WF: 30 yds.; L: 25 yds.
Color(s): Walnut brown
AFTMA Designation: DT-6-S; DT-7-S; DT-8-S; DT-9-S; WF-7-S; WF-8-S; WF-9-S;; WF-10-S; L-6-S; L-7-S; L-8-S; L-9-S

Hi-Spot Floating

Pflueger

Type: Mono-fly, mono-sink fly line
Length: 35 yd.
Color(s): Not specified
AFTMA Designation: WF-8-S; WF-9-S; WF-10-S; WF-11-S

Type: Medalist mono-fly slow sinking fly line
Length: 35 yd. coils
Color(s): Translucent
AFTMA Designation: WF-6-S; WF-7-S; WF-8-S; WF-9-S; WF-10-S; WF-11-S; WF-12-S

Type: Medalist mono-fly slow sinking fly line
Length: 35 yd. coils
Color(s): Translucent
AFTMA Designation: DT-5-S; DT-6-S; DT-7-S; DT-8-S

Type: Meadlist mono-fly floating fly line
Length: 35 yd. coils
Color(s): White
AFTMA Designation: WF-6-F; WF-7-F; WF-8-F; WF-9-F; WF-10-F; WF-11-F

Type: Medalist mono-fly floating fly line
Length: 35 yd. coils
Color(s): White
AFTMA Designation: DT-5-F; DT-6-F; DT-7-F; DT-8-F

Wet Cel Wet Head

Scientific Anglers/3M

Type: Wet Cel I slow sinking
Length: 25 yd. coils
Color(s): Medium green
AFTMA Designation: L-5-S; L-6-S; L-7-S; L-8-S; L-9-S; L-10-S; L-11-S

Type: Wet Cel I slow sinking
Length: 30 yd. coils
Color(s): Medium green
AFTMA Designation: WF-5-S; WF-6-S; WF-7-S; WF-8-S; WF-9-S; WF-10-S

Type: Wet Cel I slow sinking
Length: 30 yd. coils
Color(s): Medium green
AFTMA Designation: DT-5-S; DT-6-S; DT-7-S; DT-8-S; DT-9-S; DT-10-S

Type: Wet Cel I slow sinking
Length: 30 yd. coils
Color(s): Medium green
AFTMA Designation: ST-6-S; ST-7-S; ST-8-S; ST-9-S; ST-10-S; ST-11-S

Type: Wet Cel II fast sinking

Length: 30 yd. coils
Color(s): Dark green
AFTMA Designation: DT-4-S; DT-5-S; DT-6-S; DT-7-S; DT-8-S; DT-9-S; DT-10-S; DT-11-S; DT-12-S

Type: Wet Cel wet head
Length: 30 yd. coils
Color(s): Two-tone green
AFTMA Designation: WF-7-F/S; WF-8-F/S; WF-9-F/S; WF-10-F/S; WF-11-F/S; WF-12-F/S

Type: Air Cel
Length: 25 yd. coils
Color(s): White; light green; dark brown
AFTMA Designation: L-1-F; L-2-F; L-3-F; L-4-F; L-5-F; L-6-F; L-7-F; L-8-F; L-9-F

Type: Air Cel
Length: 30 yd. coils
Color(s): White; light green; dark brown
AFTMA Designation: WF-5-F; WF-6-F; WF-7-F; WF-8-F; WF-9-F

Type: Air Cel
Length: 30 yd. coils
Color(s): White; light green; dark brown
AFTMA Designation: DT-4-F; DT-5-F; DT-6-F; DT-7-F; DT-8-F; DT-9-F

Type: Air Cel
Length: 10 yd. coils
Color(s): White
AFTMA Designation: ST-6-F; ST-7-F; ST-8-F; ST-9-F; ST-10-F; ST-11-F

Type: Air Cel bass bug taper
Length: 10 yd. coils
Color(s): Light green
AFTMA Designation: WF-6-F; WF-7-F; WF-8-F; WF-9-F

Type: Air Cel wet tip
Length: 30 yd. coils
Color(s): Two-tone green
AFTMA Designation: WF-5-F/S; WF-6-F/S; WF-7-F/S; WF-8-F/S; WF-9-F/S; WF-10-F/S

Type: Air Cel wet tip
Length: 30 yd. coils
Color(s): Two-tone green
AFTMA Designation: DT-4-F/S; DT-5-F/S; DT-6-F/S; DT-7-F/S; DT-8-F/S

Type: Air Cel wet tip hi-d
Length: 30 yd. coils
Color(s): Yellow; dark green
AFTMA Designation: WF-5-F/S; WF-6-F/S; WF-7-F/S; WF-8-F/S; WF-9-F/S; WF-10-F/S; WF-11-F/S; WF-12-F/S; WF-13-F/S

Type: Air Cel supreme
Length: 30 yd. coils
Color(s): Ivory; mahogany; fluorescent orange
AFTMA Designation: WF-4-F; WF-5-F; WF-6-F; WF-7-F; WF-8-F; WF-9-F; WF-10-F

Type: Air Cel supreme saltwater taper
Length: 30 yd. coils
Color(s): Ivory; non-glare grey
AFTMA Designation: WF-8-F; WF-9-F; WF-10-F; WF-11-F; WF-12-F

Type: Air Cel supreme
Length: 30 yd. coils
Color(s): Ivory; mahogany; fluorescent orange

Air Cel

AFTMA Designation: DT-3-F; DT-4-F; DT-5-F; DT-6-F; DT-7-F; DT-8-F; DT-9-F; DT-10-F; DT-11-F

Type: Air Cel fisherman
Length: 25 yd. coils
Color(s): Kelly green
AFTMA Designation: L-5-I; L-6-I; L-7-I; L-8-I; L-9-I

Type: Air Cel fisherman
Length: 30 yd. coils
Color(s): Kelly green
AFTMA Designation: WF-6-I; WF-7-I; WF-8-I; WF-9-I; WF-10-I; WF-11-I; WF-12-I

Type: Air Cel fisherman
Length: 30 yd. coil
Color(s): Kelly green
AFTMA Designation: DT-5-I; DT-6-I; DT-7-I; DT-8-I; DT-9-I; DT-10-I

Type: Wet Cel Hi-D extra fast sinking
Length: 30 yd. coils
Color(s): Greenish black
AFTMA Designation: WF-7-S; WF-8-S; WF-9-S; WF-10-S; WF-11-S; WF-12-S

Type: Wet Cel Hi-D extra fast sinking
Length: 30 yd. coils
Color(s): Greenish black
AFTMA Designation: DT-7-S; DT-8-S; DT-9-S; DT-10-S

Type: Wet Cel Hi-D extra fast sinking
Length: 10 yd. coils
Color(s): Greenish black
AFTMA Designation: ST-7-S; ST-8-S; ST-9-S; ST-10-S; ST-11-S

Type: Wet Cel II fast sinking
Length: 25 yd. coils; *also 50 yd. coils
Color(s): Dark green

Air Cel

Air Cel

AFTMA Designation: L-4-S; L-5-S; L-6-S*;
L-7-S*; L-8-S*; L-9-S*; L-10-S; L-11-S

Type: Wet Cel II fast sinking
Length: 30 yd. coils
Color(s): Dark green
AFTMA Designation: WF-4-S; WF-5-S; WF-6-S;
WF-7-S; WF-8-S; WF-9-S; WF-10-S;
WF-11-S; WF-12-S

Type: Wet Cel II fast sinking
Length: 10 yd. coils
Color(s): Dark green
AFTMA Designation: ST-6-S; ST-7-S; ST-8-S;
ST-9-S; ST-10-S; ST-11-S

Shakespeare

Type: Presidential fast sinking
Length: 25 yds.
Color(s): Dark green
AFTMA Designation: L-6-S; L-7-S; L-8-S; L-9-S

Type: Presidential fast sinking
Length: 40 yds.
Color(s): Dark green
AFTMA Designation: WF-11-S; WF-12-S

Type: Presidential fast sinking
Length: 30 yds.
Color(s): Dark green
AFTMA Designation: WF-6-S; WF-7-S; WF-8-S;
WF-9-S; WF-10-S

Type: Presidential fast sinking
Length: 30 yds.
Color(s): Dark green
AFTMA Designation: DT-6-S; DT-7-S; DT-8-S;
DT-9-S

Type: Presidential floating
Length: 25 yds.
Color(s): Green

AFTMA Designation: L-4-F; L-5-F; L-6-F; L-7-F;
L-8-F; L-9-F

Type: Presidential floating
Length: 30 yds.; WF-10-F: 40 yds.
Color(s): Green
AFTMA Designation: WF-5-F; WF-6-F; WF-7-F;
WF-8-F; WF-9-F; WF-10-F

Type: Presidential floating
Length: 30 yds.
Color(s): Green
AFTMA Designation: DT-4-F; DT-5-F; DT-6-F;
DT-7-F; DT-8-F; DT-9-F

Sunset

Type: The Chancellor Chalkstream Mono-
filament fly line
Length: 30 yds.
Color(s): Chalk grey
AFTMA Designation: DT-4-F; DT-5-F; DT-6-F;
DT-7-F; DT-8-F

Type: The Chancellor Masterline floating
fly line
Length: DT: 30 yds.; WF: 30 or 40 yds.;
ST: 10 or 11⅔ yds.
Color(s): White; green
AFTMA Designation: DT-4-F; DT-5-F; DT-6-F;
DT-7-F; DT-8-F; DT-9-F; WF-5-F; WF-6-F;
WF-7-F; WF-8-F; WF-9-F; WF-10-F; WF-11-F;
ST-5-F; ST-6-F; ST-7-F; ST-8-F; ST-9-F;
ST-10-F; ST-11-F

Type: The Chancellor Masterline sinking
fly line
Length: DT: 30 yds.; WF: 30 or 40 yds.;
ST: 10 or 11⅔ yds.
Color(2): Grey
AFTMA Designation: DT-4-S; DT-5-S; DT-6-S;
DT-7-S; DT-8-S; DT-9-S; WF-5-S; WF-6-S;
WF-7-S; WF-8-S; WF-9-S; WF-10-S;
WF-11-S; ST-5-S; ST-6-S; ST-7-S; ST-8-S;
ST-9-S; ST-10-S; T-11-S

The Chancellor Masterline Floating

Type: The Chancellor Masterline sink tip fly
line
Length: 30 or 40 yds.
Color(s): Grey
AFTMA Designation: DT-6-F/S; DT-7-F/S;
DT-8-F/S; DT-9-F/S; DT-10-F/S; WT-5-F/S;
WT-6-F/S; WT-7-F/S; WT-8-F/S; WF-9-F/S;
WF-10-F/S

Type: The Graduate Masterline floating
fly line
Length: DT: 30 yds.; WF: 30 yds.; L: 20 yds.
Color(s): Green
AFTMA Designation: DT-5-F; DT-6-F; DT-7-F;
DT-8-F; DT-9-F; WF-6-F; WF-7-F; WF-8-F;
WF-9-F; L-6-F; L-7-F

Type: The Graduate Masterline sinking fly line
Length: DT: 30 yds. WF: 30 yds.; L: 20 yds.
Color(s): Brown
AFTMA Designation: DT-5-S; DT-6-S; DT-7-S;
DT-8-S; DT-9-S; WF-6-S; WF-7-S; WF-8-S;
WF-9-S; L-7-S; L-8-S

Leaders

Berkley

Type: Steelon spinning leaders
Diameter: Not specified
Breaking Strength (in lbs.): 6; 10; 20
Length: 3"; 4"; 5"; 6"; 9"
Color(s): Not specified

Type: Steelon leaders
Diameter: Not specified
Breaking Strength (in lbs.): 20; 30; 45; 60
Length: 6"; 9"; 12"; 18"; 24"; 36"; 48"; 72"
Color(s): Clear

Type: Steelon nylon casting leaders
Breaking Strength (in lbs.): 20; 30
Length: 6"; 9"; 12"

Type: Steelon cable leaders
Breaking Strength (in lbs.): 6; 10; 20; 30
Length: 4"; 5"; 6"; 9"; 12" 18"; 24"

Type: Steelon ball bearing leaders
Breaking Strength (in lbs.): 6; 10; 20; 30
Length: 4"; 5"; 6"; 9"; 12" 18"; 24"

Type: Not-a-knot-knotless trout tapered leaders
Diameter: 0X; 1X; 2X; 3X; 4X; 5X; 6X
Breaking Strength (in lbs.): 6; 5; 4; 3; 2½; 2; 1¾
Length: 6'; 7½'; 9'
Color(s): Camouflage

Type: Qwik sink knotless tapered leaders
Diameter: 0X; 1X; 2X; 3X; 4X; 5X; 6X
Breaking Strength (in lbs.): 6; 5; 4; 3; 2½; 2; 1¾
Length: 7½'; 9'
Color(s): Camouflage

Type: Knotless heavy tapered leaders
Diameter: 4X; 3X; 2X; 1X; 0X; 8/5; 6/5
Breaking Strength (in lbs.): 2½; 3; 4; 5; 6; 8; 10
Length: 7½'; 9'
Color(s): Camouflage

Type: Specialist tapered leader
Diameter: 0X; 1X; 2X; 3X; 4X; 5X; 6X
Breaking Strength (in lbs.): 6; 5; 4; 3; 2½; 2; 1¾
Length: 9'
Color(s): Clear

Nylo-Steel

Cortland

Type: 333 Knotless tapered nylon leaders
Diameter: 6X; 5X; 4X; 3X; 2X; 1X; 0X; 8/5; 6/5
Breaking Strength (in lbs.): 1.5; 2; 3; 3.5; 4.5; 6; 8; 11; 13
Length: 7½'; 9'
Color(s): Mist blue

Type: 444 Twin-Tip tapered leaders
Diameter: 0X; 1X; 2X; 3X; 4X; 5X; 6X; 8/5
Breaking Strength (in lbs.): 1.5; 2.3; 3.5; 4.5; 6; 8; 11; 13
Length: 9'
Color(s): Clear

Dragon Fly

Type: Nylon leaders
Diameter: Not specified
Breaking Strength (in lbs.): 30
Length: 24"
Color(s): Clear

Type: Nylo-steel leaders
Diameter: Not specified
Breaking Strength (in lbs.): 30
Length: 6"; 9"; 12"
Color(s): Clear

Type: Stainless steel leaders
Diameter: Not specified
Breaking Strength (in lbs.): 40
Length: 24"
Color(s): Clear

Garcia

Type: Garcia knotless tapered fly leaders
Diameter: 6X; 5X; 4X; 3X; 2X; 1X; 0X
Breaking Strength (in lbs.): 1½; 2; 4; 5; 6; 7; 8
Length: 7½'; 9'
Color(s): Clear

Gladyl Knotless Tapered

Gladding

Type: Gladding-South Bend knotless tapered leaders
Diameter: Not specified
Breaking Strength (in lbs.): 8; 9; 6.3; 2.1; 12.6
Length: 7½'; 9'
Color(s): Not specified

Type: Gladyl knotless tapered leaders
Diameter: 7X; 6X; 5X; 4X; 3X; 2X; 1X; 0X
Breaking Strength (in lbs.): 1.2; 2.1; 3.3; 4.3; 5.2; 6.3; 8.9
Length: 6' (5X, 4X only); 7½'; 9'
Color(s): Not specified

Type: Clearon knotless tapered nylon fly
Diameter: 6X; 5X; 4X; 3X; 2X; 1X; 0X
Breaking Strength (in lbs.): 3; 5; 6; 8; 9; 10
Length: 7½'; 9'
Color(s): Water clear

Martin

Type: Stainless steel leader
Diameter: Not specified
Breaking Strength (in lbs.): Not specified
Length: 13'; 6'
Color(s): Clear

Type: Mooching leaders
Diameter: Not specified
Breaking Strength (in lbs.): 10 thru 30
Length: 7'
Color(s): Clear

Type: Dodger leaders
Diameter: Not specified
Breaking Strength (in lbs.): 25
Length: 33"
Color(s): Clear

Mason

Type: Taper-Flex knotless tapered leaders
Diameter: 0X; 1X; 2X; 3X; 4X; 5X; 6X
Breaking Strength (in lbs.): 1.5; 2; 3; 4; 5; 6; 7
Length: 6'; 7½'; 9'; 12'
Color(s): Mist; grey

Type: Balanced tapered leaders
Diameter: 0X; 1X; 2X; 3X; 4X; 5X
Breaking Strength (in lbs.): 1.25; 1.75; 2.7; 3.5; 4; 5
Length: 6'; 7½'; 9'; 12'
Color(s): Mist

Type: Steelflex nylo-strand leaders
Breaking Strength (in lbs.): 12; 20; 30; 45; 60
Length: 4'; 5'; 6'; 9'; 12'

Type: Steelflex multistrand leaders
Breaking Strength (in lbs.): 12; 20; 30; 45
Length: 5'; 6'; 9'; 12'; 18'

OLM

Type: Steel leaders

Breaking Strength (in lbs.): 30
Length: 6"; 9"

Type: Salt water mooching leaders
Breaking Strength (in lbs.): 10; 15; 20; 25
Length: 7'

Type: Surf leaders
Breaking Strength (in lbs.): 10; 15; 20; 30; 40; 50
Length: 3'

Type: Wire leaders
Breaking Strength (in lbs.): 30
Length: 12"; 18"; 24"

Orvis

Type: Compound taper wet fly leaders with kwik-klips
Diameter: 0X; 1X; 2X; 3X
Breaking Strength (in lbs.): 6; 5; 4; 3½
Length: 7½'; 9'
Color(s): Not specified

Type: Hand tied knotted leaders
Diameter: 0X; 1X; 2X; 3X; 4X
Breaking Strength (in lbs.): 2; 3; 3½; 4; 5; 6
Length: 5'; 6'; 9'; 12'; 18'

Sampo

Type: Steelheart leaders
Diameter: Not specified
Breaking Strength (in lbs.): 6; 10; 20; 30; 45
Length: 3"; 4"; 5"; 6"; 9"; 12"; 18"; 24"; 36"
Color(s): Not specified

Type: Ball-bearing muskie leaders
Diameter: Not specified
Breaking strength (in lbs.): 45
Length: 9"
Color(s): Not specified

Type: Ball-bearing striper leaders
Diameter: Not specified
Breaking Strength (in lbs.): 45
Length: 18"; 24"; 36"
Color(s): Not specified

Type: Rosco steelheart leader
Diameter: Not specified
Breaking Strength (in lbs.): 6; 10; 20; 30; 45
Length: 3"; 4"; 5"; 6"; 9"; 12"; 18"; 24"; 36"
Color(s): Not specified

Type: Rosco striper leaders
Diameter: Not specified
Breaking Strength (in lbs.): 45
Length: 18"; 24"; 36"
Color(s): Not specified

Weber

Type: Monofilament nylon leaders
Diameter: Not specified
Breaking Strength (in lbs.): 10; 15; 20
Length: 6"; 9"; 12"
Color(s): Camouflage

Type: Tied tapered nylon leaders
Diameter: 5X; 4X; 3X; 2X; 1X; 0X
Breaking Strength (in lbs.): 1½; 2; 2½; 3; 3½; 4½
Length: 6', 9'
Color(s): Camouflage

Type: Kwik-cast nylon leaders
Diameter: Not specified
Breaking Strength (in lbs.): 6; 8; 10; 12; 15; 20
Length: 3'; 4½'; 6'
Color(s): Camouflage; mist

Type: 3" "shorty" kant kink wire leaders
Diameter: Not specified
Breaking Strength (in lbs.): 10
Length: 3"
Color(s): Clear nylon over bright wire

Type: Kant kink wire leaders
Diameter: Not specified
Breaking Strength (in lbs.): 20; 30
Length: 6"; 9"; 12"; 18"; 24"; 36"; 72"
Color(s): Clear nylon over bright wire

Type: "Sink" knotless tapered nylon trout leaders
Diameter: 5X; 4X; 3X; 2X; 1X
Breaking Strength (in lbs.): 2.8; 3.5; 4.2; 5.6; 7.0
Length: 7'; 9'
Color(s): Camouflage; glint-free

Type: "No-sheen" knotless tapered nylon leaders
Diameter: 6X; 5X; 4X; 3X; 2X; 1X; 0X; 8/5; 6/5
Breaking Strength (in lbs.): 1¼; 2; 2½; 3; 4; 5; 6; 8; 10
Length: 7'; 9'
Color(s): Camouflage

Type: Knotless level nylon leaders
Diameter: Not specified
Breaking Strength (in lbs.): 2; 4; 6; 8; 10; 15; 20
Length: 3'; 4'; 6'
Color(s): Camouflage; mist; natural

Sink and No-sheen Knotless Tapered

Worth

Type: Nylon leader
Diameter: Not specified
Breaking Strength (in lbs.): 10; 20; 30
Length: 6"; 9"; 12"; 18"
Color(s): Not specified

Type: Piano wire leader with attached snap and swivel
Diameter: .018
Breaking Strength (in lbs.): Not specified
Length: 6"; 9"; 12"; 18"; 24"
Color(s): Not specified

Type: Heavy duty knotless tapered leader
Diameter: 6X; 5X; 4X; 3X; 2X; 1X; 0X; 9/5; 8/5; 7/5; 6/5; 5/5
Breaking Strength (in lbs.): 1.25; 2; 2.5; 3; 4; 5; 6; 7; 8; 9; 10; 12
Length: 7½'; 9'; 12'
Color(s): Not specified

Type: Sinking knotless tapered leader
Diameter: 6X; 5X; 4X; 3X; 2X; 1X; 0X; 8/5; 6/5
Breaking Strength (in lbs.): 1.25; 2; 2.5; 3; 4; 5; 6; 8; 10
Length: 7½'; 9'; 12'
Color(s): Mist green

Piano Wire

Specifications: Accessories

1977 Product Preview
Accessories

Accessories make a day on the water more pleasurable and often play a vital role in helping an angler to catch more fish. Among the more popular items in this category are tackle boxes, electric trolling motors and electronic gear, including depth sounders. All are part of fishing by today's standards, and it is questionable whether the proverbial farm lad with bent pin would do as well as the highly skilled fisherman with a wagonload of helpful equipment.

Trends in tackle boxes appear to stretch to extremes, with large drawer boxes and smaller specialized boxes in the lead. The advantage of the drawer style is that it saves space on a boat but allows ready access to its contents. If it tips, it won't spill the contents, either. Many anglers may use a drawer box for the bulk of their tackle, but there also seems to be a switch toward individual boxes for different types of gear. Spinner bait models, plug boxes and even modular compacts that open on one side or both are finding room aboard boats of every description or on the shore alongside the angler.

Trolling motors are getting more powerful than ever, and most of the best sellers offer the 24-volt option as well as improved materials for the motors. Initially, electric motors were strictly a tool of the fresh water angler, but they are now finding more use aboard boats that fish the shallow waters of the seas. For that reason, parts must be made corrosion-resistant, and the problem of electrolysis, which causes electrical fields to set up between dissimilar metals in salt water, must be solved.

Depth sounders are becoming almost as essential to anglers as fishing rods, and many boats now boast at least two units. Flasher types are still very much in use, but recording depth sounders are becoming increasingly popular. There is also a growing use of the digital read-out models as a back-up unit and as a means to indicate sudden depth changes before they become apparent on the recording type of machine. The digitals work at very high speeds and can be monitored by the boat that is operated to detect a dropoff or shoaling.

Woodstream's Old Pal Division has added a five-drawer tackle box to its stylish Bass Boss Series. There are forty-seven compartments in the box and a large add-on bottom for holding reels, tools, filleting knife and other accessories. Both four- and five-drawer boxes are now part of the Famous Fish Series of tackle boxes. The drawers have different interior configurations, and these can be interchanged, as can a deep drawer that takes the place of two drawers of regular height.

The add-on bottom is also being offered as part of the Famous Fish Series and can be attached to standard boxes as well as the drawer designs. A thirty-six-compartment, six-tray, hip-roof box with the new "cork look" trays is now part of the same series. An even larger, fifty-six-compartment, seven-tray hip-roof box with an add-on bottom rounds out the additions to the Famous Fish Series.

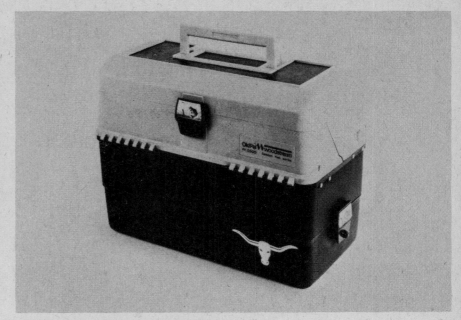

Long Horn add-on bottoms are new from Old Pal.

Old Pal's Bass Boss five-drawer tackle box.

Old Pal's Professional Series drawer box.

Vlchek Adventurer seven-drawer box.

Vlchek's Adventurer tackle boxes feature a seven-drawer molded box that has ninety-six worm-resistant compartments. It is the largest made in this style, yet requires only 1.73 square feet of deck space when it is open. The front panel tucks under the bottom drawer, keeping it out of the angler's way. A smaller, six-drawer model with forty-seven compartments is also part of the line.

Adventurer's Lure Luggage Series has the 2253 Space Saver Box and the slightly smaller 2233 version. There is two-way access (either through the top or by open-

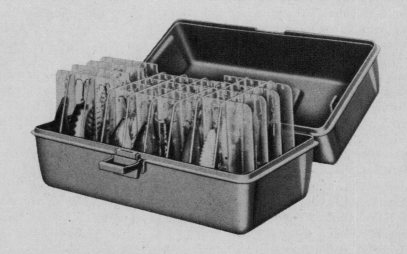

Vlchek Adventurer 1745 with slotted lift-out rack.

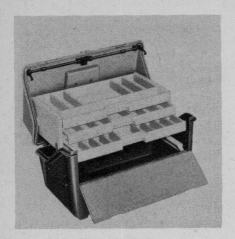

Three-drawer Space Saver box by Adventurer.

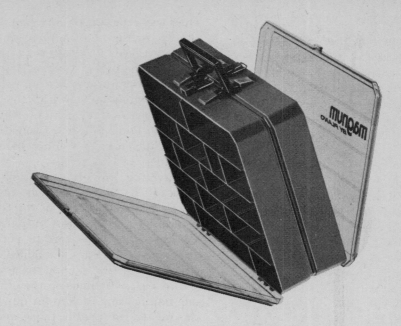

Plano's Magnum 1146.

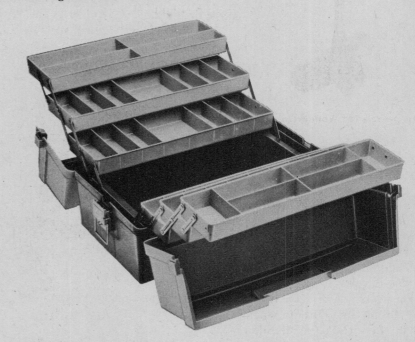

The Plano 9106.

ing the three drawers from the front), and the drawers are interchangeable so that you can add the interior configurations you need. The 2253 has fifty-seven compartments, while the 2233 has thirty-two. There is plenty of room below the drawers for reels, lure boxes, tools and other items of equipment.

Adventurer's Crank Baiter Series, designed for the angler who tosses plugs or spinner baits, uses its Lure Arranger inside a shell. The lures hang individually from slotted inserts and are easy to reach or put back. The new model 1735 has sixty-two slots, for thirty-two spinner baits and thirty crank baits.

Strengthening the trend toward modular boxes for one type of fishing, Plano offers its Magnum 1146 and Magnum 1123. These are flat boxes with movable dividers, which offer up to twenty-three compartments in the single version and forty-six in the double version. The 1146 is simply a pair of 1123's permanently riveted together. Both boxes have draw-bolt-type latches and see-through amber lids. They are wormproof and can be used for any type of tackle from panfish gear to bait-rigging equipment for offshore sport.

Plano's 9106 is a forty-two-compartment, hip-roof model with six polypropelene trays made 1½ inches deep to hold lures that don't fit in other boxes. There is plenty of extra storage space below the trays for reels, pork rind, extra spools of line and anything else. A wide drain trough runs around the box, making it leakproof in rain or when spray sweeps over the bow of the boat. The latches are of the positive variety and provide a hasp for locking.

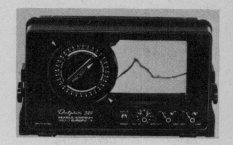

Pearce Simpson Dolphin 320.

That way, the angler can simply pick up the right box and have the tackle he needs for whatever type of fishing he expects to do. Even newer configurations are on the way, including some with transparent covers so the contents will be visible, and a model or two with slotted dividers for spinner baits and plugs.

Traveling anglers sometimes favor soft bags for their gear, and this is particularly true of the fly fisherman. The Orvis Company has completely redesigned its popular series of kit bags and added a new model or two. Among the new features are boxed lids on the outside flap pockets, Velcro for quick closure on the pocket flaps, and double slide pads. The bags are available in several sizes and have strong shoulder straps to facilitate carrying.

Garcia Electro-Sonic Flasher.

Shakespeare's Fishing Tackle Division announces that two high-performance electric fishing motors have been added to its Wondertroll line. The 712 is a 12-volt motor that produces up to 17 pounds of thrust, while the 724 is the 24-volt version and has been measured at 22½ pounds of thrust. Both motors have the new universal motor mount designed for use

Shakespeare's 724 Wondertroll motor.

Three different molded hip-roof plastic boxes are new additions to the UMCO line of tackle boxes. The all-purpose box of the trio has six cantilever trays with fifty roomy compartments. The other two boxes offer, respectively, two trays and one drawer and one tray and one drawer. A spillproof protection system will keep the box from spilling its contents when it isn't latched; the company claims that this helps improve a fisherman's language.

Plastics Research and Development are marketing a series of Bass N Boxes in both single and back-to-back, or double, mode. These flat, modular boxes have compartment dividers, and it is recommended that one box be used for only one specific type of tackle.

on deck or gunwales. An automatic locking device secures the motor in either the running or the stowed position and is easy to unlock to change the position.

The Garcia Corporation has improved its line of depth flashers and chart recorders with the introduction of the Electro-Sonic 9360A and 9350A. Both these solid-state fish finders feature a special high-speed mode control that gives clear, concise readings on fish and bottom structure at speeds up to 45 knots. The 9360A is engineered for detailed readings from 0 to 60 feet, with the potential to read down to 120 feet. It is ideal for the angler who fishes primarily in shallow water. The more powerful 9350A works in deeper waters and will read to a maximum of 300 feet. At speeds of 45 knots, it will read bottom structure down to 100 feet.

The Electro-Sonic 9500A and 9400A from Garcia have four range controls and two modes on the chart recorder, which equals a total of eight close-up increments for a super-detailed chart picture. On the 9400A, the chart can be set to any 60-foot range and then to a 30-foot close-up for an even more detailed picture. The 9500A has the same operational ability, except that the ranges are increased to 120 feet at a time.

The Pearce Simpson Division of Gladding Corporation has unveiled a new Dolphin 320 combination flasher/recorder that will read in

80-foot increments down to 320 feet. In fact, the machine will read even deeper because of its powerful transmitter, and the lower depths will repeat on the paper. Chart speed is 35 inches per hour and the width is 100 millimeters, or approximately 4 inches.

Waller Corporation's Fish Hawk 555 Oxygen Analyzer is the first one on the market that does not require calibration before use. It has a 50-foot line for deeper water and a colored scale that facilitates reading. It is also available in combination with other instruments in the Waller line.

Orvis has a Shoo Bug jacket that has proved to be the best weapon in the outdoorsman's battle against black flies and mosquitoes. The lightweight jacket comes in a charging bag and special repellent is applied. Field tests and testimonials from its first buyers have caused sales to zoom. According to Orvis, it really does a job, and once you see someone wearing one in black-fly or mosquito country, you'll never be without one.

Anyone who operates an outboard-powered boat should have a kill switch that instantly shuts off the engine if the operator leaves the helm position. The Tempo Quick Kill does just that and can be installed in a few minutes on key ignition switches on the dash or the shift-control box. There are no holes to drill, wires to cut or complex switch mechanisms to figure out. Installation requires only removing the retaining nut from the ignition switch and slipping Quick Kill in place. It could save your life.

Triangulation of objects on shore is an easy way to pinpoint fishing spots, and you can handle the assignment without sophisticated electronic gear. Ritchie Navigation Instruments has marketed a new hand-bearing compass that allows the user to sight a landmark

Waller Fish Hawk Dissolved Oxygen Meter.

and take a bearing. By using a red aiming dot, extreme accuracy is possible and there is a dial lock button that enables the angler to take the bearing.

Custom-building your own fishing rods is not only fun but can save you money. The difficult part of the operation, however, has been in achieving a slick finish on the wraps over the guides. Old-fashioned finishes took time and were built up layer after layer. Gudebrod is now marketing Hard 'N Fast, a one-coat rod finish that lasts for years after it dries to a hard, luxurious finish.

Hauling a trolling weight up with two hands rather than one takes some of the effort out of fishing, and this is one of the key features on the Luhr Jensen King Auto Track II Down-Rigger. Having a crank handle on each side, it also makes one-handed cranking easier, since the handle is never on the wrong side. Delring bearings in the cranking assembly virtually eliminate side thrust and radial load friction, making it easier to

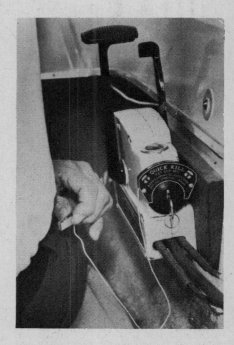

Quick Kill switch from Tempo Products.

recover the trolling weight. It has a built-in depth indicator and a plastic reel that insulates the cable against electrolysis in salt water and is available in both short-arm and long-arm models.

Ritchie hand-bearing compass.

Gudebrod's Hard 'N Fast.

Penn Reels has added the Fathom-Master 620 Downrigger with a 4-foot heavy-duty anodized-aluminum boom that can easily be removed from the downrigger for storage. Two line guides prevent the cable from jumping the pulley, and the pulley swivels with the weight to give automatic tracking. The Swivel-Matic base unit allows one-hand operation by pushing or pulling the boom. There are no locking pins with which to contend. The boom swivels 180 degrees. A drag brake control identical with the drag assembly on the well-known Penn Senator reels monitors the lowering of the trolling weight. The design of the Fath-

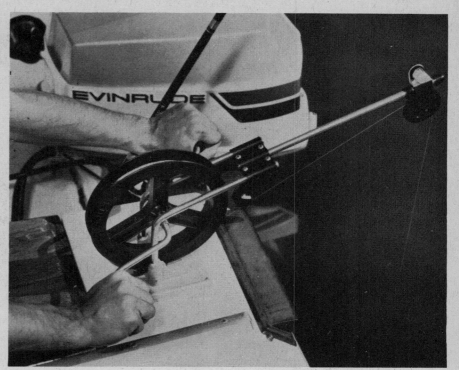

Luhr Jensen Down-Rigger.

om-Master 620 is vertical so that it occupies a minimum of space and doesn't extend back into the cockpit. This unit was designed for deep salt water trolling, and all parts are corrosion-resistant, which means that it will be equally satisfactory for fresh water use.

On boats that are 16 feet long or longer, there must be one wearable Personal Flotation Device for every person on board, and most fishermen are beginning to buy their own in order to be certain of the quality and know that the device will fit. New studies have been conducted into the area of hypothermia and its effect on human beings in water of varying temperatures. Hypothermia, the lowering of the body's core temperature, can result in loss of consciousness and death. Stearns Manufacturing Company has designed their Sans Souci line of life vests to provide extended protection against hypothermia and help to increase

survival time in cold water. These vests contain Aquafoam, a closed-cell polyvinyl chloride foam that not only provides buoyancy but acts as a heat insulator in water or air. Aquafoam cannot rot or waterlog and will keep the wearer afloat indefinitely. Among the most popular models of life vests for fishermen is the blue denim SSV-165. It has four pockets with Velcro closures on the outside and comes in small, medium, large, extra large and extra extra large sizes.

Stearns also makes a fishing vest that is inflatable. It can be inflated by mouth with a valve concealed in the breast pocket, and some models contain a 16-gram CO_2 cartridge for emergency use. The outer shell of these vests is windproof and waterproof, but a mesh lining on the inside allows the jacket to breathe and prevents moisture from developing.

Bait Boxes

Mfr.: Old Pal
Model No.: 10
Size: 6″ x 3½″ x 2″
Compartment(s): 1
Material: Steel

Mfr.: Old Pal
Model No.: P30
Size: 7⅜″ x 4⁵⁄₁₆″ x 7½″
Compartment(s): Not specified
Material: Polypropylene

Mfr.: Old Pal
Model No.: 300
Size: 6″ x 3½″ x 2″
Compartment(s): 2
Material: Polyethylene

Old Pal Bait Box

Mfr.: OLM
Model No.: 157
Size: 5¾″ x 3¼″ x 1¾″
Compartment(s): 1
Material: Plastic

Mfr.: H. S. Ross
Model: Bait Baffler
Size: Not specified
Compartment(s): Not specified
Material: Aluminum

Mfr.: Plano
Model No.: 3149-7
Size: 6½″ x 3¾″ x 1⅛″
Compartment(s): 7
Material: Acrylite

Mfr.: Plano
Model No.: 3150-8
Size: 8¼″ x 4¼″ x 1⅜″
Compartment(s): 8
Material: Acrylite

Mfr.: Vlchek
Model No.: V-661
Size: 7″ x 3⅝″ x 3½″
Material: Polypropylene

Baskets

Mfr.: Dragon Fly Company, Inc.
Model No.: 3ZDT
Material: Zinc plated
Size: 13½″ x 18½″

Mfr.: Lindy/Little Joe
Model No.: AC231
Material: Wire mesh
Length: 24″
Diameter: 14″

Nylon Net

Mfr.: Nylon Net Co.
Model No.: 430
Material: Polyethylene plastic
Length: 14½″
Diameter: 19″ top; 14½″ bottom

Mfr.: Nylon Net Co.
Model No.: WB-1
Material: Wire
Length: 21″
Diameter: 15″

Mfr.: Nylon Net
Model No.: 811
Material: Galvanized wire
Length: 14″
Diameter: 22½″ top; 16″ bottom

Mfr.: Nylon Net
Model No.: 5-X
Material: Galvanized wire
Length: 12″
Diameter: 18½″ top; 13″ bottom

Mfr.: Nylon Net
Model No.: S2B
Material: Galvanized wire
Length: 17″
Diameter: 16¾″ top; 22½″ bottom

Mfr.: OLM
Model No.: WB-1
Material: Wire mesh
Length: 21″
Diameter: 15″

Compasses

Mfr.: Olsen
Model No.: 3
Type: Pocket
Material: Chrome
Features: Luminous metal dial with stop; jeweled needle.

Mfr.: Olsen
Model No.: 6
Type: Pocket
Material: Chrome
Features: Waterproof; luminous metal dial; jeweled needle.

Mfr.: Olsen
Model No.: 7
Type: Pocket
Material: Brass
Features: Memory arrow shows return direction; luminous metal dial.

Olsen Model No. 98

Mfr.: Olsen
Model No.: 60
Type: Lensatic
Material: Plastic
Features: Luminous floating metal dial; jeweled needle.

Mfr.: Olsen
Model No.: 98
Type: Lensatic
Material: Metal
Features: Liquid glycerin filled; luminous floating metal dial; jeweled needle.

Mfr.: Olsen
Model No.: 201L
Type: Wrist & pocket
Features: Liquid glycerin filled; luminous floating dial; jeweled needle.

Mfr.: Olsen
Model No.: M-111L
Type: Lensatic
Features: Fixed focus lens system; jewel pivot; leather case.

Mfr.: Olsen
Model No.: M-111PN
Type: Prismatic
Features: Jewel pivot; gradient indicator; radium dial; black metal casing; rotatable glass cover with direction arrow; leather case.

Mfr.: Tru-Nord
Model No.: 100-C
Type: Pocket
Material: Brass
Features: Radium tipped dial; watch-type case, sealed against moisture; 1″ in diameter.

Mfr.: Tru-Nord
Model No.: 200-C
Type: Pin-on
Features: Radium tipped dial; Cobalt, high magnetic steel magnet; 2″ long fastening bracket.

Mfr.: Tru-Nord
Model No.: 300-C
Type: Wrist
Features: Black nylon watch strap; radium tipped dial.

Mfr.: Tru-Nord
Model No.: 8109

Type: Pocket
Features: Non-fluid movement; brass nickel plated case; jeweled movement with needle stop; luminous dial.

Mfr.: Tru-Nord
Model No.: 8160
Type: Underwater
Features: 35mm. card; jeweled, fluid dampened movement.

Crab Traps

Mfr.: Dragon Fly Company, Inc.
Model No.: 510T
Material: Wire mesh
Size: 10½" x 10½" x 10½"

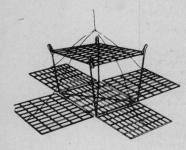

Dragon Fly Model No. 5109

Mfr.: Nylon Net
Model No.: S-12
Material: Galvanized wire
Size: 12" high

Mfr.: Nylon Net
Model No.: S-16
Material: Galvanized wire
Size: 16" high

Mfr.: Old Pal
Model No.: 666
Material: Plastic
Size: 15" x 16" x 10"
Net: Green

Mfr.: OLM
Model No.: CT-16
Material: Wire
Size: 16" x 16"

Creels

Mfr.: Colorado Tent & Awning Company
Model No.: 1 ArtiCreel
Size: 9" x 15" x 4"
Material: Flax water bag canvas with plastic sealer

Mfr.: Colorado Tent & Awning Company
Model No.: 20 ArtiCreel
Size: 10" x 14" x 4"
Material: Flax water bag canvas with plastic sealer

Mfr.: OLM
Model No.: 502
Size: 15" x 9"
Material: Canvas

Mfr.: OLM
Model No.: 506

Size: 17½" x 11"
Material: Canvas

Mfr.: OLM
Model No.: 508
Size: 19" x 12"
Material: Canvas

Colorado Tent & Awning Company ArtiCreel

Mfr.: OLM
Model No.: 510
Size: 17½" x 11"
Material: Nylon

Mfr.: Orvis
Model No.: F1823
Material: 65% dacron, 35% cotton

Mfr.: Fritz Von Schlegell
Model No.: 103 Artic Creel
Size: Not specified
Material: Plastic inner liner

Mfr.: Fritz Von Schlegell
Model No.: K-340
Size: Not specified
Material: Rubberized nylon

Down Riggers

Mfr.: Big Jon
Model No.: D-100
Type: Manual
Features: Positive brake; 4 lb. cannonball; multibead release; complete with 150 ft. 150 lb. test wire.

Mfr.: Big Jon
Model No.: D-476 Deluxe
Type: Manual
Features: Footage counter; 7½ lb. plastic coated cannonball; mounting plate; shot-pin lock; 18" rod length; complete with 200 ft. stainless steel wire.

Mfr.: Big Jon
Model No.: ES1000-1 E
Type: Electric or manual
Features: Footage counter; ball bearing tension clutch; shot-pin stop; 8 lb. cannonball; mountable handle; 12 volt motor; complete with 300 ft. stainless steel wire.

Mfr.: Big Jon
Model No.: ED500J
Type: Electric
Features: Footage counter; mounting plate; bead release; 7 lb. cannonball, 12 volt

gear head motor 15 amp; complete with 200 ft. 150 lb. test stainless steel wire.

Mfr.: Big Jon
Model No.: D400J
Type: Manual
Features: 7½ lb. cannonball; square mounting plate; footage counter; positive brakepin; clutch; complete with 200 ft. 150 lb. stainless steel wire.

Mfr.: Luhr Jensen
Model No.: 020
Type: Manual
Features: Two fisted cranking; flip-slip brake; automatic tracking; rudder release system; short arm; complete with 200 ft. 135 lb. test cable.

Mfr.: Luhr Jensen
Model No.: 026
Type: Manual
Features: Two-fisted cranking; flip-slip brake; automatic tracking; attached rod holder; short arm; includes 8 lb. weight; complete 200 ft. 135 lbs. test cable.

Mfr.: Luhr Jensen
Model No.: 030
Type: Manual
Features: Two-fisted cranking; flip-slip brake; automatic tracking; rudder release system; long arm; swivel base; complete with 200 ft. 135 lb. test cable.

Mfr.: Luhr Jensen
Model No.: 036
Type: Manual
Features: Two-fisted cranking; flip-slip brake; automatic tracking; attached rod holder; long arm; swivel base; includes 8 lb. weight; complete with 200 ft. 135 lb. test cable.

Luhr Jensen Down Rigger

Mfr.: Mac-Jac
Model No.: 160N
Type: Manual
Features: Rod holder; removable base; snag-proof roller guide; locks in five positions; complete with 150 ft. 140 lb. test cable and clip.

Mfr.: Mac-Jac
Model No.: 201
Type: Manual
Features: Stainless drag lock; sun shielded spool; complete with 150 ft. cable and clip.

Mfr.: Penn
Model No.: 600
Type: Manual
Features: Drag-brake control system; base plate; cable footage counter; complete with 200 ft. 135 lb. test stainless steel wire.

Mfr.: Riviera
Model No.: 50
Type: Manual
Features: Mounting hardware; positive tracking system; complete with 150 ft. 150 lb. stainless steel cable.

Mfr.: Riviera
Model No.: 700
Type: Manual
Features: Gear driven depth meter; safety reel clutch; positive line tracking system; mount-anywhere hardware; rod holder; complete with 200 ft. 150. lb. test stainless steel cable.

Mfr.: Riviera
Model No.: 1000 AR
Type: Electric
Features: Auto-retrieve button; circuit breaker; four position positive locking; 12 volt power unit; rod holder; safety reel clutch; complete with 200 ft. 150 lb. stainless steel cable.

Mfr.: Riviera
Model No.: 2300
Type: Manual
Features: Remote digital readout; gear driven line meter; rod holder; mounting hardware; complete with 200 ft. 150 lb. test coaxial cable.

Mfr.: Riviera
Model No.: 2700
Type: Manual
Features: Remote digital readout unit; gear driven line meter; safety reel clutch; rod holder; positive line tracking system; complete with 200 ft. 150 lb. test coaxial cable.

Mfr.: Riviera
Model No.: 2900
Type: Electric
Features: 12 volt electric retrieve system; circuit breaker; remote digital readout system; safety reel clutch; rod holder; complete with 200 ft. 150 lb. test coaxial cable.

Mfr.: Riviera
Model No.: 3000
Type: Electric
Features: Digital temperature monitor; automatic push button retrieving; 12 volt motor; gear driven depth meter; positive line tracking system; complete with 200 ft. 150 lb. test coaxial cable.

Electronic Depth-Sounding Equipment

Mfr.: Garcia
Model No.: 9299
Depth Range: 100'
Type: Flasher

Mfr.: Garcia
Model No.: 9300A
Depth Range: 100'
Type: Flasher

Mfr.: Garcia
Model No.: 9500
Depth Range: 240'
Type: Flasher

Garcia Model No. 9299

Mfr.: Gladding
Model No.: 100
Depth Range: 100'
Type: Meter

Mfr.: Gladding
Model No.: 320
Depth Range: 320'
Type: Flasher/recorder

Mfr.: Ray Jefferson
Model No.: 5200
Depth Range: 200'
Type: Flasher

Mfr.: Ray Jefferson
Model No.: 170
Depth Range: 70'
Size: 5" x 4½" x 4½"
Type: Flasher

Mfr.: Ray Jefferson
Model No.: 6006
Depth Range: 120'
Size: 6" x 9" x 6¾"
Type: Flasher

Mfr.: Lowrance
Model No.: LFG225
Depth Range: 60' low; 180' high
Size: 8¼" x 5" x 10½"
Type: Flasher

Mfr.: Lowrance
Model No.: LFG-300D
Depth Range: 60' low; 180' high
Type: Flasher

Mfr.: Lowrance
Model No.: LFG-360
Depth Range: 60' low; 180' high
Size: 6¼" x 4¾" x 6¼"
Type: Flasher

Mfr.: Lowrance
Model No.: LRG-610A
Depth Range: 60' low; 180' med.; 360' high
Size: 7½" x 6½" x 14¼"
Type: Flasher/graph

Mfr.: Lowrance
Model No.: LFP-150
Depth Range: 100'
Size: Not specified
Type: Flasher

Mfr.: Lowrance
Model No.: LFG-150

Depth Range: 100'
Size: Not specified
Type: Flasher

Mfr.: Lowrance
Model No.: LFP-300
Depth Range: 60' low; 120' high
Type: Flasher

Mfr.: Shakespeare
Model No.: DF-1
Depth Range: 200'
Size: Not specified
Type: Flasher

Mfr.: Shakespeare
Model No.: DF-3
Depth Range: 100'
Size: Not specified
Type: Flasher

Mfr.: Shakespeare
Model No.: DF-4
Depth Range. 360'
Size: Not specified
Type: Flasher

Mfr.: Shakespeare
Model No.: DF-2
Depth Range: 200'
Type: Flasher

Mfr.: Telisons
Model No.: AS-75
Depth Range: 600' with 28° x 45° beam angle
Type: Flasher

Mfr.: Telisons International Corporation
Model No.: AS-100B
Depth Range: 780' with 54° beam angle
Size: 10¾" x 6¾" x 3" (less transducer)
Type: Flasher

Mfr.: Telisons International Corporation
Model No.: AS-100C
Depth Range: 780' with 8° beam angle
Size: 10¾" x 6¾" x 3" (less transducer)
Type: Flasher

Mfr.: Telisons International Corporation
Model No.: AS-100STC
Depth Range: 780' with 54° beam angle
Size: 10¾" x 6¾" x 3" (less transducer)
Type: Flasher

Mfr.: Vexilar
Model No.: 60
Depth Range: 60'
Size: 13" x 7¼" x 6½"
Type: Meter

Mfr.: Vexilar
Model No.: 155D
Depth Range: 1300'
Type: Flasher

Mfr.: Vexilar, Inc.
Model No.: 510A
Depth Range: 200'
Size: 12½" x 9½" x 9"
Type: Flasher

Mfr.: Vexilar
Model No.: 900
Depth Range: 100'
Size: 12½" x 9½" x 9"
Type: Sounder

Mfr.: Waller Corporation
Model No.: 102A
Depth Range: 100' +
Size: 6½" x 6" x 11"
Type: Flasher

Mfr.: Waller Corporation
Model No.: 202A
Depth Range: 200' +
Size: 6½" x 6" x 11"
Type: Flasher

Mfr.: Waller Corporation
Model No.: 204
Depth Range: 60' +
Size: 8" x 6" x 8¼"
Type: Flasher

Mfr.: Waller Corporation
Model No.: 301
Depth Range: 200' +
Size: Not specified
Type: Flasher

Mfr.: Waller Corporation
Model No.: 304
Depth Range: 60' +
Size: 8" x 6" x 8¼"
Type: Flasher

Mfr.: Waller Corporation
Model No.: 530
Depth Range: 100'
Size: Not specified
Type: Digital meter

Mfr.: Waller Corporation
Model No.: 550
Depth Range: 100'
Size: Not specified
Type: Digital meter

Mfr.: Waller Corporation
Model No.: 600
Depth Range: 80'
Size: 12¾" x 2¼" x 6½" folded
Type: Meter

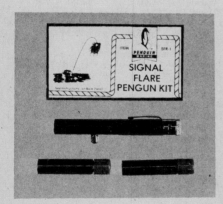

Penguin Model No. SFR-1

Flare Kits

Mfr.: Penguin
Model No.: SFR-1
Features: Anodized pengun with pocket clip;
2 red aerial signal flare cartridges.

Mfr.: Penguin
Model No.: SFR-7
Features: Military type pengun; 7 red flare
cartridges in a bandolier.

Mfr.: Penguin
Model No.: RK-1
Features: Anodized pengun; 2 smoke
cartridges; 5 red aerial signal flare
cartridges.

Mfr.: Penguin
Model No.: HFR-5
Features: Pengun, 5 red aerial signal flare
cartridges; pocket size.

Gaff Hooks

Mfr.: Jet-Aer
Model No.: 2080
Overall Length: 19"
Gaff: Tempered stainless steel
Grip: 6" sure-grip, non-slip

Mfr.: Jet-Aer
Model No.: 2090
Overall Length: 13"
Gaff: Tempered stainless steel
Grip: 6" sure-grip, non-slip

Mfr.: Martin Tackle & Manufacturing Co.
Model No.: G55
Overall Length: 6" x 2" x 16"
Gaff: Cadmium-plated steel
Grip: Wood

Mfr.: Martin Tackle & Manufacturing Co.
Model No.: G66
Overall Length: 6" x 2" x 30"
Gaff: Cadmium-plated steel
Grip: Wood

Mfr.: Martin Tackle & Manufacturing Co.
Model No.: G77
Overall Length: 7" x 3" x 36"
Gaff: Tempered steel
Grip: Wood

Mfr.: Pompanette
Model No.: 24
Gaff: 2"
Grip: 4' aluminum

Mfr.: Pompanette
Model No.: 33
Gaff: 3"
Grip: 3' aluminum

Mfr.: Pompanette
Model No.: 34
Gaff: 3"
Grip: 4' aluminum

Mfr.: Pompanette
Model No.: 36
Gaff: 3"
Grip: 6' aluminum

Mfr.: Pompanette, Inc.
Model No.: 38
Overall Length: 8'
Gaff: 3" stainless steel
Grip: Aluminum

Mfr.: Pompanette
Model No.: 44
Gaff: 4"
Grip: 4' aluminum

Mfr.: Pompanette
Model No.: 46
Gaff: 4"
Grip: 6' aluminum

Mfr.: Pompanette
Model No.: 48
Overall Length: 8'
Gaff: 4"
Grip: Aluminum

Mfr.: Pompanette, Inc.
Model No.: 56
Overall Length: Not specified
Gaff: 5" stainless steel
Grip: 6' aluminum

Mfr.: Pompanette
Model No.: 58
Overall Length: 8'
Gaff: 5"
Grip: Aluminum

Mfr.: Pompanette, Inc.
Model No.: 23
Overall Length: Not specified
Gaff: 2" stainless steel
Grip: 3' aluminum

Mfr.: Pompanette
Model No.: Fiberglass 23
Gaff: 2" fiberglass
Grip: 3' fiberglass

Mfr.: Pompanette
Model No.: Fiberglass 26
Gaff: 2" fiberglass
Grip: 6' fiberglass

Mfr.: Pompanette
Model No.: Fiberglass 33
Gaff: 3" fiberglass
Grip: 3' fiberglass

Mfr.: Pompanette
Model No.: Fiberglass 34
Gaff: 3" fiberglass
Grip: 4' fiberglass

Mfr.: Pompanette
Model No.: Fiberglass 44
Gaff: 4" fiberglass
Grip: 4' fiberglass

Mfr.: Pompanette
Model No.: Fiberglass 46
Gaff: 4" fiberglass
Grip: 6' fiberglass

Mfr.: Pompanette
Model No.: Fiberglass 56
Gaff: 5" fiberglass
Grip: 6' fiberglass

Mfr.: Pompanette
Model No.: Fiberglass 58
Gaff: 5" fiberglass
Grip: 8' fiberglass

Mfr.: Sampo
Model No.: 69
Overall Length: 10½"
Gaff: 3⁄16" diameter, cadmium plated steel
Grip: Slip-proof

Mfr.: Sampo
Model No.: G24
Overall Length: 23"

Gaff: ¼" diameter, cadmium plated steel
Grip: Slip-proof

Mfr.: Sampo
Model No.: G44
Overall Length: 44"
Gaff: ⁵⁄₁₆" diameter, forged stainless steel
Grip: Slip-proof

Guides

Aftco

Type: Regular stainless steel; roller
Size(s): #2; #3; #4; #5 (double roller);
    #2 hard; #3 hard; #4 hard; #5 hard
    (double roller)
Features: For use with regular and wire line.

Type: Heavy duty stainless steel; roller
Size(s): #41; #51 (double roller); #41 hard;
    #51 hard (double roller)
Features: For use with regular line and wire
    line.

Aftco Roller Guides

Allan

Model: CPG
Type: Spinning; stamped frame
Size(s): 8; 9; 10; 12; 14; 16; 20; 24; 30
Features: Chrome plated; stainless steel.

Model: CSWPG
Type: Spinning; wire
Size(s): 8; 9; 10; 12; 14; 16; 20; 24
Features: Lightweight; stainless steel; chrome
    plated.

Model: VSPG
Type: Surf spinning
Size(s): 8; 10; 12; 14; 16; 20; 24; 30; 35; 40;
    50; 60
Features: Lightweight; chrome plated;
    stainless wire.

Model: VSPG Braced. Same as Model VSPG
    except:
Size(s): 35; 40; 50; 60; 75

Model: VPG
Type: Spinning; stamped frame; V-type
Size(s): 8; 9; 10; 12; 14; 16; 20;
    24; 30; 35
Features: Chrome plated; stainless steel.

Model: SPG
Type: Spiralite; non-fouling
Size(s): 8; 10; 12; 14; 16; 20; 24; 30; 35; 50
Features: Chrome plated; stainlesss steel.

Model: CSNG
Type: Snake
Size(s): 4/0; 3/0; 2/0; 1/0; 1; 2; 3
Features: Stainless steel; bright or black
    finished.

Model: CG
Type: Stamped frame
Size(s): 8; 9; 10; 11; 12; 13; 14; 16; 18; 20
Features: Chromed plated; stainless steel.

Model: CWG
Type: Wire
Size(s): 8; 9; 10; 11; 12; 13; 14; 16; 18; 20; 24
Features: Chrome plated; stainless steel.

Model: CSBG
Type: Bridge type wire boat guides
Size(s): 10; 12; 14; 16; 18; 20
Features: Chrome plated; stainless steel.

Model: CCSWPG
Type: Spinning; U frame
Size(s): 8; 10; 12; 14; 16; 20; 24
Features: Tungsten carbide rings; stainless
    steel wire frame.

Model: CCVSPG
Type: Spinning; V frame
Size(s): 8; 10; 12; 14; 20; 24
Features: Tungsten carbide rings; stainless
    steel wire frame.

Model: CCSWG
Type: Casting & trolling
Size(s): 8; 10; 12; 14; 16
Features: Tungsten carbide rings; stainless
    steel wire frame.

Model: CRG
Type: Roller
Size(s): 10; 15; 20; 30
Features: Chrome plated; stainless steel.

Model: SRG
Type: Roller
Size(s): 1; 2; 3
Features: Chrome plated; stainless steel.

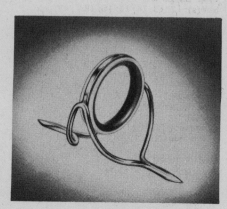

Allan Ceramic Guide

Lew Childre

Model: BSHG
Type: High frame casting and spinning
Size(s): 6; 8; 10; 12; 16; 20; 25; 30
Features: Black stainless steel frame;
    non-corroding aluminum oxide ring.

ACTUAL SIZE OF FUJI HARD SPEED RINGS

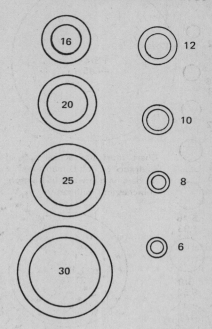

Model: BCHG
Type: Folding high frame spinning stripper
Size(s): 16; 20; 25
Features: 16: ultra lite and light spin; 20:
    light to medium spin; 25: medium to
    heavy spin.

Model: BSPHG
Type: Ultra-lite Lew-Fuji hard speed
Size(s): 8; 10; 12; 16; 20; 25; 30
Features: One foot.

Model: DHG
Type: For deep sea, trolling and bottom
    fishing; wind-on
Size(s): 6; 8; 10; 12; 16; 20
Features: Heavy duty stainless steel.

Gudebrod

Model: FT
Type: Ultra light fly; spinning
Size(s): ⁵⁄₃₂"; ³⁄₁₆"; ⁷⁄₃₂"
Features: Aetna foulproof.

Model: MSP
Type: Ultra light fly; spinning
Size(s): ⁵⁄₈"; ¾"; ⁷⁄₈"

Model: FC
Type: Fly rod; spinning; casting
Size(s): ⁵⁄₃₂"; ³⁄₁₆"; ⁷⁄₃₂"; ¼"; ⁵⁄₁₆"

Model: FM
Type: Spinning casting
Size(s): ⁵⁄₃₂"; ³⁄₁₆"; ¼"; ⁵⁄₁₆"; ³⁄₈"; ½"

Model: SP
Type: Spinning
Size(s): ¼"; ⁵⁄₁₆"; ³⁄₈"; ½"; ⁵⁄₈"; ¾"; ⁷⁄₈";
    1⅛"; 1¼"; 1¾"; 2¼"

5/32
3.97

3/16
4.76

7/32
5.55

1/4
6.35

Chart illustrates actual size of foulproof guides. Dimensions are inside ring diameters in **fractional inches** and millimeters.

1 3/4
44.45

5/16
7.93

3/8
9.52

1/2
12.70

1 1/4
31.75

5/8
15.87

1 1/8
28.57

3/4
19.05

7/8
22.22

Model: SS
Type: Light salt water
Size(s): ¼"; ⁵⁄₁₆"; ³⁄₈"; ½"

Model: SL
Type: Medium salt water
Size(s): ¼"; ⁵⁄₁₆"; ³⁄₈"; ½"

Model: SH
Type: Heavy salt water
Size(s): ¼"; ⁵⁄₁₆"; ³⁄₈"; ½"

Mildrum

Model: ME
Type: Casting; trolling
Size(s): 6; 7; 8; 9; 10; 12; 14; 16; 18; 24
Features: Mildarbide ring.

Model: SSE
Type: Casting; trolling
Size(s): 6; 7; 8; 9; 10; 11; 12; 13; 14; 15; 16; 18; 20; 22; 24
Features: Extra heavy chrome plated standard.

Model: SSBE
Type: Casting; trolling
Size(s): 7; 8; 9; 10; 11; 12; 13; 14; 15; 16
Features: Belmar frame with stainless steel ring.

Model: SRME
Type: Spinning
Size(s): 8; 10; 12; 14; 17; 20; 24; 30; 40
Features: Mildarbide ring with V-type frame.

Model: SRMC
Type: Spinning
Size(s): 8; 10; 12; 14; 17; 20; 24
Features: Mildarbide ring with standard cradle frame.

Model: SRMG
Type: Spinning
Size(s): 8; 10; 12
Features: Mildarbide ring; belmar type frame for spin-cast rods.

Model: SRB
Type: Spinning
Size(s): 7; 8; 10; 12; 14; 17; 20; 24; 30; 36; 40; 48; 60; 75
Features: Stainless steel ring; V-type frame.

Model: SRFL
Type: Spinning
Size(s): 7; 8; 10; 12; 14; 20; 24
Features: Stainless steel ring with stamped stainless steel cradle frame.

Model: MWG
Type: Big game
Size(s): 12; 14; 16; 18
Features: Mildarbide rings; winding base.

Model: MTH
Type: Big game
Size(s): 12; 14; 16; 18
Features: Mildarbide ring; strong enough to handle electric reels.

Model: SSWG
Type: Big game
Size(s): 12; 13; 14; 15; 16; 18
Features: Stainless steel rings; winding base.

Model: SSES
Type: Big game
Size(s): 12; 13; 14; 15; 16; 18
Features: Stainless steel ring.

Model: DRG
Type: Roller
Size(s): 5
Features: Double roller guide for straddle rod mounting.

Model: FBDRG
Type: Roller
Size(s): 5
Features: Double roller guide for top of rod mounting.

Model: SRG
Type: Roller
Size(s): 1; 2; 3; 4
Features: Single roller to straddle rod.

Model: FBRG
Type: Roller
Size(s): 1; 2; 3; 4
Features: Single roller for top of rod mounting.

MILLIMETER SCALE FOR GUIDES

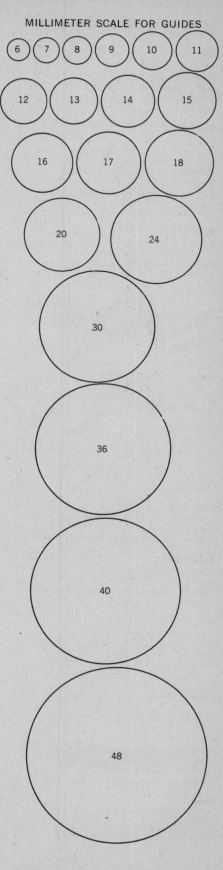

6 7 8 9 10 11
12 13 14 15
16 17 18
20 24
30
36
40
48

Knives

Buck

Model No.: 102
Overall Length: Not specified
Blade Length: 4″
Blade(s): 1 high carbon steel
Handle: Ebony
Sheath: Genuine saddle leather

Model No.: 121
Overall Length: Not specified
Blade Length: 5½″
Blade(s): 1 high carbon steel
Handle: Ebony
Sheath: Genuine saddle leather

Camillus Cutlery

Model No. 5

Model No.: 5
Overall Length: 5″ closed
Blade Length: Not specified
Blade(s): 1 chrome-plated sabre clip
Handle: Maize

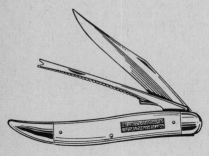

Model No. 25

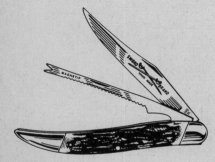

Model No. 31

Model No.: 25
Overall Length: 5″ closed
Blade Length: Not specified

Blade(s): 2 stainless steel sabre clip
(serrated tip; hook disgorger, scaler, bottle
cap lifter)
Handle: Maize

Model No.: 31
Overall Length: 5″ closed
Blade Length: Not specified
Blade(s): 2 stainless steel sabre clip
(cutting; hook disgorger-fish scaler,
cap lifter)
Handle: Indian stag

W. R. Case & Sons

Model No.: 116-8″ F w/sh
Overall Length: Not specified
Blade Length: 8″
Blade(s): 1 stainless steel
Handle: Walnut
Sheath: Leather

Model No.: 124-6″ w/sh
Overall Length: Not specified
Blade Length: 6″
Blade(s): 1 stainless steel
Handle: Rosewood
Sheath: Leather

Model No. P203-6

Model No.: P203-6″ w/sh
Overall Length: Not specified
Blade Length: 6″
Blade(s): 1 chrome-plated
Handle: Pakkawood
Sheath: Leather

Model No.: 32095 FSS
Overall Length: 5″ closed
Blade Length: Not specified
Blade(s): 2 stainless steel (cutting; disgorger,
scaler)
Handle: Composition

Fly Fisherman SS

Model: Fly Fisherman SS
Overall Length: 3⅞″ closed
Blade Length: Not specified
Blade(s): 4 stainless steel (cutting; scissors;
pick; file)
Handle: Stainless steel

Gladding

Model No.: 7-900-004
Overall Length: 11¹¹⁄₁₆″
Blade Length: 5²³⁄₃₂″
Blade(s): 1 stainless steel
Handle: Stainless steel

Model No.: 7-900-005
Overall Length: 10″

Jet-Aer

Blade Length: 4⅞″
Blade(s): 1 stainless steel
Handle: Stainless steel

Model No.: 7-900-006
Overall Length: 10″
Blade Length: 4″
Blade(s): 1 stainless steel
Handle: Stainless steel

Model No.: 7-900-007
Overall Length: 14½″
Blade Length: 9¼″
Blade(s): 1 stainless steel
Handle: Stainless steel

International

Model No.: R14010
Overall Length: 11″
Blade Length: 6½″
Blade(s): 1 stainless steel
Handle: Wood
Sheath: Molded

Model No.: R14030
Overall Length: Not specified
Blade Length: 3¼″
Blade(s): 1 stainless steel
Handle: Not specified

Model No.: R14040
Overall Length: Not specified
Blade Length: 4⅝″
Blade(s): 1 stainless steel
Handle: Paulownia wood
Sheath: Paulownia wood

Model No.: R14050
Overall Length: Not specified
Blade Length: Not specified
Blade(s): 2
Handle: Pearl plastic

Model No.: R14070
Overall Length: Not specified
Blade Length: 4⅝″
Blade(s): 1
Handle: Not specified
Sheath: Not specified

Model No.: R14350
Overall Length: Not specified
Blade Length: 6″
Blade(s): 1 stainless steel
Handle: Hardwood
Sheath: Leather

IPCO

Model No.: Mark I
Overall Length: Not specified
Blade Length: 6″
Blade(s): 1 stainless steel
Handle: Hardwood
Sheath: Ebony

Model No.: Mark V
Overall Length: Not specified

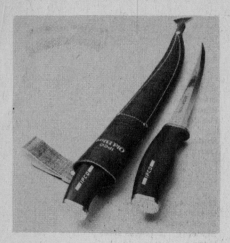

IPCO Model No. OB-6

Blade Length: 6″
Blade(s): 1 high carbon steel
Handle: Rosewood
Sheath: Leather

Model No.: Mark IX
Overall Length: Not specified
Blade Length: 9″
Blade(s): 1 high carbon steel
Handle: Rosewood
Sheath: Leather

Model No.: Pro-6
Overall Length: Not specified
Blade Length: 6″
Blade(s): 1 high carbon steel
Handle: Ebony
Sheath: Leather

Model No.: OB-6
Overall Length: Not specified
Blade Length: 6″
Blade(s): 1 high carbon steel
Handle: Molded
Sheath: Leather

Jet-Aer

Model No.: 2000
Overall Length: 9½″
Blade Length: 4¾″
Blade(s): 1 rustproof steel
Handle: Non-slip
Sheath: Plastic

Model No.: 2010
Overall Length: 11″
Blade Length: 6¼″
Blade(s): 1 rustproof steel
Handle: Non-slip
Sheath: Plastic

Model No.: 2020
Overall Length: 11½″
Blade Length: 6¾″
Blade(s): 1 rustproof steel
Handle: Non-slip
Sheath: Plastic

Model No.: 2030
Overall Length: 12¾″
Blade Length: 8″
Blade(s): 1 rustproof steel
Handle: Non-slip
Sheath: Plastic

Model No.: 2040
Overall Length: 12¾″
Blade Length: 7¾″
Blade(s): 1 rustproof steel (cutting, scaler)
Handle: Non-slip
Sheath: Plastic

Model No.: 2050
Overall Length: 16¼″
Blade Length: 11¼″
Blade(s): 1 rustproof steel (cutting, scaler)
Handle: Non-slip
Sheath: Plastic

Model No.: 2060
Overall Length: 12¼″
Blade Length: 7¼″
Blade(s): 1 rustproof steel (cutting, scaler)
Handle: Non-slip
Sheath: Plastic

Model No.: 2070
Overall Length: 4⅞″ closed
Blade Length: 4″
Blade(s): 2 rust proof steel (cutting; hook remover)
Handle: Brass and Pacca wood
Sheath: Leather

Normark

Model No.: DP306
Overall Length: 10¾″
Blade Length: 6″
Blade(s): 1 carbon, molybdenum and chromium steel
Handle: Molded
Sheath: Tooled Oxide

Model No.: FNF-4
Overall Length: 9½″ in sheath
Blade Length: 4″
Blade(s): 1 stainless steel
Handle: Reinforced birch
Sheath: Tooled leather

Model No.: FNF-6. Same as Model No. FNF-4 except:
Overall Length: 12½″ in sheath
Blade Length: 6″

Model No.: FNF-9. Same as Model No. FNF-4 except:
Overall Length: 15½″ in sheath
Blade Length: 9″

OLM

Model: No.: K-2
Blade Length: 6″
Blade(s): 1 stainless steel
Handle: Birch
Sheath: Birth

Model No.: 2806-S
Blade Length: 8″
Blade(s): 1 stainless steel
Handle: Beechwood

Model No.: 5746
Blade(s): 3 stainless steel
Handle: Pearl plastic

Model No.: 8380
Blade(s): 1 stainless steel
Handle: Wood

Model No.: 8920
Blade(s): 1 stainless steel
Handle: Wood

Olsen

Model No.: 213-F
Overall Length: Not specified
Blade Length: 6″
Blade(s): 1 carbon steel
Handle: Not specified

Model No.: 251
Overall Length: Not specified
Blade Length: 3½″
Blade(s): 1
Handle: Not specified

Model No.: 265
Overall Length: Not specified
Blade Length: 5″
Blade(s): 1 carbon steel
Handle: Not specified

Model: Fisherman Swiss Army Knife
Overall Length: 3½″ closed
Blade Length: Not specified
Blade(s): 8 (2 cutting; reamer; hook disgorger; scaler; can opener; cap lifter; phillips screwdriver; scissors; tweezers)
Handle: Elsinid plastic

Model: CK Coho Knife
Overall Length: Not specified
Blade Length: Not specified
Blade(s): 1 carbon steel
Handle: Not specified

Orvis

Model No.: U2120
Overall Length: 3½″
Blade(s): 3 stainless steel

Model No.: F2122
Overall Length: 11″
Blade Length: 6″
Blade(s): 1 stainless steel
Handle: Hardwood
Sheath: Leather

Sampo

Model No.: K706B
Overall Length: Not specified
Blade Length: 6″
Blade(s): 1 carbon steel
Handle: Hardwood
Sheath: Leather

Model No.: K736B
Overall Length: Not specified
Blade Length: 6″
Blade(s): 1 stainless steel
Handle: Hardwood
Sheath: Leather

Model No.: K755B
Overall Length: Not specified
Blade Length: 6″
Blade(s): 1 tungsten steel
Handle: Agatewood
Sheath: Leather

Model No.: K756B
Overall Length: Not specified
Blade Length: 6″
Blade(s): 1 tungsten steel
Handle: Agatewood
Sheath: Leather

Model No.: K757B. Same as K755B except:
Blade Length: 7½″

Model No.: K759B
Overall Length: Not specified
Blade Length: 9″
Blade(s): 1 tungsten stainless steel
Handle: Agatewood
Sheath: Leather

Syl-Mark

Model No.: 660
Overall Length: Not specified
Blade Length: 3½″
Blade(s): 1 stainless steel
Handle: Leather
Sheath: Leather

Tru-Nord

Model No.: S-9156-PK
Overall Length: 11″
Blade Length: 6″
Blade(s): 1 Swedish stainless steel
Handle: Polypropen

Western Cutlery

Model No.: S-751
Overall Length: 4⅜″ closed
Blade Length: Not specified
Blade(s): 2 (cutter; scaler, disgorger and cap lifter)
Handle: Composition

Model No.: SW769
Overall Length: 14″
Blade Length: 9″
Blade(s): 1 stainless steel
Handle: Hardwood

Model No.: SW766
Overall Length: 11″
Blade Length: 6″
Blade(s): 1 stainless steel
Handle: Hardwood

Model No.: SW766
Overall Length: 11″
Blade Length: 6″
Blade(s): 1 stainless steel
Handle: Hardwood

Life Jackets

Mfr.: Stearns
Model: Standard men's Sans-Souci
Size(s): S; M; L; XL; XXL; XXXL
Color(s): Blue denim; red, blue or green plaid

Mfr.: Stearns
Model: Standard ladies' Sans-Souci
Size(s): P; S; M
Color(s): Blue denim; harbor blue; red, blue or green plaid

Mfr.: Stearns
Model: Ladies' belted Sans-Souci
Size(s): P; S; M
Color(s): Blue denim; harbor blue; red, blue or green plaid

Mfr.: Stearns
Model: Sportsvest Sans-Souci
Size(s): S; M; L; XL; XXL
Color(s): Blue denim; forest green; gold; green camouflage; brown camouflage

Mfr.: Stearns
Model: Deliverance Kayak/Canoe
Size(s): S; M; L; XL
Color(s): High visibility gold; harbor blue

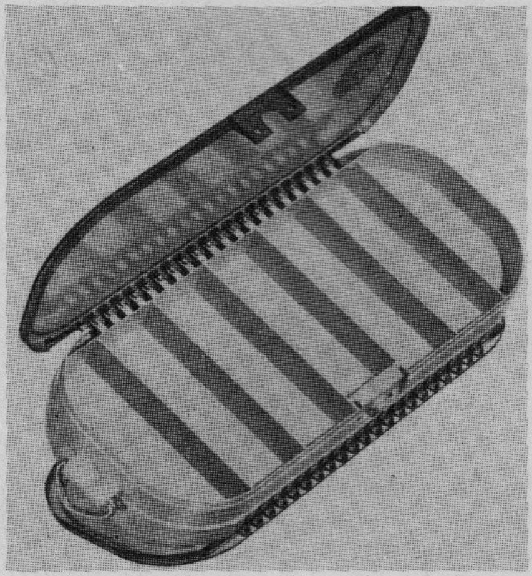

Old Pal Lure Box

Lure Boxes

Mfr.: Dragon Fly Company, Inc.
Model No.: 556
Size: 4¼″ x 8¼″
Compartments: 6
Material: Plastic

Mfr.: Luhr Jensen
Model No.: 904
Compartments: 2
Material: Plastic

Mfr.: Luhr Jensen
Model No.: 909
Compartments: 1
Material: Plastic

Mfr.: Old Pal
Model No.: 380
Size: 9¼″ x 4″ x 2″
Compartments: 16
Material: Plastic

Mfr.: Old Pal
Model No.: 360
Size: 4⅝″ x 3″ x 1³⁄₁₆″
Compartments: 4
Material: Plastic

Mfr.: Old Pal
Model No.: 365
Size: 11″ x 6¾″ x 1¾″
Compartments: 18
Material: Plastic

Mfr.: Old Pal
Model No.: P31
Size: 7⅜″ x 4⁵⁄₁₆″ x 7½″
Compartments: Not specified
Material: Polypropylene

Mfr.: OLM
Model No.: 8260
Compartments: 6
Material: Plastic

Mfr.: Orvis
Model No.: F1250
Size: ⅞″ x 3¼″ x 7½″
Compartments: 18
Material: Plastic

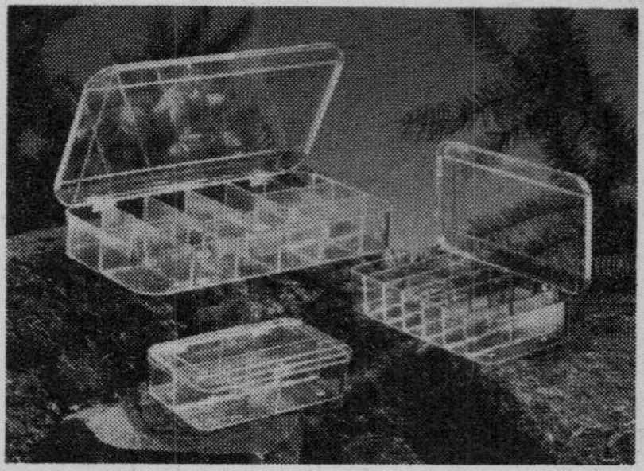

Old Pal Lure Box

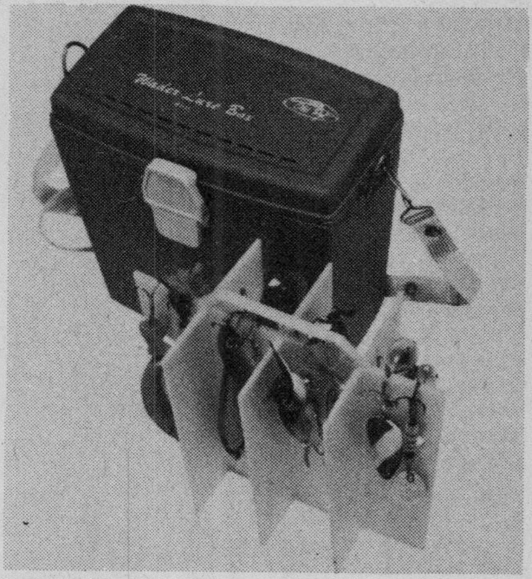

Old Pal Lure Box

Mfr.: Orvis
Model No.: F1252
Size: 1¼″ x 4¼″ x 8¼″
Compartments: 18
Material: Plastic

Mfr.: Plano
Model No.: 3000
Size: 15″ x 6″ x 1⅜″
Compartments: 9
Material: Plastic

Mfr.: Plano
Model No.: 3448-6
Size: 4⅝″ x 2⅞″ x 1″
Compartments: 6
Material: Plastic

Mfr.: Plano
Model No.: 3618
Size: 11″ x 7¼″ x 1¾″
Compartments: 18
Material: Plastic

Mfr.: Sampo
Model No.: 26A
Size: 8¼" x 4¼" x 1⅛"
Compartments: 18
Material: Butyrate

Mfr. Vlchek
Model No.: A201
Size: 8¼" x 4½" x 1⅜"
Compartments: 12
Material: Plastic

Mfr.: Vlchek
Model No.: A212
Size: 7" x 3¾" x 1¼"
Compartments: 5
Material: Plastic

Mfr.: Vlchek
Model No.: A221
Size: 4⅝" x 3" x 1⅛"
Compartments: 4
Material: Plastic

Mfr.: Vlchek
Model No.: A824
Size: 13⅛" x 9" x 2⁵⁄₁₆"
Compartments: 24
Material: Plastic

Mfr.: Vlchek
Model No.: M210
Size: 7" x 3¾" x 1¼"
Compartments: 9
Material: Polypropylene

Mfr. Vlchek
Model No.: M618
Size: 11" x 6¾" x 1¾"
Compartments: 18
Material: Polypropylene

Mfr.: Vlchek
Model No.: M806
Size: 13⅛" x 9" x 2⁵⁄₁₆"
Compartments: 6
Material: Polypropylene

Mfr.: Vlchek
Model No.: V-305
Size: 7¼" x 3½" x 1⅛"
Compartments: 5
Material: Polypropylene

Mfr.: Vlchek
Model No.: V-506
Size: 10⅜" x 4⅝" x 1¹¹⁄₁₆"
Compartments: 6
Material: Polypropylene

Nets

Mfr.: Dragon Fly
Type of net: Minnow Bucket Dip
Model No.: MBN-9
Overall Length: Not specified
Handle: Gauge wire
Frame: Gauge wire
Net: Nylon
Net Depth: Not specified

Mfr.: Hardy Brothers
Type of net: Wading
Model No.: 2
Net: Green nylon
Net Depth: 38"

Mfr.: Hardy Brothers

Type of net: Landing
Model No.: 3
Overall Length: 51"
Net: Cord
Net Depth: 23"

Mfr.: Hardy Brothers
Type of net: Trout
Model No.: 4
Overall Length: 49½"
Handle: Telescopic

Mfr.: Nylon Net
Type of net: Drop
Model: Nylon Lift Net
Overall Length: Not specified
Handle: Not specified
Frame: 4' x 4' spring steel
Net: Nylon
Net Depth: Not specified

Mfr.: Nylon Net
Type of net: Landing
Model No.: NY0-0
Overall Length: Not specified
Handle: 18" aluminum
Frame: 15" diameter aluminum
Net: 1" square nylon mesh
Net Depth: 18"

Mfr.: Nylon Net
Type of net: Minnow Bucket Dip
Model: Minnow Bucket Dip Net
Overall Length: 11"
Handle: 7" wire
Frame: Wire
Net: ⅛" square mesh
Net Depth: 3"

Mfr.: OLM
Type of net: Trout landing
Model No.: 658
Overall Length: 16"
Frame: 9" x 11" aluminum

Mfr.: OLM
Type of net: Minnow Dip
Model No.: 1119
Net: ⅛" cotton mesh

Mfr.: OLM
Type of net: Bait Well
Model No.: 3670
Handle: 18" wood
Frame: 7½" x 8" x 6"
Net: Cotton

Mfr.: Orvis
Type of net: Landing
Model No.: FO840
Frame: 8" x 13"
Net: Nylon
Net Depth: 24"

Mfr.: Orvis
Type of net: Landing
Model No.: F2903
Overall Length: 20"
Handle: Cherry wood
Frame: 9" x 12½" ash and mahogany
Net: Nylon
Net Depth: 17"

Mfr.: Orvis
Type of net: Landing
Model No.: F2904
Overall Length: 23"
Handle: Cherry wood
Frame: 10" x,14½" ash and mahogany

Net: Nylon
Net Depth: 19"

Mfr.: Sampo
Type of net: Trout
Model No.: T1200
Frame: 10" x 16"aluminum
Net: Cotton
Net Depth: 16"

Mfr.: Sampo
Type of net: Landing
Model No.: COST 17
Handle: 1⅛" x 36"
Frame: ½" x 22" x 24"
Net: Vinylon
Net Depth: 36"

Mfr.: Sampo
Type of net: Landing
Model No.: COST 21
Handle: 1⅛" x 48"
Frame: ½" x 30" x 38"
Net: Vinylon
Net Depth: 46"

Mfr.: Sampo
Type of net: Scoop
Model No.: ML 1979
Handle: 1" diameter
Frame: 19" x 19"
Net: Vinylon
Net Depth: 30"

Mfr: Sampo
Type of net: Crab
Model No.: CN 57
Handle: 4' aluminum
Frame: 13" x 14" aluminum
Net: Vinylon
Net Depth: 16"

Mfr.: Sampo
Type of net: Bait Well Dip
Model No.: DN4
Handle: 15" aluminum
Frame: 6½" x 8" bethanized wire
Net Depth: 4"

Mfr.: Nylon Net
Type of net: Dip
Model No.: HDS-1
Handle: 30" long, 1" diameter aluminum
Frame: 16" x 17"
Net: ½" square nylon
Net Depth: 12"

Mfr.: Sampo
Type of net: Shrimp & Minnow
Model No.: SM60
Overall Length: Not specified
Handle: 4" ribbed aluminum, 1" diameter
Frame: 15" x 16", ⅜" aluminum tubing
Net: ¼"-½" graduated vinylon
Net Depth: 22"

Rod Holders

Mfr.: Klamerus & Company
Model No.: 202
Size: Not specified
Bracket(s): Not specified
Material: Steel with rubber

Mfr.: Klamerus & Company
Model No.: 500

Size: Not specified
Bracket(s): Not specified
Material: Steel with rubber

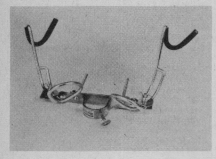

Rod Holder

Mfr.: Mac-Jac
Model No.: 525
Size: 9¼" long
Material: Aluminum

Mfr.: Joseph Mennen Company, Inc.
Model No.: 1302
Size: 1⅞" (inside diameter) x 9"
Bracket(s): Aluminum
Material: Vinyl

Mfr.: Joseph Mennen Company, Inc.
Model No.: 1303
Size: 1⅞" (inside diameter) x 9"
Bracket(s): Stainless steel
Material: Vinyl

Mfr.: Joseph Mennen Company, Inc.
Model No.: 1312
Size: 1⅞" (inside diameter) x 9"
Bracket(s): Not specified
Material: Not specified

Mfr.: OLM
Model No.: Y-95
Size: 6½" long

Mfr.: OLM
Model No.: Y-96
Size: 8¼" long

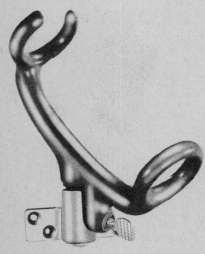

Penguin Model No. MA-1

Mfr.: Penguin Industries Inc.
Model No.: MA-1
Size: Not specified
Bracket(s): 1
Material: Aluminum with plastic coating

Mfr.: Penguin
Model No.: MA-3
Size: 2" x 10"
Bracket(s): 2 coated
Material: Aluminum

Mfr.: Sampo
Model No.: 5100
Size: 1⅞" (inside diameter) x 9"
Material: Plastic

SuperVenus

Searchlights

Mfr.: Optronics
Model: MaxiVenus Lite
Weight: 2 lbs.
Power Supply: Auto, marine, cycle or lawn
mower 12 volt battery
Features: Glare free bulb; handheld; standard
cigarette plug; complete with 10' coil or
straight cord.

Mfr.: Optronics
Model: MiniVenus Lite
Weight: 1¼ lbs.
Power Supply: Auto, marine, cycle or lawn
mower 12 volt battery
Features: Glare free bulb; standard cigarette
plug; push button switch; complete with
10' coil or straight cord.

Mfr. Optronics
Model: SuperVenus
Weight: 3¾ lbs.
Power Supply: Auto, marine, cycle or lawn
mower 12 volt battery
Features: Glare free bulb; available with
vacuum or swivel mount; standard
cigarette plug; complete with 10' cord.

Stringers

Mfr.: Dragon Fly Company, Inc.

Model No.: SCS-9
Length: Not specified
Snaps: 9
Material: Metal plated

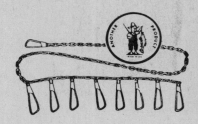

Tuffy Chain Stinger

Mfr.: International
Model No.: R21200
Length: 46"
Snaps: 9

Mfr.: Lindy/Little Joe
Model: Tuffy Chain Stringer
Length: 46"
Snaps: 9
Material: Zinc plated

Mfr.: Lindy/Little Joe
Model No.: ST115
Length: 15'
Snaps: 9
Material: Zinc-plated steel chain

Mfr.: Martin Tackle & Manufacturing Co.
Model No.: FT83
Length: Not specified
Snaps: 3

Mfr.: OLM
Model No.: T-15A-7
Length: 3'
Snaps: 7

Mfr.: OLM
Model No.: T-15A-9
Length: 3'
Snaps: 9

Mfr.: Sampo
Model No.: 300
Length: 6'
Snaps: 8
Material: Nylon

Mfr.: Sampo
Model No.: 502
Length: Not specified
Snaps: Not specified
Material: Floating polypropylene with
polyethylene cord

Mfr.: Sampo
Model No.: 310. Same as Model 300
except:
Length: 10'

Tackle Boxes

Mfr.: Old Pal
Model No.: PF1060
Type: 3 tray
Size: 12⅞" x 7⅜" x 7¼"
Compartment(s): 23

Old Pal Model No. 7400

Mfr: Old Pal
Model No.: PF1080
Type: 3 tray
Size: 15⅜" x 8¾" x 8⅛"
Compartment(s): 23

Mfr.: Old Pal
Model No.: PF1290
Type: 6 tray
Size: 15" x 8⅞" x 10⅛"
Compartment(s): 36

Mfr.: Old Pal
Model No.: PF1550
Type: 2 tray
Size: 14¾" x 8⅛" x 7⅝"
Compartment(s): 15

Mfr.: Old Pal
Model No.: PF1575
Type: 3 tray
Size: 17⅝" x 10¾" x 10"
Compartment(s): 32

Mfr.: Old Pal
Model No.: PF1585
Type: 2 drawer, 1 tray
Size: 16⅛" x 9⅜" x 9¼"
Compartment(s): 21

Mfr.: Old Pal
Model No.: SW2310
Type: 3 tray
Size: 19" x 7½" x 7½"
Compartment(s): 31
Material: Steel

Old Pal Model No. 7100

Mfr.: Old Pal
Model No.: SW2610
Type: 6 tray
Size: 19" x 7½" x 8¾"
Material: Steel

Mfr.: Old Pal
Model No.: PF5500
Type: 7 tray
Size: 19½ " x 10¼" x 14¾"
Compartment(s): 56

Mfr.: Old Pal
Model No.: PF6500
Type: 5 tray
Size: 18½" x 10" x 10⅝"
Compartment(s): 49

Mfr.: Old Pal
Model No.: PF7000
Type: 4 drawer
Size: 18¼" x 10" x 11½"
Compartment(s): 33

Old Pal Model No. PF7500

Mfr.: Old Pal
Model No.: PF7100
Type: 5 drawer
Size: 18¼" x 10" x 11½"
Compartment(s): 47

Mfr.: Old Pal
Model No.: PF7400
Type: 4 drawer
Size: 19½" x 10" x 15⅝"
Compartment(s): 33

Mfr.: Old Pal
Model No.: PF7500
Type: 5 drawers
Size: 19½" x 10" x 15⅝"
Compartment(s): 47

Mfr.: Plano
Model No.: 727
Type: 3 drawer
Size: 19⅛" x 10" x 10¾"
Compartment(s): 29
Material: ABS top, polypropylene bottom

Mfr.: Plano
Model No.: 747
Type: 3 drawer
Size: 20⅜" x 11½" x 12¾"
Compartment(s): 29
Material: ABS

Mfr.: Plano
Model No.: 777S
Type: 5 drawers

Size: 19" x 9½" x 13⅝"
Compartment(s): 28
Material: Polypropylene

Mfr.: Plano
Model No.: 1146
Type: 2 sided
Size: 14¾" x 5" x 11½"
Compartment(s): Up to 46
Material: Acrylite lids; polypropylene bottom

Mfr.: Plano
Model No.: 4901
Type: 1 tray, 1 spinner bait rack
Size: 14¾" x 7¾" x 7¾"
Compartment(s): 7
Material: Polypropylene

Mfr.: Plano
Model No.: 6300N
Type: 3 tray
Size: 16½" x 8¾" x 8"
Compartment(s): 25
Material: Polypropylene

Mfr.: Plano
Model No.: 6500
Type: 3 tray, 2 spinner bait rack
Size: 16½" x 8¾" x 8"
Compartment(s): 20
Material: Polypropylene

Mfr.: Plano
Model No.: 7530
Type: 3 tray
Size: 19" x 10¼" x 9½"
Compartment(s): 24
Material: Polypropylene

Mfr.: Plano
Model No.: 8600
Type: 6 tray
Size: 18¼" x 9⅝" x 10⅜"
Compartment(s): 36
Material: ABS top; polypropylene bottom

Mfr.: Plano
Model No.: 9106
Type: 6 tray
Size: 19½" x 11¼" x 10½"
Compartment(s): 42
Material: ABS top; polypropylene bottom

Plano Model No. 1146

Mfr.: Rebel
Model No.: BB-10
Type: 1 tray
Size: 14″ x 10″ x 2¼″
Compartment(s): Up to 20

Mfr.: Rebel
Model No.: BB-20
Type: 1 tray
Size: 14″ x 10″ x 4½″
Compartment(s): Up to 40

Mfr.: Rebel
Model No.: BB-30
Type: 1 tray, 2 spinner bait rack
Size: 14″ x 9¾″ x 4¾″
Compartment(s): Up to 20

Mfr.: UMCO
Model No.: 175A
Type: 3 tray
Size: 17½″ x 7″ x 6¾″
Compartment(s): 29
Material: Aluminum

Mfr.: UMCO
Model No.: 205A
Type: 3 tray
Size: 18¾″ x 10″ x 8¼″
Compartment(s): 36
Material: Aluminum

Mfr.: UMCO
Model No.: 1000 APB
Type: 7 tray
Size: 19″ x 10″ x 13½″
Compartment(s): 55
Material: Aluminum

Mfr.: UMCO
Model No.: 1293
Type: 3 tray
Size: 17¼″ x 8½″ x 8⅝″
Compartment(s): 25
Material: Plastic

Mfr.: UMCO
Model No.: 1852
Type: 1 tray, 1 drawer
Size: 18½″ x 11″ x 9½″
Compartment(s): 11
Material: Plastic

Mfr.: UMCO
Model No.: 1853
Type: 2 tray, 1 drawer
Size: 18½″ x 11″ x 9½″
Compartment(s): 29
Material: Palstic

Mfr.: UMCO
Model No.: 1976
Type: 6 tray
Size: 18½″ x 11″ x 9½″
Compartment(s): 50
Material: Plastic

Mfr.: UMCO
Model No.: 3060 UPB
Type: 6 tray
Size: 21½″ x 12½″ x 16¾″
Compartment(s): 49
Material: Plastic

Mfr.: UMCO
Model No.: 3500 UPB
Type: 10 tray
Size: 21½″ x 12½″ x 19″
Compartment(s): 84
Material: Plastic

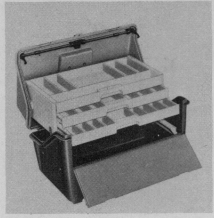
Vichek Adventurer

Mfr.: Vichek
Model No.: 1423
Type: 3 tray
Size: 14⅜″ x 7⅝″ x 7″
Compartment(s): 51
Material: Copolymer

Mfr.: Vichek
Model No.: 1726
Type: 3 tray, 1 spinner bait rack
Size: 16½″ x 8¾″ x 7½″
Compartment(s): 17
Material: Copolymer

Mfr.: Vichek
Model No.: 1733
Type: 3 tray
Size: 16½″ x 8¾″ x 7½″
Compartment(s): 40
Material: ABS copolymer

Mfr.: Vichek
Model No.: 1983
Type: 3 tray
Size: 18½″ x 10¼″ x 10⅜″
Compartment(s): 21
Material: Copolymer

Mfr.: Vichek
Model No.: 1986
Type: 6 tray
Size: 18½″ x 10¼″ x 10⅜″
Compartment(s): 40
Material: Copolymer

Mfr.: Vichek
Model No.: 1987
Type: 7 tray
Size: 18½″ x 10¼″ x 10⅜″
Compartment(s): 56
Material: Copolymer

Mfr.: Vichek
Model No.: 2000
Type: 9 cartridge
Size: 19″ x 10¾″ x 10⅛″

Mfr.: Vichek
Model No.: 1043
Type: 3 tray
Size: 12⅜″ x 7″ x 4⅝″
Compartment(s): 12

Mfr.: Vichek
Model No.: 2013
Type: 3 tray
Size: 19″ x 10¾″ x 10⅛″

Compartment(s): 36
Material: Copolymer

Mfr.: Vichek
Model No.: 2253
Type: 3 drawer
Size: 19½″ x 11½″ x 11¾″
Compartment(s): 57
Material: ABS

Mfr.: Vichek
Model No.: 2276
Type: 6 drawer
Size: 19½″ x 10⅜″ x 15″
Compartment(s): 47
Material: ABS

Mfr.: Vichek
Model No.: 2277
Type: 7 drawer
Size: 19½″ x 10⅜″ x 15″
Compartment(s): 96
Material: ABS

Vichek Adventurer Model No. 1745

Thermometers

Mfr.: Ray Jefferson
Model No.: 90
Reading Cable Depth: 100′
Temp. Reading Range: 30° to 90° F

Mfr.: Ray Jefferson
Model No.: 90S
Size: 2⅞″ x 4″ x 3¾″
Temp. Reading Range: 32° to 90° F

Lowrance Model No. LTD 250

Mfr.: Lowrance Electronics
Model No.: LTP-100
Size: 3" x 2¼" x 5¾"
Reading Cable Depth: 100'
Temp. Reading Range: 30° to 90°F

Mfr.: Lowrance
Model No.: LTD-250
Temp. Reading Range: 35° to 90° F

Mfr.: Vexilar, Inc.
Model No.: 104
Size: Not specified
Reading Cable Depth: Not specified
Temp. Reading Range: 20° to 120°F

Mfr.: Vexilar, Inc.
Model No.: 116
Size: Not specified
Reading Cable Depth: 80'
Temp. Reading Range: 35° to 95°F

Mfr.: Waller Corporation
Model No.: 505
Size: Not specified
Reading Cable Depth: 50'
Temp. Reading Range: 40° to 80°F

Mfr.: Waller Corporation
Model No.: 510
Size: Not specified
Reading Cable Depth: 100'

Mfr.: Waller Corporation
Model No. 520
Size: Not specified
Reading Cable Depth: 200'

Vexilar Model No. 116

Tops

Afteo

Type: Regular stainless steel; rollers
Size(s): #5; #6; #7; #8; #9; #10-S; #10-L;
#12; #14; #16; #18; #20; #24; #26;
#28; #30
Features: For use with regular line.

Type: Regular stainless steel; roller
Size(s): #5 hard; #6 hard; #7 hard;
#8 hard; #9 hard; #10-S hard; #10-L
hard; #12 hard; #14 hard; #16 hard;
#18 hard; #20 hard; #22 hard; #24 hard;
#26 hard; #28 hard; #30 hard; #32 hard
Features: For use with wire line.

Alan Model CPT

Type: Economy one-piece roller
Sizes: #12; #14; #16; #18; #20; #22;
#12 hard; #14 hard #16 hard; #18 hard;
#20 hard; #22 hard
Features: For use with regular or wire line.

Allan

Model: CPT
Type: Spinning; stamped frame
Size(s): 5; 5½; 6; 6½; 7; 8; 9
Features: Chrome plated; stainless steel.

Model: CSWPT same as Model CPT except:
Type: Spinning; wire
Features: Lightweight.

Model: VSPT
Type: Surf spinning
Size(s): 6; 7; 8; 9; 10; 12; 14; 16
Features: Lightweight; chrome plated;
stainless steel.

Model: VPT
Type: Stamped frame; surf spinning
Size(s): 7/10; 8/10; 9/10
Features: Chrome plated; stainless steel.

Model: CSFRT
Type: Fly rod
Size(s): 5; 5½; 6; 7; 8
Features: Stainless steel; chrome plated or
black finished.

Model: CT
Type: Stamped frame
Size(s): 5; 5½; 6; 6½; 7; 8; 9; 10; 12; 14; 16;
18; 20; 22; 24
Features: Chrome plated; stainless steel
Model: CWT. Same as Model CT except:
Type: Wire

Model: CCSWPT
Type: Spinning
Size(s): 5; 5½; 6; 6½; 7; 8; 9
Features: Tungsten carbide rings; stainless
steel wire frame.

Model: CCVSPT
Type: Surf spinning
Size(s): 7; 8; 9; 10; 12; 14
Features: Tungsten carbide rings; stainless
steel wire frame.

Alan Model CSWPT

Model: CCSWT
Type: Casting & trolling
Size(s): 5; 6; 7; 8; 9; 10; 12; 14; 16
Features: Tungsten carbide rings; stainless
steel wire frame.

Model: CRT
Type: Roller
Size(s): 10; 12; 14; 16; 18; 20; 22; 24; 26; 28
Features: Chrome plated; stainless steel.

Lew Childre

Model: BMHT
Type: Fly
Size(s): 4½; 5; 5½; 6; 6½; 7

Model: PHT
Type: Casting; spinning
Size(s): 5; 5½; 6; 6½; 7; 7½; 8; 9; 10; 11;
13; 14
Features: Chrome plated frame.

Model: DHT
Type: Heavy duty boat
Size(s): 10; 11; 13; 16; 20

Model: MT
Type: Mini-tops for telescopic rods
Size(s): 4; 5; 5½; 6

Gudebrod

Model: MLTT
Type. Foulproof
Size(s) ³⁄₁₆"

Model: LTT
Type: Foulproof
Size(s): ³⁄₁₆"

Model: CTT
Type: Foulproof
Size(s): ⁷⁄₃₂"

Model: LST
Type: Foulproof
Sizes: ⁵⁄₁₆"; ³⁄₈"

Model: SWT
Type: Foulproof
Sizes: ¼"

Model: HK
Type: Foulproof
Size(s): ⅛; ³⁄₁₆"

Mildrum

Model: MD
Type: Casting; trolling; spinning
Size(s): 5; 5½; 6; 6½; 7; 8; 9; 10; 11; 12; 13;
14; 15; 16; 17; 18; 19; 20; 22; 24; 26; 28;
30; 32
Features: Mildarbide ring.

Model: SSD. Same as Model MD except:
Features: Stainless steel rings.

Model: SSDL. Same as Model MD except:
Features: Stainless steel ring; light weight
construction.

Model: SSWT
Type: Casting; trolling; spinning
Size(s): 5; 5½; 6; 6½; 7; 8; 9; 10; 11; 12; 14;
16; 18

Features: Stainless steel wire frame top.

Model: SRMT
Type: Casting; trolling; spinning
Size(s): 4½; 5; 5½; 6; 6½; 7; 8; 9; 10; 11; 12; 14; 16; 18
Features: Light Mildarbide spin top.

Model: DTM
Type: Casting; trolling; spinning
Size(s): 4½; 5; 5½; 6; 6½ 7; 8; 9
Features: Continental style Mildarbide spin top.

Model: DTSS
Type: Casting trolling; spinning
Size(s): 4½; 5; 5½; 6; 6½; 7; 8; 9
Features: Continental design; stainless steel spin top.

Gudebrod Foulproof Tops

Model: PMT
Type: Casting; trolling; spinning
Size(s): 4; 4½; 5; 5½; 6; 6½; 7; 8
Features: Mildarbide fly top.

Model: PS
Type: Casting trolling; spinning
Size(s): 4; 4½; 5; 5½; 6; 6½; 7; 8
Features: Pear shape fly top; tapered tube.

Model: SGP. Same as Model PS except:
Features: Pear shape fly top; straight tube.

Model: RRT
Type: Roller
Size(s): 12; 14; 16; 18; 20; 22; 24; 26; 28; 30; 32
Features: Single roller top.

Model: RTT. Same as Model RRT except:
Features: Double roller top.

Model: CRT
Type: Roller
Size(s): 7; 8; 9; 10; 11; 12; 14; 16; 18; 20; 22; 24; 26; 28; 30; 32
Features: Single roller top; stamped frame.

Model: SCRT. Same as Model CRT except:
Features: Single roller top; stamped frame; riveted construction.

Model: SWVT
Type: Roller
Size(s): 12; 14; 16; 18; 20; 22; 24; 26; 28; 30; 32
Features: Single roller revolves around tip.

Trolling Motors

Mfr. Gladding
Model No. Mark II
Power: Electric 6V/12V
Mount: Transom
Shaft Length: Not specified
Weight: 4.5 lbs.
Speed(s): 2
Thrust: 5.5 lbs.; 2.2 lbs.
Reverse: 360°

Mfr.: Minn Kota
Model No.: MAG RM-4
Power: Electric 12V
Mount: Retractable
Shaft Length: 36″
Speed(s): Hi-variable
Thrust: 15 lbs.; 0-10 lbs.
Reverse: Yes

Mfr.: Minn Kota
Model No.: 10
Power: Electric 12V
Mount: Transom
Shaft Length: 27″
Speed(s): 2
Thrust: 6 lbs.; 3 lbs.

Mfr.: Minn Kota
Model No.: MAG 10
Power: Electric 12V/24V
Mount: Transom
Shaft Length: 30″
Speed(s): 3
Thrust: 24 lbs.; 13 lbs.; 9 lbs.; 6 lbs.; 5 lbs.; 2 lbs.
Reverse: Yes

Mfr.: Minn Kota
Model No.: MAG 18
Power: Electric 12V
Mount: Bow
Shaft Length: 36″
Speed(s): 4
Thrust: 18 lbs.; 12 lbs.; 7 lbs.; 4 lbs.
Reverse: 360°

Mfr.: Minn Kota
Model No.: 55
Power: Electric 12V
Mount: Transom
Shaft Length: 30″
Speed(s): Hi-variable
Thrust: 15 lbs.; 0-10 lbs.
Reverse: Yes

Mfr.: Minn Kota
Model No.: 65
Power: Electric 12V
Mount: Transom
Shaft Length: 30″
Speed(s): 4
Thrust: 18 lbs.; 12 lbs.; 7 lbs.; 4 lbs.
Reverse: Yes

Mfr.: Minn Kota
Model No.: 365
Power: Electric 12V
Mount: Retractable
Shaft Length: 36″
Speed(s): 4
Thrust: 18 lbs.; 12 lbs.; 7 lbs.; 4 lbs.

Mfr.: Minn Kota
Model No.: 375
Power: Electric 12V/24V
Mount: Retractable
Shaft Length: 36″
Speed(s): 3
Thrust: 24 lbs.; 13 lbs.; 9 lbs.; 6 lbs.; 5 lbs.; 2 lbs.

Mfr.: Minn Kota
Model No.: 535
Power: Electric 12V
Mount: Bow
Shaft Length: 36″
Speed(s): 3
Thrust: 12 lbs.; 8 lbs.; 4 lbs.
Reverse: 360°

Mfr.: Minn Kota
Model No.: 575
Power: Electric 12V/24V
Mount: Bow
Shaft Length: 36″
Speed(s): 3
Thrust: 24 lbs.; 13 lbs.; 9 lbs.; 6 lbs.; 5 lbs.; 2 lbs.
Reverse: 360°

Mfr.: Pflueger
Model No.: M7
Power: Electric
Shaft Length: 27″
Weight: 6 lbs.
Speed(s): 2
Thrust: 6 lbs.; 2 lbs.
Reverse: 360°

Mfr.: Pflueger
Model No.: M15
Power: Electric
Shaft Length: 30″
Weight: 8 lbs.
Speed(s): 3
Thrust: 8.4 lbs.; 4.5 lbs.; 2.5 lbs.
Reverse: Yes

Mfr.: Pflueger
Model No.: M40
Power: Electric 12V
Shaft Length: 36″
Weight: 15½ lbs.
Speed(s): 3
Thrust: 15 lbs.; 10 lbs.; 5 lbs.
Reverse: Yes

Mfr.: Pflueger
Model No.: RM450
Power: Electric remote control
Mount: Bow
Shaft Length: 36″
Weight: 15 lbs.
Speed(s): 3
Thrust: 10.5 lbs.; 5 lbs.; 3 lbs.
Reverse: Yes

Mfr.: Pflueger
Model No.: RM441
Power: Electric 12V
Mount: Bow
Shaft Length: 36″
Speed(s): 3
Thrust: 15 lbs.; 10 lbs.; 4 lbs.

Mfr.: Pflueger
Model No.: RM451
Power: Electric remote control
Mount: Bow
Shaft Length: 36″
Speed(s): 3
Thrust: 10.5 lbs.; 5 lbs.; 3 lbs.

Mfr.: Pflueger
Model No.: RM461
Power: Electric 12V/24V
Mount: Bow
Shaft Length: 36″
Speed(s): 3
Thrust: 20 lbs.; 12.5 lbs.; 5 lbs.

Mfr.: Rebel
Model: Super R
Power: Electric 12V/24V
Mount: Bow
Shaft Length: 36″
Thrust: 24½ lbs.

Mfr.: Rebel
Model: Rambler

Power: Electric 12V
Mount: Bow
Shaft Length: 36"

Mfr.: Shakespeare
Model No.: 505
Power: Electric 12V
Mount: Not specified
Shaft Length: 30 "
Speed(s): 21
Thrust: 1½ to 7½ lbs.
Reverse: Yes

Mfr.: Shakespeare
Model No.: 606
Power: Electric 12V
Mount: Transom
Shaft Length: 33"
Weight: 11 lbs.
Speed(s): 3
Thrust: 12 lbs.; 5.5 lbs.; 3.5 lbs.
Reverse: Yes

Mfr.: Shakespeare
Model No.: 612
Power: Electric 12V
Mount: Transom
Shaft Length: 36"
Weight: Not specified
Speed(s): 3
Thrust: 17 lbs.; 11 lbs.; 6 lbs.
Reverse: Yes

Mfr.: Shakespeare
Model No.: 888
Power: Electric
Mount: Bow
Shaft Length: Adjusts from 28" to 36"
Speed(s): 3
Thrust: 12 lbs.; 5.5 lbs.; 3.5 lbs.
Reverse: Not specified

Mfr.: Shakespeare
Model No.: 610
Power: Electric 12V
Mount: Transom
Shaft Length: 33"
Speed(s): 3
Thrust: 12 lbs.; 10 lbs.; 1.5 lbs.
Reverse: Yes

Mfr.: Shakespeare
Model No.: 924
Power: Electric 12V/24V
Mount: Bow
Shaft Length: Adjusts from 28" to 36"
Speed(s): 3
Thrust: 22.5 lbs.; 13.5 lbs.; 5.5 lbs.
Reverse: 360°

Mfr.: Shakespeare
Model No.: 988
Power: Electric 12V
Mount: Bow
Shaft Length: Adjusts from 28" to 30"
Speed(s): 3
Thrust: 12.0 lbs.; 5.5 lbs.; 3.5 lbs.
Reverse: 360°

Waders

Mfr.: Converse
Model No.: 13418
Height: Chest
Material: Fabric surface

Mfr.: Converse
Model No.: 13433
Height: Chest
Material: Cloth lined rubber surfaced

Mfr.: Converse
Model No.: 13931
Height: Chest
Material: Fabric surface and nylon

Mfr.: Converse
Model: Wadewell Hip Boot
Height: Hip
Material: Nylon cloth with wide rubber chafting tip

Mfr.: Converse
Model No.: 13932
Height: Hip
Material: Fabric surface and nylon

Mfr.: Converse
Model: Rod & Reel Hip Boot
Height: Hip
Material: Cloth lined rubber surface

Mfr.: Converse
Model No.: 13959
Height: Hip
Material: Nylon surface with felt sole

Mfr.: Converse
Model No.: 13960 Cleated or Felt Sole Nylon
Height: Chest
Material: Two rubberized layers of nylon cloth

Mfr.: Hardy Brothers
Model: Hardy Thigh Waders
Height: Thigh
Material: Stockingette lining

Mfr.: Hardy Brothers
Model: BTR Rubber-studded Thigh Waders
Height: Thigh
Material: Stockingette lineds

Mfr.: Hardy Brothers
Model: Hardy Deepwater Body Waders
Height: Chest

Mfr.: Nylon Net
Model No.: 733
Height: Hip
Material: Fully lined rubber

Mfr.: Nylon Net
Model No.: 4050
Height: Chest
Material: Rubber; insulated

Mfr.: OLM
Model No.: Hip-4N
Height: Hip
Material: Nylon outside and rubber sheeting inside

Mfr.: OLM
Model No.: Hip-4NS
Height: Hip
Material: Nylon outside and rubber sheeting; insulated boots

Mfr.: OLM
Model No. Hip-4
Height: Hip
Material: Khaki cotton sheeting

Mfr.: OLM
Model No.: Hip-4S
Height: Hip
Material: Khaki cotton sheeting; insulated

Mfr.: OLM
Model No.: W-17-1
Height: Chest
Material: Nylon outside and rubber sheeting inside

Mfr.: OLM
Model No.: W-17-1S
Height: Chest
Material: Nylon outside and rubber sheeting inside; insulated 7" high from heel

Mfr.: Orvis
Model No.: F5801
Height: Chest
Material: Calf-high felt insulated

Mfr.: Orvis
Model No.: F5805
Height: Chest
Material: Nylon uppers; rubber sole

Mfr.: Orvis
Model No.: H5806
Height: Hip
Material: Rubber soles

Mfr.: Fritz von Schlegell
Model No.: 121
Height: Chest
Material: Rubber between two layers of nylon

Mfr.: Fritz von Schlegell
Model No.: 123
Height: Chest
Material: Nylon and rubber

Mfr.: Fritz von Schlegell
Model No.: 121-I
Height: Chest
Material: Insulated with foam rubber

Mfr.: Fritz von Schlegell
Model No.: 123-I
Height: Chest
Material: Insulated with foam rubber

Mfr.: Fritz von Schlegell
Model No.: 1121
Height: Chest
Material: Nylon and rubber

Mfr.: Fritz von Schlegell
Model No.: 124
Height: Hip
Material: Nylon and rubber

Mfr.: Fritz von Schlegell
Model No.: 124-I
Height: Hip
Material: Nylon and rubber; foam rubber and felt for the feet

Mfr.: Fritz von Schlegell
Model No.: 1122
Height: Hip
Material: Nylon and rubber

Index

A selection of antique fishing tackle catalogue pages has been reproduced on the inside front and back covers to capture the flavor of a past which is gone but not forgotten.